THIRD EDITION

SEX AND INTERNAL SECRETIONS

VOLUME II

VOLUME II

CONTRIBUTORS

A. Albert
David W. Bishop
Richard J. Blandau
R. K. Burns
A. T. Cowie
John W. Everett
S. J. Folley
Thomas R. Forbes
J. W. Gowen

Roy O. Greep
A. M. Guhl
Joan G. Hampson
John L. Hampson
Frederick L. Hisaw
Frederick L. Hisaw, Jr.
James H. Leathem
Daniel S. Lehrman
Margaret Mead
John W. Money

Helen Padykula
Dorothy Price
Herbert D. Purves
Ari van Tienhoven
Claude A. Villee
H. Guy Williams-Ashman
George B. Wislocki
William C. Young
M. X. Zarrow

Baltimore • 1961

THIRD EDITION

SEX AND INTERNAL SECRETIONS

Edited by William C. Young, Ph.D.

Professor of Anatomy, University of Kansas, Lawrence

Foreword by George W. Corner, M.D., D.Sc.

Director Emeritus, Department of Embryology,

Carnegie Institution of Washington

The Williams & Wilkins Co.

Publication was supported in part by
Public Health Service Research Grant M-4648 from
the National Institute of Mental Health,
Public Health Service.

COMPOSED AND PRINTED BY THE
WAVERLY PRESS, INC.
BALTIMORE 2, MARYLAND, U.S.A.

CONTENTS

SECTION F
HORMONAL REGULATION OF REPRODUCTIVE BEHAVIOR

Biology of Sperm and Ova, Fertilization, Implantation, the Placenta, and Pregnancy

13

BIOLOGY OF SPERMATOZOA

David W. Bishop, Ph.D.

STAFF MEMBER, DEPARTMENT OF EMBRYOLOGY, CARNEGIE
INSTITUTION OF WASHINGTON, BALTIMORE, MARYLAND

I. Introduction

In no way is the present review intended to represent a renovation of the comparable section in the second edition of *Sex and Internal Secretions* (Hartman, 1939). It would be both presumptious and impracticable to attempt to update Professor Hartman's discussion of the physiologic role of spermatozoa in reproduction; this stands as a landmark now two decades old. In his review many problems were noted, some since solved, others still in the course of solution, and many even yet ignored.

The major advances in sperm biology during the intervening years have been world-wide and substantial. Stimulated in large measure by the exigencies of the animal-breeding industry, Lardy and co-workers at Wisconsin developed biochemical methods and concepts pertaining to spermatozoa, particularly those of the bull. Mann and his many able Cambridge colleagues have elucidated major aspects of the metabolic and enzymatic activities of spermatozoa in several domestic species. Significant contributions have appeared from various laboratories, too numerous to designate, from the basic demonstrations, by the Engelhardt school, of the role of adenosine triphosphate (ATP) and adenosinetriphosphatase (ATPase) in the motility of sperm, to the apparently unique metabolic characteristics of human spermatozoa reported principally by MacLeod.

A second major stride in the study of the male gamete has been provided by the development of the electron microscope. By virtue of the increase in magnification, up to 1000-fold, cells can be visually dissected down to elements on the order of 10 Å in size. Not the least of its accomplishments, the electron microscope has made possible the demonstration that *all* sperm flagella and *all* cilia throughout the plant and animal kingdoms possess the same basic pattern of longitudinal filaments, the well known 2 × 9 + 2 array. The full significance of this structural constancy is yet to be realized, but inasmuch as these filaments are generally assumed to represent the motile organelles of the cell, the physicochemical basis for motility may eventually be resolved. Likewise, the electron microscope has facilitated the study of spermatozoa during their maturation and in the initial stages of fertilization. Significant alterations in the acrosome, for example, seem to be related to the processes involved in the union of gametes.

The sperm has, in fact, been more closely scrutinized and is now recognized as something more than a uniform, finished product of the spermatogenic process. Mammalian spermatozoa from the same gonad may well differ with respect to phenotypic and antigenic characteristics. They are, moreover, far from functionally mature as they leave the testis; structural and biochemical changes occur during their sojourn and transport through both the male and female genital tracts such that their capacity for fertilization is enhanced with time and migration. Investigation of these processes constitutes a very active area of research in current studies of reproductive physiology.

Another important advance in recent years, which may here be singled out for comment, concerns the mechanism of transport of spermatozoa through the female genital tract. One of the earliest features of mammalian reproduction to be studied, only recently has the full weight of experimental attack demonstrated the important endocrinologic role involved in the process.

These, among other, developments in sperm biology are considered in some detail in the pages that follow. No attempt is made to survey completely the available literature, which is enormous; rather, what seem to be significant current principles and processes are discussed within the scope and space allotments of the present volume. The general characteristics of whole semen and its production, reviewed elsewhere (see Mann, 1954; chapters by Albert and by Price and Williams-Ashman), are necessarily slighted in favor of a fuller discussion of the internal environment of the male and female genital tracts and the probable conditions surrounding the sperm *in vivo*. Fortunately, a number of recent reviews cover many of the principal, broad points noted above and serve as background for the material reported here (MacLeod, 1943b; Ivanov, 1945; Mann, 1949, 1954; Austin and Bishop, 1957; Colwin and Colwin, 1957; Fawcett, 1958; Mann and Lutwak-Mann, 1958; Bishop, 1961; Tyler and Bishop, 1961).

The function of the male gamete is to serve as activator of the ovum and contributor of paternal hereditary components to the zygote. The sperm thus stimulates an otherwise relatively inert egg and initiates a new course of development. In Weissmannian terms, it represents a continuity, of part at least, of the germ plasm from one generation to the next. In a very real phylogenetic sense, the gamete is one haploid generation momentarily sandwiched between two extended diploid generations.

Sperm, unlike most cells, are designed to function outside of their native environment. Where fertilization is external, spermatozoa may be shed into an aqueous medium of different ionic strength which offers little shelter, scant buffering capacity, toxic ions, and a lack of energy substrate essential for extended metabolic activity. In the case of internal fertilization, on the other hand, these conditions are generally obviated, and the seminal plasma, the vehicle for transport, affords additional security features beneficial to sperm survival. However, the introduction of sperm into the female animal places them, even here, in foreign surroundings which, although natural, may not always prove hospitable. There is evidence to indicate, for example, that the normal protective and immune responses of the female against foreign invasion reach even to the oviduct and uterus and to their luminal secretions.

The motility of typical spermatozoa is certainly their most striking characteristic. Indeed, the degree of motility is frequently equated to fertilizing capacity and survival. The sperm of many nonmammalian species, however, may appear quite immotile, although they are fully capable of fertilizing normal eggs. The sperm of the herring (*Clupea*), for example, are immotile as shed and remain so until brought into the vicinity of homologous eggs (Yanagimachi, 1957). The giant sperm of the hemipteran insect, *Notonecta glauca*, show no movement until activated by fluids from the female genital system (Pantel and de Sinéty, 1906). The sperm of many invertebrate animals, moreover, are nonflagellated, a specialization particularly common among decapod *Crustacea*. Amoeboid spermatozoa are found among ascarids, and in the sponge, *Grantia*, it is claimed that the sperm lose their flagella and are engulfed by modified collar cells which transform into amoeboid forms and transport the parasite-like sperm to the oocytes (Gatenby, 1920). It thus appears

that, whereas nature has endowed the male gametes with flagella from the lowest protistan to the highest mammal, she has developed secondary modifications toward less specialized conditions among numerous organisms between the evolutionary extremes.

II. Functional State of Gametes after Spermatogenesis

The gross structure and organization of spermatozoa are generally considered complete when the gametes leave the testis. The statement is frequently seen that spermatozoa, as found in the male efferent ducts, are ready for fertilization, unlike the egg cells which often, and in all mammals, are ovulated in a cytogenetically incomplete state of development, later to be activated by the sperm. In a general way, this contrast in the functional activity of the gametes is realized, and the most cogent evidence in behalf of the fertilizing capacity (although less than normal) of testicular sperm is the record of conceptions resulting from insemination by sperm removed from the gonads of chickens and men (Munro, 1938; Adler and Makris, 1951). Normally, however, the process of sperm maturescence is not complete until some time after sperm formation, and fertilizing capacity is fully realized only after a period of sojourn in the male and female genital tracts (Redenz, 1926; Young, 1929a, 1931; Munro, 1938; Bishop, 1955).

A. THE MATURATION OF SPERMATOZOA

A number of structural and physical changes, here only briefly noted, occur in spermatozoa during transit through the ducts. Morphologically, the most obvious modification is the loss of the "kinoplasmic droplet," a cytoplasmic residuum of dubious function characteristic of immature cells and only rarely found in sperm of a normal ejaculate (Merton, 1939a; Gresson and Zlotnik, 1945; Mukherjee and Bhattacharya, 1949). Less obvious changes are a concomitant decrease in free-water content and an increase in specific gravity of sperm as they mature, as in the bull (Lindahl and Kihlström, 1952). Salisbury (1956) found evidence to indicate that changes occur in permeability to water and in intracellular concentrations of monovalent cations (Na+ and K+), modifications which might account for the increase in capacity for movement of sperm at this stage in their developmental history. Unpublished observations of electron micrographs of human sperm by Fawcett indicate that the midpiece may undergo further significant alterations after spermatogenesis, changes which involve particularly the mitochondrial sheath and the annulus at the junction of the midpiece and principal piece of the flagellum.

In the female genital tract, further sperm modifications occur which appear to be necessary for fertilization. A period of incubation in the tubal fluids is required during which changes (capacitation) occur that seem to involve both enzymatic and structural properties of the sperm (Austin and Bishop, 1958a; Chang, 1958; Noyes, 1959b). During this 2- to 6-hour interval, the sperm, at least of the rat, hamster, and rabbit, undergo certain changes in the head, which include loss of the "galea capitis" and partial dissolution of the acrosome.

What other changes occur in spermatozoa, *in vivo*, during their transport through the genital tracts, and of what consequence such modifications are to either survival or fertilization can only be surmised. In some respects, the metabolic properties of epididymal and seminal sperm differ, as studied *in vitro* (see Metabolism). Pronounced changes, of course, follow activation at the time of ejaculation, changes associated with energy production and motility. Other biochemical activities are believed to occur, moreover, which may be regarded as part of the "resting" metabolism of sperm. This will be discussed in a later section. On the other hand, certain deleterious changes may also take place, particularly during sperm storage, to such an extent that large molecular moieties, such as cytochrome *c*, are apparently lost from both bull and ram spermatozoa (Mann, 1954).

B. CYTOGENETIC DIFFERENCES IN SPERM

As the result of meiosis and segregation, spermatozoa are haploid in chromosome number and bear one-half of the hereditary complement which is carried into the next generation at fertilization. The two main types of sperm, X- and Y-bearing (in mammals), are responsible for female and male offspring, respectively, on union with the X-chromosome egg. Attempts have indeed been made, with questionable success, to separate these two kinds of sperm both by electrophoretic (Schröder, 1940a, b, 1941a, b, 1944; Gordon, 1957) and by countercurrent centrifugal methods (Lindahl, 1956).

Genetically distinct spermatozoa were long ago demonstrated by Landsteiner and Levine (1926), who showed that the A and B blood-group antigens occur in human sperm, without, however, making clear whether the specific phenotype of a given sperm is determined by its haploid set of genes or by the diploid set of the spermatocyte from which it is derived. Gullbring (1957) has recently revived this issue and claims that the A and B antigens occur on separate sperm produced by a heterozygous AB blood-group male. Further evidence of gene-induced sperm heterogeneity is afforded by the work of Beatty (1956), who studied the 3,4-dihydroxyphenylalanine (DOPA) reaction in sperm from pigmented and pale rabbits. A high correlation was found between the melanizing activity of the spermatozoa and the depth of coat color of the rabbits from which they came. It will be remembered that Snell (1944) found significant antigenic differences in the sperm of inbred strains of mice, those of strain C being readily distinguishable from those of strain C57 on a basis of their agglutination with specific antisera. Braden (1956, 1958a, 1959) has recently made an intensive study of sperm variation in pure strains of mice. Statistically significant differences in size and shape of the sperm head were demonstrated in the four inbred lines, CBA, C57BL, A, and RIII. Moreover, at fertilization, strain differences become apparent in the tendency for more than one sperm to penetrate the egg membranes, sperm of strain C57BL, for example, showing a significantly higher percentage (26 per cent) than those of other strains (12 to 14 per cent). Further, Braden (1958b) has found abnormalities in the segregation ratio of mice which tend to indicate that the actual allele present (*e.g.*, at the T-locus) in the sperm determines certain of its properties, including its relative fertilizing capacity. The precise nature of the impairment is unknown but seems to involve the ability of the sperm to traverse the uterotubal junction (Braden and Gluecksohn-Waelsch, 1958). This is the same gene which Bryson (1944) found to affect both sperm morphology and motility in the heterozygous (t^0/t^1) male. These results are yet fragmentary but are strongly indicative of the fact that spermatozoa reflect their haploid genotype and that when they bear an unfavorable allelic constitution they may display a decreased fertilizing potential. The possibility exists that subviable mutants, recessive in the heterozygous condition, might have profound detrimental effects when segregated into particular gametes.

C. REQUIREMENTS FOR LARGE SPERM NUMBERS

Any suggestion at the present time to justify the large number, or "excess," of sperm ordinarily involved in insemination is at best a hazardous supposition. The earlier speculations which presupposed a sperm "swarm" to supply hyaluronidase for the dissipation of cumulus cells (McClean and Rowlands, 1942) are inconsonant with the facts, since only a very few sperm, on the order of 25 to 250, are to be found in the presence of fertilized eggs of rats, rabbits, and ferrets, for example, while the cumulus cells are still clustered about the eggs (Braden and Austin, 1953; Chang, 1959). That many more sperm are produced and inseminated than are necessary for fertilization is not be to denied. A phenomenon implicating survival of the species can be expected to have built-in safety factors, and sperm production is no exception, particularly if the male is to be capable of frequent ejaculation. Very probably, the pattern for high gametic production was set long ago among animals which reproduced by means of external fertilization where sperm, egg, and larval loss are very high. In fact, obstacles to successful fertilization are present in mammals as well; definite blocks to sperm transport, for example, occur at the cervix, uterotubal junction, and tubal isthmus in many animals. But it is to be emphasized, in the light of evidence cited in the two preceding sections, that the waste of *healthy* spermatozoa may be less than previously conjectured. The exigencies of the complex series of cellular and functional changes which ensue during the passage of sperm through the genital tracts and the possibility of genetic variation with consequent differences in fertilizing capacity suggest that the number of physiologically effective sperm in the ejaculate may be but a fraction of the total inseminated.

III. Sperm Transport and Storage in the Male Tract

Aside from the accessory reproductive glands that supply, in large measure, the constituents of the seminal plasma (see chapter by Price and Williams-Ashman), the male genital tract of vertebrates is essentially a collection and transport system, designed to convey the spermatozoa from the testis to the ejaculatory duct (Fig. 6.1). It does more than this, however, in that the gametes, on the one hand, are altered in their capacity for fertilization and, on the other hand, are stored, motionless, often for long periods of time, preparatory to ejaculation. The intrinsic changes within the maturing sperm and the interrelations between the gametes and the various segments of the male duct system are only just beginning to be appreciated. The cytologic integrity and the functional activity of the male reproductive ducts are directly influenced by the androgen output of the testicular interstitium and presumably vary in their influence on the spermatozoa within the tract. Spermiation, the release and shedding of spermatozoa from the testes of amphibians, is, of course, hormonally induced (Van Oordt, Van Oordt and Van Dongen, 1959; Witschi and Chang, 1959); the mechanism of release is discussed elsewhere in this volume (chapter by Greep). In the cock, which has no glands analogous to the seminal vesicles or prostate, "seminal" fluids are contributed by the seminiferous tubules and vasa efferentia (Lake, 1957).

A. SPERM TRANSPORT

It can be stated with reasonable assurance that sperm migration within the male tract is, from the sperm's viewpoint, in the main a passive process (Simeone, 1933). The mechanism by which they are moved along the duct system, however, is not well understood; the mechanics may well vary in different segments. Certain workers have emphasized the currents of fluid which could sweep the sperm out of the seminiferous tubules and into the efferent ducts and epididymis (see Young, 1933; Macmillan, 1953). Resorption of fluid by the efferent ducts (Young, 1933; Ladman and Young, 1958) or epididymal epithelium (Mason and Shaver, 1952; Cleland, Jones and Reid, 1959) would complete the fluid circuit and simultaneously concentrate the sperm mass in the distal reaches of the duct system. Certain ligation experiments in which the male ducts were occluded at various levels tend to support this concept of transport by fluid currents, and circumstantial evidence is further afforded by the presence of motile cilia in the upper segment of the genital tract. On the other hand, other experiments which involved separation of the testis from the efferent ducts, thereby cutting off the supply of fluid, demonstrate unequivocally that the sperm, under these circumstances, are carried distally by some other means of tubal transport (Young, 1933; Macmillan and Harrison, 1955).

More recently acquired evidence indicates that muscular activity may play the predominant role in sperm transport through the male ducts. Roosen-Runge (1951) has observed movement in the seminiferous tubules of the dog and rat, both in the intact testis and *in vitro* in physiologic saline at 36°C. The undulating motion was attributed, by Roosen-Runge, to the contraction and relaxation of the Sertoli cells within the tubules. A more plausible explanation may rest in Clermont's recent (1958) electron micrographic demonstration of fibrous elements which lie in the wall of the seminiferous tubule of the rat and seem to resemble smooth muscle cells.

The ductuli efferentes of the adult rat can be cultured successfully in roller-tube tissue-culture preparations (Battaglia, 1958). Tubules maintained as long as 12 days show spontaneous movement, presumably due to muscular contractions. This activity could provide a mechanism whereby spermatozoa are carried along these ducts, *in vivo*.

Migration of spermatozoa through the epididymis proper is mainly, although perhaps not exclusively, brought about by spontaneous peristaltic and segmental movements of the duct. Such activity was first clearly shown in the guinea pig by Simeone (1933) and in the rat by Muratori (1953) and has been confirmed and recorded cinematographically by Risley (1958, 1960). Rhythmic contractions sweep along the adult tubule at regular intervals of 7 or 8 seconds. After gonadectomy, contractions continue in the mature duct for two more weeks. Hypophysectomy results in the loss of activity within 10 days in the head, and within 13 days in the body and tail of the epididymis. In tissue-culture preparations, the spontaneous movement of the epididymis also continues for some time (12 days), the activity being the same whether the ducts are excised from normal or from gonadectomized rats (Battaglia, 1958). It is of some historic interest to note that Moore and Quick, as early as 1924, suggested a neuromuscular mechanism for epididymal sperm transport as a result of their studies on vasectomized rabbits; at the same time they refuted the then hotly contested claims of Steinach and others that vasectomy reults in seminiferous atrophy and interstitial hypertrophy. Complete occlusion of the rat vasa efferentia, on the other hand, is claimed to lead invariably to spermatogenic destruction (Harrison, 1953).

Transport through the epididymis requires 2 to 4 days in the fowl, 4 to 7 days in the rabbit, 9 to 14 in the ram, 14 to 18 in the guinea pig, 8 in the mouse, about 15 in the rat, and 19 to 23 days in man (Toothill and Young, 1931; Munro, 1938; Edwards, 1939; Brown, 1943; MacMillan and Harrison, 1955; Asdell, 1946; Dawson, 1958; Oakberg and DiMinno, 1960). The guinea pig determinations of Toothill and Young (1931) made use of the migration of India ink particles, injected into the head of the epididymis, and not of sperm transport *per se*. The apparently rapid rate of migration of sperm in the fowl may be attributed to the relatively short length of the epididymis (Munro, 1938). Isolation of the testis from the epididymis of the guinea pig increases transport time by 1 to 2 weeks, possibly as a result of interruption of flow of fluid through the excurrent ducts, or perhaps as a consequence of operational disturbances which involve changes in the local vascularization and nerve supply.

The vas deferens serves mainly for the accumulation and storage of sperm, but what sperm migration does occur seems primarily dependent upon the muscular activity of the duct. The vasa of the rat and dog are normally quiescent in sexually inactive males, but are capable under experimental conditions, *in vitro*, of a high degree of muscular activity (Martins and do Valle, 1938; Valle and Porto, 1947). Belonoschkin (1942) claimed that peristaltic activity of the vas deferens aids in sperm transport in man.

B. SPERM SURVIVAL

Spermatozoa may reside in the genital tract for considerable periods of time before being discharged at ejaculation. They generally lose their capacity for fertilization before their capacity for motility during storage in the ducts. Survival times vary from several weeks to many months in different species. Bats normally store spermatozoa over the winter months, and this may be typical of certain other hibernating mammals as well. Knaus (1933) claimed that epididymal spermatozoa remain viable and fertile for a year in vasectomized rabbits, but the process of sperm renewal was not eliminated in his experiments. Mouse spermatozoa in the excurrent ducts maintain their capacity for fertilization for 10 to 14 days after spermatogenesis has been inhibited by x-ray irradiation (Snell, 1933). Rat epididymal spermatozoa, in animals with ligated vasa, remain capable of motility for about 6 weeks, but lose their ability to fertilize eggs within 3 weeks (White, 1933b); castration further reduces sperm survival to approximately 2 weeks (Moore, 1928). Likewise, in the guinea pig, after ligation of the efferent ducts, epididymal spermatozoa retain their capacity for motility some 60 days and for fertility 20 to 35 days; castration reduces motility to about

3 weeks (Moore, 1928; Young, 1929b). Translocation of the epididymis to the abdominal cavity further limits sperm survival to about 2 weeks. When the rabbit epididymis is anchored in the abdomen, sperm motility and fertility are reduced from about 60 and 38 days in the controls to 14 and 8 days, respectively. Demonstrations such as these seem to indicate that body temperature may have a pronounced effect even on relatively mature spermatozoa (Knaus, 1958); however, the translocation procedure may primarily affect the epididymis, which in turn alters the longevity of the spermatozoa. In at least one type of natural experiment we have evidence that excessive body temperature is seasonally avoided by the gametes. In certain passerine birds during the active breeding season a transient thermal adaptation provides lower temperatures for the storage of morphologically mature spermatozoa (Wolfson, 1954). The sperm-engorged, distal ends of the vasa deferentia here increase prominently in size and become tortuously coiled, so as to result in a cloacal, scrotum-like swelling, the internal temperature of which is about 4°C. less than body temperature.

When the testes have been separated from the epididymides and time allowed for recovery, the potential sperm capacity of the duct system can be determined. Young (1929b) found that guinea pigs, prepared in this manner, can copulate successfully as many as 20 times over a 2-month period. The relative storage facilities of the major segments of the ducts can be determined by actual sperm count. Chang (1945) diligently counted the sperm in the vasa and epididymides of several ram genital tracts and found the greatest accumulation in the tail of the epididymis (Table 13.1). By frequent ejaculation of the ram, approximately twice a day, he further was able to estimate the average rate of sperm production to be about 4.4×10^9 cells per day. In the bull the rate is less, about 2.0×10^9 sperm daily (Boyd and VanDemark, 1957); most of the epididymal sperm storage here is also in the tail (45 per cent) compared with that in the head (36 per cent) (Bialy and Smith, 1958).

TABLE 13.1

Distribution of spermatozoa in male genital tract of ram

(From M. C. Chang, J. Agric. Sc., **35**, 243–246, 1945.)

Segment	Sperm Count (× 10⁹)	Percentage of Total
Epididymis		
Caput.............	17.3	13.1
Corpus............	8.4	6.4
Cauda.............	104.3	79.1
Efferent duct		
Vas deferens.......	1.5	1.1
Ampulla...........	0.3	0.2

C. THE FUNCTIONAL MICROANATOMY OF THE EPIDIDYMIS

The epididymis has received considerable attention from microscopists bent on the elucidation of the role this part of the duct system plays in the reproductive physiology of the male. A number of recent papers have contributed to our understanding of the segmental organization of the epididymis, the cytochemistry of the mucosa, and the response of the duct to steroid influences. For many histochemical details, and historical surveys of much of the earlier literature, the following papers should be consulted: Reid and Cleland (1957), Cavazos (1958), Maneely (1958, 1959), and Reid (1958, 1959) concerning the rat; Ladman and Young (1958) on the guinea pig; Nicander (1957) for the rabbit; and Nicander (1958) concerning the stallion, ram, and bull. Although exquisite in detail and extensive in scope, these papers, with few exceptions, have added little to the earlier contributions concerning the function of the epididymis *vis-à-vis* the physiology of the spermatozoa within the lumen (*cf.* Young, 1933; Mason and Shaver, 1952). With the cytochemical background now available, however, and the current interest in epididymal physiology, the expectations to be derived from a more functional approach should now be fulfilled.

Emphasis has again been placed on the epididymal mucosa, and particularly on the vacuolar and endoplasmic reticular system as a site for the reabsorption of fluid (Nicander, 1957; Reid and Cleland, 1957; Ladman and Young, 1958), in contrast to its

function as a secretory organ (Hammar, 1897; Henry, 1900; Benoit, 1926; Maneely, 1954; Goglia and Magli, 1957). The old question as to the cause of increasing sperm density has apparently been resolved recently by ligation experiments in the rat (Cleland, Jones and Reid, 1959); a specialized region of the epididymis absorbs fluid from the lumen at the point where sperm concentration suddenly increases. Virtually nothing is known about the transport of substances, other than water and possibly inorganic ions, across the mucosal boundary, despite the elaborate cytochemical reports, which include data for acid and alkaline phosphatase activity (Bern, 1949a, b, 1951; Wislocki, 1949; Maneely, 1955, 1958; Montagna, 1955; Allen and Slater, 1957, 1958; Cavazos, 1958; Allen and Hunter, 1960), metachromatic substances (Cavazos, 1958), glycogen (Leblond, 1950; Montagna, 1955; Nicander, 1957, 1958; Cavazos, 1958; Maneely, 1958), lipids (Christie, 1955; Montagna, 1955; Cavazos and Melampy, 1956; Nicander, 1957, 1958), glycoprotein (Cavazos, 1958), and nucleic acids (Nicander, 1957, 1958; Cavazos, 1958). It would be of interest to know how these cytochemical characteristics vary, if indeed they do, with sexual activity, on the one hand, and, on the other hand, with certain functional processes, such as the reabsorption of fluid from the duct, the possible transfer of tagged molecules across the limiting membrane, the elaboration and secretion of, for example, glycerylphosphorylcholine present in the epididymis (Dawson and Rowlands, 1959), and the uptake of large molecular moieties into the mucosa from the lumen, as demonstrated with trypan blue, pyrrhol blue, fuchsin, and India ink particles (von Möllendorf, 1920; Young, 1933; Mason and Shaver, 1952; Shaver, 1954).

Nicander's studies have the added merit that cytochemical demonstrations are correlated with regional differentiation of the epididymis; the duct is divided into 6 to 8 cytologically distinct segments. Such division includes the efferent ducts as part of the epididymis, whether they appear to be nested within a depression of the testis, as in the guinea pig, or quite external to it as in the stallion, ram, bull, and rabbit. All told, the epididymis is an imposing duct, a single continuous tube about 10 feet long in the guinea pig and up to 280 feet in the stallion (Gheție, 1939; Maneely, 1959).

An impressive series of contributions pertaining to the regional differentiation and histology of the rat epididymis has been published by Reid (1958, 1959) and Reid and Cleland (1957), of the University of Sydney. They divide the rat epididymis into six discrete zones, plus the rete and efferent ducts, on the basis of cell type. The efferent ducts and zones 1 to 4 constitute the head, part of zone 4, the isthmus, and zones 5 and 6, the tail of the epididymis (Fig. 13.1). The relative lengths and diameters of the successive zones and the cellular types are represented in Figure 13.2. Six major cell types are discernible: principal, basal, ciliated, apical, halo, and clear cells (Fig. 13.3). Ciliated cells are confined to the efferent ducts—"the most beautiful ciliated cells of the vertebrate body" (von Lenhossék, 1898). Much of the remainder of the epididymis is lined with prominent, nonmotile stereocilia (Reid and Cleland, 1957). Fluid resorption from the lumen is pronounced in zone 4 (Cleland, Jones and Reid, 1959). The principal features of epididymal histogenesis in the rat are summarized in Table 13.2. During the first three weeks of postnatal development, the epididymis remains in an undifferentiated state. At about four weeks, differentiation is first noted in the head of the epididymis and is completed by day 37. Differentiation of the tail begins later than that of the head and is completed only at 14 weeks of age. Sperm are first found in the testis at 8 weeks and appear in the epididymis 2 weeks later.

The epididymis, like the accessory reproductive glands, responds to changes in circulating androgen, and its normal histologic integrity also is apparently dependent on the male hormone (Maneely, 1959). Castration is followed by reduction in tubal diameter and loss of specific cellular components (Cavazos, 1958; Maneely, 1958). Acid and alkaline phosphatase activities of the mouse epididymis decrease after gonadectomy (Allen and Slater, 1957, 1958). Intracellular polysaccharides, visualized by the

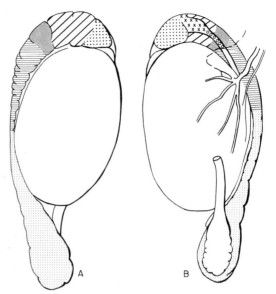

Fig. 13.1. Right testis and epididymis of rat viewed from (A) lateral and (B) medial aspects; cranial end uppermost. Small circles, efferent ducts; crosses, coni vasculosi; coarse dots, zone 1; oblique hatching, zone 2; fine horizontal hatching, zone 3; coarse horizontal hatching, zone 4; fine dots, zones 5 and 6A; unmarked, zone 6B and deferent duct. (After B. L. Reid and K. W. Cleland, Australian J. Zool., 5, 223–246, 1957.)

periodic acid-Schiff (PAS) reaction, are also reduced in the rat by castration (Maneely, 1958). All such responses can be corrected entirely or in part by the administration of testosterone propionate in adequate doses (Cavazos, 1958, and others). Maraud and Stoll (1958) have presented evidence to show, in the chicken at least, that epididymal morphogenesis from the undifferentiated Wolffian duct is dependent on a factor, presumably androgen, elaborated by the primitive testis; in the absence of the gonad, the epididymis remains in an undifferentiated state. The rat epididymis also seems to depend on testicular androgen for its early neonatal differentiation (Cieslak, 1944). Posterior hypothalamectomy of the male guinea pig is followed by extensive degeneration of the reproductive organs, including the epididymis (Soulairac and Soulairac, 1959); subsequent administration of chorionic gonadotrophin (25 I.U.) and testosterone propionate (2.5 mg.) results in only a slight recovery of the epididymal epithelium at sacrifice 8 days after injection.

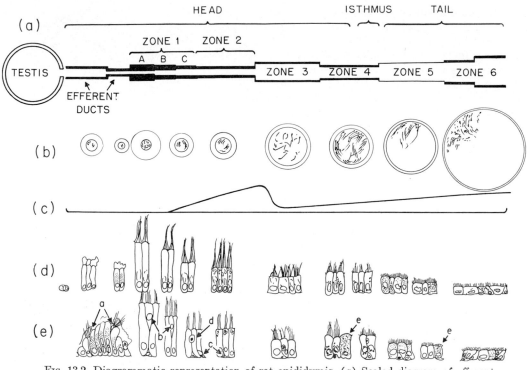

FIG. 13.2. Diagrammatic representation of rat epididymis. (*a*) Scaled diagram of efferent and epididymal ducts in longitudinal section; luminal diameter scaling one-half that of epithelial height. (*b*) Cross-sections of ducts; epithelial height and luminal diameter drawn to the same scale; sperm arrangement indicated. (*c*) Relative sperm density. (*d*) General representation of epithelium. (*e*) Specific types of cells: *a*, ciliated cells; *b*, apical cells; *c*, basal cells; *d*, halo cells; *e*, clear cells. (After B. L. Reid and K. W. Cleland, Australian J. Zool., **5**, 223–246, 1957.)

Seasonal changes in the epididymis have been demonstrated by Wislocki (1949) and others and can be interpreted as representing periodic fluctuations in androgen output.

D. THE EPIDIDYMIS IN RELATION TO SPERM PHYSIOLOGY

Until more adequate and precise information is forthcoming concerning the physiology of the epididymis, its relation to the changes undergone by the spermatozoa within the tract can only be surmised. Little enough, indeed, is known about the chemical composition of the fluids surrounding the sperm in the rete and efferent ducts, and virtually nothing is known concerning the contributions made by the epididymis as a whole to sperm welfare. Fluid is most likely resorbed from the proximal and intermediate portions of the duct, and some secretion may be contributed in exchange (Macmillan and Harrison, 1953; Macmillan, 1953). The nature of this secretion is obscure. No mechanism has been suggested to account for the significant quantity of glycerylphosphorylcholine present in the epididymis and epididymal fluid of various mammals (boar, bull, rats, and guinea pigs), although the concentration of this component is known to be androgen-dependent (Dawson, Mann and White, 1957; Dawson and Rowlands, 1959), and is presumably secreted in the proximal portion of the duct. It is unlikely that glycerylphosphorylcholine or its degradation products serve the sperm in a metabolic capacity, but its presence suggests a possible function in the further maturation of the gametes (Dawson and Rowlands, 1959). No metabolic substrates, *e.g.*, glucose or fructose, have been detected in the fluids of the epididymis. A PAS-positive glycoproteinaceous secretory product has been demonstrated in the lumen of the rat epididymis (Maneely, 1958), but its function and relation to sperm transport and survival are obscure. The most com-

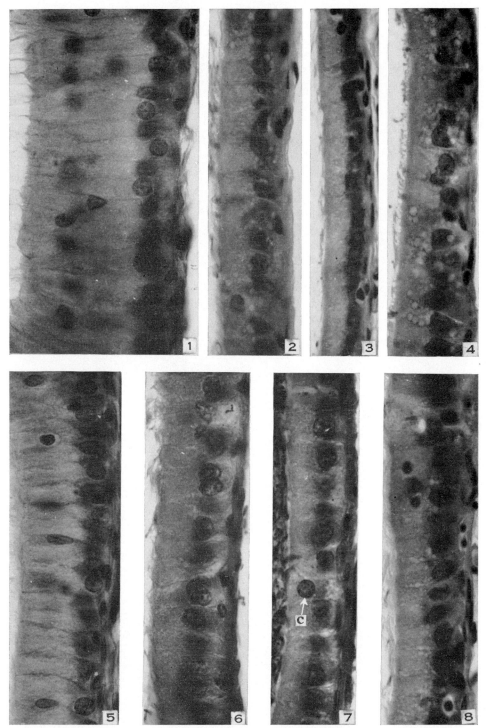

Fig. 13.3. Representative sections of rat epididymis, approx. 750 ✕. (1) Zone 1A; basal, principal, and apical cells visible. (2) Zone 4B; principal cells with perinuclear vacuoles. (3) Zone 3; clear cytoplasm in supranuclear areas. (4) Zone 4A (late); prominent vacuoles in supranuclear areas. (5) Zone 1C; basal, principal, apical, and halo cells. (6) Zone 5A; low columnar principal cells. (7) Zone 5A; as in (6); note clear cell at C. (8) Zone 4A (early); strings of small vacuoles in supranuclear regions. (From B. L. Reid and K. W. Cleland, Australian J. Zool., 5, 223–246, 1957.)

TABLE 13.2

The main changes during histogenesis of the rat epididymis
(From B. L. Reid, Australian J. Zool., **7**, 22–38, 1959.)

Day	Efferent Duct	Zone 1	Zone 2	Zone 3	Zone 4	Zone 5	Zone 6	Deferent Duct
3	Thin connective tissue investment	Undifferentiated simple cuboidal to low columnar epithelium						3 to 4 layers of concentric laminae of connective tissue
21	As for 3 days	Thicker connective tissue investment / Undifferentiated and simple cuboidal to low columnar epithelium / Connective tissue investment loose, 2 to 3 layers thick		Connective tissue investment tightly packed, 1 to 2 layers thick		Connective tissue investment as for zones 1 and 2		Pseudostratified columnar epithelium not folded, 6 to 8 layers of connective tissue
28	Differentiation by clarity of cytoplasm in initial zone and appearance of ciliated cells	Tall epithelium of stratified columnar type; mainly two rows of nuclei			Alternating segments of tall and short stratified columnar epithelium	Stratified columnar epithelium; two to four rows of nuclei; stellate lumen		Connective tissue laminae recognizable as smooth muscle
32	Advanced differentiation of terminal and initial zones. Prominent coni vasculosi region	Tall columnar epithelium of definitive structure, about 60 per cent of definitive height. Two rows of nuclei	Shorter columnar epithelium with scant apical vacuoles	Similar height columnar epithelium to zone 2 without apical vacuoles	As for 28 days	As for 28 days		As for 28 days. Folded epithelium as for adult

37	As for 32 days. Definitive pattern established	As for 32 days	As for 32 days. Increasing numbers of cells with apical vacuoles	Increased volume. Epithelium lower at 35 μ	As for 28 days	As for 28 days	Becomes differentiated from vas deferens at 39 days as pale cytoplasm with several rows of nuclei	As for 32 days
56	As for 32 days	Definitive pattern established	Definitive pattern established	As for 37 days	At junctional area with zone 3 is tall stratified columnar epithelium. More caudally it is low columnar. Juxtanuclear vacuoles appear	As for 28 days	Inactive clear cells appear. 2 or 3 rows of nuclei, occasionally 1 row	As for 32 days
				Sperm present in all zones of adult distribution				
72	As for 32 days	As for 56 days	As for 56 days	As for 56 days	Small residue of tall epithelium cranially. Remainder is low columnar	Tall columnar epithelium. 1 to 2 rows of nuclei. Rounded lumen	As for 56 days. The majority of oval nuclei now have long axes parallel to surface	As for 56 days
96	As for 32 days	As for 56 days	As for 56 days	As for 56 days	Gross increase in volume. Nuclei becoming irregular in shape	Low columnar epithelium of definitive type. Irregularity of shape of nuclei	Flattening of cells and nuclei. Nuclei irregular in shape	As for 32 days
110	As for 32 days	As for 56 days	As for 56 days	As for 56 days	As for 96 days	As for 96 days	As for 96 days. Many nuclei show peripheral distribution of chromatin	As for 32 days

TABLE 13.3

Mineral concentrations in male reproductive fluids
(From R. G. Cragle, G. W. Salisbury and J. H.
Muntz, J. Dairy Sc., **41**, 1273–1277, 1958.)

Ele-ment	Testicular Fluid (average of 12 samples)	Ampullar Fluid (average of 3 samples)	Seminal Ve-sicular Fluid (average of 10 samples)	Seminal Plasma (average of 10 samples)
	mg. per 100 ml.	mg. per 100 ml.	mg. per 100 ml.	mg. per 100 ml.
B	0.80	0.59	0.73	1.48
P	229.00	328.00	10.00	55.00
Mg	14.90	8.50	17.50	11.60
Ca	4.60	32.00	70.00	51.00
Fe	2.59	1.08	0.38	0.35
Cu	1.36	2.10	0.95	1.36
Na	178.00	137.00	251.00	273.00

plete analyses of inorganic ions in the fluids of the male tract are those by Cragle, Salisbury and Muntz (1958) for the testicular and ampullar fluids of the bull. The values are compared with those of seminal plasma and seminal vesicular fluid in Table 13.3.

One type of epididymal reaction which may be of considerable importance, although the mechanism of the process is little understood, is that concerning ionic exchange, alluded to above. Salisbury and Cragle (1956) showed that shifts in the sodium-potassium ratio occur in the luminal contents of the goat and bull when sampled at different levels of the tract. The combined "semen" (sperm and fluid) tends to show a relative increase in sodium ion and an increase in $K^+ + Na^+$ when comparisons are made of tubal contents from successively lower regions of the tract. Freezing-point determinations indicated that the fluid is initially hypertonic ($-0.600°C.$), with respect to blood, and decreases in tonicity with passage through the tube. Determinations of epididymal plasma and seminal plasma of ejaculated bull semen tended to confirm these results with respect to increase in Na^+ and the combined $K^+ + Na^+$ values (Sørenson and Andersen, 1956).

In a general way, the capacities for motility and fertility seem to be acquired about the same time, but in neither case is this brought about by a sudden change. The capacity for fertilization increases as the gametes are taken from more distal regions of the tract. In the fowl, for example, in-

semination with sperm from the testis, epididymis, and vas deferens, respectively, gave 1.6, 18.8, and 65.3 per cent fertile eggs (Munro, 1938). Similarly, in the guinea pig, sperm removed from the proximal and distal portions of the epididymis and used in artificial insemination resulted in 33.4 and 68.0 per cent pregnancies (Young, 1931). After ligation of the vasa deferentia and aging of the sperm, the percentage of fertility from proximal and distal sperm shifted to 44.2 and 32.5 per cent, respectively, for 20-day postligation sperm, and to 49.0 and 25.0 per cent for 30-day stored sperm. It seems clear that, with storage, the maturation of the sperm is followed by a process of senescence. This was further suggested by Young's experiments, since the percentage of aborted and resorbed fetuses increased apparently when fertilization was accomplished by aged spermatozoa.

Whether or not the relative fertility rates of spermatozoa from different levels of the male genital tract can be explained entirely on the assumption that motility and fertilizing capacity go hand in hand remains to be seen, since other aspects of sperm behavior also change with transit through the ducts. Young (1929c) pointed out, for example, that the heat resistance (to 46°C.) of guinea pig, rat, and ram sperm decreases as they migrate through the tract, and Lasley and Bogart (1944) showed that the resistance of boar sperm to "cold shock" is likewise reduced.

E. THE FATE OF NONUTILIZED SPERM IN THE MALE

In the absence of ejaculation, the question arises as to the fate of the millions of gametes which are continuously generated during spermatogenesis. It had been previously assumed that sperm elimination is by "insensible ejaculation"; sperm have been detected in the urinary outflow (Wilhelm and Seligmann, 1937). It was shown, however, by Young and Simeone (1930; Simeone and Young, 1931), and since confirmed by others, that the sperm of the guinea pig, for example, undergo degeneration and dissolution within the epididymis. The disposal of the degradation products of the sperm, on the other hand, is not clear from these experiments. They could very possibly be voided through the vas deferens or be absorbed by the duct mucosa and phagocytosed, as suggested by Mason and Shaver (1952) and Montagna (1955). The possibility of absorption of sperm and of sperm products by the epithelium poses a significant problem relating to self-immunization which is discussed in a later section.

F. ACQUISITION BY SPERM OF THE CAPACITY FOR MOTILITY

By the time spermatozoa are primed for union with the eggs they must be sufficiently activated to undergo independent movement, since motility, with rare exceptions, is a prerequisite for fertilization. Sperm activation is delayed in many species until the gametes are in intimate association. Among both invertebrate and vertebrate animals, instances are known in which sperm are shed in a nonmotile condition and are activated only when passively brought into association with homologous eggs as noted above. Frequently the gametes are transferred in large bundles or packets, enclosed in spermatophores, and become motile only after the casings are ruptured when in contact with the female (Drew, 1919). Generally, however, the gametes are stimulated when shed externally or ejaculated into the female genital tract. This event corresponds to a spectacular moment in the metabolic life of the cell when the exergonic processes are shifted into high gear by the abrupt supply of oxygen, substrate, or cofactors, in mammals copiously provided by the secretions of the accessory reproductive glands.

Before ejaculation, and for much of the time during their storage in the ducts, sperm are quite capable of motility but, so far as can be determined, remain, *in vivo*, in a quiescent state (Simeone, 1933). The reproductive advantage of this is obvious since, before activation, sperm survival is estimated in terms of months; after activity has been acquired, survival is a matter of days or hours (see Table 13.8). The blocks both to the excessive utilization of energy and to motility, *in vivo*, are regarded as largely of a physical nature—the relative or absolute absence of oxygen which otherwise would encourage aerobic respiration, and the lack of glycolytic substrate, such as glucose or fructose, which when present fosters anaerobic processes (Mann, 1954; Walton, 1956). Infrequent reports of transient motility by sperm immediately after removal from the genital tract, thereby implying that the cells are motile *in vivo* (White, Larsen and Wales, 1959), must be confirmed and may be attributable to the admission of oxygen during the sampling procedure. Earlier suppositions that sperm immobilization within the ducts is due to high CO_2 concentration or low pH level (Redenz, 1926) have been contraindicated (Bishop and Mathews, 1952a). Other physiologic factors, involving both intrinsic features of the gametes and exchange reactions between them and the luminal fluids, may play a role, but if so, their nature and action are unrecognized.

The *capacity* for motility on a general scale is first attained by sperm during transit through the epididymis (Redenz, 1926). Cells removed from the tail of the duct, of the bull for example, immediately become highly active when suspended in physiologic saline and given access to oxygen; under anaerobic conditions, glucose, fructose, or mannose initiates vigorous flagellation. Sperm removed from the head or the isthmus of the epididymis, on the other hand, rarely become motile and at best show only a slow nonprogressive type of undulation. Other mammals present a similar picture, the precise epididymal region where motile capacity is attained varying among species.

Some degree of flagellation, albeit of a leisurely, low-frequency type, can be observed in sperm recovered from the testes of various mammalian species (Tournade, 1913; Young, 1929a; Bishop, 1958d). These gametes are incapable of activation to full motility by the addition of oxygen, glycolytic substrate, divalent cations (Mg^{++}, Ca^{++}), or ATP (Bishop, unpublished data). Austin and Sapsford (1952) have observed that the axial filament of the living rat spermatid undergoes movement even before the flagellum begins to push out from the margin of the roughly spherical cell. In lower forms as well, particularly among insects, sperm motility can be seen during the period when the gametes are still attached to their nurse cells within the gonad

(Anderson, 1950). In conclusion, then, it would seem that spermatozoa must develop much of the machinery for movement while undergoing spermiogenesis in the testis, that subtle changes occur while they are in the mammalian epididymis such that the full capacity for motility is here acquired, and finally that this ability for flagellation is realized normally only on activation at the time of ejaculation.

Although the problem has been recognized for many years, only recently has serious attention been paid to the nature of the possible changes in spermatozoa that are responsible for the acquisition of the capacity for motility within the epididymis. In setting forth a hypothesis to account for this phenomenon, Salisbury (1956) has focused needed attention on the problem. His suggestion follows from determinations of cation concentration and freezing point depression values of fluids of the genital tract of the ram and the bull, noted above (Salisbury and Cragle, 1956). The supposition is that a decrease in K^+/Na^+ and an absolute increase in $K^+ + Na^+$ concentration, nevertheless accompanied by a total reduction in tonicity of the fluids, bring about permeability changes such that the sperm become hydrated and, as a result, capable of full metabolic activity (Salisbury, 1956). An ingenious theory, it is, nevertheless, not easily reconciled with the generally accepted demonstration that sperm *lose* water rather than gain it as they mature (Lindahl and Kihlström, 1952; Mann, 1954). Until more precise information is available concerning such details as the sodium and potassium concentrations of the sperm *vis-à-vis* those of the fluid of the ducts, the actual water- and cation-permeability of sperm at various stages, and the effect of shifts in the sodium-potassium ratio on motility of epididymal sperm, *in vitro*, this problem cannot be fully resolved.

IV. Insemination

At the time of mammalian sperm transfer, many millions of vigorously motile spermatozoa are introduced into the female genital tract. Mixed with the fluid component of the semen only at the moment of ejaculation, the sperm normally are activated by their sudden access to both oxygen and the hex-

ose energy substrate of the plasma. The source and composition of the seminal fluid have been reviewed elsewhere (Mann and Lutwak-Mann, 1951; Mann, 1954) and are further discussed in the chapter by Price and Williams-Ashman. Only certain characteristics of semen, relevant to sperm transport and welfare, need be noted here.

What is the normal function of seminal plasma, and to what extent is it dispensable? The fluid component contributed by the accessory glands can conceivably serve several functions which include its role as (1) a vehicle for sperm transport, (2) a medium containing essential inorganic ions and of adequate buffering capacity, (3) a satisfactory osmotic milieu, and (4) a source of energy substrate. Seminal plasma, by virtue of its very complex composition, also performs other duties. It supplies, for example, the enzyme and substrate responsible for vaginal-plug formation; it contains certain substances, unique to the reproductive fluids, such as antagglutin which ostensibly prevents undue sperm agglutination; it provides such ingredients as ascorbic acid, ergothioneine, and possibly glutathione, which may play a role in the adjustment of the oxidation-reduction potential. On the other hand, some components of seminal plasma may indeed be by-products with no obvious beneficial role and even, perhaps, with harmful effects on the gametes; both alcohol and sulfonamides, for example, are excreted into the plasma (Farrell, 1938; Osenkoop and MacLeod, 1947).

Since the vital process of sperm activation is accomplished by their admixture with plasma, and since a fluid vehicle is essential for sperm transport, it goes without saying that seminal plasma normally is necessary for the reproductive process. To suggest that artificial insemination with epididymal sperm suspended in saline, successful as it is, proves the dispensability of seminal plasma, is to ignore the normal biologic accomplishments of natural insemination. Nevertheless, it is a fact that artificial insemination has proved highly successful in the reproduction of many types of animals. Moreover, the collection and analysis of the ejaculate, coupled with artificial insemination by natural or modified semen, constitute the basis for much of our knowledge concerning the entire field of reproductive physiology and animal breeding.

A. EJACULATION

The ejaculatory response in many mammals occurs seasonally, corresponding to periodic activity of the testes and accessory glands, and is dependent on a variety of neurohumoral factors. In some animals, including man, potency continues throughout the period of reproductive maturity. Volume of semen and sperm concentration, being contingent on both secretory activity of the accessory glands and spermatogenic activity of the gonads, vary with successive collections. Repetitive ejaculation can "exhaust" the sperm supply (Table 13.4), and such procedures have been used, albeit without great practical success, to test the spermatogenic productivity of man and of various domestic animals.

The potential for ejaculation of many animals is quite striking. Carpenter (1942) observed that free-ranging macaque monkeys are capable of ejaculating 4 times a day for 3 or 4 days, whereas the so-called "black ape" (a baboon, *Cynopithecus*), studied by Bingham (1928), ejaculated 3 times in 20 minutes. Domestic cats have been known to inseminate 10 females within 1 hour, and rabbits, 38 to 40 does in 8 hours (Ford and Beach, 1951). White rats can ejaculate 4 times in 15 minutes and as many as 10 times during a 3-hour period. Chang and Sheaffer (1957) reported that a golden hamster copulated 50 times in an hour, with ejaculation occurring during most of the mounts. McKenzie and Berliner (1937) collected 20 ejaculates in 1 day from a ram, the 19th sample of 0.66 ml. containing over 1 billion sperm, compared with the first ejaculate of 0.7 ml. which contained 3.5 billion cells.

There is relatively little correlation between the number of intromittent thrusts and the number of actual ejaculations, or between the duration of copulation and the volume of seminal discharge. In rodents, for example, intromission may occur as many as 80 to 100 times before ejaculation, or insemination may occur on the first intromission. Copulation in the macaque may involve several dozen mountings and well over a hundred pelvic thrusts before ejaculation

TABLE 13.4
Changes in volume and sperm density of bull ejaculates collected frequently throughout a one-hour period
(From T. Mann, Advances Enzymol., **9**, 329–390, 1949.)

Number of Ejaculate	Collection Time	Volume	Number of sperm, mil. per ml. semen
	min.	*ml.*	
1	0	4.2	1664
2	10	3.9	680
3	18	3.7	254
4	28	3.7	648
5	38	3.4	135
6	45	3.5	342
7	55	2.7	390
8	63	2.9	98

occurs. The prolonged copulation of the ferret and sable, as long as 3 hours, represents, not excessive ejaculation or insemination, but rather a functional adaptation to delayed ovulation (Ford and Beach, 1951). In the dog, however, the mounting time is roughly proportional to the duration of ejaculation, averaging in several breeds about 6½ minutes (Pérez García, 1957). An important accomplishment of genital activity, at least in the rat, is the stimulation of sufficient corpus luteal function to support pregnancy (Ball, 1934).

Cerebral and constitutional influences incite and modify the physiologic processes of both erection and ejaculation (Rommer, 1952) under the direct innervation by lumbar centers operating through muscular and vascular mechanisms. Spinal section in man does not necessarily prevent seminal emission (Ford and Beach, 1951). The relevant neural pathways in man have been summarized by Whitelaw and Smithwick (1951) from their observations on partially sympathectomized patients (Fig. 13.4, *a* and *b*); sympathetic fibers and the second, third, and fourth sacral parasympathetic outflows are involved. The abolition of ejaculation through bilateral presacral sympathectomy, without loss of erection, has been demonstrated in dogs (Van Duzen, Slaughter and White, 1947) and rodents (Bacq, 1931). In man and other mammals (rat, cat, and dog), the cerebral cortex plays an important role in male sexual activity (Ford and Beach, 1951), but an evaluation of the co-ordina-

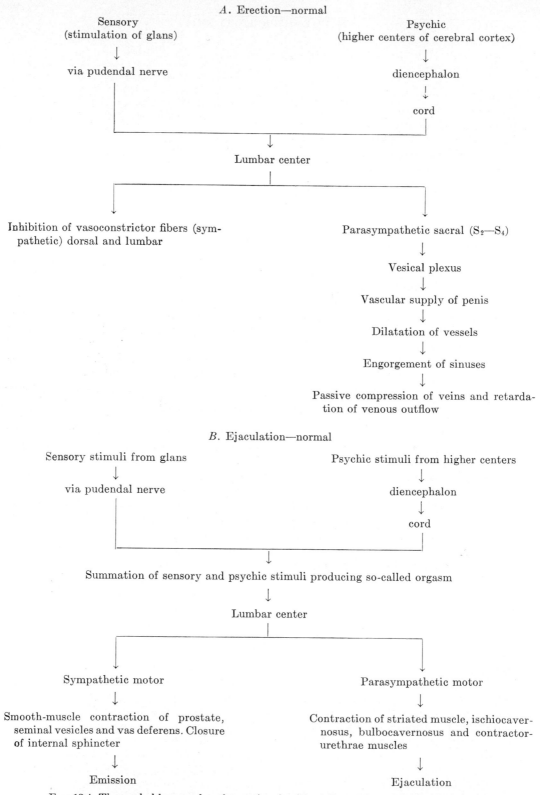

A. Erection—normal

Sensory
(stimulation of glans)
↓
via pudendal nerve

Psychic
(higher centers of cerebral cortex)
↓
diencephalon
↓
cord

Lumbar center

Inhibition of vasoconstrictor fibers (sympathetic) dorsal and lumbar

Parasympathetic sacral (S_2—S_4)
↓
Vesical plexus
↓
Vascular supply of penis
↓
Dilatation of vessels
↓
Engorgement of sinuses
↓
Passive compression of veins and retardation of venous outflow

B. Ejaculation—normal

Sensory stimuli from glans
↓
via pudendal nerve

Psychic stimuli from higher centers
↓
diencephalon
↓
cord

Summation of sensory and psychic stimuli producing so-called orgasm
↓
Lumbar center

Sympathetic motor
↓
Smooth-muscle contraction of prostate, seminal vesicles and vas deferens. Closure of internal sphincter
↓
Emission

Parasympathetic motor
↓
Contraction of striated muscle, ischiocavernosus, bulbocavernosus and contractor-urethrae muscles
↓
Ejaculation

Fig. 13.4. The probable neural pathways involved in (A) erection and (B) ejaculation in man, based on observations after partial sympathectomy. (From G. P. Whitelaw and R. H. Smithwick, New England J. Med., **245**, 121–130, 1951.)

724

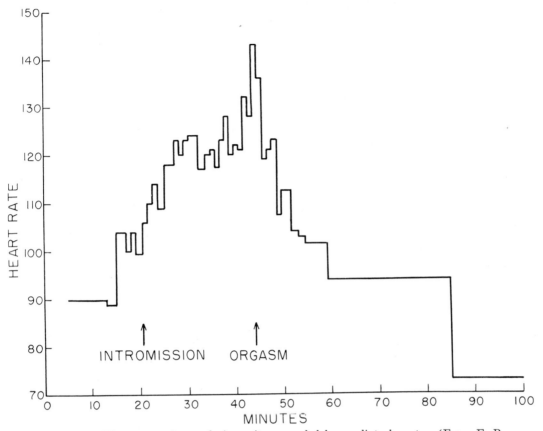

FIG. 13.5. Heart rate of man during coitus recorded by cardiotachometer. (From E. P. Boas and E. F. Goldschmidt, *The Heart Rate*, Charles C Thomas, 1932.)

tion between cerebral and spinal centers warrants considerable further study. The subject is further discussed in the chapter by Money. Ejaculation in men and dogs is accompanied by pronounced cardiovascular intensification (Pussep, 1921; Boas and Goldschmidt, 1932; Bartlett, 1956) affecting both blood pressure and pulse rate (Figs. 13.5, 13.6). Androgen administration increases libido and copulatory arousal (see chapter by Young), but the manner in which this is related to the preceding neurogenic factors is not well understood (Cheng and Casida, 1949).

B. COLLECTION OF SEMINAL COMPONENTS

Various methods of seminal collection may be employed for either whole or fractional analyses. Normal ejaculates are expected when induced by masturbation, electrical stimulation, or discharge into an artificial vagina. Sperm samples without

seminal plasma are readily obtainable from the epididymis and vas deferens of the excised tracts of many animals (*e.g.*, the guinea pig, rat, boar, bull, and stallion) by backflushing the vas and cutting the epididymis. Relatively uncontaminated prostatic fluid is procurable, *e.g.*, from men and dogs, and vesicular fluid from men, by manual massage of the appropriate glandular regions. Incomplete ejaculates are produced after extirpation of such organs as the seminal vesicles and Cowper's glands; the prostatic isolation operation, perfected on dogs by Huggins, Masina, Eichelberger and Wharton (1939) and illustrated in Chapter 6, Figure 6.2, permits the collection of large amounts of uncontaminated prostatic fluid.

C. SEMINAL VOLUME AND SUCCESSIVE FRACTIONS

Seminal volume bears some relation to animal size, but the individual contributions

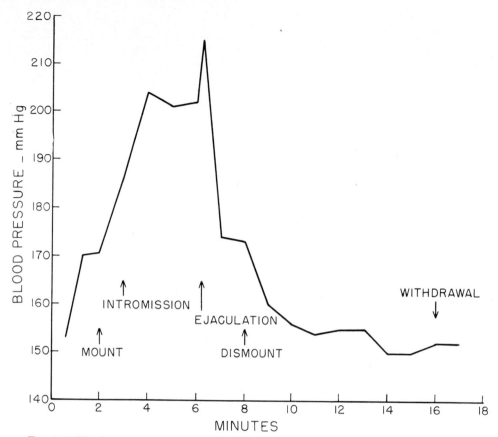

Fɪɢ. 13.6. Blood pressure of dog during coitus. (After L. M. Pussep, *Der Blutkreislauf im Gehirn beim Koitus*, Dorpat, 1921.)

TABLE 13.5

Volume and sperm density of mammalian ejaculates (From T. Mann, Advances Enzymol., **9,** 329–390, 1949; S. A. Asdell, *Patterns of Mammalian Reproduction*, Comstock Publishing Co., 1946.)

Species	Volume of Single Ejaculate		Density of Sperm in Semen	
	Range	Most common value	Range	Average value
	ml.	*ml.*	*cells per µl.*	*cells per µl.*
Man.......	2–6	3.5	50,000–150,000	100,000
Dog.	2–15	6	70,000–900,000	200,000
Rabbit ...	0.4–6	1	100,000–2,000,000	700,000
Boar.......	150–500	250	25,000–300,000	100,000
Bull.......	2–10	4	300,000–2,000,000	1,000,000
Ram......	0.7–2	1	2,000,000–5,000,000	3,000,000
Goat......	0.1–1.25	0.6	3,000,000–4,000,000	3,500,000
Stallion....	30–300	70	30,000–800,000	120,000

of the respective accessory glands determine the quantity of semen in the ejaculate. The volumes of seminal discharge from several mammals are presented in Table 13.5. The enormous volume of the boar ejaculate, as much as half a liter, may be of importance in "washing" the sperm through the uterus, inasmuch as in the sow the semen is deposited directly into the cervix, and the ejaculate is so proportioned that the spermatozoa are concentrated in the earlier fractions and are followed by a copious flood of relatively sperm-free fluid (McKenzie, Miller and Bauguess, 1938). When fractional collection is possible, the spermatozoa are found generally concentrated in the initial or middle portion of the ejaculate (ram, dog, boar, horse, and man). The ejaculate of the dog consists of a small, initial, clear, relatively sperm-free portion, followed by a milky fraction containing the bulk of the spermatozoa, and finally a slow but copious dribble largely derived from the prostate (Evans, 1933; Hartman, unpublished data). Collection by means of the electrically stimulated "split-ejaculation" technique has demonstrated in the bull an abundant sperm-free initial portion which apparently is derived from the urethral glands and presumably serves to clear the urethral passage before the transport of spermatozoa (Lutwak-Mann and Rowson, 1953). In man, however, approximately three fourths of the sperm are present in the first 40 per cent of the ejaculate (MacLeod and Hotchkiss, 1942). Qualitative contributions to the total ejaculate by the several accessory glands have been carefully studied and are discussed elsewhere (see chapter by Price and Williams-Ashman).

D. EFFECTIVE SPERM CONCENTRATION

It is not a simple matter to determine what might be the minimal effective sperm count necessary to insure fertilization. The earlier standards of what constitutes a subfertile human seminal density have undergone considerable re-evaluation. The once-acceptable value of minimal concentration, 80 to 100 million cells per ml. of semen, has now been reduced to one half or less. On the other hand, the spotty records of pregnancies in women whose husbands' sperm counts consistently average 1,000,000 per ml., or less, may be viewed with some skepticism (Michelson, 1951; Sandler, 1952). The extensive studies of MacLeod and Gold (1951) on human subjects of proved fertility, compared with men of infertile marriages, indicate a significant break between the two groups in the neighborhood of 20,000,000 cells per ml. of semen. Current trends in the evaluation of semen tend to minimize sperm density, as such, and to regard this property only with reference to other criteria, including volume, total sperm number, morphology, and, of course, motility.

A reasonable gauge of minimal effective sperm count necessary to insure fertilization has been provided by dilution tests and artificial insemination of domestic and laboratory animals. In cattle, the normal ejaculate, which contains some 4 billion sperm, can be reduced 500 to 1000 times without sacrificing high productivity (Salisbury and Bratton, 1948; Braden and Austin, 1953). Rabbit fertilization is unimpaired when the normal inseminate is decreased 500-fold (Cheng and Casida, 1948; Chang, 1951a; Chang, 1959; Braden and Austin, 1953).

That mere number of sperm is not the only factor was clarified by Chang (1946a, b) who showed that the concentration and nature of the diluent are also important. The percentage of fertile eggs recovered from does inseminated with a suboptimal number of sperm (*ca.* 40,000) decreases as a function of the volume of saline diluent (from 0.1 to 1.0 ml.). On the other hand, if rabbit seminal plasma is substituted for saline as the diluent, fertilizing capacity is enhanced (Chang, 1947b, 1949). The nature and the effect of the sperm diluent are further discussed below; it is sufficient to point out here that many factors may determine the absolute number of sperm required for a high rate of fertilization.

E. SITE OF INSEMINATION

The location of the deposition of semen during ejaculation differs in various animals and may account, in part, for the variations recorded for time of transport through the female genital tract. Intravaginal insemination predominates in the rabbit, dog, ewe, cow, and man, whereas intrauterine deposition occurs in the mouse, rat, sow, mare, and probably the hamster (Braden and Austin, 1953; du Mesnil du Buisson and Dauzier, 1955; Chang and Sheaffer, 1957).

Experimental insemination has been attempted by a number of routes. Administration of sperm into the ovarian bursa of receptive mice proved highly satisfactory (Runner, 1947). Intraperitoneal insemination has been accomplished in fowl (Van Drimmelen, 1945), guinea pigs (Rowlands, 1957), rabbits (Hadek, 1958b), and, with bare success, in the cow (Skjerven, 1955; McDonald and Sampson, 1957). In an extensive animal breeding investigation, Salisbury and VanDemark (1951) showed that artificial insemination was equally effective in cattle, as judged from the nonreturn rate, when semen was deposited in the vagina, the body of the uterus, or the uterine horns.

F. ARTIFICIAL INSEMINATION

Little more than a brief account of this special and applied subject seems appropriate at the moment. Excellent surveys of the development, techniques, and accomplishments of artificial insemination have appeared from time to time, two of the more general being those of Anderson (1944) and Emmens and Blackshaw (1956). Legal and ethical aspects of artificial insemination in man have been dwelt upon extensively in the semiclinical literature (Haman, 1947; Nicolle, 1949; Guttmacher, Haman and MacLeod, 1950; Ellis, 1952; Pope Pius XII, 1957).

According to various historic accounts, the Arabians have for centuries practiced, if not thoroughly understood, the art of artificial insemination in the breeding of their horses.[1] In more recent times Spallanzani developed a method for the artificial insemination of amphibia and, in 1782, first successfully inseminated a dog. Shortly thereafter, the first successful insemination of a woman was recorded (Home, 1799). Now it is a common practice, the world over, for the selective breeding of various species of mammals (Walton, 1958). The techniques have also been applied, both for academic and for practical aims, to other types of animals, including fowl (Quinn and Burrows, 1936; Van Drimmelen, 1945), viviparous fish (Clark, 1950), and insects (Laidlaw and Eckert, 1950; Lee, 1950).

Constant efforts are being made to improve the dilution and storage media of sperm for routine use in artificial insemination (see Salisbury, 1957). At present, 5- or 6-day survival of bull semen, diluted with egg yolk-sodium citrate and stored in the presence of antibiotics at 2 to 3°C., is about all that can be expected. Most types of semen lose their fertilizing capacity much sooner than this. It is a curious fact that fowl sperm, which survive so well (2 or more

---

[1] Walter Heape (1898) recounted an interesting tale which probably has some basis in fact: "It is taken from a book written in the year 700 of the Hejira, and therein is described how an Arab of Darfour, the owner of a valuable mare on 'heat,' armed with a handful of cotton wool which had been saturated with the discharge from the vagina of his mare, approached by stealth a valuable stallion belonging to a member of a neighbouring hostile tribe, a stallion whose services for his favourite mare the owner was desperately anxious to obtain; and having sufficiently excited the animal with the scent of the material he had brought, he obtained spermatic fluid from him on the same handful of cotton, and hastening back to his mare, which he had been obliged to leave some distance away, pushed the whole into her vagina, and obtained by that means a foal."

weeks) in the female genital tract, cannot be preserved in vitro more than a few hours without decline in fertilizing capacity (Garren and Shaffner, 1952; Carter, McCartney, Chamberlin and Wyne, 1957).

The most significant advance— certainly the most striking—in the field of sperm preservation during the past decade is the remarkable success in maintaining cells in a viable condition at extremely low temperature. The very early history began with Mantegazza's (1866) and Davenport's (1897) successful demonstrations that deep-frozen (−17°C.) human sperm could regain motility. Despite other attempts to improve the degree of recovery by the addition of various substrates and by control of temperature changes, a marked measure of success was to await the discovery of Polge, Smith and Parkes (1949), who showed that equilibration of the semen with glycerol before freezing greatly enhances sperm recovery and motility after warming to room temperature. This work, on rooster and human spermatozoa, catalyzed many investigations of the problem with the result that today there are few common mammals whose sperm have not been vitrified, stored at −79° or −196°C., and warmed up for observation of motility or used in breeding experiments (Emmens and Blackshaw, 1956; Polge, 1957; VanDemark, Miller, Kinney, Rodriguez and Friedman, 1957; Martin and Emmens, 1958). The presence of glycerol is essential, in concentrations between 10 and 15 per cent, for bull sperm, to 20 per cent for those of fowl (Martin and Emmens, 1958). Bull spermatozoa have been stored successfully in this fashion for periods up to 6 years (Walton, 1958).

Artificial insemination with previously deep-frozen, thawed sperm has resulted in conception and viable young in a number of animals. The degree of fertility varies, being low in the rabbit and as high as in normal matings in the bull (Emmens and Blackshaw, 1956). Pregnancies have been reported for several women inseminated with spermatozoa treated in this manner (Bunge and Sherman, 1954).

The advantages of the perfection of the low-temperature method for the preservation of animal sperm are obvious. In the case of bull semen, for example, the procedure permits long-term storage and, in the long run, greater use of the sperm. An additional advantage is that the storage intervals allow for progeny testing, a procedure which takes time and is of considerable importance in identifying the breeding value. As applied to man, on the other hand, the method would seem to have only limited usefulness in exceptional instances. One might suppose, for example, that successive ejaculates of an oligospermic individual could be stored and pooled in this fashion and give, upon insemination, a sufficiently high sperm count to insure fertilization. The advantage of transportability of frozen semen, practical in animal husbandry, would not be expected to play a significant role in matters concerning human fertility.

The changes which may occur in cells during storage at such low temperatures, or during the freezing or thawing process, can only be surmised. Based on the resumption of motility at room temperature and fertilizing capacity, the alterations in bull spermatozoa must be minor. In other kinds of spermatozoa, those of the rabbit for example, metabolic and permeability changes may be more pronounced. Subtle changes, such as might be induced in the cytogenetic apparatus, are unknown; there is the question of whether they have been sought.

The mechanism of the protective action of glycerol in maintaining the spermatozoa during the relatively slow freezing process and while in storage is obscure. The effect is probably not merely one of the prevention of ice crystal formation, but rather one which involves the stability of the internal ionic concentration of the cell. One can suppose that without glycerol, the withdrawal of free water would result in severe changes possibly involving an increase in ionic strength, alteration in pH, the production of toxic concentrations of such substances as urea and dissolved gases, and an actual physical reorganization of intracellular components (Lovelock, 1957). One suggestion is that the elements sensitive to deep freezing are lipoprotein complexes which, in the presence of glycerol, are prevented from denaturation (Lovelock, 1957).

Although deep freezing and cold storage of sperm are currently receiving the greatest attention, other methods of controlling metabolism and motility are being considered and may ultimately prove useful in the preservation of sperm for artificial insemination. Such metabolic blocking agents as tetrazolium compounds (Bishop and Mathews, 1952b) and carbon dioxide (Salisbury and VanDemark, 1957; VanDemark and Sharma, 1957; du Mesnil du Buisson and Dauzier, 1958) can reversibly inhibit the processes involved in the utilization of substrate and the expenditure of energy. Another approach has recently been suggested by the work of Petersen and Nordlund (1958) whose preliminary experiments indicate that bull sperm can be subjected to 150 atmospheres of pressure, in nitrogen, and survive such treatment for two weeks, after which motility is regained. Whether such a procedure destroys fertilizing capacity has not yet been ascertained.

V. Sperm Transport and Survival in the Female Tract

The vigorous motility of seminal spermatozoa has long been a source of fascination and naturally gave strong support to early suppositions that migration in the female tract is due to the activity of the cells themselves. This is now known not to be generally true, and only in certain limited segments does active sperm motility seem of possible importance in transport from the vagina to the site of fertilization in the oviduct. Suggestions have been made, in fact, that sperm motility may be unnecessary even for egg penetration (Allen and Grigg, 1957), but such has never been demonstrated in studies of fertilization of either invertebrate or vertebrate gametes.

The over-all transport system for mammalian spermatozoa is principally provided by muscular contractions of the walls of the tract, with a questionable role played by ciliary activity of the mucosa; under some circumstances, however, active flagellation of the gametes themselves is important (cf. Hartman, 1939).

A. DURATION OF TRANSPORT

The most striking evidence that sperm migration in the female tract cannot be attributed solely to sperm motility is afforded by the results of studies of the rate of transport and the time required to pass from the point of insemination to the site of fertilization or to intermediate levels of the reproductive system. Thus, for example, the mean velocity of bull sperm is on the order of 100 μ per sec. (Moeller and VanDemark, 1955; Gray, 1958), and if a straight path were followed, it would require about 1½ hours for the gametes to cover the entire length of the tract; actually the time required after natural mating is less than 2½ minutes (VanDemark and Moeller, 1951).

Rapid sperm migration through the uterus was first demonstrated by Hartman and Ball (1930) in the rat; within 2 minutes after copulation myriads of sperm had entered the tubes (Table 13.6). A subsequent investigation showed that a few sperm were present at the periovarial sac within 1½ minutes after copulation (Warren, 1938). Blandau and Money (1944) later indicated that at copulation, rat sperm are catapulted through the cervix into the uterine cornua, and within 15 minutes have entered the Fallopian tubes in considerable numbers. By clamping the middle of the tubes at various times after copulation, the distribution of sperm could be determined. After 15 minutes, sperm were found in 42 per cent of the uterine (lower) segments of the oviducts examined and 21 per cent of the ovarian (upper) segments; after 30 minutes, 85 per cent and 62 per cent, respectively; after 45 minutes, 90 per cent and 96 per cent; and at 60 minutes, both the uterine and ovarian portions of oviducts of all animals studied contained sperm.

After insemination of the mouse, sperm reach the tubal infundibulum, the site of fertilization, within 15 minutes (Lewis and Wright, 1935). In the bitch, 20 minutes or less are required (Evans, 1933; Whitney, 1937), and in the hamster about 30 minutes (Chang and Sheaffer, 1957). Rubenstein, Strauss, Lazarus and Hankin (1951) claimed that human sperm deposited at the cervix just before hysterectomy, can be recovered from the Fallopian tube 30 minutes later; the nature of the operation, however, might seriously affect the rate of transport. Other reports of sperm-transport time in women range up to 3 hours (Chang and Pincus, 1951).

As part of a series of marvelously planned and executed experiments on cattle, VanDemark and co-workers have shown that sperm migration requires only 2 to 4 minutes whether the heifers are mated or artificially inseminated. Indeed, even dead sperm, after artificial insemination, were transported to the upper reaches of the oviduct within 4.3 minutes (VanDemark and Moeller, 1951). Sperm-migration times reported for the ewe have varied considerably, ranging from several hours (Green and Winters, 1935) down to 6 to 16 minutes (Starke, 1949; Schott and Phillips, 1941). This variation is to be accounted for less by changes dependent on the estrous cycle (Dauzier and Wintenberger, 1952) than by improvements in technique.

The rabbit, in many ways a domestic anomaly in reproductive matters, apparently requires several hours for transport of a significant number of sperm, although the "vanguard" may reach the ampulla within an hour after insemination (Chang, 1952; Adams, 1956). Heape's demonstration in 1905 of approximately 4 hours for migration seems to have stood the test of time. On the basis of recovery of spermatozoa from separate segments of the genital tract, Parker (1931) and Braden (1953) found that 2.5 to 3 hours are required for transport. Confirmation is afforded by experiments involving ligation of the tubes at various intervals after copulation (Adams, 1956; Greenwald, 1956); whereas some eggs are fertilized when the tubal blocks are made prior to 2.5 hours, ligations made 3 to 5 hours after copulation do not prevent a high percentage of fertility. Whether this order of transport time is an adaptation to induced ovulation or is otherwise unique to the rabbit is not known; comparable experimentation on the cat and fer-

TABLE 13.6

Time of passage of rat spermatozoa into female genital tract

(From C. G. Hartman and J. Ball, Proc. Soc. Exper. Biol. & Med., 28, 312–314, 1930.)

Animal	Killed after Ejaculation	Uterus Clamped near Apex after Ejaculation	Sperm Located
1	1 min.	2 min.	Apex of uterine cornua
2	1 min.	100 sec.	Apex of cornua
3	30 sec.	54 sec.	Lower part of cornua
4	"Immediately"	54 sec.	Vagina

ret, for example, which also normally ovulate only when stimulated by copulation, might be instructive.

The time for sperm migration in fowl is of the same order of magnitude as that in most mammals (Mimura, 1941). Fowl sperm, labeled with inorganic P^{32}, were recovered from the infundibulum within an hour after insemination; the number found depended on the site of administration, *i.e.*, intravaginal or intrauterine (Allen and Grigg, 1957). Killed sperm also reached the infundibulum when placed in the uterus, but not when introduced intravaginally.

The study of seminal components, other than sperm, indicates that tubal transport must involve a muscular mechanism. In both the sow and the mare, certain natural seminal constituents, *e.g.*, fructose, citric acid, and ergothioneine, are found in the uterine horns within an hour after mating (Mann, Polge and Rowson, 1955). Gunn and Gould (1958) produced a Zn^{65}-labeled component of prostatic fluid in rats which served as a marker for tubal transport. In animals killed at intervals between 0.5 and 1.5 hours after mating, a significant quantity of the isotope had reached the uterotubal junction by 1 hour, and radioactive labeling was found throughout the oviduct at 1.5 hours.

B. MECHANISM OF TRANSPORT IN THE UTERUS AND OVIDUCT

The muscular contractility of the genital tract has been implicated in the process of sperm migration since the earliest studies of mating behavior and insemination (see Austin and Bishop, 1957). The normal activity of the uterus and Fallopian tube is well known (Westman, 1926; Parker, 1931; Reynolds, 1931, 1949). The contractions of the tract are not, however, peristaltic waves which might favor rapid, directed sperm transport, but rather segmentation waves which encourage dispersal from the source. Indeed, what peristalsis can be observed in the estrous oviduct (*e.g.*, the rabbit) is directed from the fimbriated toward the uterine end (Reynolds, 1949).

Both mechanical and psychic factors influence the contractility of the genital tract and appear to augment sperm migration. In the rabbit (Heape, 1898; Krehbiel and Carstens, 1939), and probably in many other animals, stimulation of the external genitalia increases uterine activity. The mating response also enhances uterine action in the mare (Millar, 1952) and cow (VanDemark and Hays, 1952). According to VanDemark and Hays (1952), the mere sight of the bull is sufficient to induce strong uterine contractions in the estrous and postestrous heifer (Fig. 13.7). The activity of the Fallopian tube of the rabbit also appears to be stimulated by the presence of a suitable buck (Westman, 1926).

In the oviducts of rabbits, Parker (1931) emphasized both the segmentation contractions and the local ab- and adovarian ciliary currents in accounting for dispersal of sperm, once they pass the uterotubal junction. In a recent series of interesting experiments, however, Black and Asdell (1958) tended to minimize ciliary activity, which is generally directed toward the uterus, and to attribute sperm distribution in the rabbit oviduct to the segmentation process brought about by the circular musculature of the tube. Tubal

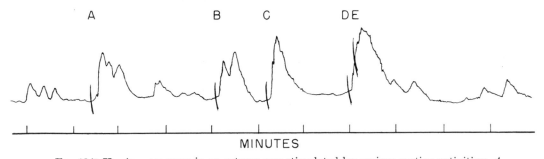

FIG. 13.7. Uterine responses in an estrous cow stimulated by various mating activities: *A*, bull brought within sight of cow; *B*, bull allowed to nuzzle vulva; *C*, bull mounts but does not copulate; *D*, bull copulates; *E*, bull ejaculates. (From N. L. VanDemark and R. L. Hays, Am. J. Physiol., **170**, 518–521, 1952.)

secretions, pronounced at the time of ovulation (Bishop, 1956a), serve as vehicle of transport for the sperm. The copious uterine fluid secreted in the rat during the proestrum performs the same role (Warren, 1938).

It is probable that ciliary activity plays a greater role in some animals than in others in distributing sperm throughout the female tract. Thus, Parker (1931) stressed the importance of adovarian ciliary currents in the oviducts of the turtle, pigeon, and chicken. With respect to *ab*ovarian currents, moreover, it should be pointed out that these, too, could serve a function by orienting the sperm toward the infundibulum; whereas unnecessary emphasis should not be placed on this as a transport mechanism, considerable evidence exists to show that sperm orient against a current and, when free-swimming, make considerable progress upstream (Adolphi, 1906a, b; Yamane and Ito, 1932; von Khreninger-Guggenberger, 1933; Brown, 1944; Sturgis, 1947).

The activity of the several segments of the female genital tract varies with phases of the ovarian cycle and, as a consequence, may alter the rate of sperm migration (see Austin and Bishop, 1957). The active motility of both the Fallopian tube and uterus, characteristic of estrus, is depressed by progestational conditions, although little change is found immediately after ovulation (Reynolds, 1949; Borell, Nilsson and Westman, 1957; Black and Asdell, 1958). Cyclic changes in sperm-transport time through the uterus and oviducts have been noted in the cow (Warbritton, McKenzie, Berliner and Andrews, 1937) and sow (du Mesnil du Buisson and Dauzier, 1955). Recent work of Noyes, Adams and Walton (1959) suggests that estrogen enhances fertilization of rabbit ova transplanted into castrates by increasing the efficacy of sperm transport, *i.e.*, by reducing the obstacles to sperm migration present in nonestrous does (Noyes, 1959a).

The most spectacular development involving endocrine control of sperm transport during the past decade has been the demonstration that oxytocin, as an important mediator of uterine activity, is essential, in some cases at least, for the rapid migration of sperm from the cervix to the site of fer-tilization (VanDemark and Moeller, 1951; VanDemark and Hays, 1952; Hays and VanDemark, 1951, 1953a). Excised and perfused cow uteri function as a transport system so long as oxytocin is present in the perfusate. Motile sperm, artificially inseminated into the cervix, are carried to the ovarian end of the oviduct in as few as 2.5 minutes. Even nonmotile sperm are transported throughout the tract within 5 minutes. In the absence of oxytocin, however, sperm migration does not occur; in fact, the cells do not even enter the fundus. Oxytocin is also apparently released during natural and artifical insemination of the cow (Hays and VanDemark, 1951, 1953b), and its administration, during mating, augments uterine contractility (Hays and VanDemark, 1953a). Oxytocin may have a general role in the uterine responses to mating and rapid transport of spermatozoa through the genital tracts of some other animals as well (Harris, 1951; Cross, 1958), although it is to be noted that coitus is claimed to abolish temporarily uterine contractions in women (Bickers and Main, 1941).

C. CRITICAL REGIONS OF SPERM TRANSPORT

The unrestricted passage of sperm, which is apparently characteristic of the heifer, is not, however, exhibited by all mammals. The cervix, the uterotubal junction, and, to a lesser degree, the isthmus of the Fallopian tube can each constitute an obstacle to free sperm transport. In these regions, active sperm motility may then assume some significance as a means of migration. In the rabbit only 1 sperm in about 50,000 reaches the site of fertilization; in the ewe and rat, the proportion is even smaller (Braden, 1953). According to Braden, of the total number of sperm deposited in the rabbit vagina during a normal insemination (about 60×10^6 cells), the proportions transmitted are roughly as follows: approximately 1 out of 40 traverses the cervix; of these, one-third reach the uterotubal junction; 1 out of 160 passes the uterotubal junction and enters the Fallopian tube; and of these, one-fourth ultimately reach the ampulla. The distribution of spermatozoa throughout the rabbit genital tract at various times after copulation is presented in Figure 13.8.

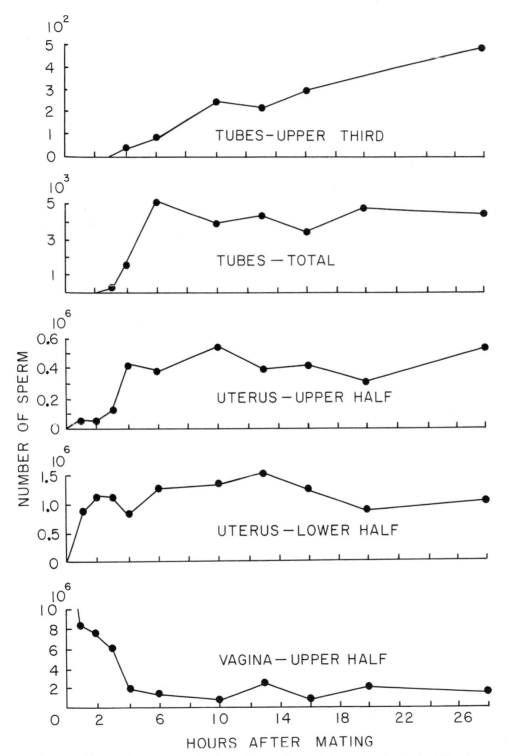

FIG. 13.8. Changes in sperm number in various sections of the genital tract of rabbit after copulation. (From A. W. H. Braden, Australian J. Biol. Sc., **6,** 693–705, 1953.)

1. The Cervix

This portal connecting the vagina and the uterus is generally regarded as constituting a partial block to sperm transport in certain animals in which ejaculation occurs in the vaginal vault, e.g., the rabbit, ewe, and man (Warbritton, McKenzie, Berliner and Andrews, 1937; Chang, 1951b; Braden, 1953; Noyes, Adams and Walton, 1958). Sperm migration through the rabbit cervix is a gradual process (Florey and Walton, 1932; Braden, 1953) and, although the mechanism certainly is not definitely known, is possibly to be attributed to active flagellation of the sperm themselves, with little or no help from the cervical duct (Noyes, Adams and Walton, 1958; cf. Hartman, 1957). Dead cells, according to Noyes and colleagues, fail to negotiate the cervical passage, as do radiopaque media. It should be noted that the latter finding is inexplicably at variance with a similar experiment of Krehbiel and Carstens (1939), who found that radiopaque medium does pass the rabbit cervix in significant amounts. Noyes, Adams and Walton (1959) also indicated that estrogen treatment facilitates cervical transport of spermatozoa, that is, decreases the resistance to migration shown by untreated animals, in this case castrated does. Whether the effect is actually on the cervical musculature, the secretion of cervical mucus, uterine motility, or some other system is not clear from these experiments.

The cervix should not be regarded as always constituting an obstacle to sperm transport. In at least two species with intravaginal insemination, namely, the heifer and dog, sperm transport is extremely rapid. The cervices in these animals, therefore, rather than retarding progress, must aid considerably in the migration of spermatozoa.

A frequently suggested theory to account for the passage of spermatozoa into the uterus envisages "insuck" of the semen through the cervix. Indeed, a transient negative uterine pressure of about 0.7 lb. per square inch has been demonstrated during coitus in the mare (Millar, 1952). However, the significance of such determinations in this animal is obscure since ejaculation normally occurs directly into the uterus (Braden and Austin, 1953). Nevertheless, in consideration of the concept relevant to women, it is reasonable to assume that the uterus can aspirate sperm and mucus into the uterine cavity by virtue of the elasticity of that organ following contraction (Belonoschkin, 1949, 1957). This subject is more extensively reviewed by Hartman (1957).

Much attention has been focused on the questions of the nature of cervical mucus, its cyclic changes, and its penetrability by spermatozoa in vitro (Shettles, 1949). The importance of cervical mucus is obvious if sperm reside in the cervix for considerable periods of time, as in women, or if the sperm have to negotiate the canal by their own motile faculties; it is of much less significance when the sperm are shot through the cervical canal at ejaculation, as in the sow, or are carried through rapidly by muscular contractions, as in the heifer.

The secretory activity of the cervix responds to variations in the ovarian cycle, and the physicochemical composition of the mucus changes accordingly. The response of the cervix to cyclic changes was first clearly stated by Allen (1922) for the mouse. Much of our current understanding stems from the important monograph of Sjövall (1938) concerning investigations of human and guinea pig cervices. There now exists adequate evidence that changes in human cervical mucus correlate well with ovulatory and with endometrial, vaginal, and other indications of estrogenic activity (Sjövall, 1938; Viergiver and Pommerenke, 1946; Shettles, 1949; Bergman, 1950; Cohen, Stein, and Kaye, 1952; Odeblad, 1959). Cervical mucus in women is most copiously secreted during the estrogenic phase; its dry weight at this time is minimal (Bergman, 1950), tonicity is low (Bergman and Lund, 1950), and pH, as generally determined, is elevated. Estrogenic mucus is also claimed to be richer in glucose and polysaccharide, but these components may be derived less from the cervical secretion than from the uterine glands higher in the tract (Bergman and Werner, 1950). Lipid is present in lower amounts at ovulation. Benaš (1958) found changes, as determined by paper electrophoresis, in the extractable protein, with a predominance of albumin in pre-ovulatory mucus and a prevalence of β- and γ-globulins in mucus collected after ovulation. No cyclical changes, however, were found by Bergman and Werner (1950) in carbohydrate hydrolysates of cervical mucus, which, when tested chromatographically, showed the presence of galactose, mannose, fucose, and hexosamine.

A recent investigation of cervical mucus from the cow (Gibbons, 1959a) has demonstrated the presence of glucose, glycogen, protein, alkaline phosphatase, lysozyme, antagglutin, and common inorganic ions. Isolation and relative purification of mucoid, prepared from bovine mucin, show that it changes in physical consistency with phases of the cycle; molecular configuration, as determined by sedimentation, viscosity, and flow-birefringence measurements, is altered and is probably due to changes in state of hydration (Gibbons and Glover, 1959). Chemically, bovine mucoid consists of about 75 per cent carbohydrate and 25 per cent amino acid residues and resembles human blood-group substances (Glover, 1959b).

The presence of glucose and hydrolyzable polysaccharide in cervical mucus suggests the availability of metabolic substrate for the spermatozoa, but the utilization of these energy sources can only be conjectured. Moricard, Gothié and Belaisch (1957) have indicated that inorganic S^{35} is apparently taken up by human sperm from cervical mucus, but the significance of this uptake cannot at present be evaluated.

Many investigators have attempted to correlate cyclical changes in cervical mucus with capacity for sperm progression, *in vitro* (Fig. 13.9). Maximal penetration by human sperm, observed in capillary tubes, occurs in estrogenic cervical secretion when the mucus is most copious and least viscous (Lamar, Shettles and Delfs, 1940; Guttmacher and Shettles, 1940; Shettles, 1940; Pommerenke, 1946; Leeb and Ploberger, 1959). Very little or no penetration is observed in pre-ovulatory or postovulatory mucus. Just before menstruation penetrability sharply increases, a change probably correlated with the premenstrual rise in circulating estrogen. During pregnancy, cervical mucus is only slightly penetrable, although the endocervical glands are hyperactive at this time (Guttmacher and Shet-

tles, 1940; Atkinson, Shettles and Engle, 1948). Postmenopausal mucus is relatively impenetrable by spermatozoa, but after adequate estrogenic administration, a mucus is secreted which is characteristic of that of the ovulatory phase. Ovariectomized women ordinarily produce a scant, viscous mucus which is increased upon estrogen administration (Moricard, 1936; Abarbanel, 1946, 1948; Pommerenke and Viergiver, 1946). It has been claimed (Cary, 1943), although not confirmed, that mucous secretion in women is enhanced by orgasm and that this facilitates sperm penetration.

These studies on sperm, *in vitro*, have in a general way largely confirmed the earlier work of Sjövall (1938), whose investigations of sperm penetration through the guinea pig cervix were mainly confined to observations *in vivo*. The penetration of sperm through the cervical mucus, *in vitro*, however, is at best only an approximation to the normal process of insemination and cervical transport, and the meaning of these carefully compiled results is not easy to assess. Their full significance must await further correlation between sperm migration *in vitro* and transit *in situ*. Certain evidence, indeed, tends to suggest that the condition of the cervical mucus in women may be of relatively little importance in sperm transport. In the series of 51 women studied by Rubenstein, Strauss, Lazarus and Hankin (1951), spermatozoa were found to have passed rapidly through the cervix at all stages of the cycle. No particulars were given concerning the condition of the cervical mucus, the presurgical coital history of the patients, or the possible effect of the operation (hysterectomy) on sperm transport. Their report, however, seems to conflict with many of the above-cited observations *in vitro* which indicate that sperm migration is limited to the ovulatory phase of the cycle.

2. The Uterotubal Junction

The speed of sperm transport through the upper genital tract is in general so rapid that in only two species, the rat and rabbit, is the junction between the uterus and the oviduct stressed in current literature as being an obstacle to sperm migration (Braden, 1953). Yet, for almost half a century, de-

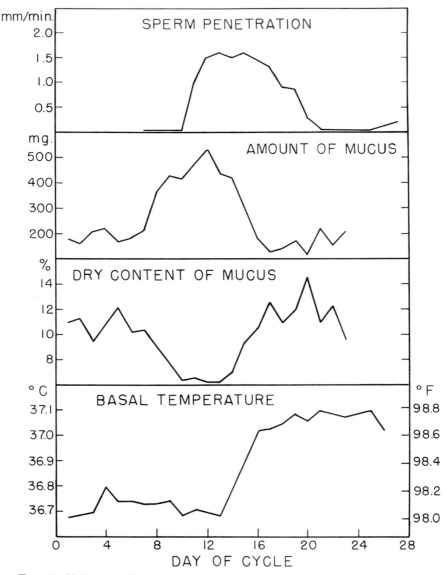

Fig. 13.9. Variation in human sperm penetration *in vitro* through cervical mucus during a single cycle (from J. K. Lamar, in *Problems of Human Fertility*, George Banta Publishing Company, 1943), correlated with cyclical changes in the mucus and in body temperature based on 35 cycles (from P. Bergman, Acta obst. et gynec. scandinav., Suppl. 4, **29**, 1–139, 1950).

scriptive and experimental investigations have pointed out the complexity of the junction and the high pressures often required to force an opening through the lumen in this region. Rubin's initial paper (1920) indicated that gas pressures of 40 to 100 mm. Hg could be considered a normal range for human tubal insufflation, the uterotubal junction being the major source of resistance. In the cat, fluid pressures of 250 to 300 mm. Hg are incapable of "forcing" the opening when injections are made through the uterus (Lee, 1925a; Anderson, 1928). On the other hand, tubo-uterine injections of fluid, that is, those from tube to uterus, require very little pressure to force the opening. Other species behave differently. With relatively little pressure, between 25 and 40 mm. Hg, fluid can be forced through the junction from the uterine to the ovarian side in both the cow and ewe (Anderson, 1928). The resistance to flow, in the cow at least, is greatest during estrus (Anderson, 1927; Whitelaw, 1933). During this early and important period of investigation, the structural aspects of the uterotubal junction of a wide variety of mammals were described, particularly the villi and folds which appear to guard the opening of the Fallopian tubes (Lee, 1925b; Anderson, 1928). Anderson's paper should be consulted for details of the comparative structure of the junction in 25 species of mammals and for her particularly thorough discussion of this region in the sow.

A general conclusion which arises from these considerations of the uterotubal junction is that the structure is sufficiently complex (Fig. 13.10) to render spurious many attempts to correlate forced-fluid determinations with sperm transport. It seems likely that in a case like the cat, for example, the fluid pressure applied would occlude the uterotubal orifices with villi or folds, and that the greater the pressure, the tighter the seal; under normal conditions the junction would remain more or less patent, at least between muscular contractions, and allow for sperm transport.

That migration through the uterotubal junction in the rat, under some circumstances, is probably accomplished by the gametes themselves was indicated by the ingenious investigation of Leonard and Perlman (1949). They injected live spermatozoa of one or more species, as well as dead sperm and India ink particles, into the rat uterus. Spermatozoa of the rat, mouse, guinea pig, and bull were injected singly, and combinations of rat-guinea pig, rat-mouse, and rat-bull sperm were introduced together. Distribution throughout the reproductive tract was determined 1 to 14 hours later. Under these conditions (cf. Table 13.6) motile rat spermatozoa freely penetrated the uterotubal junction in both estrous and diestrous animals, but dead spermatozoa and inert particles did not; foreign spermatozoa passed through only very rarely. A similar experiment on the rabbit, which also shows evidence of uterotubal blockade, should prove rewarding.

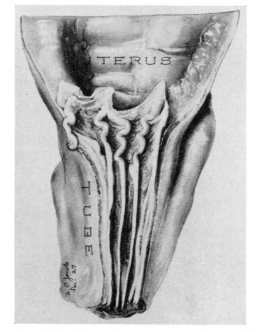

Fig. 13.10. Uterotubal junction of the rabbit. (From D. H. Anderson, Am. J. Anat., **42,** 255–305, 1928.)

3. The Isthmus

The lower segment of the oviduct constitutes a partial obstacle to sperm migration in both the rat and rabbit (Chang, 1951b; Braden, 1953). In the latter, transport of both sperm and eggs is slowed by a decrease in muscular activity, in contrast to the movements characteristic of the upper segment of the duct (Black and Asdell, 1958). The small diameter of the lumen of the isthmus, along with its kinks and extensive mucosal folding, may also retard sperm transport.

In a recent extensive study to ascertain the source of the fluctuations in gas pressures during tubal insufflation of the rabbit, Stavorski and Hartman (1958) demonstrated that the isthmus is more important than the actual uterotubal union in the degree of resistance offered to applied pressure. Sphincters were observed at both the uterotubal and tubo-ampullar junctions, but the elbow-like kinks in the isthmus were found to be the major source of resistance. The pressures necessary to force an opening were of the same order of magnitude whether a uterotubal or a tubo-uterine approach was employed. A suddenly applied high pressure was found to meet with great resistance; the more slowly the pressure was built up, the lower the peak pressure required to open the isthmian and uterotubal constrictions. The required pressures generally were higher in those animals receiving estrogen.

D. NUMBER OF SPERM AT THE SITE OF FERTILIZATION

In the few species subjected to careful investigation, the number of spermatozoa recovered from the ampulla, or what is regarded as the site of fertilization, at the approximate time of fertilization, is surprisingly low. A summary of available evidence is included in Table 13.7. Whereas these data represent, in some instances, only single determinations and, in others, mean values within a very wide range, they show quite clearly that only a minute fraction of the inseminate is present in the vicinity of the ova when fertilization occurs. In some of these studies (Moricard and Bossu, 1951; Blandau and Odor, 1949), search failed to reveal many more sperm than the number of eggs undergoing fertilization. The presence of so few sperm at this critical point is evidence enough against the once-popular view that a sperm "swarm" is essential for fertilization—either to denude the ova of their

TABLE 13.7

Number of spermatozoa found at the site of fertilization in several mammals

Species	Mean No. Sperm per Tube	Post-coital Time	Reference
		hr.	
Rat	43	?	Austin, 1948
	12	12	Blandau and Odor, 1949
	30	24	
	45	12	Braden and Austin, 1954; Moricard and Bossu, 1951
Mouse	17	10–15	Braden and Austin, 1954
Rabbit	500	?	Chang, 1951a
	38	4	Braden, 1953
	250	10	
Ferret	200	6	Hammond and Walton, 1934
	500	24	
Sheep	184*	24–48	Braden and Austin, 1954
	673†	24–48	

* Ovarian third of oviduct.
† Entire ampulla.

TABLE 13.8

Sperm survival times in the female tract

Animal	Maximal Duration of Fertility	Maximal Duration of Motility	Reference
	hr.	hr.	
Rabbit	30–32	—	Hammond and Asdell, 1926
Mouse	6	13	Merton, 1939b
Guinea pig	21–22	41	Yochem, 1929; Soderwall and Young, 1940
Rat	14	17	Soderwall and Blandau, 1941
Ferret	36–48	—	Hammond and Walton, 1934
Sheep	30–48	48	Green, 1947; Dauzier and Wintenberger, 1952
Cow	28–50	—	Laing, 1945; Vandeplassche and Paredis, 1948
Horse	144	144	Day, 1942; Burkhardt, 1949
Man	28–48	48–60	Farris, 1950; Rubenstein et al., 1951; Horne and Audet, 1958
Bat	135 days	159 days	Wimsatt, 1944

cumulous auras by hyaluronidase or to supply some ingredient for sperm penetration. Conversely, Braden and Austin (1954) have suggested that an accomplishment of the filtering out of the overwhelming majority of sperm during transport is to so limit the number of male gametes present that multiple sperm penetration of the ova is reduced, thereby preventing polyspermy and anomalous development.

E. DURATION OF FERTILIZING CAPACITY

The retention of fertilizing capacity by mammalian spermatozoa is relatively limited (Table 13.8). As in the male tract, the capacity for fertilization is lost more promptly than is their ability to move. In the female guinea pig, for example, motility of sperm continues for as long as 40 hours after mating, whereas fertilizing capacity is lost about 22 hours after copulation (Yochem, 1929; Soderwall and Young, 1940); in the mouse these periods are approximately 13½ and 6 hours, respectively (Merton, 1939b). In the consideration of sperm survival in parts of the tract other than the fertilization site, sperm motility is the most convenient, although not necessarily the only, criterion of longevity.

The values presented in Table 13.8 are the most accurate available, but the degree of precision with which such data can be obtained varies considerably among species, dependent as they are upon the estimates of the time of fertilization. Reliable figures may be expected in such forms as the guinea pig, which is known to ovulate some 10 hours after the onset of heat, or the rabbit which ovulates about 10 hours after copulation. But in women the exact time of ovulation cannot be determined with sufficient accuracy to permit a precise statement as to the duration of fertilizing capacity of the spermatozoa. The relatively long survival time reported for the mare may reflect a kind of thermal adaptation of the spermatozoa, because in the stallion the testicles are carried in shallow scrotal sacs, the temperature of which is probably close to that of the body.

Hibernating mammals which copulate in the autumn often show excessively long periods of sperm survival in the female (Hartman, 1933). In bats of the genera *Myotis* and *Eptesicus*, the spermatozoa inseminated in the fall are capable of motility and of fertilization at the time of ovulation in the spring (Wimsatt, 1942, 1944), even though subsequent copulations may occur in nature during the spring mating season (Pearson, Koford and Pearson, 1952). Long-range sperm survival is, of course, well known in various poikilothermic animals, including arthropods and lower chordates (see Hartman, 1939). Custodians of reptiles, particularly, have recorded interesting breeding data relevant to the longevity of sperm in the female. Fertile eggs have been laid by the diamond-back terrapin and various snakes, 4 to 5 years after isolation; due to the unlikelihood of delayed development, this indicates sperm survival for periods of several years (Barney, 1922; Haines, 1940; Carson, 1945).

Some attention has been directed toward the possible deleterious effect of the aging of sperm in the female tract; although still capable of fertilization, they might give rise to abnormal or nonviable embryos (Austin and Bishop, 1957). This change with senescence has been well established in fowl (Crew, 1926; Nalbandov and Card, 1943; Van Drimmelen and Oettlé, 1949; Dharmarajan, 1950), and might be expected to occur in mammals; the evidence, however, does not support it. Young's early data

(1931) indicated that guinea pig sperm, aged in the *male* tract, could lead to an increase in the percentage of abnormal embryos; but no such "overaging" effect was demonstrated in sperm maintained in the female tract (Soderwall and Young, 1940; Soderwall and Blandau, 1941).

Somewhat more recently, another type of sperm behavior was discovered which involves the capacity for fertilization (Austin, 1951; Chang, 1951b). This concerns not the maximal limit of survival, but rather the initial attainment of full fertilizing competency, a continuation, in a sense, of the process of sperm maturation long since begun in the male genital tract. This phenomenon of "capacitation," demonstrated thus far only in rats and rabbits, requires 2 to 6 hours of conditioning of the male gametes and probably involves both physiologic and structural alterations in the cells which enable them to penetrate the zonae pellucidae of the eggs (Austin, 1952; Austin and Braden, 1954; Chang, 1955, 1959). Capacitation is assumed to occur normally in the female genital tract. Under experimental conditions, the injection of rat sperm into the periovarian sac (Austin), or the introduction of rabbit sperm into the Fallopian tube (Chang), accomplishes fertilization only after a delay of several hours, unless the sperm have been previously capacitated in another suitable reproductive environment. Such a milieu for rabbit sperm is afforded by the reproductive ducts of female rabbits under a variety of hormonal conditions, and by the reproductive tracts of both immature animals and castrates, with or without the addition of gonadotrophin or estrogen (Chang, 1958). The uteri of pseudopregnant rabbits, however, and those treated with progesterone, were found unsuitable for sperm capacitation. Some doubt has been cast upon the specificity of the factors which bring about sperm conditioning by the demonstration, in the rabbit, that not only does capacitation occur in the uterus and Fallopian tube, but also in such unusual environments as the isolated bladder and colon of either male or female animals and in the anterior chamber of the eye as well (Noyes, Walton and Adams, 1958a, b; Noyes, 1959b).

As to the nature of the changes induced in

the spermatozoa during capacitation, earlier suppositions leaned toward the view that something is lost or gained by the gametes which results in enzyme activation required for fertilization (Austin and Bishop, 1957). It has since been suggested that the change, in rat sperm at least, involves processes leading to the disintegration or loss of the acrosome from the sperm head, thereby exposing structures responsible for egg penetration (Austin and Bishop, 1958a, b). The reversible counteraction of capacitation by rabbit seminal plasma, demonstrated by Chang (1957), casts some doubt, however, on the likelihood of pronounced structural changes occurring during this phase of sperm maturation. Until the physiologic changes responsible for the suggested morphologic alterations are clarified, the mechanism of capacitation will remain obscure.

F. DURATION OF SPERM MOTILITY THROUGHOUT THE TRACT

The viability of spermatozoa in the ampulla, assessed by motility, outlasts their fertilizing capacity (Table 13.8). Elsewhere in the tract, motility serves as a criterion for sperm longevity, and considerable variation in the ability of separate segments of the tract to support it has been demonstrated. Rat spermatozoa, for example, survive in the cornua about 12 hours, compared with 16 or 17 hours in the oviducts (White, 1933a). Sperm motility in the human fundus appears to be less than that in the Fallopian tube (Farris, 1950; Rubenstein, Strauss, Lazarus and Hankin, 1951).

In most mammals the alkaline cervical mucus sustains motility well, whereas the acidic vaginal depository is detrimental. Motile spermatozoa have been reported in human cervical mucus a week after coitus, although the average duration of motility here is closer to 2 days. The duration of motility in cervical mucus varies with the cycle, maximal motility coinciding with the time of ovulation (Beshlebnov, 1938; Cohen and Stein, 1951). Estrogen-induced hypersecretion of mucus is claimed to increase sperm viability as well as penetrability. Longevity in the cervical mucus of the estrous macaque is approximately 24 hours.

The primate vagina is notably inhospitable to spermatozoa, presumably because of its high acidity. Motility is sustained in the human vagina rarely longer than 3 to 4 hours (Weisman, 1939), and the duration is believed to vary inversely with changes in vaginal acidity (pH 4 to 5). The human vaginal pH, curiously enough, has been claimed to reach a minimum at the time of ovulation, an overt sign, according to Schockaert, Delrue and Férin (1939), of high estrogenic activity (Fig. 13.11). On the other hand, a sharp rise in vaginal pH of approximately 0.5 unit was claimed by Zuck and Duncan (1939) to be coincident with ovulation; this elevation is inconstant and, when it does occur, may be due to the presence of alkaline cervical mucus. Normally, in the cow, the influx of mucus renders the vagina alkaline at estrus (Lardy, Pounden and Phillips, 1940). Under normal circumstances, the inseminate is only briefly, if at all, exposed to the vaginal medium. When not ejaculated directly into the cervix or uterus, the semen may be conducted rapidly toward the cervical canal by longitudinal contraction waves (Noyes, Adams and Walton, 1958). It is doubtful, therefore, whether the high hydrogen-ion concentration, characteristic of the vagina, is of any great significance in the reproductive economy of most mammals.

G. SPERM VIABILITY IN RELATION TO TUBAL PHYSIOLOGY

In view of the great wealth of information concerning uterine and tubal transport and sperm survival, on the one hand, and uterine function and hormonal responses, on the other, there has been an appalling lack of interest in the nature of the genital fluids and the immediate environment surrounding the spermatozoa during their sojourn within the female genital tract. The corresponding deficiency of our knowledge of the male genital tract was previously noted. Difficulties in technique exist, to be sure, but they are far from insurmountable, and rich rewards should result from exploration in this virgin, but obviously fertile, field.

A review of the extensive literature on the cytochemistry of the endometrium and tubal epithelium and on the changes with variations in the estrous cycle reveals consider-

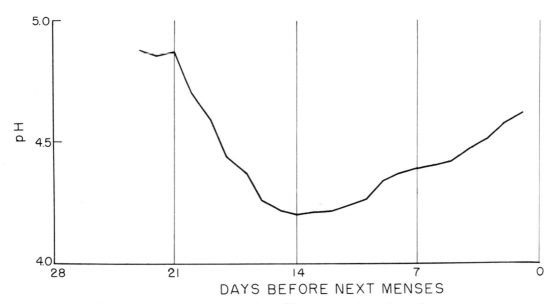

FIG. 13.11. Cyclical changes in midvaginal pH. Average values of 632 determinations on 37 normally menstruating women. (After A. E. Rakoff, L. G. Feo and L. Goldstein, Am. J. Obst. & Gynec., 47, 467–494, 1944.)

able secretory activity (Joël, 1940; Hadek, 1955, 1958a; Borell, Gustavson, Nilsson and Westman, 1959; Fredricsson, 1959a, b), but little correlation with the behavior of the gametes within the lumen. When the secretory history of specific substances has been followed, the interest has generally been in postfertilization stages, as, for example, the mucopolysaccharides released into the oviduct of the rabbit several days after ovulation (Greenwald, 1957; Zachariae, 1958).

On the other hand, several studies of the genital fluids afford some data on pH, oxygen tension, potassium and sodium ratio, enzyme content, and possible metabolic substrates. Warbritton, McKenzie, Berliner and Andrews, (1937) reported that the pH levels of the Fallopian tube, uterine horns, cervix, and vagina of the ewe are, respectively, 6.4 to 7.3, 6.6 to 7.3, 6.1 to 7.5, and 6.5 to 7.8. The wide variations to be noted here are more striking than the actual determinations. More recently, Blandau, Jensen and Rumery (1958) recorded pH values for the fluid of rat periovarian sac, ampullae, and uteri as follows: 7.7. to 8.4, 7.3 to 8.5, and 7.4 to 8.3. There thus appeared little change throughout the tract, but all regions were alkaline with respect to the peritoneal fluid

and blood. These wide variations and the pronounced alkalinity suggest that the loss of carbon dioxide from the fluids may have been responsible for the high pH values reported.

The oxygen tension of rabbit genital fluids has been determined and found adequate to support aerobic respiration (Bishop, 1957). Uterine values, determined by equilibration, range from 25 to 45 mm. Hg (Campbell, 1932). The oxygen tension of Fallopian tubal fluid, measured directly with an oxygen electrode, is approximately 40 mm. Hg (Bishop, 1956b). Birnberg and Gross (1958), however, claimed that changes in the human Fallopian tube during the ovulatory phase render it anaerobic (determined enzymatically); if this finding is confirmed, it bears significantly on the anaerobic preferences of human sperm as studied in vitro (see below).

Ionic and organic components of the luminal fluids of the cow have been analyzed (Olds and VanDemark, 1957a, b, c; VanDemark, 1958). The data for follicular, tubal, uterine, and vaginal fluids are presented in Table 13.9. Reducing substances, possibly glucose, were found in uterine fluid but were not detected in oviductal fluid. Shih, Kennedy and Huggins (1940) have

TABLE 13.9

Composition of bovine genital fluids

(From N. L. VanDemark, Internat. J. Fertil., 3, 220–230, 1958.)

Constituent	Source of Fluid			
	Vagina	Uterus	Oviduct	Follicle
Dry matter (per cent)..............	2.4	10.0	15.9	7.5
Ash (percentage of dry matter)......	41.1	10.3	7.1	9.3
Sodium (mg. per 100 ml.)............	170	220	208	304
Potassium (mg. per 100 ml.)........	166	183	223	36
Calcium (mg. per 100 ml.)..........	11	15	12	12
Total N (gm. per 100 ml.)..........	0.17	1.09	—	0.96
Reducing substance (as mg. glucose per 100 ml.)......................	9	50	—	37

contributed extensive data concerning the chemical composition of the uterine fluids of the rabbit, rat, and dog (Table 13.10).

An interesting report on potassium and sodium concentrations of uterine fluid in the proestrous rat indicates that K is relatively high (37 mEq./l.) and remains constant after copulation with a vasectomized male; Na decreases, however, by about 11 per cent from the initial value of 115 mEq./l. (Howard and DeFeo, 1959). The shift may be due to the change from follicular to luteal phase, but because of the contributions of the several accessory glands, the significance of the change is not clear. Nonetheless, the high initial K/Na ratio (0.32) suggests a marked K-tolerance on the part of the sperm and, further, a secretory action of the genital mucosa leading to the accumulation of potassium within the lumen.

The paucity of data concerning enzymatic activity by the uterine fluids was indicated by Reynolds (1949). Since that time little has been added, except for two suggestive papers dealing with amylase activity of the tube and its fluids. Human tubal cysts contain high concentrations of such an enzyme and have led to the supposition that intraluminal glycogen—if any should exist—might be hydrolyzed to provide a substrate for sperm (Green, 1957). McGeachin, Hargan, Potter and Daus (1958) confirmed the presence of amylase in the cysts and found high activities also in tubal epithelium of man, rabbit, cow, and sheep, but not of other species studied. In an electrophoretic study of the cornual fluids of the estrous rat, low concentrations of 4 major proteid components were found, which appeared to differ in their mobility characteristics from serum proteins (Junge and Blandau, 1958).

It is clear that energy substrates and other biochemical components of seminal plasma are introduced into the tubes in animals in which intrauterine ejaculation occurs (Mann, Polge and Rowson, 1955). However, the significance of these constituents for tubal physiology is highly doubtful after intravaginal insemination. Relatively little glycolytic substrate seems to be present in the fluids recovered from the tract. In the rabbit, for example, little or no hexose, and only traces of phospholipids, can be detected, either before or after copulation (Table 13.11); lactate is present in appreciable quantities and might conceivably serve as a metabolic substrate (Bishop, 1957; Mastroianni, Winternitz and Lowi, 1958). At the present time, it is not easy to ascertain which metabolic substrates and products are associated with the activities of the spermatozoa and which with the activities of the mucosal cells lining the tract. More work is necessary to fill in the metabolic and physiologic details of the sketch just barely outlined.

Abundant evidence indicates that the tubal contents are a product of active se-

TABLE 13.10

Chemical composition of uterine fluids

(From H. E. Shih, J. Kennedy and C. Huggins, Am. J. Physiol., **130**, 287–291, 1940.)

	H₂O	pH	CO₂	Total N	NPN	Protein	Cl	Na	Ca	K	Glucose	Inorganic P
	gm. per l.		*mmoles per l.*	*gm. per l.*	*gm. per l.*	*gm. per l.*	*mmoles per l.*	*mmoles per l.*	*mmoles per l.*	*mmoles per l.*	*mg. per l.*	*mmoles per l.*
Rabbit	979	7.78	53.6	0.8	0.37	2.7	98	158	4.7	6.1	0–160	0–0.20
Rat......................	982	7.55	61.8	1.0	0.29	5.1	98	169	1.5	4.3	0–150	0
Dog	984	6.09	3.0	0.8	0.20	3.8	167	162	3.5	5.2	0–80	0–0.03

TABLE 13.11

Metabolic substrates in rabbit tubular fluid
(From D. W. Bishop, Internat. J. Fertil.,
2, 11–22, 1957.)

Condition of Animal	Substrate			
	Glucose	Fructose	Lactate	Phospho-lipid
	mg. per 100 ml.	*mg. per 100 ml.*	*mg. per 100 ml.*	*mg. per 100 ml.*
Estrous......	0–2	<1	6.8	0–8
Pregnant....	0–2	<1	15.0	Trace
Castrate.....	0–1	<1	7.5	0

cretion and not merely a transudate from the vascular system or overflow from the peritoneal cavity. The presence of secretory cells in the tubal epithelium is well known; they undergo morphologic and apparent physiologic alterations which parallel changes in ovarian activity (Hadek, 1955, 1958a; Borell, Nilsson, Wersäll and Westman, 1956). In the rabbit the secretion is regarded as essential for normal development of the egg (Westman, Jorpes and Widström, 1931), and it may be necessary for the normal functioning of spermatozoa and the process of fertilization as well (*cf.* Whitten, 1957).

The secretory activity of the rabbit Fallopian tube has been investigated and the volume of flow and secretory pressure in singly and doubly ligated tubes determined (Bishop, 1956a). Mean tubal secretion rates in lightly anesthetized estrous, pregnant, and castrate rabbits were 0.79, 0.37, and 0.14 ml. per 24 hours, respectively. Secretory activity was maximal at the time when the spermatozoa are in the ampulla. Active secretion, as opposed to passive diffusion or transudation, was demonstrated by manometric determinations of the pressures developed within a closed tubal system over a 36-hour period. Pressure maxima in estrous, pregnant, and castrate rabbits averaged 46.0, 15.6, and 11.8 cm. H_2O, respectively (Fig. 13.12). Both secretory volume and pressure decreased from the 11th to the 21st day of pregnancy. Further indication that tubal secretion is an active process is shown by its sensitivity to pilocarpine; a single injection of 1 mg. of pilocarpine hydrochloride almost doubled the secretory pressure, to a value of 75 to 80 cm. H_2O, in estrogen-dominated animals (Fig. 13.13). A program initiated by Clewe and Mastroianni (1959, 1960) permits the continuous

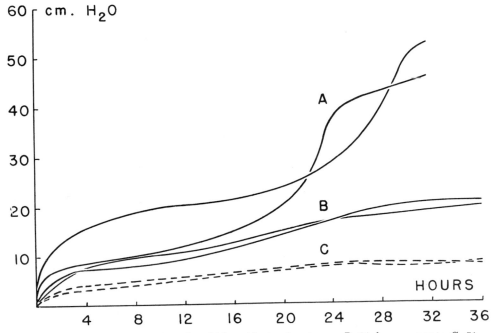

FIG. 13.12. Secretion pressures in rabbit oviducts. *A*, estrous; *B*, 14-day pregnant; *C*, 51-day castrate. (from D. W. Bishop, Am. J. Physiol., **187**, 347–352, 1956a.)

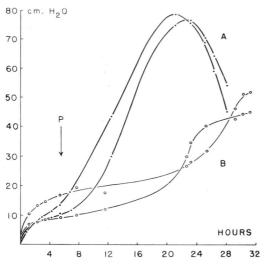

FIG. 13.13. Effect of pilocarpine on tubal secretory pressure; right and left oviducts recorded. *A*, pilocarpine-HCl (1 mg. in 1 ml. saline, I.M.) injected 5½ hours after catheterization; *B*, control estrous records. (From D. W. Bishop, Am. J. Physiol., **187**, 347–352, 1956a.)

collection of oviduct secretion over a period of many weeks. Their values for secretion rate are somewhat higher than those noted above, for example, 1.29 ml. per 24 hours for the rabbit in estrus.

Although the present state of knowledge permits only a fragile evaluation of the significance of these secretory products on the activity and viability of the gametes and fertilized eggs, tubal secretion can hardly be denied. Further chemical and physical analysis of the components of the fluids might profitably be attempted, not only in the rabbit and cow, but in other mammals as well. In the final analysis, the survival and fertilizing capacity of the sperm are functions of the relation between the cell's intrinsic properties and the environment in which it operates.

H. THE FATE OF NONFERTILIZING SPERMATOZOA

Relatively soon after insemination, excess sperm have disappeared from the lumen of the genital tract. Within 20 to 24 hours in the mouse and rat, little indication of the sperm mass can be found (Blandau and Odor, 1949; Austin, 1957). In the sow uterus, a few sperm are present about 50 hours

after copulation, but none can be found 25 hours later (du Mesnil du Buisson and Dauzier, 1955). The general fate of the unsuccessful sperm, recently reviewed by Austin (1957), has long been held to be enzymatic dissolution and phagocytic engulfment in the lumen (Königstein, 1908; Sobotta, 1920). Except for a brief spate in the Russian literature (Kushner, 1954; Vojtíšková, 1955), little credence has been given to the many claims of Kohlbrugge (1910, 1913) that sperm and sperm products are incorporated into the genital epithelium and have profound effects on the maternal physiology (see Hartman, 1939). Indeed, a subsequent paper by Vojtíšková (1956) and others by Pósalaky and colleagues in Prague (1956, 1957a, b) have been quite explicit in stating that the earlier histologic demonstrations of sperm in the epithelial mucosa can be explained on the basis of technical artifacts, principally incurred during the sectioning of tissues. Within the past year or two, however, a number of instances have come to light which make it amply clear that sperm do, under some circumstances, enter or are conducted into the uterine and tubal mucosa. Sperm in, or in association with, leukocytes have been found in the uterine glands of the guinea pig and in the tubal mucosa of other species, including the rat, rabbit, hedgehog, mole, stoat, mouse, and bat (Austin, 1959, 1960; Austin and Bishop, 1959; Edwards and Sirlin, 1959). How commonly this occurs and what its significance may be for the subsequent reproductive capacity of the female remain to be seen. The findings within seven groups of mammals indicate that the phenomenon may be widespread. The association of the spermatozoa with leukocytic infiltration further suggests that the genital tract may, under some circumstances, be regarded as a route of foreign cell invasion.

A natural skepticism regarding the ability of spermatozoa to penetrate somatic tissues is somewhat lessened by the realization that the process is a normal feature of reproduction in certain invertebrate animals. Manton (1938) cites records of this among rotifers, turbellarians, leeches, and the bedbug (*Cimex*); in *Peripatopsis* (*Onychophora*), the sperm are described as invading the body wall at the attachment site of the spermatophore and then passing into vascular channels through which they actively migrate to the ovary where sperm penetration and fertilization occur.

VI. Immunologic Problems Associated with Spermatozoa

A. ANTIGENICITY OF SPERM

The antigenic properties of spermatozoa have been recognized since the turn of the century through the pioneer studies of Landsteiner (1899), Metchnikoff (1899), and Metalnikoff (1900), who, almost simultaneously, discovered that guinea pigs produce antibodies against heterologous and homologous sperm. Landsteiner's work is of classic interest not only because it was barely the first, but also because he used an *in vivo* method to demonstrate an immune response against sperm. Bull spermatozoa, he found, remain active when injected into the peritoneal cavity of normal guinea pigs, whereas if the pigs have been previously injected parenterally with bull sperm, the peritoneally administered sperm rapidly become immotile. These early discoveries were to be followed by a great wave of interest in sperm antigens, generally assayed by *in vitro* methods, and attempts to induce sterility in female animals by injection of suspensions of spermatozoa or testicular homogenate. After a lull in activity, interest was rekindled by the development of new immunologic procedures and concepts, and the awareness of the implication of immune processes to problems of fertility and fertility control (Katsh, 1959a; Tyler and Bishop, 1961).

Specific antigens have been demonstrated in, or on, spermatozoa of many mammals, including the rabbit, rat, mouse, guinea pig, dog, ram, bull, and man. The methods used for their determination have generally involved the classical serologic procedures—agglutination, immobilization, precipitin, and complement fixation—and the more recently introduced Oudin and Ouchterlony agar gel-diffusion techniques. The results, in general, indicate a relatively high degree of species-specificity, but some cross-reactivity does occur (Mudd and Mudd, 1929;

Henle, 1938; Smith, 1949a). Tissue-specificity is also incomplete. The AB-blood group antigens, for example, as pointed out previously, are present in human sperm (Landsteiner and Levine, 1926; Gullbring, 1957), and a comparable similarity of sperm-erythrocyte agglutinins has been claimed in cattle (Docton, Ferguson, Lazear and Ely, 1952). Common antigenicity between brain and testicular tissue has been demonstrated (Lewis, 1934; Freund, Lipton and Thompson, 1953; Katsh and Bishop, 1958) and may relate to the mature germ cells themselves.

As routinely determined by means of agglutination or immobilization of fresh sperm in the presence of antisperm serum, the antigenicity of the gametes is customarily attributed to surface moieties and exposed reactive groups. Smith (1949b), however, called attention to the reactivity of the more deeply situated antigenic substances in her study of heterologous reactions among rodent sperm. In part, of course, the masking and unmasking of combining groups are a function of the technical procedures to which the cells are exposed and are features which have to be circumvented or recognized in investigations of this kind. The surface properties of, and "leakage" from, spermatozoa are known to change with storage, dilution, washing, and centrifugation, which, when severe enough (Mann, 1954), can be expected to alter the apparent natural antigenicity of the cells (Smith, 1949b; cf. Pernot, 1956).

The number of antigenic substances on the sperm surface is a moot point and may prove merely a matter of definition, if not of semantics, depending on the techniques involved (see Table 3 in Tyler and Bishop, 1961). Henle, Henle and Chambers (1938) localized three distinct antigens in bull sperm by preparing, in rabbits, agglutinating and complement-fixing antibodies against the head and tail fractions. One antigen was found to be head-specific, another tail-specific, and the third common to both head and tail of the intact sperm. On the other hand, when the agar-diffusion method was applied to the study of sperm antigenicity, many reactive substances appeared which seemed to be surface antigens.

In one series of experiments, 7 precipitin bands were observed with washed human sperm tested against rabbit antihuman sperm serum (Rao and Sadri, 1959). This investigation further indicated that 4 of the sperm antigens were common to seminal plasma, but were not present merely as contaminants. A parallel investigation, employing essentially identical procedures, led to the conclusion that *all* of the human sperm antigens are also present in plasma and the two materials cannot, immunologically, be distinguished (Weil, Kotsevalov and Wilson, 1956). A similar conclusion grew out of a study of rabbit semen, and the suggestion was made that "the effective antigens found in seminal plasma and spermatozoa of semen appear to originate in the seminal vesicle" (Weil and Finkler, 1958). Because practically all large molecular moieties and cells are potentially antigenic, and because spermatozoa may safely be assumed to arise in the testis, this statement obviously oversimplifies the facts. The point is brought up merely to emphasize the caution that should be exercised in the use of and interpretations derived from various techniques. There are sperm antigenic differences in strains of animals and in individuals within strains, as Snell (1944) and Landsteiner and Levine (1926) have long since pointed out. More, rather than less, immunologic differentiation will probably be forthcoming in the future. Indeed, Weil (1960) has recently found that the antigenic properties differ in epididymal and seminal sperm of the rabbit; the spermatozoa apparently take up and bind antigenic material from the seminal plasma during ejaculation.

B. SPERM-INDUCED IMMUNE RESPONSES IN THE MALE

Antibodies against spermatozoa, both foreign and those of the same individual, are produced with facility by members of both sexes. Why an animal should so react against autologous antigen, *i.e.*, a male against its own sperm, is not clear. According to the concepts put forward by Burnet and Fenner (1949), Billingham, Brent and Medawar (1955, 1956), and others, an organism undergoes a state of "recognition" of its own native substances during the tolerant period before antibodies are produced. Thereafter, it does not consider these, or other substances initially introduced during the tolerant period, as foreign. The formation by an adult animal of antibodies against injected autologous spermatozoa, moreover, is generally attributed to the fact that sperm are not normally produced until late in development; thus they have not had a chance to be "recognized" as native and are treated as foreign material when injected. The further supposition must be made that spermatozoa in the testis are somehow normally insulated from the rest of the body, at least from the antibody-forming sites, and therefore fail to evoke antibody production and an immune response. Such speculations are tentative and must await further understanding of the general nature of antigenic stimulation, antibody production, and antigen-antibody complex formation, subjects which are currently undergoing rapid growth and perplexing change (Talmage, 1957, 1959; Lederberg, 1959).

Because antibody production is evoked by autologous sperm, the question arises whether auto-immunization occurs and, further, whether it is of any biologic significance. Sperm agglutination occurs in otherwise normal ejaculates of rabbit, bull, and man, and the seminal plasma can be shown to contain agglutinating antibodies (Wilson, 1954; see Tyler and Bishop, 1961). The possibility exists that an antigenic stimulus for antibody formation may arise following sperm absorption or penetration into the epididymal mucosa during a period of inflammation, a process often associated with intense leukocytic infiltration (Mason and Shaver, 1952; Montagna, 1955; King, 1955). In man, such a reaction is claimed to be common after mild epididymal infection; it causes no impairment of testicular function, but produces a tissue response characterized by granulomatous lesions (Steinberg and Straus, 1946; Cronqvist, 1949; King, 1955). Similar lesions have been described in cases of granulomatous orchitis, in which spermatozoa were present in macrophage cells and in the lymphatic system (Friedman and Garske, 1949). Cruickshank and Stuart-Smith (1959) have recently described circulating antisperm antibodies in men who had previously suffered orchitis. It seems not unlikely, therefore, that certain cases of auto-agglutination of ejaculated sperm may have arisen from some kind of autosensitization and passage of the antibodies into the seminal plasma. If auto-immunization does occur by such means, it is assumed that tubal inflammation or infection must be present to effect the immune reaction; otherwise the condition should be much more common since resorption of non-ejaculated sperm from the epididymis seems to be a normal process (see above). The seminal and follicular component, antagglutin, discovered by Lindahl and Kihlström (1954), which tends to prevent abnormal clumping of sperm, does not counteract agglutination by prepared antiserum (Lindahl, 1960); it seems rather to operate through another, nonserologic type of mechanism.

Bocci and Notarbartolo (1956) suggested that immunologic factors might contribute to a state of sterility on a basis of their finding of positive antisemen skin reactions in some men suspected of infertility.

Rümke (1954) and Rümke and Hellinga (1959) made extensive studies of sperm agglutinins in the sera of sterile men. In a series of over 2000 cases, they found a considerably higher incidence of sperm-agglutinating antibodies in the sera of childless men (4.1 per cent) than in those of normal fertile controls (1.0 per cent). Among a small group of 21 relatively aspermic patients, all of whose sera had sperm agglutinins, 16 showed occlusions or obstructions of the male tract. In the light of these demonstrations, the suggestion may be ventured that auto-immunization occurs in the male, that the mechanism may result from spermatozoal reactions involving the tubal epithelium, and that the antibodies produced may impair fertility. To what extent, if any, variations in androgen levels modify the epididymal reactivity in this regard is completely unknown.

An unusual syndrome, aspermatogenesis, can be readily induced in the guinea pig by injecting homologous spermatozoa or homogenized testis combined with adjuvant (Freund, Lipton and Thompson, 1953; Freund, Thompson and Lipton, 1955; Katsh and Bishop, 1958; Tyler and Bishop, 1961). The immune response is due to a delayed sensitization and is apparently not associated with the high levels of circulating antisperm antibodies which can be detected by such methods as sperm agglutination, immobilization, and complement-fixation (Freund, 1957; Katsh and Bishop, 1958). The testicular lesion, as observed 1 to 2 months after injection, is characterized by loss of germinal epithelium and decrease in gonadal weight and volume (Fig. 13.14). The Sertoli elements are affected very little, if at all. The interstitial tissue remains functional, as judged by the normal size and activity of the accessory glands. Since the induction of aspermatogenesis by the injection of spermatozoa has been established only in the guinea pig and rat, the implications for reproductive physiology may be limited; its occurrence and the possible mechanism, however, are of substantial importance to the general areas of delayed sensitization and the immune response (Katsh, 1958, 1959c; Voisin, Toullet and Mauer, 1958).

In contrast to these investigations of *active* immunization with sperm, the introduction of antisperm serum into male animals has been shown to affect fertility in a limited number of instances. Mice and rabbits both show reproductive impairment after injection of homologous antibody serum (de Leslie, 1901; Guyer, 1922). In rats, a considerable weight loss (24 per cent) of the testes is accompanied by sloughing of germinal epithelium after injection of rat sperm antiserum produced in the rabbit (Segal, 1961). The testicular reaction appears to be a specific response against the homologous sperm.

C. SPERM-INDUCED IMMUNE RESPONSES IN THE FEMALE

The memorable statement of Charles Darwin (1871) that "the diminution of fertility may be explained in some cases by the profligacy of the women" may be taken to imply a sensitization against the male reproductive products, although another not unlikely explanation may involve the im-

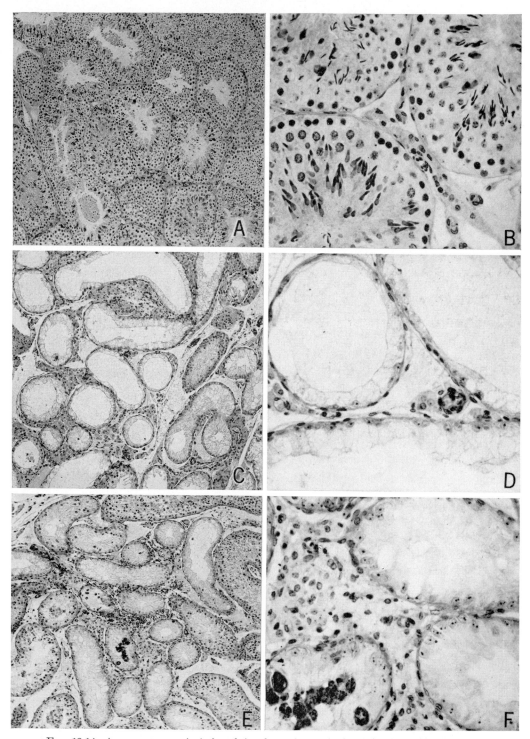

Fig. 13.14. Aspermatogenesis induced in the guinea pig by injection of testicular homogenate and adjuvant. *A*, normal adult guinea pig testis used as donor, approx. 65 ×; *B*, same, approx. 260 ×; *C*, testis of semicastrate 2 months after injection of autologous testicular homogenate, 65 ×; *D*, same, 260 ×, note normal interstitial tissue; *E*, testis of guinea pig injected at 1 week and sacrificed at 5 months of age, 65 ×; *F*, same, 260 ×. (From D. W. Bishop, unpublished photographs.)

paired health of the subjects. Three decades after Darwin, the immunization of laboratory animals against spermatozoa suggested a mechanism by which sensitization could come about. During the following half century the pros and cons of this issue were to rage. The parenteral introduction of either homologous or heterologous spermatozoa was early claimed by many workers to induce some degree of female sterility in a wide variety of animals (see Parkes, 1944; Tyler and Bishop, 1961). Some experiments seemed so successful that a patent was once granted for an antisterility preparation based on this procedure (Baskin, 1937). Such experiments, however, are beset with difficulties of control and natural biologic variation. It is not surprising, therefore, that more recent investigations have tended to discredit the earlier reports of sterility induced by sperm injection, and to provide adequate explanation for many of the apparent positive results (Eastman, Guttmacher and Stewart, 1939; Hartman, 1939; Henle and Henle, 1940; Lamoreux, 1940). The ancient role of spermotoxins in inducing female sterility seemed thus to be laid at rest.

The issue was again raised with the advent of adjuvants which have the ability of potentiating the effect of an antigenic stimulus. Quite recently, evidence has accrued indicating that reproductive capacity may indeed be impaired in female rabbits and guinea pigs when they are injected with sperm or testis homogenate combined with adjuvant (Katsh and Bishop, 1958; Isojima, Graham and Graham, 1959; Katsh, 1959b). In treated guinea pigs, the fertility (number bearing litters) was reduced to 24 per cent compared with 84 per cent for the controls. The rate of fetal death and resorption was high, but there seems to have been little effect on ovulation or fertilization. High titers of circulating antisperm antibodies were present, but their connection with the decreases in fertility is not clear. One reasonable explanation for the occurrence of these induced effects on reproductive capacity was suggested by Katsh (1957), who attributed the fetal loss to a possible anaphylactoid response of the uterus to foreign antigen. Other plausible mechanisms may involve the gametes or developing embryos

directly; circulating antibodies can pass into the uterine and tubal fluids and might impair development (McCartney, 1923).

These recent results, then, not only give some credence to the early claims for induced sterility, but also raise the question as to the possibility of naturally acquired sensitization in breeding females. Little direct evidence can be cited in support of such a hypothesis since only fragmentary immunologic studies have been made which indicate sensitization or antisperm antibody titers in the sera of animals not previously inoculated (see Tyler and Bishop, 1961). However, in a series of over 200 women, Ardelt (1933) found a positive correlation between frequency of coitus and complement-fixation titer against human spermatozoa. Studies of this sort on various species should prove rewarding.

Whereas the evidence concerning the degree of sensitization of the female is scant, the means by which antigenic stimulation might occur seems adequate. The penetration of the tubal epithelium by sperm has been noted; under some circumstances, this phenomenon may be relatively common, as when mild infections or lesions occur within the tubal mucosa. Another possible site of antigenic stimulation, particularly in animals like the rabbit, is the peritoneum, for not only do sperm pass through the tract and enter the body cavity (Hartman, 1939; Horne and Audet, 1958), but the peritoneum is an adequate site for antibody formation. Furthermore, repeated deposition of spermatozoa into the rabbit vagina results in high titers of circulating antisperm antibodies (Pommerenke, 1928). A comparable situation has also been demonstrated in heifers in which genetically tagged erythrocytes, rather than sperm, were introduced into the intra-uterine cavity, with the result that specific antibodies subsequently appeared in the blood (Kiddy, Stone, Tyler and Casida, 1959). These results have been interpreted as demonstrating the passage of antigen into the circulation where access is gained to the sites of antibody formation; it is to be noted, however, that the tissues of the reproductive tract itself do on occasion produce antibodies (Kerr and Robertson, 1953). It is worth pointing out that, in other experiments, antibodies, rather than antigens, seem to be transported across the genital epithelium, or to migrate by way of the peritoneal cavity. Parsons and Hyde (1940), for example, found circulating antibodies after introducing antisperm serum into the vaginas of rabbits, and McCartney (1923) claimed that circulating antibodies, actively produced in rats against sperm, could be detected in the uterine and vaginal fluids. Antibodies are known, of course, to pass into the uterine lumen of rabbits during pregnancy (Brambell, Hemmings and Henderson, 1951).

Very little has been attempted in altering the fertility of female animals by means of *passive* immunization with spermatozoa, perhaps because the outstanding investigation of Henle, Henle, Church and Foster (1940) was so conclusive. Repeated injection of mice with antisperm serum, produced in rabbits, failed to modify reproductive capacity in any significant way.

The treatment of fresh sperm with specific antisperm serum has profound effects on the gametes, the basis, in fact, of the sperm-agglutination and sperm-immobilization test methods. The treatment generally renders sperm, both invertebrate and vertebrate, incapable of fertilizing eggs (Godlewski, 1926; Tyler, 1948; Kiddy, Stone and Casida, 1959). A significant contribution, moreover, has been the recent demonstration that if the exposure to antiserum is carefully controlled, surprising and subtle effects may occur when these sperm are used for artificial insemination. Rabbit sperm, treated for 15 minutes with high concentrations of bovine antirabbit antiserum before insemination, were incapable of effecting fertilization, as judged from the recovery of unfertilized ova. However, a 15-minute exposure of sperm to the same, but diluted, immune serum permitted fertilization, but resulted in a high percentage of embryonic deaths (Kiddy, Stone and Casida, 1959). No such fetal wastage occurred when rabbit sperm were similarly exposed to normal bovine serum. The antisera employed in these experiments were prepared against whole semen, rather than against washed sperm, but any additional antigenic components in plasma would not be expected to have altered the results. Various inter-

pretations can be placed on these findings, including the possibility that the fertilizing sperm might have carried antibodies into the egg which impaired development, or, an alternative possibility, that the antibodies had a mutagenic action on the spermatozoa leading to abnormal development after fertilization (Kiddy, Stone and Casida, 1959). There seemed to be no injurious effect on the sperm that resulted in delayed fertilization; thus the effects cannot be attributed to aging of the ova.

An immunologic mechanism has been implicated by Gershowitz, Behrman and Neel (1958) to account for the variations from the expected ratio of offspring of couples with incompatible ABO-blood groups. These investigators found hemagglutinins in the cervical mucus of 17 out of 77 cases so distributed that they might be regarded as constituting a preconceptive selection mechanism by blood group antibodies of the uterine secretions acting on the sperm.

In conclusion, a brief survey of the immunologic literature relating to fertility indicates that spermatozoa may be deeply involved in both experimentally and naturally induced modifications in reproductive performance and capacity. Other immune-like interreactions between specific substances, fertilizin and antifertilizin, extracted from invertebrate eggs and sperm, also have been demonstrated; the possible role of these reactions in the fertilization process is discussed in the following chapter.

VII. Morphology and Composition of Spermatozoa

A. STRUCTURAL FEATURES

As one of the first objects to be viewed microscopically (van Leeuwenhoek, 1678), the spermatozoon has had a long morphologic history,[2] and still enjoys great popularity, particularly among cytochemists and electron microscopists. No exhaustive item-

[2] Reimer Kohnz (1958) calls attention to a recent "find" in the library of the Cologne Cathedral which, if genuine, would shed revolutionary light on the history of microscopic science. A manuscript, purported to have been illuminated by monks of the Reichenau Monastery ca. 1000 A.D., is interpreted as showing an egg with eight spermatozoa attached!

ization of sperm morphology is intended here, and even less is necessary by virtue of many extensive surveys which, over the years, have reviewed and collated the literature of the times, in the light of contemporary interests and in relation to other areas of biologic progress (Retzius, 1909; Wilson, 1925; Bradfield, 1955; Hughes, 1955, 1956; Franzén, 1956; Nath, 1956; Colwin and Colwin, 1957; Bishop and Austin, 1957; Ånberg, 1957; Fawcett, 1958; Schultz-Larsen, 1958; Bishop, 1961). The two historical surveys of Hughes (1955, 1956) are of particular interest to anyone mindful of the past.

Wilson (1925), among others, drew attention to the great variation in animal sperm, including the existence of nonflagellated and nonmotile gametes among certain invertebrate groups. More recently, Franzén (1956), in an admirable survey of many kinds of invertebrate spermatozoa, has emphasized what he believes is a significant correlation between sperm morphology and physiologic demands of the particular type of reproductive process concerned. Considerable attention has been paid to sperm size, from the small, microscopic sea-urchin gamete, some 40 μ long, to the relatively gigantic sperm of the hemipteran insect, *Notonecta glauca*, which is reputed to be about 12 mm. in length (Pantel and de Sinéty, 1906; Gray, 1955). The claim was once current that, because of the difference in chromosome number, a sperm population displays a bimodal size-distribution curve, but careful biometric studies by van Duijn (1958) and others have shown this to be untenable. More recently, differences in size and shape of sperm have been demonstrated in different inbred strains of mice; the characteristics seem to be genetically determined and, when intermingled, lead to extreme variation in hybrid crosses (Braden, 1959).

Gravimetric, interferometric, and refractometric methods have been applied to the study of sperm in an analysis of their physical properties. By such procedures, one can determine that bull sperm have a relative density of 1.280 (Lindahl and Kihlström, 1952), a dry mass averaging 7.1 $\times$ 10^{-9} mg. (Leuchtenberger, Murmanis, Murmanis, Ito and Weir, 1956), and a total weight of about 2.86 $\times$ 10^{-8} mg. (see Bishop, 1961). Human sperm contain at least 45 per cent "solid material" in the head, and possibly 50 per cent "solids" in the tail, as assessed by the method of immersion refractometry (Barer, Ross and Tkaczyk, 1953; Barer, 1956).

Cytochemical procedures, frequently combined with extraction procedures, have proved useful in the investigation of sperm composition, particularly in tracing the differentiation of cellular elements, such as the Golgi apparatus and *Nebenkern*, through spermiogenesis, and in identifying the chemical nature of various structures in the mature gamete. By means of PAS-positive tests for 1,2-glycol groups, for example, the acrosome was found to consist of polysaccharide associated with some proteinaceous material, complexed possibly as mucopolysaccharide (Schrader and Leuchtenberger, 1951; Leblond and Clermont, 1952; Clermont and Leblond, 1955). Further, on extraction and hydrolysis, this material from guinea pig sperm proved to contain galactose, mannose, fucose, and hexosamine (Clermont, Glegg and Leblond, 1955). These are precisely the same components found by Bergman and Werner (1950) in carbohydrate hydrolysates of human cervical mucus (see above).

The electron micrographic studies of spermatozoa, of which there have been a great number, are well summarized by Ånberg's fine treatise (1957) on human sperm and Fawcett's eloquent review (1958) of mammalian sperm in general (Fig. 13.15). Fawcett makes the historic point that in some instances the electron micrograph has confirmed details which theoretically should be invisible with the light microscope, but were seen and described, nevertheless, by an earlier generation of able microscopists— the enumeration, for example, of the 11 tail filaments of the fowl sperm by Ballowitz in 1888. But many other features have been discovered by electron microscopy. The postnuclear cap and cytoplasmic sheath, previously described as parts of the human sperm head, apparently do not exist (Fawcett, 1958). The acrosome system of the human sperm is less discrete than that observed in other types of gametes. The nu-

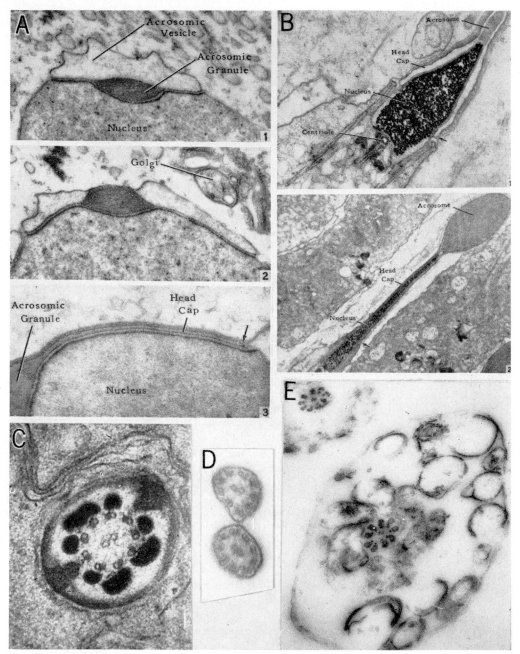

FIG. 13.15. Electron micrographs of mammalian sperm. *A*, 3 stages in the formation of the head cap of the human sperm. *B*, late spermatids of the cat (*1*) and guinea pig (*2*) in roughly longitudinal section; note approximation of axial filament to centriole. *C*, principal piece of guinea pig sperm tail; note that each peripheral doublet appears as one tubular and one solid element; 7 outermost fibers are present at this level (see Fig. 13.17*B*). *D*, terminal region of human sperm tail; the doublets appear as hollow cylinders. *E*, midpiece of human sperm; the electron-dense outermost array of filaments is surrounded by many mitochondrial bodies. (*A* and *B* from D. W. Fawcett, Internat. Rev. Cytol., **7**, 195–234, 1958; *C*, courtesy of D. W. Fawcett; *D* and *E* from Å. Ånberg, Acta obst. et gynec. scandinav., Suppl. 2, **36**, 1–133, 1957.)

cleus, instead of occupying only the posterior portion, seems rather to extend the entire length of the head (*cf.* Bishop and Austin, 1957). During differentiation, the nuclear chromatin condenses into a homogeneous, electron-dense mass, but Yasuzumi, Fujimura, Tanaka, Ishida and Masuda (1956) demonstrated in enzymatically treated bull sperm helical strands which may correspond to distinct chromosomes. During spermiogenesis in the guinea pig the four spermatids resulting from meiosis remain attached by intercellular bridges until late in the development of the gametes (Fawcett, 1959). Such connections may allow for significant interchange of materials and for mutual interaction among the members of the tetrad.

Electron microscopy has confirmed the traditional view that there are two centrioles present in the neck region of the sperm which are directly or indirectly associated with the axillary bundle extending into the flagellum (Fawcett, 1958). The homology of the centriolar body with the basal granule (blepharoplast) is assumed.

The spiral body, typical of the middle piece of the sperm, is made up principally of the mitochondrial elements, arranged spirally but not in a continuous helix. The distribution of the mitochondria, constituting in large measure the "power plant" of the cell by reason of their oxidative and phosphorylative activities, is in close association with the flagellar apparatus, particularly the fibrillar elements of the tail. The mitochondrial system is derived from or related to the *Nebenkern*, a prominent cell inclusion in spermatids of lower forms. In some insect sperm, in the absence of a true midpiece, the mitochondria extend far down into the flagellum (Rothschild, 1955). What had been considered the helical covering of the sperm tail might better be regarded as a "fibrous sheath" since the structure is neither continuous nor constituted of uniform successive gyres (Fawcett, 1958). The outer membrane, probably the true physiologic surface of the cell, is a continuous envelope and is apparently derived from the spermatid cell membrane.

Emanating from electron micrographic investigations, a universal fibrillar pattern in flagella and cilia is generally acknowledged. Modifications exist but incontestable evidence indicates that the basic arrangement, as seen in transverse sections, is the now familiar $2 \times 9 + 2$ array. Surrounding 2 central filaments is a ring of 9 double fibrils (Figs. 13.16, 13.17*A*, *B*), all of which seem to extend, uninterrupted, from proximal to distal tip of the flagellum. On extensive, but nevertheless largely circumstantial evidence, the outer filaments are generally regarded as the motile organelles. Inoué (1959), however, in summarizing the evidence pertinent to ciliary movement, suggests that the outer fibrils may actually be conductile elements, whereas the two central filaments take a more active part in motility. Certain other features of the sperm tail, including the

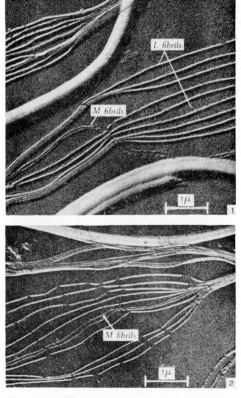

Fig. 13.16. Electron micrographs of fowl sperm flagella. Of the 11 major filaments, two (M fibrils) are differentiated from the remainder and constitute the central pair. Sperm were exposed to distilled water, fixed in formalin, and shadow-cast with platinum. (From G. W. Grigg and A. J. Hodge, Australian J. Scient. Res., ser. B, **2**, 271–286, 1949.)

chemical nature of these longitudinal filaments, their proximal association with yet
another array of 9 peripheral fibers, their
relation to the matrix of the flagellum, and
their relation to one another, are described
elsewhere in considerable detail (Bishop,
1961). As a general conclusion, the three
main divisions of sperm into head, middle
piece, and tail correspond roughly to their
genetic, metabolic, and motile functions.

B. BIOCHEMICAL FEATURES

The availability and homogeneity of spermatozoa have long appealed to the biochemist in choosing a cell type for study. Both
chemical and histochemical methods have
been employed in investigations of the composition of sperm, and recent developments
in quantitative cytochemistry show good
agreement in the results obtained by the two
general procedures. Complete analyses of the
chemical components of several types of
spermatozoa are now available and include
the full range of substances from ions to enzymes, many of which have been roughly
localized within the major regions of the
cells. For more extensive treatment concern-

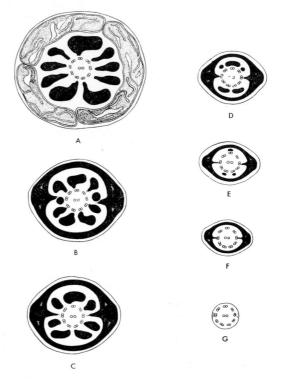

FIG. 13.17B. Diagram of rat sperm tail at various
levels from midpiece (A) to tip (G). Note bilateral
symmetry of fibrillar arrangement and termination
of outer longitudinal fibers at different levels of
flagellum. (Courtesy of D. W. Fawcett.)

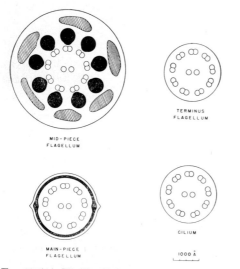

FIG. 13.17A. Highly diagrammatic representation
of transverse sections of sperm flagellum and cil-
ium; 2 central and 9 double peripheral fibrils typical of all such motile organelles. Mitochondria
(oblique hatching) present in midpiece. An additional array of 9 outermost filaments (solid) in the
midpiece of mammalian sperm extends into the
proximal portion of the flagellum. The fibrous
sheath of the tail is frequently ribbed as indicated.

ing the functional composition of sperm, the
reader is referred to several reviews (Mârza,
1930; van Duijn, 1954; Mann, 1954; Bishop,
1961); only selected features of the volumi-
nous literature will be noted here.

Just short of a century ago, Miescher, and
later Kossel, and their co-workers took up
the study of the basic proteins—protamines
and histones—of fish sperm nuclei, easily
procurable by plasmolysis of the cytoplasm
and collection of the heads by centrifugation. Progress was rapid and by the 1920's
more was known, it was claimed, about the
chemistry of the spermatozoon than about
any other cell (Marshall, 1922). These early
studies have expanded into investigations of
the basic proteins as conjugates with desoxyribonucleic acid (DNA), and particular attention has been directed toward the significant and systematic changes from the
histone- to the protamine-type protein during sperm differentiation (Miescher, 1897;
Kossel, 1928; Mirsky and Pollister, 1942;

Pollister and Mirsky, 1946; Stedman and Stedman, 1951; Felix, Fischer, Krekels and Mohr, 1951; Bernstein and Mazia, 1953a, b; Alfert, 1956; Vendrely, Knobloch and Vendrely, 1957; Ando and Hashimoto, 1958; Felix, 1958). Histone is regarded as typical of somatic chromosomes, whereas protamines characterize the nuclei of mature sperm (Daly, Mirsky and Ris, 1951). The two types of basic proteins differ in their solubility and physical properties and in their chemical composition as well; protamines are found to have fewer amino acids when compared to histones from the same animal (Daly, Mirsky and Ris, 1951). Both are very rich in arginine. This polyamino acid is reported to constitute some 70 per cent of the protamine, "gallin," of fowl sperm (Fischer and Kreuzer, 1953), and about 50 per cent and 30 per cent, respectively, of the solid matter of bovine and human sperm nuclei (Leuchtenberger and Leuchtenberger, 1958). Total amino acid composition and other chemical characteristics of sperm nucleoprotein have been reported on numerous occasions (see Sarkar, Luecke and Duncan, 1957; Daly, Mirsky and Ris, 1951; Porter, Shankman and Melampy, 1951; Dallam and Thomas, 1953).

Sperm DNA has been isolated from a variety of species and its nucleotide composition determined (Chargaff, Zamenhof and Green, 1950; Chargaff, 1951; Chargaff, Lipshitz, Green and Hodes, 1951; Elmes, Smith and White, 1952). According to Elmes, Smith, and White, the purine and pyrimidine bases of human sperm—guanine, adenine, cytosine, and thymine—are present in the molar ratio of $0.92:1.23:0.84:1.01$, which is consistent with the "thymus-type" composition of nucleic acid. The absolute amount of DNA per sperm nucleus is measurable, both by direct chemical analysis and by ultraviolet microspectrophotometry (Vendrely and Vendrely, 1948, 1949, 1953; Mirsky and Ris, 1949, 1951; Leuchtenberger, Leuchtenberger, Vendrely and Vendrely, 1952; Walker, 1956; Knobloch, Vendrely and Vendrely, 1957; Leuchtenberger and Leuchtenberger, 1958). Bull sperm contain approximately 3.3×10^{-9} mg. of DNA per nucleus. Of particular significance was the Vendrelys' (1948) demonstration that the sperm nu-

cleus contains half as much DNA as does the diploid nucleus of the corresponding somatic cell, thereby giving strong support to the theory that DNA is identical with the substance responsible for hereditary transmission. In a recent study of the sperm of bull and man, the Leuchtenbergers (1958) indicated that, whereas the amount of DNA is constant in gametes from fertile individuals, there is a tendency for DNA deficiency in the sperm from infertile individuals (see also Weir and Leuchtenberger, 1957). This finding is surely of great significance but its cause and meaning are at present obscure.

The amount of ribonucleic acid (RNA) in sperm nuclei is small, but sufficiently large to be detected. Leuchtenberger, Leuchtenberger, Vendrely and Vendrely (1952) gave a value for bull sperm of about 0.1×10^{-9} mg. of RNA per nucleus.

C. THE LOCALIZATION OF ENZYMES

The mammalian spermatozoon has a full spectrum of enzymes which enables it to carry on the usual glycolytic and oxidative processes associated with the production of energy (Mann, 1954). In addition, there are relatively specific enzyme systems associated with movement, others related to fertilization, and still others (e.g., amino acid oxidase) possibly concerned with modification of the substrate with which the sperm come in contact. Some of these enzymes have been tentatively localized in specific regions of the sperm, thereby shedding some light on the intracellular activities of the gametes and their constituent structures.

Since both mechanically separated and naturally ejaculated sperm tails, free from the heads, are capable of motility, oxidation, and glycolysis, it is obvious that the key enzyme systems concerned with these processes are relatively self-contained within the flagellum (Engelmann, 1898; Cody, 1925; Mann, 1958a). As used here, the term flagellum includes the mitochondria-containing middle piece, for without it the tail fragment rapidly loses its capacity for metabolism and motility (Bishop, 1961). The enzymes which have, by direct or indirect means, been identified in the ram sperm flagellum and are known to be involved in the Embden-Meyerhof glycolytic process, include hexokinase, phosphohexoisomerase, phosphohexokinase, aldolase, enolase, and lactic dehydrogenase (Mann, 1949, 1954). Cytochrome oxidase, determined both manometrically (Zittle and Zitin, 1942) and spectrophotometrically (Nelson, 1955a), is present in the tail fraction of bull sperm, and the complete cytochrome system can be demonstrated in flagellar preparations which include the midpieces as well (Mann, 1954). From what is known about mitochondrial activity in general, one assumes that most, if not all, of the enzyme systems associated with respiration, oxidative phosphorylation, and electron transport through the cytochrome system are concentrated in the sperm midpiece. Succinic dehydrogenase can be demonstrated in flagellar fractions both by biochemical and cytochemical methods (Mann, 1954; Nelson, 1955a; Kothare and De Souza, 1957). Nelson (1959) has further been able to show in frozen-dried sections of the rat sperm flagellum what seems to be succinic dehydrogenase activity in the outermost longitudinal fibers of the tail.

The sperm flagellum, at least in man and bull, when tested cytochemically, gives positive reactions for acid phosphatase, and the bull sperm tail shows alkaline phosphatase activity as well (Wislocki, 1950; Melampy, Cavazos and Porter, 1952). Both types of phosphatase have been cytochemically localized in the midpiece of the rat sperm (Friedlaender and Fraser, 1952; Melampy, Cavazos and Porter, 1952). The precise functions, however, of these enzymes in the sperm are not clear.

One or more adenosinetriphosphatases (ATPases) have been extracted from or demonstrated in the flagella of invertebrate and mammalian spermatozoa (Felix, Fischer, Krekels and Mohr, 1951; Nelson, 1954, 1955b; Engelhardt and Burnasheva, 1957; Burnasheva, 1958; Hoffmann-Berling, 1955; Bishop and Hoffmann-Berling, 1959). In frozen-dried sections of rat sperm flagella, ATPase has presumably been visualized in association with the outermost array of fibrils (Nelson, 1958a).

In the head of the mammalian sperm, only acid and alkaline phosphatases have been reported and these determinations were achieved by cytochemical localization (Wislocki, 1949, 1950; Melampy, Cavazos and Porter, 1952; Friedlaender and Fraser, 1952).

Thus far, no enzymes have been identified in the mammalian sperm head which compare with the invertebrate sperm lysins, believed to play some role in egg penetration (Tyler, 1948). Hyaluronidase, which effectively disperses the cumulus cell mass around mammalian ova, is present on the sperm but has not been localized in any one region. Buruiana (1956) found that hyaluronidase activity is common to mammalian sperm, whereas trypsin activity is characteristic of bird sperm; of the species studied, only the rabbit sperm showed both types of enzymatic activity. Amylase has been demonstrated in bull sperm, but because of the violence of the extraction procedure, little is known as to its site of action (Lundblad and Hultin, 1952). Other enzymatic activities have been found in intact sperm or cell homogenates, such as aconitase in bull (Lardy and Phillips, 1945; Humphrey and Mann, 1948), cholinesterases in boar and guinea pig (Sekine, 1951; Sekine, Kondo and Saito, 1954; Grieten, 1956), and glycosidases and sorbitol dehydrogenase in ram (Conchie and Mann, 1957; King and Mann, 1958). Sorbitol dehydrogenase may serve to convert the seminal plasma constituent, sorbitol, to fructose, a normal metabolic substrate for spermatozoa.

D. THE SPERM SURFACE

As far as can be determined from electron micrographs, the sperm cell membrane is identical with, or at least derived from, the spermatid membrane. In the mature ram sperm, as in many invertebrate sperm, the membrane was claimed to swell osmotically in response to hypotonic changes in the medium (Green, 1940). This is not true of bull sperm (Rothschild, 1959); in fact most mammalian sperm are resistant or indifferent to osmotic changes (Emmens, 1948; Pursley and Herman, 1950; Blackshaw, 1953a, b; M. W. H. Bishop, 1955). This feature is in contrast to the selective permeability with respect to many organic molecules, both charged and uncharged

(Mann, 1954). Rothschild (1959) investigated the anaerobic heat production in buffered suspensions of bull semen under various anisotonic conditions and found that an initial shock reaction, marked by reduced heat production and metabolic activity, was followed by gradual recovery or adaptation which in some cases was complete. Such adaptation seems particularly characteristic of bull sperm but the nature of the osmotic regulation is not entirely clear. Under severely unfavorable conditions the permeability of ram and bull sperm is so altered as to permit the apparent leakage of large molecules such as cytochrome *c* (Mann, 1951a, 1954). Pronounced changes in permeability accompany the phenomenon known as "cold-shock" (Mann and Lutwak-Mann, 1955).

Chemical analyses of ram and bull sperm by Green (1940), Zittle and O'Dell (1941), and others indicate that the surface membrane contains lipid, probably bound as phospholipoprotein; the lipid-free membrane is high in nitrogen and cystine and bears a superficial resemblance to keratin (Mann, 1954). The toughness and the elastic properties of human sperm actually have been qualitatively determined by dexterous microdissection technique (Moench, 1929).

The sperm surface at physiologic ionic strength and pH bears a negative charge which has been claimed to be higher on the tail than on the head (Joël, Katchalsky, Kedem and Sternberg, 1951). The gametes thus tend to migrate electrophoretically toward the anode. According to Machowka and Schegaloff (1935), this movement is counteracted, at certain field strengths, by a galvanotropic tendency to swim actively toward the cathode. The negative charge on the sperm surface may be attributable to phosphate, carboxyl, and/or sulfate groups attached to organic components of the membrane.

Several attempts have been made to utilize the electrophoretic properties of sperm in order to separate X- and Y-bearing gametes. Schröder (1940a, b, 1941a, b, 1944), in an interesting and apparently careful series of investigations, claimed to have accomplished this with rabbit sperm; the two types of gametes thus separated, when artificially inseminated into does, gave predominantly (78 to 80 per cent) male or female offspring. More recent work by Gordon (1957) suggests concurrence in these findings, but both the technique employed and the conclusions derived indicate the need for further confirmation. If such electrophoretic separation of the two cytogenetically distinct types of sperm is possible, it would be of interest to ascertain the reason for the behavior, whether, for example, the male- and female-producing gametes carry different ζ-potentials or otherwise vary in surface composition. Schröder's studies did indeed indicate that the electrophoretic response might be attributable to differences in the components of the lipoprotein sheaths of the two types of spermatozoa.

VIII. Sperm Metabolism

A. SOURCES OF ENERGY

In biochemical investigations of spermatozoa the focus of attention has been on the metabolic processes associated with the production of chemical energy required for motility. Although the sperm of relatively few species have been extensively explored, a fairly consistent pattern of metabolic activities has been established. Mammalian sperm, in general, display extensive glycolytic activity under both aerobic and anaerobic conditions, and carry on oxidative respiration when conditions are appropriate (Mann, 1954). Invertebrate spermatozoa, on the other hand, rely almost entirely on oxidative processes and show little, if any, glycolysis (Rothschild, 1951a). Regardless, however, of the nature of the substrate and the pattern of metabolism, the importance of the chemical conversions lies in the coupling of these exergonic reactions with the synthesis of ATP as a utilizable source of chemical energy for the performance of work (Lardy, Hansen and Phillips, 1945; Lehninger, 1955, 1959). In active spermatozoa much of this energy source is consumed by the processes underlying motility; an unknown fraction may be utilized in other activities, including possible synthetic processes, conduction, and membrane transport.

In mammalian spermatozoa, anaerobic glycolysis supplies sufficient ATP energy to support motility for long periods of time; however, respiratory processes coupled with oxidative phosphorylation are far more efficient and can be assumed to furnish sperm, as other tissues, 8 to 10 times as much ATP for the same amount of initial substrate degraded (for general discussion, see Lehninger, 1955; Slater, 1958). Sperm motility is sustained so long as a minimal concentration of intracellular ATP persists; with the exhaustion of ATP, motility ceases (Engelhardt, 1945; Lardy, Hansen, and Phillips, 1945). In 1945, Lardy and Phillips suggested the presence of ATP in bull sperm and Mann (1945) succeeded in isolating from ram sperm the nucleotide, as the barium salt, and characterizing it as ATP. Soon thereafter it was shown to be functionally identical with ATP isolated from muscle (Ivanov, Kassavina and Fomenko, 1946). ATP has since been extracted from sperm of the sea urchin, *Echinus esculentus* (Rothschild and Mann, 1950). A considerable body of evidence has suggested that phosphagen is present in mammalian sperm which might serve as a phosphorus donor for the reconstitution of ATP from adenosine diphosphate (ADP) (see Bishop, 1961, for review); recently, however, White and Griffiths (1958) re-examined the problem and failed to find any significant amount of creatine phosphate or the enzyme which might take part in transphosphorylation in the sperm of the ram, rabbit, or bull.

B. INVERTEBRATE SPERM METABOLISM

The processes underlying motility and survival of invertebrate spermatozoa are oxygen-dependent and involve the utilization of endogenous reserves (Rothschild, 1951a). In sea urchin sperm, on which such investigations have almost exclusively centered, the oxidative substrate seems to be phospholipid, mainly situated in the midpiece (Rothschild and Cleland, 1952). About 20 per cent of the intracellular phospholipid of the sperm of *Echinus esculentus* is depleted during incubation over a 7-hour period at 20°C. According to Rothschild, sea-urchin spermatozoa do not utilize glycolytic substrates (glucose or fructose), and there is scant evidence of a "sparing" of endogenous substrate by exogenous hexose.

Among certain other forms which, like the sea urchin, reproduce by external fertilization, the spermatozoa rely principally, if not entirely, on oxidative mechanisms. This is true, for example, of the starfish, *Asterias* (Barron, 1932) as well as the frog, *Rana* (Bernstein, 1954). On the other hand, some invertebrate sperm are less restricted in their metabolic capacity. The sperm of the oyster, *Saxostrea*, for example, normally depend on respiratory processes, but if these are inhibited by an oxidative inhibitor such as cyanide, and suitable substrate is present, glycolysis can occur (Humphrey, 1950). Barron (1932) indicated that sperm of various marine animals differ significantly in their tolerance for anaerobic conditions, as determined by the safranin test for oxygen; sperm of *Arbacia*, *Asterias*, and *Nereis* retain their motility and fertilizing capacity when exposed to anaerobiosis for 1, 2, and 5 hours, respectively.

The importance of oxidative phosphorylation, in contrast to oxygen consumption *per se*, to sperm motility has been clearly demonstrated in the sperm of the clam, *Spisula* (Gonse, 1959). Dinitrophenol, an uncoupling agent, inhibits sperm motility while increasing O_2 uptake several fold. Amytal, on the other hand, at a concentration which severely depresses respiration, only slightly impairs motility.

Determinations of respiratory quotients (R.Q.) of invertebrate spermatozoa yield values approximating 1.0 (Barron and Goldinger, 1941; Hayashi, 1946; Barron, Seegmiller, Mendes and Narahara, 1948; Spikes, 1949; Humphrey, 1950). Such data suggest carbohydrate rather than lipid or phospholipid as substrate. Rothschild (1951a), however, has emphasized the technical difficulties besetting such determinations and the errors which may arise; in his view, loss of bicarbonate from the seawater diluent gives erroneously high R.Q. values. Yet, in support of the possible utilization of glucose or fructose by sea urchin sperm (*Arbacia* and *Psammechinus*) stands Wicklund's demonstration that exogenous hexose significantly prolongs motility and fertilizing capacity of sperm (in Runnström, 1949), a point also suggested by the work of Spikes (1949).

It seems that, although there may exist some variation in the ability of invertebrate sperm to withstand anaerobiosis or to utilize glycolytic substrates to a limited extent, these cells generally are dependent on respiratory processes for the major production of chemical energy. Since the conditions of external fertilization deny them ready access to glycolytic substrates in the environmental milieu, the sperm have failed to develop, or have secondarily lost, their glycolytic capacity, so characteristic of mammalian and avian spermatozoa. It is unlikely, although, of course, possible, that failure to utilize hexoses rests on the impermeability of the sperm to these substrates.

C. MAMMALIAN SPERM METABOLISM

As is the case with invertebrate spermatozoa, most of what is known about the biochemical characteristics of mammalian sperm has been acquired from studies, *in vitro*. To the extent that experimental conditions may duplicate those within the genital tract, the behavior of sperm, *in vivo*, can only be surmised. Considerable variation is seemingly inherent in the metabolic characteristics of sperm of different species and in the gametes removed from different levels of the tract (see Dott, 1959). There is little doubt that such variation exists, but the causes may not be so distinctive as is generally claimed. Discounting differences in sperm behavior attributable to variations in handling and experimental procedure, it seems likely, without implying fundamental differences in metabolic patterns, that sperm, like most other types of cells, possess a lability of subcellular activity which enables them to regulate to external and intrinsic factors. The variations in sperm behavior, which at times seem so unique, are not likely to conflict with the conservative concept of the "biochemical unity of living matter" (Fruton and Simmonds, 1959).

The principal metabolic characteristics of mammalian spermatozoa have been extensively reviewed by Mann (1949, 1954); elsewhere special attention has been paid to human sperm (MacLeod, 1943b; Ivanov, 1945; Westgren, 1946; Lundquist, 1949). It is now well established that both glyco-

lytic and oxidative processes provide energy for mammalian sperm and either one or both types of metabolic pattern can serve the sperm after insemination into the female genital tract. Motility of ram and bull sperm, *in vitro*, is enhanced by the presence of *both* hexose and oxygen together (Walton and Dott, 1956). Whereas fructose is the common natural substrate at ejaculation (see chapter by Price and Williams-Ashman), most mammalian sperm also utilize glucose and mannose with equal or greater facility (Mann, 1954). The principal steps in the degradation of sperm hexose to lactic acid occur by the well known Embden-Meyerhof scheme involving ATP as phosphate donor and diphosphopyridine nucleotide (DPN) as hydrogen carrier (electron transport system); this has been demonstrated in both ram and bull sperm, mainly by the identification of individual enzyme systems and glycolytic intermediates (Mann, 1954). The several components of the cytochrome-cytochrome oxidase electron transport system have been established by manometric and spectrophotometric methods in a variety of spermatozoa, including those of man (MacLeod, 1943a; Mann, 1951a). Less direct, but nevertheless adequate, evidence further indicates that the Krebs tricarboxylic acid cycle is involved in the oxidative processes (Mann, 1954; White, 1958). Indeed, there is no evidence to suggest that the over-all metabolic systems of sperm, at least of the ram and bull, are significantly different from those of muscle or of most other mammalian tissues. The rates of glycolysis and oxidation vary, but the mechanisms are basically the same. Moreover, it is probable that under many conditions, *in vivo*, there is considerable interaction between the glycolytic and oxidative processes (for general discussion, see Racker, 1959; Racker and Gatt, 1959). Both types of metabolic pathways, glycolytic and oxidative, are complete within the sperm flagellum. This is clear from the fact that in both the guinea pig (Cody, 1925) and bull (Mann, 1958) cases have been reported in which the flagella are naturally separated from the heads at the time of ejaculation; such flagella are actively motile and show high rates of lactate production and oxygen consumption. Both turkey and cock sperm also utilize glycolytic and oxidative substrates, although at lower rates than those generally found in mammalian spermatozoa (Winberg, 1939; Pace, Moravec and Mussehl, 1952; Bade, Weigers and Nelson, 1956; Lorenz, 1958).

The range of substrates metabolized by mammalian sperm is extensive and includes carbohydrates, lipids, and amino acids. Of the three readily glycolyzable hexoses—glucose, fructose, and mannose—glucose is preferentially utilized by sperm of the bull, ram, and man (Mann, 1951b; van Tienhoven, Salisbury, VanDemark and Hansen, 1952; Flipse, 1958; Freund and MacLeod, 1958). Hexose degradation is such that one mole of glucose gives rise to two moles of lactate (Flipse and Almquist, 1955; MacLeod and Freund, 1958). Lactic acid tends to accumulate, since the rate of glycolysis, in bull sperm for example, exceeds the rate of pyruvate oxidation (Melrose and Terner, 1951). Evidence bearing on the possibility of direct oxidation of glucose by way of the hexose monophosphate shunt is fragmentary and thus far negative (Wu, McKenzie, Fang and Butts, 1959). Glycolysis can, of course, occur under both aerobic and anaerobic conditions. The addition of exogenous hexose to a respiring system of sperm tends to "spare" the respiratory substrate (Lardy and Phillips, 1941; O'Dell, Almquist and Flipse, 1959); this partial inhibition of oxidation by glycolysis is a manifestation of the well known Crabtree effect (Crabtree, 1929; Terner, 1959) and can be interpreted as a form of metabolic regulation.

Since the initial demonstration (Lardy and Phillips, 1941) that endogenous phospholipid seems to constitute the natural respiratory substrate of bull spermatozoa, many oxidizable substances have been shown to increase oxygen uptake or to support sperm motility (Mann, 1954; White, 1958). Considerable species variation occurs in the apparent facility with which such substances are oxidized, but some of this variation depends less on utilization than on the extent to which the substances penetrate specific kinds of sperm. Succinate and malate, for example, can increase the respi-

ration and motility of washed ram sperm, but are without effect on bull sperm under similar conditions, presumably because of their failure to penetrate the cells (Lardy and Phillips, 1945; Lardy, Winchester and Phillips, 1945). Changes in cell permeability induced by rough handling, severe centrifugation, storage, or specific chemical treatment, such as exposure to surface-active detergents, can alter the rate and degree of substrate penetration and thereby produce profound changes in respiratory activity (Koefoed-Johnsen and Mann, 1954).

Among the oxidative substrates which increase respiration of mammalian sperm may be included the end products of anaerobic glycolysis—pyruvate and lactate—as well as acetate, butyrate, propionate, citrate, and oxaloacetate (Lardy and Phillips, 1944; Mann, 1954). Glycerol is oxidized to lactic acid by ram and bull spermatozoa (Mann and White, 1957; White, 1957), probably by entering the Embden-Meyerhof pathway as glycerol phosphate at the triose phosphate level. In experiments involving C^{14}-tagged glycerol, it has been claimed that bull sperm can complete the oxidation to $C^{14}O_2$ under anaerobic conditions (O'Dell, Flipse and Almquist, 1956), a point which requires confirmation. The glycerol moiety of the seminal constituent, glycerylphosphorylcholine, apparently is not made available to the sperm for respiratory activity (Mann and White, 1957).

In the early work on phospholipid oxidation, it was concluded that endogenous reserves are readily utilized and that egg phospholipid can serve as an exogenous source of energy (Lardy and Phillips, 1941). This finding is supported by the study of Crawford, Flipse and Almquist (1956) who determined the uptake by bull spermatozoa of P^{32}-labeled egg phospholipid. Bomstein and Steberl (1957), on the other hand, found a negligible decrease in intracellular phospholipid and an inappreciable utilization of exogenous lecithin during incubation of well washed preparations of bull sperm. Recent re-analysis of the nature of the lipids in ram sperm indicates that 55 to 60 per cent is in the form of choline-based acetal phospholipid or plasmalogen (Lovern, Olley, Hartree and Mann, 1957).

Although this material can be oxidized by sperm with an R.Q. of about 0.71, there is no detectable change in lipid phosphorus (Hartree and Mann, 1959) ; rather, it is the fatty acid residue which is oxidized. Whatever the precise composition and nature of the intracellular oxidizable reserves, the supply must be fairly copious and the utilization efficient; some 20 years ago Moore and Mayer (1941) showed that ram sperm can remain motile in neutralized seminal plasma for 20 hours or more after the sugar, and presumably other exogenous stores, are exhausted (see Lardy, Winchester and Phillips, 1945). The details of lipid oxidation in spermatozoa have not been elaborated, but it is assumed that, as in other tissues, the fatty acid residues react with acetyl-Coenzyme A and enter the tricarboxylic acid cycle to be ultimately oxidized to carbon dioxide and water.

Earlier work had established that the addition of amino acids, particularly glycine, to suspensions of fowl or bull sperm increases many fold the duration of motility and in fowl sperm stimulates oxygen consumption as well (Lorenz and Tyler, 1951; Tyler and Tanabe, 1952). No utilization of the amino acids was detectable and the phenomenon was interpreted on a basis of the chelation of heavy metal ions, such as occurs, for example, with ethylenediaminetetraacetate (Versene) (Tyler and Rothschild, 1951). More recent experiments involving the use of C^{14}-labeled glycine have shown that this amino acid is actually taken up and metabolized by sperm of the bull, without, however, increasing oxygen consumption (Flipse, 1956; Flipse and Almquist, 1956; Flipse and Benson, 1957). Glucose depressed but did not eliminate, the utilization of glycine; on the other hand, the addition of glycine had little or no effect on the utilization of glucose (Flipse, 1958). The principal pathway of glycine catabolism in sperm seems to involve glyoxylate, formate, and carbon dioxide. This is similar to the scheme of glycine oxidation in rat liver and kidney (Nakada and Weinhouse, 1953). Certain other amino acids, namely phenylalanine, tryptophan, and tyrosine, also are metabolized by sperm of the bull and ram by a process of oxidative

deamination catalyzed by the enzyme, L-amino acid oxidase (Tosic, 1947, 1951). Hydrogen peroxide is produced in this reaction and is toxic unless eliminated by catalase (Tosic and Walton, 1950). Thus it is clear that certain amino acids are oxidized by sperm, but the significance of these reactions to the total energy-producing metabolic processes of the cells cannot be regarded as great.

D. EPIDIDYMAL SPERM AND METABOLIC REGULATION

Striking differences have been claimed for the metabolic behavior, *in vitro*, of bull sperm, from different segments of the epididymis, suggestive of metabolic regulation in relation to sperm maturation in the male genital tract (Henle and Zittle, 1942). These differences are manifested by lower rates of endogenous respiration and aerobic glycolysis, and a higher rate of anaerobic glycolysis, by epididymal sperm as compared with the rates shown by washed sperm of semen (Lardy, Hansen and Phillips, 1945; Lardy, 1952). Inasmuch as the motility of the spermatozoa from both sources is essentially similar, such metabolic behavior indicates a higher biochemical efficiency of the epididymal sperm. One can indeed demonstrate an inhibition of glycolysis by oxygen (the Pasteur effect) in epididymal sperm which is less readily displayed by washed seminal sperm.

In a search for the cause of these differences, Lardy found evidence for a so-called metabolic regulator which is present in a bound or inactive form in epididymal sperm and which is released or becomes active at the time of ejaculation (Lardy, Ghosh and Plaut, 1949). The action of the regulator was thus considered to increase respiration and aerobic glycolysis to levels characteristic of semen. This regulating activity was tentatively identified with a sulfur-containing component extractable from semen and from testicular tissue; its action was found to be similar to that of cysteine and reduced glutathione (Lardy and Ghosh, 1952; Mann, 1954). Relatively little work has since been done to identify further the metabolic regulator or to demonstrate a similar agent in other species of sperm.

Further study would be desirable to demonstrate whether bull semen contains a specific metabolic substance which might account for these effects, or whether, on the other hand, the changes noted are part of a more generally applicable type of cell regulation. For example, both the low rate of endogenous respiration and the Pasteur effect, characteristic of epididymal sperm, indicate an efficient phosphorylating system; the metabolism of seminal sperm, on the other hand, suggests that uncoupling of respiration and phosphorylation may have occurred (*cf.* Bomstein and Steberl, 1959). The similarity of action of the sperm metabolic regulator and dinitrophenol, a known uncoupling agent, further supports this interpretation (Johnson and Lardy, 1950; Lardy, 1953). Lehninger (1955) has stressed the relationship between uncoupling and the inhibition of the Pasteur effect in other (mitochondrial) metabolic systems.

A general type of metabolic regulation such as this, rather than a system unique to one type of cell, might account for some of the apparent discrepancies reported by different investigators in their studies of mammalian gametes (Melrose and Terner, 1951). White (1960), for example, working with ram sperm has failed to confirm the work of Lardy and associates; he found no significant difference in oxygen uptake or in fructolysis whether the sperm were from the epididymis or from the ejaculate. At first glance this seems to represent a marked metabolic difference in the sperm of closely related animals; considering, however, the delicate balance of cell regulation at the metabolic level (for general discussion, see Krebs, 1957; Racker and Gatt, 1959) the variation is not necessarily profound. The striking differences shown by Dott (1959) in the epididymal sperm of 5 species of domestic mammals may also represent subtle effects of metabolic control rather than overt manifestations of fundamentally different systems of cell metabolism. He found that the epididymal sperm of the bull, ram, and rabbit are activated, *in vitro*, either by oxygen or by fructose under anaerobic conditions; boar sperm, however, apparently require oxygen, and stallion sperm require fructose, to initiate motility. Once stimu-

lated, boar sperm glycolyze hexose freely, indicating perhaps that the action of the oxygen is to metabolize an intracellular inhibitor of some process necessary for motility (Dott, 1959). The response of stallion sperm suggests that the main source of energy is derived from aerobic glycolysis and, further, that endogenous oxidative reserves are scant or that the respiratory processes are inhibited at some critical point. The oxygen uptake of seminal sperm from the stallion is generally low. In certain features this situation in stallion sperm corresponds to the metabolic behavior of human seminal sperm.

E. HUMAN SPERM METABOLISM

Principally through the investigations of MacLeod (1941–1946), the metabolic activities of sperm in the human ejaculate are generally considered to present a rather unique picture. Human sperm show a high rate of anaerobic glycolysis which is only slightly depressed by oxygen; the rate of oxygen consumption in the presence of glucose is extremely low—according to Terner (1960), about one tenth that of bull sperm. When hexose is replaced by any one of a number of amino or fatty acids, sperm motility is gradually lost; it is not known, however, to what extent these exogenous substances do or do not penetrate the cell. Of the nonglycolyzable substrates employed, only succinate stimulated oxygen consumption, and this reaction was accompanied, when glucose was present, by a 40 per cent reduction in lactate production (MacLeod, 1946). MacLeod further claimed that oxygen, even at low tensions, is detrimental to human sperm suspended in Ringer glucose; after several hours at 38°C., aerobic motility is seriously impaired. Motility is also suppressed by glycolytic inhibitors (iodoacetate and fluoride), but is claimed to be unaffected by respiratory poisons (cyanide, azide, and carbon monoxide). These considerations led MacLeod to the conclusion that human sperm rely entirely on the energy of glycolysis for motility and are unable to utilize effectively oxidizable substrate, despite the fact that the cells contain the main components of the cytochrome system and tricarboxylic acid cycle.

The relatively high glycolytic activity of human sperm was compared by MacLeod (1942) to the metabolism of certain types of tumor cells (see Warburg, 1956a, b).

The apparent toxicity of oxygen on human sperm *in vitro* was attributed to the production of hydrogen peroxide, inasmuch as the effect could be eliminated by the addition of catalase. The enhanced respiration induced by succinate, noted above, was also found to be accompanied by an increase in H_2O_2 formation. As a possible mechanism of peroxide formation, the autooxidation of a flavo-like compound was suggested (MacLeod, 1943b, 1946).

These investigations on human sperm emphasize the preferential utilization of glycolytic substrates, under the conditions of the experiments. The relative failure, however, of respiratory substrates to support motility might well bear further scrutiny. This is particularly true in light of the rapid oxidation of succinate, as shown by MacLeod, and the recent report of Terner (1960) that saline suspensions of human sperm oxidize both pyruvate and acetate, as shown by $C^{14}O_2$ production from pyru-

ger, 1959; Racker, 1959). In human sperm, however, the rates of oxidative respiration and phosphorylation are low and appear to be initially metabolically suppressed. Thus the oxidative inhibition is not induced by high glycolytic activity itself (Crabtree effect), but rather, glycolysis is favored by the previous suppression of respiration. The inhibition of oxidation, in turn, can be attributed, if MacLeod is correct, to the production of toxic amounts of hydrogen peroxide, and this seems to be the relatively unique feature of human sperm metabolism. A plausible explanation for both the source of the peroxide and the failure of respiration and oxidative phosphorylation can be formulated following the suggestion by MacLeod (1942). Thus, it is characteristic of flavoprotein (FAD) that, as a "pacemaker" in the oxidative chain (Krebs, 1957), it can either transfer hydrogen atoms from reduced diphosphopyridine nucleotide (DPNH+) to the cytochrome system or, by auto-oxidation, noncatalytically combine with molecular oxygen to form hydrogen peroxide (Fruton and Simmonds, 1958) (see schema).

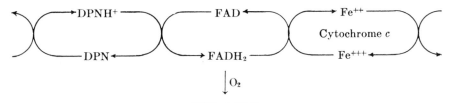

$$FAD + H_2O_2$$

vate-2-C^{14} and acetate-1-C^{14}. Dinitrophenol stimulated $C^{14}O_2$ production from both glucose-C^{14} and pyruvate-2-C^{14}.

The peculiar metabolic behavior of human sperm may be partially clarified by reference to the principles of intracellular regulation and alternative metabolic pathways, characteristic of other cellular and subcellular systems. Of the two main types of energy-producing pathways, which in a sense are normally in competition (Krebs, 1957; Racker and Gatt, 1959), the process of glycolytic phosphorylation in human sperm dominates oxidative phosphorylation. This imbalance could be brought about by the unequal distribution of such rate-limiting substances as ADP or inorganic phosphorus (for general discussion, see Lehnin-

Unlike most respiring cells which follow the first of these alternative pathways, human sperm seem to be shunted off into the nonphosphorylative peroxide-producing route. Succinate is known to bypass DPN and to donate hydrogen directly to FAD (Krebs, 1957). As previously mentioned, in human sperm succinate causes increases in both oxygen uptake and peroxide formation and a decrease in lactic acid accumulation (MacLeod, 1946). But whether this represents a shift from glycolytic to oxidative pathways or merely an inhibition of glycolysis, possibly by the poisoning of sulfhydryl-containing enzymes by excessive amounts of peroxide (MacLeod, 1951), is not known.

Speculative as these interpretations concerning human sperm may be, they have some merit. New avenues of investigation are opened by a broader approach. Moreover, some advantage is gained by attempts to relate certain aspects of the apparently exotic behavior of human sperm to the metabolic patterns and principles common to other mammalian tissues. Many issues are yet to be resolved, including the question of the utilization of oxidative substrates *vis-à-vis* their permeability, and the recently announced difference in sensitivity of human sperm to endogenous versus exogenous hydrogen peroxide (Wales, White, and Lamond, 1959). Tests might be applied to determine whether peroxide is produced in accordance with the scheme noted above or whether it may arise from endogenous nitrogenous sources, comparable to its formation from exogenous aromatic amino acids, as previously noted (Tosic, 1947; VanDemark, Salisbury and Bratton, 1949; Tosic and Walton, 1950).

F. METABOLIC-THERMODYNAMIC INTERRELATIONS

Underlying much of the above discussion are many quantitative data pertaining to the metabolic and thermodynamic properties of sperm. Rates of oxygen consumption

TABLE 13.12

Vital statistics of bull spermatozoa

(Data obtained in buffered saline, 37°C.; calculations based on free-energy change of hydrolysis of −8 kcal. per mole of adenosine triphosphate.)

Anaerobic fructolysis (Mann, 1954).....................	1.7 mg./10^9 sperm/hr.
Energy liberated............	6.27×10^{-6} erg/sperm/sec.
Energy trapped as ATP.....	1.76×10^{-6} erg/sperm/sec.
Endogenous oxygen uptake (Lardy, 1953).............	200 μl./10^9 sperm/hr.
	1000 mcal./10^9 sperm/hr.
	1.5×10^{-5} erg/sperm/sec.
Anaerobic heat production (Clarke and Rothschild, 1957).....................	220 mcal./10^9 sperm/hr.
ATP phosphorus liberated aerobically* (Nelson, 1954, 1958b)....................	2.55×10^{-6} erg/sperm/sec.
	21 μgm. P/mg. sperm N/min.
	2.5×10^{-19}M ATP/sperm/sec.
	2×10^{-12} mcal./sperm/sec.
	8.4×10^{-8} erg/sperm/sec.
Energy required for motility (Nelson, 1958b)...........	3.15×10^{-8} erg/sperm/sec.
(Rothschild, 1959).........	2.11×10^{-7} erg/sperm/sec.

* Based on fragmented cells and expressed as net result of balance between hydrolysis and synthesis of ATP.

and of fructolysis have been determined for sperm of a wide variety of species (Mann, 1954). Values have also been obtained for heat production (Bertaud and Probine, 1956; Clarke and Rothschild, 1957; Rothschild, 1959), ATP hydrolysis, and the energy requirements for flagellar movement. Some of these properties for one species are tentatively summarized in a table of vital statistics for bull spermatozoa (Table 13.12). Expressed on a per sperm basis, the energy, in ergs, calculated for substrate utilization and heat production indicate a wide thermodynamic safety factor in the balance sheet between energy generated and that required.

In Rothschild's exacting study (1959) in which he has demonstrated the changes in sperm heat production with variations in environmental factors, including pH, tonicity, and centrifugation, attention is drawn to the narrow margin between the free-energy change of anaeorbic glycolysis which is associated with ATP synthesis and the energy expenditure involved in flagellation. The data suggest that in bull sperm under anaerobic conditions the rate of ATP synthesis does not keep pace with that of ATP hydrolysis.

Although adequate data are available for the ATP-splitting activity of sperm fragments and sperm extracts (see Nelson, 1954; Burnasheva, 1958), the rate of ATP hydrolysis in whole sperm is difficult to assess, inasmuch as the value of inorganic phosphate liberated is the net result of hydrolysis over synthesis or the phosphorylation of ADP. This is clearly indicated in Table 13.12, in which the energy from ATP-splitting is seen to be insufficient for the energy requirements of movement. This procedural quandary was noted by Lardy, Hansen and Phillips (1945) who demonstrated in aerobic suspensions of bull sperm an increase in nucleotide-phosphate release in the presence of cyanide, an inhibitor of phosphorylation processes.

G. BIOSYNTHETIC ACTIVITY

Although spermatozoa are generally regarded as fully differentiated by the time they reach the epididymis, some questions have arisen with respect to their biosynthetic ability even after ejaculation. Such metabolic cofactors as ATP, for example, are most certainly synthesized (at least from ADP), at the expense of organic substrates, throughout the motile life span. More complex substances may also be synthesized. Hakim (1959) has reported that polynucleotide phosphorylases can be extracted from human sperm which, when incubated with nucleotide phosphates, cause the formation of dinucleotides, as determined chromatographically. Thus, for example, a mixture of ADP and guanosine diphosphate (GDP), in the presence of suitable enzyme, forms some ADP-GDP. In another type of study employing intact bull sperm, Bishop and Lovelock indicated that C^{14}-labeled acetate is incorporated into fatty acid (see Austin and Bishop, 1957).

The possibility of protein synthesis by sperm was suggested by Bhargava (1957), who reported the incorporation of labeled amino acids into the protein fraction of bull spermatozoa as assayed by radioactivity counting. These conclusions have since been contradicted by Martin and Brachet (1959) who suggest, on a basis of autoradiographic data, that the uptake and synthesis can be attributed to cellular components other than to the sperm in the sample. This finding falls more nearly in line with the general conclusion that RNA, essential for protein synthesis, is absent from mature sperm or is present in only very small amounts (Brachet, 1933; Friedlaender and Fraser, 1952; Leuchtenberger, Leuchtenberger, Vendrely and Vendrely, 1952; Mauritzen, Roy and Stedman, 1952). In this connection it is of interest to recall the observations of Wu, McKenzie, Fang and Butts (1959) on the contrasting metabolic capacities of testicular and seminal bull sperm. Relatively clean preparations of spermatozoa expressed from incised testis, but not sperm from the ejaculate, can oxidize glucose by way of the hexose monophosphate shunt, thereby supplying a source of ribose which is available for RNA in the earlier stages of sperm differentiation.

IX. Sperm Flagellation

The characteristics and mechanics of sperm movement are discussed in con-

siderable detail in several recent reviews dealing with both invertebrate and vertebrate material (Gray, 1953, 1955, 1958; Gray and Hancock, 1955; Bishop, 1961). Sperm motility, closely related to muscular contraction, on the one hand, and to general flagellar and ciliary activity, on the other, represents an important physiologic process with implications beyond the specific behavior of the gametes. For the present context, however, only certain more general aspects of the problem are pertinent.

By the turn of the century the significance of the flagellum for sperm motility was well established (see Wilson, 1925). As early as 1898, Engelmann had succeeded in cutting off the tails of frog spermatozoa to find that the flagella continued to move if the separations were made close to the heads. Ciaccio (1899) and particularly Koltzoff (1903) discussed the elementary mechanisms of flagellation and went so far as to compare the process with contraction of muscle. In 1911, Heidenhain postulated that the chemical energy required for motility must be distributed throughout the flagellum, a concept generally conceded today (Gray, 1958). Ballowitz (1888, 1908) emphasized the significance of the longitudinal fibrils of the axial bundle for motility. In the history of sperm biology these two decades, immediately before and after 1900, constitute the "Age of Flagellation."

A. WAVE PATTERNS

Largely through the efforts of Sir James Gray (1953–1958) many details of the process of flagellation have been recorded, most attention having been focused on the sperm of the sea urchin and bull. Although there exists much natural variation among species in the overt characteristics of the phenomenon, basically the same fundamental mechanism is involved. Propagated waves originate at the base of the flagellum and progress distally toward the tip. The major bending-couple is two-dimensional, but as it sweeps distally it is accompanied by, or is converted into, a three-dimensional wave which gives the sperm a helical spin about the axis of forward progression (Gray, 1955, 1958). In squid sperm under experimental conditions the two components of movement, lateral vibration and rotation, can be separated and analyzed individually (Bishop, 1958f). Wave co-ordination involves not only the initiation of the beat, which may be a function of the basal granule, but also the propagation of the conduction wave along the flagellum. The velocity of wave propagation has been calculated for bull sperm to be 600 to 700 μ per sec. (Bishop, 1961).

The frequency of beat, stroboscopically determined, is on the order of 20 per sec. for the bull and 15 per sec. for man (Ritchie, 1950; Rothschild, 1953; Rikmenspoel, 1957; Zorgniotti, Hotchkiss and Wall, 1958). Wave amplitude in bull sperm is 8 to 10 μ, about 20 times the diameter of the tail. These values are at best only first approximations, because wave characteristics change not only with progression along the length of the flagellum, but also with environmental conditions such as temperature and viscosity of the medium.

B. SPERM VELOCITY

Many attempts have been made to determine the speed of sperm travel (see Bishop, 1961). As a general rule, the methods used give data for translatory rather than absolute velocities (Table 13.13). Speeds up to 350 μ per sec. have been recorded for bull sperm. Rikmenspoel (1957) has presented an extensive correlation of the variations in bull sperm velocity with changes in frequency and amplitude of wave formation and with alterations in viscosity and temperature of the environment. The effect of current flow on stallion sperm velocity was demonstrated by Yam-

TABLE 13.13

Translatory velocities of mammalian spermatozoa, in vitro

(Buffered saline or saline-plasma, 37°C.)

Species	Average Velocity	Reference
	μ per sec.	
Man	23	Adolphi, 1905
	14	Botella Llusia *et al.*, 1957
Horse	87	Yamane and Ito, 1932
Ram	80	Phillips and Andrews, 1937
Bull	123	Rothschild, 1953
	114	Moeller and VanDemark, 1955
	105	Rikmenspoel, 1957
	94	Gray, 1958

ane and Ito (1932). They found that sperm orient themselves by rheotaxis, or are oriented physically, against a current, and that up to a limit, as the opposing flow is increased, the speed of movement also increases. When the opposing current flow was varied from 0 to 20 μ per sec., sperm velocity increased from 87 to 107 μ per sec. Under the conditions of the experiment, the results might be attributable merely to the direction given the sperm, thereby reducing the randomness of movement. Nevertheless, these findings may have some bearing on the problem of active sperm transport *in vivo*, where ciliary or other currents play a role. From a comparison of the data on sperm velocities (Table 13.13) and those previously cited on sperm transport, the conclusion is inescapable that in most mammals, migration is not dependent on active swimming movements alone.

C. HYDRODYNAMICS

Initiated by the theoretical speculations and mathematical derivations of Sir Geoffrey Taylor (1952), a considerable body of information has accrued which permits an evaluation of the mechanics and forces involved in sperm movement (Gray and Hancock, 1953; Hancock, 1953; Rothschild, 1953; Machin, 1958; Nelson, 1958b; Carlson, 1959). From these considerations it is clear that a spiral or three-dimensional pattern of flagellation is more efficient than a two-dimensional wave motion; Taylor calculates that the resulting sperm velocity in the former case may be up to twice as great, depending on the configuration of the sperm cell, for a given amount of energy expended. Employing these mathematical derivations and experimental data for wave characteristics such as frequency and amplitude, Gray and Hancock (1953) found good agreement in calculated and observed values for the velocity of sea-urchin sperm of about 190 μ per sec. The power output required to effect this activity has also been calculated. For sea urchin sperm, Carlson (1959) obtained a value of about 3×10^{-7} erg per sec. per sperm. Comparable figures for bull sperm have been estimated as ranging from 2×10^{-6} to 3×10^{-8} erg per sec. per sperm, depending on certain theoretical assumptions underlying the analysis (Rothschild, 1953, 1959; Nelson, 1958b).

At the present time, such information may seem limited in its application to problems of sperm physiology in relation to the reproductive process as a whole. From a broad point of view, however, it obviously affords a biophysical measure of what the sperm can accomplish, and constitutes a link between the metabolic energy produced, on the one hand, and the work performed during activity, on the other (Table 13.12).

D. MECHANISM OF MOTILITY

Speculation concerning the physical basis for activity of cilia and, by implication, flagella has a long tradition (Grant, 1833; Ankermann, 1857; Schäfer, 1904). Of the various theories proposed, the only one to persist is that which conceives of the flagellum as a diminutive contractile system (Ciaccio, 1899; Koltzoff, 1903; Ballowitz, 1908; Heidenhain, 1911). Other types of biochemical systems can be imagined to account for sperm movement, but the evidence, particularly of the past few years, favors the concept of a contractile protein mechanism, generally associated with the fibrillar system of the tail (see Bishop, 1961).

Brief mention has been made of certain salient features of the motility process. It is clear that ATP is essential for sperm activity, as it is for many other physiologic processes requiring energy. A constant supply of ATP is maintained by the glycolytic and/or oxidative processes of metabolism (Engelhardt, 1958). Certain experiments have indicated that extractable ATP is not significantly depleted during sperm activity (Hultin, 1958), thus further supporting the view that resynthesis of the nucleotide accompanies its dephosphorylation. The presence and general localization of ATPase in the flagellum have been noted; by its specific action on ATP as substrate, chemical energy associated with "high-energy" phosphate bonds is liberated.

The ATP-ATPase type of enzyme system is widely distributed throughout the animal and plant kingdoms; it has been extensively studied and closely identified with the contractile system of muscle. It was of major significance that the contractile protein itself, myosin, was found to possess the ATP-splitting activity which leads to contraction (Engelhardt and Lyubimova, 1939). ATPases thus represent the essential link between the biochemical and mechanical events (Engelhardt, 1958). Myosin alone is incapable of shortening, but when combined with actin, the complex undergoes contraction in the presence of ATP. This can be readily demonstrated in simplified muscle systems such as glycerinated fiber models (Szent-Györgyi, 1949; Varga, 1950) or actomyosin thread preparations (Portzehl and Weber, 1950).

As a result of their previous studies of the biochemistry of muscle, and the overt similarities of muscle contraction and sperm flagellation, Engelhardt and his associates undertook a detailed study of motility of bull sperm. They extracted from sperm cell homogenates a partially purified protein which showed ATPase activity and was tentatively called "spermosin" (Engelhardt, 1946). Refinements in extraction and purification procedures since that time have resulted in the preparation of a product with many of the properties of myosin, isolated by similar techniques from muscle. Meanwhile, work was being reported from several other laboratories confirming the occurrence of ATPase in sperm and sperm tail preparations of a variety of species (Felix, Fischer, Krekels and Mohr, 1951; Nelson, 1954, 1955b; Utida, Maruyama and Nanao, 1956; Bishop, 1958a; Tibbs, 1959). Although not all of these preparations are unequivocally associated with contractile protein or contractile protein alone, the evidence seems clear that the sperm tail possesses high ATPase activity.

More recent publications from Engelhardt's institute indicate that material of a high degree of purity can be extracted from bull sperm tails which probably is the contractile protein, "spermosin," responsible for movement (Engelhardt and Burnasheva, 1957; Burnasheva, 1958; Engelhardt, 1958). Approximately 80 per cent of the ATPase activity of the whole sperm is concentrated in the tail fraction, isolated by centrifugation. Substrate specificity and cationic requirements of the enzyme have led to the conclusion that it is very similar to muscle

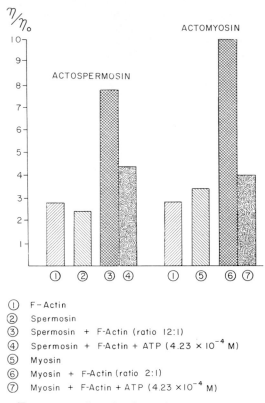

① F-Actin
② Spermosin
③ Spermosin + F-Actin (ratio 12:1)
④ Spermosin + F-Actin + ATP (4.23 × 10^{-4} M)
⑤ Myosin
⑥ Myosin + F-Actin (ratio 2:1)
⑦ Myosin + F-Actin + ATP (4.23 × 10^{-4} M)

FIG. 13.18. Complex-formation and viscosity change upon addition of adenosine triphosphate (ATP) in system composed of contractile protein extracted from bull sperm and actin from rabbit muscle. The response of muscle actomyosin is shown at the right for comparison. (From S. A. Burnasheva, Biokhimiia, **23,** 558–563, 1958.)

myosin. Further similarity is indicated by the claim that "spermosin" can combine with actin, extracted from muscle, to form an "actospermosin" complex (Burnasheva, 1958). This complex undergoes viscosity changes similar to those shown by actomyosin, upon the addition of ATP (Fig. 13.18). It is to be noted that, thus far, physical methods have not been applied to the study of the protein isolated from sperm by these investigators. Attempts to extract an actin-like protein from bull sperm have thus far proved unsuccessful. Whether the contractile system of sperm is eventually resolved as a single component system, as suggested by Burnasheva, or a double component system as in muscle, remains for further investigation to demonstrate.

Although these extraction experiments give strong evidence in favor of a myosin-

like protein in sperm flagella, the picture is far from complete. Rather striking differences have been shown, for example, in the response of fish sperm ATPase to cation concentration when compared with the behavior of muscle ATPase (Tibbs, 1959). Moreover, a comparison of structural details of the sperm flagellum before and after KCl-extraction procedures fails to indicate the source of the extractable protein; indeed, very little change can be detected in electron micrographs of mammalian sperm subjected to such treatment (Bishop, 1961).

The motile mechanism of spermatozoa has been investigated also by the preparation and reactivation of cell models, comparable to the glycerinated models of muscle. Hoffmann-Berling (1954, 1955, 1959) first accomplished this with sperm of the locust, *Tachycines*; as in the case of muscle models, glycerol-extracted sperm were reactivated by treatment with ATP at suitable concentration. This phenomenon has since been demonstrated with sperm of the squid, *Loligo*, and of several species of mammals (Bishop, 1958b, e; Bishop and Hoffmann-Berling, 1959). The methods of extraction, ATP concentrations, ionic requirements, and response to sulfhydryl inhibitors are roughly similar to those applicable to muscle models. The general nature of the response to ATP, however, is strikingly different in that the addition of the nucleotide initiates flagellation which may continue, in bull sperm for example, for as long as 2 hours (Bishop and Hoffmann-Berling, 1959). Apparently, contraction-relaxation cycles are induced in the models which in frequency and amplitude are similar to those of normal fresh sperm. However, as a result of the complete loss of permeability and co-ordination properties of the flagellar models, wave propagation along the flagellum fails to occur and forward movement is insignificant. Among other interesting features of these virtually dead but ATP-reactivated sperm models is the fact that they can be reversibly immobilized by treatment with the Marsh-Bendall (relaxing) factor, prepared from rabbit muscle according to the method of Portzehl (Bishop, 1958c). Moreover, the models are capable of flagellation against a force imposed by increasing the viscosity of the surrounding medium (Bishop, 1958f; Bishop and Hoffmann-Berling, 1959).

Such biochemical approaches as these suggest that the molecular basis of sperm motility is very similar to that of the contractile protein system of muscle. The identification of this system in the sperm is less securely established, but it is assumed to be localized in the longitudinal fibrils of the flagellum. The universality of the 2 × 9 + 2 pattern of filaments seems to demand that considerable significance be attached to them. The filaments appear on chemical grounds to resemble a fibrous protein which could be contractile in nature. Both solubility data (Schmitt, 1944; Bradfield, 1955) and the results of proteolytic digestion of sperm flagella (Hodge, 1949; Grigg and Hodge, 1949) support this view. The positive form birefringence of sperm tails further indicates an orderly arrangement of highly asymmetric structural units which may indeed be the components of the longitudinal fibrils themselves (Schmitt, 1944). X-ray diffraction measurements also suggest a high degree of organization with regular spacing of the structural elements (Lowman and Jensen, 1955). These reports on sperm flagella do not prove that the longitudinal fibrils are contractile protein, but they lend credence to that assumption. Excellent supporting evidence, moreover, is that obtained by Astbury and Weibull (1949) in their study of an entirely different type of flagellar system, the isolated flagella of bacteria. These investigators concluded that the x-ray diffraction pattern of flagellar preparations is characteristic of the k-m-e-f group of fibrous proteins and, further, that both the α- and β-configurations can be demonstrated in unstretched and stretched fibrillar preparations. Astbury and Saha (1953) refer to these bacterial flagella as "monomolecular muscles."

It is to be stressed that the longitudinal filaments of spermatozoa show no consistent cross-striation or periodicity which might be compared with that of the striated muscle fibril (Bishop, 1961). In human sperm prepared for electron micrography, Schultz-Larsen (1958) found an indication of periodicity with intervals of about 20 Å, but this phenomenon is irregular and remains to be confirmed. Cross-striations at intervals of 500 to 700 Å were found in *Arbacia* sperm by Harvey and Anderson (1943), but these have been interpreted as aggregation artifacts rather than as true components of structural periodicity.

Whereas the physical basis for sperm motility is thus fairly well established in a contractile protein system possibly associated with the flagellar filaments, no fully satisfactory theory of the operation of the mechanism has been advanced. The suggestion of Bradfield (1955) that the cylindrically arranged peripheral fibrils fire off progressive contraction waves in successive order was put forth hypothetically to describe a plausible but untested description of flagellation. Afzelius (1959) proposes, on the basis of ultrastructural differences in members of the pairs of peripheral fibrils, that the mechanism may function along the lines of the interdigitating-fibril scheme described for striated muscle by Huxley and Hanson (1954, 1957). Other more conservative speculations have been suggested (*cf.* Bishop, 1958f; Gray, 1958; Nelson, 1959), and final analysis of the precise nature of the contraction-relaxation waves and their synchronous operation in the sperm flagellum must await further experimental innovation and investigation. A striking gap currently persists between the ultrastructural interpretations of spermatozoa and the molecular characteristics associated with motility.

X. Fertilizing Capacity of Treated Spermatozoa

A wide range of environmental factors has been employed in the study of mammalian sperm responses, dating from the very earliest investigations of the gametes (van Leeuwenhoek, 1678). Three principal criteria have served as end points in the investigations of sperm physiology—motility, metabolism, and fertilizing capacity. Interrelated and interdependent *in vivo*, any of these properties alone or in combination can be assessed following experimental manipulation of the sperm *in vitro*. The chemical factors known to modify motility and metabolic behavior of sperm may be arbitrarily grouped roughly as follows: electrolytes including the hydrogen ion, enzymatic inhibitors, chelating compounds, and a variety of uncoupling agents which include sulf-hydryl-blocking agents, hormones (*e.g.*, thyroxine), antibiotics, and surface-active substances (Mann, 1954, 1958b). Other types of environmental factors which induce profound effects on sperm behavior involve dilution of the cell suspension, temperature changes, ionizing radiation, and certain biologic fluids and cell extracts.

The action of such agents on sperm motility and metabolic activity, but not necessarily on fertilizing capacity, is reviewed in detail elsewhere (Hartman, 1939; Mann, 1954; Bishop, 1961); the effect on fertilizing capacity *per se* will be briefly presented here. Alteration of the fertility rate by pretreatment of spermatozoa is, of course, an established procedure. In an extreme sense, this is accomplished by the extension of the life span of sperm for purposes of artificial insemination (Anderson, 1945; Emmens and Blackshaw, 1956; Salisbury, 1957), or, conversely, the curtailment of survival by spermicidal agents (Mann, 1958b; Jackson, 1959).

A. DILUTION OF THE SPERM SUSPENSION

Chang (1946a) drew attention to the dilution effect on mammalian sperm by demonstrating that artificial insemination of rabbits was successful with a given number of sperm suspended in a small amount (0.1 ml.) of saline medium, whereas the same number of sperm in a larger volume (1.0 ml.) failed to bring about fertilization. Mann (1954) suggested that the dilution effect in mammalian sperm might in part be the same general type of response as that occurring in invertebrate sperm, in which the phenomenon has been extensively investigated (Gray, 1928; Hayashi, 1945; Rothschild, 1948, 1956a, b; Rothschild and Tuft, 1950; Mohri, 1956a, b). The studies of mammalian sperm by Emmens and Swyer (1948), Blackshaw (1953a), and White (1953) indicate that some essential substance, or substances, is lost during dilution of the sperm suspension. Such loss can be partially counteracted by the addition to the diluent of K^+ (Blackshaw, 1953b; White, 1953) or of seminal plasma or certain large molecular compounds (Chang, 1959). The nature of the loss, the protective

effect of colloidal substances, and the intracellular changes involved in the dilution effect in mammalian sperm are still obscure. The alterations in the sperm are probably not mere physical changes but rather chemical alterations which involve the metabolic state. The dilution phenomenon in invertebrate spermatozoa, for example, seems to involve an activation of the cytochrome system or other changes in respiratory pattern induced by such factors as pH or copper ions of sea water (Rothschild, 1950, 1956b). Rothschild (1959) has shown an increase in both the initial heat production and prolonged heat production of bull sperm diluted 1:3 with balanced saline solution, compared with the heat output of sperm in seminal plasma.

B. TEMPERATURE EFFECTS

Numerous studies have indicated a direct effect of temperature change on the overt behavior and survival of spermatozoa, but little attention has been directed toward the possible effect on fertilizing capacity of pretreatment of the gametes. One earlier investigation (Young, 1929c) indicated that exposure of guinea pig sperm in the epididymis to 45°C. for 30 minutes reduced the fertility rate, and treatment at 47°C. seriously impaired motility; nevertheless, those embryos which were produced by females inseminated with sperm treated at 45 to 46°C. were apparently normal. Hagström and Hagström (1959) recently demonstrated that the fertilization rate of sea urchins is enhanced by exposure of sperm to either slight increases or decreases in temperature before union of the gametes. The pronounced temperature changes to which sperm are exposed during vitrification are of a far different order of magnitude and are surprisingly well tolerated when properly controlled (see Artificial Insemination).

C. IONIZING RADIATION

When very severe, irradiation can lead to impairment of motility and metabolism in animal spermatozoa; lower doses induce change in nuclear components with consequent abnormalities in development. Hertwig (1911) first demonstrated the paradoxical effect of fertilizing frog eggs with sperm exposed to radium emanations. At lower levels of treatment, abnormal young were produced, increasing in percentage and severity with increase in dosage. At high levels of radiation, normal young developed. The latter effect was attributed to the parthenogenetic development of eggs stimulated by sperm incapable of participating in fertilization. This was confirmed by Rugh (1939) who found an increase in embryonic abnormality and death following fertilization by sperm x-irradiated with doses from 15 to 10,000 r; sperm treated with 50,000 r, however, failed to enter the eggs and a high proportion (91 per cent) of the parthenogenetic young were viable.

Since parthenogenesis is not readily induced in mammals, no such paradoxical effect is to be expected. Impairment of fertilization and induction of embryonic abnormalities have, however, been caused by x-irradiation of sperm *in vitro*. Irradiation of rabbit and mouse sperm induced changes as manifested by embryonic abnormalities and chromosomal aberrations after fertilization of normal eggs (Amoroso and Parkes, 1947; Bruce and Austin, 1956). γ-Radiation when administered at doses of 32,000 to 65,000 r from a radiocobalt source depressed the motility of rabbit sperm (Chang, Hunt and Romanoff, 1957). After treatment with these high exposures, the sperm that were able to reach the ova showed little if any impairment in fertilizing capacity. However, even at a dosage of 800 r, blastocyst formation was retarded, and at 6500 r it was prevented altogether. Johansson (1946) had reported similar findings in fowl; high levels of x-irradiation (3000 to 12,000 r) reduced motility of sperm, whereas relatively low levels (600 to 1200 r) impaired development. The work of Edwards (1954–1957) on the mouse indicates that irradiation, either x-ray or ultraviolet (nonionizing), while permitting fertilization, can render the male gamete incapable of taking part in development. Comparable radiomimetic effects were obtained by treatment of mouse sperm with either trypaflavine or toluidine blue (Edwards, 1958).

The effect of irradiation in mammalian sperm may be similar to that suggested for invertebrate sperm. At certain levels of x-irradiation the fertilizing capacity of sea urchin sperm is reduced, and the cause has been attributed to the formation in the medium of hydrogen peroxide, produced by splitting of water molecules and recombination of free radicals (Evans, 1947). It has also been suggested that stable organic peroxides, rather than hydrogen peroxide, are formed and that these are toxic to sperm, possibly acting by the oxidation of enzymatic sulfhydryl groups (Barron, Nelson and Ardao, 1948; Barron and Dickman, 1949; Barron, Flood and Gasvoda, 1949).

D. IONIC AND OSMOTIC EFFECTS

Despite a mass of data concerning the action of electrolytes and pH changes on sperm motility, and recently on sperm heat production (Rothschild, 1959), relatively little has been done to assess the fertilizing capacity of pretreated sperm. Although certain ions in excess seem to have unusually detrimental effects on sperm survival, *in vitro*—for example, calcium, manganese, lithium, and chloride (Lardy and Phillips, 1943; MacLeod, Swan and Aitken, 1949)—of more surprising interest is the general resistance of sperm to nonbalanced saline media (see Bishop, 1961). Rabbit sperm, for instance, can tolerate 2.0 per cent NaCl for many hours if brought gradually into the hypertonic medium (Anderson, 1945), and bull sperm retain motility for several hours in isotonic KCl. Determinations of the degree to which fertilizing capacity is affected by such treatment might yield very significant results.

Chang and Thorsteinsson (1958b) have made an important beginning with this aim in view. They found that the fertilizing capacity of rabbit sperm is unimpaired by exposure for brief periods (10 to 20 minutes) before insemination in Krebs-Ringer solutions of one-half or twice isotonic concentration. Of particular interest was the finding that motility, but not fertility, was depressed by treatment with the hypertonic medium; one can assume that some recovery occurred in the female tract. Beyond the limits of this range of tonicity, fertilizing capacity was reduced, as judged by observation of recovered tubal eggs; yet even with solutions 0.1 or 4 times isotonic strength (which completely inhibited motility, *in vitro*) fertilization occurred, although at a low rate. Chang and Thorsteinsson also studied the tolerance of sperm to osmotic variation in relation to simultaneous changes in pH. In isotonic Krebs-Ringer medium, rabbit sperm withstood short exposure to acid or alkaline conditions over a pH range of about 5.6 to 10.0, based on observations of motility and conception rate. Under hypo- or hypertonic conditions, however, the upper limit of the pH range tolerated was significantly depressed. This work emphasizes once again the unusual resistance or adaptation of the mammalian germ cell to changes in ionic environment.

E. EFFECTS OF BIOLOGIC FLUIDS

Some effects of certain biologic fluids with which sperm come in contact have been discussed in previous sections. It is clear, for example, that seminal fructose serves the gametes as glycolytic substrate at the time of ejaculation; uterine fluid, or certain of its components, aids in the capacitation phenomenon of sperm during transport through the genital tract. In studies of the effect on fertilizing capacity, sperm have been treated, *in vitro*, with seminal plasma, urine, normal blood serum, and antisperm serum, as well as with isolated products of the female tract itself.

The beneficial effect of *seminal plasma* as sperm diluent, for example, was demonstrated in the rabbit by Chang (1947b). Tests on 33 rabbits showed the advantage (percentage of fertilized eggs) of homologous plasma over saline when the does were inseminated with a minimal number of sperm. It was subsequently indicated that heterologous plasma from human semen was equally effective when used as a diluent for rabbit sperm (Chang, 1949). Bull seminal plasma, however, was injurious to rabbit sperm and caused a significant reduction in fertilizing capacity. It is not clear whether the favorable action of plasma, when it occurs, is due to a specific factor or set of factors, or whether it is caused by a nonspecific action such as chelation by the amino acid or polypeptide components present. The role of chelating substances in extending the motility, metabolism, and fertilizing capacity of sperm has been demonstrated in several invertebrate and vertebrate species (Lorenz and Tyler, 1951; Tyler and Rothschild, 1951; Tyler and Tanabe, 1952; Tyler, 1953; Rothschild and Tyler, 1954). Such an effect was indeed suggested by the work of Chang, since preparations of dead heterologous sperm were as effective as seminal plasma in augmenting fertility in the rabbit (Chang, 1949). These findings may have some bearing on those cases in which, it has been claimed, resuspension of human sperm in foreign plasma improves motility and fertilizing capacity (see Rozin, 1958). A possible detrimental effect of seminal plasma on the fertilizing capacity of sperm was indicated by the demonstration of Chang (1957) that plasma destroys or counteracts the capacitation response of sperm within the rabbit genital tract (see above).

Although it is generally believed that *urine* is harmful to spermatozoa, Chang and Thorsteinsson (1958a) have shown that rabbit sperm tolerate exposure to 50 per cent urine for 10 to 15 minutes with no disturbance in conception rate. A urine concentration of 75 per cent can seriously impair sperm motility, *in vitro*, but even this treatment does not prevent fertilization when these same sperm are artificially inseminated into receptive does.

As has long been known, normal blood *serum* sometimes agglutinates spermatozoa, usually in a head-to-head type of aggregation. This is regarded as a nonspecific agglutination response, and the serum factor which brings it about can be destroyed or effectively reduced by heating to approximately 60°C. In an investigation of the effects of sera on homologous and heterologous sperm, Chang (1947a) demonstrated a complement-like agglutinating component which generally was toxic to the sperm of both its own and of other species; the one exception was the factor in human serum which was ineffective on human sperm. The substance in rabbit serum was found chemically unstable, thermolabile, and nondialyzable. Such an agent was detectable in the sera of man, bull, rabbit, guinea pig, and rat; very little is known, however, concerning its origin or possible role, if any, during normal reproductive processes.

The effects of *antiserum* on the gametes have been discussed in a previous section. It will be recalled that the typical cell-specific agglutination and immobilization responses can render the sperm incapable of fertilization. Further, the experiments of Kiddy, Stone and Casida (1959) suggest a differential effect of treatment with high and low concentrations of antisperm serum. The former impairs fertilizing capacity; the latter results in abnormal development after fertilization (see section on Immunologic Problems).

The impendency of fertilization provokes consideration of several types of sperm responses which can profitably be introduced here and further elaborated on in the chap-

ter by Blandau. These responses involve interrreactions of the sperm and egg, or egg exudates, and concern such processes as chemotaxis, sperm activation, sperm agglutination, and the acrosome reaction.

With respect to the occurrence of chemotaxis, that is, the directed movement toward the egg in response to a chemical gradient from the egg, the evidence relating to animal gametes is essentially negative (Rothschild, 1956b). Many earlier claims for sperm chemotaxis among lower animals (see Heilbrunn, 1943), and certain recent reports on mammalian species (Hübner, 1955; Schuster, 1955; Schwartz, Brooks and Zinsser, 1958), can be readily ascribed to "trap-action," that is, the accumulation of sperm in the vicinity of the egg or egg substance, and not to a nonrandom movement of the

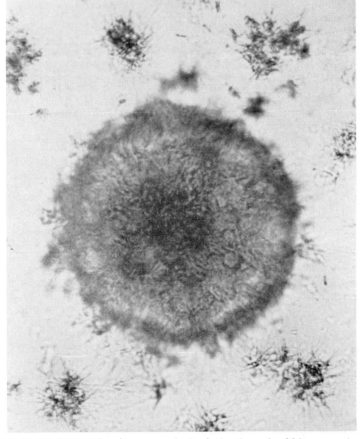

Fig. 13.19. Fertilizin reaction in mammal. Agglutination of rabbit sperm in immediate vicinity of egg collected from rabbit oviduct. Sperm agglutinates form predominantly in head-to-head patterns. (From D. W. Bishop and A. Tyler, J. Exper. Zool., **132**, 575–601, 1956.)

FIG. 13.20. Electron micrographs of sea urchin spermatozoa (*Hemicentrotus pulcherrimus*): *A*, control, formalin-fixed in sea water; *B*, formalin-fixed two seconds after addition of egg water showing breakdown in acrosomal region and extrusion of protoplasmic mass; *C*, formalin-fixed 20 seconds after addition of egg water; *D*, formalin-fixed three minutes after addition of egg water. The agglutination which results from the addition of egg water is reversed at 2.5 minutes. (Photographs courtesy of J. C. Dan.)

sperm toward it. The phenomenon of chemotaxis has, however, been established as occurring in some primitive plants, such as certain ferns, mosses, and brown algae, and the various attempts to determine the nature of the chemical stimulus and the mechanism of the response have been attended by some success (Pfeffer, 1884; Shibata, 1911; Cook, Elvidge and Heilbron, 1948; Cook and Elvidge, 1951; Rothschild, 1951b, 1956b; Wilkie, 1954; Brokaw, 1957, 1958a, b).

Activation of sperm by homologous eggs and egg exudates has been described in some invertebrate species, and the stimulating activity has been attributed to the fertilizin (gynogamone I) present in the egg jelly coat (Lillie, 1919; Tyler, 1948; Rothschild, 1956b). The source of the activator and the specificity of the reaction are, however, somewhat controversial. The increase in motility, when observed, may or may not be accompanied by a substantial enhancement in respiratory activity (Rothschild, 1956b).

The species-specific agglutination of invertebrate spermatozoa by fertilizin of homologous eggs constituted the keystone of the fertilizin theory advanced by Lillie (1919) to account for the specificity and "cell recognition" inherent in the process of fertilization. The nature of the serologic-like gametic substances—egg fertilizin and sperm antifertilizin—and the role these substances may play in the fertilization process have been extensively studied by Tyler and coworkers (1948–1959). Sperm agglutination by egg exudates has been demonstrated in many species of animals in both the invertebrate and lower vertebrate groups (see Tyler, 1948). The phenomenon is also exhibited by mammalian gametes (Fig. 13.19), among which some degree of species specificity is displayed (Bishop and Tyler, 1956). A current view of the possible significance of these gametic substances to fertilization may be found in the recent review by Tyler (1959).

Spermatozoa not only seem to interreact serologically with egg exudates resulting in agglutination and/or loss of fertilizing capacity; they also can be stimulated under some circumstances to undergo morphologic change, most spectacularly characterized by

the acrosome reaction (Dan, 1952, 1956; Colwin and Colwin, 1955, 1957). The forcible release of material from the sperm head (Fig. 13.20), apparently induced by the presence of egg fertilizin, involves the protrusion of a filamentous projection which seems to play a vital, if, as yet obscure, role in the initial stage of the fertilization process.

XI. Conclusion

The notation of a conclusion to the Biology of Spermatozoa seems singularly inappropriate. Both the intensity and the expanse of current research indicate that one is merely taking stock of accumulating data and transient concepts—that in the future lies the answer to most of the questions raised in the pages above. On the one hand, the properties of spermatozoa can be expected to become increasingly clear by our delving more deeply into the nature and activity of the cell, a fruitful approach in its own right and beneficial to the more practical concerns of fertility, sterility, and animal breeding. On the other hand, the recognition of the general characteristics of sperm behavior, movement, metabolism, and survival seems likely to shed brighter light on comparable processes and systems in other cells and tissues, including the nature of cell regulation and adaptation, energy utilization, aging, and movement inherent in ciliary activity, flagellation, and muscular contraction.

If much of the foregoing seems more fragmentary than complete, more provocative and speculative than dogmatic or resolute, this survey may then serve some purpose. The accomplishments have been many, but even more fascinating developments lie ahead.

XII. References

ABARBANEL, A. R. 1946. Spermatozoa and cervical mucus. In *The Problem of Fertility*, E. T. Engle, Ed. pp. 119–126. Princeton, N. J.: Princeton University Press.

ABARBANEL, A. R. 1948. Artificial reproduction of the cyclic changes in cervical mucus in human castrates, with clinical correlations. West. J. Surg., **56**, 26–34.

ADAMS, C. E. 1956. A study of fertilization in the rabbit: the effect of post-coital ligation of the

Fallopian tube or uterine horn. J. Endocrinol., **13**, 296–308.

ADLER, L., AND MAKRIS, A. 1951. Successful artificial insemination with macerated testicular tissue. Fertil. & Steril., **2**, 459–460.

ADOLPHI, H. 1905. Die Spermatozoen der Säugetiere schwimmen gegen den Strom. Anat. Anz., **26**, 549–559.

ADOLPHI, H. 1906a. Ueber das Verhalten von Wirbeltierspermatozoen in strömenden Flüssigkeiten. Anat. Anz., **28**, 138–149.

ADOLPHI, H. 1906b. Ueber das Verhalten von Schlangenspermien in strömenden Flüssigkeiten. Anat. Anz., **29**, 148–151.

AFZELIUS, B. 1959. Electron microscopy of the sperm tail; results obtained with a new fixative. J. Biophys. & Biochem. Cytol., **5**, 269–278.

ALFERT, M. 1956. Chemical differentiation of nuclear proteins during spermatogenesis in the salmon. J. Biophys. & Biochem. Cytol., **2**, 109–114.

ALLEN, E. 1922. The oestrous cycle in the mouse. Am. J. Anat., **30**, 297–371.

ALLEN, J. M., AND HUNTER, R. L. 1960. A histochemical study of enzymes in the epididymis of normal, castrated and hormone replaced castrated mice separated by zone electrophoresis in starch gels. J. Histochem. & Cytochem., **8**, 50–57.

ALLEN, J. M., AND SLATER, J. J. 1957. A chemical and histochemical study of alkaline phosphatase and aliesterase in the epididymis of normal and castrate mice. Anat. Rec., **129**, 255–273.

ALLEN, J. M., AND SLATER, J. J. 1958. A chemical and histochemical study of acid phosphatase in the epididymis of normal, castrate and hormone-replaced castrate mice. Anat. Rec., **130**, 731–745.

ALLEN, T. E., AND GRIGG, G. W. 1957. Sperm transport in the fowl. Australian J. Agric. Res., **8**, 788–799.

AMOROSO, E. C., AND PARKES, A. S. 1947. Effects on embryonic development of X-radiation of rabbit spermatozoa *in vitro*. Proc. Roy. Soc., London, ser. B, **134**, 57–78.

ÅNBERG, Å. 1957. The ultrastructure of the human spermatozoon; an electronmicroscopic study of spermatozoa from sperm samples and the epididymis, including some observations of the spermatid. Acta obst. et gynec. scandinav., Suppl. 2, **36**, 1–133.

ANDERSON, D. H. 1927. The rate of passage of the mammalian ovum through various portions of the Fallopian tube. Am. J. Physiol., **82**, 557–569.

ANDERSON, D. H. 1928. Comparative anatomy of The tubo-uterine junction. Histology and physiology in the sow. Am. J. Anat., **42**, 255–305.

ANDERSON, J. 1944. *The Semen of Animals and Its Use for Artificial Insemination*. Edinburgh: Imperial Bureau of Animal Breeding and Genetics, Technical Commission.

ANDERSON, J. M. 1950. A cytologic and cytochemical study of the testicular cyst-cells in the Japanese beetle. Physiol. Zool., **23**, 308–316.

ANDO, T., AND HASHIMOTO, C. 1958. Studies on protamines. V. Changes of the proteins in the cell nuclei of the testis during the formation of spermatozoa of the rainbow trout (*Salmo irideus*). J. Biochem., **45**, 529–540.

ANKERMANN. 1857. Einiges über die Bewegung und Entwicklung der Samenfäden des Frosches. Ztschr. wiss. Zool., **8**, 129–151.

ARDELT, F. 1933. Spermaresorption bei gesunden und genitalkranken Frauen. Arch. Gynäk., **156**, 357–361.

ASDELL, S. A. 1946. *Patterns of Mammalian Reproduction*. Ithaca, N. Y.: Comstock Publishing Company, Inc.

ASTBURY, W. T., AND SAHA, N. N. 1953. Structure of algal flagella. Nature, London, **171**, 280–283.

ASTBURY, W. T., AND WEIBULL, C. 1949. X-ray diffraction study of the structure of bacterial flagella. Nature, London, **163**, 280–282.

ATKINSON, W. B., SHETTLES, L. B., AND ENGLE, E. T. 1948. Histochemical studies on the secretion of mucus by the human endocervix. Am. J. Obst. & Gynec., **56**, 712–716.

AUSTIN, C. R. 1948. Number of sperms required for fertilization. Nature, London, **162**, 534–535.

AUSTIN, C. R. 1951. Observations on the penetration of the sperm into the mammalian egg. Australian J. Scient. Res., ser. B, **4**, 581–596.

AUSTIN, C. R. 1952. The "capacitation" of the mammalian sperm. Nature, London, **170**, 326.

AUSTIN, C. R. 1957. Fate of spermatozoa in the uterus of the mouse and rat. J. Endocrinol., **14**, 335–342.

AUSTIN, C. R. 1959. Entry of spermatozoa into the Fallopian-tube mucosa. Nature, London, **183**, 908–909.

AUSTIN, C. R. 1961. In *Physiological Mechanisms Concerned with Conception*, W. O. Nelson, Ed. New York: Pergamon Press, in press.

AUSTIN, C. R., AND BISHOP, M. W. H. 1957. Preliminaries to fertilization in mammals. In *The Beginnings of Embryonic Development*. A. Tyler, R. C. van Borstel and C. B. Metz, Ed., pp. 71–107. Washington: American Association for the Advancement of Science.

AUSTIN, C. R., AND BISHOP, M. W. H. 1958a. Capacitation of mammalian spermatozoa. Nature, London, **181**, 851.

AUSTIN, C. R., AND BISHOP, M. W. H. 1958b. Role of the rodent acrosome and perforatorium in fertilization. Proc. Roy. Soc., London, ser. B, **149**, 241–248.

AUSTIN, C. R., AND BISHOP, M. W. H. 1959. Presence of spermatozoa in the uterine-tube mucosa of bats. J. Endocrinol., **18**, viii–ix.

AUSTIN, C. R., AND BRADEN, A. W. H. 1954. Time relations and their significance in the ovulation and penetration of eggs in rats and rabbits. Australian J. Biol. Sc., **7**, 179–194.

AUSTIN, C. R., AND SAPSFORD, C. S. 1952. The development of the rat spermatid. J. Roy. Microscop. Soc., 71, 397–406.

BACQ, Z. M. 1931. Impotence of the male rodent after sympathetic denervation of the genital organs. Am. J. Physiol., 96, 321–330.

BADE, M. L., WEIGERS, H., AND NELSON, L. 1956. Oxygen uptake, motility and fructolysis of turkey spermatozoa. J. Appl. Physiol., 9, 91–96.

BALL, J. 1934. Demonstration of a quantitative relation between stimulus and response in pseudopregnancy in the rat. Am. J. Physiol., 107, 698–703.

BALLOWITZ, E. 1888. Untersuchungen über die Struktur der Spermatozoën, zugleich ein Beitrag zur Lehre vom feineren Bau der contraktilen Elemente. Arch. mikroskop. Anat., 32, 401–473.

BALLOWITZ, E. 1908. Fibrilläre Struktur und Contraktilität. Arch. ges. Physiol., 46, 433–464.

BARER, R. 1956. Phase contrast and interference microscopy in cytology. In Physical Techniques in Biological Research, G. Oster and A. W. Pollister, Eds., Vol. 3, pp. 30–90. New York: Academic Press, Inc.

BARER, R., ROSS, K. F. A., AND TKACZYK, S. 1953. Refractometry of living cells. Nature, London, 171, 720–724.

BARNEY, R. L. 1922. Further notes on the natural history and artificial propagation of the diamond-back terrapin. Bull. U. S. Bureau Fisheries, 38, 91–111.

BARRON, E. S. G. 1932. The effect of anaerobiosis on the eggs and sperm of sea urchin, starfish and Nereis and fertilization under anaerobic conditions. Biol. Bull., 62, 46–53.

BARRON, E. S. G., AND DICKMAN, S. 1949. Studies on the mechanism of action of ionizing radiations; inhibition of sulfhydryl enzymes by alpha, beta, and gamma rays. J. Gen. Physiol., 32, 595–605.

BARRON, E. S. G., FLOOD, V., AND GASVODA, B. 1949. Studies on the mechanism of action of ionizing radiations. V. The effect of hydrogen peroxide and of x-ray irradiated sea water on the respiration of sea urchin sperm and eggs. Biol. Bull., 97, 51–56.

BARRON, E. S. G., AND GOLDINGER, J. M. 1941. Effect of iodoacetate and malonate on the respiration of sea urchin sperm. Proc. Soc. Exper. Biol. & Med., 48, 570–574.

BARRON, E. S. G., NELSON, L., AND ARDAO, M. I. 1948. Regulatory mechanisms of cellular respiration. II. The role of soluble sulfhydryl groups as shown by the effect of sulfhydryl reagents on the respiration of sea urchin sperm. J. Gen. Physiol., 32, 179–190.

BARRON, E. S. G., SEEGMILLER, J. E., MENDES, E. G., AND NARAHARA, H. T. 1948. The effect of nitrogen mustards on the respiration and fertilization of sea urchin sperm and eggs. Biol. Bull., 94, 267–274.

BARTLETT, R. G. J. 1956. Physiologic responses during coitus. J. Appl. Physiol., 9, 469–472.

BASKIN, M. J. 1937. U. S. Patent No. 2,103,240.

BATTAGLIA, G. 1958. Sulla motilità dell'epididimo del ratto in colture organotipiche rotanti. Arch. ital. anat. e embriol., 63, 47–56.

BEATTY, R. A. 1956. Melanizing activity of semen from rabbit males of different genotype. Proc. Roy. Physical Soc., Edinburgh, 25, 39–44.

BELONOSCHKIN, B. 1942. Biologie der Spermatozoen im menschlichen Hoden und Nebenhoden. Arch. Gynäk., 174, 357–368.

BELONOSCHKIN, B. 1949. Zeugung beim Menschen im Lichte der Spermatozoenlehre. Stockholm: Sjöbergs Forlag.

BELONOSCHKIN, B. 1957. Einiges zur Biologie der Cervix uteri im Befruchtungsvorgang. Arch. Gynäk., 189, 280–285.

BENAŠ, A. 1958. Paper electrophoresis of protein extracts of cervical mucus during the menstrual cycle. Radovi med. fak. Zagreb, 2, 198–201.

BENOIT, J. 1926. Recherches anatomiques, cytologiques et histophysiologiques sur les voies excrétrices du testicule, chez les mammifères. Arch. anat., histol., et embryol., 5, 173–414.

BERGMAN, P. 1950. Sexual cycle, time of ovulation, and time of optimal fertility in women. Acta obst. et gynec. scandinav., Suppl. 4, 29, 1–139.

BERGMAN, P., AND LUND, C. G. 1950. The osmotic pressure of human cervical mucus; cyclic changes in the osmotic pressure of cervical mucus and the effect of changes in osmotic pressure on spermatozoal motility. Acta obst. et gynec. scandinav., 30, 267–272.

BERGMAN, P., AND WERNER, I. 1950. Analysis of carbohydrates in human cervical mucus by means of paper partition chromatography. Acta obst. et gynec. scandinav., 30, 273–277.

BERN, H. A. 1949a. Urinary and genital tract phosphatases of the male Dutch rabbit. Am. J. Physiol., 156, 396–404.

BERN, H. A. 1949b. The distribution of alkaline phosphatase in the genital tract of male animals. Anat. Rec., 104, 361–377.

BERNSTEIN, G. S. 1954. Some physiological propphatase activity in the genital tract of the male mouse. Endocrinology, 48, 25–33.

BERNSTEIN, G. S. 1954. Some physiologic properties of frog sperm. Biol. Bull., 107, 305.

BERNSTEIN, M. H., AND MAZIA, D. 1953a. The DNP of sea urchin sperm. I. Isolation and analysis. Biochim. et biophys. acta, 10, 600–606.

BERNSTEIN, M. H., AND MAZIA, D. 1953b. The DNP of sea urchin sperm. II. Properties. Biochim. et biophys. acta, 11, 59–68.

BERTAUD, S., AND PROBINE, M. C. 1956. Rate of heat production by bull spermatozoa. Nature, London, 178, 933.

BESHLEBNOV, A. V. 1938. "On the optimal time of insemination of cows during oestrus." Problemy zhivotnovodstva, No. 2, pp. 73–88.

BHARGAVA, P. M. 1957. Incorporation of radioactive amino acids in the proteins of bull spermatozoa. Nature, London, **179**, 1120–1121.

BIALY, G., AND SMITH, V. R. 1958. Number of spermatozoa in the different parts of the reproductive tract of the bull. J. Dairy Sc., **41**, 1781–1786.

BICKERS, W., AND MAIN, R. J. 1941. Patterns of uterine motility in normal ovulatory and anovulatory cycles, after castration, coitus and missed abortion. J. Clin. Endocrinol., **1**, 992–995.

BILLINGHAM, R. E., BRENT, L., AND MEDAWAR, P. B. 1955. Acquired tolerance of skin homografts. Ann. New York Acad. Sc., **59**, 409–416.

BILLINGHAM, R. E., BRENT, L., AND MEDAWAR, P. B. 1956. Quantitative studies on tissue transplantation immunity. III. Actively acquired tolerance. Phil. Tr. Roy. Soc., London, ser. B, **239**, 357–414.

BINGHAM, H. C. 1928. Sex development in apes. Comp. Psych. Monogr., **5**, 1–165.

BIRNBERG, C. H., AND GROSS, M. 1958. Enzymatic activities of follicular fluid. Internat. J. Fertil., **3**, 374–381.

BISHOP, D. W. 1955. Sperm maturescence. Scient. Month., **80**, 86–92.

BISHOP, D. W. 1956a. Active secretion in the rabbit oviduct. Am. J. Physiol., **187**, 347–352.

BISHOP, D. W. 1956b. Oxygen concentrations in the rabbit genital tract. In *Proceedings 3rd International Congress Animal Reproduction, Physiology,* pp. 53–55. London: Brown Knight & Truscott, Ltd.

BISHOP, D. W. 1957. Metabolic conditions within the oviduct of the rabbit. Internat. J. Fertil., **2**, 11–22.

BISHOP, D. W. 1958a. Sperm contractile protein. Anat. Rec., **131**, 533–534.

BISHOP, D. W. 1958b. Glycerine-extracted models of sperm of the squid, *Loligo pealii.* Anat. Rec., **132**, 414.

BISHOP, D. W. 1958c. Relaxing factors in ATP-induced motility of sperm models. Anat. Rec., **132**, 414–415.

BISHOP, D. W. 1958d. Reflections on recent advances in the study of the biology of spermatozoa. Bios, **29**, 73–81.

BISHOP, D. W. 1958e. Mammalian sperm cell models reactivated by ATP. Fed. Proc., **17**, 15.

BISHOP, D. W. 1958f. Motility of the sperm flagellum. Nature, London, **182**, 1638–1640.

BISHOP, D. W. 1961. Sperm motility. Physiol. Rev., in press.

BISHOP, D. W., AND HOFFMANN-BERLING, H. 1959. Extracted mammalian sperm models. I. Preparation and reactivation with adenosine triphosphate. J. Cell. & Comp. Physiol., **53**, 445–466.

BISHOP, D. W., AND MATHEWS, H. P. 1952a. The significance of intravas pH in relation to sperm motility. Science, **115**, 209–211.

BISHOP, D. W., AND MATHEWS, H. P. 1952b. Inhibition of sperm motility by tetrazolium salts. Science, **115**, 211–212.

BISHOP, D. W., AND TYLER, A. 1956. Fertilizing of mammalian eggs. J. Exper. Zool., **132**, 575–601.

BISHOP, M. W. H. 1955. The physiology of bull spermatozoa. Thesis, Cambridge University.

BISHOP, M. W. H., AND AUSTIN, C. R. 1957. Mammalian spermatozoa. Endeavour, **16**, 137–150.

BISHOP, M. W. H., AND LOVELOCK, J. E. 1957. See Austin and Bishop, 1957.

BLACK, D. L., AND ASDELL, S. A. 1958. Transport through the rabbit oviduct. Am. J. Physiol., **192**, 63–68.

BLACKSHAW, A. W. 1953a. The motility of ram and bull spermatozoa in dilute suspension. J. Gen. Physiol., **36**, 449–462.

BLACKSHAW, A. W. 1953b. The effects of potassium and calcium salts on the motility of ram, rabbit and bull spermatozoa. J. Physiol., **120**, 465–470.

BLANDAU, R., JENSEN, L., AND RUMERY, R. 1958. Determination of the pH values of the reproductive-tract fluids of the rat during heat. Fertil. & Steril., **9**, 207–214.

BLANDAU, R. J., AND MONEY, W. L. 1944. Observations on the rate of transport of spermatozoa in the female genital tract of the rat. Anat. Rec., **90**, 255–260.

BLANDAU, R. J., AND ODOR, D. L. 1949. The total number of spermatozoa reaching various segments of the reproductive tract in the female albino rat at intervals after insemination. Anat. Rec., **103**, 93–110.

BOAS, E. P., AND GOLDSCHMIDT, E. F. 1932. *The Heart Rate.* Springfield, Ill.: Charles C Thomas.

BOCCI, A., AND NOTARBARTOLO, R. 1956. Anticorpi antispermatici quale fattore di sterilità. Indagini sul siero, sullo sperma e sulle secrezioni cervico-vaginale. Minerva ginec., **8**, 957–970.

BOMSTEIN, R. A., AND STEBERL, E. A. 1957. The utilization of phospholipides by bovine spermatozoa. Exper. Cell Res., **12**, 254–264.

BOMSTEIN R. A., AND STEBERL, E. A. 1959. The effect of adenosine upon the aerobic metabolism of bovine spermatozoa. Arch. Biochem. & Biophys., **85**, 43–52.

BORELL, U., GUSTAVSON, K.-H., NILSSON, O., AND WESTMAN, A. 1959. The structure of the epithelium lining the Fallopian tube of the rat in oestrus. An electron-microscopical study. Acta obst. et gynec. scandinav., **38**, 203–210.

BORELL, U., NILSSON, O., WERSÄLL, J., AND WESTMAN, A. 1956. Electron-microscope studies of the epithelium of the rabbit Fallopian tube under different hormonal influences. Acta obst. et gynec. scandinav., **35**, 35–41.

BORELL, U., NILSSON, O., AND WESTMAN, A. 1957. Untersuchungen über die Schlagfrequenz der Cilien in der Tuba uterina des Kaninchens (mit Film). Verhandl. Anat. Gesellsch., **53**, 89–91.

BOTELLA LLUSIA, J., PURAS, A., ATECA, M., AND GOMEZ RUIZ, J. 1957. Mesure de la progression linéaire du sperme humain comme indice de la fertilité masculine. Rev. franc. gynec. et obst., **52**, 241–254.

BOYD, L. J., AND VANDEMARK, N. L. 1957. Spermatogenic capacity of the male bovine. I. A measurement technique. J. Dairy Sc., **40**, 689–697.

BRACHET, J. 1933. Recherches sur la synthèse de l'acide thymonucléique pendant le développement de l'oeuf d'Oursin. Arch. Biol., **44**, 519–576.

BRADEN, A. W. H. 1953. Distribution of sperms in the genital tract of the female rabbit after coitus. Australian J. Biol. Sc., **6**, 693–705.

BRADEN, A. W. H. 1956. Differences in morphology and behavior of sperm from different inbred strains of mice. Ph.D. Thesis, Edinburgh University.

BRADEN, A. W. H. 1958a. Variation between strains of mice in phenomena associated with sperm penetration and fertilization. J. Genetics, **56**, 37–47.

BRADEN, A. W. H. 1958b. Influence of time of mating on the segregation ratio of alleles at the T locus in the house mouse. Nature, London, **181**, 786–787.

BRADEN, A. W. H. 1959. Strain differences in the morphology of the gametes of the mouse. Australian J. Biol. Sc., **12**, 65–71.

BRADEN, A. W. H., AND AUSTIN, C. R. 1953. Fertilization and fertility in mammals. Australian Vet. J., May, 129–132.

BRADEN, A. W. H., AND AUSTIN, C. R. 1954. The number of sperms about the eggs in mammals and its significance for normal fertilization. Australian J. Biol. Sc., **7**, 543–551.

BRADEN, A. W. H., AND GLUECKSOHN-WAELSCH, S. 1958. Further studies of the effect of the T locus in the house mouse on male fertility. J. Exper. Zool., **138**, 431–452.

BRADFIELD, J. R. G. 1955. Fibre patterns in animal flagella and cilia. Symp. Soc. Exper. Biol., **9**, 306–334.

BRAMBELL, F. W. R., HEMMINGS, W. A., AND HENDERSON, M. 1951. *Antibodies and Embryos.* London: University of London, Athlone Press.

BROKAW, C. J. 1957. 'Electro-chemical' orientation of bracken spermatozoids. Nature, London, **179**, 525.

BROKAW, C. J. 1958a. Chemotaxis of bracken spermatozoids: the role of bimalate ions. J. Exper. Biol., **35**, 192–196.

BROKOW, C. J. 1958b. Chemotaxis of bracken spermatozoids: implications of electrochemical orientation. J. Exper. Biol., **35**, 197–211.

BROWN, R. L. 1943. Spermia transport in man. J. Urol., **50**, 786–788.

Brown, R. L. 1944. Rate of transport of spermia in human uterus and tubes. Am. J. Obst. & Gynec., **47**, 407–411.

BRUCE, H. M., AND AUSTIN, C. R. 1956. An attempt to produce the Hertwig effect by X-irradiation of male mice. Stud. Fertil., **8**, 121–131.

BRYSON, V. 1944. Spermatogenesis and fertility in *Mus musculus* as affected by factors at the T locus. J. Morphol., **74**, 131–187.

BUNGE, R. G., AND SHERMAN, J. K. 1954. Frozen human semen. Fertil. & Steril., **5**, 193–194.

BURKHARDT, J. 1949. Sperm survival in the genital tract of the mare. J. Agric. Sc., **39**, 201–203.

BURNASHEVA, S. A. 1958. "Characteristics of spermosin, a contractile protein, in sperm cells." Biokhimiya, **23**, 558–563.

BURNET, F. M., AND FENNER, F. 1949. *The Production of Antibodies*, 2nd ed. Melbourne: Macmillan & Company, Ltd.

BURUIANA, L. M. 1956. Sur l'activité hyaluronidasique et trypsinique du sperme. Naturwiss., **43**, 523.

CAMPBELL, J. A. 1932. Normal gas tensions in the mucus membrane of the rabbit's uterus. J. Physiol., **76**, 13P.

CARLSON, F. D. 1959. The motile power of a swimming spermatozoon. In *Proceedings 1st National Biophysical Conference*, p. 443–449. Columbus, Ohio: The Biophysical Society.

CARPENTER, C. R. 1942. Sexual behavior of free ranging rhesus monkeys (*Macaca mulatta*). I. Specimens, procedures and behavioral characteristics of estrus. J. Comp. Psych., **33**, 113–142.

CARSON, H. L. 1945. Delayed fertilization in a captive indigo snake with notes on feeding and shedding. Copeia, No. 4; 222–225.

CARTER, R. D., McCARTNEY, M. G., CHAMBERLIN, V. D., AND WYNE, J. W. 1957. The effect of storage time and temperature on fertilizing capacity of turkey semen. Poultry Sc., **36**, 618–621.

CARY, W. H. 1943. In Discussion of Lamar, J. K.: Some observations on sperm migration through cervical mucus. In *Problems of Human Fertility*, pp. 92–98. E. T. Engle, Ed. Menasha, Wisc.: George Banta Publishing Company.

CAVAZOS, L. F. 1958. Effects of testosterone propionate on histochemical reactions of epithelium of rat ductus epididymis. Anat. Rec., **132**, 209–227.

CAVAZOS, L. F., AND MELAMPY, R. M. 1956. Effects of differential testosterone propionate levels on rat accessory gland activity. Iowa State Coll. J. Sc., **31**, 19–24.

CHANG, M. C. 1945. The sperm production of adult rams in relation to frequency of semen collection. J. Agric. Sc., **35**, 243–246.

CHANG, M. C. 1946a. Effect of dilution on fertilizing capacity of rabbit spermatozoa. Science, **104**, 361–362.

CHANG, M. C. 1946b. Fertilizing capacity of rabbit spermatozoa. In *The Problem of Fertility*, E. T. Engle, Ed., pp. 169–181. Princeton, N. J.: Princeton University Press.

CHANG, M. C. 1947a. The effects of serum on spermatozoa. J. Gen. Physiol., **30**, 321–335.

CHANG, M. C. 1947b. Effects of testis hyaluronidase and seminal fluids on the fertilizing capacity of rabbit spermatozoa. Proc. Soc. Exper. Biol. & Med., **65**, 51–54.

CHANG, M. C. 1949. Effects of heterologous seminal plasma and sperm cells on fertilizing capacity of rabbit spermatozoa. Proc. Soc. Exper. Biol. & Med., **70**, 32–36.

CHANG, M. C. 1951a. Fertilization in relation to the number of spermatozoa in the Fallopian tubes of rabbits. Ann. Ostet. e Ginec., 2nd Fasc. Spec., 918–925.

CHANG, M. C. 1951b. Fertilizing capacity of spermatozoa deposited into the Fallopian tubes. Nature, London, **168**, 697–698.

CHANG, M. C. 1952. Fertilizability of rabbit ova and the effects of temperature *in vitro* on their subsequent fertilization and activation *in vivo*. J. Exper. Zool., **121**, 351–381.

CHANG, M. C. 1955. Development of fertilizing capacity of rabbit spermatozoa in the uterus. Nature, London, **175**, 1036–1037.

CHANG, M. C. 1957. A detrimental effect of seminal plasma on the fertilizing capacity of sperm. Nature, London, **179**, 258–259.

CHANG, M. C. 1958. Capacitation of rabbit spermatozoa in the uterus with special reference to the reproductive phases of the female. Endocrinology, **63**, 619–628.

CHANG, M. C. 1959. Fertilizing capacity of spermatozoa. In *Recent Progress in the Endocrinology of Reproduction*, C. Lloyd, Ed., pp. 131–163. New York: Academic Press, Inc.

CHANG, M. C., HUNT, D. M., AND ROMANOFF, E. B. 1957. Effects of radiocobalt irradiation on rabbit spermatozoa *in vitro* on fertilization and early development. Anat. Rec., **192**, 211–229.

CHANG, M. C., AND PINCUS, G. 1951. Physiology of fertilization in mammals. Physiol. Rev., **31**, 1–26.

CHANG, M. C., AND SHEAFFER, D. 1957. Number of spermatozoa ejaculated at copulation, transported into the female tract, and present in the male tract of the golden hamster. J. Hered., **48**, 107–109.

CHANG, M. C., AND THORSTEINSSON, T. 1958a. Effects of urine on motility and fertilizing capacity of rabbit spermatozoa. Fertil. & Steril., **9**, 231–237.

CHANG, M. C., AND THORSTEINSSON, T. 1958b. Effects of osmotic pressure and hydrogen-ion concentration on the motility and fertilizing capacity of rabbit spermatozoa. Fertil. & Steril., **9**, 510–520.

CHARGAFF, E. 1951. Some recent studies on the composition and structure of nucleic acids. J. Cell. & Comp. Physiol., Suppl., **38**, 41–59.

CHARGAFF, E., LIPSHITZ, R., GREEN, C., AND HODES, M. E. 1951. The composition of the desoxyribonucleic acid of salmon sperm. J. Biol. Chem., **192**, 223–230.

CHARGAFF, E., ZAMENHOF, S., AND GREEN, C. 1950. Composition of human desoxypentose nucleic acid. Nature, London, **165**, 756–757.

CHENG, P., AND CASIDA, L. E. 1948. Fertility in rabbit as affected by the dilution of semen and the number of spermatozoa. Proc. Soc. Exper. Biol. & Med., **69**, 36–39.

CHENG, P., AND CASIDA, L. E. 1949. Effects of testosterone propionate upon sexual libido and the production of semen and sperm in the rabbit. Endocrinology, **44**, 38–48.

CHRISTIE, A. C. 1955. A histochemical study of the cytoplasmic inclusions of the epithelial cells in the epididymis of the mouse. Quart. J. Microscop. Sc., **96**, 161–168.

CIACCIO, G. V. 1899. Parallelle tra gli spermatozoidi del *Triton cristatus* e quelli della *Rana esculenta*. Rendic. Accad. Sc. Ist. Bologna, **3**, 1898–1899.

CIESLAK, E. S. 1944. Evidence for early testis hormone secretion in the rat from a study of the epididymis. Endocrinology, **35**, 63–67.

CLARK, E. 1950. A method for artificial insemination of viviparous fishes. Science, **112**, 722–723.

CLARKE, E. W., AND ROTHSCHILD, LORD. 1957. Anaerobic heat production of bull spermatozoa. Proc. Roy. Soc., London, ser. B, **147**, 316–331.

CLELAND, K. W., JONES, W. G., AND REID, B. L. 1959. Physiology of the rat testis and epididymis as revealed by ligation experiments. Australian J. Sc., **21**, 185.

CLERMONT, Y. 1958. Contractile elements in the limiting membrane of the seminiferous tubules of the rat. Exper. Cell Res., **15**, 438–440.

CLERMONT, Y., GLEGG, R. E., AND LEBLOND, C. P. 1955. Presence of carbohydrates in the acrosome of the guinea pig spermatozoon. Exper. Cell Res., **8**, 453–458.

CLERMONT, Y., AND LEBLOND, C. P. 1955. Spermiogenesis of man, monkey, ram and other mammals as shown by the "PAS" technique. Am. J. Anat., **96**, 229–253.

CLEWE, T. H., AND MASTROIANNI, L., JR. 1959. A method for prolonged collection of secretions from the oviducts of unanesthetized rabbits. Anat. Rec., **133**, 261–262.

CLEWE, T. H., AND MASTROIANNI, L., JR. 1960. A method for continuous volumetric collection of oviduct secretions. J. Reprod. & Fertil., **1**, 146–150.

CODY, B. A. 1925. Observations and experiments upon spermatozoa of the guinea pig. J. Urol., **13**, 175–191.

COHEN, M. R., AND STEIN, I. F. 1951. Sperm survival at estimated ovulation time—comparative morphology; relative male infertility. Fertil. & Steril., **2**, 20–27.

COHEN, M. R., STEIN, I. F., SR., AND KAYE, B. M. 1952. Spinnbarkeit: a characteristic of cervical mucus; significance at ovulation time. Fertil. & Steril., **3**, 201–209.

COLWIN, A. L., AND COLWIN, L. H. 1955. Sperm entry and the acrosome filament (*Holothuria atra* and *Asteri amurensis*). J. Morphol., **97**, 543–568.

COLWIN, A. L., AND COLWIN, L. H. 1957. Morphology of fertilization: acrosome filament formation and sperm entry. In *The Beginnings of Embryonic Development*, A. Tyler,

R. C. van Borstel and C. B. Metz, Eds., pp. 135–168. Washington: American Association for the Advancement of Science.

CONCHIE, J., AND MANN, T. 1957. Glycosidases in mammalian sperm and seminal plasma. Nature, London, **179**, 1190–1191.

COOK, A. H., AND ELVIDGE, J. A. 1951. Fertilization in the Fucaceae: investigations on the nature of the chemotactic substance produced by the eggs of *Fucus serratus* and *F. vesiculosus*. Proc. Roy. Soc., London, ser. B, **138**, 97–114.

COOK, A. H., ELVIDGE, J. A., AND HEILBRON, I. 1948. Fertilization including chemotactic phenomena in the Fucaceae. Proc. Roy. Soc., London, ser. B, **135**, 293–301.

CRABTREE, H. G. 1929. Observations on the carbohydrate metabolism of tumours. Biochem. J., **23**, 536–545.

CRAGLE, R. G., SALISBURY, G. W., AND MUNTZ, J. H. 1958. Distribution of bulk and trace minerals in bull reproductive tract fluids and semen. J. Dairy Sc., **41**, 1273–1277.

CRAWFORD, M. D., FLIPSE, R. J., AND ALMQUIST, J. O. 1956. Uptake of phosphorus-32 from egg yolk phospholipids by bovine spermatozoa. J. Dairy Sc., **39**, 922–923.

CREW, F. A. E. 1926. On fertility in the domestic fowl. Proc. Roy. Soc., Edinburgh, **46**, 230–238.

CRONQVIST, S. 1949. Spermatic invasion of the epididymis. Acta path. et microbiol. scandinav., **26**, 786–794.

CROSS, B. A. 1958. The motility and reactivity of the oestrogenized rabbit uterus *in vivo*; with comparative observations on milk injection. J. Endocrinol., **16**, 237–260.

CRUICKSHANK, B., AND STUART-SMITH, D. A. 1959. Orchitis associated with sperm agglutinating antibodies. Lancet, **1**, 708.

DALLAM, R. D., AND THOMAS, L. E. 1953. Chemical studies on mammalian sperm. Biochim. et biophys. acta, **11**, 79–89.

DALY, M. M., MIRSKY, A. E., AND RIS, H. 1951. The amino acid composition and some properties of histones. J. Gen. Physiol., **34**, 439–450.

DAN, J. C. 1952. Studies on the acrosome. I. Reaction to egg-water and other stimuli. Biol. Bull., **103**, 54–66.

DAN, J. C. 1956. The acrosome reaction. Internat. Rev. Cytol., **5**, 365–394.

DARWIN, C. 1871. *The Descent of Man and Selection in Relation to Sex,* 2 vols. London: John Murray.

DAUZIER, L., AND WINTENBERGER, S. 1952. La vitesse de remontée des spermatozoïdes dans le tractus génital de la brebis. Ann. Inst. Nat. Rech. Agron., No. 1, 13–22.

DAVENPORT, C. B. 1897. *Experimental Morphology.* New York: Macmillan Company.

DAWSON, R. M. C. 1958. The labelling of ram semen *in vivo* with radioactive phosphate and [carboxy-^{14}C] stearic acid. Biochem. J., **68**, 512–519.

DAWSON, R. M. C., MANN, T., AND WHITE, I. G. 1957. Glycerylphosphorylcholine and phosphorylcholine in semen and their relation to choline. Biochem. J., **65**, 627–634.

DAWSON, R. M. C., AND ROWLANDS, I. W. 1959. Glycerylphosphorylcholine in the male reproductive organs of rats and guinea pigs. Quart. J. Exper. Physiol., **44**, 26–34.

DAY, F. T. 1942. Survival of spermatozoa in the genital tract of the mare. J. Agric. Sc., **32**, 108–111.

DE LESLIE, C. 1901. Influence de la spermatoxine sur la reproduction. Compt. rend. Acad. Sc., **133**, 544–546.

DHARMARAJAN, M. 1950. Effect on the embryo of staleness of the sperm at the time of fertilization in the domestic hen. Nature, London, **165**, 398.

DOCTON, F. L., FERGUSON, L. C., LAZEAR, E. J., AND ELY, F. 1952. The antigenicity of bovine spermatozoa. J. Dairy Sc., **35**, 706–709.

DOTT, H. M. 1959. Species differences in the metabolism of epididymal spermatozoa. Stud. Fertil., **10**, 73–79.

DREW, G. A. 1919. Sexual activities of the squid *Loligo pealii* (Les.). II. The spermatophore; its structure, ejaculation, and formation. J. Morphol., **32**, 379–435.

DU MESNIL DU BUISSON, F., AND DAUZIER, L. 1955. Distribution et résorption du sperme dans le tractus génital de la truie des spermatozoïdes. Ann. endocrinol., **16**, 413–422.

DU MESNIL DU BUISSON, F., AND DAUZIER, L. 1958. Maintien du pouvoir fécondant du sperme de Verrat en présence de gaz carbonique. Compt. rend. Acad. Sc., **247**, 2472–2475.

EASTMAN, N. J., GUTTMACHER, A. F., AND STEWART, E. H., JR. 1939. Experimental observations on "sperm immunity" in the rat. J. Contraception, **4**, 147–151.

EDWARDS, J. 1939. The effect of unilateral castration on spermatogenesis. Proc. Roy. Soc., London, ser. B, **128**, 407–421.

EDWARDS, R. G. 1954. The experimental induction of pseudogamy in early mouse embryos. Experientia, **10**, 499–500.

EDWARDS, R. G. 1957a. The experimental induction of gynogenesis in the mouse. I. Irradiation of the sperm by X-rays. Proc. Roy. Soc., London, ser. B, **146**, 469–487.

EDWARDS, R. G. 1957b. The experimental induction of gynogenesis in the mouse. II. Ultraviolet irradiation of the sperm. Proc. Roy. Soc., London, ser. B, **146**, 488–504.

EDWARDS, R. G. 1958. The experimental induction of gynogenesis in the mouse. III. Treatment of sperm with trypaflavine, toluidine blue, or nitrogen mustrad. Proc. Roy. Soc., London, ser. B, **149**, 117–129.

EDWARDS, R. G., AND SIRLIN, J. L. 1959. Fate of spermatozoa penetrating into the tissues of the Fallopian tube. Nature, London, **183**, 1744–1745.

ELLIS, W. H. 1952. The socio-legal problem of

artificial insemination. Indiana Law J., **28**, 620–640.

ELMES, P. C., SMITH, J. D., AND WHITE, J. C. 1952. See Mann, 1954.

EMMENS, C. W. 1948. The effect of variations in osmotic pressure and electrolyte concentration on the motility of rabbit spermatozoa at different hydrogen-ion concentrations. J. Physiol., **107**, 129–140.

EMMENS, C. W., AND BLACKSHAW, A. W. 1956. Artificial insemination. Physiol. Rev., **36**, 277–306.

EMMENS, C. W., AND SWYER, G. I. M. 1948. Observations on the motility of rabbit spermatozoa in dilute suspension. J. Gen. Physiol., **32**, 121–138.

ENGELHARDT, V. A. 1945. "Phosphoric acid and cell functions." Bull. acad. sc. U.R.S.S., ser. biol., No. 2, 182–195.

ENGELHARDT, V. A. 1946. Adenosinetriphosphatase properties of myosin. Advances Enzymol., **6**, 147–191.

ENGELHARDT, V. A. 1958. Enzymology and mechanochemistry of tissues and cells. In *Proceedings International Symposium Enzyme Chemistry, Tokyo and Kyoto, 1957*, pp. 34–39. Tokyo: Igaku Shion, Ltd.

ENGELHARDT, V. A., AND BURNASHEVA, S. A. 1957. Localization of the protein spermosin in sperm cells. Biochemistry, **22**, 513–518.

ENGELHARDT, V. A., AND LYUBIMOVA, M. N. 1939. Myosine and adenosinetriphosphatase. Nature, London, **144**, 668–669.

ENGELMANN, T. W. 1898. Cils vibratils. In *Dictionnaire de Physiologie,* C. Richet, Ed., Vol. 3, pp. 783–799. Paris: F. Alcan.

EVANS, E. I. 1933. The transport of spermatozoa in the dog. Am. J. Physiol., **105**, 287–293.

EVANS, T. C. 1947. Effects of hydrogen peroxide produced in the medium by radiation on spermatozoa of *Arbacia punctulata*. Biol. Bull., **92**, 99–109.

FARRELL, J. I. 1938. The secretion of alcohol by the genital tract. J. Urol., **40**, 62–73.

FARRIS, E. J. 1950. *Human Fertility and Problems of the Male*. White Plains, N. Y.: The Author's Press.

FAWCETT, D. W. 1958. The structure of the mammalian spermatozoon. Internat. Rev. Cytol., **7**, 195–234.

FAWCETT, D. W. 1959. Changes in the fine structure of the cytoplasmic organelles during differentiation. In *Developmental Cytology*, D. Rudnick, Ed., pp. 161–189. New York: Ronald Press.

FELIX, K. 1958. Formation et fonction des nucléoprotamines. Bull. Soc. Chim. Biol., **40**, 17–33.

FELIX, K., FISCHER, H., KREKELS, A., AND MOHR, R. 1951. Nucleoprotein. II. Mitteilung. Ztschr. physiol. Chem., **289**, 10–19.

FISCHER, H., AND KREUZER, L. 1953. Über Gallin. Ztschr. physiol. Chem., **293**, 176–182.

FLIPSE, R. J. 1956. Metabolism of glycine by bovine spermatozoa. Science, **124**, 228.

FLIPSE, R. J. 1958. Isotopic studies of semen metabolism. In *Proceedings IIIrd Symposium Reproduction and Infertility*, pp. 233–243. New York: Pergamon Press.

FLIPSE, R. J., AND ALMQUIST, J. O. 1955. Metabolism of bovine semen. II. Qualitative anaerobic catabolism of glucose-C^{14} by bovine spermatozoa. J. Dairy Sc., **38**, 782–787.

FLIPSE, R. J., AND ALMQUIST, J. O. 1956. Diluters for bovine semen. IX. Motility of bovine spermatozoa in milk-glycine and egg yolk-glycine diluents with and without glycerol. J. Dairy Sc., **39**, 1690–1696.

FLIPSE, R. J., AND BENSON, A. A. 1957. Catabolism of glycine-C^{14} by washed bovine spermatozoa. Exper. Cell Res., **13**, 611–614.

FLOREY, H., AND WALTON, A. 1932. Uterine fistula used to determine the mechanism of ascent of the spermatozoon in the female genital tract. J. Physiol., **74**, 5P–6P.

FORD, C. S., AND BEACH, F. A. 1951. *Patterns of Sexual Behavior*. New York: Harper and Brothers.

FRANZÉN, Å. 1956. On spermatogenesis, morphology of the spermatozoon, and biology of fertilization among invertebrates. Zool. Bidrag f. Uppsala, **31**, 355–482.

FREDRICSSON, B. 1959a. Proliferation of rabbit oviduct epithelium after estrogenic stimulation, with reference to the relationship between ciliated and secretory cells. Acta morphol. neerl.-scandinav., **2**, 193–202.

FREDRICSSON, B. 1959b. Histochemical observations on the epithelium of human Fallopian tubes. Acta obst. et gynec. scandinav., **38**, 109–134.

FREUND, J. 1957. Sensitization with organ specific antigens and the mechanism of enhancement of the immune response. J. Allergy, **28**, 18–28.

FREUND, J., LIPTON, M. M., AND THOMPSON, G. E. 1953. Aspermatogenesis in the guinea pig induced by testicular tissue and adjuvants. J. Exper. Med., **97**, 711–726.

FREUND, J., THOMPSON, G. E., AND LIPTON, M. M. 1955. Aspermatogenesis, anaphylaxis, and cutaneous sensitization induced in the guinea pig by homologous testicular extract. J. Exper. Med., **101**, 591–604.

FREUND, M., AND MacLEOD, J. 1958. Effect of addition of fructose and of glucose on the fructolysis and motility of human semen. J. Appl. Physiol., **13**, 506–509.

FRIEDLAENDER, M. H. G., AND FRASER, M. J. 1952. Cytochemical reactions of ram spermatozoa. Exper. Cell Res., **3**, 462–474.

FRIEDMAN, N. B., AND GARSKE, G. L. 1949. Inflammatory reactions involving sperm and the seminiferous tubules: extravasation, spermatic granulomas, and granulomatous orchitis. J. Urol., **62**, 363–374.

FRUTON, J. S., AND SIMMONDS, S. 1958. *General Biochemistry*, 2nd ed. New York: John Wiley and Sons, Inc.

GARREN, H. W., AND SHAFFNER, C. S. 1952. The

effect of temperature and time of storage on the fertilizing capacity of undiluted fowl sperm. Poultry Sc., **31**, 137–145.

GATENBY, J. B. 1920. The germ cells, fertilization and early development of *Grantia* (*Sycon*) *compressa*. J. Linnean Soc., London, Zool., **34**, 261–297.

GERSHOWITZ, H., BEHRMAN, S. J., AND NEEL, J. V. 1958. Hemagglutinins in uterine secretions. Science, **128**, 719–720.

GHEȚIE, V. 1939. Präparation und Länge des Ductus epididymis beim Pferd und Schwein. Anat. Anz., **87**, 369–374.

GIBBONS, R. A. 1959a. Physical and chemical properties of mucoids from bovine cervical mucin. Biochem. J., **72**, 27P–28P.

GIBBONS, R. A. 1959b. Chemical properties of two mucoids from bovine cervical mucin. Biochem. J., **73**, 209–217.

GIBBONS, R. A., AND GLOVER, F. A. 1959. The physicochemical properties of two mucoids from bovine cervical mucin. Biochem. J., **73**, 217–225.

GODLEWSKI, E. 1926. L'inhibition réciproque de l'aptitude à féconder de spermes d'espèces éloignées comme conséquence de l'agglutination des spermatozoïdes. Arch. Biol., **36**, 311–350.

GOGLIA, G., AND MAGALI, G. 1957. Ricerche istochimiche sui processi secretori dei coni vascolosi e del condotto dell'epididimo della cavia. Boll. Soc. ital. biol. sper., **33**, 418–421.

GONSE, P. H. 1959. Respiration and motility in Spisula spermatozoa. Biol. Bull., **117**, 433–434.

GORDON, M. J. 1957. Control of sex ratio in rabbits by electrophoresis of spermatozoa. Proc. Nat. Acad. Sc., **43**, 913–918.

GRANT, R. E. 1833. On the nervous system of *Beroë Pileus*, Lam., and on the structure of its cilia. Tr. Zool. Soc., London, **1**, 9–12.

GRAY, J. 1928. The effect of dilution on the activity of spermatozoa. J. Exper. Biol., **5**, 337–344.

GRAY, J. 1953. Undulatory propulsion. Quart. J. Microscop. Sc., **94**, 551–578.

GRAY, J. 1955. The movement of sea-urchin spermatozoa. J. Exper. Biol., **32**, 775–801.

GRAY, J. 1958. The movement of the spermatozoa of the bull. J. Exper. Biol., **35**, 96–108.

GRAY, J., AND HANCOCK, G. J. 1955. The propulsion of sea-urchin spermatozoa. J. Exper. Biol., **32**, 802–814.

GREEN, C. L. 1957. Identification of alpha-amylase as a secretion of the human Fallopian tube and "tubelike" epithelium of Müllerian and mesonephric duct origin. Am. J. Obst. & Gynec., **73**, 402–408.

GREEN, W. W. 1940. The chemistry and cytology of the sperm membrane of sheep. Anat. Rec., **76**, 455–472.

GREEN, W. W. 1947. Duration of sperm fertility in the ewe. Am. J. Vet. Res., **8**, 299–300.

GREEN, W. W., AND WINTERS, L. M. 1935. Studies on the physiology of reproduction in the sheep.

III. The time of ovulation and rate of sperm travel. Anat. Rec., **61**, 457–469.

GREENWALD, G. S. 1956. Sperm transport in the reproductive tract of the female rabbit. Science, **124**, 586.

GREENWALD, G. S. 1957. Interruption of pregnancy in the rabbit by the administration of estrogen. J. Exper. Zool., **135**, 461–478.

GRESSON, R. A. R., AND ZLOTNIK, I. 1945. A comparative study of the cytoplasmic components of the male germ-cells of certain mammals. Proc. Roy. Soc., Edinburgh, **62**, 137–170.

GRIETEN, J. 1956. Apparition de cholinestérase au cours de la maturation des spermatozoïdes du cobaye. Compt. rend. Soc. biol., **150**, 1015–1016.

GRIGG, G. W., AND HODGE, A. J. 1949. Electron microscopic studies of spermatozoa. I. The morphology of the sperm of the common domestic fowl. Australian J. Scient. Res., ser. B, **2**, 271–286.

GULLBRING, B. 1957. Investigation on the occurrence of blood group antigens in spermatozoa from man, and serological demonstration of the segregation of characters. Acta med. scandinav., **159**, 169–172.

GUNN, S. A., AND GOULD, T. C. 1958. Role of zinc in fertility and fecundity in the rat. Am. J. Physiol., **193**, 505–508.

GUTTMACHER, A. F., HAMAN, J. O., AND MacLEOD, J. 1950. The use of donors for artificial insemination. A survey of current practices. Fertil. & Steril., **1**, 264–270.

GUTTMACHER, A. F., AND SHETTLES, L. B. 1940. Cyclic changes in cervical mucus and its practical importance. Human Fertil., **5**, 4–9.

GUYER, M. F. 1922. Studies on cytolysins. III. Experiments with spermatoxins. J. Exper. Zool., **35**, 207–223.

HADEK, R. 1955. The secretory process in the sheep's oviduct. Anat. Rec., **121**, 187–201.

HADEK, R. 1958a. Histochemical studies on the uterus of the sheep. Am. J. Vet. Res., **19**, 882–886.

HADEK, R. 1958b. Intraperitoneal insemination of rabbit doe. Proc. Soc. Exper. Biol. & Med., **99**, 39–40.

HAGSTRÖM, B. E., AND HAGSTRÖM, B. 1959. The effect of decreased and increased temperature on fertilization. Exper. Cell Res., **16**, 174–183.

HAINES, T. P. 1940. Delayed fertilization in *Leptodeira annulata polysticta*. Copeia, No. 2, 116–118.

HAKIM, A. A. 1959. Synthetic activity of polynucleotide phosphorylase from sperm. Nature, London, **183**, 334.

HAMAN, J. O. 1947. Medico-legal aspects of artificial insemination. Tr. Am. Soc. Study Steril., **3**, 19–25.

HAMMAR, J. A. 1897. Ueber Secretionserscheinungen im Nebenhoden des Hundes; zugleich ein Beitrag zur Physiologie des Zellkerns. Arch. Anat. u. Ent.-gesch., Suppl. **1**, 1–42.

HAMMOND, J., AND ASDELL, S. A. 1926. The vitality of the spermatozoa in the male and female reproductive tract. J. Exper. Biol., **4**, 155–185.

HAMMOND, J., AND WALTON, A. 1934. Notes on ovulation and fertilisation in the ferret. J. Exper. Biol., **11**, 307–319.

HANCOCK, G. J. 1953. The self-propulsion of microscopic organisms through liquids. Proc. Roy. Soc., London, ser. A, **217**, 96–121.

HARRIS, G. W. 1951. Neural control of the pituitary gland. I. The neurohypophysis. Brit. M. J., **2**, 559–564.

HARRISON, R. G. 1953. The effect of ligation of the vasa efferentia on the rat testis. Proc. Soc. Stud. Fertil., **5**, 97–100.

HARTMAN, C. G. 1933. On the survival of spermatozoa in the female genital tract of the bat. Quart. Rev. Biol., **8**, 185–193.

HARTMAN, C. G. 1939. Ovulation, fertilization and the transport and viability of eggs and spermatozoa. In *Sex and Internal Secretions,* E. Allen, C. H. Danforth and E. A. Doisy, Eds., pp. 630–719. Baltimore: The Williams & Wilkins Company.

HARTMAN, C. G. 1957. How do sperms get into the uterus? Fertil. & Steril., **8**, 403–427.

HARTMAN, C. G., AND BALL, J. 1930. On the almost instantaneous transport of spermatozoa through the cervix and the uterus of the rat. Proc. Soc. Exper. Biol. & Med., **28**, 312–314.

HARTREE, E. F., AND MANN, T. 1959. Plasmalogen in ram semen and its role in sperm metabolism. Biochem. J., **71**, 423–434.

HARVEY, E. B., AND ANDERSON, T. F. 1943. The spermatozoon and fertilization membrane of *Arbacia punctulata* as shown by the electron microscope. Biol. Bull., **85**, 151–156.

HAYASHI, T. 1945. Dilution medium and survival of the spermatozoa of *Arbacia punctulata.* I. Effect of the medium on fertilizing power. Biol. Bull., **89**, 162–179.

HAYASHI, T. 1946. Dilution medium and survival of the spermatozoa of *Arbacia punctulata.* II. Effect of the medium on respiration. Biol. Bull., **90**, 177–187.

HAYS, R. L., AND VANDEMARK, N. L. 1951. Stimulatory action of breeding on the release of oxytocin as measured by intramammary pressure. J. Dairy Sc., **34**, 496–498.

HAYS, R. L., AND VANDEMARK, N. L. 1953a. Effects of oxytocin and epinephrine on uterine motility in the bovine. Am. J. Physiol., **172**, 557–560.

HAYS, R. L., AND VANDEMARK, N. L. 1953b. Effects of stimulation on the reproductive organs of the cow on the release of an oxytocin-like substance. Endocrinology, **52**, 634–637.

HEAPE, W. 1898. On the artificial insemination of mares. Veterinarian, **71**, 202–212.

HEAPE, W. 1905. Ovulation and degeneration of ova in the rabbit. Proc. Roy. Soc., London, ser. B, **76**, 260–268.

HEIDENHAIN, M. 1911. *Plasma und Zelle,* Pt. II, pp. 945–1110. Jena: Gustav Fischer.

HEILBRUNN, L. V. 1943. *An Outline of General Physiology,* 2nd ed. Philadelphia: W. B. Saunders Company.

HENLE, G., AND ZITTLE, C. A. 1942. Studies of the metabolism of bovine epididymal spermatozoa. Am. J. Physiol., **136**, 70–78.

HENLE, W. 1938. The specificity of some mammalian spermatozoa. J. Immunol., **34**, 325–336.

HENLE, W., AND HENLE, G. 1940. Spermatozoal antibodies and fertility. II. Attempt to induce temporary sterility in female guinea pigs by active immunization against spermatozoa. J. Immunol., **38**, 105–115.

HENLE, W., HENLE, G., AND CHAMBERS, L. A. 1938. Studies on the antigenic structure of some mammalian spermatozoa. J. Exper. Med., **68**, 335–352.

HENLE, W., HENLE, G., CHURCH, C. F., AND FOSTER, C. 1940. Spermatozoal antibodies and fertility. I. Attempt to induce temporary sterilization in female white mice by passive immunization with spermatozoal antisera. J. Immunol., **38**, 97–103.

HENRY, A. 1900. Étude histologique de la fonction sécrétoire de l'épididyme chez les vértébrés supérieurs. Arch. Anat. microscop., **3**, 229–292.

HERTWIG, O. 1911. Die Radiumkrankheit tierischer Keimzellen. Arch. mikroskop. Anat., **77**, 97–164.

HODGE, A. J. 1949. Electron microscopic studies of spermatozoa. II. The morphology of the human spermatozoon. Australian J. Scient. Res., ser. B, **2**, 368–378.

HOFFMANN-BERLING, H. 1954. Adenosintriphosphat als Betriebsstoff von Zellbewegungen. Biochim. et biophys. acta, **14**, 182–194.

HOFFMANN-BERLING, H. 1955. Geisselmodelle und Adenosintriphosphat (ATP). Biochim. et biophys. acta, **16**, 146–154.

HOFFMANN-BERLING, H. 1959. The role of cell structures in cell movements. In *Cell, Organism and Milieu,* D. Rudnick, Ed., pp. 45–62. New York: Ronald Press.

HOME, E. 1799. The dissection of an hermaphrodite dog. With observations on hermaphrodites in general. Philos. Tr. Roy. Soc., **89**, 485–496.

HORNE, H. W., JR., AND AUDET, C. 1958. Spider cells, a new inhabitant of peritoneal fluid; a preliminary report. Obst. & Gynec., **11**, 421–423.

HOWARD, E., AND DEFEO, V. J. 1959. Potassium and sodium content of uterine and seminal vesicle secretions. Am. J. Physiol., **196**, 65–68.

HÜBNER, K. A. 1955. Tierexperimentelle Untersuchungen über den Transport des Sperma im weiblichen Genitaltrakt. Zentralbl. Gynäk., **77**, 1220–1229.

HUGGINS, C., MASINA, M. H., EICHELBERGER, L., AND WHARTON, J. D. 1939. Quantitative studies of prostatic secretion. I. Characteristics of the normal secretion; the influence of thyroid, suprarenal, and testis extirpation and androgen substitution on the prostatic output. J. Exper. Med., **70**, 543–556.

HUGHES, A. 1955. Studies in the history of microscopy. I. The influence of achromatism. J. Roy. Microscop. Soc., **75**, 1–22.

HUGHES, A. 1956. Studies in the history of microscopy. II. The later history of the achromatic microscope. J. Roy. Microscop. Soc., **76**, 47–60.

HULTIN, T. 1958. The contents of nucleotide pyrophosphates in ageing sea urchin sperms. Exper. Cell. Res., **14**, 633–635.

HUMPHREY, G. F. 1950. The metabolism of oyster spermatozoa. Australian J. Exper. Biol. & Med. Sc., **28**, 1–13.

HUMPHREY, G. F., AND MANN, T. 1948. Citric acid in semen. Nature, London, **161**, 352.

HUXLEY, H. E. 1957. The double array of filaments in cross-striated muscle. J. Biophys. & Biochem. Cytol., **3**, 631–648.

HUXLEY, H. E., AND HANSON, J. 1954. Changes in cross-striations of muscle during contraction and stretch and their structural interpretation. Nature, London, **173**, 973–976.

INOUÉ, S. 1959. Motility of cilia and the mechanism of mitosis. In *Biophysical Science—A Study Program*, J. L. Onkley, Ed., pp. 402–408. New York: John Wiley & Sons, Inc.

ISOJIMA, S., GRAHAM, R. M., AND GRAHAM, J. B. 1959. Sterility in female guinea pigs induced by injection with testis. Science, **129**, 44.

IVANOV, I. I. 1945. Metabolism and motility of spermatozoa. Human Fertil., **10**, 33–42.

IVANOV, I. I., KASSAVINA, B. S., AND FOMENKO, L. D. 1946. Adenosine triphosphate in mammalian spermatozoa. Nature, London, **158**, 624.

JACKSON, H. 1959. Antifertility substances. Pharmacol. Rev., **11**, 135–172.

JOËL, C. A. 1940. Zur Histologie und Histochemie der menschlichen Eileiter wahrend Zyklus und Schwangerschaft. Monatsschr. Geburtsch. Gynäk., **110**, 252–265.

JOËL, C. A., KATCHALSKY, A., KEDEM, O., AND STERNBERG, N. 1951. Electrophoretic measurements of human spermia. Experientia, **7**, 274–275.

JOHANSSON, K.-I. 1946. Experiments with X-rays on cock sperms in regard to motility and fertility. Acta agric. suecana, **1**, 335–343.

JOHNSON, R. B., AND LARDY, H. A. 1950. Mode of action of the sperm "regulator," 2,4-dinitrophenol and usnic acid. Fed. Proc., **9**, 187.

JUNGE, J. M., AND BLANDAU, R. J. 1958. Studies on the electrophoretic properties of the cornual fluids of rats in heat. Fertil. & Steril., **9**, 353–367.

KATSH, S. 1957. *In vitro* demonstration of uterine anaphylaxis in guinea pigs sensitized with homologous testis or sperm. Nature, London, **180**, 1047–1048.

KATSH, S. 1958. Demonstration *in vitro* of an anaphylactoid response of the uterus and ileum of guinea pigs injected with testis or sperm. J. Exper. Med., **107**, 95–108.

KATSH, S. 1959a. Immunology, fertility and infertility: a historical survey. Am. J. Obst. & Gynec., **77**, 946–956.

KATSH, S. 1959b. Infertility in female guinea pigs induced by injection of homologous sperm. Am. J. Obst. & Gynec., **78**, 276–278.

KATSH, S. 1959c. The contribution of the bacterial components of adjuvant in the induction of aspermatogenesis and in the sensitization of the ilea of guinea pigs. Internat. Arch. Allergy & Appl. Immunol., **15**, 172–188.

KATSH, S., AND BISHOP, D. W. 1958. The effects of homologous testicular and brain and heterologous testicular homogenates combined with adjuvant upon the testes of guinea pigs. J. Embryol. & Exper. Morphol., **6**, 94–104.

KERR, W. R., AND ROBERTSON, M. 1953. Active and passive sensitization of the uterus of the cow *in vivo* against *Trichomonas foetus* antigen and the evidence for the local production of antibody in that site. J. Hyg., **51**, 405–415.

KIDDY, C. A., STONE, W. H., AND CASIDA, L. E. 1959. Immunologic studies on fertility and sterility. II. Effects of treatment of semen with antibodies on fertility in rabbits. J. Immunol., **82**, 125–130.

KIDDY, C. A., STONE, W. H., TYLER, W. J., AND CASIDA, L. E. 1959. Immunologic studies on fertility and sterility. III. Effect of isoimmunization with blood and semen on fertility in cattle. J. Dairy Sc., **42**, 100–109.

KING, E. S. J. 1955. Spermatozoal invasion of the epididymis. J. Path. & Bact., **70**, 459–467.

KING, T. E., AND MANN, T. 1958. Sorbitol dehydrogenase in spermatozoa. Nature, London, **182**, 868–869.

KNAUS, H. 1933. Zur Physiologie der Samenblasen. Klin. Wchnschr., **12**, 1609–1609.

KNAUS, H. 1958. Die Reifung der Spermatozoen in den männlichen Samenwegen. Wein. med. Wchnschr., **108**, 790–791.

KNOBLOCK, A., VENDRELY, C., AND VENDRELY, R. 1957. The amount of desoxyribonucleic acid in a single trout sperm. Exper. Cell Res., **24**, 201–202.

KOEFOED-JOHNSEN, H. H., AND MANN, T. 1954. Studies on the metabolism of semen. 9. Effect of surface active agents with special reference to the oxidation of succinate by spermatozoa. Biochem. J., **57**, 406–410.

KOHLBRUGGE, J. H. F. 1910. Der Einfluss der Spermatozoïden auf den Uterus. Ein Beitrag zur Telogonie. Ztschr. Morphol. Anthropol., **12**, 359–368.

KOHLBRUGGE, J. H. F. 1913. Die Verbreitung der Spermatozoiden im weiblichen Körper und im befructeten Ei. Roux' Arch. Entwicklungsmech. Organ., **35**, 165–188.

KOHNZ, R. 1958. Mikroscopie im Mittelalter; eine seltsame Entdeckung. München. med. Wchnschr., **100**, 1395–1396.

KOLTZOFF, N. K. 1903. Ueber formbestimmende elastische Gebilde in Zellen. Biol. Centralbl., **23**, 680–696.

KÖNIGSTEIN, H. 1908. Ueber das Schicksal Spermatozoen, welche nicht zur Befruchtung gelangen. Wien. klin. Wchnschr., **21**, 971–973.

KOSSEL, A. 1928. *The Protamines and Histones,* transl. by W. V. Thorpe. London: Longmans, Green and Company.

KOTHARE, S. N., AND DE SOUZA, E. J. 1957. A preliminary report on the cytochemical demonstration of succinic dehydrogenase patterns in human spermatozoa. Current Sc. (India), **26,** 355.

KREBS, H. A. 1957. Control of metabolic processes. Endeavour, **16,** 125–132.

KREHBIEL, R. H., AND CARSTENS, H. P. 1939. Roentgen studies of the mechanism involved in sperm transportation in the female rabbit. Am. J. Physiol., **125,** 571–577.

KUSHNER, K. F. 1954. "The effect of heterospermic insemination in animals and its biological nature." Bull. acad. sc., U.R.S.S., ser. biol., No. 1, 32.

LADMAN, A. J., AND YOUNG, W. C. 1958. An electron microscopic study of the ductuli efferentes and rete testis of the guinea pig. J. Biophys. & Biochem. Cytol., **4,** 219–226.

LAIDLAW, H. H., JR., AND ECKERT, J. E. 1950. *Queen Rearing.* Hamilton, Ill.: Dadant and Sons.

LAING, J. A. 1945. Observations on the survival time of the spermatozoa in the genital tract of the cow and its relation to fertility. J. Agric. Sc., **35,** 72–83.

LAKE, P. E. 1957. The male reproductive tract of the fowl. J. Anat., **91,** 116–129.

LAMAR, J. K. 1943. Some observations on sperm migration through cervical mucus. In *Problems of Human Fertility,* E. T. Engle, Ed., pp. 92–98. Manasha, Wisc.: George Banta Publishing Company.

LAMAR, J. K., SHETTLES, L. B., AND DELFS, E. 1940. Cyclic penetrability of human cervical mucus to spermatozoa *in vitro.* Am. J. Physiol., **129,** 234–241.

LAMOREUX, W. F. 1940. Spermatozoal antibodies and infertility in the fowl. J. Exper. Zool., **85,** 419–430.

LANDSTEINER, K. 1899. Zur Kenntnis der spezifisch auf Blutkörperchen wirkenden Sera. Zentralbl. Bakt., **25,** 546–549.

LANDSTEINER, K., AND LEVINE, P. 1926. On group specific substances in human spermatozoa. J. Immunol., **12,** 415–418.

LARDY, H. A. 1952. The metabolic regulator in mammalian spermatozoa. In *Studies on Testis and Ovary, Eggs and Sperm,* E. T. Engle, Ed., pp. 111–122. Springfield, Ill.: Charles C Thomas.

LARDY, H. A. 1953. Factors controlling rates of metabolism in mammalian spermatozoa. In *Mammalian Germ Cells,* G. E. W. Wolstenholme, M. P. Cameron, and J. S. Freeman, Eds., pp. 59–65. London: J. & A. Churchill, Ltd.

LARDY, H. A., AND GHOSH, D. 1952. Comparative metabolic behavior of epididymal and ejaculated mammalian spermatozoa. Ann. New York Acad. Sc., **55,** 594–596.

LARDY, H. A., GHOSH, D., AND PLAUT, G. W. E.
1949. A metabolic regulator in mammalian spermatozoa. Science, **109,** 365–367.

LARDY, H. A., HANSEN, R. G., AND PHILLIPS, P. H. 1945. The metabolism of bovine epididymal spermatozoa. Arch. Biochem., **6,** 41–51.

LARDY, H. A., AND PHILLIPS, P. H. 1941. Phospholipids as a source of energy for motility of bull spermatozoa. Am. J. Physiol., **134,** 542–548.

LARDY, H. A., AND PHILLIPS, P. H. 1943. The effect of pH and certain electrolytes on the metabolism of ejaculated spermatozoa. Am. J. Physiol., **138,** 741–746.

LARDY, H. A., AND PHILLIPS, P. H. 1944. Acetate utilization for maintenance of motility of bull spermatozoa. Nature, London, **153,** 168–169.

LARDY, H. A., AND PHILLIPS, P. H. 1945. Studies of fat and carbohydrate oxidation in mammalian spermatozoa. Arch. Biochem., **6,** 53–61.

LARDY, H. A., POUNDEN, W. D., AND PHILLIPS, P. H. 1940. H-ion concentration of various fluids of the genital tract of the cow. Proc. Soc. Exper. Biol. & Med., **44,** 517–519.

LARDY, H. A., WINCHESTER, B., AND PHILLIPS, P. H. 1945. The respiratory metabolism of ram spermatozoa. Arch. Biochem., **6,** 33–40.

LASLEY, J. F., AND BOGART, R. A. 1944. Some factors affecting the resistance of ejaculated and epididymal spermatozoa of the boar to different environmental conditions. Am. J. Physiol., **141,** 619–624.

LEBLOND, C. P. 1950. Distribution of periodic acid-reactive carbohydrates in the adult rat. Am. J. Anat., **86,** 1–49.

LEBLOND, C. P., AND CLERMONT, Y. 1952. Spermatogenesis of the rat, mouse, hamster, and guinea pig as revealed by the "periodic acid-fuchsin sulfurous acid" technique. Am. J. Anat., **90,** 167–215.

LEDERBERG, J. 1959. Genes and antibodies. Science, **129,** 1649–1653.

LEE, F. C. 1925a. A preliminary note on the physiology of the uterine opening of the Fallopian tube. Proc. Soc. Exper. Biol. & Med., **22,** 335–336.

LEE, F. C. 1925b. A brief note on the anatomy of the uterine opening of the Fallopian tube. Proc. Soc. Exper. Biol. & Med., **22,** 470–471.

LEE, H. T. Y. 1950. A preliminary histological study of the insemination reaction in *Drosophila gibberosa.* Biol. Bull., **98,** 25–33.

LEEB, H., AND PLOBERGER, U. 1959. Zur Frage der Spermienwanderung im Bereiche des weiblichen Genitales. Wien. med. Wchnschr., **109,** 267–270.

LEHNINGER, A. L. 1955. Oxidative phosphorylation. The Harvey Lectures, **49,** 176–215.

LEHNINGER, A. L. 1959. Respiratory-energy transformation. Rev. Mod. Physics, **31,** 136–146.

LEONARD, S. L., AND PERLMAN, P. L. 1949. Conditions effecting the passage of spermatozoa through the utero-tubal junction of rat. Anat. Rec., **104,** 89–102.

LEUCHTENBERGER, C., AND LEUCHTENBERGER, R.
1958. Die Desoxynucleoproteide im Säuge-
tiersperma; eine quantitative Studie am
menschlichen und Stierspermatozoen mittels
Mikrospektrophotometrie und Interferenzmi-
kroskopie. Ztschr. physiol. Chem., **313**, 130–
137.

LEUCHTENBERGER, C., LEUCHTENBERGER, R., VEN-
DRELY, C., AND VENDRELY, R. 1952. The quantitative estimation of desoxyribosenucleic
acid (DNA) in isolated individual animal
nuclei by the Caspersson ultraviolet method.
Exper. Cell Res., **3**, 240–244.

LEUCHTENBERGER, C., MURMANIS, I., MURMANIS, L.,
ITO, S., AND WEIR, D. R. 1956. Interferometric dry mass and microspectrophotometric
arginine determinations on bull sperm nuclei
with normal and abnormal DNA content.
Chromosoma, **8**, 73–86.

LEWIS, J. H. 1934. The antigenic relationship
of the alcohol-soluble fractions of brain and
testicle. J. Immunol., **27**, 473–478.

LEWIS, W. H., AND WRIGHT, E. S. 1935. On the
early development of the mouse egg. Contr.
Embryol., Carnegie Inst. Washington, **25**,
113–144.

LILLIE, F. R. 1919. *Problems of Fertilization*.
Chicago: University of Chicago Press.

LINDAHL, P. E. 1956. Counter-streaming centrifugation of bull spermatozoa. Nature, London,
178, 491–492.

LINDAHL, P. E. 1960. On some factors influencing the biological activity of sperm antag-
glutins. J. Reprod. & Fertil., **1**, 3–22.

LINDAHL, P. E., INGELMAN-SUNDBERG, A., AND
FURUHJELM, M. 1956. The sperm anti-ag-
glutinic factor in women. J. Obst. & Gynec.,
63, 363–371.

LINDAHL, P. E., AND KIHLSTRÖM, J. E. 1952. Alterations in specific gravity during the ripening
of bull spermatozoa. J. Dairy Sc., **35**, 393–
402.

LINDAHL, P. E., AND KIHLSTRÖM, J. E. 1954. An
antagglutinic factor in mammalian sperm
plasm. Fertil. & Steril., **5**, 241–255.

LINDAHL, P. E., AND NILSSON, A. 1957. The isolation of sperm antagglutin from the follicle
fluid, and some of its properties. Biochim. et
biophys. acta, **25**, 22–32.

LORENZ, F. W. 1958. Carbohydrate metabolism
of cock spermatozoa. Nature, London, **182**,
397–398.

LORENZ, F. W., AND TYLER, A. 1951. Extension of
motile life span of spermatozoa of the domestic
fowl by amino acids and proteins. Proc. Soc.
Exper. Biol. & Med., **78**, 57–62.

LOVELOCK, J. E. 1957. The demonstration of
lipid-protein complexes as a cause of damage
by freezing. Proc. Roy. Soc., London, ser. B,
147, 427–433.

LOVERN, J. A., OLLEY, J., HARTREE, E. F., AND MANN,
T. 1957. The lipids of ram spermatozoa.
Biochem. J., **67**, 630–643.

LOWMAN, F. G., AND JENSEN, L. H. 1955. Preliminary note on X-ray diffraction studies with

the tails of spermatozoa of silver salmon (*Oncorhynchus kisutch*). Biochim. et biophys. acta,
16, 438–439.

LUNDBLAD, G., AND HULTIN, E. 1952. Amylase in
bull spermatozoa. Exper. Cell Res., **3**, 506–
507.

LUNDQUIST, F. 1949. Aspects of the biochemistry
of human semen. Acta physiol. scandinav.,
Suppl. 66, **19**, 1–105.

LUTWAK-MANN, C., AND ROWSON, L. E. A. 1953.
The chemical composition of the pre-sperm
fraction of bull ejaculate obtained by electrical
stimulation. J. Agric. Sc., **43**, 131–135.

MACHIN, K. E. 1958. Wave propagation along
flagella. J. Exper. Biol., **35**, 796–806.

MACHOWKA, W. W., AND SCHEGALOFF, S. B. 1935.
Die Reaktion der Spermatozoen auf konstan-
ten Strom (Galvanotaxis). Roux' Arch.
Entwicklungsmech. Organ., **133**, 694–700.

MACLEOD, J. 1941a. The metabolism of human
spermatozoa. Am. J. Physiol., **132**, 193–201.

MACLEOD, J. 1941b. The effect of glycolysis inhibitors and of certain substrates on the metabolism and motility of human spermatozoa.
Endocrinology, **29**, 583–591.

MACLEOD, J. 1942. The relation between the
metabolism and motility of human spermatozoa. Human Fertil., **7**, 129–141.

MACLEOD, J. 1943a. The rôle of oxygen in the
metabolism and motility of human spermatozoa. Am. J. Physiol., **138**, 512–518.

MACLEOD, J. 1943b. The physiology of mammalian semen. Ann. Rev. Physiol., **5**, 399–412.

MACLEOD, J. 1946. Metabolism and motility of
human spermatozoa. In *The Problem of Fertility*, E. T. Engle, Ed., pp. 154–166. Princeton,
N. J.: Princeton University Press.

MACLEOD, J. 1951. Sulfhydryl groups in relation to the metabolism and motility of human
spermatozoa. J. Gen. Physiol., **34**, 705–714.

MACLEOD, J., AND FREUND, M. 1958. Influence of
spermatozoal concentration and initial fructose
level on fructolysis in human semen. J. Appl.
Physiol., **13**, 501–505.

MACLEOD, J., AND GOLD, R. S. 1951. The male
factor in fertility and infertility. II. Spermatozoa counts in 100 men of known fertility
and in 100 cases of infertile marriages. J.
Urol., **66**, 436–449.

MACLEOD, J., AND HOTCHKISS, R. S. 1942. The
distribution of spermatozoa and of certain
chemical constituents in the human ejaculate.
J. Urol., **48**, 225–229.

MACLEOD, J., SWAN, R. C., AND AITKEN, G. A., JR.
1949. Lithium; its effect on human spermatozoa, rat testicular tissue and upon rats *in
vivo*. Am. J. Physiol., **157**, 177–183.

MACMILLAN, E. W. 1953. The effects of interruption of the vasal and inferior epididymal
arteries on the cauda epididymidis and testis.
Proc. Soc. Stud. Fertil., **5**, 12–19.

MACMILLAN, E. W., AND HARRISON, R. G. 1955.
The rate of passage of radiopaque medium
along the ductus epididymidis of the rat.
Proc. Soc. Stud. Fertil., **7**, 35–40.

MANEELY, R. B. 1954. Some aspects of epididymal structure and function. Thesis, Liverpool.

MANEELY, R. B. 1955. The distribution of polysaccharide complexes and of alkaline glycerophosphatase in the epididymis of the rat. Acta anat., Basel, **32**, 361–380.

MANEELY, R. B. 1958. The effect of bilateral gonadectomy on the histology and histochemistry of the surviving epididymis in rats. Acta. anat., Basel, **32**, 361–380.

MANEELY, R. B. 1959. Epididymal structure and function: a historical and critical review. Acta zool., **41**, 1–21.

MANN, T. 1945. Studies on the metabolism of semen. 1. General aspects, occurrence and distribution of cytochrome, certain enzymes and coenzymes. 2. Glycolysis in spermatozoa. Biochem. J., **39**, 451–458; 458–465.

MANN, T. 1949. Metabolism of semen. Advances Enzymol., **9**, 329–390.

MANN, T. 1951a. Studies on the metabolism of semen. 7. Cytochrome in human spermatozoa. Biochem. J., **48**, 386–388.

MANN, T. 1951b. Mammalian semen: composition, metabolism and survival. Biochem. Soc. Symp., **7**, 11–22.

MANN, T. 1954. *The Biochemistry of Semen.* New York: J. Wiley & Sons, Inc.

MANN, T. 1958a. Aspetti biochimici della riproduzione. Rendic. Ist. Super. Sanita. Roma, **21**, 16–29.

MANN, T. 1958b. Biochemical basis of spermicidal activity. Stud. Fertil., **9**, 3–27.

MANN, T., AND LUTWAK-MANN, C. 1951. Secretory function of male accessory organs of reproduction in mammals. Physiol. Rev., **31**, 27–55.

MANN, T., AND LUTWAK-MANN, C. 1955. Biochemical changes underlying the phenomenon of cold-shock in spermatozoa. Arch. Sc. biol., **39**, 578–588.

MANN, T., AND LUTWAK-MANN, C. 1958. Reproduction. Ann. Rev. Physiol., **20**, 275–304.

MANN, T., POLGE, C., AND ROWSON, L. E. A. 1955. Participation of seminal plasma during the passage of spermatozoa in the female reproductive tract of the pig and horse. J. Endocrinol., **13**, 133–140.

MANN, T., AND WHITE, I. G. 1957. Glycerol metabolism by spermatozoa. Biochem. J., **65**, 634–639.

MANTEGAZZA, P. 1866. Sullo sperma umano. Rendic. Ist. Lomb. di sc. e lett. Rendic. Cl. di lett. e sc., mor. e polit. Milano, **3**, 183–198.

MANTON, S. M. 1938. Studies on the Onychophora. IV. The passage of spermatozoa into the ovary in *Peripatopsis* and the early development of the ova. Philos. Tr. Roy. Soc., London, ser. B, **228**, 421–442.

MARAUD, R., AND STOLL, R. 1958. Sur le rôle inducteur du testicule dans la morphogénèse épididymaire chez les vértébrés; résultats de la castration. Compt. rend. Soc. biol., **152**, 346–350.

MARSHALL, F. H. A. 1922. *The Physiology of Reproduction*, 2nd ed., Ch. VIII. London: Longmans, Green and Company.

MARTIN, F., AND BRACHET, J. 1959. Autoradiographic studies on the incorporation of amino acids into spermatozoa. Exper. Cell Res., **17**, 399–404.

MARTIN, I., AND EMMENS, C. W. 1958. Factors affecting the fertility and other characteristics of deep-frozen bull semen. J. Endocrinol., **17**, 449–455.

MARTINS, T., AND DO VALLE, J. R. 1938. Influence de la castration sur la motilité du canal déférent du rat. Compt. rend. Soc. biol., **127**, 464–466.

MÂRZA, V. D. 1930. Histochimie du spermatozoïde. Rev. Med.-Chirurg. din Iasi, Bul. Soc. Med. Natur. (Romîn.), **41**, 521–630.

MASON, K. E., AND SHAVER, S. L. 1952. Some functions of the caput epididymis. Ann. New York Acad. Sc., **55**, 585–593.

MASTROIANNI, L., JR., WINTERNITZ, W. W., AND LOWI, N. P. 1958. The *in vitro* metabolism of the human endosalpinx. Some preliminary studies. Fertil. & Steril., **9**, 500–509.

MAURITZEN, C. M., ROY, A. B., AND STEDMAN, E. 1952. The ribosenucleic acid content of isolated cell nuclei. Proc. Roy. Soc., London, ser. B, **140**, 18–31.

McCARTNEY, J. L. 1923. Further observations on the antigenic effects of semen. Mechanism of sterilization of female rat from injections of spermatozoa. Am. J. Physiol., **66**, 404–407.

McCLEAN, D., AND ROWLANDS, I. W. 1942. Role of hyaluronidase in fertilization. Nature, London, **150**, 627–628.

McDONALD, L. E., AND SAMPSON, J. 1957. Intraperitoneal insemination of the heifer. Proc. Soc. Exper. Biol. & Med., **95**, 815–816.

McGEACHIN, R. L., HARGAN, L. A., POTTER, B. A., AND DAUS, A. T., JR. 1958. Amylase in Fallopian tubes. Proc. Soc. Exper. Biol. & Med., **99**, 130–131.

McKENZIE, F. F., AND BERLINER, V. 1937. The reproductive capacity of rams. Univ. Missouri Agric. Exper. Sta. Res. Bull., No. 265, pp. 1–143.

McKENZIE, F. F., MILLER, J. C., AND BAUGUESS, L. C. 1938. The reproductive organs and semen of the boar. Univ. Missouri Agric. Exper. Sta. Res. Bull., No. 279, pp. 1–122.

MELAMPY, R. M., CAVAZOS, L. F., AND PORTER, J. C. 1952. Cytochemical reactions of bovine spermatozoa and seminal plasma. J. Dairy Sc., **35**, 140–148.

MELROSE, D. R., AND TERNER, C. 1951. The influence of 2:4-dinitrophenol on the Pasteur effect in bull spermatozoa. Biochem. J., **49**, i–ii.

MERTON, H. 1939a. Studies on reproduction in the albino mouse. II. Contributions on maturation of the sperm cells. Proc. Roy. Soc., Edinburgh, **59**, 145–152.

MERTON, H. 1939b. Studies on reproduction in the albino mouse. III. The duration of life of spermatozoa in the female reproductive tract. Proc. Roy. Soc., Edinburgh, **59**, 207–218.

METALNIKOFF, S. 1900. Études dur la spermatoxine. Ann. Inst. Pasteur, **14**, 577–590.

METCHNIKOFF, É. 1899. Études sur la résorption des cellules. Ann. Inst. Pasteur, **13**, 737–770.

MICHELSON, L. 1951. In discussion of "Semen studies and fertility" by E. T. Tyler. J. A. M. A., **146**, 314.

MIESCHER, F. 1897. *Die Histochemischen und Physiologischen Arbeiten*. Leipzig: F. C. W. Vogel.

MILLAR, R. 1952. Forces observed during coitus in thoroughbreds. Australian Vet. J., **28**, 127–128.

MIMURA, H. 1941. Studies on the mechanism of travel of spermatozoa through the oviduct in the domestic fowl. J. Dept. Agric. Kyusyu Imp. Univ., **6**, 167–251.

MIRSKY, A. E., AND POLLISTER, A. W. 1942. Nucleoproteins of cell nuclei. Proc. Nat. Acad. Sc., **28**, 344–352.

MIRSKY, A. E., AND RIS, H. 1949. Variable and constant components of chromosomes. Nature, London, **163**, 666–667.

MIRSKY, A. E., AND RIS, H. 1951. The desoxyribonucleic acid content of animal cells and its evolutionary significance. J. Gen. Physiol., **34**, 451–462.

MOELLER, A. N., AND VANDEMARK, N. L. 1955. *In vitro* speeds of bovine spermatozoa. Fertil. & Steril., **6**, 506–512.

MOENCH, G. L. 1929. The investigation of the relation of sperm morphology to fertility by means of microdissection. Am. J. Obst. & Gynec., **18**, 53–56.

MOHRI, H. 1956a. Studies on the respiration of sea-urchin spermatozoa. I. The effect of 2,4-dinitrophenol and sodium azide. J. Exper. Biol., **33**, 73–81.

MOHRI, H. 1956b. Studies on the respiration of sea-urchin spermatozoa. II. The cytochrome oxidase activity in relation to the dilution effect. J. Exper. Biol., **33**, 330–337.

MONTAGNA, W. 1955. Some cytochemical observations on human testes and epididymides. Ann. New York Acad. Sc., **55**, 629–642.

MOORE, B. H., AND MAYER, D. T. 1941. The concentration and metabolism of sugar in ram semen. Res. Bull. Univ. Missouri Agric. Exper. Sta., No. 338, 1–35.

MOORE, C. R. 1928. On the properties of the gonads as controllers of somatic and psychical characteristics. X. Spermatozoon activity and the testis hormone. J. Exper. Zool., **50**, 455–494.

MOORE, C. R., AND QUICK, W. J. 1924. Properties of the gonads as controllers of somatic and psychical characteristics. VII. Vasectomy in the rabbit. Am. J. Anat., **34**, 317–336.

MORICARD, R. 1936. Méiose et mitosines. La Presse Méd., **44**, 314–316.

MORICARD, R., AND BOSSU, J. 1951. Arrival of fertilizing sperm at the follicular cell of the secondary oocyte. Fertil. & Steril., **2**, 260–266.

MORICARD, R., GOTHIÉ, S., AND BELAISCH, J. 1957. De l'utilisation du soufre radioactif (35S) pour l'étude de la sécrétion muqueuse cervicale et de certaines modifications spermatiques. Bull. Féd. soc. gynec. et obst. fr., Paris, **9**, 15–18.

MUDD, S., AND MUDD, E. B. H. 1929. The specificity of mammalian spermatozoa, with special reference to electrophoresis as a means of serological differentiation. J. Immunol., **17**, 39–52.

MUKHERJEE, D. P., AND BHATTACHARYA, P. 1949. Study of spermatozoa from different levels of the male reproductive tracts of the sheep, goat and buffalo. Proc. Zool. Soc., Bengal, **2**, 149–161.

MUNRO, S. S. 1938. Functional changes in fowl sperm during their passage through the excurrent ducts of the male. J. Exper. Zool., **79**, 71–92.

MURATORI, G. 1953. Sulla motilità spontanea del canale dell'epididimo del ratto. Ann. Univ. Ferrara, Anat. umana, **1**, 29–36.

NALBANDOV, A., AND CARD, L. E. 1943. Effect of stale sperm on fertility and hatchability of chicken eggs. Poultry Sc., **22**, 218–226.

NAKADA, H. I., AND WEINHOUSE, S. 1953. Studies of glycine oxidation in rat tissues. Arch. Biochem. & Biophys., **42**, 257–270.

NATH, V. 1956. Cytology of spermatogenesis. Internat. Rev. Cytol., **5**, 395–453.

NELSON, L. 1954. Enzyme distribution in fragmented bull spermatozoa. I. Adenylpyrophosphatase. Biochim. et biophys. acta, **14**, 312–320.

NELSON, L. 1955a. Enzyme distribution in fragmented bull spermatozoa. II. Succinic dehydrogenase and cytochrome oxidase. Biochim. et biophys. acta, **16**, 494–501.

NELSON, L. 1955b. Adenosinetriphosphatase of Mytilus spermatozoa. I. Effects of pH, calcium, and magnesium, and concentration of enzyme and substrate. Biol. Bull., **109**, 295–305.

NELSON, L. 1958a. Cytochemical studies with the electron microscope. I. ATPase in rat spermatozoa. Biochim. et biophys. acta, **27**, 634–641.

NELSON, L. 1958b. ATP—an energy source for sperm motility. Biol. Bull., **115**, 326–327.

NELSON, L. 1959. Cytochemical studies with the electron microscope. II. Succinic dehydrogenase in rat spermatozoa. Exper. Cell Res., **16**, 403–410.

NICANDER, L. 1957. On the regional histology and cytochemistry of the ductus epididymidis in rabbits. Acta morphol. neerl.-scandinav., **1**, 99–118.

NICANDER, L. 1958. Studies on the regional histology and cytochemistry of the ductus epididymidis in stallions, rams and bulls. Acta morphol. neerl.-scandinav., **1**, 337–362.

NICOLLE, J. 1949. Les aspects sociaux, moraux, religieux, médicaux-légaux, et juridiques de l'insémination artificielle en race humaine. Ouest méd., **2**, 530–533.

NOYES, R. W. 1959a. The endocrine control of the passage of spermatozoa and ova through the female genital tract. Fertil. & Steril., **10**, 480–487.

NOYES, R. W. 1959b. The capacitation of spermatozoa. Obst. & Gynec. Surv., **14**, 785–797.

NOYES, R. W., ADAMS, C. E., AND WALTON, A. 1958. Transport of spermatozoa into uterus of the rabbit. Fertil. & Steril., **9, 288–299.**

NOYES, R. W., ADAMS, C. E., AND WALTON, A. 1959. The passage of spermatozoa through the genital tract of female rabbits after ovariectomy and oestrogen treatment. J. Endocrinol., **18**, 165–174.

NOYES, R. W., WALTON, A., AND ADAMS, C. E. 1958a. Capacitation of rabbit spermatozoa. J. Endocrinol., **17**, 374–380.

NOYES, R. W., WALTON, A., AND ADAMS, C. E. 1958b. Capacitation of rabbit spermatozoa. Nature, London, **181**, 1209–1210.

OAKBERG, E. F., AND DiMINNO, R. L. 1960. X-ray sensitivity of primary spermatocytes of the mouse. Internat. J. Radiol. Biol., **2**, 196–209.

ODEBLAD, E. 1959. The physics of the cervical mucus. Acta obst. et gynec. scandinav., Suppl. 1, **38**, 44–58.

O'DELL, W. T., ALMQUIST, J. O., AND FLIPSE, R. J. 1959. Metabolism of bovine semen. VI. Effect of fructose and arabinose on the uptake and metabolic utilization of glycerol-1-C^{14} by bovine spermatozoa. J. Dairy Sc., **42**, 89–93.

O'DELL, W. T., FLIPSE, R. J., AND ALMQUIST, J. O. 1956. Metabolism of bovine semen. III. Uptake and metabolic utilization of glycerol-1-C^{14} by bovine spermatozoa. J. Dairy Sc., **39**, 214–217.

OLDS, D., AND VANDEMARK, N. L. 1957a. Physiologic aspects of fluids in the female genitalia with special reference to cattle. Am. J. Vet. Res., **18**, 587–602.

OLDS, D., AND VANDEMARK, N. L. 1957b. The behavior of spermatozoa in luminal fluids of bovine female genitalia. Am. J. Vet. Res., **18**, 603–607.

OLDS, D., AND VANDEMARK, N. L. 1957c. Composition of luminal fluids in bovine female genitalia. Fertil. & Steril., **8**, 345–354.

OSENKOOP, R. S., AND MACLEOD, J. 1947. Sulfadiazine: its effect on spermatogenesis and its excretion in the ejaculate. J. Urol., **58**, 80–84.

PACE, D. M., MORAVEC, D. F., AND MUSSEHL, F. E. 1952. Physiological characteristics of turkey semen. 1. Effect of type of diluent and degree of dilution on duration of motility in turkey spermatozoa. Poultry Sc., **31**, 577–580.

PANTEL, J., AND DE SINÉTY, R. 1906. Les cellules de la lignée mâle chez le *Notonecta glauca* L., avec des détails plus étendus sur la période d'accroissement et sur celle de transformation. La Cellule, **23**, 87–303.

PARKER, G. H. 1931. The passage of sperms and eggs through the oviducts in terrestrial vertebrates. Phil. Tr. Roy. Soc., London, **219**, 381–419.

PARKES, A. S. 1944. Reproduction and its endocrine control. Ann. Rev. Physiol., **6**, 483–516.

PARSONS, E. I., AND HYDE, R. R. 1940. An evalua-

tion of spermatoxic sera in the prevention of pregnancy. Am. J. Hyg., **31**, 89–113.

PEARSON, O. P., KOFORD, M. R., AND PEARSON, A. K. 1952. Reproduction in the lump-nosed bat (*Corynorhinus rafinesquei*) in California. J. Mammal., **33**, 273–320.

PÉREZ GARCÍA, T. 1957. Aportaciones a los métodos de recogida y contrastación del esperma de perro. Rev. Patronato Biol. Anim., **3**, 97–150.

PERNOT, E. 1956. Recherches sur les constituants antigéniques des spermatozoïdes de cobayes. Bull. Soc. chim. biol., **38**, 1041–1054.

PETERSEN, P., AND NORDLUND, S. 1958. Survival of bull spermatozoa after exposure to 150 atm N_2 for 15 days. Experientia, **14**, 223–225.

PFEFFER, W. 1884. Locomotorische Richtungsbewegungen durch chemische Reize. Untersuch. bot. Inst. Tübingen, **1**, 304–382.

PHILLIPS, R. W., AND ANDREWS, F. N. 1937. The speed of travel of ram spermatozoa. Anat. Rec., **68**, 127–132.

POLGE, C. 1957. Low-temperature storage of mammalian spermatozoa. Proc. Roy. Soc., London, ser. B, **147**, 498–508.

POLGE, C., SMITH, A. U., AND PARKES, A. S. 1949. Revival of spermatozoa after vitrification and dehydration at low temperatures. Nature, London, **164**, 666.

POLLISTER, A. W., AND MIRSKY, A. E. 1946. The nucleoprotamine of trout sperm. J. Gen. Physiol., **30**, 101–116.

POMMERENKE, W. T. 1928. Effects of sperm injections into female rabbits. Physiol. Zool., **1**, 97–121.

POMMERENKE, W. T. 1946. Cyclical changes in the physical and chemical properties of cervical mucus. Am. J. Obst. & Gynec., **52**, 1023–1028.

POMMERENKE, W. T., AND VIERGIVER, E. 1946. The effect of the administration of estrogens upon the production of cervical mucus in castrated women. J. Clin. Endocrinol., **6**, 99–108.

POPE PIUS XII. 1957. Editorial: Address of His Holiness, Pope Pius XII, to the Second World Congress on Fertility and Sterility. Internat. J. Fertil., **2**, 1–10.

PORTER, J. C., SHANKMAN, S., AND MELAMPY, R. M. 1951. Chemical composition of bovine spermatozoa. Proc. Soc. Exper. Biol. & Med., **77**, 53–56.

PORTZEHL, H., AND WEBER, H. H. 1950. Zur Thermodynamik des ATP-Kontraktion des Aktomyosinfadens. Ztschr. Naturf., **5b**, 123.

PÓSALAKY, Z., AND HAJDI, G. 1956. Experimental studies of the destiny of spermatozoa not participating in the fertilization process. Acta biol. acad. sc., Hungary, Suppl., **1**, 16.

PÓSALAKY, Z., AND TÖRŐ, I. 1957a. Experimental investigations into the destiny of spermatozoa not participating in fertilization. Acta biol. acad. sc., Hungary, **8**, 1–10.

PÓSALAKY, Z., AND TÖRŐ, I. 1957b. Fate of spermatozoa not participating in the fertilization process. Nature, London, **179**, 150–151.

PURSLEY, G. R., AND HERMAN, H. A. 1950. Some

effects of hypertonic and hypotonic solutions on the livability and morphology of bovine spermatozoa. J. Dairy Sc., **33**, 220–227.

PUSSEP, L. M. 1921. *Der Blutkreislauf im Gehirn beim Koitus.* Tartu, URSS: Dorpat (transl. 1922, Stuttgart: J. Puttnam).

QUINN, J. P., AND BURROWS, W. H. 1936. Artificial insemination in fowls. Heredity, **27**, 31–37.

RACKER, E. 1959. Multienzyme systems. Am. Naturalist, **93**, 237–244.

RACKER, E., AND GATT, S. 1959. Interactions of glycolysis and oxidative pathways. Ann. New York Acad. Sc., **72**, 427–438.

RAKOFF, A. E., FEO, L. G., AND GOLDSTEIN, L. 1944. The biologic characteristics of the normal vagina. Am. J. Obst. & Gynec., **47**, 467–494.

RAO, S. S., AND SADRI, K. K. 1959. Immunological studies with human semen and cervical mucus. in *Proceedings 6th International Conference Planned Parenthood (1959)*, p. 313. London: International Planned Parenthood Federation.

REDENZ, E. 1926. Nebenhoden und Supermienbewegung. Würzb. Abhandl. ges. Med., **24**, 107–150.

REID, B. L. 1958. Some cytological features of epididymal cells in the rat. Quart. J. Microscop. Sc., **99**, 295–313.

REID, B. L. 1959. The structure and function of the epididymis. II. The histogenesis of the rat epididymis. Australian J. Zool., **7**, 22–38.

REID, B. L., AND CLELAND, K. W. 1957. The structure and function of the epididymis. I. The histology of the rat epididymis. Australian J. Zool., **5**, 223–246.

RETZIUS, G. 1909. *Biologische Untersuchungen,* Vol. 14, pp. 1–230. Jena: Gustav Fischer.

REYNOLDS, S. R. M. 1931. Studies on the uterus. V. The influence of the ovary on the motility of the non-gravid uterus of the unanaesthetized rabbit. Am. J. Physiol., **97**, 706–721.

REYNOLDS, S. R. M. 1949. *The Physiology of the Uterus,* 2nd ed. New York: Paul B. Hoeber, Inc.

RIKMENSPOEL, R. 1957. *Photoelectric and Cinematographic Measurements of the "Motility" of Bull Sperm Cells.* Utrecht: H. J. Smits.

RISLEY, P. L. 1958. The contractile behavior *in vivo* of the ductus epididymidis and vasa efferentia of the rat. Anat. Rec., **130**, 471.

RISLEY, P. L. 1961. Physiology of the male accessory organs. In *Physiological Mechanisms Concerned with Conception,* W. O. Nelson, ed., Ch. 2. New York: Pergamon Press, in press.

RITCHIE, D. 1950. The frequency of beat of sperm tails. Science, **111**, 172–173.

ROMMER, J. J. 1952. *Sterility, Its Cause and Its Treatment.* Springfield, Ill., Charles C Thomas.

ROOSEN-RUNGE, E. C. 1951. Motions of the seminiferous tubules of rat and dog. Anat. Rec., **109**, 413.

ROTHSCHILD, LORD. 1948. The physiology of sea-urchin spermatozoa. Senescence and the dilution effect. J. Exper. Biol., **25**, 353–368.

ROTHSCHILD, LORD. 1951a. Sea-urchin spermatozoa. Biol. Rev., **26**, 1–27.

ROTHSCHILD, LORD. 1951b. Cytochrome-catalysis of the movements of bracken spermatozoids. Proc. Roy. Soc., London, ser. B, **138**, 272–277.

ROTHSCHILD, LORD. 1953. The movements of spermatozoa. In: *Mammalian Germ Cells,* G. E. W. Wolstenholme, M. P. Cameron, and J. S. Freeman, Eds., pp. 122–130. London: J. & A. Churchill, Ltd.

ROTHSCHILD, LORD. 1955. The spermatozoa of the honey-bee. Tr. Roy. Entomol. Soc., London, **107**, 289–294.

ROTHSCHILD, LORD. 1956a. The respiratory dilution effect in sea-urchin spermatozoa. Vie et Milieu, **7**, 405–412.

ROTHSCHILD, LORD. 1956b. *Fertilization.* London: Methuen and Company, Ltd.

ROTHSCHILD, LORD. 1959. Anaerobic heat production of bull spermatozoa. II. The effects of changes in the colligative and other properties of the suspending medium. Proc. Roy. Soc., London, ser. B, **151**, 1–22.

ROTHSCHILD, LORD, AND CLELAND, K. W. 1952. The physiology of sea-urchin spermatozoa; the nature and location of the endogenous substrate. J. Exper. Biol., **29**, 66–71.

ROTHSCHILD, LORD, AND MANN, T. 1950. Carbohydrate and adenosinetriphosphate in sea-urchin semen. Nature, London, **166**, 781.

ROTHSCHILD, LORD, AND TUFT, P. H. 1950. The physiology of sea-urchin spermatozoa. The dilution effect in relation to copper and zinc. J. Exper. Biol., **27**, 59–72.

ROTHSCHILD, LORD, AND TYLER, A. 1954. The physiology of sea-urchin spermatozoa. Action of Versene. J. Exper. Biol., **31**, 252–259.

ROWLANDS, I. W. 1957. Insemination of the guinea-pig by intraperitoneal injection. J. Endocrinol., **16**, 98–106.

ROZIN, S. 1958. The role of seminal plasma in motility of spermatozoa; therapeutic insemination with husband's spermatozoa in heterologous seminal plasma; preliminary report. Acta med. orient., Jerusalem, **17**, 24–25.

RUBENSTEIN, B. B., STRAUSS, H., LAZARUS, M. L., AND HANKIN, H. 1951. Sperm survival in women. Motile sperm in the fundus and tubes of surgical cases. Fertil. & Steril., **2**, 15–19.

RUBIN, I. C. 1920. Nonoperative determination of patency of Fallopian tubes in sterility; intrauterine inflation with oxygen, and production of an artificial pneumoperitoneum; preliminary report. J. A. M. A., **74**, 1017.

RUGH, R. 1939. Developmental effects resulting from exposure to X-rays. I. Effects on the embryo of irradiation of frog sperm. Proc. Am. Phil. Soc., **81**, 447–465.

RÜMKE, P. 1954. The presence of sperm antibodies in the serum of two patients with oligozoospermia. Vox Sanguinis, **4**, 135–140.

RÜMKE, P., AND HELLINGA, G. 1959. Autoantibodies against spermatozoa in sterile men. Am. J. Clin. Path., **32**, 357–363.

RUNNER, M. 1947. Attempts at *in vitro* semination of mouse egg. Anat. Rec., **99**, 564–565.

RUNNSTRÖM, J. 1949. The mechanism of fertilization in metazoa. Advances Enzymol., **9**, 241–327.

SALISBURY, G. W. 1956. The function of the epididymis of the bull. I. A theory for the activation of spermatozoan motility. Tijdschr. Diergeneesk., **81**, 616–623.

SALISBURY, G. W. 1957. Recent developments with bull semen diluents. Anim. Breed. Abstr., **25**, 111–123.

SALISBURY, G. W., AND BRATTON, R. W. 1948. Fertility level of bull semen diluted at 1 : 400 with and without sulfanilamide. J. Dairy Sc., **31**, 817–822.

SALISBURY, G. W., AND CRAGLE, R. G. 1956. Freezing point depressions and mineral levels of fluids of the ruminant male reproductive tract. In *Proceedings 3rd International Congress Animal Reproduction, Physiology*, pp. 25–28. London: Brown Knight & Truscott, Ltd.

SALISBURY, G. W., AND VANDEMARK, N. L. 1951. The effect of cervical, uterine and cornual insemination on fertility of the dairy cow. J. Dairy Sc., **34**, 68–74.

SALISBURY, G. W., AND VANDEMARK, N. L. 1957. Carbon dioxide as a reversible inhibitor of spermatozoan metabolism. Nature, London, **180**, 989–990.

SANDLER, B. 1952. The relation of cervical mucus and asthenospermia in sterility. J. Obst. & Gynec., **59**, 202–207.

SARKER, B. C. R., LUECKE, R. W., AND DUNCAN, C. W. 1957. The amino acid composition of bovine semen. J. Biol. Chem., **171**, 463–465.

SCHÄFER, E. A. 1904. Theories of ciliary movement. Anat. Anz., **24**, 497–511.

SCHMITT, F. O. 1944. Structural proteins of cells and tissues. Advances Protein Chem., **1**, 25–68.

SCHOCKAERT, J. A., DELRUE, G., AND FÉRIN, J. 1939. Action comparée de l'oestradiol et du dioxy-diéthylstilbène sur le pH vaginal de la femme. Compt. rend. Soc. biol., **131**, 1309–1311.

SCHOTT, R. G., AND PHILLIPS, R. W. 1941. Rate of sperm travel and time of ovulation in sheep. Anat. Rec., **79**, 531–540.

SCHRADER, F., AND LEUCHTENBERGER, C. 1951. The cytology and chemical nature of some constituents of the developing sperm. Chromosoma, **4**, 404–428.

SCHRÖDER, V. 1940a. Über die künstliche Geschlechtsregulation bei den Säugetieren mittels der Elektrophorese und deren biologische Kontrolle. Compt. rend. (Doklady) Acad. sc. URSS, **26**, 687–691.

SCHRÖDER, V. 1940b. Die physikalisch-chemische Analyse der Spermienphysiologie (Säugetierspermien). Über die Natur der Lipoide der anodisch und kathodisch wandernden Kaninchenspermien. Compt. rend. (Doklady) Acad. sc. URSS, **26**, 692–697.

SCHRÖDER, V. 1941a. Künstliche Geschlechtsregulation der Nachkommenschaft der Säugetiere und ihre biologischen Kontrolle. Ztschr. Tier. Zucht. Biol., **50**, 1–15.

SCHRÖDER, V. 1941b. Über die biochemischen und physiologischen Eigentümlichkeiten der X- und Y-Spermien. Ztschr. Tier. Zucht. Biol., **50**, 16–23.

SCHRÖDER, V. 1944. Les spermatoxines et le problème de la régulation artificielle du sexe chez les mammifères. Compt. rend. (Doklady) Acad. Sc., URSS, **44**, 396–400.

SCHULTZ-LARSEN, J. 1958. The morphology of the human sperm. Acta path. et microbiol. scandinav., Suppl., **128**, 1–121.

SCHUSTER, A. 1955. Experimenteller Nachweis zweiter voneinander abhändiger chemotaktischer Systeme beim Transport der Spermien. Arch. Gynäk., **187**, 231–242.

SCHWARTZ, R., BROOKS, W., AND ZINSSER, H. H. 1958. Evidence of chemotaxis as a factor in sperm motility. Fertil. & Steril., **9**, 300–308.

SEGAL, S. 1961. In *Physiological Mechanisms Concerned with Conception*, W. O. Nelson, Ed., Ch. 8. New York: Pergamon Press, in press.

SEKINE, T. 1951. Cholinesterase in pig spermatozoa. J. Biochem., **38**, 171–179.

SEKINE, T., KONDO, C., AND SAITO, M. 1954. Acetylcholinesterase in animal spermatozoa. II. The distribution of the enzyme in cell particulate components. Seitai no Kagaku, **6**, 89–94.

SHAVER, S. L. 1954. The role of stereocilia in removing India ink particles from the lumen of the rat epididymis. Anat. Rec., **119**, 177–185.

SHETTLES, L. B. 1940. A method for studying the penetrability of human cervical mucus. Fed. Proc., **7**, 114.

SHETTLES, L. B. 1949. Cervical mucus: cyclic variations and their clinical significance. Obst. & Gynec. Surv., **4**, 614–623.

SHIBATA, K. 1911. Untersuchungen über die Chemotaxis des Pteridophyten Spermatozoiden. Jahrb. wiss. bot., Berlin, **49**, 1–60.

SHIH, H. E., KENNEDY, J., AND HUGGINS, C. 1940. Chemical composition of uterine secretions. Am. J. Physiol., **130**, 287–291.

SIMEONE, F. A. 1933. A neuromuscular mechanism in the ductus epididymis and its impairment by sympathetic denervation. Am. J. Physiol., **103**, 582–591.

SIMEONE, F. A., AND YOUNG, W. C. 1931. A study of the function of the epididymis. IV. The fate of non-ejaculated spermatozoa in the genital tract of the male guinea pig. J. Exper. Biol., **8**, 163–175.

SJÖVALL, A. 1938. Untersuchungen über die Schleimhaut der Cervix Uteri. Acta obst. et gynec. scandinav., Suppl. 4, **18**, 1–253.

SKJERVEN, O. 1955. Conception in a heifer after deposition of semen in the abdominal cavity. Fertil. & Steril., **6**, 66–67.

SLATER, E. C. 1958. Oxidative phosphorylation. Australian J. Exper. Biol. & Med. Sc., Suppl., **36**, S1–S12.

SMITH, A. U. 1949a. Some antigenic properties of mammalian spermatozoa. Proc. Roy. Soc., London, ser. B, **136**, 46–66.

SMITH, A. U. 1949b. The antigenic relationship of some mammalian spermatozoa. Proc. Roy. Soc., London, ser. B., **136**, 472–479.

SNELL, G. D. 1933. X-ray sterility in the male house mouse. J. Exper. Zool., **65**, 421–441.

SNELL, G. D. 1944. Antigenic differences between the sperm of different inbred strains of mice. Science, **100**, 272–273.

SOBOTTA, J. 1920. Was wird aus den in den Uterus ejaculierten und nicht zur Befruchtung verwandeten Spermatozoen? Arch. mikroskop. Anat., **94**, 185–207.

SODERWALL, A. L., AND BLANDAU, R. J. 1941. The duration of the fertilizing capacity of spermatozoa in the female genital tract of the rat. J. Exper. Zool., **88**, 55–63.

SODERWALL, A. L., AND YOUNG, W. C. 1940. The effect of aging in the female genital tract on the fertilizing capacity of guinea pig spermatozoa. Anat. Rec., **78**, 19–29.

SØRENSEN, E., AND ANDERSEN, S. 1956. The influence of sodium and potassium ions upon the motility of sperm cells. In *Proceedings 3rd International Congress Animal Reproduction, Physiology*, pp. 45–47. London: Brown Knight & Truscott, Ltd.

SOULAIRAC, A., AND SOULAIRAC, M. L. 1959. Actions de la gonadotrophine chorionique et de la testostérone sur le comportement sexuel et le tractus génital du rat male porteur de lésions hypothalamiques postérieures. Ann. endocrinol., **20**, 137–146.

SPALLANZANI, L. 1785. Fecondation artificielle. In *Expériences pour Servir a l'Histoire de la Génération des Animaux et des Plantes*. Geneva: B. Chirol.

SPIKES, J. D. 1949. Metabolism of sea urchin sperm. Am. Naturalist, **83**, 285–298.

STARKE, N. C. 1949. The sperm picture of rams of different breeds as an indication of their fertility. II. The rate of sperm travel in the genital tract of the ewe. Onderstepoort J. Vet. Sc. & Anim. Husbandry, **22**, 415–525.

STAVORSKI, J., AND HARTMAN, C. G. 1958. Uterotubal insufflation: A study to determine the origin of fluctuations in pressure. Obst. & Gynec., **11**, 622–639.

STEDMAN, E., AND STEDMAN, E. 1951. The basic proteins of cell nuclei. Philos. Tr. Roy. Soc., London, ser. B, **235**, 565–596.

STEINBERG, J., AND STRAUS, R. 1946. Sperm invasion of the epididymis. Tr. West. Sect. Am. Urol. A., **13**, 70–75.

STURGIS, S. H. 1947. The effect of ciliary current on sperm progress in excised human Fallopian tubes. Tr. Am. Soc. Study Steril., **3**, 31–39.

SZENT-GYÖRGYI, A. 1949. Free energy relations and contractions of actomyosin. Biol. Bull., **96**, 140–161.

TALMAGE, D. W. Allergy and immunology. Ann. Rev. Med., **8**, 239–256.

TALMAGE, D. W. 1959. Immunological specificity. Science, **129**, 1643–1648.

TAYLOR, G. 1952. The action of waving cylindrical tails in propelling microscopic organisms. Proc. Roy. Soc., London, ser. A, **211**, 225–239.

TERNER, C. 1959. The effects of 2,4-dinitrophenol and p-nitrophenol on the aerobic and anaerobic metabolism of bull spermatozoa. Biochim. et biophys. acta, **36**, 479–486.

TERNER, C. 1960. Oxidation of exogenous substrates by isolated human spermatozoa. Am. J. Physiol., **198**, 48–50.

TIBBS, J. 1959. The adenosine triphosphatase activity of perch sperm flagella. Biochim. et biophys. acta, **33**, 220–226.

TOOTHILL, M. C., AND YOUNG, W. C. 1931. The time consumed by spermatozoa in passing through the ductus epididymides of the guinea-pig as determined by means of India ink injections. Anat. Rec., **50**, 95–107.

TOSIC, J. 1947. Mechanism of hydrogen peroxide formation by spermatozoa and the role of amino-acids in sperm motility. Nature, London, **159**, 544.

TOSIC, J. 1951. Hydrogen peroxide formation by spermatozoa and its relation to sperm survival. Biochem. Soc. Symp., **7**, 22–23.

TOSIC, J., AND WALTON, A. 1950. Metabolism of spermatozoa. The formation and elimination of hydrogen peroxide by spermatozoa and effects on motility and survival. Biochem. J., **47**, 199–212.

TOURNADE, A. 1913. Différence de motilité de spermatozoïdes prélévés dans les diverses segments de l'épididyme. Compt. rend. Soc. biol., **74**, 738.

TYLER, A. 1948. Fertilization and immunity. Physiol. Rev., **28**, 180–219.

TYLER, A. 1949. Properties of fertilizin and related substances of eggs and sperm of marine animals. Am. Naturalist, **83**, 195–219.

TYLER, A. 1953. Prolongation of life-span of sea urchin spermatozoa, and improvement of the fertilization-reaction, by treatment of spermatozoa and eggs with metal-chelating agents (amino acids, Versene, DEDTC, oxine, cupron). Biol. Bull., **104**, 224–239.

TYLER, A. 1959. Some immunological experiments on fertilization and early development in sea urchins. Exper. Cell Res., Suppl., **7**, 183–199.

TYLER, A., AND BISHOP, D. W. 1961. Immunological phenomena. Chapter 8. In *Physiological Mechanisms Concerned with Conception*. W. O. Nelson, Ed. New York: Pergamon Press, in press.

TYLER, A., AND ROTHSCHILD, LORD. 1951. Metabolism of sea urchin spermatozoa and induced anaerobic motility in solutions of amino acids. Proc. Exper. Soc. Biol. & Med., **76**, 52–58.

TYLER, A., AND TANABE, T. Y. 1952. Motile life of bovine spermatozoa in glycine and yolk-citrate diluents at high and low temperatures. Proc. Soc. Exper. Biol. & Med., **81**, 367–371.

UTIDA, S., MARUYAMA, K., AND NANAO, S. 1956. Effects of zinc and some chelating agents on the apyrase activity in suspensions of the tail of starfish spermatozoa. Jap. J. Zool., **12**, 11–17.

VALLE, J. R., AND PORTO, A. 1947. Gonadal hormones and the contractility *in vitro* of the vas deferens of the dog. Endocrinology, **40**, 308–315.

VANDEMARK, N. L. 1958. Spermatozoa in the female genital tract. Internat. J. Fertil., **3**, 220–230.

VANDEMARK, N. L., AND HAYS, R. L. 1952. Uterine motility responses to mating. Am. J. Physiol., **170**, 518–521.

VANDEMARK, N. L., MILLER, W. J., KINNEY, W. C., JR., RODRIGUEZ, C., AND FRIEDMAN, M. E. 1957. Preservation of bull semen at sub-zero temperatures. Bull. Univ. Illinois Agric. Exper. Sta., No. 621, 2–39.

VANDEMARK, N. L., AND MOELLER, A. N. 1951. Speed of spermatozoan transport in reproductive tract of estrous cow. Am. J. Physiol., **165**, 674–679.

VANDEMARK, N. L., SALISBURY, G. W., AND BRATTON, R. W. 1949. Oxygen damage to bull spermatozoa and its prevention by catalase. J. Dairy Sc., **32**, 353–360.

VANDEMARK, N. L., AND SHARMA, U. D. 1957. Preliminary fertility results from the preservation of bovine semen at room temperatures. J. Dairy Sc., **40**, 438–439.

VANDEPLASSCHE, M., AND PAREDIS, F. 1948. Preservation of the fertilizing capacity of bull semen in the genital tract of the cow. Nature, London, **162**, 813.

VAN DRIMMELEN, G. C. 1945. Intraperitoneal insemination of birds. J. S. African Vet. M. A., **16**, 1–6.

VAN DRIMMELEN, G. C., AND OETTLÉ, A. G. 1949 Changes in sperm quality. Proc. Soc. Study Fertil., **1**, 5–10.

VAN DUIJN, C., JR. 1954. Cytomicrochemistry of human spermatozoa. J. Roy. Microscop. Soc., **74**, 69–107.

VAN DUIJN, C., JR. 1958. Biometry of human spermatozoa. J. Roy. Microscop. Soc., **77**, 12–27.

VAN DUZEN, R. E., SLAUGHTER, D., AND WHITE, B. 1947. The effect of presacral neurectomy on fertility of man and animals. J. Urol., **57**, 1206–1209.

VAN LEEUWENHOEK, A. 1678. Observationes D. Anthonii Leeuwenhoek, de Natis è semine genitali Animalculis. Nec non Auctoris harum Transactionum Responsa. Philos. Tr. Roy. Soc., London, **12**, 451–453.

VAN OORDT, G. J., VAN OORDT, P. G. W. J., AND VAN DONGEN, W. J. 1959. Recent experiments on the regulation of spermatogenesis and the mechanism of spermiation in the common frog, *Rana temporaria*. In *Comparative Endocrinology*. A. Gorbman, Ed., pp. 488–498. New York: John Wiley & Sons.

VAN TIENHOVEN, A., SALISBURY, G. W., VANDEMARK, N. L., AND HANSEN, R. G. 1952. The preferential utilization by bull spermatozoa of glucose as compared to fructose. J. Dairy Sc., **35**, 637–641.

VARGA, L. 1950. Observations on the glycerol-extracted *musculus psoas* of the rabbit. Enzymologia, **14**, 196–211.

VENDRELY, C., AND VENDRELY, R. 1949. Sur la teneur individuelle en acide désoxyribonucléique des gamètes d'oursins *Arbacia* et *Paracentrotus*. Compt. rend. Soc. biol., **143**, 1386–1387.

VENDRELY, R., KNOBLOCH, A., AND VENDRELY, C. 1957. An attempt of using biochemical methods for cytochemical problems: The DNP of spermatogenetic cells of bull testis. Exper. Cell Res., Suppl., **4**, 279–283.

VENDRELY, R., AND VENDRELY, C. 1948. La teneur du noyan cellulaire en acide désoxyribonucléique à travers les organes, les individus et les espèces animales. Experientia, **4**, 434–436.

VENDRELY, R., AND VENDRELY, C. 1953. Arginine and deoxyribonucleic acid content of erythrocyte nuclei and sperms of some species of fishes. Nature, London, **172**, 30-31.

VIERGIVER, E., AND POMMERENKE, W. T. 1946. Cyclic variations in the viscosity of cervical mucus and its correlation with amount of secretion and basal temperature. Am. J. Obst. & Gynec., **51**, 192–200.

VOISIN, G. A., TOULLET, F., AND MAUER, P. 1958. The nature of testicular antigens, with particular reference to autosensitization and transplantation immunity. Ann. New York Acad. Sc., **73**, 726–744.

VOJTÍŠKOVÁ, M. 1955. "Sperm in the genital tract in chicks." Cesk. biol., **4**, 141–145.

VOJTÍŠKOVÁ, M. 1956. The question of the participation of non-fertilizing sperms in the sexual process. Folia Biol., Prague, **2**, 239–248.

VON KHRENINGER-GUGGENBERGER, J. 1933. Experimentelle Untersuchungen über die vertikale Spermienwanderung. Arch. Gynäk., **153**, 64–66.

VON LENHOSSÉK, M. 1898. Ueber Flimmerzellen. Verhandl. anat. Gesellsch., Jena, **14**, 106–128.

VON MÖLLENDORF, W. 1920. Vitale Färbungen an tierischen Zellen. Grundlagen, Ergebnisse und Ziele biologischer Farbstoffversuche. Ergebn. Physiol., **18**, 141–306.

WALES, R. G., WHITE, I. G., AND LAMOND, D. R. 1959. The spermicidal activity of hydrogen peroxide *in vitro* and *in vivo*. J. Endocrinol., **18**, 236–244.

WALKER, P. M. B. 1956. Ultraviolet absorption techniques. In *Physical Techniques in Biological Research*, G. Oster and A. W. Pollister, Eds., pp. 401–487. New York: Academic Press, Inc.

WALTON, A. 1956. The initiation of motility in mammalian spermatozoa. Stud. Fertil., Oxford, **8**, 53–57.

WALTON, A. 1958. Artificial insemination in retrospect and prospect. J. Roy. Agric. Soc., London, **119**, 63–69.

WALTON, A., AND DOTT, H. M. 1956. The aerobic metabolism of spermatozoa. In *Proceedings 3rd International Congress Animal Reproduction. Physiology*, pp. 33–35. London: Brown Knight & Truscott, Ltd.

WARBRITTON, V., McKENZIE, F. F., BERLINER, V., AND ANDREWS, F. N. 1937. Sperm survival in the genital tract of the ewe. In *Proceedings American Society Animal Production*, pp. 142–145.

WARBURG, O. 1956a. On the origin of cancer cells. Science, **123**, 309–314.

WARBURG, O. 1956b. The origin of cancer cells. Triangle, **2**, 202–208.

WARREN, M. R. 1938. Observations on the uterine fluid of the rat. Am. J. Physiol., **122**, 602–608.

WEIL, A. J. 1960. Immunological differentiation of epididymal and seminal spermatozoa of the rabbit. Science, **131**, 1040–1041.

WEIL, A. J., AND FINKLER, A. E. 1958. Antigens of rabbit semen. Proc. Soc. Exper. Biol. & Med., **98**, 794–797.

WEIL, A. J., KOTSEVALOV, O., AND WILSON, L. 1956. Antigens of human seminal plasma. Proc. Soc. Exper. Biol. & Med., **92**, 606–610.

WEIR, D. R., AND LEUCHTENBERGER, C. 1957. Low sperm desoxyribose nucleic acid as possible cause for otherwise unexplained human infertility. Fertil. & Steril., **8**, 373–378.

WEISMAN, A. I. 1939. The endurance of spermatozoa within the vagina as compared with spermatozoal vitality outside of the body. Med. Rec., **150**, 87–88.

WESTGREN, A. 1946. Metabolism and sterility of human spermatozoa. Acta. physiol. scandinav., Suppl. 39, **12**, 1–80.

WESTMAN, A. 1926. A contribution to the question of the transit of the ovum from the ovary to the uterus in rabbits. Acta obst. et gynec. scandinav., Suppl. 8, **5**, 1–104.

WESTMAN, A., JORPES, E., AND WIDSTRÖM, G. 1931. Untersuchungen über den Schleimhautzyklus in der Tuba uterina, seine hormonale Regulierung und die Bedeutung des Tubensekrets für die Vitalität der befruchteten Eier. Acta obst. et gynec. scandinav., **11**, 278–292.

WHITE, I. G. 1953. Metabolic studies of washed and diluted ram and bull spermatozoa. Australian J. Biol. Sc., **6**, 706–715.

WHITE, I. G. 1957. Metabolism of glycerol and similar compounds by bull spermatozoa. Am. J. Physiol., **189**, 307–310.

WHITE, I. G. 1958. Biochemical aspects of mammalian semen. Anim. Breed. Abst., **26**, 109–123.

WHITE, I. G. 1961. In *Physiological Mechanisms Concerned with Conception*, W. O. Nelson, Ed. New York: Pergamon Press, in press.

WHITE, I. G., AND GRIFFITHS, D. E. 1958. Guanidines and phosphagens of semen. Australian J. Exper. Biol. & Med. Sc., **36**, 97–101.

WHITE, I. G., LARSEN, L. H., AND WALES, R. G. 1959. Method for the *in vivo* collection of epididymal spermatozoa and for their comparison with ejaculated cells. Fertil. & Steril., **10**, 571–577.

WHITE, W. E. 1933a. The extrauterine survival of spermatozoa. J. Physiol., **79**, 230–233.

WHITE, W. E. 1933b. The duration of fertility and the histological changes in the reproductive organs after ligation of the vasa efferentia in the rat. Proc. Roy. Soc., London, ser. B, **113**, 544–550.

WHITELAW, G. P., AND SMITHWICK, R. H. 1951.

Some secondary effects of sympathectomy. New England J. Med., **245**, 121–130.

WHITELAW, M. J. 1933. Tubal contractions in relation to the estrous cycle as determined by uterotubal insufflation. Am. J. Obst. & Gynec., **25**, 475–484.

WHITNEY, L. F. 1937. *How to Breed Dogs*. New York: Orange Judd Publishing Company.

WHITTEN, W. K. 1957. Culture of tubal ova. Nature, London, **179**, 1081–1082.

WILHELM, S. F., AND SELIGMANN, A. W. 1937. Spermatozoa in urine. Am. J. Surg., **35**, 572–574.

WILKIE, D. 1954. The movements of spermatozoa of bracken (*Pteridium aquilinum*). Exper. Cell Res., **6**, 384–391.

WILSON, E. B. 1925. *The Cell in Development and Heredity*, 3rd ed. New York: The Macmillan Company.

WILSON, L. 1954. Sperm agglutinins in human semen and blood. Proc. Soc. Exper. Biol. & Med., **85**, 652–655.

WIMSATT, W. A. 1942. Survival of spermatozoa in the female reproductive tract of the bat. Anat. Rec., **83**, 299–305.

WIMSATT, W. A. 1944. Further studies on the survival of spermatozoa in the female reproductive tract of the bat. Anat. Rec., **88**, 193–204.

WINBERG, H. 1939. Beitrag zur Kenntnis des Stoffwechsels der Vogelspermien. Ark. Zool., **32A**, 1.11.

WISLOCKI, G. B. 1949. Seasonal changes in the testes, epididymides and seminal vesicles of deer investigated by histochemical methods. Endocrinology, **44**, 167–189.

WISLOCKI, G. B. 1950. Cytochemical reactions of human spermatozoa and seminal plasma. Anat. Rec., **108**, 645–661.

WITSCHI, E., AND CHANG, C. Y. 1959. Amphibian ovulation and spermiation. In *Comparative Endocrinology*, pp. 149–160. A. Gorbman, Ed., New York: John Wiley & Sons.

WOLFSON, A. 1954. Sperm storage at lower-than-body temperature outside the body cavity in some passerine birds. Science, **120**, 68–71.

WU, S. H., MCKENZIE, F. F., FANG, S. C., AND BUTTS, J. S. 1959. Pathways of glucose utilization in epididymal and testicular sperm cells. J. Dairy Sc., **42**, 110–114.

YAMANE, J., AND ITO, T. 1932. Über die Geschwindigkeit der Pferdespermatozoen in strömenden und nichtströmenden Flussigkeiten. Cytologia, **3**, 188–199.

YANAGIMACHI, R. 1957. Studies of fertilization in *Clupea pallasii*. III. Manner of sperm entrance into the egg. Dobutsugaku Zasshi (Zool. Mag.), **66**, 226–233.

YASUZUMI, G., FUJIMURA, W., TANAKA, A., ISHIDA, H., AND MASUDA, T. 1956. Submicroscopic structure of the sperm-head as revealed by electron microscopy. Okajimas Folia Anat. Japon., **29**, 133–138.

YOCHEM, D. E. 1929. Spermatozoön life in the female reproductive tract of the guinea pig and rat. Biol. Bull., **56**, 274–297.

YOUNG, W. C. 1929a. A study of the function of the epididymis. I. Is the attainment of full spermatozoon maturity attributable to some specific action of the epididymal secretion? J. Morphol., **47,** 479–495.

YOUNG, W. C. 1929b. A study of the function of the epididymis. II. The importance of an aging process in sperm for the length of the period during which fertilizing capacity is retained by sperm isolated in the epididymis of the guinea pig. J. Morphol., **48,** 475–491.

YOUNG, W. C. 1929c. The influence of high temperature on the reproductive capacity of guinea-pig spermatozoa as determined by artificial insemination. Physiol. Zool., **2,** 1–8.

YOUNG, W. C. 1931. A study of the function of the epididymis. III. Functional changes undergone by spermatozoa during their passage through the epididymis and vas deferens in the guinea pig. J. Exper. Biol., **8,** 151–162.

YOUNG, W. C. 1933. Die Resorption in den Ductuli Efferentes der Maus und ihre Bedeutung für das Problem der Unterbindung im Hoden-Nebenhodensystem. Ztschr. Zellforsch., **17,** 729–759.

YOUNG, W. C., AND SIMEONE, F. A. 1930. Development and fate of spermatozoa in the epididymis and vas deferens in the guinea pig. Proc. Soc. Exper. Biol. & Med., **27,** 838–841.

ZACHARIAE, F. 1958. Autoradiographic (^{35}S) and histochemical studies of sulphomucopolysaccharides in the rabbit uterus, oviducts and vagina; variations under hormonal influence. Acta endocrinol., Copenhagen, **29,** 118–134.

ZITTLE, C. A., AND O'DELL, R. A. 1941. Chemical studies of bull spermatozoa. Lipid, sulfur, cystine, nitrogen, phosphorus, and nucleic acid content of whole spermatozoa and the parts obtained by physical means. J. Biol. Chem., **140,** 899–907.

ZITTLE, C. A., AND ZITIN, B. 1942. The amount and distribution of cytochrome oxidase in bull spermatozoa. J. Biol. Chem., **144,** 99–104.

ZORGNIOTTI, A. W., HOTCHKISS, R. S., AND WALL, L. C. 1958. High-speed cinephotomicrography of human spermatozoa. M. Radiog. & Photog., **34,** 44–49.

ZUCK, T. T., AND DUNCAN, D. R. L. 1939. The time of ovulation in the human female. Am. J. Obst. & Gynec., **38,** 310–313.

14

BIOLOGY OF EGGS AND IMPLANTATION

Richard J. Blandau, Ph.D., M.D.

PROFESSOR OF ANATOMY, UNIVERSITY OF WASHINGTON SCHOOL OF MEDICINE, SEATTLE, WASHINGTON

I. Introduction

In recent years there has been much more intense research activity on the morphology, physiology, and biochemistry of spermatozoa and semen of mammals than on their eggs and the fluids forming their environment. The significant increase in the investigations of the male gametes is due largely to stimuli resulting from the necessity of perfecting techniques of artificial insemination in domestic animals and of elucidating the problems of infertility and contraception in man. A distinct advantage with respect to investigations of the male is the ready availability and large number of gametes which can be obtained from a single subject. In contrast, the mammalian egg is available in restricted numbers and then only at very specific times in the reproductive cycle. Furthermore, there are very real difficulties in maintaining mammalian eggs in a normal physiologic state after they have been removed from their usual environment.

Even though there have been notable advances in the investigations of the complicated physiologic and biochemical mechanisms which exist in the development, storage, transport, and syngamy of the gametes since Dr. Carl G. Hartman's erudite discussions of the subject in 1932 and 1939, our understanding of the fundamental problems involved in maintaining the continuous stream of life from generation to generation is still in its infancy. As we proceed 20 years later, it will be clear that the older methods of classical histology have not yet outlived their usefulness. But it will also be apparent that many of the advances which have been made, particularly in the investigation of mammalian materials, can be attributed largely to the use of new and improved techniques for the collection and study of living gametes and embryos. For this reason, the subject to which this chapter is devoted will be introduced with an enumeration and description of some of the methods which have contributed so much to the work of the last two decades. Most important of these are the methods which have been developed for recovering eggs and embryos from the oviducts and uterus, and they, therefore, will be described as a preliminary to the discussion which follows.

Methods

A. METHODS FOR RECOVERING MAMMALIAN EGGS AND EMBRYOS

1. Collecting Ova from the Oviducts

In animals such as the guinea pig, rat, mouse, and hamster, in which the oviducts are highly coiled, several procedures may be followed for obtaining the tubal eggs. The coils of oviduct can be trimmed from the mesosalpinx with iridectomy scissors. By stroking the length of the tube with a fine, curved, blunt probe, the entire contents can be expressed and the ova separated from the debris.

Another method is that of placing the oviducts in a balanced salt solution and

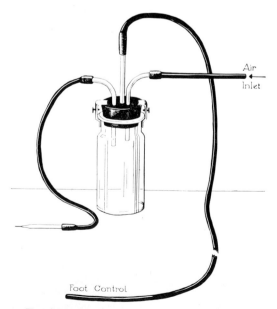

Fig. 14.1. Apparatus for washing ova from the oviducts of mammals.

mincing them into small pieces with a pair of fine, pointed scissors, and then searching for the ova. Both of the above methods are wasteful of time and material, because the ova may be damaged and the full number frequently is not recovered.

The best method for obtaining ova from the coiled oviducts of the rat, mouse, hamster, and guinea pig is to insert a fine pipette filled with a suitable solution into the lumen of the fimbriated end. The pipette is held in place with fine watchmaker's forceps. Gentle pressure is exerted on the fluid in the pipette by a simple arrangement whereby air pressure can be controlled in the manner illustrated in Figure 14.1. If the oviducts are removed and cut just above the uterotubal junction, ova may be seen to escape slowly from the cut end. By controlling the pressure, all of the ova can be kept within a circumscribed area and any other contents of the oviduct, such as spermatozoa, can be accurately counted or evaluated (Rowlands, 1942; Simpson and Williams, 1948; Blandau and Odor, 1952; Noyes and Dickmann, 1960; Dickmann and Noyes, 1960).

2. Collecting Free Ova from the Uterus

Flushing of free ova from the uterus has been performed in the monkey (Hartman, 1944) and cow (Rowson and Dowling, 1949; Dracy and Petersen, 1951). In the monkey the uterine lumen may be entered with a hypodermic needle inserted into the uterus through the abdominal wall. The contents of the uterus are then flushed through a funnel, the stem of which has been inserted into the cervical lumen. Several segmenting eggs were obtained by this procedure. The disadvantages of this method are two: first, a large quantity of fluid must be examined, and, second, the presence of cellular debris in the washings makes it difficult to locate the single egg.

In rodents the cornua may be removed from the body and separated into their right and left halves. Each cornu is then flushed with physiologic saline by inserting a fine hypodermic needle into the oviductal end. During the flushing, the cornu should be gently stretched so as to release ova that may be trapped within the endometrial folds.

In the cow relatively large quantities of physiologic solutions are used to flush out the cornu on the side on which the corpus luteum has been detected by rectal palpation (Rowson and Dowling, 1949). The recovered fluid is poured into a series of French separatory funnels and allowed to stand for 20 minutes. Ordinarily, this interval is long enough for the ovum to gravitate to the bottom. A few milliliters of fluid are removed from each funnel and the egg searched for. By this method, Dracy and Petersen reported the recovery of 10 fertilized ova from a single cow which had been superovulated.

3. Recovery of Attached Embryos

The techniques devised by Dr. Chester Heuser, thus far unsurpassed in the degree of their perfection, provide the safest method of obtaining blastocysts or early implanting embryos. Uteri of man or other primates which have been removed by hysterectomy are completely immersed in Locke's solution. The uterus is cut coronally into dorsal and ventral halves. The surface of the mucosa can then be examined under a binocular dissecting microscope in order to locate the site of the implanting embryo (Heuser and Streeter, 1941; Hertig and Rock, 1951).

A somewhat similar procedure can be followed in observing and recovering implanting embryos of the guinea pig, rat, and rabbit. The cornu is cut longitudinally along the mesometrial border with iridectomy scissors and the entire cornu laid open as a book. The mucosa of the antimesometrial area is examined under a binocular dissecting microscope in order to find the implanting embryos and, when they are found, fixatives can be added directly and only a small segment of the uterus removed for sectioning (Blandau, 1949b; Böving, personal communication).

B. EGG CULTURE AND PRESERVATION
IN VITRO

Studies of the effects of various environmental conditions on mammalian eggs and zygotes are of more than academic interest. The possibility of applying such knowledge to artificial insemination and intergeneric

and reciprocal transplantation of eggs is of economic importance, especially in animal husbandry. Consequently, for years special attention has been given to the problem of finding satisfactory media for the successful culture and transplantation of eggs.

Gates and Runner (1952) compared Ortho-bovine semen-diluter containing egg yolk with regular Locke's solution as a medium for transplanting mouse ova and concluded that the semen diluter was the more satisfactory medium. Many other media have proved successful. These include, to list only a few, Ringer-Locke solution with an equal volume of homologous blood serum (Pincus, 1936), Krebs' solution (Black, Otto and Casida, 1951), phosphate-buffered Ringer-Dale solution mixed with an equal volume of homologous plasma (Chang, 1952b), and Krebs-Ringer bicarbonate containing 1 mg. per ml. glucose and 1 mg. per ml. crystalline bovine plasma albumin (Armour) (McLaren and Biggers, 1958).

Rabbit eggs have been used most often as test objects in the evaluation of media. The eggs of this animal are particularly hardy during manipulation and storage in vitro, a condition which may be related to the presence of the mucous coat. Aqueous humor from sheep's eyes has been used successfully for the transfer of eggs from sheep to sheep (Warwick and Berry, 1949). Willett, Buckner and Larson (1953) obtained pregnancies in cows from eggs suspended in homologous blood serum during transfer.

Except when the rabbit was used, attempts at growing fertilized eggs in vitro in the same media used for their transfer have not been successful. The pioneering work on the cultivation of mammalian eggs under conditions of tissue culture must be attributed to Brachet (1913), Long (1912), Lewis and Gregory (1929), Pincus (1930), and Nicholas and Hall (1942). Lewis and Gregory recorded their notable success in culturing fertilized rabbit ova in homologous blood serum in vitro by means of cinemicrophotography. Fertilized rabbit ova will cleave regularly in vitro up to and beyond the initial stages of blastocyst expansion (Pincus and Werthessen, 1938). Lewis and Hartman (1933) succeeded in culturing the fertilized eggs of Macacus rhesus for a number of divisions. Eggs of guinea pigs, cultured *in vitro*, rarely divide beyond the first few blastomeres (Squier, 1932). Guinea pig blastocysts, however, grow quite well in a culture medium consisting of equal parts Locke's solution (pH 7.5), serum from guinea pigs pregnant from 20 to 24 days, and embryo extract prepared from 19- to 20-day-old guinea pig embryos (Blandau and Rumery, 1957). As yet, no success has been obtained with the very early fertilized eggs of the hamster and rat (Wrba, 1956).

Hammond (1949) cultured fertilized mouse ova in dilute suspensions of whole hen's egg in saline to which had been added Ca, K, Mg, and glucose. No 2-cell ova developed beyond the 4-cell stage; 8-cell ova ordinarily developed into blastocysts. Whitten (1956) found that 8-cell mouse eggs developed into blastulae in an egg white-saline mixture or in Krebs-Ringer bicarbonate solution to which 0.003 M glycine had been added. There seems to be some physiologic difference between the 2- and 8-celled ova in this animal because the 2-celled mouse eggs are refractory to *in vitro* cultivation unless calcium lactate replaces the calcium chloride in the culture medium (Whitten, 1957).

Considerable success has attended the *in vitro* culture of embryos which are beyond the blastocyst stage at the time of transfer to tissue culture (Brachet, 1913; Waddington and Waterman, 1933; Jolly and Lieure, 1938; Nicholas, 1947; Moog and Lutwak-Mann, 1958). Nicholas (1933) obtained better growth *in vitro* when the embryos were cultured in a circulating medium.

Several investigators have studied the effects of cooling mammalian eggs *in vitro*. Chang (1948a, b) found that rapid lowering of the temperature of 2-celled rabbit ova that had been suspended in a mixture of equal parts of buffered Ringer's solution and rabbit serum was harmful to subsequent development. However, the important factor was not the rate of cooling but whether the process was continued until +10°C. was reached. Apparently, that is the optimal temperature for the storage of fertilized rabbit eggs. At this temperature eggs can be kept *in vitro* up to 168 hours without loss of viability. At +22°C. to +24°C. ova lived for only 24 to 48 hours. Attempts to maintain glycerol-treated rabbit ova at temperatures ranging from −79° to −190°C. have so far been unsuccessful (Smith, 1953).

C. INTRASPECIFIC EGG TRANSFER

The technique for the transfer of unfertilized and fertilized eggs between the members of the same species was first described by Heape (1890). He used this method in rabbits to demonstrate that the genetical characteristics of mammals are fixed at the time of fertilization and are not influenced by the intra-uterine environment of the foster mother. Biedl, Peters and Hofstatter (1922) and Pincus (1930) used Heape's technique during investigations on fertility and demonstrated that it is possible to transplant fertilized rabbit eggs to pseudopregnant does.

In animal husbandry artificial insemination has been an important method for the widespread distribution of desirable genes by way of the spermatozoa. Similar genetical improvement through the egg has been greatly limited in domestic farm animals by the small number of offspring. A single cow, for example, will produce 1 calf per year and seldom more than 5 in a lifetime. If transplantation of eggs could be perfected, the number of genetical experiments could be increased at least 2-fold. That the prospect is favorable, is indicated by the fact that transfers which have resulted in pregnancies have been reported for mice (Bittner and Little, 1937; Fekete and Little, 1942; Fekete, 1947; Runner, 1951; Gates and Runner, 1952; Runner and Palm, 1953; McLaren and Michie, 1956; Tarkowski, 1959; McLaren and Biggers, 1958); rats (Nicholas, 1933; Noyes, 1952); rabbits (Heape, 1890; Biedl, Peters and Hofstatter, 1922; Pincus, 1936, 1939; Chang, 1947, 1948a, b, 1949a, 1952b; Chang, Hunt and Romanoff, 1958; Venge, 1953; Avis and Sawin, 1951; Black, Otto and Casida, 1951; Adams, 1953); sheep and goats (Warwick and Berry, 1949; Averill and Rowson, 1958); swine (Kvasnickii, 1951); and cows (Willett, Buckner and Larson, 1953).

The majority of successful egg transfers have been accomplished by exposing the oviducts and cornua surgically and placing the eggs within them (Fig. 14.2). Introducing fertilized eggs into the cornua by way of the vagina and cervix has usually failed to result in pregnancy (Dowling, 1949; Umbaugh, 1949; Rowson, 1951). Two exceptions have so far been reported. Kvasnickii (1951) obtained one pregnancy in the sow from eggs placed in the uterus *per vaginam* and Beatty (1951) obtained 5 young from 55 mice morulae and blastulae introduced into the cornua by the same approach. Since the normal development of ova in artificial pregnancy is wholly dependent upon the environment into which they have been placed, day-old rabbit ova would develop into normal young only when transferred to oviducts of animals in which ovulation had been induced at approximately the same time. Similarly, blastocysts would develop into young only when transplanted into 2-day or 5-day cornua (Chang, 1950c). Again in transferring fertilized tubal ova to the cornua of rats, Nicholas (1933) reported that when the host animal ovulated later than the donors, implantations were greatly reduced as compared to those instances in which the cycles were more closely synchronized. Dickmann and Noyes (1960) transferred ova that were one day younger than the cornua to host females and found that they developed at a normal rate until the fifth day, when they degenerated and failed to implant. On the other hand, ova that were one day older than the host's cornua delayed their development until the endometrium had "caught up" and was ready for implantation. This implies that there is a very critical egg-uterine interrelationship that is established on the fifth day of pregnancy in the rat. Transplantation of rat ova beneath the kidney capsule (Nicholas, 1942) and of mouse ova into the abdominal cavity and anterior chamber of the eye (Fawcett, Wislocki and Waldo, 1947; Runner, 1947) have resulted in only partial embryonic development.

D. THE PRODUCTION OF EGGS BY SUPEROVULATION

Many studies have been directed to methods for superovulating various animals, then fertilizing the eggs *in vivo*, recovering and transferring them to recipient females (Clewe, Yamate and Noyes, 1958; Noyes, 1952; and Chang, 1955a).

Such possibilities have been realized es-

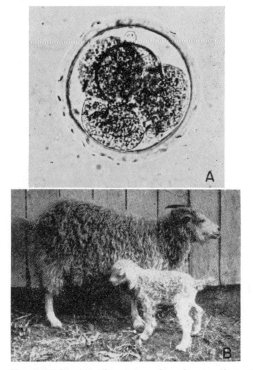

FIG. 14.2. Result of autotransfer of a 4-cell goat egg, *B*. The mother was operated upon on the second day after breeding, the oviduct was removed and the 4-cell egg (*A*) was washed out. The egg was then injected into the opposite horn of its mother (Warwick and Berry, 1949).

pecially by Chang (1948a), who obtained 53 2-celled rabbit ova from a single doe. These ova were transplanted to 4 other females and yielded 45 normal young. Using somewhat similar techniques of superovulation and *in vivo* fertilization in rabbits, Avis and Sawin (1951) obtained 81 per cent successful impregnations and Dowling (1949) 78 per cent pregnancies.

Subsequently, Marden and Chang (1952) performed the novel experiment of shipping superovulated, fertilized rabbit ova by way of aerial transport from Shrewsbury, Massachusetts, to Cambridge, England, for successful transplantation into recipient does. While in transport, the eggs were stored in a flask containing whole rabbit serum kept at temperatures from 12 to 16°C. In domestic animals, the economic importance of such transfer of eggs from genetically superior animals is receiving considerable attention (see Proceedings of the First National Egg Transfer Breeding Conference, 1951). Unfortunately, superovulation in cattle which has been achieved by the administration of gonadotrophic hormones (Casida, Meyer, McShan and Wesnicky, 1943; Umbaugh, 1949; Hammond, 1950a, b) has met with little success as a means of inducing pregnancy (Willett, Black, Casida, Stone and Buckner, 1951).

III. Biology of the Mammalian Egg

A. OOGENESIS

The literature is now revealing a more clear cut opinion as to whether or not the primordial germ cells from the yolk sac of the embryo are set aside at the beginning of ontogenesis, or whether they arise *de novo* from the somatic cells of the gonadal peritoneum in the embryo and particularly the sexually mature female. Knowledge in this field has been significantly advanced by employing the techniques of experimental embryology, organ and tissue culture, histochemistry, x-rays, ultraviolet irradiation, genetics and statistics. The Gomori alkaline phosphatase procedure has been used by a number of investigators to distinguish selectively the primordial germ cells in the human (McKay, Hertig, Adams and Danziger, 1953), the mouse (Chiquoine, 1954; Mintz, 1959), and the rat (McAlpine, 1955). Using the same technique, Bennett (1956) reported the absence of germ cells in strains of mice known to be sterile. It has been suggested that the high alkaline phosphatase activity in the germ cells may be related to their active movement through tissues. This speculation has merit when it is noted that alkaline phosphatase activity is greatly reduced in amblystoma, in which the germ cells do not actively migrate, and in the chick where these cells are apparently transported by way of the blood stream (Chiquoine and Rothenberg, 1957, Simon, 1957a, b). It should be noted that the primordial germ cells may be identified by other techniques. For example, in the rat and man the use of the periodic acid-Schiff (PAS) reaction and a hematoxylin counter stain gives such excellent cytologic differentiation of the germ cells that they can be counted and their migratory course followed (Roosen-Runge, personal communication).

It is beyond the scope of our discussion to present the details of the controversy of germ cell origin, migration, localization, and proliferation. Excellent reviews of the better-known theories are contained in the papers and monographs of Heys (1931), Cheng (1932), Swezy (1933), Pincus (1936), Bounoure (1939), Everett (1945), Nieuwkoop (1949), Zuckerman (1951), Brambell (1956), and Nieuwkoop and Suminski (1959). Evidence for the extragonadal origin of the primordial germ cells has been significantly enhanced by the more recent investigations in amphibia, birds, and various mammals such as the armadillo, mouse, rat, cat, rabbit, and man. In an excellent paper dealing with the migration of the germ cells in the human, Witschi (1948) points out that in embryos of less than 16 somites all of the primitive germinal elements are located in the endoderm of the yolk sac splanchnopleure near the site of evagination of the allantois (Fig. 14.3). From this location the individual germ cells appear to migrate to the genital folds by various routes. Witschi concludes from studies of sectioned human embryos that the migration of the germ cells is accomplished by active autonomous movements and cites evidence of proteolysis of the cells and tissues in the immediate vicinity of the forward moving cells. He suggests that the specific orientation of the cell is directed by some chemical substance released by the peritoneum of the gonadal regions.

A very important contribution to the solution of the problem of seeding the primitive gonads by germ cells from extragonadal origin is described in the contributions of Mintz (1957, 1959) and Mintz and Russell (1957). These authors noted that the gonads of mice of the WW, W^vW^v and WW^v genotypes are almost devoid of germ cells at birth. The application of the alkaline phosphatase technique revealed that the cells are present in their usual numbers in the yolk sac splanchnopleure by the 8th day of development. The mutant genes apparently do not impair the initial formation of the primordial germ cells. By the 9th day of development, however, many of the germ cells had already degenerated at their site of origin. Some of them escape destruction and migrate toward the genital ridge. The migratory cells fail to divide so that the

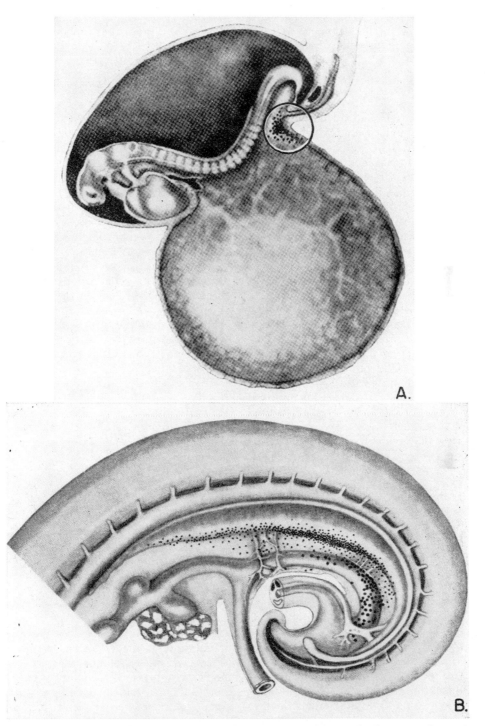

FIG. 14.3. Drawings of graphic reconstructions of a 16- and 32-somite human embryo. *A.* The black dots within the circle represent the location of the germ cells in the yolk sac and ventral wall of the hind-gut in the 16-somite embryo. *B.* Position of individual germ cells (black dots) in the 32-somite embryo. Larger dots indicate an endodermal position. Few germ cells remain in the ventral mesenchyme. (After E. Witschi, Contr. Embryol., Carnegie Inst. Washington, **32,** 67–80, 1948.)

total number reaching the gonads is small. These findings were in strong contrast to the behavior of germ cells of the normal mouse.

By use of a genetical marker, further experimental proof of extragonadal origin of germ cells was obtained. From theoretic expectations, experimental matings using heterozygotes should yield 25 per cent defective offspring. The actual frequency of embryos with gonads containing few germ cells was 28 to 29 per cent. The observations of Mintz and Russell give significant verification of the initial extragonadal origin of primordial germ cells in the mouse. Their work demonstrates further that mice of different strains lose oocytes at different rates depending on their genetical characteristics.

In some of the mutant mice, there is a complete absence of ovocytes in the ovaries of the adults. Russell and Fekete (1958) have shown that when chimeric organ cultures were made *in vitro*, combining one-half of a fetal ovary from the mutant strain with one-half of an ovary from a normal animal, no germ cell differentiation occurred despite active proliferation of the germinal epithelium.

The sterility pattern described for the female has been observed also in the male mouse. Primordial germ cells are very poorly represented in the testes of WW, WW^v and W^{v}W^v embryos and newborn. The mature males of these strains are invariably sterile. Veneroni and Bianchi (1957) reported some success in treating such sterile males with follicle stimulating hormone and testosterone propionate. They conclude that the problem of sterility is related not only to the reduction in the number of primordial germ cells but also to an endocrinologic deficiency.

Willier (1950) studied the developmental history of the primordial germ cells in the chick by preparing chorio-allantoic grafts of the blastoderm at certain critical stages, namely, (1) at the time the germ cells were still near the site of their origin, (2) during their migration, and (3) when they had arrived in the prospective gonadal areas. He found that under these experimental conditions the ovarian cortex never forms; he attributed this deficiency, at least in part,

to a failure of the development of a mechanism in the graft for transporting the primordial germ cells to the areas of the developing gonad. Swift (1914), Dantschakoff, Dantschakoff and Bereskina (1931), Willier (1950), and Weiss and Andres (1952), suggested that the primary germ cells are carried to the primitive sex glands of the chick embryo by way of the blood stream. Thus the cells are originally distributed at random, but they accumulate and persist only in the gonadal primordium.

Recently, Simon (1957a, b) confirmed the vascular transport of the germ cells in the chick by the application of several ingenious experimental embryologic techniques of transplantation and parabiosis. In the developing chick of less than 10 somites the primitive germ cells are localized in the germinal crescent zone in the anterior part of the yolk sac. The caudal part of the embryo containing the future genital ridge was severed and moved some distance from the original embryo. Vascularity of both parts was interfered with as little as possible. Stained sections of embryos examined on the 4th day of development revealed that the gonads had been populated by germ cells which could have reached them only by way of the vascular stream. In other experiments the caudal areas of 10 somite embryos, where gonads were not seeded by germ cells, were transplanted to the area vasculosa of other 10 somite embryos. The developing gonads in the transplants were colonized by germ cells. In still another experiment chick embryos were placed in parabiosis. In one of the transplanted embryos the anterior crescent containing the primordial germ cells was cut away. In cases of successful parabiosis the gonads of both embryos were seeded by germ cells.

Even though it is recognized that in many mammals and the chick the germ cells of the primitive sex glands are derived from migratory primordial germ elements, a more difficult problem remains of a possible second source of germ cells arising from somatic cells in the gonad of embryos, fetuses, and mature animals. It has been proposed that the original germ cells degenerate after having reached the gonads and having effected their inductive roles, and that new cells arise secondarily by proliferation of cells in the germinal epithelium (Allen, 1911; Firket, 1914; Kingery, 1917). On the other hand, Essenberg (1923), Butcher (1927), Brambell (1927, 1928), and Swezy and Evans (1930) postulated a dual origin for the germ cells, *i.e.*, they may arise both from the primordial germ cells, and directly from somatic cells.

The ingrowth of new cells from the germinal epithelium, resulting in the production of new oocytes, was thought to have been demonstrated for both the eutherian mammals (Pincus, 1936; Duke, 1941; Slater and Dornfeld, 1945), and birds (Bullough and Gibbs, 1941). However, various opinions flourished as to whether these oocytes were produced continuously throughout the reproductive life of the female (Robinson, 1918; Papanicolaou, 1924; Hargitt, 1930), or whether they arose from a cyclically stimulated germinal epithelium. On the basis of Allen's (1923) investigations on the mouse, and Evans' and Swezy's (1931) work on a variety of mammalian species, it was widely accepted that a large number of oocytes make their appearance from the germinal epithelium about the time of estrus. According to these investigations the oocytic population reaches its peak during the period of heat and ovulation. On the other hand, Green and Zuckerman (1951a, b, 1954) analyzed the difference in the number of oocytes during the menstrual cycle in 12 pairs of ovaries of *Macaca mulatta* by both quantitative and statistical methods. Their results did not support the accepted view that the total number of oocytes in the ovaries of the monkey varies during the cycle and reaches a maximum near the time of ovulation. They concluded that there is no significant difference between the average total number of oocytes present at the beginning, middle, and end of the cycle. From the results of the experiments of Papanicolaou (1924), Moore and Wang (1947), Mandl and Zuckerman (1951), Mandl and Shelton (1959), Enders (1960), and others, one would assume that the germinal epithelium is not essential for oogenesis in the adult mammal. If oogenesis is to continue after puberty in the absence of a germinal epithelium, are there alternative sources for the new oocytes? It has been proposed that either the concentration

of primordial germinal cells in the region of the hilum of the ovary, redescribed by Vincent and Dornfeld (1948), may be a source, or that specialized cells, histologically indistinguishable from other stromal cells, may be transformed into germ cells. In support of the latter, Dawson (1951) suggested that in polyovular follicles in which there is a great disproportion in the size of the ova, the accessory egg may have arisen by delayed oocytic differentiation of a cell temporarily incorporated in the follicular epithelium.

Of the numerous experimental approaches to the problem of the origin of the germ cells in the sexually mature animal, the action of various hormones on the germinal epithelium has received particular attention. Bullough (1946) claimed that at the time of ovulation the estrogen-rich follicular fluid which bathes the ovary induces mitotic activity of the germinal epithelium. Stein and Allen (1942) demonstrated a stimulating effect of estrogen on the proliferation of the germinal epithelium of the mouse when this hormone was injected directly into the periovarial sac. On the other hand, thyroxine similarly applied retarded mitoses of the germinal epithelium (Stein, Quimby and Moeller, 1947). More recently Simpson and van Wagenen (1953) reported an enhancement of all the processes concerned with the development of oocytes and follicles in prepubertal monkeys (*Macaca mulatta*) that had been injected subcutaneously with either highly purified follicle-stimulating hormone (FSH) extracted from the sheep pituitary or extracts from homologous pituitaries (also see van Wagenen and Simpson, 1957, and Simpson and Van Wagenen, 1958). The germinal epithelium was stimulated to such an extent that there was an active ingrowth of germinal cords which closely simulated the development of Pflüger's tubes. Small oocytes appeared to be developing within the germinal cords and there were evidences which one could interpret as reactivated oogenesis. An attempt was made to carefully quantify the response of the ovaries by counting the number of oogonia and growing follicles. In general the follicular counts remained unchanged, but primary follicles with a single granulosa cell layer were fewer in the stimulated ovaries than in the controls, indicating that more of them had been started on the course of further development. From the evidence presented in the monkey and from a variety of other observations one must conclude that, once reproductive life has begun, there is *no* neonatal growth of germinal epithelium.

One of the major difficulties is the problem of distinguishing germinal epithelial cells from adjacent oogonia. A similar difficulty is encountered when attempts are made to remove only the germinal epithelial cells by surgical or chemical means (Moore and Wang, 1947; Mandl and Zuckerman, 1951). This problem is further emphasized by Everett (1945) when he states, "It seems probable that the cells of the epithelium, which form functional sex elements, are not and never were a part of the mesothelial covering, but are cells which were segregated early and are merely stored in the epithelium."

From some of the earlier work, it was felt that much would be gained if some technique were devised whereby individual cells could be marked and their subsequent fate determined. Latta and Pederson (1944) initiated such experimentation when they injected India ink into the periovarian space and examined the ovaries at varying intervals thereafter. Ova and follicular cells with carbon particle inclusions were seen in various stages of growth and maturation and these observations were interpreted as demonstrations of the origin of ova and follicular cells from "vitally stained" germinal epithelium. It is suggested, however, in light of recent evidence that many cells are capable of moving such particles across the cells and transferring them to others (Odor, 1956; Hampton, 1958), that the validity of using colloidal particles for labeling epithelial cells should be re-evaluated.

Theoretically, the study of tissue culture preparations of fetal and adult ovaries by phase contrast and time-lapse cinematography might be a better approach to the problem of the neoformation of oocytes in mammals and a few experiments of this type have been performed. Long (1940) reported oocytes developing from newborn and adult mice ovaries growing *in vitro*. These findings were not confirmed by simi-

lar studies of Ingram (1956) in which he found no signs of oogenesis in tissue culture preparations of either mouse or rat ovaries. Gaillard (1950) suggested that the germinal epithelium was essential for survival of explants of human embryonic ovaries in that explants without germinal epithelium invariably died. On the other hand, Martinovitch (1939) cultured fetal mouse ovaries for as long as $3\frac{1}{2}$ months. Although the ovarian epithelium disappeared after one week *in vitro*, the ovocytes continued to grow.

The covering epithelium of the ovary is capable of proliferation, and mitotic figures are frequently demonstrable. As the size of the ovary changes during the normal cycle or upon stimulation with exogenous hormones, the covering epithelium must keep pace with the changing surface contour. As mentioned above, the primordial germ cells in the embryo are strongly phosphatase-positive. Careful evaluation of the cells arising from the germinal epithelium have so far shown negative enzymatic reactions.

Furthermore it is a consistent finding that when mice are x-rayed in late fetal life or at birth with sufficient dosages to eliminate the ovogonia, no new ovocytes form from the cells of the germinal epithelium (Brambell, Parkes and Fielding, 1927; Mintz, 1958).

It is an obvious conclusion that any attempt to ascertain the origin of germ cells cannot be considered adequate without thoroughly investigating the entire germ-cell cycle from the very earliest stages to the formation of the definitive sex elements in the fetal and postnatal periods. This must include also the origin of the functional germinal cells in the sexually mature animal. There is an urgent need for a comprehensive comparative study of the cytology, distribution, and migration of these cells. Inasmuch as the germ cells often contain nuclear and cytoplasmic features which are highly characteristic, they offer unusual advantages for various experimental analyses using some of the more modern techniques of experimental embryology, tissue culture, and microscopy.

Even though we have confined our remarks here to the chick and mammal, we recognize the importance of the considerable body of descriptive and experimental information that has been recorded for the amphibia and invertebrates (Tyler, 1955). Heteroplastic transplantations and other experimental procedures which can be performed more easily in these animals may lead to explanations of the fundamental patterns of germ cell-inducing influences by the surrounding cells and to other problems bearing on the question of the origin of second generation germ cells in the genital ridge.

B. GROWTH, COMPOSITION, AND SIZE OF THE MAMMALIAN EGG

The rate of growth of the oocyte in relation to the stage of development of the ovarian follicle has been investigated in a number of placental mammals (Brambell, 1928, mouse; Parkes, 1931, rat, ferret, rabbit, pig; Zuckerman and Parkes, 1932, baboon; Green and Zuckerman, 1951a, 1954, *Macaca mulatta* and man). The available information indicates that size relationship of ovum and follicle has the same quantitative aspect in all animals studied. It is interesting that the regression line relating to the size of egg and follicle is steep in the first phase and almost horizontal in the second (Fig. 14.4). It is generally believed that the ovum attains its mature size about the time antrum formation begins in the follicle. Further, it is also believed that follicular response to pituitary hormones is confined primarily to those follicles in which the ova have attained their full dimensions (Pincus, 1936). It is well known that not all ova grow to mature size. Factors determining which of the ovarian eggs are destined to begin their growth or to complete their growth during a reproductive cycle are unknown and present very challenging problems. Growth of the follicle beyond the antrum stage may be quite independent of the presence of an ovum. This has been demonstrated in a variety of ways, but particularly by the observation that in senile rats large anovular follicles are of common occurrence (Hargitt, 1930). The converse has been reported; ova may grow to full size within the stroma of an ovary without being invested by follicular cells.

Of particular interest, also, are the questions raised by Gaillard (1950) and Dawson (1951) of the histogenetic relationship between the oocyte and follicular cells and the oocytic potentiality of the follicular cells themselves. In tissue culture explants from human fetal ovarian cortex, Gaillard described the development of cord-like groups of cells from the germinal epithelium. A second group of cord-like outgrowths developed from the follicular cells of the primordial follicles in which the oocytes had degenerated. New oocytes developed within these follicular cords and the surrounding cuboidal epithelial cells arranged themselves in a single layer to form the corona radiata. The observations of Gaillard emphasize the potential histogenetic interrelationships between the egg and the first layer of follicular cells. The possible inductive relationships of the ovarian egg and the various components

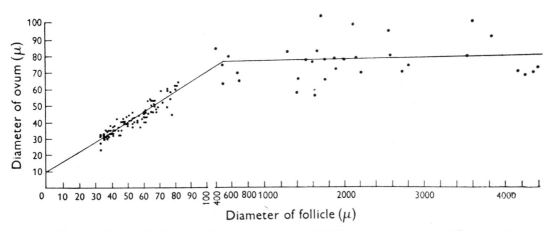

FIG. 14.4. Regression lines relating size of ovum and follicle in human ovaries (Green and Zuckerman, 1951b).

of the follicle need to be clarified and offer excellent opportunities for more detailed investigation.

Studies of the various microscopically visible components of the ooplasm of mammalian eggs have not advanced as rapidly and significantly as have studies dealing with similar elements in the eggs of the lower vertebrates and invertebrates (Claude, 1941; Holtfreter, 1946a, b; Schrader and Leuchtenberger, 1952; Rebhun, 1956; Yamada, Muta, Motomura and Koga, 1957; Nath, 1960).

Relatively little information is available on the history, biochemical significance, and function of the cytoplasmic inclusions during the period of growth, maturation, or fertilization of the mammalian oocyte. In the dog, cat, and rabbit Golgi material of the young oocyte is first localized in the region of the nucleus, but it is later distributed throughout the ooplasm and finally aggregates near the cell periphery. The submicroscopic details of these shifts in the organelles of the oocyte have now been described for the rat and mouse. In oocytes with a single layer of granulosa cells the large Golgi complex lies at one pole of the nucleus (Fig. 14.5). This position of the Golgi complex is characteristic of primary

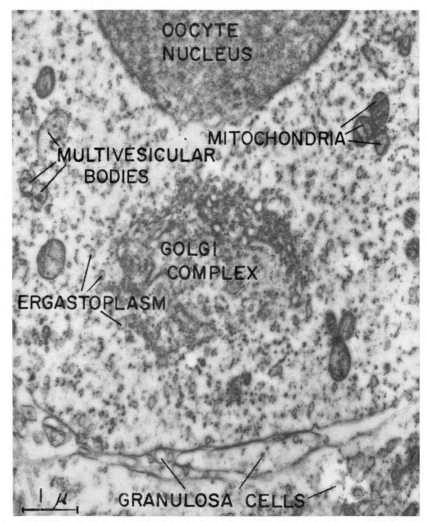

Fig. 14.5. Electron micrograph of a portion of a unilaminar or primary follicle obtained from a rat 2 days postpartum. The large mitochondria have much matrix and few cristae. The large Golgi complex is located at one pole of the nucleus. Note close apposition of granulosa cell membranes to oolemmal membrane. (Courtesy of Dr. L. Odor.)

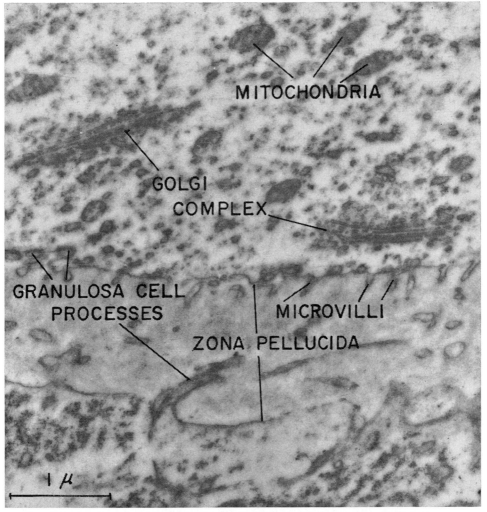

Fig. 14.6. An electron micrograph of a small segment of a multilaminar follicle from a 15-day-old rat. The peripheral location of the Golgi elements, its parallel stacked double membranes and associated vesicles are well shown. The relations between the microvilli and the granulosa cell profiles in contact with the oolemma may be observed. (Courtesy of Dr. L. Odor.)

follicles before zona pellucida formation. Large mitochondria with relatively few cristae are present also and at this stage are rather evenly distributed throughout the egg.

As the egg continues to develop the follicle becomes multilayered and the Golgi complex now appears as a number of smaller units with a complex of stacked, parallel, double membranes lying relatively near the surface of the egg (Fig. 14.6). The mitochondria and other organelles also assume a more peripheral position. The behavior of the Golgi complex varies greatly from ani-

mal to animal (Zlotnik, 1948), and there are diverse opinions concerning its role in yolk production. Some investigators suggest that the Golgi material is concerned with the production of protein yolk, whereas others, working on different animals, maintain that it is always associated with the fatty yolk (Gresson, 1948).

During the early stages in the development of the follicle, the Golgi material in those cells arranged to form the corona radiata lies nearest the zona pellucida. Small granules from the vicinity of the Golgi material have been described, in fixed and stained cells, as migrating toward the egg (Gresson, 1933; Moricard, 1933; Aykroyd, 1938; Beams and King, 1938; Zlotnik, 1948). How the yolk material is transferred from the cells of the corona radiata into the egg itself has not been unequivocally demonstrated. A reversal of the polarity of the Golgi complex in the follicular cells of the more mature follicles suggested to Henneguy (1926), Gresson (1933), and Aykroyd (1938) that it may be responsible, at least in part, for the elaboration of the follicular fluid.

The appearance and distribution of the mitochondria in the mammalian egg also vary greatly from animal to animal. Rodlike or granular mitochondria have been described as being concentrated around the Golgi material in the fixed and stained eggs of the dog (Zlotnik, 1948) and in the cortical zones of the eggs of the bat, cat, and dog (Van der Stricht, 1923). In the mature unfertilized eggs of the rabbit, mouse, and hamster the mitochondria are concentrated in the peripheral zones. At the time of fertilization they migrate to the region of the developing pronuclei and tend to aggregate around them (Lams, 1913; Gresson, 1940).

Observations of the living eggs of the rat and guinea pig by time-lapse cinematography at the time of fertilization do not reveal a significant displacement of the cytoplasmic inclusions such as have been described in fixed and stained preparations.

The ultracentrifuge has been used in an investigation of the cytoplasmic components of the eggs of the mouse and human (Gresson, 1940; Aykroyd, 1941). In the human ovarian egg coagulated cytoplasm occupies more than one-half of the cell, whereas the nucleus, mitochondria, and Golgi material are confined in the remaining half. During ultracentrifugation the mouse egg is stratified into four distinct layers: (1) a centripetal layer, which stains very lightly and which may contain a few small Golgi aggregations, (2) a thin layer of yolk, (3) a relatively wide band containing the major portion of the Golgi material and the nucleus, and (4) a wider band containing principally the mitochondria (Gresson, 1940).

The distribution of nucleic acids in the developing and the mature rat and rabbit egg has been studied histochemically by Vincent and Dornfeld (1948), Dalcq (1956), Dalcq and Jones-Seaton (1949), Austin (1952b), Van de Kerckhove (1959); and Sirlin and Edwards (1959). As the oocyte grows, the desoxyribonucleic acid content of the nucleus is reduced and a perinuclear band of ribonucleic acid makes its appearance in the cytoplasm. Vincent and Dornfeld attributed the organization of the primary follicle to the evocating action of the ribonucleic acid elaborated by the oocyte. Microphotometric determinations of desoxyribonucleic acid (DNA) have been reported on Feulgen-stained nuclei of mouse oocytes and of cleaving eggs (Alfert, 1950). The data indicate that the amount of DNA present in a primary oocyte nucleus is constant, but that as the nucleus grows the DNA is progressively diluted. On the other hand, just before the first cleavage in fertilized eggs the amount of DNA in the pronuclei is doubled. The nuclei of each of the succeeding cleavage stages contain twice the amount of DNA present in the early pronuclei. In addition, studies were carried out on the protein concentration in oocytes and cleavage nuclei using the Millon reaction. The ripe egg contains a reserve of proteins which is divided among the cells and nuclei of the cleavage stages.

Attention should be directed to the rapidly expanding literature dealing with the cytology and biochemistry of the eggs of amphibia and the chick. Clues for experimental methodology on the eggs of mammals may be found within these reports (Bieber, Spence and Hitchings, 1957; Flickinger and Schjeide, 1957; Rosenbaum, 1957, 1958; Wischnitzer, 1957, 1958; Bellairs, 1958; Tandler, 1958; also see Tyler, 1955, and Brown and Ris, 1959).

The use of compounds labeled with radioisotopes is an important tool for the study of the transport and utilization of various substances by eggs (Moricard and Gothié, 1955, 1957, Lin, 1956; Friz, 1959). Most of the tracer experiments have been done in the chick and amphibia in which it is clear that such egg storage materials as lecithin, cephalin, and vitellin are formed in organs outside the ovary and transported by way of the plasma to the egg. Greenwald and Everett (1959) injected pregnant mice with S^{35} methionine and subsequently studied the eggs by radioautographic techniques. Ovarian ova and the blastocysts recovered from the cornua showed active protein synthesis. Similar synthesis was noted in the early fertilization stages. However, eggs in the 2-cell through the morula stages contained no demonstrable S³⁵ methionine. From these observations one would conclude that there is a basic difference in the metabolism of tubal and cornual ova, and again raises the question of the importance of the environmental fluids in providing materials necessary for the growth and development of the eggs.

Earlier investigators directed attention to the fact that in many mammalian eggs the deutoplasm is arranged in such a way as to exhibit an obvious polarity. Such polarity was described particularly for the eggs of the guinea pig by Lams (1913) and is conspicuous in a newly ovulated egg found in section by Myers, Young and Dempsey (1936). Such a polarity has been observed also in eggs of the cat (Van der Stricht, 1911), bat (Van Beneden, 1911), dog (Van der Stricht, 1923), and ferret (Hamilton, 1934).

Attention has recently been redirected to the fact that the mammalian egg may have a specific cytologic organization which is important in establishing its symmetry and polarity. This pattern of symmetry is based on the crescentic distribution of a primary basophilia and the localization of the mitochondria. The significance of the cytoplasmic organization in relation to the morphogenetic pattern in the mammalian egg must await the elaboration of new techniques of experimental embryology which can be applied to mammalian material (Jones-Seaton, 1949; Dalcq, 1951, 1955; Austin and Bishop, 1959).

There are striking species differences in the amount and distribution of yolk material within the cytoplasm of living mammalian eggs. In the eggs of the horse, cow, dog, and mink the cytoplasm is so filled with fatty and highly refractile droplets that the vitellus under phase microscopy appears as a dark mass obscuring the nucleus (Squier, 1932; Enders, 1938; Hamilton and Day, 1945; Hamilton and Laing, 1946). In living eggs of the monkey, rat, mouse, rabbit, hamster, and goat the yolk granules are finely

divided and uniformly distributed; thus the various nuclear changes occurring during meiosis and fertilization are more readily visible (Long, 1912; Lewis and Gregory, 1929; Lewis and Hartman, 1941; Amoroso, Griffiths and Hamilton, 1942; Samuel and Hamilton, 1942; Austin and Smiles, 1948; Blandau and Odor, 1952). The ooplasm of human and guinea pig eggs is of intermediate density when compared to the two groups mentioned above (Squier, 1932; Hamilton, 1944).

The mature mammalian egg is a cell of extraordinary size, and even the smallest (field vole, 60 μ) is large when compared with any of the somatic cells within its environment. It is remarkable that throughout the eutheria there should be so little relationship between the size of the adult animal and the volume of the egg (Hartman, 1929). Data on the apparent sizes of the vitelli of living eggs of various animals are summarized in Table 14.1. The need for more accurate measurements on the diameters and volumes of the living eggs of mammals still exists.

C. EGG MEMBRANES

1. The Zona Pellucida

The *zona pellucida* is usually classified as a secondary egg membrane. It is believed to be a product of the primary layer of follicular cells which surround the oocytes in the ovary (Corner, 1928a). Under the light microscope the fresh zona pellucida appears as a more or less homogeneous membrane with a somewhat irregular surface, the amount of irregularity depending upon the species. As mentioned earlier the immature mammalian oocyte is surrounded by a single layer of cuboidal "follicle cells" whose plasma membranes are in intimate contact with the vitelline membrane. This relationship is partially altered in the growing egg by the gradual deposition of a mucopolysaccharide membrane which when fully formed constitutes the zona pellucida. At first the zona pellucida appears in irregular patches and in the form of an homogeneous secretion (Fig. 14.7). Slender microvilli which extend from the surface of the vitelline membrane are embedded in the zona. Short, blunt cellular processes also arise from the granulosa

TABLE 14.1

Estimates of the diameter of the vitellus of various mammalian ova

(Modified from C. G. Hartman, Quart. Rev. Biol., **4**, 373–388, 1929)

Animal	Most Probable Size of Egg
	μ
Monotremata	
Platypus	2.5 mm.
Echidna	3.0 mm.
Marsupialia	
Dasyurus	240
Didelphys	140–160
Edentata	
Armadillo	80
Cetacea	
Whale	140
Insectivora	
Mole (Talpa)	125
Hedgehog (Erinaceus)	100
Rodentia	
Mouse	75–87.8
Rat	70–75
Guinea pig	75–85
Hamster	72.2
Field vole	60
Lagomorpha	
Rabbit	120–130
Carnivora	
Mink	107
Dog	135–145
Cat	120–130
Ferret	153
Ungulata	
Cow	138–143
Horse	105–141
Sheep	147
Goat	145
Pig	120–140
Chiroptera	
Bat	95–105
Lemurs	
Tarsius	90
Primates	
Gibbon	110–120
M. mulatta	125–143
Gorilla	130–140
Man	130–140

cell surfaces facing the zona and as the cells recede due to the thickening of the zona they maintain contact with the vitelline membrane (Fig. 14.6). Several investigators have called attention to an agranular layer of cytoplasm of the granulosa cells in contact with the developing zona (Trujillo-Cenóz and Sotelo, 1959; Odor, 1960). This layer may indicate the elaboration of secretory material for the building of the zona pellu-

cida. The agranular layer is certainly suggestive but not conclusive evidence for the follicular cell origin of the zona, for a similar layer of dense substance has been described just below the oolemmal membrane (Fig. 14.8). Some interpret the granular layer below the plasma membrane of the egg as indicative of the transfer of material of large molecular weight from the granulosa cells into the egg.

As the zona pellucida increases in thickness the number of microvilli also greatly increase and extend into the zona for approximately one-third of its width (Figs. 14.6 and 14.8). In eggs with fully developed zonae pellucidae, membrane profiles of the granulosa cell processes traversing this membrane have been observed in intimate contact with the oolemma (Fig. 14.8) (Yamada, Muta, Motomura and Koga, 1957; Odor, 1959; Sotelo and Porter, 1959; Anderson and Beams, 1960).

If the living tubal ova of mammals are examined with the phase microscope, the protoplasmic extensions of the corona radiata cells also may be seen penetrating the zona pellucida in an oblique or irregular direction. These canaliculi are the radial striations of the zona pellucida described by Heape (1886) and Nagel (1888).

It is well known that after ovulation and sperm penetration the egg shrinks and the perivitelline space makes its appearance. At this time the surface of the vitellus appears quite smooth with the microvilli no longer demonstrable.

As mentioned above, the protoplasmic extensions of the corona radiata are in intimate contact with the surface of the egg membrane. A number of investigators have described the passage of Golgi material from the follicle cells into the eggs in fixed preparations in fishes, reptiles, birds, the squirrel, rabbit, and rat (Brambell, 1925; Bhattacharya, Das and Dutta, 1929; Bhattacharya, 1931). Zlotnik (1948) described the migration of small sudanophilic granules from the vicinity of the follicular Golgi material into the oocytes of the dog, cat, and the rabbit. There is great need for clarification of the role of the cells of the corona radiata in the transport of various materials into the ooplasm and in the formation of yolk in the mammalian egg (Gatenby and

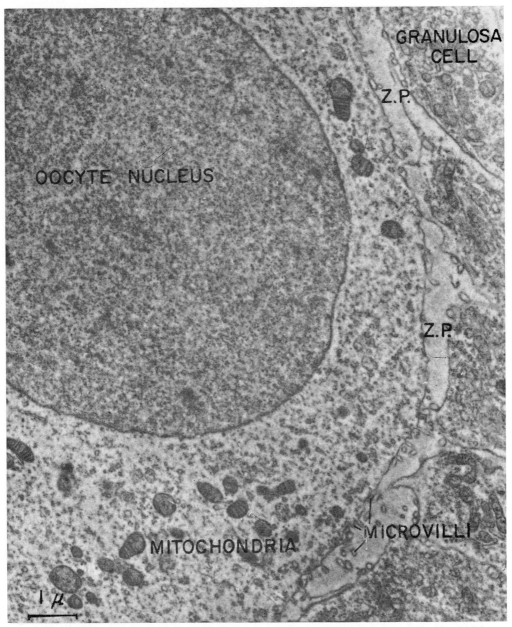

Fig. 14.7. Portion of unilaminar follicle from an 8-day-old rat. The zona pellucida (*Z.P.*) is just forming, and is deposited in irregular patches. The Golgi complex, not shown in this micrograph has begun to break up into smaller units. The mitochondria still have a random distribution. (Courtesy of Dr. L. Odor.)

Woodger, 1920; Kirkman and Severinghaus, 1938).

Also awaiting clarification is the problem as to whether the retraction of the corona radiata cell processes alters the morphology and/or physical characteristics of the zona pellucida. The zona apparently is able to function as a differential membrane. It has been observed in the rat that accessory spermatozoa within the perivitelline space remain intact even until the time of implantation whereas those suspended in the fluids of the oviduct and not incorporated in phagocytic cells undergo complete disintegration

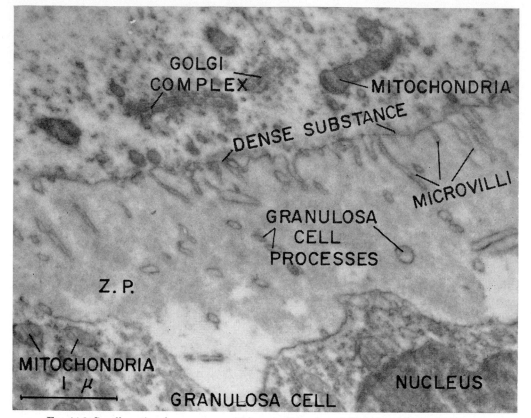

Fig. 14.8. Small section from an egg within a multilaminar follicle in which a small antrum was present. Continuity and extent of ovular microvilli are well shown. Note dense substance just inside the oolemma. (Courtesy of Dr. L. Odor.)

within 12 to 24 hours after insemination. Furthermore, if the zona pellucida of a rat ovum is removed mechanically, the ooplasm then lying free in Ringer-Locke's solution will undergo visible plasmolysis within a few minutes.

The physical properties of the zona pellucida vary according to the animal species and the experimental conditions under which the membrane is examined. Ordinarily the zona pellucida of a newly ovulated ovum is glassy, resilient, and tough. It is moderately elastic and may be considerably indented with fine needles without rupturing. Chemically the zona is composed chiefly of neutral or weakly acidic mucoproteins (Leach, 1947; Wislocki, Bunting and Dempsey, 1947; Harter, 1948; Leblond, 1950; Konecny, 1959; Da Silva Sasso, 1959). It is exceedingly sensitive to changes in hydrogen ion concentration: for example, the rat zona pellucida softens in buffers more acid than pH 5 and

passes into solution in pH 4.5, but the rabbit zona requires buffers of pH 3 or lower to accomplish the same effect (Hall, 1935; Braden, 1952).

The dissolution of the zona may also be effected by hydrogen peroxide and certain other oxidizing and reducing agents. Furthermore, the zona pellucida in fresh rat eggs may be dissolved readily by trypsin, chymotrypsin, and mold protease (Braden, 1952). In the rabbit the zona is removed by trypsin but is not affected by chymotrypsin or mold protease (Braden, 1952). These data indicate that in both rat and rabbit ova the zona contains protein, but that the type of protein is not the same in the two species (Chang and Hunt, 1956). In rat eggs which are undergoing cleavage and which are examined immediately after being flushed from the oviduct the external surface of the zona is sufficiently smooth so that the eggs may roll down the incline of a concave dish containing them. But after a short interval in the new environment, the zonae may become sticky and cling to the glass surface of the dish or to the pipettes and needles used in transporting them. Nonmotile spermatozoa caught within or on the zona pellucida have been pictured many times in the eggs of the human (Shettles, 1953), the rhesus monkey (Lewis and Hartman, 1941), the guinea pig (Squier, 1932), and the rabbit (Pincus, 1930). The same phenomenon has been observed only on rare occasions in rat eggs, again emphasizing differences in the physical characteristics of the zona from animal to animal.

There is very little information as to the permeability of the various membranes enclosing the mammalian egg. Recently the eggs of the rabbit, rat, and hamster were exposed to dyes such as toluidine blue and alcian blue and to a 1 per cent solution of heparin and digitonin in order to test the selectivity of the membranes (Austin and Lovelock, 1958). It was found that the zonae pellucidae of all three animals were permeable to the dyes and digitonin but not to heparin.

There is too little known of the changes which occur in the zona pellucida and other egg membranes under varying environmental conditions to draw conclusions as to the nature of its selectivity. Techniques whereby invertebrate egg membranes are impaled with microelectrodes have yielded new information as to membrane potentials and resistance at varying stages of fertilization (Tyler, Monroy, Kao and Grundfest, 1956). Similar investigations on mammalian eggs would be valuable in solving the problems of selectivity of the egg membranes and in evaluating the response of eggs to various environmental fluids.

The question should also be raised as to whether or not the zona pellucida and/or the mucin coating may present barriers to the diffusion of gases and thus constitute a limiting factor to the rate of development. Fridhandler, Hafez and Pincus (1957) found no differences in the O_2 uptake when comparing normal rabbit eggs and eggs in which the mucin coat and zona pellucida had been punctured. Other properties of the zona pellucida will be considered later when the problem of the means by which spermatozoa penetrate it is discussed.

2. The Mucous or "Albuminous" Layer

Unlike the zona pellucida, which is formed in the ovary, the "albumin" or mucous layer is deposited on the zona by secretions of the glandular cells in the oviducts or uterus and is therefore classified as a tertiary membrane.

In the monotremes (Hill, 1933) and many marsupials (Hartman, 1916; McCrady, 1938) an abundant albuminous coat is deposited on the zona pellucida as the egg moves through the oviduct. A similar deposit, but composed principally of mucopolysaccharides has been described for the eggs of various animals forming the order Lagomorpha (Cruikshank, 1797; Gregory, 1930; Pincus, 1936). A thinner but chemically identical coat has been described in the ova of the horse and dog (Lenhossek, 1911; Hamilton and Day, 1945). It is only in the rabbit that the mucous coat has been charged with limiting the period during which the ovum can be penetrated by spermatozoa. A very thin layer of mucus has been observed on rabbit eggs removed from 5 to 8 hours after ovulation (Pincus, 1930; Braden, 1952). Furthermore, it has been shown that the rabbit egg must be penetrated by a spermatozoon before the 6th hour after ovulation if normal development is to ensue (Hammond, 1934). That the mucous membrane inhibits sperm penetration is confirmed by the fact that unfertilized rabbit ova may be stored in vitro for 48 to 72 hours without, in many instances, losing their fertilizing capacity after being transferred into the oviducts of properly timed recipients (Chang, 1953). It has been clearly demonstrated that the mucin is stored in the secretory cells of the oviduct and that estrogens are necessary for the synthesis of the mucin granules (Greenwald, 1958a). Discharge of the mucin granules is apparently controlled by progesterone. The thickness of the mucin coat on rabbit eggs, or glass beads placed in the oviduct, can be either significantly increased by injecting progesterone in properly conditioned females, or greatly reduced by injecting estrogens immediately after ovulation.

Apparently the ovum plays only a passive role in the process of mucin deposition. The remarkably even distribution of mucin on living eggs or glass beads implies that the oviduct has a specific pattern of muscular contraction so as to rotate the eggs as they move forward.

If the mucous coat is vitally stained with toluidine blue, one observes a concentric stratification which may indicate an appositional growth as the egg proceeds through the oviduct. Chemically the mucous coat is composed chiefly of strongly acid mucopolysaccharides. It is readily dissolved by trypsin, chymotrypsin, and pepsin. It is not affected by hydrochloric acid solutions as strong as 0.1 M but it may be slowly removed by solutions more alkaline than pH 9. A peculiar and important property of the albuminous coat is that at pH 9 or 10 it becomes exceedingly sticky. As will be noted later, this may be of importance for the adherence of the egg to uterine tissue at the time of implantation. The possible role of the mucous coat in the development of the egg was not realized until the investigations of Böving (1952c) in which certain details of rabbit blastocyst implantation were observed directly. A plastic chamber was developed for examining the interior of the pregnant rabbit uterus. It was noted that the mucous coat participates actively in the initial adhesive attachment of the blastocyst to the uterus. Such localized attachment precedes by several days the cellular adhesion and invasion of the uterus by the blastocyst. Böving observed further that the adhesion to the uterus is localized in the abembryonic hemisphere of the blastocyst, probably because it is in this region that an alkaline reaction, produced by secretions of the embryo, enhances the stickiness of the mucous coat. The polar localization of the adhesive attachment of the mucous coat not only provides a mechanism for the initial blastocyst attachment, but also is important in establishing the orientation of the blastocyst within the uterus (see section on "Spacing and orientation of ova *in utero*").

Böving (1954) observed that still another membrane is deposited on the rabbit egg by secretions of the uterus. The membrane forms a sticky covering that stains meta-chromatically in toluidine blue and functions as an adhesive attachment during positioning and orientation of the blastocyst *in utero*. He proposed that the noncellular, adhesive layer be called the "gloiolemma."

D. THE FIRST MATURATION DIVISION

Meiotic division is not a phenomenon which is confined entirely to the ova in the preovulatory follicles. It may be encountered in egg cells in the latter part of embryonic development, in immature follicles undergoing atresia, and in ovaries stimulated excessively by the animal's own pituitary hormones, or by pituitary hormone preparations which have been injected (Evans and Swezy, 1931; Guthrie and Jeffers, 1938; Dempsey, 1939; Witschi, 1948).

Fairly complete descriptions of the various stages in the formation of the first polar body and second maturation spindles are available for a number of mammals (Hartman and Corner, 1941, the macaque; Hoadley and Simons, 1928, Hamilton, 1944, and Rock and Hertig, 1944, the human; Kirkham and Burr, 1913, Blandau, 1945, Odor, 1955, the rat; Long and Mark, 1911, the mouse; Moore, 1908, the guinea pig; Langley, 1911, the cat; Van Beneden, 1875, Pincus and Enzmann, 1935, the rabbit; Robinson, 1918, the ferret).

Specific data on the temporal relationship between ovulation and the first maturation division are available primarily for the rabbit (Pincus and Enzmann, 1935–1937), guinea pig (Myers, Young and Dempsey, 1936), cat (Dawson and Friedgood, 1940), rat (Odor, 1955), and mouse (Edwards and Gates, 1959).

The rabbit is an animal particularly suited for studies of maturation phenomena because it ovulates regularly between 9 and 10 hours after copulation. The first evidence of change in the nucleus of a ripe ovum may be seen 2 hours after copulation. At this time the nuclear membrane is intact but tetrad formation is in evidence. Four hours after copulation the nuclear membrane has disappeared and the first polar spindle, with tetrads located on the metaphase plate, occupies a paratangential position near the periphery of the ooplasm. Abstriction of the first polar body is completed about 8 hours after copulation. Shortly thereafter, the second metaphase spindle is formed and remains in position just below the surface of the primary egg membrane. It remains in this condition until the fertilizing spermatozoon penetrates the egg.

Similar observations on successive phases of the first maturation division have now been completed for the rat (Odor, 1955). In over 1500 living and fixed eggs examined at specific times before and after the onset of heat it was observed that by the onset of heat, the germinal vesicle has lost its membrane in most animals, and has been transformed into a a dense chromatic mass which then quickly moves towards the periphery of the ooplasm. Between the 3rd and 4th hours the chromosomes have arranged themselves in the metaphase plate. Abstriction of the first polar body is usually completed between the 6th and 7th hour, and positioning of the second metaphase spindle by the 8th hour. It is interesting that, even though there was considerable variation in the stages of maturation found in animals killed at the same time after the onset of heat, 83 per cent of all the ova were in the same stage of maturation or in a very closely related phase.

In all mammals studied, except the dog and fox (Van der Stricht, 1923; Pearson and Enders, 1943), the first maturation division is completed within the ovarian follicle several hours before it ruptures.

There is evidence that a specific correlation exists between the gonadotrophins and the maturation phenomena within the oocytes (Bellerby, 1929; Friedman, 1929; Friedgood and Pincus, 1935). Apparently the threshold of response of oocytes for maturation is lower than is the threshold for ovulation (Hinsey and Markee, 1933). Moricard and Gothié (1953) injected small quantities of chorionic gonadotrophin directly into the ovarian follicles of unmated rabbits and observed the formation of the first metaphase spindles and the abstriction of the first polar bodies. This was interpreted as showing the direct effect of pituitary hormones in inducing meiosis. On the basis of a study on oocytes recovered from rabbit ovaries Chang (1955b) concluded that once the oocytes have attained the ve-

sicular stage maturation can be readily induced by a variety of experimental procedures the most effective of which is the subnormal temperature treatment of unfertilized ova. According to his investigations first polar body formation is not immediately dependent on gonadotrophic stimulation.

A number of investigators who have examined mammalian ova have commented on the rapid disappearance of the first polar body. Sobotta and Burckhard (1910) saw the first polar body in only 2 of 100 recently ovulated mouse ova. The infrequent presence of the first polar body in postovulatory ova in which the second maturation spindle was completed suggested that possibly the first polar body was not always formed (Sobotta, 1895). Yet from a variety of studies on meiosis in fixed and living eggs, it may be concluded that the abstriction of the first polar body invariably occurs. In addition it may not disappear as rapidly as some of the older investigators believed. The first and second polar bodies are visible in a 4-celled guinea pig embryo photographed by Squier (1932). There has been considerable speculation as to the method whereby the first polar body disappears. Kirkham (1907) suggested that the first polar body in the mouse either was forced through the zona pellucida or escaped from the perivitelline space by its own ameboid movement. Similar theories have been held by Moricard and Gothié (1953) for the rat, in which they maintain that the polar body passes directly through the zona pellucida. From the observations of Lams and Doorme (1908) in the mouse, Mainland (1930) in the ferret, and Odor (1955) in the rat, it is almost certain that the first polar body undergoes rapid fragmentation and cytolysis within the perivitelline space so that only some finely granular material remains. Ameboid movement of the first body has never been documented in the thousands of living mammalian eggs examined.

E. THE OVULATED EGG

The appearance of tubal ova from a single animal varies considerably depending on the lapse of time between ovulation and examination and the environmental fluids in which they are kept. When the eggs are shed from the follicles they are ordinarily surrounded by a variable number of layers of granulosa cells and a matrix of more or less viscid follicular fluid. The vitellus does not completely fill the zona pellucida, and the first polar body, if it has not already disintegrated, may be pressed between the zona and the ooplasmic membrane. An exception to this may be found in the Canidae in which formation of the first polar body is apparently delayed for some time after ovulation. The length of time that the coronal cells persist varies greatly in the eggs of different species.

A well developed corona radiata is regularly found in newly ovulated ova of the mouse (Lewis and Wright, 1935), the hamster (Ward, 1946), the rat (Gilchrist and Pincus, 1932), the rabbit (Gregory, 1930), the cat (Hill and Tribe, 1924), the dog (Evans and Cole, 1931), the monkey (Lewis and Hartman, 1941), and man (Hamilton, 1944; Shettles, 1953). The rapid dispersal or even absence of the cells forming the corona radiata has been reported for the sheep (McKenzie and Terrill, 1937), the cow (Evans and Miller, 1935; Hamilton and Laing, 1946; Chang, 1949b), the pig (Corner and Amsbaugh, 1917; Heuser and Streeter, 1929), the horse (Hamilton and Day, 1945), and the deer (Bischoff, 1854), and would seem to be a characteristic of the newly ovulated guinea pig ovum (Myers, Young and Dempsey, 1936).

The eggs of unmated females gradually lose their investment of granulosa cells as they pass through the oviducts. The cells become rounded and drop away from the cumulus, a process that occurs first in the more peripheral cells. The cells of the corona radiata which are adjacent to the zona pellucida are the last to fall away and when they are brushed from the surface of the zona in living eggs *in vitro* their long and irregularly shaped protoplasmic processes extending into the zonal canaliculi can be seen (Squier, 1932; Duryee, 1954; Shettles, 1958). The mechanism which effects the dispersal and final dissolution of the cumulus oophorus and corona radiata in unmated females is not known. It has been suggested that an enzyme, elaborated by the tubal mucosa, is responsible for the dispersal of the cells (Shettles, 1958).

When an observer follows the cytologic changes in the cells forming the cumulus oophorus as ovulation approaches and notes their behavior in tissue culture preparations *in vitro* he is impressed with the suggestion that separation of the cells involves a gradual depolymerization of the intercellular cement substance and a change in the activity of the cell surface.

If time-lapse photographs are made of the coronal cells surrounding ovulated eggs, a very active bubbling and "blister" formation of the surface membranes is apparent. "Bubbling" activity of the cell surfaces is frequently seen in cells which are losing their vitality (Zollinger, 1948). These surface changes occur at the time when the cells are undergoing most active separation and accounts for the withdrawal of the cytoplasmic processes from the zona pellucida. Further evidence that the behavior of the cell is related to loss of vitality is shown by their very poor growth in tissue culture.

F. RESPIRATORY ACTIVITY OF
MAMMALIAN EGGS

There have been only limited investigations on the energy-yielding mechanisms and energy-requiring processes of the developing eggs of mammals (rat, Boell and Nicholas, 1948; rabbit, Smith and Kleiber, 1950, Fridhandler, Hafez and Pincus, 1957; and cow, Dragoiu, Benetato and Oprean, 1937).

The fertilized ovum during its various stages of cleavage and differentiation is an ideal experimental object for such studies and has been used extensively in the invertebrates, amphibia, and birds where large numbers of eggs are readily available (Boell, 1955). Refinements in the Cartesian diver technique have made possible the measurement of gas exchange of less than 1 $m\mu l.$; thus the number of mammalian eggs required to obtain significant data need not be large (Sytina, 1956). Furthermore, the effectiveness of gonadotrophins in inducing ovulation in the sexually immature female rodents and their willingness to mate after such treatment provides a ready source of eggs independent of ovulation at specific phases of the sexual cycle.

The type of information which can be obtained by measuring the O_2 uptake of fertilized rabbit ova placed in the Cartesian diver and subjected to a variety of metabolites and inhibitors can be seen in Tables 14.2 and 14.3 (Fridhandler, Hafez and Pincus, 1957). In the rabbit egg, as in other cells, cyanide has a markedly inhibiting effect on respiration. This inhibition is reversible and presumably cyanide acts through the cytochrome oxidase system. Of significance is the finding that glucose is not an obligatory substrate for respiratory activity of the fertilized rabbit egg.

If glucose is added to the medium containing 2- to 8-cell eggs, there is little capacity to carry out glycolysis. However, such capacity develops during the late morula and blastocyst stages. This change may indicate either an alteration in the membrane characteristics of the egg, or the development of a new enzyme system as the egg develops.

The electrical characteristics of eggs and their changes during activation and fertilization have been studied in frogs, echinoderms, and fish (Maéno, 1959; Ito and Maéno, 1960). The electrical properties and membrane characteristics of mammalian eggs are entirely unknown. The use of the ultramicro-electrode which has been so helpful in nerve and muscle electrophysiology offers an unusual research tool for examining the primary process of activation of eggs.

G. TRANSPORT OF TUBAL OVA

The mammalian oviducts must perform a variety of functions in the transport and development of the gametes (also see "Sperm transport in the female genital tract"). They must provide some means for transporting the ovulated ova from the ovary or periovarial space into the infundibulum. Secretions must be elaborated within the infundibulum in order to provide an environment favorable for sperm penetration. In some animals, such as the rabbit, opossum, horse, and dog, specialized cells secrete materials which form tertiary membranes for the eggs. Still other cells secrete nutritional and possibly other substances which may be essential for the normal growth and development of the fertilized eggs. Furthermore, the peristaltic and anti-peristaltic activities of the oviducts must be regulated in such a way that the ova are propelled forward at a definite rate and in proper rotational sequence so as to be evenly coated with the tertiary membranes. The oviducts are indeed highly specialized organs whose anatomic differences in the various regions have been described by many investigators but whose specific physiologic functions still present many unsolved problems.

As evidence accumulates, a happier middle ground of opinion is forming as to the roles of the musculature and ciliary activity in the downward propulsion of the eggs and in the ascent of the spermatozoa. Comprehensive summaries of observations and theories dealing with these particular problems may be found in the papers and monographs of Westman (1926), Parker (1931), Hartman (1939), Alden (1942b), Kneer and Cless (1951).

The more extensive investigations of the oviducts during the estrous cycle include: (1) The observations of Snyder (1923, 1924), Andersen (1927a, b), Anopolsky (1928), Westman (1932), and Stange (1952), on the lymphatics, the size of muscle fibers, and the cyclic changes in the epithelium of the Fallopian tubes of the rabbit, sow, and man. (2) The alterations of rhythmic contractions in the oviducts of the rat (Alden, 1942b; Odor, 1948), the sow (Seckinger, 1923, 1924), the rabbit (Westman, 1926), the rhesus monkey (Seckinger and Corner, 1923; Westman, 1929), and man (Seckinger and Snyder, 1924, 1926; Westman, 1952).

The specific method whereby the newly ovulated egg is moved from the site of rupture of the ovarian follicle to the infundibulum is poorly understood. There is considerable species variation in the relationship of the fimbriated end of the oviduct to the ovary proper. In the Muridae and Mustelidae the ovaries are almost enclosed by the thin, membranous periovarial sac (Alden, 1942a; Wimsatt and Waldo, 1945). The medusa-like infundibulum is enclosed within the sac but occupies a relatively small area of the periovarial space. It is believed that in those animals in which fluids accumulate within the ovarian bursa at the time of ovulation the ova are directed to the ostium by

TABLE 14.2

Effect of pre-incubation on O_2 uptake of fertilized ova

Incubating medium: Ca^{++}-free Krebs-Ringer phosphate, pH 7.4. Gas phase: air. (After L. Fridhandler, E. S. E. Hafez, and G. Pincus, Exper. Cell Res., **13**, 132–139, 1957.)

Developmental Stage		Pre-incubation of Ova		Metabolites Added to RP in Diver	Average O_2 Uptake
Morphology	Hr postcoitum	$T°C$	Time		
			min.		*mμl./ovum/hr.*
		23	120	None	0.45
		23	120	0.1% glucose	0.49
		23	120	10^{-2} M pyruvate	0.47
2–4 cell	20–28	29	90	None	0.45
		29	90	0.1% glucose	0.42
		29	90	10^{-2} M pyruvate	0.41
		29	180	None	0.39
		29	180	0.1% glucose	0.59
		29	180	10^{-2} M pyruvate	0.53
		37	150	None	1.84
Blastocyst	108	37	150	10^{-2} M pyruvate	2.42

TABLE 14.3

O_2 uptake of fertilized ova in different media

Gas phase: air. (After L. Fridhandler, E. S. E. Hafez, and G. Pincus, Exper. Cell Res., **13**, 132–139, 1957.)

Developmental Stage		Medium in the Divers		Average O_2 Uptake
Morphology	Hr. Postcoitum	Basic medium	Added substances (M)	
				mμl./ovum/hr.
2–8 cells	24–30	RPG	None	0.41
			10^{-3} M NaCN (appr.)	0.02
			10^{-3} M phlorizin	0.41
		RPG	None	0.56
			2×10^{-3} M Na fluoride	0.47
Morulae	68	RP	None	0.48
			10^{-2} M malonate	0.42
			10^{-2} M malonate plus 10^{-3} M fumarate	0.47
Blastocysts	78	RP	None	1.71
			10^{-2} M malonate	1.69
			10^{-2} M malonate plus 10^{-3} M fumarate	1.74
Blastocysts	88	RP	None	2.92
			10^{-2} M malonate	2.36
			10^{-2} M malonate plus 10^{-3} M fumarate	2.70
Blastocysts	115	RPG	None	78.00
			10^{-3} M NaCN (appr.)	0.00

movement of these fluids into the oviduct (Fischel, 1914). However, observations on normal fluid flow within the periovarial sac are very limited. It has been demonstrated that if dyes such as Janus green or particulate material are introduced into the periovarial space in the immediate vicinity of the ostium, the material quickly passes into the first loop of the oviduct (Alden, 1942b). Transport is effected primarily by the ciliary activity of the fimbriated end of the ostium (Clewe and Mastroianni, 1958). Furthermore, if newly ovulated eggs are placed on the surfaces of the fimbriae in the rat, mouse, or hamster the cilia will sweep them into the infundibulum within 8 seconds (Blandau, unpublished observations). How those ova located at some distance from the oviduct reach the fimbria has not been observed.

Under normal physiologic conditions the ovary moves backwards and forwards within the periovarial sac. These movements are accentuated at the time of ovulation and are effected by the abundant smooth muscle in the mesovarium. Such activity keeps the fluids of the periovarial sac in motion. Those eggs ovulated at the opposite side of the ovary away from the infundibulum are passively moved into its vicinity where ciliary currents then aid in completing transport.

A potentially wide communication between the ostium of the oviduct and the peritoneal cavity exists in a variety of animals such as the guinea pig, rabbit, monkey, and man (Sobotta, 1917; Westman, 1952). The extent of the communication varies with the stage of the menstrual or estrous cycle. Ordinarily in a rabbit not in heat, the fimbriae do not cover the ovary. As the time of ovulation approaches, there is a great increase in motility and turgidity of the fimbriae so that they almost enclose the ovary (Westman, 1926, 1952). Recently attempts have been made to observe the activities of the human fimbriae by means of abdominal peritoneoscopy or exploratory culdotomy. Elert (1947) has seen the elongated fimbria grasp the lower pole of an ovary for as long as 2 minutes. Doyle (1951, 1954), however, failed to observe either a sweeping or grasping motion of the fimbriae before or during the rupture of the follicle. He suggests that in the human female the initial transport of the ovum is by a process in which it floats into the cul-de-sac and from there is siphoned into the ampulla by simple peristaltic contractions which originate at the region of the fimbriae. Doyle's (1956) recent observations are more in line with those described by Elert above.

It has been suggested that the activity of the abundant smooth musculature of the adnexa and the fimbriae produces a powerful suction effect on the ovary, thus drawing the ovulated eggs into the tube (Sobotta, 1917; Westman, 1952). It is a fact, however, that no one has made measurements of this presumed negative pressure, nor, as pointed out earlier, has anyone observed a newly ovulated mammalian ovum transported from the surface of the ovary into the oviduct in animals in which the ovaries are not enclosed in periovarial sacs. During laparotomy there are very real problems in maintaining the normal anatomic position and physiologic condition of the oviducts so that their actual function *in vivo* can be assessed accurately. In general the muscular activity of the fimbriae has received more enthusiastic support than the cilia as being the agent for the transport of eggs from ovary to oviduct. However, in the few instances in which eggs were placed close to the fimbriae and egg transport observed directly, the ciliary activity of the fimbriae appeared to be primarily responsible.

The rate of the ciliary beat in the rabbit Fallopian tubes has been studied by Borell, Nilsson and Westman (1957); during estrus the cilia beat at a rate of 1500 beats per minute.

The rate increases about 20 per cent on the 2nd and 3rd day after copulation and at the time of implantation. By the 14th day of pregnancy the rate of beat had returned to normal. There was no significant difference in the rate of beat in cilia removed from various segments of the oviduct. Many more direct and continuous observations on the intact oviducts of different animals are needed before definite conclusions may be reached as to the mechanics of egg transport from the ovary to the infundibulum.

In the rat, mouse, and hamster, one of the

most striking changes in the oviduct is the dilation of the ampulla during the heat period (Sobotta, 1895; Alden, 1942b; Burdick, Whitney and Emerson, 1942). In the rat several of the loops of the ampulla begin to dilate between the 3rd and 4th hours after the onset of heat, maximal dilation being about the time of ovulation (Odor, 1948). A constriction at the distal end of the dilated loop is frequently visible as a distinct blanched segment a few millimeters in length and in which the mucosal folds fit snugly against each other. This valve-like constriction is responsible for the retention of the oviducal fluids and eggs for at least 18 to 20 hours. Nothing is known of the nervous or hormonal mechanisms effecting the constriction, nor how spermatozoa cope with the stenosis as they proceed through the oviducts to reach the ampullae where sperm penetration occurs. The eggs of the mouse, rat, and hamster are fertilized in the dilated ampullae and remain there for approximately 20 to 30 hours after ovulation (Burdick, Whitney and Emerson, 1942; Odor and Blandau, 1951; Strauss, 1956). In the rabbit the freshly ovulated eggs pass through the upper half of the oviduct within 2 hours after ovulation and come to lie at the junction of the ampulla and isthmus. They remain here for the next day and a half (Greenwald, 1959).

Normally sperm penetration into the eggs of mammals takes place in the ampullae. There are, however, several interesting exceptions. In ferrets, tenrecs, and shrews spermatozoa somehow enter the ovarian follicles containing the ripe eggs and penetrate them before ovulation.

Both ciliary activity and peristalsis are involved in moving the eggs into the dilated ampullae. Burdick, Whitney and Emerson (1942) showed that ciliary action in the second loop of the oviduct in the mouse is sufficiently strong to rotate a whole cluster of eggs. Vigorous, localized peristaltic waves, spaced 12 to 16 seconds apart, seemed to be more important than the cilia in moving the eggs towards the entrance of the isthmus. Almost identical observations have been reported for the transport of eggs in the ampulla of the rat (Alden, 1942b; Odor, 1948).

As the time of ovulation approaches in the rat, the contractions of the dilated loops of the ampulla increase in amplitude more than in rate. The force of the aduterine contraction waves, measured by the rate of movement of particulate matter in the lumen, greatly exceeds that of the antiperistaltic activity. The contraction waves do not extend beyond the constriction at the uterine end of the dilated ampulla. Clumps of ovulated eggs, stained lycopodium spores, or ascaris eggs were moved vigorously backwards and forwards within the lumen of the tube and then forced gradually into the distal, most dilated loop. This vigorous activity subsided rapidly after ovulation and would have been missed completely if continuous observations had not been made. It would be important to determine more accurately the temporal relationship between ovulation, the dilation of the ampulla, and the changes in the pattern of muscular contractions of this area as compared with the remaining coils of the oviduct.

The passage of ova through the isthmus and intramural regions proceeds at a remarkably constant rate in various animals. The principal forces invoked are muscular or ciliary or both. Whatever the mechanism for propulsion may be, it is not necessarily similar for all species nor for any particular segment of the oviduct within a single animal (Sobotta, 1914; von Mikulicz-Radecki, 1925; von Mikulicz-Radecki and Nahmmacher, 1925, 1926; Kok, 1926; Alden, 1942b; Burdick, Whitney and Emerson, 1942; Odor, 1948).

On the basis of their studies on the behavior of the rabbit oviduct *in vitro*, Black and Asdell (1958) suggested that the movement of the luminal contents imparted by the circular muscles is ample to account for the transport of sperm and eggs through all of the oviduct except the isthmus. When the ova reach the isthmus they wait until sufficient fluid "surges down the tube to sweep them through the tubo-uterine junction" (Black and Asdell, 1959).

When the *in vivo* movements of oviducts are studied by short interval time-lapse cinematography one is impressed with the variety of contraction patterns exhibited at different times in the cycle. These observations re-emphasize the importance of applying a host of techniques to clarify the physiology of the oviducts.

The normal functional state of the oviducts is dependent on the maintenance of a delicate balance between estrogen and progesterone. In the mated mouse and rabbit, injections of estrogen result in tube-locking the ova for as long as 7 days after copulation, at which time the eggs degenerate (Burdick and Pincus, 1935; Burdick, Whitney and Pincus, 1937). By contrast, the injection of progesterone (Alden, 1942c) and induced superovulation (Wislocki and Snyder, 1933) accelerate the passage of eggs. Fertilized ova introduced into the oviducts of pseudopregnant rabbits will continue to develop normally but they are not transported into the uterus. Similarly the eggs of donor rabbits will not be transported if they are introduced into the oviducts of estrous females in which there is no luteal growth (Austin, 1949b). Alden (1942c) carefully removed the ovaries from the periovarial sacs in mated rats and observed the position and development of ova. Ovariectomy after ovulation did not prevent the normal development or transport of the eggs through the oviduct and, in fact, hastened their transport. Noyes, Adams and Walton (1959) ovariectomized rabbits and found that when freshly ovulated eggs from donor females were transplanted into the ampulla of the oviduct, the eggs were transported into the uterus in 14 hours.

There is very little pertinent information concerning the role of the cilia in moving the ova through the isthmus and intramural portions of the oviduct. Because of the thickness of the muscular wall in these areas it is difficult to observe the activity of the cilia in living specimens even by transillumination (Alden, 1942b). Also the number, size, and arrangement of the ciliated cells in the oviduct varies greatly from species to species. In addition, individual variations within a given species have been described throughout the reproductive cycle (Sobotta, 1914; Novak and Everett, 1928; Hartman, 1939; Burdick, Whitney and Emerson, 1942; Odor, 1948).

The earlier observations of Parker (1928, 1931) on the ciliary currents in the opened oviduct of the turtle, *Chrysemys picta*, have recently been repeated and extended by Yamada (1952) to the tortoise, *Clemmys japonicus*, and the frog, *Rana nigromaculata*. Yamada described a reverse ciliary movement beating toward the ovarian end of the oviduct in both animals. The rate of the descending current was about two times faster than that of the ascending current. In the frog the activities of the cilia cause the eggs to rotate as they descend. This may be an important mechanism for coating the eggs evenly with egg jelly. Crowell (1932) also described a tract of cilia beating toward the infundibulum in the oviducts of several species of lizards. It is generally assumed that during the period in which eggs are being transported the oviducts of most mammals undergo a secretory phase, but it is not known what proportion of the fluid within the lumen is contributed by the secretions of the oviduct, the lining of the periovarial sac when present, the follicular fluid, and the peritoneal fluid. Even less is known concerning the chemistry of these fluids. The rabbit, hare, opossum, and possibly the dog and horse present peculiar problems because of the specialized mucous secretions which coat the eggs and form the tertiary membranes.

The cytology and secretory activity of the epithelial lining of the oviduct have been the subjects of many studies in mammals, but there is little unanimity of opinion regarding (1) the changes in cellular morphology during the cycle, (2) the types of secretions elaborated, and (3) the cyclic variations of the particular secretory products which have been identified. In the oviducts of the pig and man both secretory and ciliated cells are present in the same proportions in all phases of the cycle. The height of the ciliated cells varies periodically, reaching a maximum during the time the eggs are passing through the tubes (Snyder, 1923, 1924; Novak and Everett, 1928; Bracher, 1957). Allen (1922), among others, expressed the view that there are no ciliated cells in the isthmus of the oviduct of the mouse or rat. This interpretation must be modified at least for the rat, in view of the findings of Alden (1942b), Kellog (1945), and Deane (1952) that both ciliated and secretory cells are present in the isthmus of this animal. Alden (1942b) and Deane (1952) were unable to observe cyclic variations in the histologic or histochemical picture of the oviducts of the rat. In the mouse the primary cyclic alteration of the epithelium is restricted to a slight but significant variation in the height of the ciliated cells ('Espinasse, 1935). In the sheep the majority of the secretory cells are confined to the ampulla, few being found in the isthmus (Hadek, 1953). Hadek describes a significant increase of secretory products in the lumen of the oviduct during estrus and early in the metestrum.

Studies of electron micrographs of ultrathin sections of oviducts of the mouse, man (Fawcett and Porter, 1954), rabbit (Borell, Nilsson, Wersäll and Westman, 1956; Nilsson, 1957), and rat (Odor, 1953; Nilsson, 1957, 1959) have demonstrated the similarity of the ciliary apparatus of epithelial cells in the various species. Of special interest was the presence of tiny, filiform projections on certain of the cells interspersed among the ciliated cells (Fig. 14.9). Similar projections are also found on the luminal surface of

what are probably the secretory cells. These processes do not have the longitudinal fibrils nor basal corpuscles that are essential components of cilia. A comparative study of the fine structure of the mammalian oviducts at carefully timed intervals and under different hormonal influences may lead to important observations of cyclic variations in both the ciliated and secretory cells (Borell, Nilsson and Westman, 1957).

The histochemical characteristics of the epithelium of the oviduct have been studied particularly by Deane (1952) and Milio (1960) in the rat, Hadek (1955) in the sheep, Fredricsson (1959b) in the rabbit, Fawcett and Wislocki (1950) and Fredricsson (1959a) in man. In the rat alkaline phosphatases occur on the ciliated borders of the cells of the isthmus, which suggests that this material has a role in the transfer of phosphorylated compounds. The rat differs from many other species in that glycogen could not be demonstrated in the epithelium of the oviduct at any time of the cycle. Quantities of esterase were present in the cells of all regions but only the cells of

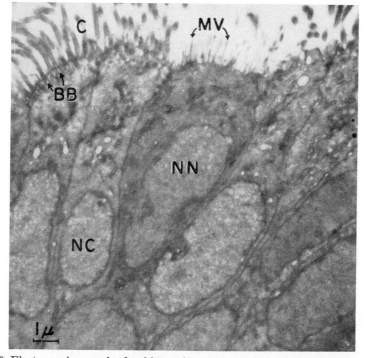

FIG. 14.9. Electron micrograph of a thin section of the oviduct of the rat. Note nonciliated cell with microvilli wedged between ciliated cells. *NN*, nucleus of nonciliated cell; *NC*, nucleus of ciliated cell; *BB*, basal bodies; *C*, cilia; *MV*, microvilli. (Courtesy of Dr. L. Odor.)

the fimbriated end contained lipid droplets. It is interesting as noted earlier that in the rat no histochemical changes could be demonstrated during the various phases of the estrous cycle. In the sheep an acid mucopolysaccharide is secreted by the oviduct most profusely at the time of ovulation (Hadek, 1955). Amylase is present in the secretions of the oviducts of man, cow, rabbit, and sheep in concentrations above that found in homologous sera. The significance of the relatively high concentrations of this enzyme in relation to the reproductive process is not clear (McGeachin, Hargan, Potter and Daus, 1958).

In man glycogen occurs not only in the ciliated cells but also in the nonciliated epithelia. Even though it is impossible to draw a firm conclusion regarding the correlation of glycogen in tubal epithelium with the menstrual cycle, it is generally believed that the maximal amount is present during the follicular phase (Fawcett and Wislocki, 1950).

It is generally assumed that the luminal fluids of the oviducts and cornua undergo cyclic changes, not only in amounts secreted, but also in their chemical composition. Such assumptions are based on very tenuous evidence; actually these fluids have received very little attention primarily because of the problems in obtaining adequate samples and in correlating the chemical and physical characteristics of the tract fluids with the endocrinologic and histochemical activity of the cells forming the stroma. With the development of a method for the volumetric collection of tubal fluid (Clewe and Mastroianni, 1960; Mastroianni, Beer, Shah and Clewe, 1960), accurate information with respect to the quantity and nature of the secretion may now be obtained. In the meantime we are dependent on the reports by Bishop (1956a, c) and Olds and Van Demark (1957a, b) who have recently summarized and extended the information available on the composition and endocrine control of luminal fluids in the female genital tracts of the rabbit and cow.

Observations on hydrogen ion concentrations of the fluids within the periovarial sac, the dilated ampullae, and uterine cornua in the rat have revealed that the fluids of the periovarial sac and oviduct have a pH of approximately 8.05 ± 0.18, whereas the mean pH of the cornual fluid is 7.74 ± 0.12 (Blandau, Jensen and Rumery, 1958). The fluids from the reproductive tract were significantly more basic than the peritoneal fluids. The results from biochemical studies on tubal fluid and ligation experiments reveal clearly that tubal fluid is the product of the oviduct itself and that contributions from the peritoneal cavity or uterus are either minimal or absent. Much more information is necessary to learn the nature of the molecular species present in the fluids of the reproductive tract. Free electrophoretic patterns of the cornual fluids of rats in heat demonstrate the presence of four major components in low concentrations. The leading major component has mobility values somewhat faster than albumen and the remaining components have mobilities within the range of normal serum proteins. Studies of cornual fluids by paper electrophoresis, however, suggest that the distribution of the proteins is not the same as in rat serum (Junge and Blandau, 1958). Previous observations on the washings of a sheep's oviduct examined 45 to 60 minutes after death showed a pH of 6 to 6.4 during the diestrum and 6.8 to 7.0 during estrus and the metestrum (Hadek, 1953). The pH of the uterine fluids in cattle has been reported as ranging from 5.8 to 7.0 with very minor changes during the cycle (Sergin, Kuznecov, Kozlova and Nesmejanova, 1940).

Respiratory differences between the epithelium of the ampulla and the infundibulum of the human oviduct have been studied by Kneer, Burger and Simmer (1952) and Mastroianni, Winternitz and Lowi (1958). They found an increase in the respiratory rate of both segments during the follicular phase, but not during the secretory phase. During all phases of the cycle the oxygen consumption of the epithelium of the ampulla was consistently higher than that of the epithelium of the infundibulum. Bishop (1956b) measured oxygen tension in the lumen of the rabbit oviduct by electrochemical techniques and found that the luminal environment is aerobic and that the oxygen tension is in equilibrium with that of the

TABLE 14.4

Volume of fluid secreted by the doubly ligated rabbit oviduct during a three-day interval

(After D. W. Bishop, Am. J. Physiol., **187**, 347–352, 1956a.)

Condition of Animal	Number of Tracts Ligated	Volume of Tubal Secretion	
		Range	Average
		ml.	*ml.*
Estrogen-dominated..	18	1.3–4.5	2.62
Progestational.......	11	0.3–2.3	1.10
Castrate (9-day).....	8	0.0–2.1	0.80

arterioles within the endometrium.

Finally, it has been established that secretions of the oviduct undergo changes in response to hormonal variations (Table 14.4). Bishop (1956a) studied the rates of fluid production and the secretion pressures in rabbit oviducts under a variety of experimental conditions. Ligatures were secured around the uterotubal junctions. Polyethylene tubes were then inserted into the fimbriated ampullae and securely tied, and manometric changes in fluid pressures were recorded continuously for periods up to 52 hours. The mean rates of oviduct secretion are recorded in Table 14.4 and the maximal secretory pressures graphically in Fig. 14.10. The data indicate that the oviducts of rabbits exhibit an active process of secretion against a gradient. The variations in secretory pressures are related to changes in hormonal activity in the normal female or to hormonally induced responses in the castrate animal. Corner (1928b) showed that if the ovaries of rabbits are removed 4 to 8 hours after ovulation, all of the eggs are transported to the uterus, but that the blastocysts die soon after entering the uterine cavity. He concluded that the presence of actively secreting corpora lutea is essential for the continued nutrition of the free blastocyst. Westman (1930) also removed the ovaries of rabbits 12 hours after mating. All the ova recovered from the oviducts 72 hours later showed some signs of degeneration. Subsequently Westman, Jorpes and Widström (1931) cauterized the corpora lutea of mated rabbits and recorded a degeneration of the tubal ova similar to that

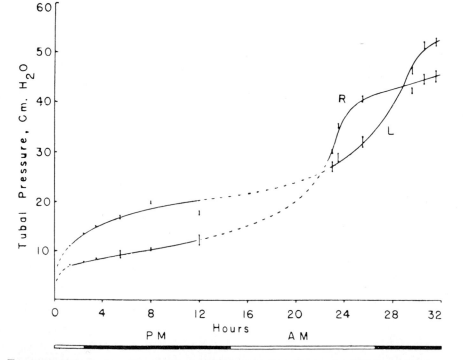

Fig. 14.10. Tubular secretion pressure of right and left oviducts of rabbit under Dial anesthesia. Vertical bars indicate pulsations due to visceral movements at the time of reading. (After D. W. Bishop, Am. J. Physiol., **187**, 347–352, 1956.)

observed after ovariectomy. Injections of corpus luteum extract into the operated animals prevented degeneration of the ova.

Current investigations on fluids of the rabbit oviduct have shown that the secretions of the upper, fimbriated third are necessary for normal enlargement of the blastocyst (Bishop, unpublished data). The oviducts of pregnant females and castrates who have received progesterone secrete copious quantities of fluids. If these fluids are prevented from entering the uterus about the 5th day, by double ligation, the blastocysts remain small and do not reach their normal size by the 8th day or the time of implantation.

If fertilized ova of the Muridae are prevented from entering the uterus, either by ligation of the oviduct or by the administration of hormones which inhibit the normal propulsive mechanism of the tube, the eggs develop to the blastocyst stage before degeneration begins (Burdick, Whitney and Pincus, 1937; Burdick, Emerson and Whitney, 1940; Alden, 1942d). The occurrence of tubal pregnancies, especially in the human female, indicates that under some circumstances development may continue within the oviduct beyond the stage of normal implantation.

IV. Fertilization and Implantation

Fertilization involves the penetration of a fully developed egg by a motile, mature spermatozoon, and the subsequent formation, growth, and karyogamy of the sperm and egg nuclei. An integral part of this process is the physical act of penetration of the spermatozoon into the "karyocytoplasm" which results in the "activation" of the egg. The classical experiments of Loeb (1913) in the invertebrates and Rugh (1939) in amphibia have shown that "activation" does not depend on a specific property of the spermatozoon, but may be effected by chemical, mechanical, or physical stimuli (see also Wilson, 1925). Unfertilized mammalian eggs may likewise be activated by a variety of stimuli, but ordinarily do not proceed far in embryonic development (Pincus and Enzmann, 1936, Chang, 1954, 1957, in the rabbit; Thibault, 1949, Austin, 1951a, in the rabbit, rat, and sheep).

Although Barry (1843) was the first investigator to observe a spermatozoon within the mammalian egg, no detailed description of the process of fertilization appeared until Van Beneden published his observations on the rabbit in 1875. Since then, numerous investigations on the cytology and physiology of fertilization in the mammal have formed a large volume of literature (Van der Stricht, 1910, the bat; Sobotta, 1895, Lams and Doorme, 1908, Gresson, 1948, the mouse; Rubaschkin, 1905, Lams, 1913, the guinea pig; Gregory, 1930, Pincus and Enzmann, 1932, the rabbit; Tafani, 1889, Sobotta and Burckhard, 1910, Kirkham and Burr, 1913, Huber, 1915, Kremer, 1924, Gilchrist and Pincus, 1932, MacDonald and Long, 1934, Austin, 1951a, b, Blandau and Odor, 1952, Austin and Bishop, 1957, the rat; Van der Stricht, 1910, Hill and Tribe, 1924, the cat; Mainland, 1930, the ferret; Van der Stricht, 1923, the dog; Pearson and Enders, 1943, the fox; Wright, 1948, the weasel; Hamilton and Laing, 1946, Piykianen, 1958, the cow; Amoroso, Griffiths and Hamilton, 1942, the goat; and others). The specific point of emphasis and the degree of completeness of these studies vary widely and in a number of instances only discontinuous and isolated stages were observed and reported.

Certain of the many changes occurring during the process of sperm penetration and fertilization can be studied best in fixed material properly sectioned and stained. Many features, however, can be observed most clearly only in the living egg. Obviously one way of studying fertilization phenomena is to look at them. But microscopic observations on the living egg even with the newer phase-contrast objectives and other techniques have been disappointing to many because of the problems in establishing and maintaining an environment in which the processes can take place. There is such an array of observations of sperm penetration and fertilization in the invertebrates that there has been a tendency to translate these observations directly to the mammalian egg. It is becoming increasingly clear that there is not necessarily a common denominator for these vital processes and that they vary widely. The interesting differences in the shape of the heads of sper-

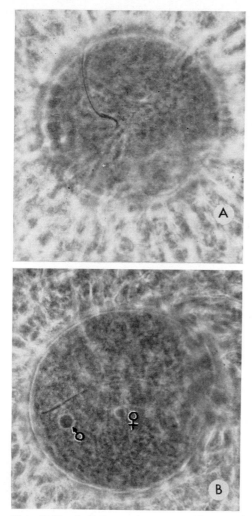

FIG. 14.11. A living rat ovum with cumulus oophorus intact and a fertilizing spermatozoon in the ooplasm (A). B. Living rat ovum with cumulus intact and showing the early development of the male and female pronuclei. × 450.

matozoa from species to species alone may indicate the existence of a variety of mechanisms for penetrating the various barriers encountered before the vitellus can be entered.

Quantitative data on the temporal relationship between ovulation, penetration of sperm, and syngamy are lacking for most mammals. Before this information can be had for any animal, the time of ovulation must be easily and accurately determinable, the rate of ascent of spermatozoa to the site of fertilization must be known, and the rate

of sperm passage through the cumulus oophorus, zona pellucida, and vitelline membrane must be established. Information of this sort is now available for several species, particularly that obtained by the use of phase-contrast microscopy and time-lapse cinemicrophotography in the study of living eggs. These methods have supplemented the earlier observations and made possible a more complete account of the process of fertilization (Austin and Smiles, 1948; Odor and Blandau, 1951; Austin, 1951b, 1952a).

A. THE CUMULUS OOPHORUS AND SPERM PENETRATION

The number of layers of cells and the compactness of the cumulus oophorus of newly ovulated eggs varies greatly in different animals. Cumulus cells and the mucopolysaccharide matrix enclosing them have been reported as sparse or absent in the tubal eggs of the sheep (Assheton, 1898; McKenzie and Allen, 1933; Clark, 1934), the roe deer (Bischoff, 1854), the cow (Hartman, Lewis, Miller and Swett, 1931), the pig (Corner and Amsbaugh, 1917), the horse (Hamilton and Day, 1945), and the opossum (Hartman, 1928). In other species such as the rat, mouse, hamster, mink, rabbit, monkey, and man (Boyd and Hamilton, 1952), many layers of granulosa cells form the cumulus oophorus. Furthermore, in certain rodents the ovulated eggs clump together within the dilated ampullae of the oviducts, greatly increasing the number of cell layers and viscous gels the spermatozoa must penetrate in order to reach the more centrally lying eggs. If attempts are made to remove the cells forming the cumulus of newly ovulated eggs by pulling them away with fine needles, the tenaciousness of this investment is impressive and one wonders how a spermatozoon ever reaches the vitellus (Fig. 14.11).

In the preovulatory follicle the cells of the cumulus oophorus become loosened from the follicular wall and somewhat separated one from another. This is seen most spectacularly in the guinea pig and cat (Myers, Young, and Dempsey, 1936; Dawson and Friedgood, 1940). The ovum and enveloping cumulus cells have frequently been observed to lie free within the antrum before the follicle ruptures. Although only limited observations have been made, some reports indicate that the cumulus oophorus in the preovulatory follicles cannot be dispersed as readily by the methods that are effective in ovulated eggs (Farris, 1947; Shettles, 1953). It is important to determine what chemical or physical alterations occur in the intercellular cement substances of the cumulus during the time the follicle is ripening and to learn why this should differ in the cells surrounding the egg from other similar cells lining the walls of the follicle.

The existence of a "cumulus-dispersing" factor in mammals was brought to light by the experiments of Gilchrist and Pincus (1932), Yamane (1935), Pincus (1936), and Pincus and Enzmann (1936). These investigators demonstrated that either living sperm suspensions or sperm extracts of the rabbit, rat, and mouse rapidly disperse the cells of the cumulus oophorus of tubal ova. Yamane (1930) inferred that the presence of a proteolytic enzyme in the spermatozoa was responsible for both follicle-cell dispersion and "activation" of the egg to produce the second polar body.

In a series of carefully controlled experiments Pincus (1936) showed that a heat-labile substance was present in sperm extracts which caused follicle-cell dispersion, but that this substance would not effect second polar body formation. Pincus demonstrated further that the rate of cell dispersion in vitro was roughly proportional to the number of spermatozoa in the suspension. It was discovered later that the "cumulus-cell-dispersing substance" was the enzyme hyaluronidase (Duran-Reynolds, 1929). The enzyme depolymerizes and hydrolyzes the hyaluronic acid cement substance binding the granulosa cells together. This discovery at first seemed to provide a happy solution to the problem of how spermatozoa penetrate the cumulus oophorus (McClean and Rowlands, 1942; Fekete and Duran-Reynolds, 1943; Leonard and Kurzrok, 1945). Numerous observations quickly demonstrated that the testes and spermatozoa of mammals are the richest sources of animal hyaluronidase. The enzyme first appears in the testes when spermatogenesis begins in the pubertal animal and before

fully developed spermatozoa are present in the tubules (Riisfeldt, 1949).

It became clear that there is a proportional relationship in vitro between sperm count and the hyaluronidase concentration; further, that the enzyme is associated with the spermatozoa and not with the seminal plasma (Werthessen, Berman, Greenberg and Gargill, 1945; Kurzrok, Leonard and Conrad, 1946; Swyer, 1947a; Michelson, Haman and Koets, 1949). Hyaluronidase concentration per sperm is highest in the bull and rabbit, somewhat less in the boar and man, still lower in the dog, and very low in birds and reptiles (Swyer, 1947a, b; Mann, 1954). Observations on the in vitro dispersal of granulosa cells by hyaluronidase suggested that large numbers of spermatozoa are necessary in the semen in order to provide a sufficient concentration of the enzyme.

The in vitro observations of Pincus and Enzmann (1936) strengthened this assumption when they demonstrated that a minimum number of 20,000 spermatozoa per cubic millimeter of rabbit semen is necessary if the cumulus cells surrounding one ovulated egg are to be dispersed. Such observations seemed to explain the necessity of the "sperm swarms" described in the oviducts of mated rabbits. The swarms created and maintained a sufficiently high concentration of the enzyme to permit the denudation of the eggs so that certain of the spermatozoa could approach and penetrate the zona pellucida.

Attempts were then made to increase the fertilizing capacity of a subnormal number of spermatozoa by adding hyaluronidase extracts to semen suspensions used for artificial inseminations. In 1944, Rowlands proposed that such a procedure had increased the fertilizing capacity of rabbit spermatozoa. This could not be confirmed by Chang (1950b); indeed, it was observed that seminal plasma in which the hyaluronidase had been inactivated by heat was as effective as untreated plasma. Kurzrok, Leonard and Conrad (1946) outlined a method for adding bull hyalurodinase to oligospermic specimens of human semen which was to be used for artificial insemination. This method was employed in the treatment of sterility and reported to have been notably successful.

Many further attempts to demonstrate the therapeutic value of hyaluronidase in mammalian infertility have met with failure (see Siegler, 1947; Tafel, Titus and Wightman, 1948; Johnston and Mixner, 1950). The generally poor results obtained by the addition of hyaluronidase to semen introduced into the vagina or uterus by artificial insemination may be explained by the later experiments of Leonard, Perlman and Kurzrok (1947), which conclusively demonstrated that hyaluronidase inserted into the lower reproductive tract is not transported to the oviducts. The systematic studies of Austin (1949b) and Chang (1947, 1951a) revealed that in the rabbit only 100 to 1000 spermatozoa reach the site of fertilization. Even though in one experiment 600,000,000 spermatozoa were artificially introduced into the female reproductive tract, only approximately 2000 of them were found in the tubes. An even smaller number (10 to 50) have been shown to reach the ampulla of the rat oviduct at the time of sperm penetration (Blandau and Odor, 1949; Moricard and Bossu, 1951).

It is probably correct to assume that any hyaluronidase which reaches the cumulus at the time of semination is transported by relatively few spermatozoa. Although the enzyme has not been localized in the sperm itself, it is assumed that it is an integral part of the cell and is liberated in a relatively localized region as the spermatozoon makes its way through the cement substance. The spermatozoon is remarkably permeable in that such large molecules as cytochrome c or hyaluronidase can detach themselves from the sperm cell and pass into the extracellular environment by the so-called "leakage" phenomenon (Mann, 1954).

In vitro tests have shown that the enzyme hyaluronidase diffuses into the suspending fluid at a definite rate depending on the type of medium and the temperature. New formation of the enzyme by spermatozoa does not seem to occur (Meyer and Rapport, 1952). The possibility exists that the enzyme may be able to exert its action while still bound to the sperm cell.

A recent development in the study of hyaluronidase action and its possible role in fertilization has been the attempt to utilize certain inhibitors of the enzyme as systemic contraceptives. Among the naturally occurring and extraneous inhibitors may be listed heavy metals, heparin, quinones, "rehibin" or trigentisic acid, and antihyaluronidase antibodies, as well as a nonspecific, electrophoretically identifiable serum factor (Leonard and Kurzrok, 1945; Beiler and Martin, 1947; Glick and Moore, 1948; Meyer and Rapport, 1952; Hahn and Frank, 1953; Parkes, 1953). Many of these substances are highly active inhibitors of hyaluronidase and may reduce or prevent fertilization when added to semen *in vitro* before artificial insemination. Attempts to inhibit fertilization by giving these substances orally or by injection have not been repeatedly successful, but several derivatives of hyaluronic acid obtained by acetylation or nitration and added to rabbit semen *in vitro* seemed to have inhibited dispersion of follicle cells and to have impaired fertility (Pincus, Pirie and Chang, 1948).

It has now been demonstrated repeatedly that ova in the ampulla of the oviduct may have been penetrated by spermatozoa without evident dispersal of the granulosa cells (Lewis and Wright, 1935; Leonard, Perlman and Kurzrok, 1947; Austin, 1948b; Bowman, 1951; Odor and Blandau, 1951, in the rat; Chang, 1950b, in the rabbit; Amoroso, personal communication, in the cat). Again, dog spermatozoa do not contain hyaluronidase yet they are capable of penetrating the many layers of granulosa cells comprising the cumulus. Inasmuch as a generalized dispersal of the cells of the cumulus does not occur at the time of sperm penetration, the pendulum has swung to the present view that the individual spermatozoon carries sufficient enzyme to make a path for itself through the cumulus layer and the gel matrix. If rat spermatozoa are added to slides containing cumulus masses from freshly ovulated eggs and their movement through the cumulus matrix observed with phase objectives, one is led to conclude that an intact cumulus is essential if sperm penetration is to be successful, *i.e.*, the cumulus may act as a base against which the sperm flagellum can push as it moves forward towards the zona pellucida. The spermatozoa may move through the cumulus with broad sweeps of their flagella and at a rate of forward progression which makes it difficult to conceive of the depolymerization of the matrix to form a tunnel for the sperm. It must be concluded therefore that the role of hyaluronidase in sperm penetration is unknown and that much more critical evaluation needs to be directed into this area.

Even though the outer layers of the cumulus oophorus of ovulated eggs *in vitro* may be removed readily by hyaluronidase, the corona radiata may not be dispersed with the same rapidity, especially in eggs treated immediately after ovulation. The basis for this difference lies in the fact that the cells forming the corona radiata send polar, cytoplasmic extensions into the zona pellucida, thereby anchoring them firmly, although temporarily. In the newly ovulated eggs of the rat, hamster, and mouse the corona cells cannot be removed mechanically without breaking the zona pellucida. It is only after the eggs have been in contact with spermatozoa or have resided in the oviducts for a number of hours that the corona cells may be either brushed off the zona pellucida or drop away spontaneously.

Swyer (1947b) and Chang (1951b) suggested that the coronal cells are removed mechanically by being more or less brushed off by the ciliary and muscular activity of the oviduct. This may be true for human and rabbit eggs, but in the rat, mouse, and hamster in which the eggs lie in the dilated ampulla, and thus at a distance from the wall of the oviduct, it would seem appropriate to assume that factors other than mechanical are involved in dispersing the corona. If rat eggs are examined approximately 24 hours after ovulation, one can observe that their zonae are completely free of the coronal cells, but that they may be still enclosed in an abundant viscous matrix. It appears that the corona cells gradually retract their cytoplasmic extensions from the zonal canaliculi.

Interesting observations can be made by growing freshly ovulated eggs and their attached corona cells in tissue culture. Time-lapse cinematography reveals that the cells forming the cumulus and corona, although alive, have lost much of their vitality. The surfaces of the cells undergo peculiar bubbling movements. This "bubbling" is similar to that described in cells in the late stages of cell division or in cells which are about to die. Changes in the fluidity of the cell surface apparently account for the bubbling which continues for hours in favorable preparations. This phenomenon accounts for the retraction of the cell processes from the zona and the gradual dispersal of the cells. That the cumulus and coronal cells lose their vitality rather quickly after ovulation is shown further by their very poor growth in tissue culture compared with that of similar cells removed from young follicles.

The rate of the dispersal of cumulus cells after ovulation varies in different animals. In mated rabbits the eggs are completely denuded of cumulus and corona cells 4 to 6 hours after ovulation. After sterile matings, however, the cumulus and corona are not dispersed until 7 to 8 hours after ovulation (Pincus, 1930; Chang, 1951b; Braden, 1952). In the rat there is relatively little change, either in the cumulus mass or in the corona cells for many hours after ovulation and fertilization (Blandau, 1952). Shettles (1953) suggested that in addition to hyaluronidase there may be a tubal factor which is important in the removal of the cumulus oophorus in the human egg. He found that hyaluronidase had little effect in removing the cumulus cells in ovarian eggs, but, if bits of homologous tubal mucosa were added, the cumulus oophorus was dispersed readily.

In spite of the formidable barriers interposed by the cumulus and corona, they do not prevent the entrance of sperm into the egg; in fact, as suggested earlier, their presence seems to be important in some animals if penetration is to be effected (Fig. 14.11). Chang (1952a) demonstrated that, in the rabbit at least, there is a relationship between the loss of the granulosa cells and fertilizability. He counted the spermatozoa in eggs fixed at different intervals after ovulation and found that the greatest number entered the eggs between the 2nd and 4th hours. Once the denudation of the eggs is completed (approximately 6 hours after ovulation), penetration of spermatozoa no longer occurs, despite the presence of adequate numbers in the environs. It is important to remember that the deposition of the mucous coat in the rabbit ovum may limit its fertilizable life (Pincus, 1930; Hammond, 1934). The actual time after ovulation that mucous deposition begins has been variously reported as 5, 6, 8, and 14 hours (Pincus, 1930; Hammond, 1934; Chang, 1951b; Braden, 1952). It remains to be determined whether failure of sperm penetration into the rabbit egg after 6 hours' sojourn in the ampulla is related to the loss of the cumulus, the deposition of the mucous coat, or to a specific change in the physical characteristics of the zona pellucida itself.

B. THE ZONA PELLUCIDA AND SPERM PENETRATION

The general appearance and properties of the zona pellucida were described earlier. The manner whereby spermatozoa penetrate the zona pellucida and the conditions influencing this process are poorly understood. Despite the numerous attempts to fertilize mammalian ova *in vitro*, only a few investigators have described isolated stages in the process of sperm penetration through the zona pellucida or into the vitellus. Shettles (1953) described in some detail the behavior of a human spermatozoon passing through the zona pellucida of an isolated follicular ovum. As the spermatozoon became attached to the zona it rotated on its longitudinal axis. As the head was observed in focus in the equatorial plane, the rate of rotation decreased until, by the time the tip of the head was midway in the zona, the front and side views of the head could be seen to alternate. The progression of the head through the zona pellucida was intermittent until only the tail lay within it. The head and body then underwent several intermittent side-to-side, jerky movements and finally slipped into the perivitelline space. It required 18 minutes for a spermatozoon to traverse the zona pellucida. Duryee (1954) described the consistency of the zona pellucida of the human follicular egg as jelly-like, much less

tough and resilient than the tubal egg. It would be interesting to know whether these differences in the physical properties of the zonae of ovarian and tubal eggs in the human affect the manner of spermatozoon penetration.

On two occasions Pincus (1930) found rabbit ova with the heads of spermatozoa partially embedded within the zonae, and described the slow yet perceptible forward progress until the heads penetrated the vitelli. Pincus believed that the flagellae did not enter the ooplasm but were left behind in the zonae pellucidae.

There is no sound evidence of a predetermined pathway or "micropyle" in the zona pellucida of mammals. In the few instances where attention has been paid to this matter, spermatozoa seem to be able to penetrate the zona at any point on its surface. A small elliptical slit with the sperm tail partially projecting through it has been noted in the zona pellucida of living fertilized eggs of the rat, guinea pig, and Libyan jird (Austin, 1951b; Austin and Bishop, 1958). The slits in the zona are not seen in eggs which do not contain spermatozoa. It is usually possible to discern as many slits as there are sperm within the perivitelline space. The general appearance of the slit and the manner in which the perforatorium of the sperm head attacks the zona pellucida *in vitro* creates the impression that the zona may be fractured by the spermatozoon. Similar slits can be made by fracturing rat zonae with tungsten needles sharpened electrolytically to several micra in thickness.

Recently Austin and Bishop (1958) have presented observations suggesting that the acrosome is lost as the sperm passes through the female reproductive tract and postulate that the perforatorium elaborates an enzyme which depolymerizes the zona pellucida in a very restricted zone as the sperm moves through it.

Discussions on the mechanisms involved in sperm penetration of the zona have implicated a variety of conditions and substances as being of importance in changing the physical characteristics of the zona in the localized area of contact. As mentioned earlier, the zona pellucida can be softened or disintegrated in rat and rabbit eggs by buffers with pH values from 3 to 5 (Hall, 1935; Harter, 1948; Braden, 1952). Various reducing agents such as glutathione and cysteine in Tyrode's solution cause rapid dissolution of the zona. Oxidizing agents such as the hydrogen peroxide which is produced by sperm (Tosic and Walton, 1946) are particularly efficacious in removing this membrane. Several investigators favor the possibility that a specific mucolytic enzyme, "zona lysin" (Austin and Bishop, 1958) may be secreted by the sperm as it makes contact with the zona pellucida (Leblond, 1950; Austin, 1951b). It seems likely that the passage of the spermatozoon through the zona pellucida may occur in a variety of ways in different animals. Too few observations have been made to significantly implicate any of the physical, chemical, or mechanical mechanisms suggested for sperm penetration of the zona pellucida in the mammalian egg.

It has been suggested that the physical properties of the zona pellucida in the dog, hamster, and sheep are altered after the first sperm passes through it and enters the vitellus. It is postulated that a substance is secreted by the vitellus which "tans" the zona so that additional sperm cannot penetrate it (Braden, Austin and David, 1954). Smithberg (1953) reported that the zonae pellucidae of the unfertilized mouse eggs are more readily removed by proteolytic enzymes than those of fertilized eggs.

Chang and Hunt (1956) tested the effects of a variety of proteolytic enzymes on the zonae pellucidae of fertilized and unfertilized eggs of rabbits, rats, and hamsters. Even though none of the fertilized hamster eggs contained more than one sperm, there was no evidence that the zonae pellucidae of the fertilized eggs were more resistant to digestion than those of unfertilized eggs. In contrast Austin (1956c) reported that the zonae pellucidae of fertilized hamster eggs were dissolved more quickly by trypsin than those of unfertilized eggs. Blockage of the zona pellucida in the rat and rabbit egg is not as definite, yet there are indications that fertilized and unfertilized eggs react differently to proteolytic enzymes.

In many animals the sequence of the re-

productive processes are arranged in such a manner that spermatozoa must wait at the site of fertilization for several hours before ovulation occurs and the eggs have arrived in the ampullae. If freshly ejaculated spermatozoa of rats or rabbits are transferred directly to oviducts containing newly ovulated eggs, relatively few if any of the eggs will be fertilized. If, however, spermatozoa are introduced into the genital tract several hours before the expected time of ovulation, they undergo some kind of change by which they gain the capacity to fertilize eggs on contact. Chang (1951) was the first to report this phenomenon in the rabbit and termed it "development." In the same year, Austin (1951) working in Australia independently described the phenomenon and called it "capacitation." Chang (1959a) further approached this question by artificially inseminating rabbits that acted as "incubator" hosts. He subsequently withdrew sperm samples at stated intervals and injected them into the oviducts of rabbits that had just ovulated. Chang concluded that 6 hours of such "host incubation" was necessary before rabbit sperm could fertilize the majority of ova ovulated. Similar observations by Austin (1951), Noyes (1953), and Noyes, Walton and Adams (1958) on rats indicated that approximately 3 hours is the time required for capacitation in this animal. There has been some success in the intraperitoneal insemination of the rabbit doe 8 hours before ovulation with sperm which had been washed several times in a sodium citrate buffer solution (Hadek, 1958). Attempts to induce capacitation *in vitro* by exposing rabbit spermatozoa for varying lengths of time to a variety of physiologic solutions and solutions containing endometrial tissue have been largely unsuccessful (Chang, 1955b). Partial capacitation has been reported when rabbit spermatozoa are incubated in diverticula of the bladder and colon which had been created surgically (Noyes, Walton and Adams, 1958). Capacitation was also effected when spermatozoa were stored in the seminal vesicles and anterior chamber of the eye. There is no evidence as yet which favors the need for capacitation in the mouse and guinea pig during normal mating. According to Austin and Bishop (1958) there are changes in the optical properties of the acrosomes of rabbit, rat, and hamster spermatozoa as they traverse the female reproductive tract. When a sperm reaches the egg in the ampulla, the acrosome is detached, exposing the perforatorium. Austin and Bishop propose that the acrosome is the carrier of the enzyme hyaluronidase which allows the sperm to depolymerize the hyaluronic acid jelly of the cumulus oophorus. The exposed perforatorium, then, may be a carrier of a lysin which may alter the physical characteristics of the zona pellucida so that the sperm may pass through it. There has been much speculation on the importance of capacitation in fertilization, but there is little significant evidence to support the various theories proposed (Chang, 1955a, b, and 1959b; Strauss, 1956).

C. SPERM-EGG INTERACTING SUBSTANCES

The phenomenon of agglutination by "egg water" has been observed and described many times for the spermatozoa of echinoderms, annelids, molluscs, ascidians, cyclostomes, fish, and amphibia (Rothschild, 1956; Tyler, 1957). The compound in the egg water responsible for the effect is derived from a jelly-like membrane which is secreted on the egg by the follicular cells. On ovulation the jelly gradually dissolves in sea water and composes the fertilizin first described by Lillie (1919). Experiments with invertebrate eggs have demonstrated that fertilizin is responsible for the specific sperm-agglutinating power and for the initial specific adherence of the sperm to the egg. One of the interesting chapters in biology has been the attempt to characterize the biologic and chemical properties of these interacting substances.

Whether sperm-egg interacting substances are present in the fluids forming the environment of ovulated mammalian eggs has been very little investigated. Recently Bishop and Tyler (1956) and Thibault and Dauzier (1960) have reported the presence of fertilizin in the eggs of rabbits, mice, and cows. The reaction was found to be primarily species specific and its source is believed to be the zona pellucida.

Much more experimental testing must be done to amplify knowledge in the field of interacting substances of mammalian eggs and spermatozoa.

D. SPERM PENETRATION OF THE VITELLINE MEMBRANE

The penetration of a spermatozoon into the ooplasm *in vitro* has been observed on so few occasions in mammals that it is not yet possible to give an accurate account of this phenomenon. Pincus (1930) records a slight bulging of the ooplasm in rabbit eggs at the point where the head of the sperm made contact with the vitelline membrane. Because of the opacity of the egg cytoplasm, no further progress of the head could be observed. Studying rat, mice, and hamster eggs, Austin (1951b) and Austin and Braden (1956) described a more or less passive penetration of the ooplasm by the fertilizing spermatozoon, as if the ooplasm "pulled" the entire sperm into its substance or "phagocytized" it. Austin (1951b) and Austin and Bishop (1957) ascribed some peculiar property to the head of the sperm which results in its being "absorbed" into the vitellus. The investigations of Dan (1950) on the changes in the acrosome of the sea urchin at the time of sperm penetration of the egg have an interesting bearing on this problem. She believed that as the spermatozoon swims actively through the jelly layer of the egg, the acrosome responds to the chemical stimulation of the egg jelly by a localized breakdown of its membrane. By the time the spermatozoon reaches the vitelline membrane a few seconds later, it carries at its tip a labile mass of lysin with which it effects penetration of the ooplasm.

The observations of Austin are at variance with those made by others also in the rat and in which it appeared that ooplasmic penetration was accomplished primarily by the activities of the flagellum of the fertilizing sperm (Blandau and Odor, 1952). Although discontinuous, the forward progression of the spermatozoon into the ooplasm seemed to depend on a propulsive type of undulating movement of the tail which forced the head forward a distance of 10 to 20 μ at a time. While that portion of the flagellum within the ooplasm was retarded in its amplitude of motion by the viscosity of the egg cytoplasm, that which was still in the perivitelline space lashed about vigorously. These observations are similar to those described by Shettles (1960) in the human. As mentioned earlier, the technical problems in observing *in vitro* fertilization will no doubt be solved when the molecular species of the fluids forming the normal egg environment is known.

There is no specific information with respect to the nature of the vitelline membrane of the mammalian egg or to the changes it may undergo on sperm entry. It would be desirable to know whether the vitelline membrane undergoes modification after penetration by the fertilizing spermatozoon. An interesting procedure for measuring the solidification of the egg membranes of salmonid eggs has been described recently by Zotin (1958). Even though there is no clear evidence of a comparable phenomenon in mammalian eggs, some factor appears to control the number of spermatozoa which enter the vitellus. Cortical granules have been described in the unfertilized hamster egg which disappear on fertilization, but apparently they are not associated with the block of polyspermy (Austin, 1956a). Quantitative data are necessary to clarify the relationship between the number of spermatozoa which may enter the periovarial space, the rate of the "tanning" reaction of the zona, if such a phenomenon exists, and the reaction of the perivitelline membrane which blocks the entry of further spermatozoa.

Shrinkage of the vitellus after sperm penetration has been described in the rabbit and rat (Gilchrist and Pincus, 1932; Pincus and Enzmann, 1932), but a comparable shrinkage can be noted in unfertilized ova recovered from the oviduct several hours after ovulation, and thus shrinkage *per se* cannot be used as a criterion for sperm penetration. The shrinkage of the vitellus is related in some way to changes in the vitelline membrane because the numerous microvilli present in the young ovarian egg have disappeared and the total surface of the egg has been greatly reduced.

E. FERTILIZATION *IN VITRO*

During the past century one of the most challenging and frustrating problems was the attempt to fertilize mammalian ova *in vitro* and to follow their cleavage. Even though several successes were recorded, it could not be maintained unequivocally until the recent work of Chang (1959a) that sperm penetration has been accomplished and that the divisions of the eggs noted were the result of fertilization rather than of an "activation" of the egg instituted by some other factor in the environment, or just plain fragmentation.

Relatively little has been added to our understanding of the mechanism of sperm penetration into the ooplasm since the extensive experiments of Long (1912) in which he attempted to fertilize rat and mice eggs *in vitro*. He described penetration of the follicle cells and observed the sinuous movements of the sperm as they advanced within the cumulus. The role of the spermatozoa in the dispersal of the granulosa cells was noted and this was interpreted as being due to the lashing activities of the sperm flagellum. Long also described the formation of the second polar body in eggs which had been placed in sperm suspensions. Polar body formation began within 2 hours and abstriction was completed within 4 hours of the time of immersion. Unfortunately, his description leaves one uncertain as to whether penetration by the sperm was actually observed or merely confirmed by sectioned material.

Some success with fertilization *in vitro* was also achieved by Pincus (1930, 1939), Pincus and Enzmann (1934, 1935), Venge (1953), and Thibault and Dauzier (1960) in their extensive experiments with both ovarian and tubal eggs of rabbits. These investigators described the abstriction of the second polar body, the shrinkage of the vitellus, the penetration of the zona by spermatozoa partially embedded within it, and the presence of spermatozoa in the perivitelline space in fixed and stained preparations. Transplantation of living eggs into the oviducts of pseudopregnant rabbits, following the addition of sperm to the eggs, resulted in the birth of live young possessing the genetic characteristics of coat color which had been used as markers. It is suggested in a later report (Chang and Pincus, 1951) that the results "may have been due to adherent sperm effecting fertilization in the fallopian tubes."

The mammalian egg may be "activated" to various degrees according to the balance of thermal, osmotic, and chemical factors in its environment. Thus eggs "activated" by being placed in a cold environment may form double nuclei which closely resemble normal pronuclei (Thibault, 1947a, b, 1948). The eggs of the opossum, rat, mouse, hamster, mink, and ferret also will show varying degrees of "activation" and may be difficult to differentiate from normally cleaving ova (Smith, 1925; Chang, 1950a; Austin, 1951a, 1956c; Blandau, 1952). Attempts to fertilize the timed human ovarian ova recovered by Corner, Farris and Corner (1950), were unsuccessful. Rock and Menkin (1944) and Menkin and Rock (1948) also attempted to achieve fertilization of human ovarian eggs in vitro and reported several successes. The first egg recovered from a large follicle was cultured in the patient's serum for 27 hours. It was then placed in a washed suspension of sperm for 1 hour and observed continuously. Penetration of the ovum by sperm was not observed. When the same egg was inspected 40.5 hours later, it consisted of two blastomeres each measuring 86 μ in diameter. A second egg treated in much the same manner also was found to contain two blastomeres 45 hours after exposure to spermatozoa. The stage of maturation of these ovarian eggs could not be determined and it is assumed that the meiotic divisions occurred in vitro. Since the fertilizable life of the human ovum is unknown, and there is no specific information on sperm penetration, the role of the flagellum in semination, pronuclei formation, karyogamy, and the rate of cleavage, it is clear that the true identification of a fertilized human ovum has not been achieved. In the rat, for example, one can find unfertilized cleaved ova which on first inspection closely resemble fertilized eggs even containing modified nuclei or nuclear fragments. When examined in detail the fragmenting eggs do not contain the flagellae of spermatozoa, a positive indication that penetration has not been accomplished (compare 2 and 3 in Figure 14.15).

Various criteria have been accepted as an indication of fertilization in vitro such as polar body formation, shrinkage of the vitel-lus, presence of one or more pronuclei, and cleavage of the ooplasm. As emphasized earlier, all of these phenomena have been observed many times in eggs which have not been penetrated by a spermatozoon and which are in varying stages of degeneration and fragmentation. Too little is known concerning the processes of semination and fertilization in mammals, with the possible exceptions of the rat and rabbit, to judge unequivocally whether normal sperm penetration and fertilization have been accomplished in vitro.

The freshly ovulated eggs of most mammals are notoriously sensitive to changes in environment and one is concerned lest the eggs cultured in vitro may simulate the events occurring in vivo without activation by a spermatozoon. If sperm penetration and the various fertilization phenomena cannot be followed continuously by direct visualization, it is generally agreed that, unless viable embryos are obtained by transplanting the supposedly fertilized eggs to recipient animals, the success of fertilization is not sufficiently proven. Recently Chang (1959a) was successful in fertilizing the rabbit egg in vitro and obtaining living young by transplanting them to host animals. Thus for the first time a repeatable procedure for fertilizing mammalian ova in vitro has been perfected. Chang obtained unfertilized rabbit eggs by intravenous injection of sheep pituitary extract into estrous rabbits. Sperm were obtained 12 hours after mating females with fertile bucks by washing the uterus with a Krebs-Ringer bicarbonate solution. Unfertilized ova were obtained by flushing the oviducts of the animals which had received the gonadotrophins. Both sperm and eggs were placed in a small Carrel flask and kept at 38°C. Three to 4 hours later the ova were transferred to a second Carrel flask containing rabbit serum and cultured for another 18 hours. At this time the eggs were recovered and examined, and those that appeared to be cleaving were transferred to recipient rabbits. Approximately 42 per cent of the transferred ova that appeared to be fertilized were delivered at term as viable young.

F. FATE OF THE UNFERTILIZED EGG

Evidence that ovulation without fertilization is followed by rapid degeneration and fragmentation of the vitellus has been obtained for many different species (Hartman, 1924, Smith, 1925, in the opossum; Sobotta, 1895, Kirkham, 1907, Long, 1912, Charlton, 1917, in the mouse; Chang and Fernandez-Cano, 1958, in the hamster; Long and Evans, 1922, Mann, 1924, Blandau, 1943, 1952, in the rat; Squier, 1932, Blandau and Young, 1939, in the guinea pig; Chang, 1950a, in the ferret; Heape, 1905, Pincus, 1936, in the rabbit; Dziuk, 1960, in the gilt; Hartman, Lewis, Miller and Swett, 1931, in the cow; and Allen, Pratt, Newell and Bland, 1930, in man).

With the possible exception of the rat, the problem of the ultimate fate of the degenerating ova has not been satisfactorily resolved for any mammal. It is generally accepted that as the unfertilized eggs undergo complete fragmentation and dissolution they are absorbed either in the oviducts or uterus (Corner, 1928a; Pincus, 1936). Charlton (1917) suggested that final disintegration of unfertilized ova in the mouse is effected by means of phagocytic leukocytes. It is assumed further that the unfertilized ova disappear from the female reproductive tract before the succeeding ovulation. However, Hensen (1869) described the retention of approximately 100 rabbit ova in a blocked oviduct in which presumably the eggs had accumulated from a number of ovulations.

The unfertilized ova in the rat do not undergo complete dissolution during the normal 4- to 5-day estrous cycle. The vitellus fragments ordinarily into a number of units of varying sizes and the eggs, with their zonae intact, are eliminated near the end of the succeeding heat period by being washed out through the vagina (Blandau, 1943). Attention has been directed to the frequent occurrence of abortive "cleavages" in the unfertilized tubal eggs of the ferret and rat (Austin, 1949a; Chang, 1950a). This phenomenon is more common in the prepubertal rat treated with gonadotrophins than in the adult animal. In the "cleaved" unfertilized ova, the blastomeres and their nuclear configurations may appear identical with those of fertilized ova and can, indeed, be differentiated only by the absence of the flagellum of the fertilizing sperm. Most unfertilized ova, however, fragment into a number of units of unequal size, each containing one or more abortive nuclei.

G. FORMATION OF THE SECOND POLAR BODY

The penetration of the vitellus by a spermatozoon is not the only stimulus which will induce the formation of the second polar body. Yamane (1930) observed that if rabbit eggs are placed in solutions containing rat or horse spermatozoa, or immersed in pancreatic solutions, cytoplasmic masses similar to the second polar body will be abstricted. Similar "false polar bodies" or extrusions of clear, chromatin-free masses were produced when rabbit eggs were immersed in various concentrations of trypsin (Pincus and Enzmann, 1936). Both the abstriction of the second polar body and shrinkage of the ooplasm may be induced in rabbit, rat, and mouse eggs by a variety of other nonspecific stimuli such as ether, Nembutal, nitrous oxide anesthesia, and "cold shock" (Pincus and Enzmann, 1936; Thibault, 1949; Austin and Braden, 1954b; Braden and Austin, 1954). By contrast, colchicine or "hot shock" inhibits the emission of the second polar body (Austin and Braden, 1954b). Austin (1951b) described the formation of the second polar body in rat eggs in which spermatozoa were in the perivitelline space but had not yet penetrated the vitelline membrane. It is uncertain whether "activation" is caused by a substance released into the perivitelline space by the spermatozoa, or by the mechanical impact of the spermatozoa on the vitelline membrane. There are relatively few data on the temporal relationship between penetration of the vitellus by the sperm and the abtrusion of the second polar body. Pincus and Enzmann (1932) reported that in rabbit ova 45 minutes or more elapse between the time the sperm enters the vitellus and the formation of the second polar body is completed. Formation of the second polar body *in vitro* has also been observed in mouse eggs that had been penetrated by spermatozoa. The time required for the complete process was over 2 hours (Lewis and Wright, 1935). Long (1912) pointed out that second polar body formation in the rat began within 5 minutes to 2 or more hours after the spermatozoa were added to the eggs in *in vitro* preparations. Abstrictions of the polar bodies were completed 45 minutes later.

The interesting observations of Austin (1951c) on the sequence of events during formation of the second polar body in the living rat ova deserve special mention. In the unfertilized egg the chromosomes are arranged on the metaphase plate with the spindle lying paratangentially to the surface, usually in close association with the abstricted first polar body. Within a few minutes after the sperm head has penetrated the vitellus, and before it shows any detectable change, the chromosomes on the second maturation spindle pass to anaphase. The telophase stage is reached about 75 minutes after the initial penetration by the sperm. Then, there is a 20-minute period during which no further change is noted. Subsequently, the spindle slowly moves away from the surface and begins to rotate in such a way that its final position is at right angles to its original location. Rotation is completed in about 50 minutes. The spindle then elongates and becomes narrower, the process terminating in abstriction of a clear vesicle containing the clumped chromosomes. Since it was necessary to flatten the egg considerably in order to be able to observe the spindle under the phase microscope, complete abstriction of the polar body did not occur.

Similar observations on the formation of second polar bodies in rat ova were reported by Odor and Blandau (1951). Approximately 2000 eggs were removed at varying intervals after ovulation and sperm penetration. The eggs were examined either in the fresh condition or after histologic preparation. In the majority of ova, the second polar body had been abstricted completely by the end of the 4th hour after semination.

H. PRONUCLEI FORMATION, SYNGAMY, AND FIRST SEGMENTATION DIVISION

As mentioned earlier, the general concept of the mechanism of fertilization in mammals has been based almost entirely on the examination of fixed and stained material. Even so, it is remarkable that a story of continuing development should have evolved by the piecing together of evidence from killed eggs, the age of which could not be determined within narrow limits. The more recent

advances involving an evaluation of the temporal relationship between ovulation and the various phenomena of fertilization may be said to be due largely to the application of phase contrast microscopy to the studies of living rat ova (Austin and Smiles, 1948; Odor and Blandau, 1951; Austin, 1951a, b, 1952a; Blandau and Odor, 1952; Austin and Braden, 1954a, b).

Employing this method, Austin and Smiles observed fertilized eggs that were obtained by inducing ovulation in immature rats by means of gonadotrophins and subsequently allowing the females to mate. The recovered zygotes were kept at body temperature and development was followed continuously with the phase microscope. The details of the fertilization process described by Odor and Blandau were the result of examining several thousand living and fixed fertilized eggs recovered from sexually mature females at specific time intervals after ovulation and fertilization.

In the rat the complete process of fertilization, from the penetration of the ooplasm by sperm until the first segmentation division, requires approximately 24 hours. In general, the first 8 hours after sperm penetration is the period of the formation of the second polar body and the initial development of the male and female pronuclei (Fig. 14.12).

Changes in the morphology of the living sperm head can be noted as early as 10 minutes after penetration of the ooplasm and involve a loss of sharpness of outline and contrast, first in the posterior and caudal regions of the head. The decrease in contrast continues until finally the whole nuclear part is almost invisible in the living specimen, even under the phase-contrast objectives (Fig. 14.12, *4*). Concomitantly the head increases greatly in size and fluidity. During the initial period of swelling of the nuclear portion, the bifid perforatorium becomes detached (Fig. 14.12, *3*). Approximately 2 hours after the sperm has entered, the primary nucleoli make their appearance within the enlarged sperm nucleus. Time-lapse cinemicrophotography has shown that the nucleoli enlarge by the fusion of minute nucleolar aggregations. The larger nucleoli then fuse one with another until only a single large nucleolus is present (Fig. 14.13, *1* and

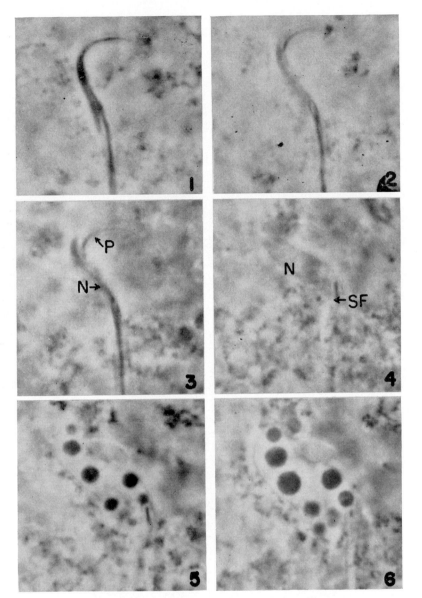

FIG. 14.12. Various stages in the transformation of the head of the fertilizing sperm leading to the formation of the male pronucleus. Note loss of contrast of the head as it enlarges. The changes in the head from *1* through *6* require 2 to 3 hours. Observations were made on the living egg, *in vitro*, and examined with phase contrast objectives. *P*, perforatorium; *N*, sperm nucleus; *SF*, sperm flagellum (Austin, 1951c).

2). Throughout this period of transformation, the flagellum may remain attached to the head and may undergo a very fine, intermittent, vibratory motion, especially in the region of the middle piece. The formation of the definitive female pronucleus begins soon after the second polar body has been completely abstricted. The chromosomes remaining within the ooplasm after extrusion of the polar body are clumped together in the form of a small, compact mass (Fig. 14.13). The first indication of transformation of this chromosomal mass into the female pronucleus is the appearance of several minute nucleoli within a homogeneous nucleoplasm. As the nucleoli increase in size

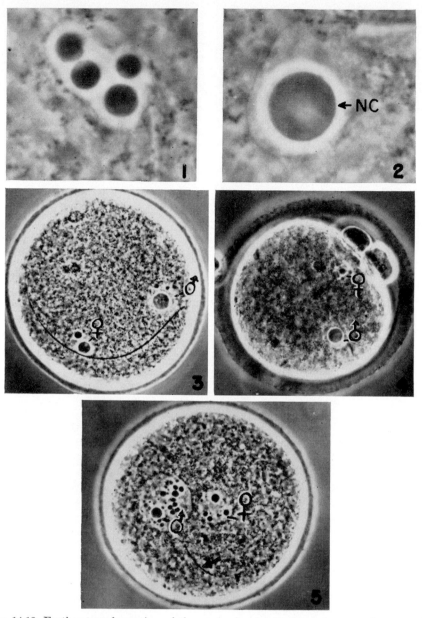

FIG. 14.13. Further transformation of the sperm head into the male pronucleus, *1* and *2*. Note the large nucleolus, formed by fusion of smaller nucleoli. *NC*, nucleolus. This stage has been reached approximately 5 hours after that in part *1*, Figure 14.12, *1* and *2* (Austin, C. R., 1952). Developing male (♂) and female (♀) pronuclei, *in situ*, as observed in living rat eggs, *3, 4* and *5*. The entire sperm flagellum enters the ooplasm at the time of sperm penetration, *3* (Odor and Blandau, 1951).

and number, certain of them coalesce, eventually producing one or two large nucleoli. As the pronucleus grows, the optical density of its nucleoplasm decreases to such an extent that it becomes clear and translucent.

Although there may be considerable variation in the development of the pronuclei between the 9th and 19th hours after sperm penetration, this is the time of active growth of the pronuclei and of increase in the number of their nucleoli (Fig. 14.13, *5*). During the early hours of this period, the male pronucleus grows at a more rapid rate than that of the female, and this differential is maintained even until karyogamy. At the stage of greatest development, the number of nucleoli in the male pronucleus may have increased to approximately 30 and that within the female nucleus to 10. Near the end of this interval, the pronuclei gradually approach one another. For some time after actual contact, the pronuclei retain their identity and the female pronucleus may considerably indent the larger male pronucleus (Fig. 14.14, *2*). Approximately one-half hour before karyogamy begins, the nucleoli in both pronuclei disappear from view and there is some shrinkage in the size of the pronuclei (Fig. 14.14, *3*). Even after the complete disappearance of the nucleoli, the nuclear membranes may still be intact. Soon, however, they become irregular in outline and disappear. Shortly before the first segmentation division, an aggregation of the prophase chromosomes may be observed. Within a brief period, the chromosomes are arranged on the metaphase plate. After an interval of 30 to 40 minutes, the chromosomes begin to divide and pass through the anaphase and telophase stages (Fig. 14.14, *4* and *5*). The first segmentation spindle is observed most commonly between the 21st and 23rd hours after the entrance of the sperm. Even though Austin (1951c) followed the formation of the segmentation spindle, cleavage of the rat zygote did not occur *in vitro*.

It is often difficult to differentiate between the male and female pronuclei in sectioned material. Hence, their identification has not been clearly established for most mammals. The male pronucleus has been reported to be larger in the cat (Hill and Tribe, 1924), vole (Austin, 1957), guinea pig (Lams, 1913), and rat (Odor and Blandau, 1951; Austin, 1951c; Austin and Braden, 1953), and of approximately equal size in the mouse, guinea pig (Lams and Doorme, 1908), bat (Van der Stricht, 1910), cat (Van der Stricht, 1911), and hamster (Boyd and Hamilton, 1952; Austin, 1956b).

Edwards and Sirlin (1956a, b, 1959) have demonstrated that the male pronucleus within the fertilized mouse egg could be identified by injecting adult males with C^{14}-labeled adenine approximately 1 month before mating. The male pronuclei showed autoradiographs which could be related to the labeled sperm particularly in di- and trispermic eggs. Lin (1956) labeled unfertilized mouse eggs with DL-methionine while they were still within the follicles. Ovulation was induced by gonadotrophins and the unfertilized eggs were transplanted to mated females where they were fertilized and subsequently delivered as normal young.

The acridine orange-staining technique has been applied recently to living rat eggs and the localization of the stain determined by fluorescence microscopy (Austin and Bishop, personal communication). The distribution of DNA may be determined by this technique and the preliminary data give support to the earlier reports of Dalcq and Pasteels (1955) that duplication of DNA occurs within the pronuclei.

Information regarding the temporal relationship between the formation of the first segmentation spindle and karyogamy is also very meager. In the guinea pig (Rubaschkin, 1905; Lams, 1913), bat (Van der Stricht, 1910), and rat (Odor and Blandau, 1951), the pronuclei have not completely fused by the time the spindle is formed. Isolated phases of this stage have been described also for the mouse (Lams and Doorme, 1908), rabbit (Gregory, 1930), and goat (Amoroso, Griffiths and Hamilton, 1942).

I. FATE OF THE CYTOPLASMIC COMPONENTS OF THE FERTILIZING SPERM FLAGELLUM

Observations on the extent to which the flagellum of the fertilizing spermatozoon is carried into the ooplasm of the mammalian egg are contradictory and incomplete. The majority of the reports deal with sectioned material in which the identification of the whole flagellum may be very difficult. Yet, knowledge of the fate of the cytoplasmic components of the sperm is essential to an understanding of the role of the male gamete and must be pursued further.

In the mammals, the entire tail has been reported to be lodged within the ooplasm in the bat (Van der Stricht, 1923); mouse (Van der Stricht, 1923; Gresson, 1948); guinea pig

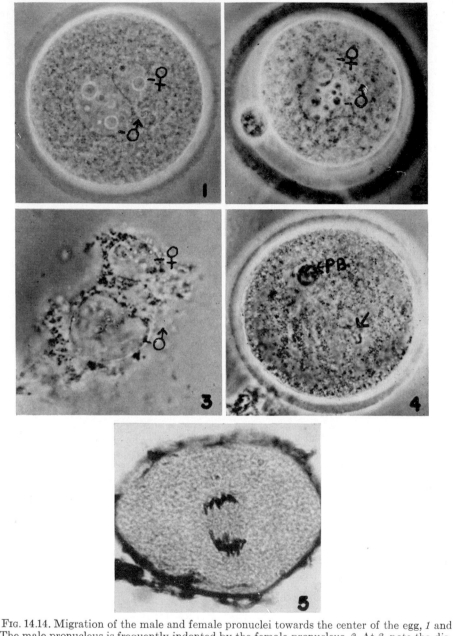

FIG. 14.14. Migration of the male and female pronuclei towards the center of the egg, *1* and *2*. The male pronucleus is frequently indented by the female pronucleus, *2*. At *3*, note the disappearance of the nucleoli in the pronuclei immediately before the appearance of recognizable chromosomes as seen in *4*. Telophase stage during first segmentation division in *5*. *PB*, polar body (Odor and Blandau, 1951).

(Lams, 1913); rat (Gilchrist and Pincus, 1932; Austin, 1951b; Blandau and Odor, 1952); and ferret (Mainland, 1930). Pincus (1930) and Nihoul (1926) were not convinced that in rabbits the flagellum enters the ooplasm. In the vole the flagellum enters

the vitellus in only 55 per cent of fertilized eggs (Austin, 1957).

Except for the investigations by Gresson in the mouse, and Blandau and Odor in the rat, there are no detailed accounts of the fate of the flagellum after it enters the fertilized egg. In the mouse the mitochondria and Golgi material of the sperm become dispersed throughout the egg cytoplasm and the axial filament of the flagellum disappears before the first cleavage. But in the rat the flagellum is of such length and rigidity that it assumes an eccentric position within the periphery of the cell. Probably this explains why the male pronucleus ordinarily begins its development in the outer zones of the egg. Between the 15th and 19th hour after penetration, the external sheaths of the middle- and main-pieces begin to lose their smooth contours and they gradually disappear (Fig. 14.15). When this has been accomplished, the spiral mitochondrial sheath of the middle piece and the axial filament of the main piece can be clearly visualized. Immediately before the first cleavage, the continuous helical mitochondrial thread begins to swell. During the 2-cell stage, the mitochondrial thread is

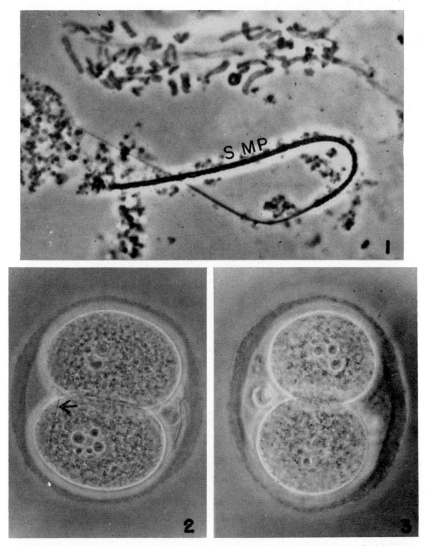

Fig. 14.15. Chromosomes from the metaphase of the first segmentation division removed from a living, fertilized rat egg, *1*. The sperm flagellum from the same egg lies just below the chromosomes. Note that the spiral mitochondrial sheath (SMP) is still present. At *2*, two-cell rat egg with the remains of the sperm flagellum at arrow. At *3*, unfertilized rat egg in which the fragments appear similar to the blastomeres of a normally fertilized egg but there is no sperm flagellum present (Blandau and Odor, 1952).

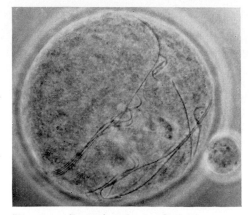

Fig. 14.16. Somewhat flattened, living rat ovum with 13 accessory spermatozoa in the perivitelline space and a single fertilizing spermatozoon in the ooplasm. × 450.

broken up into globules that are dispersed throughout the egg cytoplasm. The remains of the axial filament have been observed in the 2-cell stage of the bat (Van der Stricht, 1902), guinea pig (Lams, 1913), and vole (Austin, 1957) and as late as the blastocyst stage of the rat (Blandau and Odor, 1952).

Van der Stricht (1902) and Lams (1913) believed that, in the 2-cell stage of the bat and guinea pig, the sperm tail is present in only one of the blastomeres. This was partially substantiated for the rat by Blandau and Odor, who noted that in 58 per cent of 329 2-celled ova a greater portion of the axial filament was located within one blastomere and that in 12 per cent it lay entirely within a single blastomere. In the remaining 30 per cent, the axial filament was equally divided between the two. The significance of the various positions of the axial filament in the cleaving egg is not clear. It may represent merely the mechanical difficulty of moving an inert body. Of greater significance is the meaning of the cytoplasmic contribution of the sperm midpiece to the developing embryo in those animals in which its component parts are dispersed within the vitellus.

J. SUPERNUMERARY SPERMATOZOA AND POLYSPERMY IN MAMMALIAN OVA

The terms "supernumerary sperm," "accessory sperm," and "polyspermy" have been used to mean either the penetration of more than one spermatozoon into the ooplasm with the subsequent development of multiple sperm nuclei, or the location of one or more spermatozoa in the perivitelline space. Inasmuch as polyspermy is used widely in the literature of invertebrates to designate the penetration of the ooplasm by multiple spermatozoa, it is suggested that this meaning should be retained for mammals and that the terms supernumerary or accessory spermatozoa should be utilized just to indicate the presence of nonfertilizing spermatozoa in the perivitelline space.

Intact spermatozoa have been observed many times within the perivitelline spaces of ova of various mammals (Sobotta and Burckhard, 1910, Gilchrist and Pincus, 1932, Odor and Blandau, 1949, Austin, 1951b, in the rat; Lams and Doorme, 1908, Lewis and Wright, 1935, in the mouse; Van der Stricht, 1910, in the bat; Hensen, 1876, Lams, 1913, in the guinea pig; Hill and Tribe, 1924, in the cat; Heape, 1886, in the mole; Harvey, 1958, in the pika; Pincus and Enzmann, 1932, Chang, 1951c, in the rabbit; Hancock, 1959, in the pig). Quantitative data on the presence of supernumerary spermatozoa are available for the rat and several strains of mice. Austin (1953) and Odor and Blandau (1951) found that approximately 23 per cent of seminated rat ova contained supernumerary spermatozoa. The number of sperm per egg ranged from 1 to 23 (Fig. 14.16). After mating various strains of mice, Braden (1958a, b); and Piko, 1958) reported that the percentage of ova containing more than one sperm was more significantly related to the strain of the male than to the female. Matings with C57 males resulted in a consistently higher number of eggs with more than one sperm, irrespective of the strain of the females used.

Apparently supernumerary spermatozoa have no effect on the rate of development of the ovum. In the rat, at least, the fluids of the perivitelline space offer an environment which is considerably more favorable for these spermatozoa than that of the oviduct. Except for a separation of the head from the neck-piece, the accessory spermatozoa in the rat, at least, show no evidence of cytolysis in any of the developmental stages including the late blast-ocyst. As mentioned earlier, spermatozoa from the same insemination that are lying free in the oviduct will have undergone extensive cytolysis in less than 24 hours. Finally, with the disappearance of the zona pellucida at the time of implantation, the accessory spermatozoa are cast forth into the uterine lumen. Austin (1957) suggests that the flagellum within the perivitelline space of the vole egg may undergo dissolution *in situ*.

The penetration of more than one sperm into the ooplasm is a common phenomenon in birds, reptiles, urodeles, selachians, and insects (Fankhauser and Moore, 1941). Ordinarily, the additional sperm nuclei do not interfere with the development of the egg.

Until recently, polyspermy in eutherian eggs was considered to be relatively rare (Austin and Braden, 1953). Nevertheless, trinucleate eggs have been described in the rat (Tafani, 1889; Kremer, 1924; Pesonen, 1949; Austin and Braden, 1953); cat (Van der Stricht, 1911; Hill and Tribe, 1924); ferret (Mainland, 1930); and rabbit (Amoroso and Parkes, 1947; Austin and Braden, 1953).

According to Austin and Braden, the incidence of polyspermy in the normally mated rat is approximately 1.2 per cent; in the rabbit 1.4 per cent. If mating is delayed until after ovulation or if rats are subjected to hyperthermia, the figure rises to as much as 8.8 per cent. The incidence of polyspermy is no doubt influenced by a variety of conditions including hereditary variations within various strains (Odor and Blandau, 1956; Braden, 1958a, b). Austin and Braden (1953) concluded from their work that polyspermy in rats gives rise to triploidy in the embryo and that the polyspermic male pronuclei and the female pronucleus contribute to the formation of the first cleavage spindle. To the present, the polyspermic rat embryos have been found to develop to at least the 8-cell stage without showing abnormality. Fischberg and Beatty (1952a, b) have observed a normal-appearing triploid mouse embryo at 9½ days. It is not known whether the triploid embryos can survive to birth. More recently, Gates and Beatty (1954) have stated that delay of fertilization by 5½ hours or more in the mouse did not result in an increased number of triploid embryos.

K. STAGES OF DEVELOPMENT AND LOCATION OF EGGS

The zygotes of the eutherian mammals are remarkably similar in their appearance and rate of development through the various stages of cleavage and formation of the blastocyst. Cleavage consists of a succession of mitotic divisions of the zygote at specific time intervals after karyogamy. The partitioning of the zygote occurs with little or no increase in the total amount of cytoplasm. Salient features of the mechanism of cleavage in different vertebrate types have been reviewed by Boyd and Hamilton (1952).

Data on the rate of cleavage and transport of fertilized ova through the oviduct in different animals have accumulated much more slowly than one would expect from the availability of material. The most complete information has been obtained for some of the ungulates and laboratory rodents and is presented in tabular form (Table 14.5) from the summary of Hamilton and Laing (1946). The rate of cleavage is an inherent property of the zygote. Thus the cleavage rates of different species of amblystoma reared at the same temperature are significantly different. Similarly, in the rabbit the cleavage rate is consistently more rapid in strains of larger-sized animals than in the smaller-sized races (Castle and Gregory, 1929; Gregory and Castle, 1931). It is interesting that, although the zygotes of the larger-sized race divided more rapidly and contained more cells, embryonic differentiation occurred at the same rate in both races.

Altering the environment of zygotes may also effect the rate or cleavage. Thus the early fertilized eggs of the rat, mouse, hamster, and guinea pig cleave only irregularly if at all under tissue-culture conditions. If various thio-amino acids are added to the medium in which rabbit zygotes are being cultured, cell division will proceed normally and may even be accelerated (Pincus, 1937; Pincus and Werthessen, 1938; Miller and Reimann, 1940).

TABLE 14.5
Stages of development of fertilized ova, in hours, of different species

Animal	Observer	1 cell	2 cell	3-4 cell	5-8 cell	9-16 cell	Morula	Blastocyst	Time and Stage at Which Egg Reaches Uterus (hr.)
Opossum.........	Hartman (1928)	—	60	66	72	—	84	96	24 (1 cell pronuclear stage)
Mouse............	Lewis and Wright (1935)	0-24	24-38	38-50	50-64	60-70	68-80	74-82	72 (morula)
Mouse............	Sobotta (1895)	0-24	24-38	50	60	70	—	—	—
Rat..............	Huber (1915)	0-24	42-70	63-73	89	80-96	—	—	—
Rat..............	Gilchrist and Pincus (1932)	8.5-27	27-44	60-85	71-95	—	—	—	—
Rat..............	Macdonald and Long (1934)	12-20 (15)	37-61 (45)	57-85 (65)	64-87 (79)	84-92 (90)	—	105-109 (107)	—
Guinea pig.......	Squier (1932)	3-30	30-35	30-75	80	—	100-115	115-140	80-85 (8-cell)
Rabbit...........	Gregory (1930)	up to 22	22-26	26-32	32-40	40-47	47-68	68-76	70 (blastocyst)
Rabbit...........	Assheton (1894)	12-24	24-28	28	—	—	48	75-96	—
Rabbit...........	Gilchrist and Pincus (1932)	11-21	21-24	—	—	—	—	—	72-75 (blastocyst)
Ferret...........	Hamilton (1934)	31-53	—	64-72	64-116	74-120	120-146	146-264	120-140 (32-cell)
Pig..............	Heuser and Streeter (1929)	0-51	51-66	66-72	90-110	—	110-114	114	75 (4-cell)
Sheep............	Clark (1934)	0-38	38-39	42	44	65-77	96	113-138	77-96 (16-cell)
Goat.............	Amoroso, Griffiths and Hamilton (1942)	30	30-48	60	85	98	120-140	158	98 (10-13-cell)
Cow..............	Winters, Green and Comstock (1942)	34	50-62	—	62-64	110	134	182	110 (16-cell)
Cow..............	Hamilton and Laing (1946)	23-51	40-55	44-65	46-96	71-141	144	190	96 (8 to 16-cell)
Horse............	Hamilton and Day (1945)	—	24	(3)27-33 (4)30-36	(5)50-60	(15)96 ± 6	98±6	—	—
Macacus rhesus..	Lewis and Hartman (1941)	—	0-24	24-36	36-48	48-72	72-96	—	96 (16-cell)

Again cleavage may be either partially or completely inhibited by the addition of colchicine to a culture medium containing the fertilized eggs of frogs (Samartino and Rugh, 1946) or rabbits (Pincus and Waddington, 1939). A similar effect is observed when this drug is injected into mated mice (Waldo and Wimsatt, 1945). The rate of cleavage also depends on the amount of stored yolk. This is particularly true in the macrolecithal eggs of frogs and birds.

The peculiar phenomenon of deutoplasmolysis, or extrusion of yolk from fertilized and cleaving eggs, has been described in the bat (Van der Stricht, 1909), various marsupials (Hartman, 1928), the horse (Hamilton and Day, 1945), the guinea pig (Lams, 1913), the cat (Hill and Tribe, 1924), the pig (Heuser and Streeter, 1929), and the ferret (Hamilton, 1934). In the cleaving eggs of the horse, a large amount of the yolk is extruded into the perivitelline space. The significance of this process is unknown, but it has been suggested that elimination of yolk may be necessary in order to establish a normal nucleocytoplasmic ratio (Levi, 1915).

Except for the monotremes, all mammals have meiolecithal eggs which undergo a complete or holoblastic type of cleavage. A discrepancy in the size of the first two blastomeres has been reported for a number of mammals and seems to be the usual condition (see Amoroso, Griffiths and Hamilton, 1942, for review of this subject).

The second cleavage division occurs in two planes at right angles to each other. Division of the two blastomeres is not necessarily synchronous and accounts for the frequent observation of a 3-cell stage. In an ovum containing two blastomeres of unequal size, the larger cell apparently has some priority in the next two divisions and this probably explains the origin of eggs containing an unequal number of cells. In the 4-cell stage, the blastomeres are arranged in the form of a tetrahedron, due to the preceding orientation of the two mitotic spindles at right angles to each other. Differences in the size of the blastomeres have been recorded in almost every species.

By the end of the 16-cell stage, several of the blastomeres have been moved centrally thus forming the morula. In subsequent cleavages, the smaller, peripheral cells divide more rapidly and an asynchrony, already present, is accentuated. Then fluids begin to accumulate between peripheral and central cells, giving rise to the cavity of the blastocyst.

During cleavage there is a significant diminution in the volume of the total ooplasm. In the first cleavage division of the monkey (Macacus rhesus), Lewis and Hartman (1933) recorded a shrinkage of 44 per cent. During the 1-cell stage of the mouse, Lewis and Wright (1935) noted shrinkage of as much as 25 per cent with a further decrease in volume as cleavage continued. The hamster egg is even more remarkable for the very large volume of its perivitelline space (Austin, 1957).

As mammalian ova of various species are studied, attention is being directed to the differences in the size of blastomeres and rate of cleavage in the hope of finding evidence for the sorting and localization of specific determining substances in the zygote. It has been suggested that in the eggs of the monkey (Lewis and Hartman, 1941), pig (Heuser and Streeter, 1929), goat (Amoroso, Griffiths and Hamilton, 1942), rabbit (Van Beneden, 1875), and mouse (Sobotta, 1924), the more rapidly dividing blastomeres are the precursors of the trophoblast and the more slowly cleaving cells the precursors of the inner cell mass or the embryo proper.

Even though discrepancies in the size of the first two blastomeres have been described in many mammals, there is at yet little evidence of a qualitative difference between them. Heuser and Streeter (1929) could not find a demonstrable cytologic difference between the first two blastomeres of the pig. Hamilton (1934) suggested that, at least in the ferret, size differences of the blastomeres can be explained by the chance division of the cytoplasm in the first cleavage. Despite the difference in size of the first two blastomeres in the mouse, Gresson (1941) has shown that the mitochondria are equally divided between them. Furthermore, the observations of Nicholas and Hall (1942) do not support the theory of absolute determination of the early blastomeres.

These investigators obtained normal young after separating the first two blastomeres of a rat embryo and transplanting them into pregnant host females. From the results of these experiments, they concluded that "the rat egg possesses the capacity to satisfy two of the criteria for equipotentiality: (1) each of the first two parts of the egg may form a whole embryo which develops further than the cleavage stages, and (2) the fusion of two eggs produces one single individual of large size." More recently, Tarkowski (1959) destroyed a single blastomere in 2- and 4-celled mouse eggs by piercing them with a micropipette directly through the zona pellucida. The eggs were then transferred to properly timed recipients. Of 175 half-blastomeres transplanted, 30 per cent had implanted and appeared to be normal except that they were significantly smaller than the controls. Three females gave birth to a total of 6 young which had developed from the experimental eggs. All of the animals were fertile and subsequently gave birth to several litters. Much more experimental work is needed in this area, and perhaps the techniques of transplanting individual blastomeres to the anterior chamber of the eye may open possibilities for further investigations (Fawcett, Wislocki and Waldo, 1947; Runner, 1947).

L. THE AGE OF THE EGG AT THE TIME OF FERTILIZATION

In 1913, Jacques Loeb in his book "Artificial Parthenogenesis and Fertilization" wrote as follows: "The unfertilized mature egg dies in a comparatively short time, which may vary from a few hours to a few weeks according to the species or the conditions under which the egg lives. The death of the unfertilized egg is possibly the only clear case of natural death of a cell, *i.e.*, of death which is not caused by external injuries, and the act of fertilization is thus far the only known means by which the natural death of a cell can be prevented." As studies on the physiology of mammalian gametes are pursued, it is evident that these cells must indeed be listed among those having the shortest life span in the body.

The reproductive processes in most mammals are so timed that spermatozoa reach the site of fertilization and are ready to penetrate the eggs almost immediately after their extrusion from the follicles.

Developmental defects which result from the over-ripening of gametes before fertilization have been studied in greatest detail in invertebrates and lower vertebrates (Gemmill, 1900; Bataillon, 1901; Grave and Oliphant, 1930). Because of their ready availability, the eggs of the fish and amphibia have been found particularly useful in experimental investigations of this type (Mrsić, 1923, 1930; Witschi, 1952).

Witschi described a method whereby frogs were induced to retain their mature eggs within the uteri for varying intervals by separating the females from the males and keeping them in dry containers at room temperature. By subsequent removal of the eggs, by either laparotomy or stripping, the aging gametes could be fertilized by artificial insemination and their development followed. He found that fertilization and development remained relatively normal in eggs which had been retained for 3 to 4 days. However, the sex-determining mechanism was affected in that almost 90 per cent males were produced. Similar alterations in the sex ratio have been reported by Mrsić in the aging eggs of the rainbow trout. If the frog eggs were retained for more than 4 days without fertilization, they gradually became over-ripe and either failed to be fertilized or, if penetrated by a spermatozoon, developed abnormally. After approximately 1 week, all of the eggs retained in the genital ducts became unfertilizable. In amphibia, as in other species, the aging eggs gradually lose their vitality. Witschi's observations are particularly significant in that he followed the development of the over-ripe eggs beyond the stage of metamorphosis and described a number of teratogenic effects of widely divergent nature. Some of the developmental abnormalities encountered were polymyelia, polydactyly, axial duplications (especially in the region of the head), anencephaly, microcephaly, and failure of normal differentiation of various tissues and organs.

In evaluating the bases for the widely divergent nature of these abnormalities, Witschi suggested that they are expressions of an

TABLE 14.6

The fertilizable life of the mammalian ovum

Animal	Length of Fertilizable Life	Investigator
Opossum	Morphologic signs of degeneration appear within 24 hours after ovulation.	Hartman (1924a)
Mouse	(a) 12 hours. Matings 13 hours after ovulation results in reduced fertility (b) 6 hours, estimation (c) 8 hours, experimental	Long (1912) Lewis and Wright (1935) Runner and Palm (1953)
Hamster	5 hours, experimental	Chang and Fernandez-Cano (1958)
Rat	>12 hours, experimental	Blandau and Jordan (1941)
Guinea pig	>20 hours, experimental	Blandau and Young (1939); Rowlands (1957)
Ferret	>30 hours, experimental	Hammond and Walton (1934)
Rabbit	6 hours, experimental 8 hours, experimental	Hammond (1934) Chang (1953) Braden (1952)
Sheep	24 hours, estimation	Green and Winters (1935)
Cow	18–20 hours, experimental	Barrett (1948)
Mare	Short	Day (1940)
Monkey	23 hours, estimation	Lewis and Hartman (1941)
Man	6–24 hours, estimation	Hartman (1936)

interference with either the normal processes of producing or liberating evocators, or the capacity of the embryonic tissues to respond to induction. Of special interest is the finding that the older fertilized eggs frequently gave rise to teratomatous proliferations in the endoderm. When these tumor-like masses were transplanted to older larvae they grew rapidly and metastasized. Needham (1950) proposed that, because the primary evocator, the principal sex-hormone, and various carcinogens belong to the steroid compounds, the effect of over-ripeness may be related to a disturbance of embryonic sterol metabolism.

The fertilizable life of the mammalian ovum has been experimentally determined in only a few rodents, carnivores, and ungulates (Table 14.6). In the ferret, for example, Hammond and Walton (1934) found that the ovum remains capable of fertilization for not more than 30 hours after ovulation. In the rabbit, delay in fertilization

results in lowered fertility and smaller size of litters (Hammond, 1934). In the hamster 50 per cent of ova are incapable of fertilization 4 to 5 hours after ovulation (Chang and Fernandez-Cano, 1958).

In rats the spermatozoa may penetrate eggs which have been aged 12 hours before fertilization or to a point of devitalization but not of death. In such eggs they may even undergo transformation into the male pronuclei and form segmentation spindles, but the female nucleus in the same egg either fails to develop or fragments into a number of nuclei of varying sizes. Even though 70 per cent of the greatly over-ripe rat eggs may be penetrated by spermatozoa, various abnormalities of development result which are not compatible with continued growth and development. Thus, at the time of implantation only 4 per cent of the experimental rats are impregnated. Furthermore, the ova which do implant successfully are retarded in their development, and the majority die before the fetal period is reached (Blandau, 1952; also see Braden, 1959).

A strikingly similar picture is presented by delayed fertilization in the guinea pig. The fertilizable life of the egg in this species is approximately twice (20 hours) that of the rat (Blandau and Young, 1939; Rowlands, 1957). The first effects of over-ripeness are seen in embryos from females inseminated approximately 8 hours after ovulation. No normal development followed inseminations more than 20 hours after ovulation. As far as could be determined, the principal effects of aging were either the early death of the zygote in the pre-implantation period or retardation in the rate of growth in embryos which were capable

of implanting. A moderate delay in fertilization has been shown to lead to polyspermy particularly in rats and rabbits (Austin and Braden, 1953; Odor and Blandau, 1956).

M. IMPLANTATION

The blastula of the placental mammal is called the blastocyst. In the fully developed stage it is still enclosed in the zona pellucida and shows the inner cell-mass attached to the embryonic pole of the trophoblast. During the early period of its existence the blastocyst is spherical to somewhat oval in shape and except for size appears remarkably similar from animal to animal (Fig. 14.17).

In most mammals, the blastocyst does not come into firm contact with the maternal

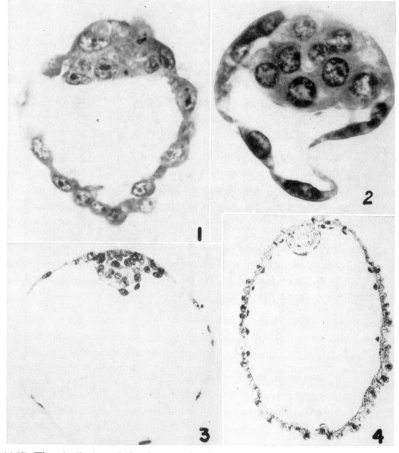

FIG. 14.17. The similarity of the free uterine blastocysts of various mammals: 1, 5½-day human blastocyst (photograph courtesy, Hertig, A., and Rock, J.); 2, 6-day guinea pig blastocyst; 3, 9-day monkey blastocyst (Heuser and Streeter, 1941); and 4, 9-day sheep blastocyst (Boyd and Hamilton, 1952).

endometrium for a number of days after reaching the uterus. In the mouse, mole, shrew, and guinea pig, the free uterine period is from 3 to 3½ days; in the rabbit, 5 to 6 days; in the rhesus monkey and possibly the human, 4 to 6 days; in the cat, 8 to 9 days; in the dog, 9 to 10 days; and in the ungulates probably somewhat longer.

Under the conditions of "developmental diapause" or delayed implantation, the free uterine period of the blastocysts may be significantly prolonged. Delayed implantation occurs naturally in a variety of species such as the pine marten, 6 months; American badger, 2 months; European badger, 3 to 10 months; European roe deer, 4 months; armadillo, 14 weeks; fishers, 9 months; and bears, 6 months. Delayed implantation has also been recorded in the stoat, weasel, sable, and fur seal. In the rat, mouse, and certain insectivores, implantation may be delayed several days to 2 weeks if there is concurrent lactation (Lataste, 1887; Daniel, 1910; King, 1913; Hamlett, 1935; Brambell, 1937; Weichert, 1940, 1942). In the mouse and rat the delay varies roughly with the number of young suckled, and this, in turn, prolongs the period of gestation. According to Lataste, the duration of gestation is normal in mice suckling only 1 or 2 young but prolonged in those suckling 3 or more. If certain hormonal conditions are satisfied, implantation will occur in normal females suckling large litters (Kirkham, 1916; Weichert, 1940, 1942, 1943; Krehbiel, 1941). Delay of implantation is very likely due to an inhibitory effect by some uterine or nutritional factor acting on the blastocysts (Whitten, 1958). Various experimental methods may successfully delay implantation without destroying the ova. Ovariectomy the second day after mating in the rat, followed by subliminal doses of progesterone (0.5 mg. per day), will keep the eggs alive for 6 to 45 days, but the decidual cell response and implantation do not take place. If more progesterone than 0.5 mg. per day is injected into these animals, implantation may occur. A combination of injections in which a small dose of estradiol benzoate is added to the subliminal dose of progesterone is very effective in consummating implantation. In contrast, if the ovaries are removed from pregnant rats on the fourth day when the blastocysts have reached the cornua, progesterone, even in dosages of 10 mg., cannot effect implantation. If estrogen and progesterone are injected simultaneously, the blastocysts will resume their growth and will implant (Canivenc and Laffargue, 1957; Cochrane and Meyer, 1957; Mayer, 1959).

The blastocysts of pregnant rats spayed the 4th day may remain alive for as long as or longer than 21 days. Rat blastocysts apparently do not require adrenocortical hormones to remain viable. Mayer (1959) and his co-workers have demonstrated that the blastocysts in the cornua of rats which have been ovariectomized and adrenalectomized on the 4th day after mating can implant on the 10th day, provided estrogen and progesterone are both injected simultaneously.

The experiments of Cochrane and Meyer, and others that have been mentioned, suggest that the optimal conditions for embryo attachment and implantation depend on a delicately balanced, synergistic action of estrogen and progesterone on the endometrium. But nothing is known as to what is happening within the egg during its dormant state and what factors control the dormancy, nor do we understand what changes occur within the uterine lumen which may eventually satisfy the conditions of the embryo to continue its growth, make attachment to the uterine epithelium, and implant. Our point of view will no doubt be broadened as experimental approaches to the problem are varied and more species are studied.

Runner (1947), Fawcett (1950), and Kirby (1960) found that, irrespective of the state of the host's gonads, implantation occurred when mouse ova were transplanted either to the kidney capsule or to the anterior chamber of the eye. Whitten (1958) transplanted 8-celled mouse eggs to the surface of the kidneys of normal and hypophysectomized mice. Ten days later successful grafts were found in 10 of 15 normal and in 13 of 18 hypophysectomized animals. Successful implantation of mouse eggs onto the kidney apparently does not depend on the secretion of the pituitary.

Buchanan, Enders and Talmage (1956)

reported that implantation occurs in ovariectomized armadillos that are not receiving hormonal replacement. In the European badger ovulation occurs during delayed implantation. The new set of corpora lutea does not hasten implantation because delay in implantation may continue for 2 months after the last ovulation (Harrison and Neal, 1959).

The phenomenon of delayed implantation offers an excellent experimental approach to the general problem of embryo-endometrial interrelationships and the specific factors that control embryo attachment and implantation.

N. SPACING AND ORIENTATION OF OVA
IN UTERO

The specific sites of implantation in mammals having multiple young, as related both to the longitudinal axis and to the surface of the endometrium, are remarkably constant (Mossman, 1937). Even in animals having only a single young and a simplex uterus, such as man, monkey, sloths, and others, the location of the implantation site and the orientation of the blastocyst to the endometrium are quite definitely regulated (Mossman, 1937; Heuser and Streeter, 1941).

Various explanations have been proposed to account for the intra-uterine spacing of blastocysts in polytocous mammals. Mossman suggested that the implanting blastocyst may interact in some manner with the surrounding endometrium so as to create a local refractory zone in which no other embryos can implant. The results obtained by Fawcett, Wislocki and Waldo (1947) after transplanting several mouse ova into the same anterior chamber of the eye are of interest in this connection. They found that fertilized eggs continue to develop in close proximity to one another only until one of them begins to implant. Thereafter, the remaining embryos degenerate. The onset of the degenerative changes in the surrounding blastocysts is coincident with the extravasation of blood into the tissues in the immediate vicinity of the attaching embryo. They suggest that possibly a cytolytic ferment of the trophoblast may cause edema or hemorrhage into the maternal tissues which so alters the local environment that it is untenable for the remaining blastocysts.

According to Mossman's theory, the blastocyst that enters the uterine cavity first establishes a refractory zone near the uterotubal junction and begins the process of attachment. The remaining blastocysts establish similar zones in the fashion of a gradient toward the cervix until all become evenly spaced. It has been frequently observed in pregnant animals with bicornuate uteri that the embryos which are implanted nearest the oviducts are slightly more advanced in development than those nearest the cervix. It has also been observed that the embryos which are implanted nearest the cervix show a higher incidence of resorption than those implanted at other sites.

Recently McLaren and Michie (1959) have taken issue with Mossman's theory that implantation is serial and that refractory zones are established. These investigators induced ovulation and mating in mice by hormone treatment. At 18½ days after mating, the cornua were divided into 6 equal segments and the embryos weighed. They found that the embryos in the middle of the cornua actually weighed less, on the average, than those at either end. The embryo lying nearest the oviduct was usually significantly lighter than its neighbor.

It may be questioned whether the differences in weight of mice fetuses at 18½ days *post coitum* have any relationship to differences in size and differentiation of the embryos during the first 5 to 10 days of development or during the period of orientation *in utero* or of attachment and implantation.

Investigators who have observed blastocysts and implanting embryos have frequently commented on the variations in the early stages of development in the same animal and the variation from animal to animal when they are killed at identical times after mating. The variations in the rate of differentiation are particularly striking if the development of the attachment cones of the guinea pig embryos are observed in tissue culture. The attachment cones of each of the 2 to 3 blastocysts recovered from the cornua of the same animal may be in a different stage of development and may retain this difference throughout the period of cultivation.

The successful transplantation of eggs from animal to animal in certain rodents is feasible and may be the means whereby an experimental approach to the problem of spacing can be made. One or more fertilized eggs could be transferred to the oviducts of properly timed hosts and their sites of attachment observed. One of the problems in evaluating implantation grossly in transplantation experiments is the possibility of inert objects (lint, clumps of cells, etc.) affecting the decidual response and mimicking implantation.

In normal, pregnant rats the embryos are more evenly spaced *in cornu* when the number of young is 5 or more. If the number of implanting blastocysts is less than 4, there is a tendency to occupy chiefly the caudal halves of the horns (Frazer, 1955).

Information is needed as to the manner in which eggs enter the cornua, *i.e.*, whether they enter singly or as a group and what the relationship of the multiple eggs may be one to another during the several days that they lie free within the uterine lumen. It is quite clear that embryonic spacing *in utero* is more even than random. This raises the question as to what controls the size of the refractory area if the cornu is crowded by superovulation, transplantation of eggs, or more than normal numbers of eggs from compensatory hypertrophy in cases where one ovary has been removed.

It has long been known that in bicornuate uteri blastocysts may pass from one cornu into the other through the body of the uterus (Boyd, Hamilton and Hammond, 1944; Boyd and Hamilton, 1952; and many others). Bischoff (1845) interpreted transuterine migration as a method by which the distribution of embryos could be equalized in cases where there is a disparity in the number of eggs ovulated from each ovary. The means by which this migration is accomplished has been the subject of speculation and some investigation.

At present, there is no direct evidence that the unimplanted embryo has the power of independent movement. If this is true then the positioning of the blastocyst *in utero* and its orientation in relation to the endometrium must depend on chemical and/or physical forces. Markee and Hinsey (1933) suggested that alternate contractions of the cornu transport blastocysts from one to another. Krehbiel (1946) anastomosed the cornua of ovariectomized rats in a variety of ways and concluded that each uterine cornua retains its individuality in effecting the distribution of embryos.

The role of the myometrium in the distribution and spacing of the blastocysts *in utero* has received considerable attention. Corner (1923) and Wislocki and Guttmacher (1924) found active myometrial contractions in the sow during the preimplantation period. Even though the postovulatory contractions occurred with greater frequency, they were greatly diminished in amplitude compared with those recorded during the estrous phase. The motility pattern of the myometrium changes gradually from day to day so that, by the time of implantation (12th or 13th day), the spontaneous contractions continue at a rate of 4 to 8 per minute, but their amplitude is so slight that the kymographic tracings are almost level. Similar observations were reported for the excised uterine horns of the rabbit (Knaus, 1927). Using a more refined technique and beginning their observations immediately after the muscle strips were put into the bath, Csapo and Corner (1951) and Csapo (1955) showed that uterine muscle under the dominance of progesterone displays a high state of irritability but poor conduction, and it develops spontaneously a state of "contracture" when it is first placed in the muscle bath. Spontaneous contractions begin after a short interval but they are of very low amplitude. The initial "contracture" is reversible and may be suspended by electrical stimulation or anoxia. Progesterone in some way alters the response of the myometrium to stimuli.

The motility pattern of the myometrium under the dominance of progesterone is certainly different from that when the animal is in estrus, but the nature of these differences is still puzzling (Reynolds, 1949; Csapo and Goodall, 1954). A strip from an estrous uterus placed in the bath relaxes immediately. After a short interval, spontaneous contractions begin and continue with increasing amplitude. Thereafter, contractions occur at intervals of 1 to 2 minutes followed by prompt relaxation. In contrast, similar relaxation was not observed in uterine strips under the influence of progesterone. Instead they slowly shorten.

Ivy, Hartman and Koff (1931) observed that muscular contraction waves in the monkey uterus originate from an area slightly ventral and cranial to the insertions of each of the oviducts and then proceed medially to meet in the midline. They concluded that in the monkey the area of the endometrium where implantation usually occurs is affected by contractions to a lesser extent than the remainder of the uterus.

Nicholas (1936) interposed a section of duodenum into the rat's uterus and found embryos in the lower uterine segment. Lim and Chao (1927) reversed the middle portion of one or both cornua of the rabbit and reported that pregnancy was not prevented.

Markee (1944) introduced sea urchin eggs, celloidin balls, and glass beads into the tubal ends of rabbit cornua and observed their distribution at varying intervals from estrus to 10 days after ovulation. He found that the sea urchin eggs were distributed most evenly in the uteri of estrous rabbits, especially at the time of ovulation. Fairly good distribution was recorded at 5 days and poor distribution at 10 days after ovulation. As noted below, none of these inert objects or sea urchin eggs expand with time as do rabbit blastocysts before attachment. It is doubtful that the movements of these objects in utero could be considered as the normal state of affairs in the transport of blastocysts. In order to study this problem further, Markee observed uterine contractions directly through a glass window which had been sewn into the abdominal wall. Three types of contractions were observed during estrus and for 5 days after ovulation: (1) local ring-type contractions persisting for approximately 10 seconds, (2) peristaltic contractions proceeding throughout the length of the cornu, and (3) antiperistaltic waves of approximately the same intensity as the peristaltic contractions. After the 5th day, the peristaltic and antiperistaltic contractions decreased greatly in amplitude and in the length of their excursions.

Recent studies on the mechanisms contributing to the distribution of the implanting rabbit blastocysts have directed attention to the possibility that both physical and chemical interactions between the blastocyst and uterus are important (Böving, 1952a, b, 1954, 1956, 1959). Böving has found that by 7 days post coitum, rabbit blastocysts have achieved an almost even distribution, not only with reference to the space between them, but also with respect to the entire length of the uterine cornu (Fig. 14.18). If the number of blastocysts in utero varies, the spacing is nevertheless appropriate to their number. The cornua reacts to the presence of each blastocyst and positions it in relation to all other blastocysts present until a remarkably even distribution is achieved by the 7th day post coitum. There is evidence from the work on the rabbit at least that the movement and positioning of blastocysts in utero coincide with their increase in size. Rabbit blastocysts of approximately 1-mm. size are propelled much more slowly than blastocysts or glass beads 3 to 6 mm. in diameter. Böving suggested that each blastocyst acts as a localized stimulus which initiates the propulsive muscular activity and that the size of the blastocysts determines the way in which the myometrium responds. Cessation of positioning is coincident with a local loss of uterine tone and a ballooning out of the antimesometrial wall to form a "dome."

The blastocysts of the leporid family of rodents, the carnivores, some insectivores, and bats undergo considerable expansion in the uterine cavity before and at the time of attachment. In these animals, then, the spacing of the blastocysts may be arranged according to Böving's theory that myogenic uterine contraction is the effector of both propulsion and spacing.

As mentioned earlier, during the 6th and 7th days after copulation in rabbits, the expanded blastocysts occupy a distended, antimesometrial "dome" caused by a local decrease in uterine muscle tone. From in vivo observations of the pregnant uterus, Böving (1952b, c) observed that the blastocysts of the rabbit undergo a rotational

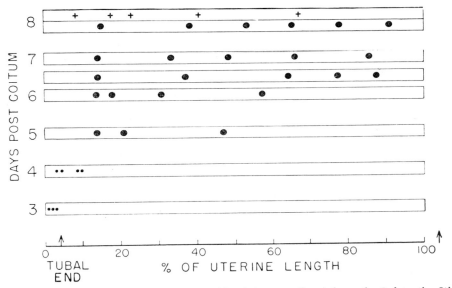

FIG. 14.18. Positions of rabbit blastocysts (dots) *in utero* (bars) from the 3rd to the 8th day *post coitum*. There is little change in position during days 3 and 4. Even distribution is achieved 6 to 7 days *post coitum*. The crosses in the 8-day uterine horn represent the position of blastocyst models which had been in the uterus for 2 days (Böving, 1954).

and to-and-fro motion approximately every 30 seconds. This seems to be effected by a change in the tone of the muscles forming the uterine dome. The rotational motion could provide an orientational mechanism, because eventually all surfaces of the blastocyst would come in contact with the dome. In the *in vivo* observations, it seemed that the blastocyst is "grasped" by the muscular action of the uterus, and by the 7th day *post coitum* is confined along the antimesometrial border.

As implied earlier, the orientation of the blastocyst with reference to the uterus and mesometrium varies considerably in different species. It may be mesometrial as in the Pteropodidae and Tarsiidae, antimesometrial as in most rodents and insectivores, or orthomesometrial as in the Centetes and Hemicentetes (Mossman, 1937).

The orientation of the embryonic disk within the uterus is remarkably constant in closely related species but varies greatly in different orders. Thus the inner cell mass at the time of attachment may be directed toward the mesometrium in the rodents, toward the antimesometrial side in the vesperilionid bats and some insectivores, or toward the lateral side as in the golden mole. With the possible exception of the

rabbit and guinea pig, the role of the blastocyst in determining the pole of attachment is unknown.

Alden (1945) reversed the mesometrial-antimesometrial axis of the uterus of the rat by surgical means and demonstrated that, regardless of the position of the altered segment, the implanting embryos were correctly oriented relative to the uterus. Apparently, gravity alone is not of great importance in determining the pole of attachment, at least not for the rat egg.

Before the cells of the trophoblast can come into contact with the uterine epithelium, either the tough and resistant zona pellucida must be removed or the cells of the living trophoblast must penetrate the zona. A number of investigators have thought chiefly in terms of the removal of the mucous coat and zona pellucida by uterine factors. As we will see, others have been impressed by the possibility of participation by the trophoblast.

In 1935 Hall presented evidence which seemed to support the former view. He found that in rats and mice the zonae pellucidae disappear rapidly when immersed in fluids of pH 3.7 or below. In less acid solutions (pH 4 to 5), they were affected much more slowly. Acidified Ringer's fluid at first caused a swelling of the zonae, and the ordinarily smooth outer contour became wavy and fringe-like. In measuring the hydrogen ion concentration of the fluids in the vicinity of deciduomata of the rat, values as low as pH 5.7 were recorded. Such values were of sufficient acidity to effect the gradual softening of the zona pellucida. Pincus and Enzmann (1936) also measured the pH of uterine luminal fluids in pseudopregnant rats and at no time observed values below 6.7. From Hall's work it was concluded that "as the decidua develops around the implanting egg and as the metabolic activities of the dividing blastocyst increase, the fluid bathing the blastocyst may become sufficiently acid to be a factor in the removal of the oolemma." Fertilized mouse ova, transplanted to the anterior chamber of the eye, lost their zonae independently of a change in hydrogen ion concentration of the environmental fluids (Fawcett, Wislocki and Waldo, 1947). Other factors which alter the physical properties of the secondary and tertiary membranes were described earlier. At this point, however, it is important to direct attention to Lutwak-Mann's (1959) recent comments on the toughness and resilience of the zona in the rabbit and the difficulty in dissolving it except by harsh enzyme and chemical means.

Results obtained during work on the guinea pig and rabbit have prompted investigators to think of other methods by which the zona pellucida and other investing membranes might be shed. Remnants of the zona pellucida have been found adhering to the blastocyst wall in sections of early implanting guinea pig ova (von Spee, 1901; Maclaren and Bryce, 1933). This fact indicates that the zona pellucida is not uniformly lost by chemical action of the fluids of the uterus. In the guinea pig the abembryonal pole of the blastocyst first makes contact with the endometrial

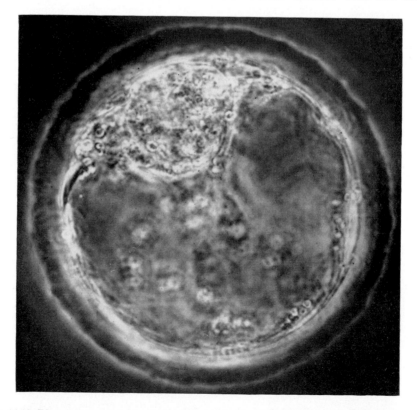

Fig. 14.19. Photomicrograph of a living guinea pig blastocyst removed on the 6th day after ovulation. The inner cell mass is directed towards the top of the page. Abembryonal cells form but a single layer (compare with Figure 14.17, 2). × 900.

epithelium of the antimesometrial border of the cornu. In 1883 von Spee described an increase in the size and number of the abembryonal pole cells of the guinea pig shortly before implantation of the blastocyst and gave an account of the pseudopodia-like processes of these cells penetrating the zona. These processes were regarded by other investigators as fixation artifacts or "as of the nature of a secretion" (Sansom and Hill, 1931). Recently, the early implantation of the guinea pig has been reinvestigated and the observations of van Spee have been confirmed (Blandau, 1949b). It is remarkable that there should be so little change in the zona of the guinea pig egg during its 3 day sojourn in the cornu. The blastocyst completely fills the perivitelline space and the abembryonal pole cells comprise but a single layer (Fig. 14.19). Within a few hours before the ovum attaches itself to the uterine epithelium, the abembryonal pole cells proliferate to form the implantation cone. The trophoblast cells lying next to the zona send numerous slender protoplasmic processes through it (Fig. 14.20) until the abembryonal pole is riddled with them. The cytoplasmic extensions increase rapidly in size and may extend as bulbous expansions of varying shape for some distance beyond the zona pellucida (Fig. 14.21). It is only in the region where the zona is perforated by the extension of the abembryonal pole cells that it gradually becomes thinner and disappears. The remainder of the zona pellucida has been observed *in vitro* to slough off from the attaching blastocyst, much as a grape skin is removed from the flesh of the grape. Attachment cones have been de-

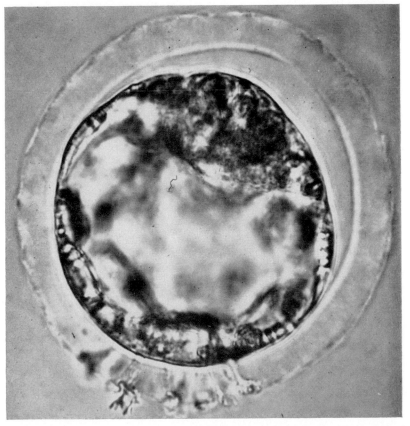

Fig. 14.20. Appearance of living guinea pig blastocyst approximately one hour before attachment of the abembryonal pole to the endometrium. Note the increase in the number of the abembryonal pole cells and the cytoplasmic extensions of these cells through the zona pellucida. × 900.

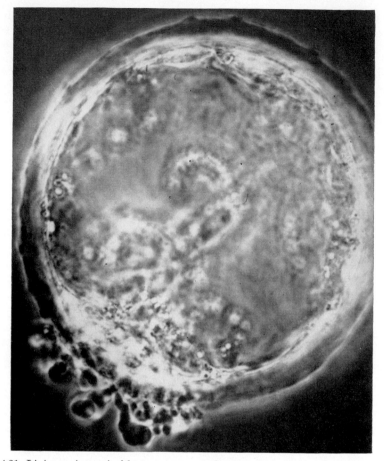

Fig. 14.21. Living guinea pig blastocyst removed approximately one-half hour before attachment to the endometrium. The blastocyst is slightly rotated to show the extensive protoplasmic projections at the abembryonal pole. × 900.

scribed in fixed preparations of a number of genera of ground squirrels and chipmunks (Lee, 1903; Mossman, 1937). Although the extension of conclusions based on the study of one species to other species is precarious, it is possible that the same relationship of the attachment cone to the zona pellucida exists in other forms (Mossman, 1937). Böving noted a change in the viscosity and adhesiveness of the rabbit egg investments at the time of implantation which he attributed to local alkalinity (pH 9) released from one or more regions of the abembryonic hemisphere. Following adhesion, the outer investments of the blastocyst in this area disintegrate. Inasmuch as remnants of the membranes are sometimes observed in the areas between the implanting blastocysts, their final removal ap-

parently is similar to that described for the guinea pig. When the membranes have been shed the abembryonic trophoblast adheres to the uterine epithelium, particularly in areas where blood vessels are subjacent to the epithelium. The trophoblast penetrates the epithelium by displacement, and the invasion of the stroma at first is not destructive.

O. BLASTOCYST EXPANSION

In the guinea pig, rat, mouse, and hamster, the diameter of the blastocyst at the time of attachment is approximately the same as that of the tubal ova. In these species implantations are more or less regularly spaced but not invariably so, because placental fusion occurs frequently. Thus there does not seem to be the same purposeful interplay between the embryos and cornua as described for the rabbit. The blastocysts of these rodents are definitely polarized in relation to the uterine epithelium at the time of attachment and invasion. Although it is universally stated that the blastocyst does not have the capacity for independent movement *in utero,* observations on the behavior of the guinea pig blastocyst in tissue culture and the cytologic descriptions of the attachment cones in the monkey, ground squirrels, and chipmunks suggest that the blastocyst plays an active role in its positioning at the time of attachment. This possibility would encourage one to examine more carefully the living blastocysts of various animals at the time of attachment. From some of the earlier investigations, it would seem that the expansion of the rabbit blastocyst is dependent on physiologic factors external to the egg itself (Pincus and Werthessen, 1938). Thus, blastocyst expansion is interfered with if ovariectomy is performed or estrogen is injected 3 to 5 days after mating. On the other hand, injections of progesterone can reverse the effect of estrogen (Burdick and Pincus, 1935; Pincus, 1936; Pincus and Kirsch, 1936). Allen and Corner (1929) showed that if progesterone is injected into rabbits ovariectomized shortly after fertilization, the fertilized eggs will implant normally. If fertilized rabbit ova are grown in watch glass cultures, they will cleave normally, but they herniate and collapse during the blastocyst stage (Lewis and Gregory, 1929). If crystalline progesterone is added to these cultures, there is no increase in the rate of cleavage nor is herniation or collapse prevented (Pincus and Werthessen, 1937). The same investigators have shown that regular expansion of the blastocyst is obtained if the morulae or blastocysts are cultured in homologous serum and the medium is continually circulated. Recently, Bishop observed that expansion is suppressed if the oviducts of rabbits are ligated soon after the blastocysts have entered the uterus. The implication is that some oviducal factor is necessary for expansion. The problem is complicated by the fact that the egg does not expand during its 3 day sojourn in the oviduct.

From the observations recorded above, it seems that in order to stimulate normal growth and expansion of the blastocyst, in the leporid family of rodents at least, progesterone must act in some way on oviducal and uterine metabolism since both parts of the genital tract are probably involved.

The specific physicochemical processes in blastocyst expansion are not known. A plausible explanation is that the expansion may be due simply to the processes of osmosis, the changes in size being related to ionic variations of the fluid within the blastocyst cavity and the surrounding environment. It is more likely, however, that complex processes of active transport are involved, and, if these are to be elucidated, help from the biochemist and physical chemist is essential.

One of the difficulties confronting investigators so trained is the small amount of material obtainable for study by the conventional chemical methods. This is particularly true in such laboratory animals as the mouse, rat, hamster, guinea pig, and monkey, in which the blastocyst undergoes very little expansion before implantation and in which uterine secretions are present in very minute amounts. Nevertheless the recent approaches to the study of embryo attachment and implantation in the rabbit, particularly those by Böving (1954), Bennett (1956) and Lutwak-Mann (1959), offer a methodological approach that is essential if the dynamic aspects of nidation are to be understood. Lutwak-Mann especially and her co-workers have been the most active in discerning the practical problems in the handling of early embryologic material for biochemical study and in devising sound methodologic approaches.

In 1938 Pincus and Werthessen described a crystalline deposit in the abembryonal membranes of certain blastocysts of rabbits removed on the 5th day after mating from females which had been ovariectomized 18 to 20 hours after copulation. Böving (1954) identified this crystalline material as calcium carbonate and noted that there is little or none present 3 to 4 days after mating, but that the deposit increases to a maximum at the 6th day *post coitum.* He suggested that the osmotic effect of the blastocyst fluid is increased by the ionization of the inherent calcium carbonate reserve. Deficient respiration of the free blastocyst may perhaps lead to the production of acids which react with the calcium carbonate reserve. At the time of uterine attachment, there is improved gas exchange due to the embryo's close proximity to subepithelial blood vessels. Thus the bound alkali is liberated, the ionic concentration of the fluid is decreased, and blastocyst turgidity is lessened.

In measuring the bicarbonate of the rabbit blastocyst cavity fluid, Lutwak-Mann and Laser (1954) found a remarkably high content in 6- and 7-day-old embryos. Thereafter, the level of bicarbonate fell rapidly so that on the 8th day, when implantation is completed, the level was somewhat below that for maternal blood. The occurrence of high concentrations of bicarbonate in the unattached blastocysts led to assays of carbonic anhydrase activity in extracts of pregnant and nonpregnant rabbit uterine mucosa. It was found that carbonic anhydrase activity was very low in the uteri from nonpregnant animals but very high in the uteri from pregnant individuals. The oviducts, endometrium, and placental tissues are the main loci of carbonic anhydrase activity in the female reproductive tract. There are, however, species differences in the extent and the time at which the enzyme can be demonstrated. The endometria of pregnant or nonpregnant hamsters, rats, and guinea pigs do *not* contain measurable quantities of carbonic anhydrase. However, significant enzyme activity has been found in the maternal portions of the placenta of these animals (Lutwak-Mann, 1955).

It has been clearly established for the rabbit that the enzyme is hormone-dependent. Progesterone and progesterone-like compounds greatly increase the amounts of the enzyme measured in the endometrium and this increase is proportional to the dosage of the hormone injected. There is no concomitant increase of carbonic anhydrase in the blood (Lutwak-Mann and Adams, 1957a, b).

There is a 10- to 30-fold increase in the weight of the blastocyst between the 5th and 6th days. Dry weight measurements have shown that this increase is due primarily to water. The enzyme system responsible for the active transport of water is as yet unknown, but is being actively sought. Concentrations of Na, K, and Cl ions in the yolk sac fluid approach or, in the case of K, exceed that of the maternal serum. Glucose, on the other hand, is present in less than half the amount found in maternal blood on the 7th day and two-thirds the amount on the 8th day. Data are also available on total nitrogen, phosphorus, bicarbonate, and various vitamins, particularly the components of the B complex, in the unimplanted blastocyst (Kodicek and Lutwak-Mann, 1957; Lutwak-Mann, 1959). Obviously the opportunities for utilizing isotopes for transfer studies in the fresh and implanting blastocysts are many indeed, and one may confidently expect a rapid unravelling of the manifold functional aspects of implantation if these techniques are employed by competent investigators.

P. EMBRYO-ENDOMETRIAL RELATIONSHIPS

The interrelationship between the blastocyst and the endometrium at the time of attachment and implantation is not only exceedingly complex but also highly variable in different species. Irrespective of the complexity of the attachment, each type has as its purpose the apposition or intimate fusion of the fetal membranes to the maternal endometrial epithelium or stroma so that adequate physiologic exchange can take place.

Earlier studies on the experimental production of deciduomas by mechanical stimulation of the sensitized endometrium, and the dependence of implantation on the proper hormonal stimulation of the uterine mucosa, had the effect of swinging the pendulum of opinion toward the endometrium as being the most active agent in the process of nidation (Huber, 1915; Kirkham, 1916; Selye and McKeown, 1935; Krehbiel, 1937; Rossman, 1940). More recently, however, the observations (1) on the development of the attachment cone in some specific area of the trophoblastic wall just before attachment, (2) the changes in the viscosity and adhesiveness of the egg envelopes at the time of attachment, and on the developmental potentialities of ova transplanted to the anterior chamber of the eye and other sites have swung the pendulum back to the embryo and the role that it may play in nidation (Assheton, 1894; von Spee, 1901; Schoenfeld, 1903; Mossman, 1937; Fawcett, Wislocki and Waldo, 1947; Runner, 1947; Blandau, 1949a; and Böving, 1954, 1961).

The extensive proliferation and differentiation in the endometrium of certain animals after ovulation undoubtedly are important in the nourishment and maintenance of the ovum *in utero* and in providing a suitable implantation site. The considerable growth and differentiation which the blastocysts of many animals undergo before they make contact with the uterine mucosa would indicate that more nutrients are required than are stored in the ooplasm of most mammalian eggs. The widespread occurrence of glucose, glycogen, lipids, phosphatases, iron, calcium, and many other substances, including vitamins and enzymes, in the endometrium may provide the necessary nourishment during the very early stages of implantation (Wislocki and Dempsey, 1945). Bloch (1939) described the secretion of an osmophilic substance by the uterine epithelium which is thought to be absorbed by the free mouse blastocyst. The work of Daron (1936), Markee (1940), Phelps (1946), Parry (1950), and Böving (1952a, 1961) has demonstrated that there is an increased blood supply immediately below the uterine epithelium at about the time of blastocyst attachment. The increased vascularity may not only provide nutrition to the uterine epithelium, but more importantly it provides blood vessels for specific physicochemical reactions between the trophoblast and endometrium (Böving, 1959a). A similar increase in the blood supply in the antimesometrial area has been observed in the guinea pig (Bacsich and Wyburn, 1940). This is the area in which implantation invariably occurs in this species, and the localized hyperemia is considered to be a factor in the antimesometrial implantation.

It is well established that the presence of an actively secreting corpus luteum is essential if implantation is to be complete and successfully maintained. In rabbits progesterone is necessary, not only for the nutrition of the free blastocyst *in utero*, but also for implantation (Fraenkel, 1903; Corner,

1928b; Corner and Allen, 1929; Hafez and Pincus, 1956a, b). Histochemical and quantitative tests have indicated that lipids are present in the endometrium in greater amounts during the luteal phase of the reproductive cycle than at any other time (Krehbiel, 1937; van Dyke and Chen, 1940; Alden, 1947).

It is clear that the presence of an embryo in the cornu exerts a significant effect on the secretion of luteotrophic hormone and on the functional life of the corpus luteum. How these effects are produced remains a challenging problem. We need to determine whether direct invasion of the endometrium is essential or whether mere expansion of the embryo can act as a trigger mechanism. Nalbandov and St. Clair (1958) have shown that if plastic beads of more than 2 mm. in diameter are inserted into the cornua on the 8th day of the estrous cycle in sheep, the cycle is significantly lengthened. Denervation of the cornu containing the beads prevented this change in length.

It has been found repeatedly that endometrial sensitivity to the formation of deciduomata is limited normally to the period of implantation and placentation (Loeb, 1908; Allen, 1931; Selye and McKeown, 1935; Krehbiel, 1937; Greenwald, 1958b). The traumatizing substances were physical, chemical, and electrical stimuli. From these studies, three facts were revealed: (1) The formation of the "maternal placenta" can be induced in the complete absence of the blastocyst (Krehbiel, 1937; Mossman, 1937; Dawson and Kosters, 1944). (2) Even though tissue destruction in the endometrium can be brought about by specific and nonspecific stimuli and even though the end-result may appear similar, the mechanisms producing the changes do not necessarily stem from the same basic stimulus. (3) All of the stimuli used are presumed to have as the basis of their action some kind of tissue injury.[1] Notwithstanding, the histologic transformations of the deciduomas correspond exactly to those occurring normally in

[1] The passage of an electric current of sufficient magnitude through the endometrium to induce the decidual response gives no evidence of tissue damage that can be detected microscopically. This of course does not eliminate the possibility that cellular injury has not occurred.

early pregnancy. Krehbiel (1937) found, for example, in the experimentally induced deciduomas of the rat that glycogen and lipids appeared intracellularly in cells which cytologically seemed identical with those of the normal endometrium of pregnancy.

It would be interesting to know whether the same intensity of artificial stimulus would induce the decidual response in the uteri of a variety of animals. In the rat, for example, the slightest pressure against the superficial uterine epithelium, at the proper time after ovulation, is sufficient to initiate the decidual response. Thus a bit of lint, small clumps of cells, and glass or paraffin beads the approximate size of eggs effect an endometrial response identical with the response to the normally implanting embryo (Blandau, 1949a). In this species the very earliest changes in the subepithelial stroma begin when the blastocyst is attached only very tenuously to the uterine epithelium (Fig. 14.22). From this response of the endometrium, perhaps localized pressure is sufficient to induce the decidual reaction. Equally impressive is the fact that the decidual response begins before there is any alteration in the superficial uterine epithe-

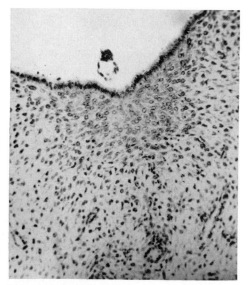

Fig. 14.22. Longitudinal section through the antimesometrial wall of a pregnant rat killed on the 5th day. The loosely attached rat blastocyst has initiated the subepithelial decidual response. There is no detectable alteration in the superficial epithelium. × 450.

lium detectable by microscopic means. Thus, any stimulus from living eggs or inert objects within the lumen is transmitted to the underlying stroma directly through the intact lining epithelium. Wimsatt (1944), in describing the earliest phases of implantation in the bat, came to the conclusion that the changes in the epithelium of the pocket into which the blastocyst comes to rest is "an expression of a localized physiologic reaction of the uterus to some chemical stimulus of unknown nature liberated by the ovum, which may produce this effect by acting locally on the epithelium or by inducing a local relaxation in the uterine muscle."

It is important to recall again that the destruction and removal of the uterine epithelium by the trophoblastic cells of the rat blastocyst do not begin until the embryo lies deeply within the decidual crypt and a sizable decidual response has been elicited (Alden, 1948). Therefore, the initiation of the decidual reaction and the active invasion of the endometrium by the trophoblast are two distinctly different phenomena separated by a considerable interval of time. In the guinea pig, rabbit, monkey, man, and possibly other mammals, the normal decidual response is not elicited until the embryo has effected the removal of the superficial uterine epithelium. Recently, it has been shown that there is a definite species difference in the response of the endometrium to glass or paraffin beads inserted into the uterus of properly timed females (Blandau, 1949a). In the rat, the beads initiated the decidual response and were implanted in a manner similar to blastocysts. In the guinea pig, the beads did not effect the removal of the uterine epithelium, and only occasionally was a minimal decidual response induced. Thus it would appear for the guinea pig, at least, not only that the stimulus must be a direct one to the underlying stroma but that a certain amount of tissue injury or invasion is necessary before the decidual response can be initiated.

As we suggested earlier, the initiation of the decidual reaction may be the result of a localized pressure exerted by the blastocyst, or of the action of some chemical substance secreted by the egg, which is transmitted to a properly sensitized subepithelial stroma. Recently, Shelesnyak (1952, 1954, 1959a,

1959b) undertook to investigate the nature of the non-specific stimulus required to initiate the deciduomas by determining the effects of histamine and histamine antagonists on the endometrium. He theorized that some degree of injury was a common factor to all methods of uterine stimulation, that a histamine or histamine-like substance was present at the site of injury, and further, that at the time of blastocyst attachment there is an "estrogen surge" which acts to release histamine from the endometrium and which in turn initiates the decidual cell response. Evidence for the role of histamine in deciduoma production also includes the depletion of the mast cell population of the endometrium just before attachment. On this basis, after instilling diphenhydramine hydrochloride or other antihistamines into one horn, both cornua of pseudopregnant rats were stimulated to induce deciduoma development. Definite inhibition of deciduoma was noted in the cornu receiving the antihistamine, particularly if the drug was instilled before the transformation of endometrial cells to decidual cells. Consistent with this finding are the indications from extensive tests that drugs having a specific histamine antagonism are effective in suppressing the decidual cell reaction when introduced into the uterine lumen of rats and mice during pseudopregnancy. On the other hand, antihistamines injected subcutaneously in these animals ordinarily fail to prevent implantation. Species differences must also be considered. Böving (1959) was unable to find mast cells associated with rabbit trophoblast invasion.

The theory that some mechanism of histamine release is responsible for initiating the decidual cell reaction would logically imply that the blastocyst is an active histamine secretor or that it indirectly effects a rise of "free" histamine in the cornua, or interferes with its destruction. In all of the work that has been reported in the attempt to establish histamine as the primary evocator in the decidual cell response and implantation, the blastocyst has been ignored. There has been no attempt to examine the living blastocyst itself and to determine the effects of the various drugs used on it. Con-

sequently, the conclusions drawn as to the failure of implantation are equivocal because the condition of the implanting agent in the experiment has not been evaluated. Also relevant is the fact mentioned earlier that the decidual response in the rat and mouse is evoked, not only by living embryos, but also by many inert objects inducing the response without evidence of epithelial destruction. The mechanism of histamine release under these conditions must be based on some unknown factor.

The appearance of implantation cones, just before and during attachment of the blastocyst to the endometrium in guinea pigs, rabbits, squirrels, chipmunks, and probably primates, raises the question as to whether the embryo may not initially send protoplasmic extensions between the epithelial cells lining the lumen and thus secrete some substance which not only initiates the decidual response, but also effects the removal of underlying endometrial tissue (compare Figs. 14.23, 14.24 and 14.25) (Mossman, 1937; Wislocki and Streeter, 1938; Böving, 1954, 1959a). It is interesting that during this initial invasion in the guinea pig, rabbit, and man, there is a negligible amount of endometrial necrosis. In the description of the implantation stages of the macaque, Wislocki and Streeter also emphasized that during the earliest

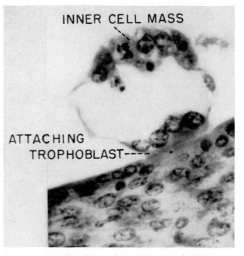

FIG. 14.23. Section of a guinea pig blastocyst showing the very earliest stage in the attachment of the abembryonal pole cells to the maternal endometrium. × 500.

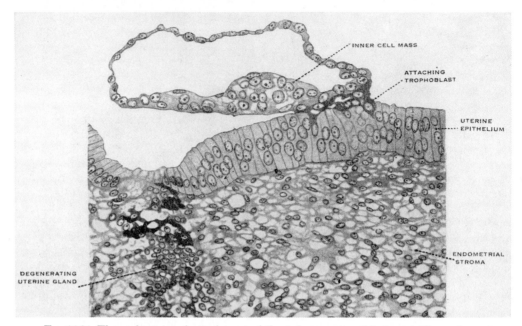

FIG. 14.24. The early stage of attachment of the 9-day macaque blastocyst. The embryonic pole is directed towards the uterine epithelium (Wislocki and Streeter, 1938).

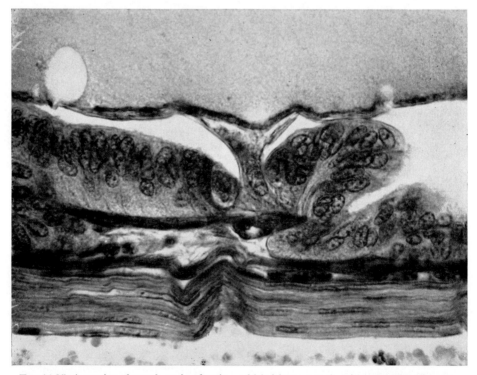

FIG. 14.25. A section through an implanting rabbit blastocyst showing an unusually narrow trophoblast invasion of the uterine epithelium. There is no evidence of epithelial debris within the trophoblast cells. A group of clumped uterine epithelial nuclei surrounded by pale cytoplasm lies to the left of the invading foot (Böving, 1959a). Fixation: Sousa, Azan stain. × 600.

phases of embryonic attachment to the uterine epithelium, the subepithelial mucosa shows no reaction whatever. When joined, these observations remind us that as yet there is no conclusive evidence that the implanting embryo secretes cytolytic enzymes but may secrete other substances.

The most imaginative experimental approach to the problems of embryo spacing, attachment, and implantation is the work of Böving (1959a, b and c, 1961) on the rabbit. He has clearly shown that, in this animal, invasion is promoted by a chemical substance elaborated within the blastocyst and transferred to the maternal circulation. The invasion-promoting substance has been characterized as being in the form of bicarbonate which induces a localized high pH. Circulating progesterone increases the level of endometrial carbonic anhydrase and accelerates the removal of bicarbonate from the embryo by catalyzing the formation of carbonic acid. The carbonic acid is converted to carbon dioxide which is removed by the maternal circulation. The local pH rises and the various blastocysts' membranes become very sticky, particularly at the site of attachment. The physicochemical interrelationship of the trophoblast and endometrial epithelium effects a dissociation of the epithelium, thus opening a path for the trophoblast.

At this writing, the precise roles of the egg and endometrium during implantaton are unknown and remain a challenging problem. The numerous modifications of the implantation processes in the different mammalian families create difficulties of interpretation in what is already an unusually complex problem. As more detailed descriptions of the embryo-endometrial relationships appear, it seems clear that neither the ovum nor the endometrium is primarily responsible for implantation, but that both play mutual and overlapping roles. One of the greatest gaps in our knowledge of implantation for any animal is a detailed description of the process itself and the precise timing of the events in this phenomenon. The various experimental approaches to the physiologic and biochemical mechanisms of implantation have quickened our interest and broadened our view of the complex metabolic

processes required if implantation is to be successful, but our efforts to interpret correctly the data from biochemical, physiologic, and pharmacologic investigations will be limited until more accurate information has been obtained bearing on the morphologic features of the process itself.

V. References

ADAMS, C. E. 1953. Some aspects of ovulation, recovery and transplantation of ova in the immature rabbit. In *Mammalian Germ Cells*, pp. 198–216. Boston: Little, Brown and Company.

ALDEN, R. H. 1942a. The periovarial sac in the albino rat. Anat. Rec., **83**, 421–434.

ALDEN, R. H. 1942b. The oviduct and egg transport in the albino rat. Anat. Rec., **84**, 137–169.

ALDEN, R. H. 1942c. Aspects of the egg-ovary-oviduct relationship in the albino rat. I. Egg passage and development following ovariectomy. J. Exper. Zool., **90**, 159–169.

ALDEN, R. H. 1942d. Aspects of the egg-ovary-oviduct relationship in the albino rat. II. Egg development within the oviduct. J. Exper. Zool., **90**, 171–181.

ALDEN, R. H. 1945. Implantation of the rat egg. I. Experimental alteration of uterine polarity. J. Exper. Zool., **100**, 229–235.

ALDEN, R. H. 1947. Implantation of the rat egg. II. Alteration in osmiophilic epithelial lipids of the rat uterus under normal and experimental conditions. Anat. Rec., **97**, 1–19.

ALDEN, R. H. 1948. Implantation of the rat egg. III. Origin and development of primary trophoblast giant cells. Am. J. Anat., **83**, 143–182.

ALFERT, M. 1950. A cytochemical study of oogenesis and cleavage in the mouse. J. Cell. & Comp. Physiol., **36**, 381–409.

ALLEN, B. M. 1911. The origin of the sex-cells of Amia and Lepidosteus. J. Morphol., **22**, 1–36.

ALLEN, E. 1922. The oestrus cycle in the mouse. Am. J. Anat., **30**, 297–371.

ALLEN, E. 1923. Ovogenesis during sexual maturity. Am. J. Anat., **31**, 439–481.

ALLEN, E., PRATT, J. P., NEWELL, Q. U., AND BLAND, L. J. 1930. Human tubal ova; related early corpora lutea and uterine tubes. Contr. Embryol., Carnegie Inst. Washington, **22**, 45–76.

ALLEN, W. M. 1931. I. Cyclic alterations of the endometrium of the rat during the normal cycle, pseudopregnancy, and pregnancy. II. Production of deciduomata during pregnancy. Anat. Rec., **48**, 65–103.

ALLEN, W. M., AND CORNER, G. W. 1929. Physiology of the corpus luteum. III. Normal growth and implantation of embryos after very early ablation of the ovaries, under the influence of the corpus luteum. Am. J. Physiol., **88**, 340–346.

AMOROSO, E. C., GRIFFITHS, W. F. B., AND HAMILTON, W. J. 1942. The early development of the goat (*Capra hircus*). J. Anat., **76**, 377–406.

AMOROSO, E. C., AND PARKES, A. S. 1947. Effects on embryonic development of x-irradiation of rabbit spermatozoa *in vitro*. Proc. Roy. Soc., ser. B, **134**, 57–78.

ANDERSEN, D. H. 1927a. Lymphatics of the Fallopian tube of the sow. Contr. Embryol., Carnegie Inst. Washington, **19**, 135–147.

ANDERSEN, D. H. 1927b. The rate of passage of the mammalian ovum through various portions of the Fallopian tube. Am. J. Physiol., **82**, 557–569.

ANDERSEN, E., AND BEAMS, H. W. 1959. Cytological observations on the fine structure of the guinea pig ovary with special reference to the oogonium, primary oocyte and associated follicle cells. J. Ultrastruct. Res., **3**, 432–446.

ANOPOLSKY, D. 1928. Cyclic changes in the size of muscle fibers of the Fallopian tube of the sow. Am. J. Anat., **40**, 459–469.

ASSHETON, R. 1894. A re-investigation into the early stages of the development of the rabbit. Quart. J. Microscop. Sc., **32**, 113–164.

ASSHETON, R. 1898. The segmentation of the ovum of the sheep, with observations on the hypothesis of a hypoblastic origin of the trophoblast. Quart. J. Microbiol. Sc., **41**, 205–261.

AUSTIN, C. R. 1948a. Number of sperms required for fertilization. Nature, London, **162**, 534–535.

AUSTIN, C. R. 1948b. Function of hyaluronidase in fertilization. Nature, London, **162**, 63–64.

AUSTIN, C. R. 1949a. The fragmentation of eggs following induced ovulation in immature rats. J. Endocrinol., **6**, 104–110.

AUSTIN, C. R. 1949b. Fertilization and the transport of gametes in the pseudopregnant rabbit. J. Endocrinol., **6**, 63–70.

AUSTIN, C. R. 1951a. Activation and the correlation between male and female elements in fertilization. Nature, London, **168**, 558–559.

AUSTIN, C. R. 1951b. Observations on the penetration of the sperm into the mammalian egg. Australian J. Sc. Res., **4**, 581–596.

AUSTIN, C. R. 1951c. The formation, growth and conjugation of the pronuclei in the rat egg. J. Roy. Microscop. Soc., **71**, 295–306.

AUSTIN, C. R. 1952a. The development of pronuclei in the rat egg, with particular reference to quantitative relations. Australian J. Sc. Res., ser. B, **5**, 354–365.

AUSTIN, C. R. 1952b. Nucleic acids associated with the nucleoli of living segmented rat eggs. Exper. Cell Res., **4**, 249–251.

AUSTIN, C. R. 1956a. Cortical granules in hamster eggs. Exper. Cell Res., **10**, 533–540.

AUSTIN, C. R. 1956b. Activation of eggs by hypothermia in rats and hamsters. J. Exper. Biol., **33**, 338–347.

AUSTIN, C. R. 1956c. Ovulation, fertilization, and early cleavage in the hamster (*Mesocricetus auratus*). J. Roy. Microscop. Soc., **75**, 141–154.

AUSTIN, C. R. 1957. Fertilization, early cleavage and associated phenomena in the field vole. (*Microtus agrestis*). J. Anat., **91**, 1–11.

AUSTIN, C. R. 1960. Capacitation and the release of hyaluronidase from spermatozoa. J. Reprod. & Fertil., **3**, 310–311.

AUSTIN, C. R., AND BISHOP, M. W. H. 1957. Fertilization in mammals. Biol. Rev., **32**, 296–349.

AUSTIN, C. R., AND BISHOP, M. W. H. 1958. Role of the rodent acrosome and perforatorium in fertilization. Proc. Roy. Soc., ser. B, **149**, 241–248.

AUSTIN, C. R., AND BISHOP, M. W. H. 1958. Differential fluorescence in living rat eggs treated with acridine orange. Exper. Cell. Res., **17**, 35–43.

AUSTIN, C. R., AND BRADEN, A. W. H. 1953. An investigation of polyspermy in the rat and rabbit. Australian J. Biol. Sc., **6**, 674–692.

AUSTIN, C. R., AND BRADEN, A. W. H. 1954a. Time relations and their significance in the ovulation and penetration of eggs in rats and rabbits. Australian J. Biol. Sc., **7**, 179–194.

AUSTIN, C. R., AND BRADEN, A. W. H. 1954b. Induction and inhibition of the second polar division in the rat egg and subsequent fertilization. Australian J. Biol. Sc., **7**, 195–210.

AUSTIN, C. R., AND BRADEN, A. W. H. 1956. Early reactions of the rodent egg to spermatozoon penetration. J. Exper. Biol., **33**, 358–365.

AUSTIN, C. R., AND LOVELOCK, J. E. 1958. Permeability of rabbit, rat and hamster egg membranes. Exper. Cell Res., **15**, 260–261.

AUSTIN, C. R., AND SMILES, J. 1948. Phase-contrast microscopy in the study of fertilization and early development of the rat egg. J. Roy. Microscop. Soc., **68**, 13–19.

AVERILL, R. L. W., AND ROWSON, L. E. A. 1958. Ovum transfer in the sheep. J. Endocrinol., **16**, 326–336.

AVIS, F. R., AND SAWIN, P. B. 1951. A surgical technique for the reciprocal transplantation of fertilized eggs in the rabbit. J. Hered., **42**, 259–260.

AYKROYD, O. E. 1938. The cytoplasmic inclusions in the oogenesis of man. Ztschr. Zellforsch. mikroskop. Anat., **27**, 691–710.

AYKROYD, O. E. 1941. The effects of ultracentrifuging human oocytes. Proc. Roy. Irish Acad. Dublin, **46**, 101–108.

BACSICH, P., AND WYBURN, G. M. 1940. Cyclic variation in the vascular architecture of the uterus of the guinea pig. Tr. Roy. Soc. Edinburgh, **60**, 79–86.

BARRETT, G. R. 1948. Time of insemination and conception rates in dairy cows. Ph.D. Thesis, University of Wisconsin.

BARRY, M. 1843. Spermatozoa observed a second time within the ovum. Philos. Tr. Roy. Soc., **22**, 415.

BATAILLON, E. 1901. La pression osmotique et les grands problemes de la biologie. Roux' Arch. Entwicklungsmech. Organ., **11**, 149–184.

BEAMS, H. W., AND KING, R. L. 1938. A study of the cytoplasmic components and inclusions of the developing guinea pig egg. Cytologia, **8**, 353–367.

BEATTY, R. A. 1951. Transplantation of mouse eggs. Nature, London, **168**, 995.

BEILER, J. M., AND MARTIN, G. L. 1947. Inhibitory

action of vitamin-P compounds on hyaluronidase. J. Biol. Chem., **171**, 507–511.

BELLERBY, C. W. 1929. The relation of the anterior lobe of the pituitary to ovulation. J.
Physiol., **67**, xxxiii.

BELLAIRS, R. 1958. The conversion of yolk into
cytoplasm in the chick blastoderm as shown by
electron microscopy. J. Embryol. & Exper.
Morphol., **6**, 149–161.

BENNETT, D. 1956. Developmental analysis of a
mutation with pleiotropic effects in the mouse.
J. Morphol., **98**, 199–234.

BHATTACHARYA, D. R. 1931. The infiltration of
Golgi bodies from follicular epithelium to the
egg in mammals. Allahabad Univ. Stud. Sc.
Sect., **7**, 1–8.

BHATTACHARYA, D. R., DAS, R. J., AND DUTTA, S. K.
1929. On the infiltration of Golgi bodies from
the follicular epithelium to the egg. Ztschr.
Zellforsch. mikroskop. Anat., **8**, 566–577.

BIEBER, S., SPENCE, J. A., AND HITCHINGS, G. H.
1957. The isolation and identification of the
nucleic acids and their derivatives in the ovum
of *Rana pipiens*. Anat. Rec., **128**, 523–524.

BIEDL, A., PETERS, H., AND HOFSTATTER, R. 1922.
Experimentelle Studien über die Einnistung
und Weiterentwicklung des Eies im Uterus.
Ztschr. Geburtsh. u. Gynäk., **84**, 59–130.

BISCHOFF, T. L. W. 1845. *Entwicklungsgeschichte
des Hundeseies*. Braunschweig: Friedrich Vie-
weg und Sohn.

BISCHOFF, T. L. W. 1854. *Entwicklungsgeschichte
des Rehes*. Giessen: J. Ricker.

BISHOP, D. W. 1956a. Active secretion in the
rabbit oviduct. Am. J. Physiol., **187**, 347–352.

BISHOP, D. W. 1956b. Oxygen concentrations in
the rabbit genital tract. In *Proceedings Third
International Congress on Animal Reproduction*, Part I. Cambridge.

BISHOP, D. W. 1956c. Metabolic conditions
within the oviduct of the rabbit. *Proceedings
Second World Congress on Fertility and Sterility*, pp. 1134–1145. International Fertility Association.

BISHOP, D. W., AND TYLER, A. 1956. Fertilizin
of mammalian eggs. J. Exper. Zool., **132**, 575–
601.

BITTNER, J. J., AND LITTLE, C. C. 1937. Transmission of breast and lung cancer in mice. J.
Hered., **28**, 117–121.

BLACK, D. L., AND ASDELL, S. A. 1958. Transport
through the rabbit oviduct. Am. J. Physiol.,
192, 63–68.

BLACK, D. L., AND ASDELL, S. A. 1959. Mechanisms controlling entry of ova into rabbit
uterus. Am. J. Physiol., **197**, 1275–1278.

BLACK, W. G., OTTO, G., AND CASIDA, L. E. 1951.
Embryonic mortality in pregnancies induced
in rabbits of different reproductive stages. Endocrinology, **49**, 237–243.

BLANDAU, R. J. 1943. The fate of the unfertilized
ova in the albino rat. Anat. Rec., **87**, 17–27.

BLANDAU, R. J. 1945. The first maturation division of the rat ovum. Anat. Rec., **92**, 449–457.

BLANDAU, R. J. 1949a. Embryo-endometrial interrelationships in the rat and guinea pig. Anat.
Rec., **104**, 331–360.

BLANDAU, R. J. 1949b. Observations on implantation of the guinea pig ovum. Anat. Rec., **103**,
19–47.

BLANDAU, R. J. 1952. The female factor in fertility and infertility. I. The effects of delayed
fertilization on the development of the pronuclei in rat ova. Fertil. & Steril., **3**, 349–365.

BLANDAU, R., JENSEN, L., AND RUMERY, R. 1958.
Determination of the pH values of the repro-
ductive-tract fluids of the rat during heat.
Fertil. & Steril., **9**, 207–214.

BLANDAU, R. J., AND JORDAN, E. S. 1941. The effect
of delayed fertilization on the development of
the rat ovum. Am. J. Anat., **68**, 275–287.

BLANDAU, R. J., AND ODOR, D. L. 1949. The total
number of spermatozoa reaching various segments of the reproductive tract in the female
albino rat at intervals after insemination. Anat.
Rec., **103**, 93–110.

BLANDAU, R. J., AND ODOR, D. L. 1952. Observations on sperm penetration into the ooplasm
and changes in the cytoplasmic components of
the fertilizing spermatozoon in rat ova. Fertil.
& Steril., **3**, 13–26.

BLANDAU, R. J., AND YOUNG, W. C. 1939. The effects of delayed fertilization on the development of the guinea pig ovum. Am. J. Anat., **64**,
303–329.

BLOCH, S. 1939. Contributions to research on the
female sex hormones. The implantation of the
mouse egg. J. Endocrinol., **1**, 399–408.

BOELL, E. J. 1955. Energy exchange and enzyme
development during embryogenesis. In *Analysis of Development*, Sect. VIII, B. J. Willier,
P. A. Weiss, and V. Hamburger, Eds., pp. 520–
555. Philadelphia: W. B. Saunders Company.

BOELL, E. J., AND NICHOLAS, J. S. 1948. Respiratory metabolism of the mammalian egg. J.
Exper. Zool., **109**, 267–281.

BORELL, U., GUSTAVSON, K.-H., NILSSON, O., AND
WESTMAN, A. 1959. The structure of the epithelium lining the Fallopian tube of the rat in
oestrus. Acta obst. et gynec. scandinav., **38**,
203–218.

BORELL, U., NILSSON, O., WERSÄLL, J., AND WEST-
MAN, A. 1956. Electron-microscope studies of
the epithelium of the rabbit Fallopian tube
under different hormonal influences. Acta obst.
et gynec. scandinav., **35**, 35–41.

BORELL, U., NILSSON, O., AND WESTMAN, A. 1957.
Ciliary activity in the rabbit fallopian tube
during oestrus and after copulation. Acta obst.
et gynec. scandinav., **36**, 22–28.

BOUNOURE, L. 1939. *L'origine des cellules repro-
ductrices et le problème de la lignée germinale*.
Paris: Gauthiers-Villars.

BÖVING, B. G. 1952a. Rabbit trophoblast invades
uterine epithelium overlying blood vessels.
Anat. Rec., **112**, 12.

BÖVING, B. G. 1952b. Mechanisms contributing
to the orientation of implanting rabbit blasto-

868 SPERM, OVA, AND PREGNANCY

cysts (Am. A. Anatomists Mtg. abstr.). Anat. Rec., **112,** 170.

BÖVING, B. G. 1952c. Internal observation of rabbit uterus. Science, **116,** 211–214.

BÖVING, B. G. 1954. Blastocyst-uterine relationships. Cold Spring Harbor Symposia Quant. Biol., **19,** 9–28.

BÖVING, B. G. 1956. Rabbit blastocyst distribution. Am. J. Anat., **98,** 403–434.

BÖVING, B. 1959a. The biology of trophoblast. Ann. New York Acad. Sc., **80,** 21–43.

BÖVING, B. G. 1959b. Implantation. Ann. New York Acad. Sc., **75,** 700–725.

BÖVING, B. G. 1959c. Endocrine influences on implantation. In: *Recent Progress in the Endocrinology of Reproduction.* New York: Academic Press, Inc.

BÖVING, B. G. 1961. Anatomical analyses of rabbit trophoblast invasion. Contr. Embryol., Carnegie Inst. Washington, **37,** in press.

BOWMAN, R. H. 1951. Fertilization of undenuded rat ova. Proc. Soc. Exper. Biol. & Med., **76,** 129–130.

BOYD, J. D., AND HAMILTON, W. J. 1952. Cleavage, early development and implantation of the egg. In *Marshall's Physiology of Reproduction.* London: Longmans, Green and Company.

BOYD, J. D., HAMILTON, W. J., AND HAMMOND, J. 1944. Transuterine ("internal") migration of the ovum in sheep and other mammals. J. Anat., **78,** 5–14.

BRACHER, F. 1957. Der Cyclus des Goldhamster-Epoophorons. Ztschr. Anat., **120,** 201–210.

BRACHET, A. 1913. Recherches sur le déterminisme héréditaire de l'oeuf mammifères développement "in vitro" de jaunes vésicules blastodermique de lapin. Arch. Biol., **28,** 477–503.

BRADEN, A. W. H. 1952. Properties of the membranes of rat and rabbit eggs. Australian J. Sc. Res., ser. B, **5,** 460–471.

BRADEN, A. W. H. 1957. Variation between strains in the incidence of various abnormalities of egg maturation and fertilization in the mouse. J. Genet., **55,** 476–486.

BRADEN, A. W. H. 1958a. Strain differences in the incidence of polyspermia in rats after delayed mating. Fertil. & Steril., **9,** 243–246.

BRADEN, A. W. H. 1958b. Variation between strains of mice in phenomena associated with sperm penetration and fertilization. J. Genet., **56,** 37–47.

BRADEN, A. W. H. 1959. Are nongenetic defects of the gametes important in the etiology of prenatal mortality? Fertil. & Steril., **10:** 285–298.

BRADEN, A., AND AUSTIN, C. R. 1954. Reactions of unfertilized mouse eggs to some experimental stimuli. Exper. Cell Res., **7,** 277–280.

BRADEN, A. W. H., AUSTIN, C. R., AND DAVID, H. A. 1954. The reaction of the zona pellucida to sperm penetration. Australian J. Biol. Sc., **7,** 391–409.

BRAMBELL, F. W. R. 1925. The oogenesis of fowl (*Gallus bankira*). Philos. Tr. Roy. Soc., ser. B, **214,** 113–151.

BRAMBELL, F. W. R. 1927. The development and morphology of the gonads of the mouse. I. The morphogenesis of the indifferent gonad and of the ovary. Proc. Roy. Soc., ser. B, **101,** 391–409.

BRAMBELL, F. W. R. 1928. The development and morphology of the gonads of the mouse. III. The growth of the follicles. Proc. Roy. Soc., ser. B, **103,** 258–272.

BRAMBELL, F. W. R. 1937. The influence of lactation on the implantation of the mammalian embryo. Am. J. Obst. & Gynec., **33,** 942–953.

BRAMBELL, F. W. R. 1956. Ovarian changes. In *Marshall's Physiology of Reproduction,* A. S. Parkes, Ed., Ch. 5. London: Longmans, Green and Company.

BRAMBELL, F. W. R., PARKES, A. S., AND FIELDING, U. 1927. Changes in the ovary of the mouse following exposure to X-rays. II. Irradiation at or before birth. Proc. Roy. Soc., ser. B, **101,** 95–114.

BRAREN, F. 1957. Parthenogenetisches Teilungsstadium einer menschlichen Eizelle. Anat. Anz., **104,** 372–375.

BROWN, C. A., AND RIS, H. 1959. Amphibian oocyte nucleoli. J. Morphol., **104,** 377–414.

BRUNER, J. A., FAILER, G., WENK, P., AND WITSCHI, E. 1951. The respiratory metabolism of overripe eggs and embryos of the frog *Rana temporaria* (Abstr.). Anat. Rec., **111,** 452.

BUCHANAN, G. D., ENDERS, A. C., AND TALMAGE, R. V. 1956. Implantation in armadillos ovariectomized during the period of delayed implantation. J. Endocrinol., **14,** 121–128.

BULLOUGH, W. S. 1946. Mitotic activity in the adult female mouse (*Mus musculus* L.). A study of its relation to the oestrous cycle in normal and abnormal conditions. Philos. Tr. Roy. Soc., ser. B, **231,** 453–516.

BULLOUGH, W. S., AND GIBBS, H. F. 1941. Oogenesis in adult mice and starlings. Nature, London, **148,** 439–440.

BURDICK, H. O., EMERSON, B. B., AND WHITNEY, R. 1940. Effects of testosterone propionate on pregnancy and on passage of ova through the oviducts of mice. Endocrinology, **26,** 1081–1086.

BURDICK, H. O., AND PINCUS, G. 1935. The effect of oestrin injection upon the developing ova of mice and rabbits. Am. J. Physiol., **111,** 201–208.

BURDICK, H. O., WHITNEY, R., AND PINCUS, G. 1937. The fate of mouse ova tube-locked by injection of oestrogenic substances. Anat. Rec., **67,** 513–519.

BURDICK, H. O., WHITNEY, R., AND EMERSON, B. 1942. Observations on the transport of tubal ova. Endocrinology, **31,** 100–108.

BUTCHER, E. O. 1927. The origin of the definitive ova in the white rat (*Mus norvegicus albinus*). Anat. Rec., **37,** 13–29.

CANIVENC, R., AND LAFFARGUE, M. 1957. Survie des blastocystes de Rat en l'absence d'hormones ovariennes Compt. rend. Acad. Sc., **254,** 1752–1754.

CASIDA, L. E., MEYER, R. K., MCSHAN, W. H., AND
WESNICKY, W. 1943. Effects of pituitary
gonadotropins on the ovaries and the induction
of superfecundity in cattle. Am. J. Vet. Res.,
4, 76–94.

CASTLE, W. E., AND GREGORY, P. W. 1929. The
embryological basis of size inheritance in the
rabbit. J. Morphol., 48, 81–93.

CHANG, M. C. 1947. Effects of testis hyaluronidase and seminal fluids on the fertilizing capacity of rabbit spermatozoa. Proc. Soc. Exper.
Biol. & Med., 66, 51–54.

CHANG, M. C. 1948a. Transplantation of fertilized rabbit ova: the effect on viability of age,
in vitro storage period, and storage temperature. Nature, London, 161, 978–979.

CHANG, M. C. 1948b. The effects of low temperature on fertilized rabbit ova in vitro, and the
normal development of ova kept at low temperature for several days. J. Gen. Physiol., 31,
385–410.

CHANG, M. C. 1949a. Effects of heterologous sera
on fertilized rabbit ova. J. Gen. Physiol., 32,
291–300.

CHANG, M. C. 1949b. The problems of superovulation and egg transfer in cattle. In Proceedings National Egg Transfer Breeding Conference, pp. 39–46. San Antonio, Texas: Foundation for Applied Research.

CHANG, M. C. 1950a. Cleavage of unfertilized
ova in immature ferrets. Anat. Rec., 108, 31–
44.

CHANG, M. C. 1950b. Fertilization, male infertility, and hyaluronidase. Ann. New York Acad.
Sc., 52, 1192–1195.

CHANG, M. C. 1950c. Development and fate of
transferred rabbit ova or blastocyst in relation
to ovulation time of recipients. J. Exper. Zool.,
114, 197–225.

CHANG, M. C. 1951a. Fertilization in relation to
the number of spermatozoa in the Fallopian
tubes of rabbits. Ann. Ostet. e Ginec., 2nd
Fasc. Spec., 918–925.

CHANG, M. C. 1951b. Fertility and sterility as revealed in the study of fertilization and development of rabbit eggs. Fertil. & Steril., 2, 205–222.

CHANG, M. C. 1951c. Fertilizing capacity of spermatozoa deposited in the Fallopian tubes. Nature, London, 168, 697–698.

CHANG, M. C. 1952a. An experimental analysis
of female sterility in the rabbit. Fertil. & Steril.,
3, 251–262.

CHANG, M. C. 1952b. Fertilizability of rabbit ova
and the effects of temperature in vitro on their
subsequent fertilization and activation in vivo.
J. Exper. Zool., 121, 351–370.

CHANG, M. C. 1953. Fertilizability of rabbit germ
cells. In Mammalian Germ Cells, pp. 226–242.
Boston: Little, Brown and Company.

CHANG, M. C. 1954. Development of parthenogenetic rabbit blastocysts induced by low temperature storage of unfertilized ova. J. Exper.
Zool., 125, 127–149.

CHANG, M. C. 1955a. The maturation of rabbit
oocytes in culture and their maturation, activa-

tion, fertilization and subsequent development
in the Fallopian tubes. J. Exper. Zool., 128,
379–406.

CHANG, M. C. 1955b. Fertilization and normal
development of follicular oocytes in the rabbit.
Science, 121, 867–869.

CHANG, M. C. 1957. Natural occurrence and artificial induction of parthenogenetic cleavage of
ferret ova. Anat. Rec., 128, 187–200.

CHANG, M. C. 1959a. Fertilization of rabbit ova
in vitro. Nature, London, 184, 466–467.

CHANG, M. C. 1959b. Fertilizing capacity of spermatozoa. In Recent Progress in the Endocrinology of Reproduction, C. W. Lloyd, Ed., pp.
131–165. New York: Academic Press, Inc.

CHANG, M. C., AND FERNANDEZ-CANO, L. 1958.
Effects of delayed fertilization on the development of pronucleus and the segmentation of
hamster ova. Anat. Rec., 132, 307–319.

CHANG, M. C., AND HUNT, D. M. 1956. Effects of
proteolytic enzymes on the zona pellucida of
fertilized and unfertilized mammalian eggs.
Exper. Cell Res., 11, 497–499.

CHANG, M. C., HUNT, D. M., AND ROMANOFF, E. B.
1958. Effects of radiocobalt irradiation of unfertilized or fertilized rabbit ova in vitro on
subsequent fertilization and development in
vivo. Anat. Rec., 132, 161–177.

CHANG, M. C., AND PINCUS, G. 1951. Physiology
of fertilization in mammals. Physiol. Rev., 31,
1–26.

CHARLTON, H. H. 1917. The fate of the unfertilized egg in the white mouse. Biol. Bull., 33,
321–331.

CHENG, T. H. 1932. The germ cell history of
Rana cantabrigensis Baird. I. Germ cell origin
and gonad formation. Ztschr. Zellforsch. mikroskop. Anat., 16, 497–541.

CHIQUOINE, A. D. 1954. The identification, origin,
and migration of the primordial germ cells in
the mouse embryo. Anat. Rec., 118, 135–146.

CHIQUOINE, A. D., AND ROTHENBERG, E. J. 1957. A
note on alkaline phosphatase activity of germ
cells in amblystoma and chick embryos. Anat.
Rec., 127, 31–35.

CLARK, R. T. 1934. Studies on the physiology of
reproduction in the sheep. II. The cleavage
stages of the ovum. Anat. Rec., 60, 135–151.

CLAUDE, A. 1941. Particulate components of the
cytoplasm. Cold Spring Harbor Symposia
Quant. Biol., 9, 263–271.

CLEWE, T. H., AND MASTROIANNI, L., JR. 1958.
Mechanisms of ovum pickup. I. Functional
capacity of rabbit oviducts ligated near the
fimbria. Fertil. & Steril., 9, 13–17.

CLEWE, T. H., AND MASTROIANNI, L., JR. 1960. A
method for continuous volumetric collection of
oviduct secretions. J. Reprod. & Fertil., 1, 146–
150.

CLEWE, T. H., YAMATE, A. M., AND NOYES, R. W.
1958. Maturation of ova in mammalian ovaries in the anterior chamber of the eye. Internat.
J. Fertil., 3, 187–192.

COCHRANE, R. L., AND MEYER, R. K. 1957. Delayed

nidation in the rat induced by progesterone. Proc. Soc. Exper. Biol. & Med., **96**, 155–159.

CORNER, G. W. 1923. The problem of embryonic pathology in mammals, with observations upon intrauterine mortality in the pig. Am. J. Anat., **31**, 523–545.

CORNER, G. W. 1928a. Cytology of the ovum, ovary and fallopian tube. In *Special Cytology*, E. V. Cowdry, Ed. Vol. 3, pp. 1567–1607. New York: Paul B. Hoeber, Inc.

CORNER, G. W. 1928b. Physiology of the corpus luteum. I. The effect of early ablation of the corpus luteum upon embryos and uterus. Am. J. Physiol., **86**, 74–81.

CORNER, G. W., AND ALLEN, W. M. 1929. Physiology of the corpus luteum. II. Production of a special uterine reaction (progestational proliferation) by extracts of the corpus luteum. Am. J. Physiol., **88**, 326–339.

CORNER, G. W., AND AMSBAUGH, A. E. 1917. Oestrus and ovulation in swine. I. The period of ovulation. Anat. Rec., **12**, 287–292.

CORNER, G. W., SR., FARRIS, E. J., AND CORNER, G. W., JR. 1950. The dating of ovulation and other ovarian crises by histological examination in comparison with the Farris test. Am. J. Obst. & Gynec., **59**, 514–528.

CROWELL, P. S. 1932. The ciliation of the oviducts of reptiles. Proc. Nat. Acad. Sc., **18**, 372–373.

CRUIKSHANK, W. 1797. Experiments in which, on the third day after impregnation, the ova of rabbits were found in the Fallopian tubes; and on the fourth day after impregnation in the uterus itself; with the first appearance of the foetus. Philos. Tr., **87**, 197–214.

CSAPO, A. 1955. The mechanism of myometrial function and its disorders. In *Modern Trends in Obstetrics and Gynaecology*, Second Series, Ch. 2, pp. 20–49. London: Butterworth and Company, Ltd.

CSAPO, A., AND CORNER, G. W. 1951. *In vitro* contracture of pseudopregnant uterine muscle contrasted with estrous motility. Endocrinology, **49**, 349–368.

CSAPO, A., AND GOODALL, M. 1954. Excitability, length tension relation and kinetics of uterine muscle contraction in relation to hormonal status. J. Physiol., **126**, 384–395.

DALCQ, A. M. 1951. New descriptive and experimental data concerning the mammalian egg, principally of the rat. I and II. Proc. Roy. Netherlands Acad. Sc. Amsterdam, **54**, 351–372; 469–479.

DALCQ, A. M. 1955. Processes of synthesis during early development of rodents' eggs and embryos. In *Proc. Soc. Stud. Fertil.*, Vol. VII, Chap. XI.

DALCQ, A. M. 1956. Effets du réactif de Schiff sur les oeufs en segmentation du rat et de la souris. Exper. Cell Res., **10**, 99–119.

DALCQ, A. M., AND JONES-SEATON, A. 1949. La répartition des éléments basophiles dans d'oeuf du rat et du lapin et son intérêt pour la mor-

phogénese. Bull. Acad. Belge. Clin. Sc., sér. 5, **35**, 500–511.

DALCQ, A. M., AND PASTEELS, J. 1955. Détermination photométrique de la teneur relative en DNA des noyaux dans les oeufs de segmentation du rat et de la souris. Exper. Cell Res., suppl., **3**, 72–97.

DAN, J. C. 1950. Sperm entrance in echinoderms, observed with the phase contrast microscope. Biol. Bull., **99**, 399–411.

DANIEL, J. F. 1910. Observation on the period of gestation in white mice. J. Exper. Zool., **9**, 865–870.

DANTSCHAKOFF, W., DANTSCHAKOFF, W., JR., AND BERESKINA, L. 1931. Keimzelle und Gonade. Identität der Urkeimzellen und der entodermalen Wanderzellen. Experimentelle Beweise. Ztschr. Zellforsch. mikroskop. Anat., **14**, 323–375.

DARON, G. H. 1936. The arterial pattern of the tunica mucosa of the uterus in *Macacus rhesus*. Am. J. Anat., **58**, 349–419.

DA SILVA SASSO, W. 1959. Existence of hyaluronic acid at the zona pellucida of the rabbit's ovum. Acta Anat., **36**, 352–357.

DAWSON, A. B. 1951. Histogenetic interrelationships of oocytes and follicle cells. Anat. Rec., **110**, 181–197.

DAWSON, A. B., AND FRIEDGOOD, H. B. 1940. The time and sequence of preovulatory changes in the cat ovary after mating or mechanical stimulation of the cervix uteri. Anat. Rec., **76**, 411–429.

DAWSON, A. B., AND KOSTERS, B. A. 1944. Preimplantation changes in the uterine mucosa of the cat. Am. J. Anat., **75**, 1–38.

DAY, F. T. 1940. Clinical and experimental observations on reproduction in the mare. J. Agric. Sc., **30**, 244–261.

DEANE, H. W. 1952. Histochemical observations on the ovary and oviduct of the albino rat during the estrous cycle. Am. J. Anat., **91**, 363–414.

DEMPSEY, E. W. 1939. Maturation and cleavage figures in ovarian ova. Anat. Rec., **75**, 223–235.

DICKMANN, Z., AND NOYES, R. W. 1960. The fate of ova transferred into the uterus of the rat. J. Reprod. & Fertil., **1**, 197–212.

DOWLING, D. F. 1949. Problems of the transplantation of fertilized ova. J. Agric. Sc., **39**, 374–396.

DOYLE, J. B. 1951. Exploratory culdotomy for observation of tubo-ovarian physiology at ovulation time. Fertil. & Steril., **2**, 475–486.

DOYLE, J. B. 1954. Ovulation and the effects of selective uterotubal denervation. Fertil. & Steril., **5**, 105–130.

DOYLE, J. B. 1956. Tubo-ovarian mechanism: observation at laparotomy. Obst. & Gynec., **8**, 686–690.

DRACY, A. E., AND PETERSEN, W. E. 1951. Technique for isolating fertilized bovine ova by flushing the uterus with physiological solutions. In *Proceedings National Egg Transfer Breeding*

Conference, pp. 13–17. San Antonio: Foundation for Applied Research.

DRAGOIU, I., BENETATO, G., AND OPREAN, R. 1937. Recherches sur la respiration des ovocytes des Mammifères. Compt. rend. Soc. biol., **126**, 1044–1046.

DUKE, K. L. 1941. The germ cells of the rabbit ovary from sex differentiation to maturity. J. Morphol., **69**, 51–81.

DURAN-REYNOLDS, F. 1929. The effect of extracts of certain organs from normal and immunized animals on the infecting power of vaccine virus. J. Exper. Med., **50**, 327–340.

DURYEE, W. R. 1954. Microdissection studies of human ovarian eggs. Tr. New York Acad. Sc., **17**, 103–108.

DZIUK, P. 1960. Frequency of spontaneous fragmentation of ova in unbred gilts. Proc. Soc. Exper. Biol. & Med., **103**, 91–92.

EDWARDS, R. G., AND GATES, A. H. 1958. Timing of the stages of the maturation divisions, ovulation, fertilization and the first cleavage of eggs of adult mice treated with gonadotrophins. J. Endocrinol., **18**, 292–304.

EDWARDS, R. G., AND SIRLIN, J. L. 1956a. Labelled pronuclei in mouse eggs fertilized by labelled sperm. Nature, London, **177**, 429.

EDWARDS, R. G., AND SIRLIN, J. L. 1956b. Studies in gametogenesis, fertilization and early development in the mouse, using radioactive tracers. In *Proceedings Second World Conference Fertility and Sterility*, pp. 18–26. International Fertility Association.

EDWARDS, R. G., AND SIRLIN, J. L. 1959. Identification of C^{14}-labelled male chromatin at fertilization in colchicine-treated mouse eggs. J. Exper. Zool., **140**, 19–27.

ELERT, R. 1947. Der Mechanismus der Eiabnahme im Laparoskop. Zentralbl. Gynäk., **69**, 38–43.

ENDERS, R. K. 1938. The ovum of the mink (*Mustela vison*). Anat. Rec., **72**, 469–471.

ENDERS, A. C. 1960. A histological study of the cortex of the ovary of the adult armadillo, with special reference to the question of neoformation of oocytes. Anat. Rec., **136**, 491–500.

'ESPINASSE, P. G. 1935. The oviducal epithelium of the mouse. J. Anat., **69**, 363–368.

ESSENBERG, J. M. 1923. Sex-differentiation in the viviparous teleost *Xiphophrous helleri* Heckel. Biol. Bull., **45**, 46–97.

EVANS, E. I., AND MILLER, F. W. 1935. An unfertilized tubal ovum in the cow. Anat. Rec., **62**, 25–30.

EVANS, H. M., AND COLE, H. H. 1931. An introduction to the study of the oestrous cycle in the dog. Mem. Univ. California, **9**, 66–118.

EVANS, H. M., AND SWEZY, O. 1931. Ovogenesis and the normal follicular cycle in adult mammalia. Mem. Univ. California, **9**, 119–225.

EVERETT, N. B. 1945. The present status of the germ-cell problem in vertebrates. Biol. Rev., **20**, 45–55.

FANKHAUSER, G., AND MOORE, C. 1941. Cytological and experimental studies of polyspermy in the newt, *Triturus viridescens*. I. Normal fertilization. J. Morphol., **68**, 347–385.

FARRIS, E. J. 1947. Critical evaluation of methods of hyaluronidase assay in human semen. In *Proceedings Third Conference Sterility and Fertility*, p. 112.

FAWCETT, D. W. 1950. Development of mouse ova under the capsule of the kidney. Anat. Rec., **108**, 71–92.

FAWCETT, D. W., AND PORTER, K. R. 1954. A study of the fine structure of ciliated epithelial cells with the electron microscope. Anat. Rec., **113**, 33.

FAWCETT, D. W., AND WISLOCKI, B. 1950. Histochemical observations of the human Fallopian tube. J. Nat. Cancer Inst., **12**, 213–214.

FAWCETT, D. W., WISLOCKI, G. B., AND WALDO, C. M. 1947. The development of mouse ova in the anterior chamber of the eye and in the abdominal cavity. Am. J. Anat., **81**, 413–443.

FEKETE, E. 1947. Differences in the effect of uterine environment upon development in the DBA and C^{57} black strains of mice. Anat. Rec., **98**, 409–415.

FEKETE, E., AND DURAN-REYNOLDS, F. 1943. Hyaluronidase in fertilization of mammalian ova. Proc. Soc. Exper. Biol. & Med., **52**, 119–121.

FEKETE, E., AND LITTLE, C. C. 1942. Observations on the mammary tumor incidence in mice born from transferred ova. Cancer Res., **2**, 525–530.

FIRKET, J. 1914. Recherches sur l'organogénèse des glandes sexuelles chez les oiseaux. Arch. Biol., **29**, 201–351.

FISCHBERG, M., AND BEATTY, R. A. 1952a. Heteroploidy in mammals. II. Induction of triploidy in pre-implantation mouse eggs. J. Genet., **50**, 455–470.

FISCHBERG, M., AND BEATTY, R. A. 1952b. Heteroploidy in mouse embryos due to crossing of inbred strains. Evolution, **6**, 316–324.

FISCHEL, A. 1914. Zur normalen Anatomie und Physiologie der weiblichen Geschlechtsorgane von Mus decumanus sowie über die experimentelle Erzeugung von Hydro- und Pyosalpinx. Arch. Entwicklungsmech. Organ., **39**, 578–616.

FLICKINGER, R. A., AND SCHJEIDE, O. A. 1957. The localization of phosphorus and the site of calcium binding in the yolk protein of the frog's egg. Exper. Cell Res., **13**, 312–316.

FRAENKEL, L. 1903. Die Function des Corpus Luteum. Arch. Gynäk., **68**, 438–545.

FRAZER, J. F. D. 1955. The site of implantation of ova in the rat. J. Embryol. & Exper. Morphol., **3**, 332–334.

FREDRICSSON, B. 1959a. Studies on the morphology and histochemistry of the Fallopian tube epithelium. Acta Anat., **38**, 5–23.

FREDRICSSON, B. 1959b. Proliferation of rabbit oviduct epithelium after estrogenic stimulation, with reference to the relationship between ciliated and secretory cells. Acta morphol. neerl. scandinav., **2**, 193–202.

FREDRICSSON, B. 1959c. Histochemical observations on the epithelium of human Fallopian tubes. Acta obst. et gynec. scandinav., **38**, 109–134.

FRIDHANDLER, L., HAFEZ, E. S. E., AND PINCUS, G. 1957. Developmental changes in the respiratory activity of rabbit ova. Exper. Cell Res., **13**, 132–139.

FRIEDGOOD, H. B., AND PINCUS, G. 1935. The nervous control of the anterior pituitary as indicated by maturation of ova and ovulation after stimulation of cervical sympathetics. Endocrinology, **19**, 710–718.

FRIEDMAN, M. H. 1929. Mechanism of ovulation in the rabbit. II. Ovulation produced by the injection of urine from pregnant woman. Am. J. Physiol., **90**, 617–622.

FRIZ, M. 1959. Experimenteller Beitrag zur Frage der Milieübeziehungen frühester Entwicklungsstudien des Säugereies. Gynaecologia, **148**, 215–224.

FRIZ, M., AND MEY, R. 1959. Ist das Ei während seiner Wanderung autark? Ztschr. Geburtsh. Gynäk., **154**, 1–8.

GAILLARD, C. J. 1950. Sex cell formation in explants of the foetal human ovarian cortex. Konink. Nederl. Akad. Wetensch., **53**, 1300–1316.

GATENBY, J. B., AND WOODGER, J. H. 1920. On the relationship between the formation of yolk and the mitochondria and Golgi apparatus during oogenesis. J. Roy. Microscop. Soc., **41**, 129–156.

GATES, A. H., AND BEATTY, R. A. 1954. Independence of delayed fertilization and spontaneous triploidy in mouse embryos. Nature, London, **174**, 356–357.

GATES, A., AND RUNNER, M. 1952. Factors affecting survival of transplanted ova of the mouse. Anat. Rec., **113**, 555.

GEMMILL, J. F. 1900. On the vitality of the ova and spermatozoa of certain animals. J. Anat. & Physiol., **34**, 163–181.

GILCHRIST, F., AND PINCUS, G. 1932. Living rat eggs. Anat. Rec., **54**, 275–287.

GLICK, D., AND MOORE, D. H. 1948. Hyaluronidase inhibitor in electrophoretically separated fractions of human serum. Arch. Biochem., **19**, 173–175.

GRAVE, B. H., AND OLIPHANT, J. F. 1930. The longevity of unfertilized gametes. Biol. Bull., **59**, 233–239.

GREEN, S. H., AND ZUCKERMAN, S. 1951a. The number of oocytes in the mature rhesus monkey (*Macaca mulatta*). J. Endocrinol., **7**, 194–202.

GREEN, S. H., AND ZUCKERMAN, S. 1951b. Quantitative aspects of the growth of the human ovum and follicle. J. Anat., **85**, 373–375.

GREEN, S. H., AND ZUCKERMAN, S. 1954. Further observations on oocyte numbers in mature rhesus monkeys (*Macaca mulatta*). J. Endocrinol., **10**, 284–290.

GREEN, W. W., AND WINTERS, L. M. 1935. Studies on the physiology of reproduction in the sheep. III. The time of ovulation and rate of sperm travel. Anat. Rec., **61**, 457–469.

GREENWALD, G. S. 1958a. Endocrine regulation of the secretion of mucin in the tubal epithelium of the rabbit. Anat. Rec., **130**, 477–495.

GREENWALD, G. S. 1958b. Formation of deciduomata in the lactating mouse. J. Endocrinol., **17**, 24–28.

GREENWALD, G. S. 1959. Tubal transport of ova in the rabbit. Anat. Rec., **133**, 368.

GREENWALD, G. S., AND EVERETT, N. B. 1959. The incorporation of S^{35}-methionine by the uterus and ova of the mouse. Anat. Rec., **134**, 171–184.

GREGORY, P. W. 1930. The early embryology of the rabbit. Contr. Embryol., Carnegie Inst. Washington, **21**, 141–168.

GREGORY, P. W., AND CASTLE, W. F. 1931. Further studies on the embryological basis of size inheritance in the rabbit. J. Exper. Zool., **59**, 199–211.

GRESSON, R. A. R. 1933. A study of the cytoplasmic inclusions and nuclear phenomena during the oogenesis of the mouse. Quart. J. Microscop. Sc., **75**, 697–721.

GRESSON, R. A. R. 1940. A cytological study of the centrifuged oocyte of the mouse. Quart. J. Microscop. Sc., **81**, 569–583.

GRESSON, R. A. R. 1941. A study of the cytoplasmic inclusions during maturation, fertilization and the first cleavage division of the egg of the mouse. Quart. J. Microscop. Sc., **83**, 35–59.

GRESSON, R. A. R. 1948. Fertilization, parthenogenesis, and the origin of the primitive germ-cell of some animals. In *Essentials of General Cytology*, pp. 64–75. Edinburgh: University Press.

GUTHRIE, M. J., AND JEFFERS, K. R. 1938. The ovaries of the bat *Myotis lucifugus lucifugus* after injection of hypophyseal extract. Anat. Rec., **72**, 11–36.

HADEK, R. 1953. Mucin secretion in the ewe's oviduct. Nature, London, **171**, 750.

HADEK, R. 1955. The secretory process in the sheep's oviduct. Anat. Rec., **121**, 187–205.

HADEK, R. 1958. Intraperitoneal insemination of rabbit doe. Proc. Soc. Exper. Biol. & Med., **99**, 39–40.

HAFEZ, E. S. E., AND PINCUS, G. 1956a. Inhibition of implantation by deciduoma formation in the rabbit. Fertil. & Steril., **7**, 422–429.

HAFEZ, E. S. E., AND PINCUS, G. 1956b. Hormonal requirements of implantation in the rabbit. Proc. Soc. Exper. Biol. & Med., **91**, 531–534.

HAHN, L., AND FRANK, E. 1953. Synthetic inhibitors of hyaluronidase. II. New polycondensed diphenylmethane and triphenylmethane derivatives. Acta. chem. scandinav., **7**, 806–812.

HALL, B. V. 1935. The reactions of rat and mouse eggs to hydrogen ions. Proc. Soc. Exper. Biol. & Med., **32**, 747–748.

HAMILTON, W. J. 1934. The early stages in the development of the ferret. Fertilisation to the formation of the prochordal plate. Tr. Roy. Soc. Edinburgh, **58**, 251–278.

HAMILTON, W. J. 1944. Phases of maturation and fertilization in human ova. J. Anat., **78**, 1–4.

HAMILTON, W. J., AND DAY, F. T. 1945. Cleavage stages of the ova of the horse, with notes on ovulation. J. Anat., **79**, 127–130.

HAMILTON, W. J., AND LAING, J. A. 1946. Development of the egg of the cow up to the stage of blastocyst formation. J. Anat., **80**, 194–204.

HAMLETT, G. W. D. 1935. Notes on the embryology of a Phyllostamid bat. Am. J. Anat., **56**, 327–353.

HAMMOND, J. 1934. The fertilisation of rabbit ova in relation to time. A method of controlling litter size, the duration of pregnancy and weight of young at birth. J. Exper. Biol., **11**, 140–161.

HAMMOND, J., AND WALTON, A. 1934. Notes on ovulation and fertilisation in the ferret. J. Exper. Biol., **11**, 307–319.

HAMMOND, J., JR. 1949. Recovery and culture of tubal mouse ova. Nature, London, **163**, 28–29.

HAMMOND, J., JR. 1950a. Induced twin ovulation and multiple pregnancy in cattle. J. Agric. Sc., **39**, 222–225.

HAMMOND, J., JR. 1950b. The possibility of artificial pregnancy in cattle. J. Ministry Agric., **57**, 67–70.

HAMPTON, J. C. 1958. An electron microscope study of the hepatic uptake and excretion of submicroscopic particles injected into the blood stream and into the bile duct. Acta Anat., **32**, 262–291.

HANCOCK, J. L. 1959. Polyspermy of pig ova. Anim. Prod., **1**, 103–106.

HARGITT, G. T. 1930. The formation of the sex glands and germ cells of mammals. V. Germ cells in the ovaries of adult, pregnant, and senile albino rats. J. Morphol. & Physiol., **50**, 453–473.

HARRISON, R. J., AND NEAL, E. G. 1959. Delayed implantation in the badger (*Meles meles* L.). In *Implantation of Ova*, P. Eckstein, Ed., pp. 19–25. London: Cambridge University Press.

HARTER, B. T. 1948. Glycogen and carbohydrate-protein complexes in the ovary of the white rat during the oestrous cycle. Anat. Rec., **100**, 40.

HARTMAN, C. G. 1916. Studies on the development of the opossum (*Didelphys virginiana* L.) I. History of early cleavage. II. Formation of the blastocyst. J. Morphol., **27**, 1–83.

HARTMAN, C. G. 1924. Observations on the viability of the mammalian ovum. Am. J. Obst. & Gynec., **7**, 40–43.

HARTMAN, C. G. 1928. The breeding season of the opossum (*Didelphys virginiana* L.) and the rate of intra-uterine and postnatal development. J. Morphol. & Physiol., **46**, 143–215.

HARTMAN, C. G. 1929. How large is the mammalian egg? A review. Quart. Rev. Biol., **4**, 373–388.

HARTMAN, C. G. 1932. Ovulation and the transport and viability of ova and sperm in the female genital tract. In *Sex and Internal Secretions*, 1st ed., E. Allen, Ed., pp. 674–733. Baltimore: The Williams & Wilkins Company.

HARTMAN, C. G. 1936. *The Time of Ovulation in Women*. Baltimore: The Williams & Wilkins Company.

HARTMAN, C. G. 1939. Ovulation, fertilization and the transport and viability of eggs and spermatozoa. In *Sex and Internal Secretions*, 2nd ed., E. Allen, C. H. Danforth and E. A. Doisy, Eds., pp. 630–719. Baltimore: The Williams & Wilkins Company.

HARTMAN, C. G. 1944. Recovery of primate eggs and embryos. Methods and data on the time of ovulation. West. J. Surg., **52**, 41–61.

HARTMAN, C. G., AND CORNER, G. W. 1941. The first maturation division of the Macaque ovum. Contr. Embryol., Carnegie Inst. Washington, **29**, 1–6.

HARTMAN, C. G., LEWIS, W. H., MILLER, F. W., AND SWEET, W. W. 1931. First findings of tubal ova in the cow, together with notes on oestrus. Anat. Rec., **48**, 267–275.

HARVEY, E. B. 1958. Tubal ovum in Ochotonidae (Lagomorpha). Anat. Rec., **132**, 113–120.

HEAPE, W. 1886. The development of the mole (*Talpa europea*), the ovarian ovum, and segmentation of the ovum. Quart. J. Microscop. Sc., **26**, 157–174.

HEAPE, W. 1890. Preliminary note on the transplantation and growth of mammalian ova within a uterine foster-mother. Proc. Roy. Soc., **48**, 457–458.

HEAPE, W. 1905. Ovulation and degeneration of ova in the rabbit. Proc. Roy. Soc., ser. B, **76**, 260–268.

HENNEGUY, L. F. 1926. Sur la situation de l'appareil de Golgi dans les cellules folliculaires de l'ovaire de Cobaye. Compt. rend. Soc. biol., **94**, 764.

HENSEN, V. 1869. Über die Züchtung unbefruchteter Eier. Zentralbl. med. Wiss., **7**, 403–404.

HENSEN, V. 1876. Beobachtung über die Befruchtung und Entwicklung des Kaninchens und Meerschweinchens. Ztschr. Anat., **1**, 213–273.

HERTIG, A. T., AND ROCK, J. 1951. Two human ova of the pre-villous stage, having an ovulation age of about eleven and twelve days respectively. Contr. Embryol., Carnegie Inst. Washington, **29**, 127–156.

HEUSER, C. H., AND STREETER, G. L. 1929. Early stages in the development of pig embryos, from the period of initial cleavage to the time of the appearance of limb-buds. Contr. Embryol., Carnegie Inst. Washington, **20**, 1–30.

HEUSER, C. H., AND STREETER, G. L. 1941. Development of the Macaque embryo. Contr. Embryol., Carnegie Inst. Washington, **29**, 15–55.

HEYS, F. 1931. The problem of the origin of germ cells. Quart. Rev. Biol., **6**, 1–45.

HILL, J. P. 1933. The development of the Monotremata. II. The structure of the egg-shell. Tr. Zool. Soc., London, **21**, 413.

HILL, J. P., AND TRIBE, M. 1924. The early development of the cat (*Felis domestica*). Quart. J. Microscop. Sc., **68**, 514–602.

HINSEY, J. C., AND MARKEE, J. E. 1933. Studies on prolan-induced ovulation in midbrain and midbrain-hypophysectomized rabbits. Am. J. Physiol., **106**, 48–54.

HOADLEY, L., AND SIMONS, D. 1928. Maturation phases in human oocytes. Am. J. Anat., **41**, 497–509.

HOLTFRETER, J. 1946a. Experiments on the formed inclusions of the amphibian egg. I. The effect of pH and electrolytes on yolk and lipochondria. J. Exper. Zool., **101**, 355–405.

HOLTFRETER, J. 1946b. Experiments on the formed inclusions of the amphibian egg. III. Observations on microsomes, vacuoles, and on the process of yolk resorption. J. Exper. Zool., **103**, 81–112.

HOOKER, C. W., AND FORBES, T. R. 1949. Specificity of the intrauterine test for progesterone. Endocrinology, **45**, 71–74.

HUBER, G. C. 1915. The development of the albino rat, *Mus norvegicus albinus*. I. From the pronuclear stage to the stage of the mesoderm anlage; end of the first to the end of the ninth day. J. Morphol., **26**, 247–358.

INGRAM, D. L. 1956. Observations on the ovary cultured *in vitro*. J. Endocrinol., **14**, 155–159.

ITO, S., AND MAÉNO, T. 1960. Resting potential and activation potential of the Oryzias egg. I. Response to electrical stimulation. Kumamoto J. Sc., **5**, 100–107.

IVY, A. C., HARTMAN, C. G., AND KOFF, A. 1931. The contractions of the monkey uterus at term. Am. J. Obst. & Gynec., **22**, 388–399.

JOHNSTON, J. E., AND MIXNER, J. P. 1950. Relationship of hyaluronidase concentration to fertility of dairy bull semen. J. Dairy Sc., **33**, 847–850.

JOLLY, J., AND LIEURE, C. 1938. Recherches sur la culture des oeufs des mammifères. Arch. Anat. microscop., **34**, 307–373.

JONES-SEATON, A. 1949. A study of cytoplasmic basophily in the egg of the rat and some other mammals. Ann. Soc. Roy. Zool. Belgique, **80**, 76–86.

JUNGE, J. M., AND BLANDAU, R. J. 1958. Studies on the electrophoretic properties of the cornual fluids of rats in heat. Fertil. & Steril., **9**, 353–367.

KELLOG, M. 1945. The postnatal development of the oviduct of the rat. Anat. Rec., **93**, 377–399.

KING, H. D. 1913. Some anomalies in the gestation of the albino rat. Biol. Bull., **24**, 377–391.

KINGERY, H. M. 1917. Oogenesis in the white mouse. J. Morphol., **30**, 261–316.

KIRBY, D. R. 1960. Development of mouse eggs beneath the kidney capsule. Nature, London, **187**, 707–708.

KIRKHAM, W. B. 1907. The maturation of the mouse egg. Biol. Bull., **12**, 259–265.

KIRKHAM, W. B. 1916. The prolonged gestation in suckling mice. Anat. Rec., **11**, 31–40.

KIRKHAM, W. B., AND BURR, H. S. 1913. The breeding habits, maturation of eggs and ovulation of the albino rat. Am. J. Anat., **15**, 291–317.

KIRKMAN, H., AND SEVERINGHAUS, A. E. 1938. A review of the Golgi apparatus. I and II. Anat. Rec., **70**, 413–431; 557–575.

KNAUS, H. 1927. Experimentelle Untersuchungen zur Physiologie und Pharmakologie der Uterusmuskulatur im Puerperium. Arch. exper. Path. u. Pharamakol., **134**, 225–246.

KNEER, M., BURGER, H., AND SIMMER, H. 1952. Über die Atmung der Schleimhaut menschlicher Eileiter. Arch. Gynäk., **181**, 561–574.

KNEER, M., AND CLESS, H. 1951. Flimmerung und Strömung im menschlichen Eileiter. Geburtsh. u. Frauenh., **11**, 233–239.

KODICEK, E., AND LUTWAK-MANN, C. 1957. The pattern of distribution of thiamine, riboflavin and nicotinic acid in the early rabbit embryo. J. Endocrinol., **15**, liii–liv.

KOK, F. 1926. Bewegund des muskulösen. Rohres der Fallopischen Tube. Arch. Gynäk., **127**, 384–430.

KONECNY, M. 1959. Étude histochimique de la zone pellucide des ovules de Chatte. Compt. rend. Soc. biol., **153**, 893–894.

KREHBIEL, R. H. 1937. Cytological studies of the decidual reaction in the rat during early pregnancy and in the production of deciduomata. Physiol. Zool., **10**, 212–233.

KREHBIEL, R. H. 1941. The effects of theelin on delayed implantation in the pregnant lactating rat. Anat. Rec., **81**, 381–392.

KREHBIEL, R. H. 1946. Distribution of ova in combined uteri of unilaterally ovariectomised rats. Anat. Rec., **96**, 323–340.

KREMER, J. 1924. Das Verhalten der Vorkerne im befruchteten Ei der Ratte und der Maus mit besonderer Berücksichtigung ihrer Nucleolen. Ztschr. mikroskop. Anat., **1**, 353–390.

KURZROK, R., LEONARD, S. L., AND CONRAD, H. 1946. Role of hyaluronidase in human fertility. Am. J. Med., **1**, 491–506.

KVASNICKII, A. U. 1951. Opyt mejporodnoi peresadkĭ jaĭcekletok. Experiments with intergeneric transplants of ova. Sovet. Zootekh., **1**, 36–42. In Anim. Breed. Abst., **19**, 224, 1951.

LAMS, H. 1913. Etude de l'oeuf de Cobaye aux premiers stades de l'embryogenèse. Arch. biol., **28**, 229–323.

LAMS, H., AND DOORME, J. 1908. Nouvelles recherches sur la maturation et la fécondation de l'oeuf des mammifères. Arch. biol., **23**, 259–365.

LANGLEY, W. H. 1911. The maturation of the egg and ovulation in the domestic cat. Am. J. Anat., **12**, 139–172.

LATASTE, F. 1887. Recherches de Zooethique sur les Mammifères de l'orde des Rongeurs. Acta Soc. Linneus Bordeau, **40**, 202.

LATTA, J. S., AND PEDERSON, E. S. 1944. The origin of ova and follicle cells from the germinal epithelium of the ovary of the albino rat as demonstrated by selective intravital staining with India ink. Anat. Rec., **90**, 23–35.

LEACH, E. H. 1947. Bismark Brown as a stain for mucoproteins. Stain Technol., **22**, 73–76.

LEBLOND, C. P. 1950. Distribution of periodic acid reactive carbohydrates in the adult rat. Am. J. Anat., **86**, 1–50.

LEE, T. G. 1903. Implantation of the ovum in *Spermaphilus tridecemlineatus* Mitch. In *Mark Anniversary Volume*, pp. 419–436.

LENHOSSEK, M. 1911. In *Fejlödéstani Jergyzetek*, L. Nagy, Ed. Budapest: Mai Henrik és Fia.

LEONARD, S. L., AND KURZROK, R. 1945. A study of hyalurodidase: effects on the follicle cells of ovulated rat ova. Endocrinology, **37**, 171–176.

LEONARD, S. L., PERLMAN, P. L., AND KURZROK, R. 1947. Relation between time of fertilization and follicle-cell dispersal in rat ova. Proc. Soc. Exper. Biol. & Med., **66**, 517–518.

LEVI, G. 1915. Il comportamento dei condriosomi durante i piu precoci periodi dello suiluppo dei mammiferi. Arch. Zellforsch., **13**, 471–524.

LEWIS, W. H., AND GREGORY, P. W. 1929. Cinematographs of living developing rabbit-eggs. Science, **69**, 226–229.

LEWIS, W. H., AND HARTMAN, C. G. 1933. Early cleavage stages of the eggs of the monkey (*Macacus rhesus*). Contr. Embryol., Carnegie Inst. Washington, **24**, 187–201.

LEWIS, W. H., AND HARTMAN, C. G. 1941. Tubal ova of the rhesus monkey. Contr. Embryol., Carnegie Inst. Washington, **29**, 1–6.

LEWIS, W. H., AND WRIGHT, E. S. 1935. On the early development of the mouse egg. Contr. Embryol., Carnegie Inst. Washington, **25**, 113–146.

LILLIE, F. R. 1913. The mechanism of fertilization. Science, **38**, 524–528.

LILLIE, F. R. 1919. *Problems of Fertilization.* Chicago: University of Chicago Press.

LIM, R., AND CHAO, C. 1927. On the mechanism of the transportation of ova. I. Rabbit uterus. Chinese J. Physiol., **1**, 175–198.

LIN, T. P. 1956. DL-Methionine (sulphur-35) for labelling unfertilised mouse eggs in transplantation. Nature, London, **178**, 1175–1176.

LOEB, J. 1913. *Artificial Parthenogenesis and Fertilization.* Chicago: University of Chicago Press.

LOEB, L. 1908. The production of deciduomata. J. A. M. A., **50**, 1897–1901.

LONG, J. A. 1912. III. The living eggs of rats and mice, with a description of apparatus for obtaining and observing them. Univ. California Pub. Zool., **9**, 105–136.

LONG, J. A. 1940. Growth *in vitro* of ovarian germinal epithelium. Contr. Embryol., Carnegie Inst. Washington, **28**, 91–96.

LONG, J. A., AND EVANS, H. M. 1922. The oestrus cycle in the rat and its associated phenomena. Mem. Univ. California, **6**, 1–148.

LONG, J. A., AND MARK, E. L. 1911. The maturation of the egg of the mouse. Carnegie Inst. Washington, No. 142, 1–72.

LUTWAK-MANN, C. 1955. Carbonic anhydrase in the female reproductive tract. Occurrence, distribution and hormonal dependence. J. Endocrinol., **13**, 26–38.

LUTWAK-MANN, C. 1959. Biochemical approach to the study of ovum implantation in the rabbit. In *Implantation of Ova*, P. Eckstein, Ed., pp. 35–49. London: Cambridge University Press.

LUTWAK-MANN, C., AND ADAMS, C. E. 1957a. The effect of methyloestronolone on endometrial carbonic anhydrase and its ability to maintain pregnancy in the castrated rabbit. Acta endocrinol., **25**, 405–411.

LUTWAK-MANN, C., AND ADAMS, C. E. 1957b. Carbonic anhydrase in the female reproductive tract. II. Endometrial carbonic anhydrase as indicator of luteoid potency: correlation with progestational proliferation. J. Endocrinol., **15**, 43–55.

LUTWAK-MANN, C., AND LASER, H. 1954. Bicarbonate content of the blastocyst fluid and carbonic anhydrase in the pregnant rabbit uterus. Nature, London, **173**, 268–269.

MACDONALD, E., AND LONG, J. A. 1934. Some features of cleavage in the living egg of the rat. Am. J. Anat., **55**, 343–361.

MACLAREN, W., AND BRYCE, T. H. 1933. The early stages in development of cavia. Tr. Roy. Soc. Edinburgh, **57**, 647–664.

MAÉNO, T. 1959. Electrical characteristics and activation potential of *Bufo* eggs. J. Gen. Physiol., **43**, 139–157.

MAINLAND, D. J. 1930. Early development of ferret: the pronuclei. J. Anat., **64**, 262–287.

MANDL, A. M., AND SHELTON, M. 1959. A quantitative study of oocytes in young and old nulliparous laboratory rats. J. Endocrinol., **18**, 444–450.

MANDL, A. M., AND ZUCKERMAN, S. 1951. The effect of destruction of the germinal epithelium on the numbers of oocytes. J. Endocrinol., **7**, 103–111.

MANN, M. C. 1924. Cytological changes in unfertilized tubal eggs of the rat. Biol. Bull., **46**, 316–327.

MANN, T. 1954. *The Biochemistry of Semen.* New York: John Wiley and Sons, Inc.

MARDEN, W. G. R., AND CHANG, M. C. 1952. The aerial transport of mammalian ova for transplantation. Science, **115**, 705–706.

MARKEE, J. E. 1940. Menstruation in intraocular endometrial transplants in the rhesus monkey. Contr. Embryol., Carnegie Inst. Washington, **28**, 223–308.

MARKEE, J. E. 1944. Intrauterine distribution of ova in the rabbit. Anat. Rec., **88**, 329–336.

MARKEE, J. E., AND HINSEY, J. C. 1933. Internal migration of ova in the cat. Proc. Soc. Exper. Biol. & Med., **31**, 267–270.

MARTINOVITCH, P. M. 1939. The effect of subnormal temperature on the differentiation and survival of cultivated *in vitro* embryonic and infantile rat and mouse ovaries. Proc. Roy. Soc. London, ser. B., **128**, 138–143.

MASTROIANNI, L., JR., BEER, F., SHAH, U., AND CLEWE, T. 1961. Endocrine regulation of oviduct secretions in the rabbit. Endocrinology, **68,** 92–100.

Mastroianni, L., Jr., Winternitz, W. W., and Lowi, N. P. 1958. The *in vitro* metabolism of the human endosalpinx. Fertil. & Steril., **9,** 500–509.

Mayer, G. 1959. Recent studies on hormonal control of delayed implantation and super-implantation in the rat. In *Implantation of Ova,* P. Eckstein, Ed., pp. 76–83. London: Cambridge University Press.

McAlpine, R. J. 1955. Alkaline glycerophosphatase in the developing adrenal, gonads, and reproductive tract of the white rat (abstr.). Anat. Rec., **121,** 407–408.

McClean, D., and Rowlands, I. W. 1942. Role of hyaluronidase in fertilization. Nature, London, **150,** 627–628.

McCrady, E. 1938. The embryology of the opossum. Am. Anat. Mem., No. 16, 11–125.

McGeachin, R. L., Hargan, L. A., Potter, B. A., and Daus, A. T., Jr. 1958. Amylase in Fallopian tubes. Proc. Soc. Exper. Biol. & Med., **99,** 130–131.

McKay, D. S., Hertig, A. T., Adams, E. C., and Danziger, S. 1953. Histochemical observations on the germ cells of human embryos. Anat. Rec., **117,** 201–220.

McKenzie, F. F., and Allen, E. 1933. The estrual cycle in the ewe; a histological study of the genital tract of the non-pregnant ewe. Missouri Agric. Exper. Sta. Res. Bull., No. 328, 14.

McKenzie, F. F., and Terrill, C. E. 1937. Estrus, ovulation and related phenomena in the ewe. Missouri Agric. Exper. Sta. Res. Bull., No. 264.

McLaren, A., and Biggers, J. D. 1958. Successful development and birth of mice cultivated *in vitro* as early embryos. Nature, London, **182,** 877–878.

McLaren, A., and Michie, D. 1956. Studies on the transfer of fertilized mouse eggs to uterine foster mothers. I. Factors affecting the implantation and survival of native and transferred eggs. J. Exper. Biol., **33,** 394–416.

McLaren, A., and Michie, D. 1956. The spacing of implantations in the mouse uterus. In *Implantation of Ova,* P. Eckstein, Ed., pp. 65–75. London: Cambridge University Press.

Menkin, M. F., and Rock, J. 1948. *In vitro* fertilization and cleavage of human ovarian eggs. Am. J. Obst. & Gynec., **55,** 440–452.

Meyer, K., and Rapport, M. M. 1952. Hyaluronidases. Advances Enzymol., **13,** 199–236.

Michelson, L., Haman, J. O., and Koets, P. 1949. A study of hyaluronidase in the semen of the husband in infertile marriages. J. Urol., **61,** 799–802.

Milio, G. 1960. Alkaline phosphatase activity and PAS reactivity of the tubal epithelium of *Rattus albino.* Boll. Soc. ital. biol. sper., **36,** 394–396.

Miller, B. J., and Reimann, S. P. 1940. Effect of dl-methionine and l-cysteine on the cleavage

rate of mammalian eggs. Arch. Path., **29,** 181–188.

Mintz, B. 1957. Embryological development of primordial germ-cells in the mouse: influence of a new mutation, W^J. J. Embryol. & Exper. Morphol., **5,** 396–403.

Mintz, B. 1958. Irradiation of primordial germ cells in the mouse embryo. Anat. Rec., **130,** 341.

Mintz, B., and Russell, E. S. 1957. Gene-induced embryological modifications of primordial germ cells in the mouse. J. Exper. Zool., **134,** 207–238.

Moog, F., and Lutwak-Mann, C. 1958. Observations on rabbit blastocysts prepared as flat mounts. J. Embryol. & Exper. Morphol., **6,** 57–67.

Moore, C. R., and Wang, H. 1947. Ovarian activity in mammals subsequent to chemical injury of cortex. Physiol. Zool., **20,** 300–321.

Moore, J. E. S. 1908. On the maturation of the ovum in the guinea-pig. Proc. Roy. Soc., ser. B, **80,** 285–287.

Moricard, R. 1933. Zone de Golgi du follicule ovarien. (Discussion sur la fonction du liquide folliculaire et de la folliculine). Ann. anat. path., **10,** 1222–1226.

Moricard, R., and Bossu, J. 1951. Arrival of fertilizing sperm at the follicular cell of the secondary oöcyte. Fertil. & Steril., **2,** 260–266.

Moricard, R., Bossu, J., and Moricard, F. 1950. Premières observations de la pénétration du spermatozoide dans la membrane pellucide d'ovocytes de lapines fécondées *in vitro*; niveau de potential d'oxydo-reduction de la sécretion tubaire. An. brasil. ginec., **30,** 81–92.

Moricard, R., and Gothié, S. 1953. Hormonal mechanisms of the first polar body formation in the follicle. In *Mammalian Germ Cells,* pp. 180–197. Boston: Little, Brown & Company.

Moricard, R., and Gothié, S. 1955. Etude de la répartition en S^35 dans les cellules folliculaires périovocytaires au cours de l'ovogenèse et de la terminaison de la première mitose de maturation chez la lapine adulte. Compt. rend. Soc. biol., **149,** 1918–1922.

Moricard, R., and Gothié, S. 1957. De l'utilisation des traceurs 32 P et 35 S en physiologie sexuele. Rev. gynec. e obst., **100,** 19–34.

Mossman, H. W. 1937. Comparative morphogenesis of the fetal membranes and accessory uterine structures. Contr. Embryol., Carnegie Inst. Washington, **26,** 129–246.

Mrsić, W. 1923. Die Spätbefruchtung und deren Einfluss auf Entwicklung und Geschlechtsbildung, experimentelle nachgeprüt an der Regenbogenforelle. Arch. mikroskop. Anat., **98,** 129–206.

Mrsić, W. 1930. Über die Eireifung bei der Forelle und deren Bedeutung für die übliche Methode der Künstlichen Laichgewinnung. Arch. Hydrobiol., **21,** 649–678.

Myers, H. I., Young, W. C., and Dempsey, E. W. 1936. Graafian follicle development throughout the reproductive cycle in the guinea pig, with especial reference to changes during oestrus (sexual receptivity). Anat. Rec., **65**, 381–401.

NAEGL, W. 1888. Das menschliche Ei. Arch. mikroskop. Anat., **31**, 342–423.

NALBANDOV, A. V., AND ST. CLAIR, L. E. 1958. Relation of the nervous system to implantation. In Proceedings Third Symposium on Reproduction and Infertility, F. X. Gassner, Ed. New York: Pergamon Press.

NATH, V. 1960. Hstochemistry of lipids in oogenesis. Int. Rev. Cytol., **9**, 305–320.

NEEDHAM, J. 1950. *Biochemistry and Morphogenesis*. London: Cambridge University Press.

NICHOLAS, J. S. 1933. Development of transplanted rat eggs. Proc. Soc. Exper. Biol. & Med., **30**, 1111–1113.

NICHOLAS, J. S. 1936. The development of the rat egg after its implantation in a foreign cavity. Anat. Rec., Suppl., **67**, 33–34.

NICHOLAS, J. S. 1942. Experiments on developing rats. IV. The growth and differentiation of eggs and egg-cylinders when transplanted under the kidney capsule. J. Exper. Zool., **90**, 41–64.

NICHOLAS, J. S. 1947. Experimental approaches to problems of early development in the rat. Quart. Rev. Biol., **22**, 179–195.

NICHOLAS, J. S., AND HALL, B. V. 1942. Experiments on developing rats. II. The development of isolated blastomeres and fused eggs. J. Exper. Zool., **90**, 441–458.

NIEUWKOOP, P. D. 1949. The present state of the problem of the "Keimbahn" in the vertebrates. Experientia, **5**, 308–312.

NIEUWKOOP, P. D., AND SUMINSKI, E. H. 1959. Does the so-called "germinal cytoplasm" play an important role in the development of the primordial germ cells? Arch. Anat. microscop et Morphol. expér., Suppl., **48**, 189–198.

NIHOUL, J. 1926. Recherches sur l'appareil endocellulaire de Golgi dans les premières stades du développment des mammifères. La Cellule, **37**, 23–40.

NILSSON, O. 1957. Observations on a type of cilia in the rat oviduct. J. Ultrastruct. Res., **1**, 170–177.

NOVAK, E., AND EVERETT, H. S. 1928. Cyclical and other variations in the tubal epithelium. Am. J. Obst. & Gynec., **16**, 499–530.

NOYES, R. W. 1952. Fertilization of follicular ova. Fertil. & Steril., **3**, 1–12.

NOYES, R. W. 1953. The fertilizing capacity of spermatozoa. West. J. Surg., **61**, 342–349.

NOYES, R. W., ADAMS, C. E., AND WALTON, A. 1959. The transport of ova in relation to the dosage of oestrogen in ovariectomized rats. J. Endocrinol., **18**, 108–117.

NOYES, R. W., AND DICKMANN, Z. 1960. Relationship of ovular age to endometrium development. J. Reprod. & Fertil., **1**, 186–196.

NOYES, R. W., WALTON, A., AND ADAMS, C. E. 1958. Capacitation of rabbit spermatozoa. J. Endocrinol., **17**, 374–380.

ODOR, D. L. 1948. Some physiologic and histo-

logic observations on the tubal sac of the oviduct in the rat. Master's Thesis, University of Rochester.

ODOR, D. L. 1953. Electron microscopy of the rat oviduct. Anat. Rec., **115**, 434–435.

ODOR, D. L. 1955. The temporal relationship of the first maturation division of rat ova to the onset of heat. Am. J. Anat., **97**, 461–491.

ODOR, D. L. 1956. Uptake and transfer of particulate matter from the peritoneal cavity of the rat. J. Biophys. & Biochem. Cytol., Suppl., **2**, 105–108.

ODOR, D. L. 1960a. Polar body formation in the rat oocyte as observed with the electron microscope. Anat. Rec., **137**, 13–24.

ODOR, D. L. 1960b. Electron microscopic studies on ovarian oocytes and unfertilized tubal ova in the rat. J. Biophys. & Biochem. Cytol., **7**, 567–574.

ODOR, D. L., AND BLANDAU, R. J. 1949. The frequency of occurrence of supernumerary sperm in rat ova. Anat. Rec., **104**, 1–10.

ODOR, D. L., AND BLANDAU, R. J. 1951. Observations on fertilization and the first segmentation division in rat ova. Am. J. Anat., **89**, 29–62.

ODOR, D. L., AND BLANDAU, R. J. 1956. Incidence of polyspermy in normal and delayed matings in rats of the Wistar strain. Fertil. & Steril., **7**, 456–467.

OLDS, D., AND VAN DEMARK, N. L. 1957a. Physiological aspects of fluids in female genitalia with special reference to cattle: a review. Am. J. Vet. Res., **18**, 587–602.

OLDS, D., AND VAN DEMARK, N. L. 1957b. Composition of luminal fluids in bovine female genitalia. Fertil. & Steril., **8**, 345–354.

PAPANICOLAOU, G. H. 1924. Oogenesis during sexual maturity as elucidated by experimental methods. Proc. Soc. Exper. Biol. & Med., **21**, 393–396.

PARKER, G. H. 1928. The direction of the ciliary currents in the oviducts of vertebrates. Am. J. Physiol., **87**, 93–96.

PARKER, G. H. 1931. The passage of sperms and eggs through the oviducts in terrestrial vertebrates. Philos. Tr. Roy. Soc., **219**, 381–419.

PARKES, A. S. 1931. The reproductive processes of certain mammals. II. The size of the Graafian follicle at ovulation. Proc. Roy. Soc., ser. B, **109**, 185–196.

PARKES, A. S. 1953. Prevention of fertilization by a hyaluronidase inhibitor. Lancet, **265**, 1285–1287.

PARRY, H. J. 1950. The vascular structure of the extra-placental uterine mucosa of the rabbit. J. Endocrinol., **7**, 86–99.

PEARSON, O. P., AND ENDERS, R. K. 1943. Ovulation, maturation and fertilization in the fox. Anat. Rec., **85**, 69–83.

PESONEN, S. 1949. On abortive ova; on cytology of fertilized ova in the white mouse, on the cytology of maturation division. Ann. Chir. et gynaec., Fenn. suppl., 3, **38**, 337–352.

PHELPS, D. 1946. Endometrial vascular reactions

and the mechanism of nidation. Am. J. Anat., **79,** 167–197.

PIKO, L. 1958. Etude de la polyspermie chez le Rat. Compt. rend. Soc. biol., **152,** 1356.

PINCUS, G. 1930. Observations on the living eggs of the rabbit. Proc. Roy. Soc., ser. B, **107,** 132–167.

PINCUS, G. 1936. *The Eggs of Mammals.* New York: Macmillan Company.

PINCUS, G. 1937. The metabolism of ovarian hormones, especially in relation to the growth of the fertilized ovum. Cold Spring Harbor Symposia Quant. Biol., **5,** 44–56.

PINCUS, G. 1939. The comparative behavior of mammalian eggs *in vivo* and *in vitro.* IV. The development of fertilized and artificially activated rabbit eggs. J. Exper. Zool., **82,** 85–129.

PINCUS, G., AND ENZMANN, E. V. 1932. Fertilisation in the rabbit. J. Exper. Biol., **9,** 403–408.

PINCUS, G., AND ENZMANN, E. V. 1934. Can mammalian eggs undergo normal development *in vitro?* Proc. Nat. Acad. Sc., **20,** 121–122.

PINCUS, G., AND ENZMANN, E. V. 1935. The comparative behavior of mammalian eggs *in vivo* and *in vitro.* I. The activation of ovarian eggs. J. Exper. Med., **62,** 655–676.

PINCUS, G., AND ENZMANN, E. V. 1936. The comparative behavior of mammalian eggs *in vivo* and *in vitro.* II. The activation of tubal eggs of the rabbit. J. Exper. Zool., **73,** 195–208.

PINCUS, G., AND ENZMANN, E. V. 1937. The growth, maturation and atresia of ovarian eggs in the rabbit. J. Morphol., **61,** 351–376.

PINCUS, G., AND KIRSCH, R. E. 1936. The sterility in rabbits produced by injections of oestrone and related compounds. Am. J. Physiol., **115,** 219–228.

PINCUS, G., PIRIE, N. W., AND CHANG, M. C. 1948. The effects of hyaluronidase inhibitor on fertilization in the rabbit. Arch. Biochem., **19,** 388–396.

PINCUS, G., AND WADDINGTON, C. H. 1939. The effects of mitosis-inhibiting treatments on normally fertilized pre-cleavage rabbit eggs. J. Hered., **30,** 515–518.

PINCUS, G., AND WERTHESSEN, N. T. 1937. A quantitative method for the bio-assay of progestin. Am. J. Physiol., **120,** 100–104

PINCUS, G., AND WERTHESSEN, N. T. 1938. The comparative behavior of mammalian eggs *in vivo* and *in vitro.* III. Factors controlling the growth of the rabbit blastocyst. J. Exper. Zool., **78,** 1–18.

PIYKIANEN, I. G. 1958. Fertilization and early development of sheep embryos (in Russian). Izv. Akad. Nauk. SSSR, Ser. Biol., **3,** 291–298.

REBHUN, L. 1956. Electron microscopy of basophilic structures of some invertebrate oocytes. I. Periodic lamellae and the nuclear envelope. II. Fine structure of the yolk nuclei. J. Biophys. & Biochem. Cytol., **2,** 93–104; 159–170.

REYNOLDS, S. R. M. 1949. *The Physiology of the Uterus,* 2nd ed., pp. 20–23. New York: Paul B. Hoeber, Inc.

RIISFELDT, O. 1949. Origin of hyaluronidase in rat testis. Nature, London, **163,** 874–875.

ROBINSON, A. 1918. The formation, rupture and closure of ovarian follicles in ferrets and ferret-polecat hybrids, and some associated phenomena. Tr. Roy. Soc. Edinburgh, **52,** 303–362.

ROCK, J., AND HERTIG, A. T. 1944. Information regarding the time of human ovulation derived from a study of three unfertilized and eleven fertilized ova. Am. J. Obst. & Gynec., **47,** 343–356.

ROCK, J., AND MENKIN, M. F. 1944. *In vitro* fertilization and cleavage of human ovarian eggs. Science, **100,** 105–107.

ROOSEN-RUNGE, E. C. 1951. Quantitative studies on spermatogenesis in the albino rat; duration of spermatogenesis and some effects of colchicine. Am. J. Anat., **88,** 163–176.

ROSENBAUM, R. 1957. Glycogen as an expression of basic ground organization in the egg of *Rana pipiens.* Anat. Rec., **127,** 359.

ROSENBAUM, R. 1958. Histochemical observations on the cortical region of the oocytes of Rana pipiens. Quart. J. Microscop. Sc., **99,** 159–169.

ROSSMAN, I. 1940. The deciduomal reaction in the rhesus monkey (*Macaca mulatta*). I. Epithelial proliferation. Am. J. Anat., **66,** 277–342.

ROTHSCHILD, V. 1956. *Fertilization.* New York: John Wiley & Sons, Inc.

ROWLANDS, I. W. 1942. Collection of eggs from the Fallopian tube of the rat. Nature, London, **150,** 267.

ROWLANDS, I. W. 1944. Capacity of hyaluronidase to increase the fertilizing power of sperm. Nature, London, **154,** 332–333.

ROWLANDS, I. W. 1957. Insemination of the guinea pig by intraperitoneal injection. J. Endocrinol., **16,** 98–106.

ROWSON, L. E. 1951. Methods of inducing multiple ovulations in cattle. J. Endocrinol., **7,** 260–270.

ROWSON, L. E., AND DOWLING, D. F. 1949. An apparatus for extraction of fertilized eggs from the living cow. Vet. Rec., **61,** 191.

RUBASCHKIN, W. 1905. Über die Reifungs- und Befruchtungsprozesse des Meerschweincheneis. Anat. Hefte, **29,** 509–553.

RUGH, R. 1939. Developmental effects resulting from exposure to x-rays. I. Effect on the embryo of irradiation of frog sperm. Proc. Am. Philos. Soc., **81,** 447–465.

RUNNER, M. N. 1947. Development of mouse eggs in the anterior chamber of the eye. Anat. Rec., **98,** 1–17.

RUNNER, M. N. 1951. Differentiation of intrinsic and maternal factors governing intrauterine survival of mammalian young. J. Exper. Zool., **116,** 1–20.

RUNNER, M. N., AND PALM, J. 1953. Transplantation and survival of unfertilized ova of the mouse in relation to postovulatory age. J. Exper. Zool., **124,** 303–316.

RUSSELL, E. S., AND FEKETE, E. 1959. Analysis of W-series pleiotropism in the mouse: Effect of W^vW^v substitution on definitive germ cells and on ovarian tumorigenesis. J. Nat. Cancer Inst., **21**, 365–381.

SAMARTINO, G. T., AND RUGH, R. 1946. Effects of colchicine in the frog in relation to ovulation and early development. Proc. Soc. Exper. Biol. & Med., **63**, 424–427.

SAMUEL, D. M., AND HAMILTON, W. J. 1942. Living eggs of the golden hamster. J. Anat., **76**, 204–209.

SANSOM, G. S., AND HILL, J. P. 1931. Observations on the structure and mode of implantation of the blastocyst of Cavia. Tr. Soc. Zool., **21**, 295–354.

SCHOENFELD, H. 1903. Contribution à l'étude de la fixation de l'oeuf des mammifères dans la cavité uterine, et des premiers stades de la placentation. Arch. Biol., **19**, 701–830.

SCHRADER, F., AND LEUCHTENBERGER, C. 1952. The origin of certain nutritive substances in the eggs of Hemiptera. Exper. Cell Res., **3**, 136–146.

SECKINGER, D. L. 1923. Spontaneous contractions of the Fallopian tube of the domestic pig with reference to the oestrous cycle. Bull. Johns Hopkins Hosp., **34**, 236–239.

SECKINGER, D. L. 1924. The effect of ovarian extracts upon the spontaneous contractions of the Fallopian tube of the domestic pig with reference to the oestrous cycle. Am. J. Physiol., **70**, 538–549.

SECKINGER, D. L., AND CORNER, G. W. 1923. Cyclic variations in the spontaneous contraction of the fallopian tube of *Macacus rhesus*. Anat. Rec., **26**, 299–301.

SECKINGER, D. L., AND SNYDER, F. F. 1924. Cyclic variations in the spontaneous contractions of the human Fallopian tube. Proc. Soc. Exper. Biol. & Med., **21**, 519–521.

SECKINGER, D. L., AND SNYDER, F. F. 1926. Cyclic changes in the spontaneous contractions of the human fallopian tube. Bull. Johns Hopkins Hosp., **39**, 371–378.

SELYE, H., AND MCKEOWN, T. 1935. Studies on the physiology of the maternal placenta in the rat. Proc. Roy. Soc., ser. B, **119**, 1–31.

SERGIN, N. P., KUZNECOV, M. P., KOZLOVA, V. M., AND NESMEJANOVA, T. N. 1940. Physicochemical conditions in the genital tract of the cow and survival of spermatozoa. Dokl. Akad. seljskohoz. Nauk, **15**, 24–28; Anim. Breed. Abst., **9**, 18–19, 1941.

SHELESNYAK, M. C. 1952. Inhibition of decidual cell formation in the pseudopregnant rat by histamine antagonists. Am. J. Physiol., **170**, 522–527.

SHELESNYAK, M. C. 1954. Comparative effectiveness of antihistamines in suppression of the decidual cell reaction in the pseudopregnant rat. Endocrinology, **54**, 396–401.

SHELESNYAK, M. C. 1959a. Histamine and the nidation of the ovum. In *Implantation of Ova,* P. Eckstein, Ed., pp. 84–95. London: Cambridge University Press.

SHELESNYAK, M. C. 1959b. Fall in uterine histamine associated with ovum implantation in

pregnant mice. Proc. Soc. Exper. Biol. & Med., **100**, 380–381.

SHERMAN, J. K., AND TEH PING LIN. 1958. Survival of unfertilized mouse eggs during freezing and thawing. Proc. Soc. Exper. Biol. & Med., **98**, 902–905.

SHETTLES, L. B. 1947. A clinical evaluation of bull testis hyaluronidase in infertility. Tr. Am. Soc. Stud. Steril., **3**, 98–107.

SHETTLES, L. B. 1953. Observations on human follicular and tubal ova. Am. J. Obst. & Gynec., **66**, 235–247.

SHETTLES, L. B. 1958. Corona radiata cells and zona pellucida of living human ova. Fertil. & Steril., **9**, 167–170.

SHETTLES, L. B. 1960. *Ovum Humanum.* New York: Hofner Publishing Company, Inc.

SIEGLER, S. L. 1946. The value of physiological stubstrates in sperm migration in selected cases of human infertility. Am. J. Obst. & Gynec., **51**, 13–21.

SIMON, D. 1957a. Sur la localisation des cellules germinales primordiales chez l'embryon de Poulet et leur mode de migration vers les ébauches gonadiques. Compt. rend. Acad. Sc., **244**, 1541–1543.

SIMON, D. 1957b. La migration des cellules germinales de l'embryon de Poulet vers les ébauches gonadiques: preuves expérimentales. Compt. rend. Soc. biol., **151**, 1576–1580.

SIMPSON, M. E., AND VAN WAGENEN, G. 1953. Response of the ovary of the monkey (*Macaca mulatta*) to the administration of pituitary follicle stimulating hormone (FSH). Anat. Rec., **115**, 370.

SIMPSON, M. E., AND VAN WAGENEN, G. 1958. Experimental induction of ovulation in the Macaque monkey. Fertil. & Steril., **9**, 386–399.

SIMPSON, S. A., AND WILLIAMS, P. C. 1948. Improved method of getting rats' eggs from the Fallopian tubes. Nature, London, **161**, 237.

SIRLIN, J. L., AND EDWARDS, R. G. 1959. Timing of DNA synthesis in ovarian oocyte nuclei and pronuclei of the mouse. Exper. Cell. Res., **18**, 190–196.

SLATER, D. W., AND DORNFELD, E. J. 1945. Quantitative aspects of growth and oocyte production in the early prepubertal rat ovary. Am. J. Anat., **76**, 253–275.

SMITH, A. H., AND KLEIBER, M. 1950. Size and oxygen consumption in fertilized eggs. J. Cell. & Comp. Physiol., **35**, 131–140.

SMITH, A. U. 1953. *In vitro* experiment with rabbit eggs. In *Mammalian Germ Cells,* pp. 217–225. Boston: Little, Brown & Company.

SMITH, S. C. 1925. Degenerative changes in the unfertilized eggs of the opossum (*Didelphis virginiana*), with remarks on the so-called parthenogenesis in mammals. Am. J. Anat., **35**, 81–103.

SMITHBERG, M. 1953. The effect of different proteolytic enzymes on the zona pellucida of mouse ova. Anat. Rec., abstr., **117**, 554.

SNYDER, F. F. 1923. Changes in the fallopian

tube during the ovulation cycle and early pregnancy. Bull. Johns Hopkins Hosp., **34**, 121–125.

SNYDER, F. F. 1924. Changes in the human oviduct during the menstrual cycle and pregnancy. Bull. Johns Hopkins Hosp., **35**, 141–146.

SOBOTTA, J. 1895. Die Befruchtung und Furchung des Eies der Maus. Arch. mikroskop. Anat. **45**, 15–92.

SOBOTTA, J. 1914. Zur Frage der Wanderung des Säugetiereis durch den Eileiter. Anat. Anz., **47**, 448–464.

SOBOTTA, J. 1917. Über den Mechanismus der Aufnahme der Eier der Säugetiere in den Eileiter und des Transportes durch diesen in den Uterus. Anat. Hefte, **54**, 359–446.

SOBOTTA, J. 1924. Beiträge zur Forschung des Eies der Säugetiere mit besonderer Berücksichtigung der Frage der Determination der Forschung. I. Die Forschung des Eies der Maus. (*Mus musculus*). Zschtr. Anat., **72**, 94–116.

SOBOTTA, J., AND BURCKHARD, G. 1910. Reifung und Befruchtung des Eies der weissen Ratte. Anat. Hefte, **42**, 435–494.

SOTELO, J. R., AND PORTER, K. R. 1959. An electron microscope study of the rat ovum. J. Biophys. & Biochem. Cytol., **5**, 327–342.

SQUIER, R. R. 1932. The living egg and early stages of its development in the guinea pig. Contr. Embryol., Carnegie Inst. Washington, **23**, 225–250.

STANGE, H. H. 1952. Zur funktionellen Morphologie des Fimbrienendes der menschlichen Tube und des Epoophoron. Arch. Gynäk., **182**, 77–103.

STEIN, K., AND ALLEN, E. 1942. Attempts to stimulate proliferation of the germinal epithelium of the ovary. Anat. Rec., **82**, 1–9.

STEIN, K. F., QUIMBY, J., AND MOELLER, A. 1947. Response of germinal epithelium to thyroid tissue or thyroxin in the ovarian capsule of the mouse. Anat. Rec., **99**, 249–264.

STRAUSS, F. 1956. The time and place of fertilization of the golden hamster egg. J. Embryol. & Exper. Morphol., **4**, 42–56.

SWEZY, O. 1933. The changing concept of ovarian rhythms. Quart. Rev. Biol., **8**, 423–433.

SWEZY, O., AND EVANS, H. M. 1930. The human ovarian germ cells. J. Morphol. & Physiol., **49**, 543–577.

SWIFT, C. H. 1914. Origin and early history of the primordial germ-cells in the chick. Am. J. Anat., **15**, 483–516.

SWYER, G. I. M. 1947a. The release of hyaluronidase from spermatozoa. Biochem. J., **41**, 413–417.

SWYER, G. I. M. 1947b. A tubal factor concerned in the denudation of rabbit ova. Nature, London, **159**, 873–874.

SYTINA, M. V. 1956. Study of oxygen absorption by rabbits' ova and zygotes (in Russian). Doklady Vaskhnil, **9**, 11–13.

TAFANI, A. 1889. La fécondation et la segmentation étudiées dans les oeufs des rats. Arch. Biol. ital., **11**, 112–117.

TAFEL, R. E., TITUS, P., AND WIGHTMAN, W. A. 1948. Hyaluronidase in treatment of human sterility. Am. J. Obst. & Gynec., **55**, 1023–1029.

TANDLER, C. J. 1958. The localization of inorganic phosphate in the oöcytes of *Bufo arenarum*: heterogeneity of the nucleoli. Exper. Cell Res., **14**, 408–413.

TARKOWSKI, A. K. 1959. Experiments on the development of isolated blastomeres of mouse eggs. Nature, London, **184**, 1286–1287.

THIBAULT, C. 1947a. Essai de parthénogenèse expérimentale chez le rat. Compt. rend. Soc. biol., **141**, 607–608.

THIBAULT, C. 1947b. La parthénogenèse expérimentale chez le lapin. Compt. rend. Soc. biol., **224**, 297–299.

THIBAULT, C. 1948. L'activation et la régulation de l'ovocyte parthénogénétique de lapine. Compt. rend. Soc. biol., **142**, 495–497.

THIBAULT, C. 1949. L'oeuf des mammifères son développement parthénogénétique. Ann. Des. Sc. Nat. Zool., **11**, 136–219.

THIBAULT, C., AND DAUZIER, L. 1960. "Fertilisines" et fécondation *in vitro* de l'oeuf de lapine. Compt. rend. Acad. Sc., **250**, 1358–1359.

TOSIC, J., AND WALTON, A. 1946. Formation of hydrogen peroxide by spermatozoa and its inhibiting effect on respiration. Nature, London, **158**, 485.

TRUJILLO-CENÓZ, O., AND SOTELO, J. R. 1959. Relationships of the ovular surface with follicle cells and origin of the zona pellucida in rabbit oöcytes. J. Biophys. & Biochem. Cytol., **5**, 347–350.

TYLER, A. 1955. Gametogenesis, fertilization and parthenogenesis. In *Analysis of Development*, B. H. Willier, P. A. Weiss, and V. Hamburger, Eds., Ch. 1, Sect. V, pp. 170–212. Philadelphia: W. B. Saunders Company.

TYLER, A. 1957. Immunological studies of early development. In *The Beginnings of Embryonic Development*, pp. 341–382. Washington: American Association for Advancement of Science.

TYLER, A., MONROY, A., KAO, C. Y., AND GRUNDFEST, H. 1956. Membrane potential and resistance of the starfish egg before and after fertilization. Biol. Bull., **111**, 153–177.

UMBAUGH, R. E. 1949. Superovulation and ovum transfer in cattle. Am. J. Vet. Res., **10**, 295–305.

VAN BENEDEN, E. 1875. La maturation de l'oeuf, la fécondation, et les premiéres phases du développement embryonaire des mammifères d'après les recherches faites sur le lapin. Bull. Acad. Roy. Sc. Belgique, **40**, 686–736.

VAN BENEDEN, E. 1911. Recherches sur l'embryologie des mammifères. De la segmentation de la formation de la cavité blastodermique et de l'embryon didermique chez le Murin. Arch. Biol., **26**, 1–63.

VAN DE KERCKHOVE, D. 1959. Content of deoxyribonucleic acid of the germinal vesicle of the primary oocyte in the rabbit. Nature, London, **183**, 4657.

VAN DER STRICHT, O. 1902. Le spermatozoid dans l'oeuf de chauve-souris (*V. noctula*). Verhand-

lungen der Anatomie Gesellschaft auf der 16 Versammlung in Halle, p. 163.

VAN DER STRICHT, O. 1909. La structure de l'oeuf des mammifères (chauve-souris Vesperugo noctula). Mém. Acad. roy. Belgique, ser. 2, **2**, 1.

VAN DER STRICHT, O. 1910. La structure de l'oeuf des mammifères (*Chauve-souris, Vesperugo noctula*). Troisième partie. L'oocyte à la fin du stade d'accroissement, au stade de la maturation, au stade de la fecondation et au début de la segmentation. Acad. roy. Belgique Clin. Sc. Mém., ser. 2, 1–176.

VAN DER STRICHT, O. 1923. Étude, comparée des ovules des mammifères aux différentes périodes de l'ovogenèse, l'après les travaux du Laboratoire d'Histologie et d'Embryologie de l'Université de Gand. Arch. Biol., **33**, 229–300.

VAN DER STRICHT, R. 1911. Vitellogenese dans l'ovule de chatte. Arch. Biol., **26**, 365–481.

VAN DYKE, H. B., AND CHEN, G. 1940. The distribution of lipoids in the genital tract of the monkey at different stages of the menstrual cycle. Am. J. Anat., **66**, 411–427.

VAN WAGENEN, G., AND SIMPSON, M. E. 1957. Induction of multiple ovulation in the Rhesus monkey (*Macaca mulatta*). Endocrinology, **61**, 316–318.

VENERONI, G., AND BIANCHI, A. 1957. Correcting the genetically determined sterility of W^v/W^v male mice. J. Embryol. & Exper. Morphol., **5**, 422–427.

VENGE, O. 1953. Experiments on fertilization of rabbit ova *in vitro* with subsequent transfer to alien does. In *Mammalian Germ Cells*, p. 243–252. Boston: Little, Brown & Company.

VINCENT, W. S., AND DORNFELD, E. J. 1948. Localization and role of nucleic acids in the developing rat ovary. Am. J. Anat., **83**, 437–469.

VON KAULLA, K. N., AIKAWA, J. K., AND PETTIGREW, J. D. 1959. Ist das menschliche Ei für in den Kreislauf gelangende radioaktive Substanzen und für Medikamente erreichbar? Klin. Wchnschr., **37**, 1248.

VON MIKULICZ-RADECKI, F. 1925. Zur Physiologie der Tube 1. Mitteilung. Experimentelle Studien über die Spontanbewegungen der Kaninchentube *in situ*. Zentralbl. Gynäk., **49**, 1655–1662.

VON MIKULICZ-RADECKI, F., AND NAHMMACHER, W. 1925. Zur Physiologie der Tube. II. Mitteilung. Beobachtung von Fortbewegung korpuskulärer Elemente in der Kaninshentube durch Muskelkontraktionen. Zentralbl. Gynäk., **49**, 2322–2327.

VON MIKULICZ-RADECKI, F., AND NAHMMACHER, W. 1926. Zur Physiologie der Tube. III. Mitteilung. Beobachtung und Registrierung von Bewegung der Kaninchentube durch ein neues Bauchfenster. Zentralbl. Gynäk., **50**, 1309–1313.

VON SPEE, F. 1883. Beitrag zur Entwickelungsgeschichte der früheren Stadien des Meerschweinchens bis zur Vollendung der Keimblase. Arch. Anat. Physiol., **7**, 44–60.

VON SPEE, F. 1901. Die Implantation des Meerschweinscheneies in die Uteruswand. Ztschr. Morphol. Anthropol., **3**, 130–182.

WADDINGTON, C. H., AND WATERMAN, A. J. 1933. The development *in vitro* of young rabbit embryos. J. Anat., **67**, 355–370.

WALDO, C. M., AND WIMSATT, W. A. 1945. The effect of colchicine on early cleavage of mouse ova. Anat. Rec., **93**, 363–375.

WARD, M. C. 1946. A study of the estrous cycle and the breeding of the golden hamster (*Cricetus auratus*). Anat. Rec., **94**, 139–161.

WARWICK, B. L., AND BERRY, R. O. 1949. Intergeneric and intra-specific embryo transfers in sheep and goats. J. Hered., **40**, 297–303.

WEICHERT, C. K. 1940. The experimental shortening of delayed pregnancy in the albino rat. Anat. Rec., **77**, 31–47.

WEICHERT, C. K. 1942. The experimental control of prolonged pregnancy in the lactating rat by means of estrogen. Anat. Rec., **83**, 1–17.

WEICHERT, C. K. 1943. Effect of environmental stilbestrol in shortening prolonged gestation in the lactating rat. Proc. Soc. Exper. Biol. & Med., **53**, 203–204.

WEISS, P., AND ANDRES, G. 1952. Experiments on the fate of embryonic cells (chick) disseminated by the vascular route. J. Exper. Zool., **121**, 449–488.

WERTHESSEN, N. T., BERMAN, S., GREENBERG, B. E., AND GARGILL, S. C. 1945. A technique for the assay of hyaluronidase in human semen and its correlation with the sperm concentration. Am. J. Urol., **54**, 565–570.

WESTMAN, A. 1926. A contribution to the question of the transit of the ovum from ovary to uterus in rabbits. Acta obst. et gynec. scandinav., **5**, 1–104.

WESTMAN, A. 1929. Untersuchunger über die Physiologie der Tuba uterina bei *Macacus rhesus-Affen*. Acta obst. et gynec. scandinav., **8**, 307–314.

WESTMAN, A. 1930. Studies on the functions of the mucous membrane of the uterine tube. Acta obst. et gynec. scandinav., **10**, 288–298.

WESTMAN, A. 1932. Studien über den Sexualzyklus bei *Macacus rhesus-Affen*. Acta obst. et gynec. scandinav., **12**, 282–328.

WESTMAN, A. 1952. Investigations into the transport of the ovum. In *Proceedings Conference Studies on Testis and Ovary Eggs and Sperm*, E. T. Engle, Ed., pp. 163–175. Springfield, Ill.: Charles C Thomas.

WESTMAN, A., JORPES, E., AND WIDSTRÖM, G. 1931. Untersuchungen über den Schleimhautzyklus in der Tuba uterina, seine hormonale Regulierung und die Bedeutüng des Tubensekrets für die Vitalität der befruchteten Eier. Acta obst. et. gynec. scandinav., **11**, 279–292.

WHITTEN, W. K. 1956. Culture of tubal mouse ova. Nature, London, **177**, 96.

WHITTEN, W. K. 1957. Culture of tubal ova. Nature, London, **179**, 1081–1082.

WHITTEN, W. K. 1958. Endocrine studies on delayed implantation in lactating mice: role of the pituitary in implantation. J. Endocrinol., **16**, 435–440.

WILLETT, E. L., BUCKNER, P. J., AND LARSON, G. L. 1953. Three successful transplantations of fertilized bovine eggs. J. Dairy Sc., **36**, 520–523.

WILLETT, E. L., BLACK, W. G., CASIDA, L. E., STONE, W. H., AND BUCKNER, P. J. 1951. Successful transplantation of a fertilized bovine ovum. Science, **113**, 247.

WILLIER, B. H. 1950. Sterile gonads and the problem of the origin of germ cells in the chick embryo. Arch. Anat. Microscop., **39**, 269–273.

WILSON, E. B. 1925. *The Cell in Development and Heredity*. New York: Macmillan Company.

WIMSATT, W. A. 1944. Further studies on the survival of spermatozoa in the female reproductive tract of the bat. Anat. Rec., **88**, 193–204.

WIMSATT, W. A., AND WALDO, C. M. 1945. The normal occurrence of a peritoneal opening in the bursa ovarii of the mouse. Anat. Rec. **93**, 47–57.

WINBERG, H. 1941. Physiologic behavior of bird sperm at varying temperatures. Arch. Zool., **33**, 1–12.

WINTERS, L. M., GREEN, W. W., AND COMSTOCK, R. E. 1942. Prenatal development of the bovine. Minnesota Agric. Exper. Sta., Tech. Bull. 151.

WISCHNITZER, S. 1957. A study of the lateral loop chromosomes of amphibian oocytes by phase contrast microscopy. Am. J. Anat., **101**, 135–167.

WISCHNITZER, S. 1958. An electron microscope study of the nuclear envelope of amphibian oocytes. J. Ultrastruct. Res., **1**, 201–222.

WISLOCKI, G. B., BUNTING, H., AND DEMPSEY, E. W. 1947. Metachromasia in mammalian tissues and its relationship to mucopolysaccharides. Am. J. Anat., **81**, 1–37.

WISLOCKI, G. B., AND DEMPSEY, E. W. 1945. Histochemical reactions of the endometrium in pregnancy. Am. J. Anat., **77**, 365–403.

WISLOCKI, G. B., AND GUTTMACHER, A. F. 1924. Spontaneous peristalsis of the excised whole uterus and fallopian tubes of the sow with reference to the ovulation cycle. Bull. Johns Hopkins Hosp., **35**, 246–252.

WISLOCKI, G. B., AND SNYDER, F. F. 1933. The experimental acceleration of the rate of transport of ova through the Fallopian tube. Bull. Johns Hopkins Hosp., **52**, 379–386.

WISLOCKI, G. B., AND STREETER, G. L. 1938. On the placentation of the macaque (*Macaca mulatta*), from the time of implantation until the formation of the definitive placenta. Contr. Embryol., Carnegie Inst. Washington, **27**, 1–66.

WITSCHI, E. 1948. Migration of the germ cells of human embryos from the yolk sac to the primitive gonadal folds. Contr. Embryol., Carnegie Inst. Washington, **32**, 67–80.

WITSCHI, E. 1952. Overripeness of the egg as a cause of twinning and teratogenesis: a review. Cancer Res., **12**, 763–786.

WRBA, H. 1956. Behavior of the fertilised rat egg *in vitro*. Naturwissenschaften, **43**, 334.

WRIGHT, P. L. 1948. Preimplantation stages in the long-tailed weasel (*Mustela frenata*). Anat. Rec., **100**, 593–607.

YAMADA, F. 1952. Studies on the ciliary movements of the oviduct. Japan. J. Physiol., **2**, 194–197.

YAMADA, E., MUTA, T., MOTOMURA, A., AND KOGA, H. 1957. The fine structure of the oocyte in the mouse ovary studied with electron microscope. Kurume M. J., **4**, 148–171.

YAMANE, J. 1930. The proteolytic action of mammalian spermatozoa and its bearing upon the second maturation division of ova. Cytologia, **1**, 394–403.

YAMANE, J. 1935. Kausal-analytische Studien über die Befruchtung des Kanincheneies. I. Die Dispersion der Follikezellen und die Ablösung der Zellen der Corona radiata des Eies durch Spermatozoen. Cytologia, **6**, 233–255.

ZLOTNIK, I. 1948. A comparative study of the cytoplasmic components during the oögenesis of dog, cat, and rabbit. Proc. Roy. Soc. Edinburgh, ser. B, **63**, 200–212.

ZOLLINGER, H. U. 1948. Cytologic studies with the phase microscope. I. The formation of "blisters" on cells in suspension (potocytosis), with observations on the nature of the cellular membrane. Am. J. Path., **24**, 545–567.

ZOTIN, A. I. 1958. The mechanism of hardening of the salmonid egg membrane after fertilization or spontaneous activation. J. Embryol. & Exper. Morphol., **6**, 546–568.

ZUCKERMAN, S. 1951. The number of oocytes in the mature ovary. Recent Progr. Hormone Res., **6**, 63–109.

ZUCKERMAN, S., AND PARKES, A. S. 1932. The menstrual cycle of the primates. II. The cycle of the baboon. Proc. Zool. Soc. London, Pt. 1, 139–191.

15

HISTOCHEMISTRY AND ELECTRON MICROSCOPY OF THE PLACENTA

George B. Wislocki, M.D., Sc.D. (Hon.)

LATE JAMES STILLMAN PROFESSOR OF COMPARATIVE ANATOMY
AND HERSEY PROFESSOR OF ANATOMY

and

Helen A. Padykula, Ph.D.

ASSISTANT PROFESSOR OF ANATOMY,
HARVARD MEDICAL SCHOOL, BOSTON, MASSACHUSETTS

Between 1951 and 1955 George B. Wislocki worked enthusiastically on the original manuscript of this review. He viewed it as one of his most important contributions. A long delay in its publication, since his death in October 1956, has necessitated considerable revision to permit current publication. Helen A. Padykula, who worked in close association with Dr. Wislocki, agreed to make this revision. Although the original manuscript has been altered in many ways, a genuine attempt has been made to preserve the dynamic approach to the study of placentation which characterized Dr. Wislocki.

I. Introduction

Histochemistry has elucidated the complicated architectural relationships of the mammalian placenta to an important degree. The localization of chemical constituents in tissue sections has provided a framework of evidence and suggestions for the function of various parts of the maternal-fetal placental complex. Evidence for the sites of hormonal synthesis is principally of a histochemical nature. Furthermore, as has been true in the study of many tissues and organs, histochemical methods have also permitted further definition and differentiation of placental cell types. This is well illustrated in the use of histochemical methods to study the cellular intermingling which occurs at the maternal-fetal junction in the human placenta (Wislocki, 1951).

Descriptions of the ultrastructure of the placenta appeared soon after the introduction of methods for preparing sections thin enough to allow study with the electron microscope (Boyd and Hughes, 1954; Wislocki and Dempsey, 1955a; Wislocki and Dempsey, 1955b; Dempsey, Wislocki and Amoroso, 1955; Dempsey and Wislocki,

1956). There was immediate interest in defining the fine structure of membranes of great physiologic exchange (Low, 1953, pulmonary alveolar lining; Pease, 1955, nephron; Yamada, 1955, glomerulus; Palay and Karlin, 1959a, b, intestinal epithelium). Some comparisons of ultrastructure are already possible between the placental membranes and those mediating exchange in the kidney, intestine, and lung. Observations on ultrastructure and histochemistry are closely related, and this correlation will be delineated here for the placenta.

In this review, emphasis will be placed on the human and rodent placentas, although there will also be a consideration of the comparative histochemistry and histophysiology of the placental barrier. Amoroso's chapter in Marshall's *Physiology of Reproduction* gives an excellent account of comparative placentation, and thus no attempt will be made in the present review to cover that subject, except for a brief introductory description of placental histology in man and the rhesus monkey. Huggett and Hammond (1952), in a chapter in Marshall's book, drew, to a slight degree, on cytologic and histochemical data in discussing various aspects of fetal nutrition, placental metabolism, and the placental barrier. The endocrine functions of the placenta and the transport activities of the placental barrier will be considered only in so far as studies of the morphology have contributed to an understanding of them.

Placental morphology is relatively difficult to understand, because of the complex structural relationships between the developing embryo and the uterus. These comprise a succession of stages of placental development involving implantation or nidation, followed by the gradual formation of

PLATE 15.I

Fig. 15.1. A normal human gestation sac containing an embryo approximately 1 month of age. The chorion laeve has been dissected away to reveal the embryo, amnion, exocoelom, yolk sac and chorionic membrane. Numerous delicate chorionic villi extend outward from the chorion, constituting the fetal placenta. × 3½. (Carnegie Institution of Washington.)

Fig. 15.2. A section through a 16-day-old human ovum. Observe the embryonic shield (*h*) with the amniotic cavity above it and the yolk sac below (*i*). The dark stained chorion (*ch*) encloses the large exocoelomic cavity (*j*). Secondary villi (*b*) containing cores of mesoderm are in process of development. The villi are separated from one another by the intervillous space (*f*) which contains maternal blood. Peripheral to the secondary villi is a zone composed largely of cytotrophoblast comprising cell columns (*d*) and the trophoblastic shell (*c*). The latter is poorly demarcated from the surrounding decidua basalis (*a*) and decidua capsularis (*e*). × 30. (Rock and Hertig, 1948.)

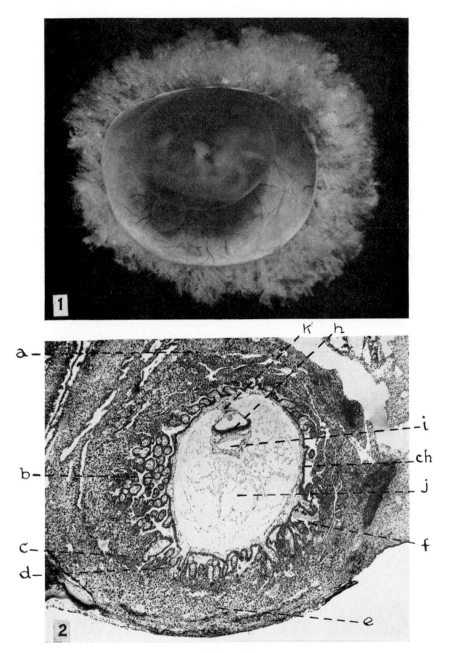

PLATE 15.I

the so-called definitive placenta. Through its brief life history, the mammalian placenta displays a pattern of differentiation which is manifested by structural, physiologic, and biochemical changes. Studies which define these changes emphasize that the placenta is different at various points in gestation. Histochemical methods have aided in tagging these changes in structure and function. It should be emphasized that, despite the kaleidoscopic changes which take place while the fetal membranes are variously differentiating into the so-called definitive placenta, the structures involved are functionally adequate at all times to meet the metabolic demands of the developing embryo and fetus.

In various groups of mammals further complications arise from the variety of modes of placentation, involving several kinds of nidation and subsequent intercrescence of the fetal and maternal membranes to constitute the placenta. The walls of the yolk sac and the allantois fuse in different ways with the chorion of mammals so that either a choriovitelline or chorio-allantoic placenta, or both, may differentiate. The former occurs in many orders of mammals (but not in man and monkey), usually preceding the latter in time of appearance, and disappearing after the allantoic placenta has become established. However, in some groups (*e.g.*, rodents) the two types of placentas continue to function concurrently throughout gestation. Until recently, the significance of the yolk sac placenta has been largely overlooked. The elegant physiologic experiments of Brambell and his associates (1948, 1950, 1951, 1956, 1957) have high-lighted this membrane by establishing it as the exclusive mediator of antibody transport from mother to fetus in rodents and lagomorphs.

As a consequence of the many varieties of placentas and numerous stages of differentiation of the various types, much research has been devoted to comparative placentation, seeking to elucidate the phylogenetic relationships, the topographic structure, and functional roles of the fetal membranes and placenta as they manifest themselves in different groups of mammals (Mossman, 1937; Amoroso, 1952). Despite extensive investigations of these questions, there are still large areas of uncertainty and lack of agreement in reference to the phylogeny of the placenta and of the structural homologies and functional significance of its various parts. As a result of the complexities of placental structure and the attendant preoccupation with comparative placental topography, the placenta is less well known histologically, cytologically, and histochemically than most organs of the body.

PLATE 15.II

FIG. 15.3. A section through the placenta of a rhesus monkey on the 29th day of gestation. Secondary chorionic villi are visible, each comprising a core of vascularized mesoderm surrounded by a darkly stained mantle of cytotrophoblast and syncytium, bordering the intervillous space (*i*) in which maternal blood circulates. The tips of the definitive villi extend downward as columns of cellular trophoblast (primary villi). The distal ends of these cell columns (*c*) unite on the periphery of the growing placenta to form the trophoblastic shell (*s*). The latter merges indistinctly with the underlying decidually-transformed endometrium (*d*); uterine gland (*g*). Iron hematoxylin stain. × 6½.

FIG. 15.4. Localization of alkaline phosphatase in an anchoring villus from a human placenta of 8 weeks. The enzyme occurs only in the outer margin of the syncytium. × 235. (Dempsey and Wislocki, 1945.)

FIG. 15.5. Indophenol oxidase reaction in a human chorionic villus of the 6th week of pregnancy. The oxidase activity is confined to the syncytial trophoblast. × 100. (Dempsey and Wislocki, 1944.)

FIG. 15.6. The birefringent lipids in the syncytium of a monkey's placenta. A fresh spread of the placenta was photographed between crossed prisms. × 80. (Dempsey and Wislocki, 1944.)

FIG. 15.7. Localization of basophilic substance in a villus from a human placenta of 13 weeks. An outer, eosinophilic zone (*e*) and a deeper, basophilic region (*b*) may be seen. Zenker formol fixative. Eosin methylene blue stain. × 1440. (Dempsey and Wislocki, 1945.)

FIG. 15.8. A chorionic villus of a normal human placenta of 10 weeks' gestation stained for iron by the Turnbull blue method. The iron is concentrated in the outermost part of the stroma just beneath the trophoblast. Some particles staining for iron extend into the interior of the villus. × 250.

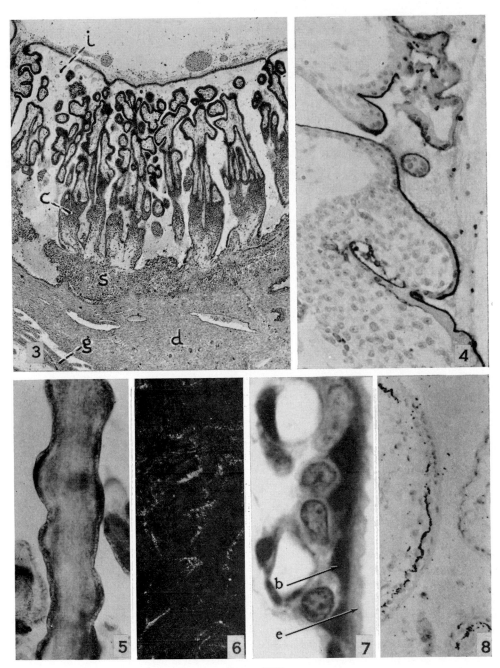

PLATE 15.II

In view of the above considerations, a brief review of the topography and histologic structure of the placentas of man and rhesus monkey will be given early in this chapter. Later a histologic description of yolk sac placentation, as it occurs in the rat, will be presented. These morphologic descriptions will provide a background against which the various features of the localization of hormones, enzymes, and other compounds in these placentas will be more readily understood.

II. Histochemical Methods Utilized in the Study of the Placenta

The placenta is a most reactive organ histochemically; some portion of it reacts positively in most histochemical tests. This is not surprising in view of its manifold functions which surpass those of any other organ, with the possible exception of the adult liver. The cytologic methods which have been applied to placentas, such as those for the demonstration of mitochondria, Golgi apparatus, brush borders, reticular fibers, and nuclear morphology, are standard and need not be specifically cited here. On the other hand, histochemical methods have been more recently developed, and are also changing constantly in the light of new advances. To aid the reader in assessing the localizations illustrated in this review, a brief outline of some of the histochemical methods, as they were used in this laboratory, will be presented. The reader is referred to Pearse's *Textbook of Histochemistry* (1960) for fuller accounts of methods.

A. BASOPHILIA AND ACIDOPHILIA

Nucleoproteins and acid mucopolysaccharides are conspicuously basophilic substances. Desoxyribonucleoprotein is responsible for most of the basophilia of cell nuclei, whereas much cytoplasmic basophilia, especially in cells which are rapidly growing or synthesizing large amounts of protein, is attributable to ribonucleoprotein. The latter is also present in the nucleoli. The strong affinity of nucleoproteins and acid mucopolysaccharides for cationic or basic dyes is dependent on the presence in them of phosphate and sulfate groups which bear strong negative charge under many routine conditions of staining. Under controlled conditions of staining, in which the pH of the staining solution is varied, it is possible to distinguish basophilia caused by nucleic acids and acid mucopolysaccharides from that of proteins. Because the isoelectric point of proteins differs, some stain readily with basic dyes whereas others react with acid dyes at a given pH. A discussion of the factors influencing basophilia and acidophilia of tissues is given in papers by Singer and Morrison (1948) and Singer (1952). The controlled use of acid and basic dyes on the human and rat placenta is illustrated in the papers by Singer and Wislocki (1948) and Wislocki, Weiss, Burgos and Ellis (1957).

Many cell types of the growing, differentiating placenta are rich in cytoplasmic ribonucleoprotein (Dempsey and Wislocki, 1946). It can be identified by comparing histologic sections stained by methylene blue with control sections treated with ribonuclease before staining (Brachet, 1953). Desoxyribonucleoprotein can be distinguished from ribonucleoprotein by the Feulgen method.

The acid mucopolysaccharides which contain sulfuric acid, such as heparin, chondroitin sulfuric acid esters, and certain mucoid substances, are strikingly basophilic. This class of mucopolysaccharides can be identified in tissue sections which have been stained with basic dyes in a series of solutions of descending pH, inasmuch as the sulfate-containing moiety continues to stain at pH as low as 1 and 2, whereas the weaker acid groupings of polysaccharides, such as hyaluronic acid, cease to stain at pH 4.5 (Dempsey, Bunting, Singer and Wislocki, 1947).

In addition to exhibiting basophilia, acid mucopolysaccharides possess the property of shifting the absorption spectrum of certain thiazine dyes, thereby inducing metachromatic staining. Thus, toluidin blue and thionin, which color most basophilic substances blue, will stain acid mucopolysaccharides and, under some conditions, nucleoproteins red (Wislocki, Bunting and Dempsey, 1947). Michaelis (1947) attributed the metachromasia of dye molecules to their polymerization. An excellent analysis of the phenomenon of metachromasia was made recently by Bergeron and Singer (1958).

B. CARBOHYDRATES

Modern histochemistry of carbohydrates revolves principally around the periodic acid-Schiff (PAS) reaction developed by McManus (1945) and Hotchkiss (1948). This procedure involves the oxidation by periodic acid of 1,2-glycol linkages which are common in sugars. The resulting aldehydic groups are colored by the Schiff's reagent. The periodic acid-Schiff reaction also stains other carbohydrate containing substances including glycoproteins, mucoproteins, and glycolipoproteins (Leblond, 1950). Glycogen can be differentiated histochemically from these substances by the use of saliva or malt diastase on control sections. In earlier studies of the placenta, glycogen storage was assessed by Best's carmine stain as well as by means of alkaline silver nitrate (Mitchell and Wislocki, 1944). Also in much of the earlier work a digested control section was not used.

C. LIPIDS

Sudan dyes, which dissolve readily in triglycerides, are most commonly used to demonstrate these lipids. Sudan black B has superseded Sudan III and IV by virtue of its more favorable color and also because it reveals many lipids in addition to triglycerides. Mitochondria are stained by Sudan black B presumably through their phospholipid content. There is some evidence that staining by Sudan black occurs also through chemical binding (Pearse, 1960). Osmium tetroxide is also employed for demonstrating lipid, although it is less specific than Sudan staining. This energetic agent, which is the principal fixative-stain for electron microscopy, will oxidize unsaturated compounds turning them grey or black. For the demonstration of phospholidips, Baker (1946) introduced an acid hematein test.

A group of histochemical reactions is characteristic of the lipid droplets of the *steroid-producing organs*. Besides staining intensely with Sudan black B, these lipid droplets, in frozen sections of formalin-fixed material, react positively in tests for carbonyl groups, such as the Schiff test and

hydrazine methods (phenylhydrazine method of Bennett (1940) and the naphthoic acid hydrazide method of Ashbel and Seligman (1949)). They are fluorescent when viewed with ultraviolet light and contain birefrigent crystals (Dempsey and Wislocki, 1944; Wislocki and Dempsey, 1946a, b; Rockenschaub, 1952). The droplets also give colored products when treated with mineral acids, as in the Liebermann-Burchardt reaction or the Schultz reaction for cholesterol. All of the above reactions are prevented following extraction of the sections with acetone at room temperature.

In the past it was proposed that all or some of these reactions might be given by ketosteroids, *i.e.*, by hormones and their immediate precursors (Dempsey and Wislocki 1946). Seligman and Ashbel (1951) adduced evidence for the ketonic nature of some of the carbonyls and for the specificity of the naphthoic acid-hydrazide reaction in the steroid hormone-producing glands. However, it was gradually realized that none of the above reactions is specific for ketosteroids, and a reevaluation of their significance was undertaken by Deane and Seligman (1953). More recently Karnovsky and Deane (1954, 1955) have shown by both chemical and histochemical means that the carbonyl groups in adrenal cortical lipids seem to be exclusively aldehydes produced by the auto-oxidation of unsaturated fatty acids during fixation. The reaction is inhibited by the addition of various anti-oxidants and chelating agents to the fixative. Moreover, hydrazine reactivity occurs only when there is reactivity to the Schiff reagent, and the appearance of aldehydes is correlated with the disappearance of double bonds in the lipids.

On the other hand, the experimental observations of Karnovsky and Deane proved rather conclusively that the percentage of unsaturated fatty acids which are the source of the aldehyde groups is high in functionally active adrenals and declines in inactive glands, thus confirming the earlier assertions (Bennett, 1940; Wislocki and Bennett, 1943; Dempsey and Wislocki, 1946) that the intensity of the carbonyl reaction correlates well with secretory activity.

Furthermore, despite the fact that none of the various reactions is specific for ketosteroids, their occurrence in lipid droplets of the adrenal cortex, gonads, and placenta, and their variations under different physiologic conditions of these organs suggest that the methods are empirically useful in identifying the probable sites of ketosteroid hormone formation. Application of the above procedures for the identification of sites of steroid hormone production will be found in the following papers: for the adrenal cortex (Bennett, 1940; Deane and Greep, 1946), ovary (Dempsey and Bassett, 1943; Deane, 1952), testis (Pollock, 1942), and placenta (Wislocki and Bennett, 1943; Dempsey and Wislocki, 1944; Wislocki, 1952).

D. ENZYMES

Numerous histochemical methods have been devised for preserving enzymes so that they will retain activity toward either naturally occurring or synthetic substrates. In most of these procedures an insoluble primary reaction product is precipitated *in situ* in frozen sections, and it is then visualized by a color reaction which reveals the location of the enzyme. The methods of Gomori (1941a, b) for *acid* and *alkaline phosphatases*, utilizing a variety of substrates, were applied to the study of the placentas of various animals (Dempsey and Wislocki,

1947). Observations by Padykula (1958) on fluctuations of phosphatase activity of the rat placenta included changes in adenosine triphosphatase, as well as acid and alkaline phosphatases.

The presence of the *cytochrome oxidase-cytochrome c system* has been demonstrated by the indophenol blue oxidase reaction by treating fresh spreads of placental villi with the nadi reagents (paraphenylene-diamine and α-naphthol (Dempsey and Wislocki, 1944). A series of oxidation-reduction indicator dyes was applied similarly to determine the oxidation-reduction potential of various placental elements.

Succinic dehydrogenase activity of the human placenta, as illustrated in this review, was localized by the tetrazolium method developed by Seligman and Rutenburg (1951) and modified by Padykula (1952). The localization of this enzyme in the rodent placenta was reported by Telkkä and Lehto (1954), Reale and Pipino (1957), and Padykula (1958). A comparative study of the distribution of this oxidative enzyme in various placental types was made by Reale and Pipino (1959).

Esterase activity was localized in the human placenta in this review according to the procedures of Nachlas and Seligman (1949) and Barrnett and Seligman (1952). In the rat placenta, Padykula (1958) demonstrated this enzymatic activity by the

---

PLATE 15.III

FIG. 15.9. The trophoblast of a secondary chorionic villus of a 30-day human placenta stained with Mallory's connective tissue stain. Observe the syncytium which contains small nuclei and possesses a brush-border on its free surface facing the intervillous space. Notice the large chromophobic Langhans cells which rest upon a deeply stained basement membrane contiguous to a fetal capillary which contains several nucleated erythrocytes. × 1600. (Wislocki and Bennett, 1943.)

FIG. 15.10. The localization of basophilic substances in a human villus of 13 weeks. Zenker formol fixative. Methylene blue staining. Basophilia is intense in the inner layer of the syncytial cytoplasm whereas the marginal zone and brush border are unstained. The cytoplasm of the Langhans cells is also unstained. The basophilic staining of the syncytial cytoplasm, but not that of the nuclei, is prevented by prior exposure of sections to ribonuclease, a result which indicates that the cytoplasmic basophilia is due to the presence of ribonucleoprotein. × 10 ocular; × 60 objective. (Dempsey and Wislocki, 1945.)

FIG. 15.11. Localization of basophilic substances in a cytotrophoblastic cell island from a human placenta of 13 weeks. The cytotrophoblastic cells contain strongly basophilic material in their cytoplasm, arranged in a fashion reminiscent of Nissl substance in neurons. In addition, the intercellular matrix is weakly basophilic. Zenker formol fixative. Methylene blue staining. (Dempsey and Wislocki, 1945.)

FIG. 15.12. The same region as in Figure 15.11, from a contiguous section, stained following treatment with ribonuclease. The basophilia of nuclei and the intercellular matrix is unchanged, whereas the cytoplasmic basophilia has been abolished. (Dempsey and Wislocki, 1945.)

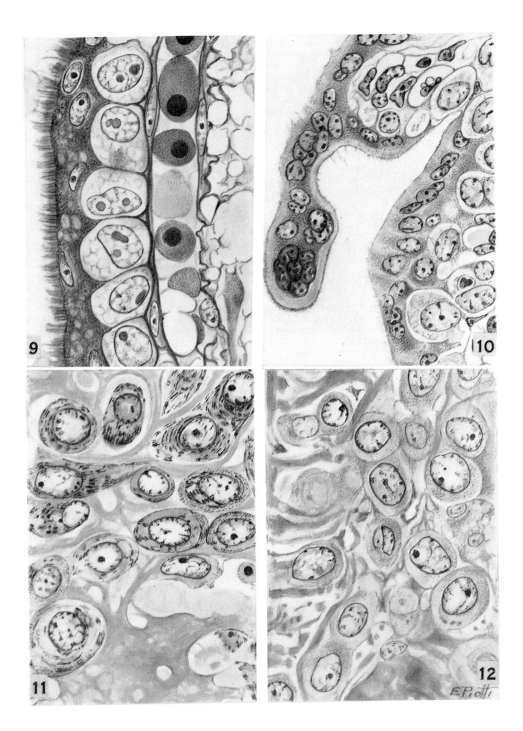

Pearse procedure. Gomori (1945) devised a method for *lipase* which has been applied to placentas of several different groups.

E. IRON AND SULFHYDRYL AND AMINO GROUPS OF PROTEINS

Microincineration of tissue sections (Scott, 1933) is a well known means of demonstrating minerals in cells. It was used for the identification of placental *iron* by Dempsey and Wislocki (1944). Placental iron is also demonstrable in tissue sections by various methods involving the Prussian blue reaction.

Protein-linked *sulfhydryl* groups have been demonstrated in the human placenta in the present study by the method of Barrnett and Seligman (1952).

Amino groups of proteins were demonstrated in the granular cells of the metrial gland of the rat by the method of Weiss, Tsou and Seligman (1954).

III. The Placentas of Man and Rhesus Monkey

A. TOPOGRAPHY AND GENERAL HISTOLOGY

The comparative placentation of primates has been extensively studied by Wislocki (1929), Hill (1932), and Stieve (1944). The placentation of the rhesus monkey (*Macaca mulatta*) has been described in detail by Wislocki and Streeter (1938).

The human placenta in its earliest stages has been the subject of recent observations by Hertig and Rock (1941, 1945), Rock and Hertig (1948), Hertig, Rock and Adams (1956). In subsequent stages it has been investigated by Grosser (1925a), Spanner (1935a, b, 1940), Stieve (1940, 1941), Stieve and von der Heide (1941), Wislocki and Bennett (1943), and Hamilton and Boyd (1951, 1960).

The *chorion*, or outer membrane surrounding the developing implanted egg, unites with the vascular, allantoic body stalk in man, apes, and monkeys to give rise to the definitive placenta which is hemochorial and villous in form. The essential cells or parenchyma of the chorion and placenta are collectively called the *trophoblast*, a term introduced by the Dutch embryologist Hubrecht, signifying "nutritive layer."

At the site of implantation of the developing blastocyst in the uterine endometrium, cords of trophoblast grow out from the initially smooth surface of the chorion. These tongues which penetrate and erode the endometrium are called the *primary chorionic villi*. On approximately the 15th day after fertilization of human and rhesus monkey eggs, mesoderm begins to appear in the proximal, attached portions of the villi and differentiates progressively toward their growing distal ends. The differentiation of mesoderm in this manner converts the primary chorionic villi into *secondary villi*. With the development of embryonic blood vessels in them, the secondary villi become converted into *tertiary* or *definitive placental villi*. The secondary and tertiary villi are covered by a mantle of trophoblast differentiated into an inner layer of large, vesicular trophoblastic cells or trophoblasts designated as *Langhans cells* after their discoverer, and an outer layer of syncytially transformed cells referred to as the *syncytial trophoblast* or *syncytium*. The latter, as the name implies, consists of a continuous mass of cytoplasm devoid of cell boundaries and containing small, darkly stained nuclei (Fig. 15.9).

The distal ends of the chorionic or placental villi continue to grow for a considerable period in the form of columns of cytotrophoblast preceding the differentiation of mesoderm in them. These are designated as the *trophoblastic cell columns*. The distal tips of these columns unite on the periphery of the growing placenta to constitute the *trophoblastic shell*. These structures will be referred to collectively as the *peripheral cytotrophoblast*, and the cells comprising them as *peripheral trophoblasts*, in contradistinction to the Langhans cells associated with the secondary and tertiary villi. As will be shown, the peripheral trophoblasts have numerous cytologic and histochemical properties which distinguish them from the Langhans cells. The beginning of many of these features can be seen in a human blastocyst on the 16th day following fertilization (Fig. 15.2) and their further development is illustrated in a placenta of a rhesus monkey of the 29th day of gestation (Fig. 15.3).

Placental villi grow initially everywhere over the circumference of the human chorion (Fig. 15.1). However, on one side, where the thick, well vascularized endometrium favors their growth, the villi become long, branched, and profuse, forming the *chorion frondosum* which eventually gives rise to the definitive, discoidal placenta.

As the trophoblast invades the endometrium giving rise to the placental villi, dilated endometrial blood vessels are eroded and tapped, their contents providing nourishment for the proliferating blastocyst. The maternal blood lacunae become increasingly confluent, forming a more or less continuous *intervillous space* between the placental villi. This space acquires afferent and efferent connections with the arteries and veins of the uterine wall, as a consequence of which maternal blood begins to circulate in the intervillous space and to bathe the surface of the villi. In the mesodermal stroma of the placental villi, newly formed blood vessels become connected with the blood vessels and developing heart within the growing embryo, so that toward the end of the first month, fetal blood begins to circulate in the capillaries of the villi. The secondary and tertiary villi continue to lengthen and branch. A number of large stem or anchoring villi extend across the intervillous space to attach to the tropho-

blastic shell or basal plate which is apposed to the uterine decidua.

As the blastocyst grows, the endometrium surrounding it undergoes significant changes. The zone in which the trophoblastic shell and the endometrium meet has been variously called the "junctional," "composite," or "penetration" zone. The endometrium subjacent to the junctional zone comprises an outer cellular portion, the *stratum compactum* and a deeper glandular part, the *stratum spongiosum*, the latter characterized by the presence of conspicuous, actively secreting glands. The spongy layer extends down to the *basal zone*, the latter forming a narrow strip which is contiguous to the myometrium and contains the fundic ends of the uterine glands. The stromal cells of the compact zone and, later, of the glandular zone, become transformed into large polygonal elements termed *decidual cells*. This decidual transformation occurs throughout the entire extent of the endometrium. That portion of the *decidua* directly beneath the implanted blastocyst constitutes the maternal part of the placenta and is called the *decidua basalis*. It is attacked and resorbed to a large degree by the growing placenta. Its remnants, at the time of birth, are either expelled or undergo resorption. The endometrium renews

---

PLATE 15.IV

All of the figures (excepting Fig. 15.13) on this plate are drawings of frozen sections of material fixed in 10 per cent buffered formalin.

FIG. 15.13. The trophoblast of a human chorionic villus of 30 days. Stained with osmic acid by Champy's fixation, a procedure which differentiates lipids. The syncytium contains numerous fat droplets, whereas the Langhans cells contain none. In the stroma beneath the trophoblast a typical, vacuolated Hofbauer cell is visible. These fat droplets are similarly revealed after staining with sudan dyes. × 1600. (Wislocki and Bennett, 1943.)

FIG. 15.14. Human placental villus at full term stained with sudan black B showing minute lipid droplets in the syncytium. Some villi contain more lipid particles than this one. × 7 ocular; × 60 objective. Compare Figures 15.13 and 15.14 with Figures 15.18 and 15.19, the latter stained by the Ashbel-Seligman carbonyl method.

FIG. 15.15. Placenta of a pig (fetal crown to rump length, 120 mm.), showing the chorion in apposition to the endometrium. Sudan black B. The uterine epithelium contains numerous black, sudanophilic droplets whereas none are visible in the faintly gray staining trophoblastic cells of the chorion. Compare with Figure 15.22, showing the Ashbel-Seligman carbonyl reaction which is identical in its distribution with the sudanophilia. × 10 ocular; × 20 objective.

FIG. 15.16. The labyrinth of the chorio-allantoic placenta of a rat on the 18th day of gestation, showing numerous sudanophilic lipid droplets in the cytotrophoblasts. Compare with Figure 15.21, showing the Ashbel-Seligman carbonyl reaction.

FIG. 15.17. The labyrinth of the chorio-allantoic placenta of a mouse on the 18th day of gestation stained by the Ashbel-Seligman carbonyl reaction. The placental labyrinths of mouse and rat are identical in respect to their sudanophilia and carbonyl reactions. × 10 ocular; × 60 objective.

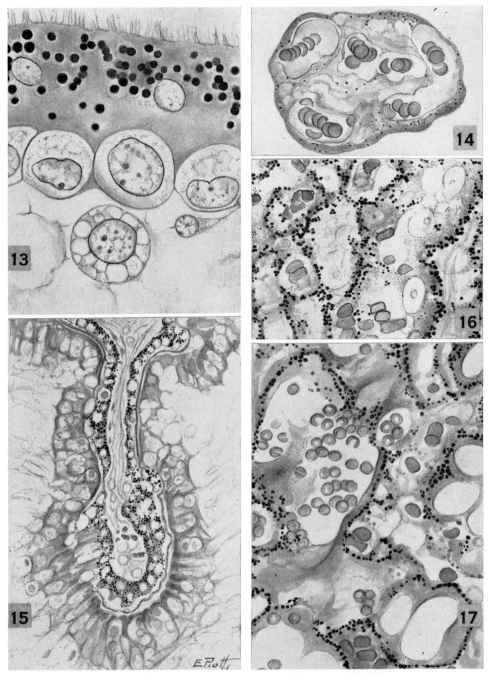

PLATE 15.IV

itself in the puerperium from the basal zone and the deep residual portion of the stratum spongiosum.

The trophoblast forms the parenchyma of the placenta and the major element of the placental barrier. It mediates the metabolic exchange between mother and fetus. It provides for the nutrition of the embryo, at first, by the local destruction and absorption of the uterine decidua, and later, by transmission of metabolites through the syncytial trophoblast from the maternal to the fetal blood streams. It serves also as an avenue for the excretion of various fetal waste products. The human trophoblast is also an important endocrine organ which produces steroid hormones, chorionic gonadotrophin and other hormones.

B. CHORIONIC VILLI

1. Trophoblasts: the Langhans Cells

These conspicuous cells which possess large nuclei constitute a germinal bed in which mitoses are frequently seen and from which in the early part of gestation the syncytium is evidently derived. The Langhans cells gradually diminish in number, but some of them survive until the end of gestation (Wislocki and Bennett, 1943; Wislocki and Dempsey, 1955). Electron micrographs show that the Langhans cells are closely apposed on their outer surfaces to the syncytium and on their basal surfaces to the basement membrane of the stroma of the chorionic villi.

The cytoplasm of the Langhans cells is characteristically chromophobic (Wislocki, Dempsey and Fawcett, 1948), exhibiting only faint cytoplasmic basophilia (Fig. 15.10), little affinity for acid dyes (Fig. 15.9), and no metachromasia. This lack of basophilia correlates with their meager endoplasmic reticulum, i.e., ergastoplasm (Wislocki and Dempsey, 1955). In the first 4 to 6 weeks of gestation their cytoplasm contains a considerable amount of glycogen, stainable by the PAS method. This glycogen subsequently disappears. Except for slight staining adjacent to the nuclear membrane (Fig. 15.54), the cytoplasm is negative with the PAS reagents following the removal of glycogen. There are no lipid droplets.

There is a moderate number of rod-shaped and granular mitochondria (Wislocki and Bennett, 1943). In electron micrographs, the mitochondria of the Langhans cells are relatively few in number but larger than those in the syncytium. A moderate degree of succinic dehydrogenase activity is demonstrable in these cells (Figs. 15.37 and 15.38). The Golgi apparatus is situated on the side of the nucleus toward the syncytium (Baker, Hook and Severinghaus, 1944).

The cytoplasm is faintly stained in the reaction for protein-linked sulfhydryl groups (Figs. 15.33 and 15.34). The acid and alkaline phosphatase activities are of a low order.

2. Trophoblastic Syncytium in the First and Second Trimesters of Pregnancy

FREE SURFACE. The syncytium constitutes a broad layer of cytoplasm without cell boundaries and possesses small, irregularly shaped, darkly staining nuclei which are rather uniformly dispersed in its inner zone (Fig. 15.9). It possesses an outer surface, facing the intervillous space, which is extremely variable in structure, ranging from a foamy, vacuolated border possessing delicate streamers and fronds, through various intermediate appearances, to regions where it bears a well defined brush border (Wislocki and Bennett, 1943). In the earliest stages the former appearances predominate, but as gestation advances, the brush border increases in amount. It was suggested by Wislocki and Bennett that these variable surface appearances in fixed material indicate that the living syncytial cytoplasm is pleomorphic and plastic. The parts that are foamy and vacuolated and possess streamers are probably constantly moving and flowing, a physiologic activity that would promote the absorption of fluid and metabolites from the intervillous space by the process of pinocytosis (Wislocki and Bennett, 1943). In confirmation of this, observations of explanted bits of placenta growing in tissue cultures show that the cytoplasm of both the syncytial and cellular trophoblast moves quite actively, giving rise to a variety of streamers and threadlike processes (Friedheim, 1929; Jones, Gey and Gey, 1943).

The ultrastructure of the free surface of

the syncytium at 9 to 10 weeks typifies that of a pinocytotic membrane (Wislocki and Dempsey, 1955).[1] A profusion of microvilli of various shapes reach into the maternal blood. Some microvilli are long and slender with enlarged tips; others are short and thick; and occasionally peninsulas of cytoplasm studded with microvilli extend into the maternal blood space. Often in the marginal zone immediately beneath the microvilli there are large vesicles containing finely stippled or flocculent material. They are occasionally seen in the large tongues of cytoplasm which protrude from the free surface. These vesicles are most likely formed as a result of pinocytotic activity.

BASAL SURFACE. The inner surface of the syncytium is approximated to the surfaces of the Langhans cells or the subjacent stroma of the placental villus (Fig. 15.9). As mentioned previously, the Langhans cells gradually diminish in number so that the syncytium eventually comes widely in contact with the chorionic stroma. However, even early in gestation, there are occasional gaps between the Langhans cells where the syncytium is in direct contact with the subjacent mesenchyma. Through these gaps metabolites traversing the placental barrier can by-pass the Langhans cells.

CELL ORGANELLES. Cytoplasmic basophilia is very intense in the broad inner zone of the syncytium, especially surrounding the nuclei (Figs. 15.7 and 15.10). Since this basophilia is abolished by ribonuclease, it has been attributed to the presence of ribonucleic acid (Dempsey and Wislocki, 1945). Further evidence supporting this identification is derived from: (1) the similarity of this basophilia to that of Nissl substance (Singer and Wislocki, 1948), (2) the metachromasia of this region in young placentas (Wislocki and Dempsey, 1948), and (3) the concentration of the endoplasmic reticulum (ergastoplasm) in the inner two-thirds of the syncytium (Wislocki and Dempsey, 1955). This rich cytoplasmic basophilia, which has been shown to constitute the

microsomal fraction of the biochemist (Palade and Siekevitz, 1956) points toward an active participation by these cells in protein synthesis.

In contrast to the inner zone, the outer zone of the syncytium is strongly acidophilic, although the narrow outermost zone corresponding to the brush border is less acidophilic (Singer and Wislocki, 1948). This acidophilia suggests the occurrence of basic proteins in the outer zone. The ultrastructure of this region shows that there are relatively fewer ergastoplasmic elements but there is a concentration of large vesicles which most likely are the products of pinocytosis. Higher resolution electron microscopy of this region is needed. It should be mentioned at this point that protein-bound sulfhydryl groups are concentrated especially at the inner and outer borders of the syncytial cytoplasm (Figs. 15.33 and 15.34).

Mitochondria are abundant in the syncytium, occurring as small granules and rods (Figs. 15.26 and 15.30). There is the indication of high succinic dehydrogenase activity here at 6 weeks of gestation, although this histochemical determination was complicated by the presence of lipid in the syncytium (Figs. 15.37 and 15.38). With the electron microscope, it was observed that the mitochondria are smaller but more numerous than those in the Langhans cells (Wislocki and Dempsey, 1955).

The Golgi apparatus forms a dispersed network in the syncytium. This organelle has been described in the various cells of the placenta by Acconci (1912), Wislocki and Bennett (1943), and Baker, Hook and Severinghaus (1944).

GLYCOGEN AND OTHER PAS POSITIVE MATERIAL. In the human placenta in the first month of gestation a moderate amount of glycogen is stored in the syncytial trophoblast. It disappears almost entirely by the end of the second month. Similar early storage and loss of glycogen occur in the Langhans cells and stromal fibroblasts.

PAS positive material which is resistant to digestion by saliva is conspicuous in the brush border and marginal cytoplasm of the syncytium (Figs. 15.29 and 15.54). A faint red stippling of reactive material is also visible in the deeper cytoplasm (Fig. 15.54). A dark red reaction occurs also in

---

[1] Bargmann and Knoop (1959) have also described the ultrastructure of the human placental barrier. They emphasize the syncytial nature of the outer trophoblastic layer, and offer further description of the ultrastructure of the Langhans cells, Hofbauer cells, and stromal cells.

the basement membrane upon which the Langhans cells or syncytium rest (Fig. 15.54).

LIPIDS. Birefringent, sudanophilic *lipid droplets* are abundantly present in both the inner and outer zones of the syncytium (Figs. 15.6 and 15.13). The droplets are acetone soluble. They react with phenyl-hydrazine (Wislocki and Bennett, 1943), give a positive Schiff reaction, exhibit yellowish green fluorescence (Dempsey and Wislocki, 1944; Rockenschaub, 1952), and give a positive naphthoic acid-hydrazide reaction (Fig. 15.18) (Ashbel and Seligman, 1949; Seligman, Ashbel and Cohen, 1951; Wislocki, 1952; Ashbel and Hertig, 1952). These histochemical reactions occur also in the lipid droplets of the gonads and adrenal cortex, and their occurrence in the syncytium suggests that it is the site of steroid hormonal synthesis in the placenta. Previous and later paragraphs discuss this problem more fully.

ENZYMES. *Alkaline phosphatase* (Figs. 15.4, 15.41, and 15.42) occurs in the syncytial trophoblast (Buno and Curi, 1945), where it is slight in amount at 6 weeks, but it increases tremendously as gestation advances (Dempsey and Wislocki, 1945). It varies in degree of activity according to the substrate used, the enzymatic reaction being most intense following the use of fructose diphosphate and nucleic acid, and less so with glycerophosphate and adenylic acid (Dempsey and Wislocki, 1947). The reaction occurs earliest and reaches its maximal intensity in the brush border, although, as gestation proceeds, it spreads throughout the syncytial cytoplasm and also involves the nuclei. However, the localization of the enzymatic reaction within the nuclei may not represent the actual distribution in the living state, for investigations have shown that the reaction products are capable of migrating, especially from cytoplasm to nuclei (Martin and Jacoby, 1949; Leduc and Dempsey, 1951; Herman and Deane, 1953). This enzyme is a distinguishing feature of the great absorptive surfaces of the small intestine, proximal convoluted tubule of the kidney, and syncytial trophoblast of the placenta.

Acid phosphatase (Figs. 15.39 and 15.40) occurs in great intensity in the syncytium in both cytoplasm and nuclei (Wislocki and Dempsey, 1948). The nuclear staining may

PLATE 15.V

All of the drawings on this plate (except Fig. 15.23) are of frozen sections of material fixed in 10 per cent buffered formalin and stained by the Ashbel and Seligman method for carbonyl groups. Compare the illustrations on this plate with those on Plate 15.IV.

FIG. 15.18. The syncytial trophoblast of a human villus at 5 months of gestation, stained by the carbonyl method. The reaction is localized in the lipid droplets of the syncytium. Compare with Figure 15.13. × 7 ocular; × 90 objective.

FIG. 15.19. A human placental villus at full term illustrating the positive carbonyl reaction of the minute lipid droplets in the syncytium as well as a diffuse reaction of the entire syncytial cytoplasm. Compare with Figure 15.14. × 7 ocular; × 60 objective.

FIG. 15.20. The placental labyrinth of a cat (fetal crown to rump length, 75 mm.) showing an intense carbonyl reaction in lipid droplets located in the cytotrophoblasts of the placental lamellae. A diffuse lavender reaction is present in the contiguous trophoblastic syncytium. × 10 ocular; × 40 objective.

FIG. 15.21. The carbonyl reaction in the placenta of a rat of 18 days of gestation. Compare with Figure 15.16 illustrating the distribution of sudanophilic lipids in the rat's placenta, and with Figure 15.17 illustrating the carbonyl reaction in the labyrinth of the mouse. × 10 ocular; × 40 objective.

FIG. 15.22. The carbonyl reaction in the placenta of a pig (crown to rump length, 90 mm.). The reaction is localized in the uterine epithelium, whereas little staining is apparent in the chorion. The distribution of the reaction coincides with that of lipids revealed by sudan dyes (Fig. 15.15). × 10 ocular; × 40 objective.

FIG. 15.23. The placenta of a pig (fetal crown to rump length, 235 mm.). Bouin's fixation. Masson's stain. This figure is shown to illustrate the detailed structure and relative thinness of the pig's placental barrier. It shows "intra-epithelial" maternal capillaries (*m.c.*) in the uterine epithelium (*ep*), and "intra-epithelial" fetal capillaries (*f.c.*) in the chorionic syncytium (*ch*); the distance separating the two sets of capillaries varies between 6 and 8 μ. Compare with Figures 15.28 and 15.64 which also illustrate the extreme thinness of the trophoblast and the narrow distance separating the maternal from the fetal capillaries in the placenta of the pig. × 70 ocular; × 40 objective.

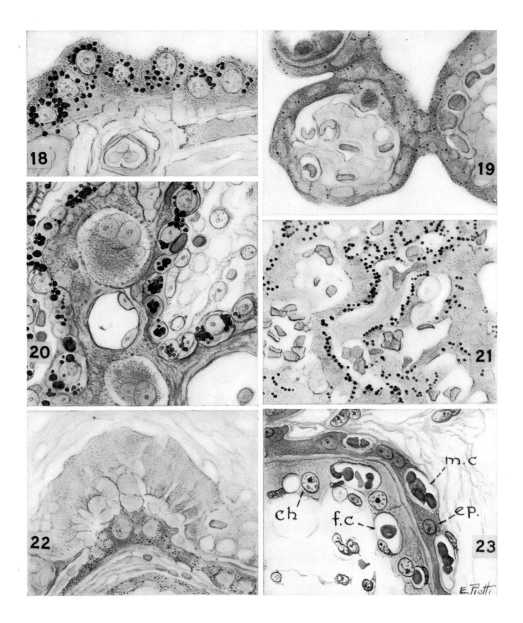

ch f.c m.c ep.

E.Piotti

not represent the true location of the enzyme, because on localizing the enzyme by both histochemical and biochemical methods and comparing the results, Palade (1951) found in the case of the hepatic cells of the rat that the enzyme was confined almost entirely to the cytoplasm. Furthermore, recent biochemical evidence indicates that this enzyme is located in a particular cytoplasmic fraction, the lysosomes (De-Duve, 1959).

High *esterase* activity is demonstrable in the trophoblast following the use of the method of Barrnett and Seligman (1952) on unfixed frozen sections (Wislocki, 1953). It could not be determined with certainty whether the intense but poorly localized crystalline reaction product was entirely in the syncytium or whether some was present in the Langhans cells (Fig. 15.36). With the method for esterase (Nachlas and Seligman, 1949) carried out on sections of acetone-fixed, paraffin-embedded material, the trophoblast shows no reaction. Acetone fixation destroys cholinesterases and some aliesterase, as a consequence of which a tissue poor in aliesterase would be negative. The combination of the positive Barrnett and Seligman reaction on unfixed frozen sections and of the negative reaction by the method of Nachlas and Seligman on acetone-fixed sections indicates that cholinesterases and possibly a small amount of aliesterase are present in the trophoblast. Cholinesterase has been found in high activity in the human placenta by chemical means (Torda, 1942; Ord and Thompson, 1950). Acetylcholine has been reported by a histochemical method devised by Wen, Chang and Wong (1936) as occurring in large amounts in the border and on the surface of the syncytium.

The *indophenol oxidase reaction* was performed with the nadi reagents on fresh, unfixed, teased villi, and on unfixed, frozen sections of human placenta of the 6th week of gestation (Dempsey and Wislocki, 1944). Indophenol blue appeared in the syncytium (Fig. 15.5), where it was interpreted as revealing the presence of the cytochrome oxidase-cytochrome c system. In contrast to the syncytium, the stroma of the villi did not give the indophenol reaction.

A series of reduction-oxidation indicators was similarly applied to placental villi. The syncytium concentrated the dyes in their oxidized form, whereas the stroma of the villi reacted far less intensely. These results indicate that the syncytium is maintained in the air at a more positive *reduction-oxidation potential* than the stroma and are in keeping with the similar distribution of indophenol blue.

3. Stroma of the Chorionic Villi; Hofbauer Cells

The stroma of the villi consists of mesenchymal connective tissue composed of cells, argyrophil reticular fibers, and fetal blood vessels. The surface of the stroma upon which the syncytium and Langhans cells rest is condensed into a basement membrane assumed to be composed of argyrophilic reticular fibers and ground substance. This membrane stains deeply with connective tissue stains, such as Mallory's and Heidenhain's azan (Fig. 15.9). It is stained also with varying intensity by the PAS reagents (Figs. 15.29, 15.32 and 15.54), the reaction probably being attributable to a ground substance consisting of mucopolysaccharide or glycoprotein which surrounds the reticular collagenous fibers. The membrane is quite variable in intensity of staining and definition, being best differentiated at the distal ends of the growing secondary villi (Fig. 15.32). In the latter region the basement membrane also exhibits metachromatic staining with toluidin blue (Wislocki and Dempsey, 1948), a response interpreted as indicating the presence of acid mucopolysaccharide.

It is of interest that the basement membrane described here, as being rich in mucopolysaccharide, is also a site in which iron (Fig. 15.8) (Hofbauer, 1905; Zancla, 1912; Wislocki and Dempsey, 1946c), calcium (Schönig, 1929; Wislocki and Dempsey, 1946c), and variable amounts of alkaline phosphatase (Wislocki and Dempsey, 1946c) are concentrated. It should be noted that in the early months of gestation these substances are demonstrable principally toward the growing tips of the villi, a finding which suggests possible functional differences in various regions.

The surface of contact between the Langhans cells, the syncytium, and the stroma also merits discussion with reference to the basement membrane. With connective tissue stains, such as Mallory's, each of the clear, chromophobic Langhans cells seems to be enclosed by a deeply stained surface film or membrane which seems to be continuous with the subjacent reticular basement membrane (Fig. 15.9). However, unlike the latter, these encapsulating membranes of the Langhans cells are neither argyrophilic nor stained by the PAS reagents (Fig. 15.54). Grosser (1925a, b) concluded that the "capsules" represent a secretion liberated by the Langhans cells, which he designated as "fibrinoid" (Wislocki and Bennett, 1943). Electron micrographs of early and late human placentas demonstrate that these cells are not separated from the syncytium or encapsulated by a collagenous material (Wislocki and Dempsey, 1955). However, narrow clefts often occur between the plasma membranes of the syncytial and Langhans cells and also between two contiguous Langhans cells.

The mesenchymal cells or fibroblasts of the chorionic villi contain a moderate quantity of glycogen in the first 2 months of gestation, but this substance declines thereafter. They possess numerous mitochondria (Fig. 15.26) and also give faint cytoplasmic reactions for sulfhydryl groups (Figs. 15.33 and 15.35), esterase (Fig. 15.36), and succinic dehydrogenase (Fig. 15.38). Gersh and Catchpole (1949) described glycoprotein granules in the mesenchymal cells, which increase in number up to 4 months of gestation, after which they decline. To these cells they ascribed the role of producing the ground substance of the villi. The endoplasmic reticulum is conspicuous in these cells, being highly branched and irregular in shape, and its matrix has unusually high density (Wislocki and Dempsey, 1955).

Besides mesenchymal cells, the stroma contains peculiar, large, predominantly round, vacuolated cells designated as *Hofbauer cells* (Fig. 15.13). They are numerous in human villi in the first months of gestation but diminish in number afterwards. In the first 6 weeks of gestation these cells contain some glycogen which is located between the cytoplasmic vacuoles. On removal of the glycogen they exhibit a residual PAS

reaction in the cytoplasm surrounding the nucleus and vacuoles (Fig. 15.57). They contain a moderate number of mitochondria (Fig. 15.26), and succinic dehydrogenase activity has been demonstrated in these cells. They do not exhibit alkaline phosphatase activity, but give a moderately strong cytoplasmic reaction for acid phosphatase. Hofbauer (1905) described osmicated droplets in some of them. Lipids occur in finely granular form, when demonstrated by sudan black. Ashbel and Hertig (1952), utilizing the Ashbel-Seligman reaction, reported that a carbonyl reaction occurs in some of the Hofbauer cells. Wislocki and Bennett (1943, Fig. 16) observed them to be filled occasionally with vacuoles or droplets deeply stained with iron hematoxylin.

The nature of the Hofbauer cells is uncertain. Some investigators have regarded them as degenerating cells (Mall and Meyer, 1921), whereas Lewis (1924) considered them to be macrophages because of the affinity of their cytoplasm for neutral red. The latter opinion also receives support from their observed increase in numbers in syphilitic infections (Hofbauer, 1925). Their histochemical properties enumerated above, particularly the presence of a positive PAS reaction after removal of glycogen, of finely dispersed lipids, and of acid phosphatase activity, are also compatible with similar reactions encountered in macrophages (Leblond, 1950; Doyle, 1950; Weiss and Fawcett, 1953). The Hofbauer cells differentiate presumably from the mesenchymal cells of the villi, although an origin from the Langhans cells has also been suggested; the latter, although unproven, is a distinct possibility. It seems quite unlikely, as some have thought, that they originate from either erythroblasts or endothelial cells (Mall and Meyer, 1921).

4. Age Changes in the Chorionic Villi

The chorionic villi undergo changes as the placenta ages. They become more branched, numerous, and slender. The Langhans cells diminish in number and assume a flattened shape, while the syncytium becomes thinned out over the distended sinusoidal capillaries. The stroma becomes less cellular, denser, and more fibrous. The basement membrane upon which the tropho-blast rests becomes increasingly thick and continuous; it contains collagenous fibers which are strongly argyrophilic and a ground substance which stains intensely with PAS reagents (cf. Figs. 15.29 and 15.50).

As the human chorionic villi age, the cytoplasmic basophilia of the syncytium, revealed by staining with methylene blue, undergoes a steady decline, whereas the affinity for acid dyes, as shown by the curve of staining with orange G, increases sharply up to the middle of pregnancy and then continues at a constant level until full term (Singer and Wislocki, 1948). Thus, as ribonucleoprotein undergoes a gradual decline, the basic protein component rises.

As ribonucleoprotein diminishes, alkaline phosphatase, which is minimal in amount in the first 2 months of gestation, increases tremendously, becoming maximal in the last trimester (cf. Figs. 15.4, 15.41, and 15.42). This reaction is confined mainly to the syncytium, especially to its outer border where it is extremely intense. It is apparent that the amounts of ribonucleoprotein and alkaline phosphatase in the syncytium are inversely related, the former being seemingly peculiar to the period of rapid growth, whereas the latter is associated with the phases of maturity and aging of the placenta. Acid phosphatase is also present in the cytoplasm of the syncytium, although it does not increase to the degree to which alkaline phosphatase does (cf. Figs. 15.39 and 15.40).

Glycogen is not detectable in the syncytium at full term, but a saliva-resistant PAS reaction is evident in the cytoplasm of its outer border (Fig. 15.50) (Wislocki, 1950). This marginal staining occurs in minute, stubble-like microvilli which have replaced the luxuriant brush border of the first half of pregnancy. This change in surface area is clearly evident in both light and electron microscopes.

With age the stroma of the villi has become more fibrous and less cellular, the fibers being markedly argyrophilic (Wislocki and Bennett, 1943, Fig. 20). Associated with the fibers, there is a ground substance which is strongly periodic acid-Schiff positive and

is condensed to form a conspicuous basement membrane upon which the syncytium rests, besides forming sheaths which enclose the sinusoidal fetal capillaries (Fig. 15.50).

The lipid droplets present in the syncytium in the first trimester (Fig. 15.13) become reduced in size and relative number (Wislocki and Bennett, 1943, Figs. 9, 10, 11, 12, and 21). Nevertheless, numerous, minute, sudanophilic droplets are still demonstrable at full term (Wislocki and Bennett, 1943, Figs. 14 and 21), and these also give a positive Ashbel-Seligman reaction for carbonyl groups (Fig. 15.19), (Wislocki, 1952). Besides the lipid droplets which react with the Ashbel-Seligman reagents, the entire syncytium exhibits a diffuse reaction (Fig. 15.19). In contrast to the above findings, Ashbel and Hertig (1952) did not observe a carbonyl reaction in 9 placentas examined at term, although Ashbel and Seligman (1949) reported a sparse reaction in 1 case at term.

The syncytium at term exhibits a large number of mitochondria (Wislocki and Bennett, 1943, Fig. 19) and also gives a positive Baker's acid hematein reaction for phospholipids (Fig. 15.24).

The conspicuous sinusoidal capillaries of the chorionic villi in the last trimester become closely pressed against the syncytium in many places. The latter becomes stretched over the capillaries to form a thin membrane. These thinned out membranous areas (Figs. 15.14, 15.24, and 15.50) (Wislocki and Bennett, 1943, Plates 5 and 6) have been termed "epithelial plates" and have been equated with Bowman's capsule of renal glomeruli (Bremer, 1916). It has been supposed that through them at this period the most active transfer of substances occurs. The thinnest areas of the hemochorial placental barrier, separating the maternal and fetal blood streams, are composed of the following layers: (1) a thin lamina of syncytium which rests on a thick basement membrane, (2) a connective tissue space which contains ground substance, and collagenous fibers, and (3) the wall of the sinusoidal capillary composed of another basement membrane which is lined internally by endothelium (Wislocki and Dempsey, 1955). The cytochemical and structural complexity of the syncytium makes it more comparable with the epithelia of the proximal convoluted tubule of the kidney and of the small intestine than with the pulmonary alveolar lining or the glomerular membrane.

Degenerative age changes that occur in the human placenta have been variously described. Tenny (1936a, b) and Tenny and Parker (1940) reported hyaline degeneration of the syncytium clothing the terminal villi of aging placentas, a change which according to them occurs to a greater degree, as well as prematurely, in toxemia, preeclampsia, and eclampsia. Wislocki and Dempsey (1946a) examined the placentas from two cases diagnosed respectively as severe preeclampsia and eclampsia. Both cases were atypical, because in each the condition was present at 4.5 months of gestation. Thinning of the syncytium with some nuclear deterioration was observed, as well as a premature decrease in basophilia associated with early accumulation of alkaline and acid phosphatases and an increased acidophilia. Some of the smallest villi showed hyaline necrosis of both syncytium and stroma. These changes were ascribed to premature aging of the chorionic villi. Subsequently, however, in a further series of placentas from cases of toxemia in the last trimester of gestation (unpublished data), changes from normal, based on loss of basophilia and an increase in phosphatases, were not apparent.

Tenney and Parker (1940) observed that a variable number of the terminal placental villi undergo hyaline degeneration in both normal and toxemic pregnancies. Wislocki and Dempsey (1948) noticed that the stroma of degenerating villi develops intense metachromasia (Figs. 15.51 and 15.57), in contrast to the ground substance of normal villi, which does not exhibit metachromatic staining, except as noted above in the basement membrane at the growing tips of secondary villi. The metachromatic transformation of the stroma of fibrous, degenerating villi is probably attributable to the formation and accumulation of an acid mucopolysaccharide. This development, it seems probable, is the equivalent of, or allied to, changes described in some

PLATE 15.VI

FIG. 15.24. Human placental villus at full term. Frozen section stained by Baker's acid hematein method for phospholipids following fixation in formalin-calcium-chloride. Observe the positive reaction in the syncytium covering the villus. The reaction coincides with the presence of mitochondria revealed in similar distribution by appropriate methods (Wislocki and Bennett, 1943, Fig. 19). × 10 ocular; × 60 objective.

FIG. 15.25. Cells of the basal plate (cytotrophoblastic shell) of a human placenta of 3½ months gestation. Frozen section stained by Baker's acid hematein method for phospholipids. Observe the cytotrophoblasts which contain variable amounts of reactive material; the latter coincides with mitochondria demonstrable by other methods. × 10 ocular; × 60 objective.

FIG. 15.26. A portion of a human placental villus at 3½ months of gestation. Frozen section stained by Baker's acid hematein method for phospholipids. Notice the dense concentration of reactive material in the cytoplasm of the syncytial trophoblast. The distribution corresponds to similarly abundant mitochondria demonstrable by other means (Wislocki and Bennett, 1943, Figs. 15.13 and 15.14). Observe also the positive Baker reaction in the cytoplasm of the Langhans cells beneath the syncytium as well as in a group of Hofbauer cells in the stroma of the villus. × 10 ocular; × 60 objective.

FIG. 15.27. The junction of the trophoblastic shell (upper half) and the decidua (lower half) in the placenta of a monkey of 4 weeks gestation. Section stained by Pap's method for reticulum. Bodian's fixative No. 2. Observe that the reticular fibers of the decidually transformed endometrium cease abruptly at the border of the trophoblastic shell. As a result of this, the boundary between the decidua and the trophoblastic shell is sharply demarcated. The metachromatic ground substance of the decidua (*cf.* Fig. 15.58) also ceases abruptly at the line of junction between the decidua and the fetal elements. × 800. (Wislocki and Bennett, 1943.)

FIG. 15.28. A chorionic fold of the placenta of a pig (fetal crown to rump length, 64 mm.), illustrating two sinusoidal fetal capillaries (surrounded by black-stained reticular fibers), penetrating the chorionic epithelium and creating thin epithelial surface plate (arrows). Compare with Figures 15.23 and 15.64 which illustrate collectively the thinness of the placental barrier in the pig's epitheliochorial placenta. Pap's stain for reticulum; Bouin's fixative. × 10 ocular; × 90 objective. (Wislocki and Dempsey, 1946b.)

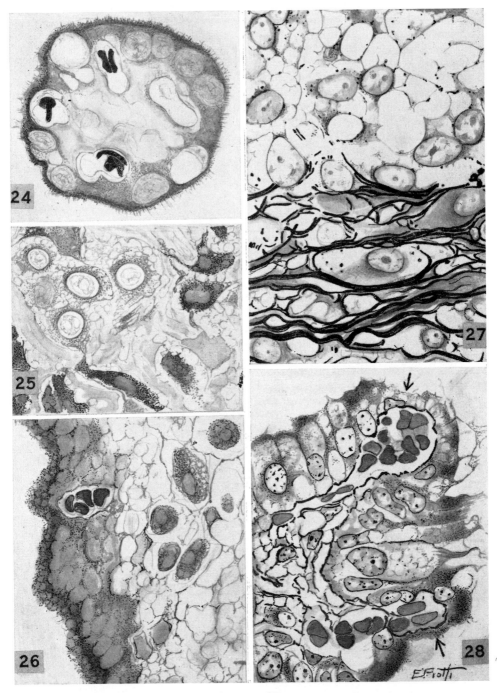

PLATE 15.VI

pathologic conditions as "mucoid degeneration." This placental change occurs in villi as early as the sixth week of gestation and is especially evident in the regressing villi of the chorion laeve.

Ashbel and Hertig (1952), using the carbonyl reaction of Ashbel and Seligman, have reported that "otherwise normal-appearing placentas from 6 cases of toxemia of pregnancy with gestational ages of 34 to 39 weeks contained increased amounts of ketosteroid, indicating a distinct metabolic abnormality." On the basis of the belief that there is an increased degeneration of the syncytium in pre-eclampsia, Smith and Smith (1948) postulated a marked decline in the production and secretion of ketosteroids by this tissue. The findings of Ashbel and Hertig would not seem to be in harmony with the supposition of the Smiths. However, one might interpret the increase in carbonyl compounds observed by them as possibly representing increased storage associated with diminished secretion of ketosteroids. The observations of Deane, Shaw and Greep (1948) on the cells of the adrenal cortex provided the basis for this speculation; they found that on stimulation of the adrenal cortex the lipid droplets of the cortical cells diminished in size, whereas on gradual reduction of normal stimulation the droplets first enlarged but subsequently diminished with extreme shrinkage of the cells. The extent and direction of the changes depended on the degree and duration of stimulation or its cessation. It should be recalled in this connection that Bienenfeld (1912) reported an unusually high content of lipid in the placenta in eclampsia.

The main difficulty in relating eclampsia and the toxemias of pregnancy to premature and excessive age changes in the placenta is that the alterations differ from those characterizing normal placental aging in degree only, there being no really distinctive qualitative or absolute quantitative histopathologic changes that can be readily ascertained. Inasmuch as the topography of the placental villi and cotyledons is complex and variable, and many of the age changes are spottily disseminated, the human placenta presents grave obstacles to adequate histologic sampling for the purpose of establishing relative degrees of age changes, whether they be normal or pathologic. Methods depending on the use of frozen sections combined with drastic histochemical procedures are especially unsuitable. The suggestion is offered that the placenta should be investigated for possible structural and functional differences with relationship to the various segments or divisions of the villous tree. The possibility that there are differences which characterize various portions of the villi is suggested by several of the histochemical findings reported in the previous pages. There is also the possibility that the structure and function of different segments of the villi, in a regional pattern from the basal plate to the surface of the placenta, may be related to the direction and manner of flow of the maternal blood in the intervillous space. With respect to this, although investigations of the uteroplacental circulation in man (Spanner, 1935b) and rhesus monkey (Ramsey, 1949, 1954) have shed much light on the uterine decidual vessels, practically nothing is known about the character and flow of the maternal blood in the intervillous space in relation to the villous trees. Moreover, because definitive information on the topography of the placental villi is lacking, previous descriptions of the pattern of the fetal villous circulation have not seemed particularly helpful (Spanner, 1935b; Boe, 1953). When the pattern of the fetal villi is worked out and correlated with the pathways of both the fetal and maternal blood streams, differing functional segments of the villi may become apparent, thus permitting deeper insight into questions of placental exchange of metabolites and aging of the placenta, both normally and in the toxemias.

C. PERIPHERAL CYTOTROPHOBLAST

The peripheral cytotrophoblast of the first trimester of gestation comprises the trophoblastic cell columns, cell islands, and the trophoblastic shell (Figs. 15.2 and 15.3). A detailed account of the differentiation and growth of these structures in the rhesus monkey was given by Wislocki and Streeter (1938). Eventually the trophoblastic cell columns (primary villi) are converted into vascularized secondary and tertiary villi covered by Langhans cells and syncytium. However, the trophoblastic shell persists and, through the expansion and growth of the placental cotyledons, is transformed into a basal plate contiguous to the decidua basalis and placental septa forming the boundaries between the cotyledons (Fig. 15.43). The septa placentae consist of masses of cells associated with a ground substance termed "fibrinoid" by Grosser (1925a, b), which is distinguishable histologically from actual fibrin intermingled with it by the fact that with Mallory's connective stain, as well as with azan, it is colored blue, whereas the fibrin stains red.

Contrary to earlier opinion, the septa placentae are now regarded as being fetal in origin and the component cells as trophoblasts (Spanner, 1935a; Stieve, 1940; Stieve and von der Heide, 1941). On the other hand, the nature and origin of the elements of the basal plate have not been so well clarified. Grosser (1948), for example, states that, in the mature placenta, decidua constitutes the foundation of the basal plate, but that it contains remnants of the "junctional" or "penetration" zone and that "the fetal side is clothed by trophoblastic cell derivatives in various stages of regression." However, more recent work has shown that the basal plate is composed mainly of functional trophoblasts (Wislocki, 1951). The so-called cell islands which preponderate in the first half of gestation (Stieve and von der Heide, 1941) also consist of clusters of trophoblasts. The cells in these various sites, from the beginning until the end of gestation, will be referred to in the present chapter as peripheral trophoblasts and the sum total of them as the peripheral cytotrophoblast. It has been demonstrated (Wislocki, 1951) that the peripheral trophoblasts are chromophilic and differ in several important cytochemical respects from the chromophobic Langhans cells of the secondary and tertiary chorionic villi. Furthermore, whereas the Langhans cells become inconspicuous and diminish by the end of gestation, the peripheral trophoblasts in the placental septa and basal plate persist in large numbers until term (Wislocki, 1951).

1. Trophoblasts Forming the Cell Columns and Trophoblastic Shell

At the junction of the primary villi with the stroma-containing secondary villi during the first 4 weeks of gestation the trophoblastic cells are large and chromophobic, resembling Langhans cells. The proximal ends of the cell columns constitute a germinal bed of cells exhibiting numerous mitoses. It is from these cells that the peripheral trophoblasts apparently arise. Moving outward from the germinal region, along the columns into the shell, the trophoblastic cells change their character. In the first months of gestation they are laden with *glycogen* as revealed by the PAS method (Figs. 15.31 and 15.32). By the end of the first month, however, a type of cell which is characterized by *cytoplasmic basophilia* and lower glycogen content has arisen and these cells increase in number. When fully developed, they contain clumps of strongly basophilic cytoplasmic material, reminiscent of the Nissl substance of neurones (Fig. 15.11), and the staining of the basophilic substance is abolished after treatment of the sections with ribonuclease (Fig. 15.12), a result indicating that the basophilic substance contains ribonucleoprotein (Dempsey and Wislocki, 1945). The staining and nature of this basophilic substance have been confirmed by Ortmann (1949). The cytoplasm of these trophoblasts also stains moderately strongly with *acid dyes* (Figs. 15.46 and 15.47). When stained with the PAS reagents following exposure to saliva, many of the trophoblasts exhibit delicate red stippling against a diffuse reddish background (Figs. 15.49 and 15.55) (Wislocki, 1950), a staining reaction indicative of the presence of a mucopolysaccharide or glycoprotein. The cytoplasm does not stain metachromatically with *toluidin blue*, a finding which indicates the absence of strongly acid mucopolysaccharides. The cells do not contain triglycerides or *lipids* of the type occurring in the syncytium. However, sudan black and Baker's method for *phospholipids* differentiate minute granules in variable numbers in the cytotrophoblasts (Figs. 15.25 and 15.48). These particles correspond in size and number to *mitochondria* revealed by other methods. *Succinic dehydro-*

genase activity is demonstrable by the formation of blue formazan crystals in the cytoplasm (Fig. 15.38). The cytotrophoblasts contain little *acid* and *alkaline phosphatase* (Dempsey and Wislocki, 1947).

From the observations cited above, it is apparent that the peripheral trophoblasts differ cytologically in several significant respects from the Langhans cells of the chorionic villi (Wislocki, Dempsey and Fawcett, 1948). The latter are chromophobic, whereas the peripheral trophoblasts are distinctly chromophilic, exhibiting marked cytoplasmic basophilia and containing a diastase-resistant polysaccharide.

2. Ground Substance of the Trophoblastic Cell Columns and Shell

The nature of the ground substance (Figs. 15.12, 15.44, 15.45, 15.46, 15.47, 15.48, 15.49 and 15.55) lying between the peripheral trophoblasts has not been clearly established. Grosser (1925a, b) designated it "fibrinoid" and regarded it as a secretion of the trophoblastic cells which becomes variously admixed with fibrin of maternal origin. He observed that the fibrinoid substance stained blue with Mallory's connective tissue stain in contrast to the fibrin which was stained red. Spanner (1935a) concurred, stressing that the ground substance surrounding the trophoblasts does not contain a collagenous reticular network, in this respect differing from the matrix of the maternal decidua basalis which possesses well defined reticular fibers surrounding its cells (Fig. 15.27). Wislocki and Bennett (1943) concluded that the ground substance of the trophoblastic shell and cell columns is probably a mixture of maternal and fetal substances. They pointed out that with other triacid stains, such as Heidenhain's azan and Masson's stain, fibrin is distinguishable from the component which Grosser termed "fibrinoid." The ground substance is also stained by basic dyes (Fig. 15.11), but, unlike the cytoplasmic basophilia of the trophoblasts, that of the ground substance is not influenced by exposure to ribonuclease (Fig. 15.12). However, Singer and Wislocki (1948) were unable to distinguish two separate components on the basis of the affinity of the ground substance for *methylene*

blue and *orange G* as measured under conditions of controlled pH staining; under these conditions the reactions to both dyes were found to be similar to that of purified fibrin. On the other hand, PAS reagents stain the fibrin an intense scarlet (Fig. 15.55), whereas the "fibrinoid" component assumes a much paler color (Fig. 15.32), a result which again indicates a distinct difference between them. *Acid* and *alkaline phosphatases* are present only in traces. The Turnbull blue reaction for iron occurs intensely in the ground substance (Dempsey and Wislocki, 1944).

It is noteworthy that the ground substance of the peripheral trophoblast is neither metachromatic (Fig. 15.58) nor provided with argyrophilic reticular fibers (Fig. 15.27) (Wislocki and Dempsey, 1948). Thus, although fibrin of maternal origin appears to gain ready access to the ground substance of the cytotrophoblast, the metachromatic component of the decidua as such does not appear to diffuse into the trophoblastic shell.

3. Cytotrophoblast of the Basal Plate and Septa Placentae at Term

It is generally believed that the peripheral trophoblast undergoes regression and degeneration in the second half of gestation, no longer playing any significant functional role. Spanner (1935a) states that the septa consist of fibrinoid, containing lacunae from which the trophoblastic cells gradually disappear. Baker, Hook and Severinghaus (1944) maintained that both cell columns and cell islands are characteristic of early pregnancy, the former persisting as late as 3.5 months. Furthermore, according to them, some cells continue to show indications of secretory activity, but for the most part they degenerate into fibrinoid. Similarly, Grosser (1948) remarked that the basal plate in the ripe placenta is clothed on its fetal side with trophoblastic cells in various states of regression.

The results obtained by the use of histochemical methods differ in two major respects from the views expressed above. First, the occurrence of cytoplasmic basophilia, of a positive PAS reaction (Figs. 15.49 and 15.55), and of numerous mitochondria in the placental septa and basal plate at full term indicate the presence of large numbers of viable and functionally active trophoblastic cells (Wislocki, 1951). Very few of the trophoblasts appear to be undergoing degeneration.

Secondly, in normal human placentas delivered at full term, the basal plate is composed predominantly of masses of cells which are identifiable as trophoblasts by cytologic and histochemical means (Wislocki, 1951). Only a few maternal decidual cells which differ cytologically from trophoblasts are attached irregularly to the maternal surface of the expelled placenta. The ground substance of the basal plate gives an intense PAS reaction which seems to be mainly attributable to fibrin (Figs. 15.49, 15.45, and 15.55), and contains no acid phosphatase (Fig. 15.40) and only traces of alkaline phosphatase (Fig. 15.42). In these respects it differs completely from the matrix of the decidua. However, after abnormal implantation, culminating in the condition termed placenta accreta, the basal plate and septa placenta are modified by the unusually deep penetration of the trophoblast into the uterine wall, resulting in widespread intercrescence of the fetal and maternal tissues (Irving and Hertig, 1937) with obliteration of the usually well defined demarcation of the basal trophoblast from the decidua.

4. Cytologic Comparisons of the Cytotrophoblasts with Decidual Cells

The decidua, as revealed by histochemical means, is composed mainly of rather large cells exhibiting many reactions, some of which distinguish them clearly from the peripheral cytotrophoblasts. In the first months of gestation both the trophoblasts and the decidual cells contain large amounts of glycogen which make it difficult to tell them apart; as gestation advances glycogen diminishes in both cell types, although a considerable quantity persists in the decidual cells until term. On the other hand, the cytoplasm of the decidual cells does not have the strong cytoplasmic basophilia which characterizes the peripheral cytotrophoblasts. Furthermore, unlike the trophoblasts, most of the decidual cells contain droplets of neutral fat and give a strong

reaction for acid phosphatase (Fig. 15.53) (Wislocki and Dempsey, 1948). Also the stippling observed in the trophoblasts following staining with PAS reagents after exposure to saliva (Figs. 15.49 and 15.55) is not seen in the decidual cells (Fig. 15.52); instead they are stained a diffuse pink. Thus certain features sharply differentiate the two types of cells.

In contrast to the ground substance of the cytotrophoblastic cell columns, the matrix of the decidua is characterized by the presence of an argyrophilic collagenous reticulum surrounding the decidual cells (Fig. 15.27). The matrix also contains an amorphous ground substance which stains metachromatically with toluidin blue (Fig. 15.58) and is quite deeply stained by PAS reagents (Fig. 15.52). The metachromasia indicates the presence in the matrix of an acid mucopolysaccharide. These reactions characterize the matrix throughout the entire period of gestation, as has been demonstrated on pieces of decidua vera and basalis obtained at cesarian removal of human placentas at full term (Wislocki, 1953).

The basal plate of the delivered human placenta exhibits, as a rule, a sharp line of demarcation between a wide zone of trophoblasts and fibrin and an incomplete, irregularly narrow lamina of decidua attached to its outer surface. The decidual cells of this narrow strip or border, which represents the "junctional" or "penetration" zone, differ from those in the general bulk of the decidua in that the cells are markedly degenerated. This zone gives a strong enzymatic reaction for acid phosphatase (Figs. 15.40 and 15.53) and a faint, irregular, nonenzymatic reaction by the method for alkaline phosphatase, the latter attributable mainly to the presence of calcium salts in this region (Fig. 15.42) (Dempsey and Wislocki, 1946).

5. Cytolytic and Proteolytic Activities of Peripheral Trophoblasts

In the first weeks of gestation the cytotrophoblast of the trophoblastic shell seems to produce proteolytic and cytolytic substances capable of attacking the endometrium (Wislocki and Bennett, 1943; Wislocki, Dempsey and Fawcett, 1948). In the early stages of normal gestation in primates, hemorrhage in the decidua coincides with the erosion of the uterine mucosa by the advancing trophoblast. However, the trophoblast elaborates a substance which initiates changes in the decidual tissue even before the ovum has become attached. In the rhesus monkey, evidence of such a chemical factor is seen in the fact that the epithelium at the secondary implantation site begins to proliferate before actual erosion of the uterine surface has taken place (Wislocki and Streeter, 1938). Similarly, in a previllous human ovum of 11 days' ovulation age, an area of congestion and hemorrhage was found on the opposite endometrial wall which had merely been in close proximity to the implantation site (Hertig and Rock, 1941).

The histologic appearances at the margin of the growing trophoblastic shell of the human placenta in the early months of gestation suggest that the cells and matrix of the decidua are attacked and slowly destroyed by the action of the advancing, growing cytotrophoblast. In sections which have been impregnated by silver, the dissolution of the fibers of the reticulum can be observed. Immediately adjacent to the border of the trophoblast, the fibers become broken up and the individual bits dissolve apparently in the outermost part of the matrix of the trophoblastic shell (Wislocki and Bennett, 1943, Plate 9). Similar fragmentation of collagen fibers in the vicinity of the

trophoblast has been noted in the placenta of rodents (Wislocki, Deane and Dempsey, 1946, Plate 10) and cat (Wislocki and Dempsey, 1946a, Fig. 5). The metachromatic ground substance between the decidual cells, close to the cytotrophoblast, is also destroyed.

Similar proteolytic activity has been demonstrated experimentally in the presence of fertilized mouse ova transplanted to various extra-uterine sites including the anterior chamber of the eye (Runner, 1947; Fawcett, Wislocki and Waldo, 1947). In the eye of a mouse containing proliferating ova, leakage of blood from engorged vessels in the iris and cornea took place before a blastocyst had actually become attached to the wall of the anterior chamber. It is noteworthy also that blood began to accumulate behind the iris at the same time that it appeared in the anterior chamber. Inasmuch as the vessels on the back of the iris and ciliary body were not in contact with the blastocyst and hence had not presumably been disrupted by actual invasion, the most satisfactory way to account for the bleeding in the posterior chamber was to attribute it to some chemical released by the trophoblast. Although the trophoblast invades maternal vessels in later stages of implantation, direct observation and study of histologic sections of ova transplanted to the eye suggested that the interstitial hemorrhage and edema in the early hours of nidation were the result of diffuse damage to

PLATE 15.VII

FIG. 15.29. Human placental villi at 2½ months of gestation, stained by the periodic acid-Schiff (PAS) procedure. Section exposed to saliva before staining. Zenker's acetic acid fixative. Observe the positive PAS reaction in the outer zone of the syncytium as well as the variable reaction of the basement membrane on which the trophoblast rests. Note also the reaction in the cells of the stroma. Compare with Figure 15.33. × 150.

FIG. 15.30. Human placental villi at 3½ months of gestation stained by Baker's acid hematein method for phospholipids. Formalin-calcium-chloride fixative. Observe the intense reaction of the syncytial trophoblast clothing the villi, as well as the staining of the stromal cells, particularly of large, vacuolated Langhans cells. Compare with Figure 15.26, which shows more details. × 240.

FIGS. 15.31 and 15.32. Sections illustrating the tip of a secondary chorionic villus attached to the trophoblastic shell (or basal plate) of a human placenta at 2 months of gestation. PAS stain after Rossman's fixative. In Figure 15.31, glycogen is abundantly revealed in the cytotrophoblasts of the basal plate (left side of figure). In Figure 15.32, the section was immersed in saliva before staining it, to remove glycogen; as a result the trophoblasts (left side of figure) are now only very faintly stained, the outer zone of the syncytial trophoblast is moderately stained and there is an intense reaction visible in the basement membrane between the stroma of the secondary villus and the cytotrophoblastic cell column. These residual reactions are attributable to carbohydrates (glycoproteins, mucopolysaccharides) other than glycogen. × 300.

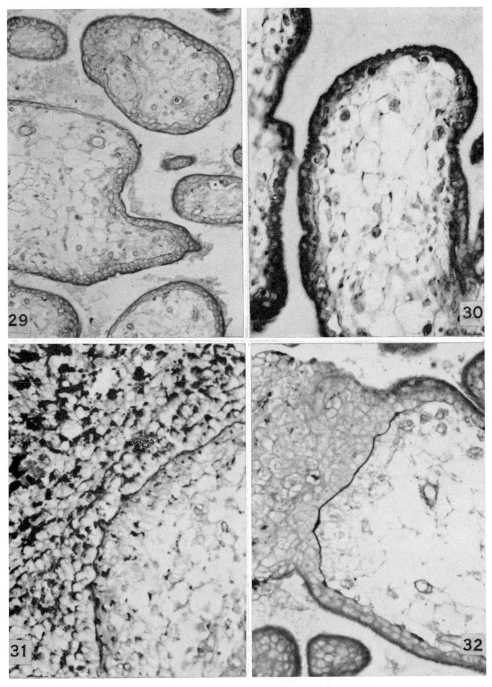

PLATE 15.VII

vessels by cytolytic substances emanating from the trophoblast. Further evidence of a cytolytic factor was demonstrated by the observation that ova placed in the eye were capable of developing in close proximity, but only until the most precocious one among them began to implant. Thereafter, the others quickly degenerated. In connection with the question of cytolytic substances produced by the placenta, it should be recalled that bits of human chorionic villi obtained from placentas of the first months of pregnancy and grown on plasma clots liquefied the medium (Gräfenberg, 1909a, b; Friedheim, 1929; Caffier, 1929).

IV. The Structure of the Placental Barrier

Two concepts have dominated the subject of placental physiology. The first of these states that, as gestation advances and the placenta ages in a given species of mammal, the placental barrier becomes progressively more permeable to physiologic exchange between mother and fetus. The second concept proposes that the placentas of mammals can be arranged in an ascending order or phylogenetic series with reference to the relative facility and rapidity with which metabolites traverse them.

The placental barrier can be defined for Mammalia as "an apposition or fusion of the fetal membranes to the uterine mucosa for physiologic exchange" (Mossman, 1937). The membranes involved are the chorion, allantois, and yolk sac, which in various relations to one another and to the uterine tissues give rise to a variety of placental structures, the nature of which will be discussed below.

A. GROSSER'S CLASSIFICATION

The relative permeability of the placenta in eutherian mammals, with reference to both ontogeny and phylogeny, has been generally related to four morphologic placental types defined by Grosser (1909). According to this doctrine, the chorioallantoic placentas of mammals can be arranged in an ascending order from the most primitive to the most advanced on the basis of the successive disappearance of 3 out of 6 layers which intervene between the maternal and fetal blood streams. The dis-

appearance of the maternal layers is attributed to the invasive and aggressive properties of the trophoblast of the chorion. In the most primitive placentas the layers comprise (1) the uterine vascular endothelium, (2) the uterine stroma, (3) the uterine epithelium, (4) the fetal trophoblast, (5) the fetal stroma, and (6) the fetal capillary endothelium. When these layers are all present, they form the so-called *epitheliochorial* type of placenta encountered in some ungulates (*e.g.*, pig, mare), Cetacea, and lemurs. Next, the uterine epithelium disappears through the invasive activity of the trophoblast, with the formation of the *syndesmochorial* type of placenta of other ungulates (*e.g.*, cow, sheep). Then with the loss of the maternal connective tissue, the *endotheliochorial* type of placenta of carnivores (dog, cat), sloths (Bradypodidae), Tupaiidae, some Insectivora (shrew, mole), and some bats (Chiroptera) arises. Finally, with the ultimate loss of the maternal endothelium, the *hemochorial* type of placenta of rodents, Tarsiidae, monkeys, anthropoid apes, and man is formed. This series has been widely accepted as having phylogenetic significance, in that it is supposed to begin with a primitive, six-layered placental barrier which is the least permeable, and to progress, by a successive reduction of the three maternal layers and a gradual diminution in width of the remaining fetal layers, to the most advanced evolutionary type in which transmission is most rapid and complete.

As an extension to Grosser's classification, Mossman (1926, 1937) sought to demonstrate that in lagomorphs and higher rodents, especially rabbit, rat, and guinea pig toward the end of gestation, the trophoblastic syncytium is normally, and very generally, lost, so that the placental membrane consists merely of fetal capillaries composed of endothelium. For the rabbit's placenta, he stated that after the 22nd day the syncytium disappears so that the placental barrier becomes reduced to a layer of "endothelium and a very thin plasmodium, the latter entirely absent in many places." This he designated as a *hemoendothelial* type of placenta, and it has been accepted as the most advanced stage of the series both morphologically and functionally.

In some groups of eutherian mammals (carnivores, some insectivores) a further provision for placental transfer exists in the paraplacental and central *hematomas*. These structures, illustrated by the paraplacental "green" and "brown" borders in dog and cat, consist of extensive extravasations of maternal blood between the chorion and endometrium. The extravasated blood is absorbed by the chorionic epithelium, with the result that the iron of the phagocytized red blood cells becomes available to the fetus. These paraplacental structures, which are epitheliochorial according to Grosser's classification but which occur mainly in association with endotheliochorial placentas, represent another important but poorly studied route of nutritive exchange between mother and fetus which has not been adequately evaluated with reference to Grosser's doctrine.

Hemotrophe is the name given to the nutritive materials absorbed by the placenta or fetal membranes directly from the circulating maternal blood stream. *Histotrophe*, on the contrary, refers to secretions and degradation products of the endometrium, as well as extravasated maternal blood, which undergo absorption. According to Grosser (1927), there is a correlation between the kind of nutriment supplied to the fetus and the degree of association between the maternal and fetal blood streams. Thus, in epitheliochorial placentas, histotrophe in the form of secretions and transudations is stated to be the almost exclusive form of nourishment. However, the higher the organization of the placenta is, the more important hemotrophic nourishment is said to become, so that it is maximal in species with hemochorial placentas. In man, and possibly the hedgehog, transmission becomes exclusively hemotrophic, so that according to Grosser, the human placenta in this respect represents a developmental end-stage. Amoroso (1952) concluded similarly that "in the hemochorial and hemo-endothelial placentas of man and higher rodents, histotrophic nutrition is insignificant after the early stages of development and nourishment of the foetus becomes possible, largely by direct absorption from the maternal blood." In regard to man, this conclusion seems entirely warranted, but in respect to rodents it should be borne in mind that they possess, in addition to a hemochorial placenta, a well developed yolk sac placenta which engages actively throughout gestation in the absorption of transudate and secretion, representing histotrophe derived from the endometrium. This illustrates again the paradox that, in the presence of what is regarded as the most highly developed and "efficient" type of placenta, namely, the hemochorial one of the higher rodents, a complex yolk sac placenta is also present which certainly functions principally by the absorption of histotrophe, a process which is generally regarded as being most primitive.

B. ULTRASTRUCTURE OF THE CHORIO-ALLANTOIC PLACENTA

A knowledge of the ultrastructure of the placental barriers of mammals is necessary to form hypotheses for the mechanism of transport across these membranes. Although our information on ultrastructure is fragmentary now, many significant observations have already been presented.

The placenta of the *pig* is classified as epitheliochorial since it consists of a simple apposition of the chorion to the endometrial epithelium without erosion. Observations have been made on the ultrastructure of the definitive pig placenta in which the corrugated surfaces of the chorion and uterine mucous membrane interdigitate closely (Dempsey, Wislocki and Amoroso, 1955). Chorionic ridges fit into matching uterine depressions (Figs. 15.23, 15.28, 15.64). These macroscopic interdigitations are further extended by the "submicroscopic" interdigitation of the free surfaces of the chorionic and uterine epithelia. In the regions of the chorionic ridges, the chorionic surface is thrown into numerous microvilli which align with the uterine microvilli to form simple interdigitations. The bovine fetal-maternal junction is similarly constructed (Björkman and Bloom, 1957). In the chorionic fossae, the fetal-maternal junction is similarly constructed; however, in addition, there are deep, thread-like invaginations of the fetal plasma membranes. Thus, there is far more intimate apposition than was previously realized and also these ultrastructural devices result in a great expansion of surface area. Furthermore, the uterine space at this maternal-fetal junction is so slight that the possibility of absorption of uterine secretions through the chorionic ridges and fossae seems to be excluded. Uterine secretions are most likely absorbed through the chorionic areolae which occur in regions where the uterine lumen is patent and filled with secretion. The special chorionic epithelium of the areolae shows great complexity at its surface. In addition to possessing irregularly shaped, often bulbous, projections which extend into the uterine lumen, these cells have complicated infoldings of the plasma membrane both apically and laterally. During the latter half of gestation, the fetal capillaries burrow into the chorionic epithelium where they acquire a so-called intra-epithelial position; fetal capillaries are especially rich in the chorionic ridges. The electron microscope has revealed that two basement membranes remain interposed between the chorionic epithelium and endothelium. Further interesting observations on the pig placenta concern the possibility of secretory activity by the cells lining the chorionic fossae and the occurrence of occasional cilia in the uterine glands.

The placenta of the *cat*, according to Grosser's classification, is of the endotheliochorial type in which erosion of the uterine epithelium and connective tissue occurs. The placenta proper consists of a series of roughly parallel trophoblastic plates or lamellae (Figs. 15.56, 15.60, and 15.61). In the center of the lamellae, maternal blood flows through closed capillaries surrounded by a relatively thick amorphous matrix and occasional giant decidual cells of maternal origin. The syncytiotrophoblast abuts on the amorphous matrix. The cytotrophoblast, which diminishes as gestation proceeds, is situated between the syncytiotrophoblast and the fetal connective tissue. The trophoblastic lamellae are separated from each other by a layer of fetal connective tissue through which fetal capillaries course.

Some observations on the ultrastructure of the placental and paraplacental regions of the cat's chorion were reported by Dempsey and Wislocki (1956). Substances passing from the maternal blood to that of the fetus first encounter the unusually thick and basophilic maternal endothelium which typifies the capillaries of the carnivore placentas. The endothelial cytoplasm evaginates to form surface projections and appears to have a well developed endoplasmic reticulum; however, inadequate preservation of these cells does not permit further

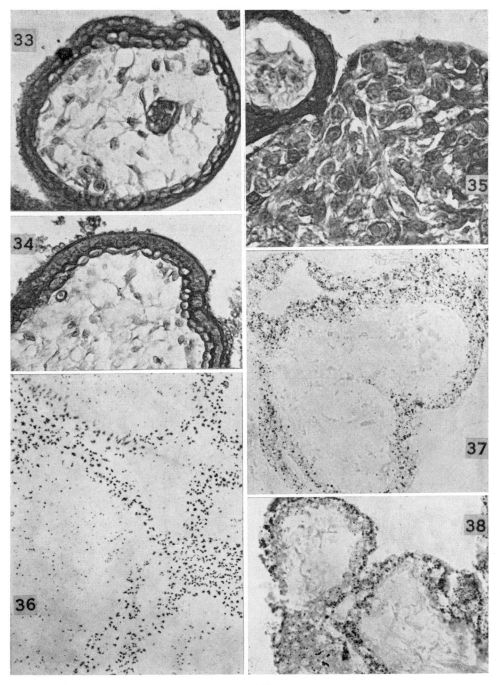

PLATE 15.VIII

evaluation of their ultrastructure. The transported substance next traverses the amorphous perivascular ground substance which varies in amount regionally, being abundant, moderate, or entirely absent. In areas in which this ground substance is lacking, the syncytium abuts on maternal endothelium. The endothelial margin of the ground substance is regular, but its opposite border, which is in contact with the syncytium, is irregular and seems to be sculptured by the syncytium. The lipid-rich syncytium sends branched processes between the cytotrophoblast to end in foot-like expansions on the trophoblastic basement membrane. Later in gestation, as the cytotrophoblasts diminish in number, these processes extend through large extracellular spaces. After crossing the two trophoblastic layers and the chorionic basement membrane, a substance then passes through a thin connective tissue space containing fibroblasts and collagen fibers. From there it next passes through the basement membrane and endothelium of ordinary fetal capillaries. Thus, despite the loss of two uterine layers, the placental barrier in the cat is structurally complex.

The paraplacental or brown border of the cat's chorion is a specialized region composed of cells rich in iron and capable of phagocytosing red blood cells, trypan blue, and other substances (Figs. 15.62 and 15.63). The absorptive surface of these cells bears a striking resemblance to that of the visceral endoderm of the rodent yolk sac. The surface plasma membrane of these columnar cells evaginates to form elaborate microvilli and invaginates to form a system of canals immediately beneath the cell surface. It is assumed that pinocytotic vesicles are formed as ingested substances are segregated in the canalicular system. In the paraplacental cells, ingested erythrocytes in various stages of breakdown were frequently observed.

The hemochorial type of placenta, in which extensive erosion of the uterine wall occurs, has been studied in the *human* and *rodents* by several investigators (Boyd and Hughes, 1954; Wislocki and Dempsey, 1955a, b; Wislocki, Weiss, Burgos and Ellis, 1957; Bargmann and Knoop, 1959; Schieb-

ler and Knoop, 1959). In the "definitive" hemochorial placenta the trophoblast is bathed directly by circulating maternal blood. Observations on the ultrastructure of the human placenta (Wislocki and Dempsey, 1955a) have been incorporated with the histochemical findings in Section III of this review. The syncytium of the human placenta resembles a pinocytotic epithelium having numerous pleomorphic microvilli and containing many large vesicles which probably represent engulfed material (Wislocki and Dempsey, 1955a, Plates 1–4). Although the Langhans cells diminish in number as gestation proceeds, some flattened cytotrophoblasts remain at term interposed between the syncytium and the trophoblastic basement membrane. At term, when the placental barrier is thinnest, a maternal substance encounters the following successive layers in reaching the fetal blood: syncytium, trophoblastic basement membrane, fetal connective tissue, basement membrane, and endothelium of the fetal sinusoidal capillary.

Many significant observations have been made on the fine structure of the chorio-allantoic placenta of the *rat*. To aid in orienting the reader, a brief description of the histology of the rat placenta follows. In the established chorio-allantoic disc of this species, three general zones are recognizable in the fetal portion: (1) a trophoblastic *labyrinth* which is served by both maternal and fetal blood vessels and is considered to be the principal area of transport; (2) a *spongiotrophoblastic zone* which partially surrounds the labyrinth and which, although it is not penetrated by fetal blood vessels, is perfused by maternal blood; and (3) a meshwork of *giant cells* which caps the spongy zone, is permeated by maternal blood, and forms the frontier of the fetal tissue.

The first description of the ultrastructure of the labyrinth of the rat at 15, 17, and 21 days of gestation quickly established two important points (Wislocki and Dempsey, 1955b). It was demonstrated that the rat and rabbit placentas are hemochorial rather than hemoendothelial as had been proposed by Mossman (1926, 1937). Furthermore, it was shown that there is no syncytial trophoblast in the labyrinth, as had been described by Grosser (1908, 1909) ; the fetal blood vessels are clothed by two or three thin layers of overlapping individual cytotrophoblasts which together constitute a laminated membrane (Wislocki and Dempsey, 1955b, Plate 2). These trophoblasts are held together by small cytoplasmic pegs which fit into depressions in adjacent cell surfaces. Wislocki and Dempsey (1955b) observed that the labyrinthine lipid droplets are located mainly in the cytoplasm of the innermost trophoblasts. Schiebler and Knoop (1959) reported that there is a relatively wide space between the outer and middle layers which communicates with the maternal blood but that the deeper cells are closely apposed. The latter investigators also observed that pinocytotic vesicles occur in numerous trophoblasts and claimed that two kinds of trophoblastic cells can be differentiated in the labyrinth with the electron microscope.

According to Wislocki and Dempsey, the placental barrier in the labyrinth of the rat is composed of: (1) two or three sheets of laminated cytotrophoblast; (2) the basement membrane supporting the trophoblast; and (3) the basement membrane and endothelium of the fetal capillary. Schiebler and Knoop did not see two separate basement membranes and report the occurrence of a single basement membrane between the trophoblast and fetal endothelium.

Schiebler and Knoop (1959) also presented some interesting observations on the fine structure and histochemistry of the spongiotrophoblasts and giant cells. The cytotrophoblasts of the spongy zone have an intensely basophilic cytoplasm, and this is consonant with the presence of an extensive, highly oriented endoplasmic reticulum. This luxuriant endoplasmic reticulum is comparable in its arrangement and abundance to that of the pancreatic acinar cells and of the Nissl bodies of neurones. The function of the spongiotrophoblast remains unknown, but this observation points toward a special role in protein synthesis. Padykula (1958) reported a striking increase in acid phosphatase and adenosine triphosphatase activity in this zone during the last week of gestation.

In the same report, Schiebler and Knoop offered much new information about the fetal giant cells, and their observations suggest a dynamic role for these strategically placed cells. The giant cells are contiguous with the spongiotrophoblasts, and with the aid of the electron microscope they can be differentiated into several types. The nuclei of the giant cells are invaginated in many places, and these recesses contain cytoplasm. In some planes of section, this morphologic arrangement gives the false impression of intranuclear inclusions, especially when the invagination contains lipid or glycogen. However, the cytoplasmic mass enclosed by the nucleus maintains its connection with the main body of cytoplasm. The cytoplasm proper is highly differentiated. It contains a great complexity and variety of vesicles and membranes, and resembles the cytoplasm of phagocytic cells in several aspects of fine structure. The surface of the giant cells presents a complicated interwoven array of microvillus-like projections to the intercellular space. This space is filled with a material which contains mucopolysaccharide, is fibrous, and appears to be continuous in some regions with Reichert's membrane. In some regions the maternal blood spaces among the giant cells are lined by a thin layer of cytoplasm which is judged to be endothelium by Schiebler and Knoop. In this location a subendothelial basement membrane seems to be lacking. Elsewhere the surfaces of the giant cells are in direct contact with the maternal blood.

The fine structure of the granular cells of the metrial gland of the pregnant rat was described by Wislocki, Weiss, Burgos and Ellis (1957). The suggestion was offered that the basic protein granules of these cells contain relaxin.

The fine structure of the hemochorial placenta of the nine-banded armadillo (*Dasypus novemcinctus*) was recently reported by Enders (1960).

Some generalizations may be made concerning the fine structure of the placental barriers. Certainly the absorptive trophoblasts resemble the cells of the proximal convoluted tubule of the kidney and the absorptive cells of the small intestine more closely than the components of the pulmonary alveolar lining or the renal glomerular membrane. The trophoblastic cells are characterized by microvilli and other surface projections which are pleomorphic and often branched. Many observations suggest that absorption by pinocytosis occurs in many types of placental cells. Whether or not erosion of the uterine wall occurs, the placental barrier is structurally complex. Along with the cellular layers, basement membranes are regularly interposed between the maternal and fetal bloodstreams. Further discussion is presented in the section on yolk sac placentation where some experimental cytologic observations have been made during the process of absorption.

C. REDUCTION IN NUMBER OF THE LAYERS OF THE CHORIO-ALLANTOIC PLACENTA

The successive elimination of the maternal layers of chorio-allantoic placentas as envisioned by Grosser's scheme has met with general acceptance. However, Wislocki and Dempsey (1946a) pointed out that the endotheliochorial type of placenta is probably nonexistent, because in carnivores and sloths the endothelial-lined maternal blood vessels are surrounded by a basement membrane and in some species, as in the cat, large decidual cells are present in the labyrinth. Consequently, in some carnivores the placenta is syndesmochorial rather than endotheliochorial.

The hemoendothelial type of placenta postulated by Mossman finds no support in recent observations by Wislocki and Dempsey (1955b) and Schiebler and Knoop (1960) with the electron microscope. These investigators found in the chorio-allantoic placental labyrinths of rat and rabbit late in gestation a complete trophoblastic membrane, consisting of 2 or 3 layers of flattened, imbricated trophoblastic cells. The presence of these layers is not detectable with the light microscope. These findings indicate that the placentas of these species are hemochorial and not hemoendothelial.

D. REDUCTION IN WIDTH OF THE LAYERS OF THE CHORIO-ALLANTOIC PLACENTA

The diminution in width of the tissues separating the maternal blood channels from the fetal capillaries, as postulated in Grosser's scheme of chorio-allantoic placentas, seems to be borne out by histologic observations of both his phylogenetic series and successive ontogenetic stages. However, some have pictured the layers in a schematic way (Huggett, 1944; Arey, 1946) with no regard for their relative widths and relationships. Actually, in progressing from epitheliochorial to hemochorial placentas, the gradual reduction in width of the thinnest areas is not nearly as striking as the theoretic concept of the removal of successive layers implies. This is due partly to the fact that in all species the connective tissue layers at the sites of the thinnest places consist only of basement membranes. Furthermore, the capillaries in the thin areas of all animals are pressed against the adjacent epithelia and in some, for example in the sow (Figs. 15.23, 15.28 and 15.64) and many ungulates, the fetal capillaries follow intra-epithelial courses in the trophoblast (Wislocki and Dempsey, 1946b: Amoroso, 1947, 1952). In addition, in the

---

PLATE 15.IX

FIG. 15.39. Human placental labyrinth at 4 months, showing acid phosphatase activity in the syncytium and stroma of the chorionic villi. Gomori's method, using glycerophosphate as substrate at pH 4.7. × 140. (Wislocki and Dempsey, 1948.)

FIG. 15.40. The basal plate of a human placenta at full term, showing the presence of acid phosphatase in the chorionic villi (above), its almost complete absence in the basal plate (center), and a marked reaction at the line of junction of the basal plate with the decidua (below). Gomori's method using glycerophosphate as substrate at pH 4.7. × 175.

FIG. 15.41. Human placental labyrinth at full term, showing the activity of alkaline phosphatase in the syncytium clothing the chorionic villi. Gomori's method using glycerophosphatase as substrate at pH 9.4. × 220.

FIG. 15.42. The basal plate of a human placenta at full term, showing an intense alkaline phosphatase reaction in the chorionic villi (above), its nearly complete absence in the basal plate (center) and a slight reaction at the line of junction of the basal plate with the decidua (below). Gomori's method using glycerophosphate as substrate at pH 9.4.

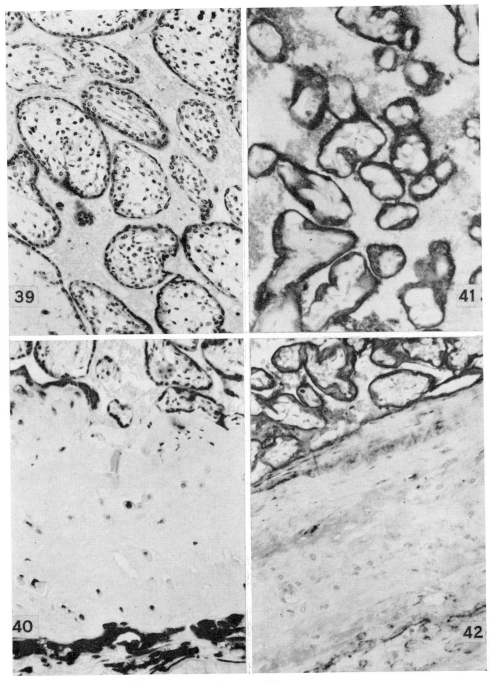

PLATE 15.IX

sow, Amoroso (1952) has described the trophoblast at one period as sending actual processes between and past the maternal epithelium into the region of the underlying maternal capillaries, establishing an endotheliochorial relationship. Despite the presence of six theoretic layers in the sow, provisions exist which tend to by-pass or materially reduce the width of several of them, thus diminishing the distance between the two blood streams. Similarly, in the cat, in the last half of pregnancy, Amoroso (1952) observed "that the foetal capillaries come to lie so near the surface of the lamellae that only the thinnest laminae of syncytial trophoblast separate them from the maternal tissues."

Measurements of the width of the maternal epithelium in the sow, made by Gellhorn, Flexner and Pohl (1941), show that its height changes from 18 μ at midgestation to 10 μ just before term. Nevertheless, in many of the thinner places between the capillaries by midgestation (Fig. 15.23 of the present study), the width of the intervening cytoplasm of the combined chorion and uterine epithelium is reduced to no more than 6 or 8 μ. In the sheep at 100 days of gestation Barcroft (1947) reported that none of the fetal and maternal capillaries is closer than 20 μ and none is separated by more than 120 μ. This offers no clue, however, as to what the average distance may be. It is apparent, nevertheless, from some excellent figures of the sheep's placenta submitted by Wimsatt (1950, Figs. 54 and 56), that the numerous maternal capillaries are about 10 to 20 μ from the fetal capillaries at 100 days and less at 133 days. In the cat at term, the distance between the two blood streams is narrowed in many places to 6 or 8 μ. In the human at term, the thinnest places vary between 3 and 6 μ in width. More extensive and careful measurements of the distances between the blood streams should be obtained in various animals at different stages of gestation, in order to provide a better basis than now exists for comparisons. In making such measurements the degree of shrinkage and separation of the layers in preparing the tissues should be carefully evaluated.

A more important consideration than the actual diminution in width of the layers in the thinnest regions might be the apparent much larger extent of thin areas in hemochorial placentas than in other placental types. Thus, for example, although the thinnest places in the sow's placenta do not seem to differ greatly from the human in respect to their actual widths, the relative extent of the thin areas is very much greater in the latter than the former. In this respect, hemochorial placentas differ greatly from epitheliochorial ones. This consideration, although possibly inherent in Grosser's doctrine, has never been clearly brought out and documented, but instead has been subordinated to the prevailing concepts of the phylogenetic reduction in number and widths of the layers.

A further point of interest concerns the placentas of rodents. The physiologic advantages obtained presumably by the reduction in width of the trophoblastic membrane and the increased extent of the thin areas would seem to be offset by the functional disadvantage of the laminated arrangement of the trophoblastic cells as revealed by electron microscopy. Here, where a syncytium with only inner and outer surfaces was believed to exist, the trophoblast is laminated, so that 4- or 6-cell surfaces extend across the placental barrier. Thus, with respect to cell surfaces and cell layers forming the placental barrier, the hemochorial placentas of rodents seem to be quite as complex as epitheliochorial and syndesmochorial placentas. The most important difference between them would seem to lie in the relatively greater extent of the thin regions, rather than in any extreme reduction of the number of cell layers in the rodent's hemochorial placenta.

Some degree of cytologic and histochemical simplification is apparent in successive stages of gestation in any given species, but striking cytologic differences between the placental membranes of Grosser's phylogenetic series at equivalent stages of gestation are not very evident. Even the thinnest regions of the different types of chorio-allantoic placentas possess a far greater cytochemical complexity than the glomerular and pulmonary membranes. Several writers have postulated that toward the end of pregnancy some of the human chorionic villi lose their syncytial covering entirely; the increase in placental permeability is attributed to this structural alteration. However, it should be pointed out that the nature and degree of degeneration and loss of the syncytium in human villi have not been carefully analyzed. Moreover, it is not known whether such altered villi are functionally active or dead and functionless. However, the assumption that a fraction of the villi becomes functionless would be consonant with an observation of Flexner, Cowie, Hellman, Wilde and Vosburgh (1948) that there is a sharp terminal decline in placental permeability after the 36th week of gestation.

V. Yolk Sac Placentation

In those lower vertebrates, such as some fishes, amphibians, and reptiles which are either ovoviviparous or viviparous, the yolk sac plays the principal role as the fetal membrane subserving the transfer of metabolic materials (Amoroso, 1952). An exception to this is encountered in some reptiles (Weekes, 1935) in which chorio-allantoic placentation occurs. In marsupials, the yolk sac is very large, whereas the allantois is always relatively small, and in only three species does the latter vascularize a placenta. In accordance with Grosser's terminology, the chorio-allantoic placenta of Perameles is "endothelio-endothelial" in character, thus differing fundamentally from the types he defined. "In all other marsupials so far investigated the embryo is nourished exclusively through the yolk-sac and a definite yolk-sac placenta of somewhat complex character is present" (Amoroso, 1952). Thus it is apparent that Grosser's theory does not apply to placentation in the majority of lower placental vertebrates or to the Metatheria (marsupials).

In eutherian mammals, on the other hand, the most typical structure subserving physiologic exchange between mother and fetus and which is constantly present, is the chorio-allantoic placenta (Hamilton, Boyd and Mossman, 1952). The yolk sac in these mammals is the most variable of the fetal membranes. It may occur as a primitive bi-

laminar yolk sac, or as a vascularized trilaminar yolk sac which develops early and is temporary. In some orders of mammals (rodents, bats, insectivores, armadillos), a very different and more complex structure, an "inverted" yolk sac placenta, develops. This usually increases in extent during gestation and in most species becomes covered with elaborately branched, vascularized villi which are in contact with the uterine mucosa (Amoroso, 1952; Hamilton, Boyd and Mossman, 1952). In ungulates, cetaceans, lemurs, sloths, and the Simiae (monkeys, apes, man), it has been assumed that the yolk sac, although present as a vesicle, plays little or no role in the metabolic exchange between mother and fetus. However, some histochemical findings on the human yolk sac challenge this assumption. In a histochemical study of 5-, 6-, and 7-mm. human embryos, McKay, Adams, Hertig and Danziger (1955a, b) localized the following substances in the yolk sac endoderm: glycogen, glycoprotein, ribonucleoprotein, acid and alkaline phosphatase, 5-nucleotidase, and nonspecific esterase. These investigators suggested that the large amount of glycogen in the yolk sac and its absence from the fetal liver may indicate that the yolk sac is supplying glucose to the embryo during the first weeks of embryonic life. McKay and his associates pointed out that there is no iron in the human yolk sac endoderm, whereas the rodent yolk sac is rich in this substance (Wislocki, Deane and Dempsey, 1946).

The inverted yolk sac placenta of rodents and lagomorphs has received more attention since Brambell and his associates (1948, 1949, 1951, 1957) demonstrated that maternal antibodies are transferred exclusively by this ancient membrane. A short description of the histology of the inverted yolk sac of the rat follows for the purpose of general orientation. A good diagram of the histology of the rat placenta was published by Anderson (1959). The yolk sac placenta of the rat is divided into two morphologic zones. (1) An outer, nonvascular *parietal wall* (bilaminar omphalopleure) consists of scattered cuboidal endodermal cells which form an incomplete lining on the interior surface of Reichert's membrane.

This thick and unusual basement membrane adheres externally to a meshwork of trophoblastic giant cells. Maternal blood flows through the interstices of this meshwork of giant cells and presumably is a regional source of some of the substances which gain entrance to the vitelline circulation. A portion of the parietal wall of the yolk sac is firmly attached to the fetal surface of the chorio-allantoic disc. (2) An inner, vascular, *visceral wall* (visceral splanchnopleure) is composed of a simple columnar endodermal epithelium which rests on a mesenchymal layer which carries the vitelline blood vessels. A serosal basement membrane (Wislocki and Padykula, 1953) separates this mesenchymal layer from a narrow, basophilic layer of mesothelium which lines the exocoelom. As the allantoic vessels penetrate the placental labyrinth, portions of both visceral and parietal walls of the yolk sac are invaginated into the labyrinth, forming perivascular recesses which were called "endodermal sinuses" by Duval (1892). In the rat the parietal wall of the yolk sac breaks down on the 15th day of gestation, and this event makes the yolk sac cavity confluent with the uterine cavity and also puts the visceral endoderm into direct contact with the uterine contents.

On the basis of histophysiologic studies on the absorption of dyes, Everett (1935) concluded that the yolk sac of the rat is a significant organ of exchange and that it is more permeable to dyes than the labyrinth. Vital dyes, such as trypan blue, which are relatively large molecules, find their way rapidly into the yolk sac where they are absorbed and stored by the visceral endoderm. These dyes reach the yolk sac, apparently, either by way of the uterine mucosa or through that portion of Reichert's membrane covering the fetal surface of the allantoic placenta. Brambell and his coworkers (1948, 1950, 1951, 1957) have established experimentally in the rabbit and rat that antibodies find their way from the maternal circulation into the embryos, not by passage through the thin and supposedly more permeable layers of the chorio-allantoic placenta, but by way of the yolk sac placenta, the latter mode of entry necessitating transfer across several layers of cells and tissues, including the structurally elaborate vitelline epithelium. Histologic evidence in support of transport of antibodies and serum proteins by the yolk sac placenta comes from the localization of absorbed serum proteins labeled by fluorescent dyes (Mayersbach, 1958), and from autoradiographic studies (Anderson, 1959). Both investigations substantiate the impermeability of the labyrinthine trophoblasts to these labeled proteins and demonstrate the accumulation of proteins in the visceral endoderm. Brambell and Halliday (1956) and Mayersbach (1958) have suggested from different kinds of evidence that the endodermal sinuses of Duval may also participate in antibody transport. Padykula (1958) demonstrated a rise in the succinic dehydrogenase activity of the visceral component of the endodermal sinuses shortly before term in the rat.

The absorptive visceral endodermal cells are interesting from the points of view of both cytology and placentation, since these cells are capable of transporting certain large molecules, such as antibodies and serum proteins, and withholding and segregating other colloidal substances, such as trypan blue. In the latter respect, they func-

---

PLATE 15.X

Fig. 15.43. Semischematic drawing of a human placenta delivered at full term. Two cotyledons are illustrated, bounded above by the so-called chorionic or closing plate (*c.p.*) and on the sides and below by septa placentae (*s.*) and the basal plate (*b.p.*). Placental branches of the umbilical blood vessels are seen in the closing plate and in the anchoring villi (*a.v.*).

Fig. 15.44. A section through a delivered placenta at full term, showing a darkly stained placental septum extending up from the base of the placenta and forming the boundary between two cotyledons. At the top of the figure, blood vessels in the closing plate are apparent. Buffered formalin fixative. Azan stain. × 3.

Fig. 15.45. A photograph of a placenta at full term showing a portion of a placental septum at a higher magnification. Buffered formalin fixation. Periodic acid-Schiff stain. By this method the septum is seen to consist of darkly stained ground substance composed principally of fibrin in which there are numerous lacunae containing faintly stained individual trophoblasts or colonies of them. × 90.

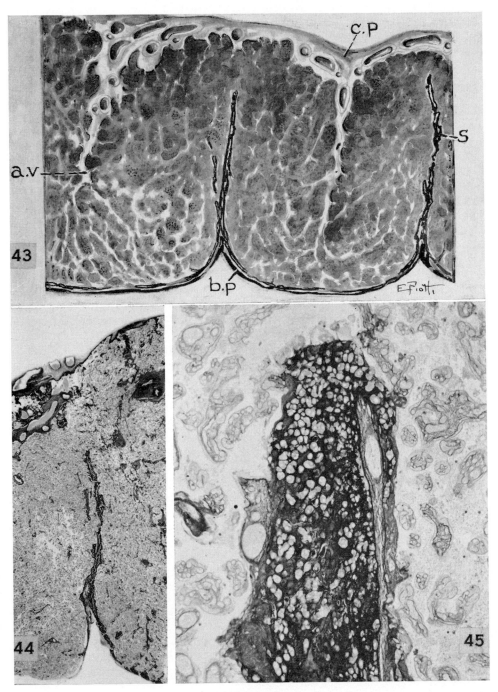

PLATE 15.X

tion as phagocytes. The absorption of large molecules is believed to occur by the process of pinocytosis. The fine structure of these cells has been described in the guinea pig (Dempsey, 1953) and rat (Wislocki and Dempsey, 1955b). Some recent electron micrographs of the rat yolk sac (Figs. 15.80–15.83) are presented in this review by Padykula. The free surface of these cells typifies that of a membrane engaged in pinocytosis. There are numerous surface projections or microvilli which are pleomorphic and branch frequently (Figs. 15.81 and 15.82). These projections form the brush border which has long been recognized with the light microscope, and which is rich in glycoprotein and, at certain times in gestation, in alkaline phosphatase. In both the rat and guinea pig these surface projections become simpler and shorter near term. In addition to these evaginations, the surface plasma membrane is invaginated in the form of minute anastomosing tubules which have a denser thicker wall than the microvilli (Fig. 15.82). It seems fairly certain that during pinocytosis a local enlargement of such a tubule is produced and a pinocytotic vesicle is formed. Vesicles fill much of the supranuclear cytoplasm, and there is considerable heterogeneity in the size and content of the supranuclear vesicles (Fig. 15.80). Filamentous mitochondria occur throughout the cytoplasm. The endoplasmic reticulum is most concentrated around the nuclei, although it is also diffusely distributed throughout the cytoplasm. The typical agranular membranes and vesicles of the Golgi apparatus can be recognized near the nucleus (Fig. 15.83). Glycogen is stored in the lower half of the cell, especially in the infranuclear region. Lipid droplets occur throughout the cytoplasm, but the larger ones are usually infranuclear where they are often in close association with the basal surface of the nucleus (Figs. 15.81 and 15.83). The supranuclear lipid is often in the form of aggregations in complicated associations with membranes (Figs. 15.79 and 15.81). Minute lipid droplets are also found within the nucleus (Figs. 15.78 and 15.80). The lateral cell boundaries of these cells are closely apposed early in gestation, whereas near term large lateral intercellular dilatations occur. Between these dilations, where the plasma membranes are closely apposed, desmosomes are evident. The bases of the cells rest on a narrow basement membrane.

With the electron microscope, experimental cytologic analyses of absorption by the visceral endoderm of the rabbit and mouse have been made by Luse and her associates (Luse, 1957; Luse, Davies and Smith, 1959; Luse, Davies and Clark, 1959). The following materials were injected into the uterus of the rabbit and mouse: colloidal gold, egg albumin, lipids, saccharated iron, bovine γ-globulin, and salivary gland virus. All of these materials entered cytoplasmic pinocytotic vesicles. However, more interestingly, iron, colloidal carbon, and salivary gland virus penetrated the nuclei. Further work suggests that pinocytosis by the nuclear membrane is the method of nuclear penetration. Similar nuclear inclusions arise in the nuclei of newborn rat duodenum after suckling. This amazing intracellular pathway of absorption probably occurs naturally as witnessed by the occurrence of lipid in the nuclei of normal visceral endoderm, duodenum, and liver.

The inverted yolk sac placenta of the rat undergoes a striking differentiation during

---

PLATE 15.XI

FIG. 15.46. A portion of a placental septum showing cytotrophoblasts surrounded by ground substance. Human placenta at 3¾ months of gestation. Masson's triacid stain. × 240.

FIG. 15.47. A cell island containing a group of cytotrophoblasts surrounded by ground substance. Human placenta at 2 months of gestation. Azan stain. × 240.

FIG. 15.48. Cytotrophoblasts of the trophoblastic shell stained by Baker's acid hematein method for phospholipids. Human placenta at 3½ months of gestation. Observe the intense reaction in the cytoplasm of the trophoblasts. Compare with Figure 15.25. × 160.

FIG. 15.49. A portion of a placental septum of a human placenta at full term, stained by the periodic acid-Schiff method after exposure of the section to saliva. The cytoplasm of the cytotrophoblasts exhibits a faint reaction which should be compared with Figure 15.55 which illustrates the cells at higher magnification. The clumps of cells are surrounded by masses of intensely stained fibrin. Compare with Figures 15.32 and 15.46 which illustrate the trophoblastic shell at 3 to 3¾ months of gestation before a great deal of fibrin has appeared. × 300.

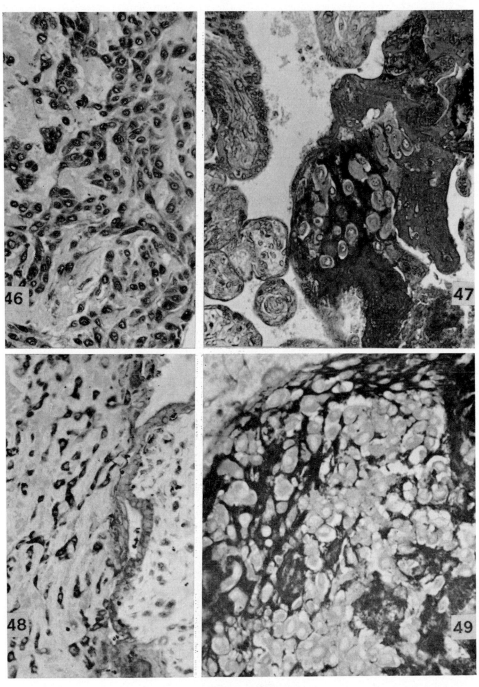

PLATE 15.XI

its brief life history (Padykula, 1958a, b). A major architectural reorganization occurs with the loss of the parietal wall shortly after mid-gestation. A short period of lipid storage for from 10 to 15 days is succeeded by a phase of glycogen storage from 15 to 20 days. After the loss of the parietal wall, there is a sharp rise in certain enzymatic activities (alkaline phosphatase, adenosine triphosphatase, acid phosphatase, succinic dehydrogenase). This burst of vitelline activity in this last third of gestation suggests greater functional activity after direct exposure of the visceral endoderm to the uterine contents. As in the case of the chorio-allantoic placentas, the reduction in the number of layers of the yolk sac probably increases the rate of absorption by the vascularized splanchnopleure. Shortly before term there is a sharp decline in glycogen content and certain enzymatic activities in the visceral endoderm. As these particular histochemical properties decline in the visceral yolk sac, they appear in the fetal liver with good temporal correlation. If the yolk sac functions in part as a fetal liver, then the terminal decrease in enzymatic activity should not be interpreted as placental aging, but rather as a redistribution of the functional activities of the placental-fetal complex (Padykula, 1958). Further morphologic aspects of aging in the placenta were discussed by Wislocki (1956).

With the ascendency of the chorio-allantoic placenta in eutherian mammals and its postulated progression in the sense of Grosser's series from a simple epitheliochorial placenta to the physiologically more "efficient" hemochorial type, one might have expected that the mammalia would have abandoned yolk sac placentation altogether. But that is not the case, for paradoxically the greatest placental development of the yolk sac, involving inversion, is associated with hemochorial placentas (rodents, lagomorphs, bats, some insectivores), whereas the least developed yolk sacs occur in animals possessing epitheliochorial placentas which are the most primitive, according to Grosser's scheme. The general adoption of Grosser's concept of the chorio-allantoic placenta has resulted in the almost complete exclusion of the yolk sac. For example,

Needham (1931, Table 227) attributes the entire transfer of substances in mammals to the chorio-allantoic placenta, without reference to other avenues of exchange. In view of the observations and experiments described here, it is evident that Grosser's doctrine will have to be re-evaluated and modified to include yolk sac placentation.

VI. Histochemistry with Reference to Comparative Placentation

It is beyond the scope of this chapter to describe in detail the structure and cytology of the placentas of various mammals. However, certain histochemical observations on lipids will be presented because they afford some clues to the probable sites of localization of placental steroid compounds. In addition, the localization of glycogen, other complex carbohydrates, and phosphatases in several types of placentas will be summarized. This histochemical information will serve as a basis for subsequent comparisons of placental structures and functions.

However, before proceeding to these matters, attention should be drawn, for readers who may wish to familiarize themselves with comparative placentation, to the compendia of this subject by Grosser (1925b), Mossman (1937), and Amoroso (1952). Recent papers on placental histochemistry of various animals will be listed here. These include investigations of the chemical morphology of the placentas of the pig (Wislocki and Dempsey, 1946b), sheep and cow (Wimsatt, 1950, 1951), shrews (Wislocki and Wimsatt, 1947), cat (Wislocki and Dempsey, 1946a), and bat (Wimsatt, 1948, 1949). In rodents histochemical observations are more numerous, including earlier investigations of fat, glycogen, and iron in placentas of the rabbit (Chipman, 1902) and rat (Goldmann, 1912). More recent studies describe glycogen in the rat's placenta (Szendi, 1933; Krehbiel, 1937; Bridgman, 1948; Bulmer and Dickson, 1960), alkaline phosphatase in the guinea pig's placenta (Hard, 1946; Nataf, 1953), and in the pregnant uterus of the rat (Pritchard, 1947), and multiple histochemical reactions in placentas of rats, mice, guinea pigs, and rabbits (Wislocki, Deane and Dempsey,

1946; Bridgman, 1948a, b; Wislocki and Padykula, 1953; Davies, 1956; Padykula, 1958). The Ashbel-Seligman reaction for carbonyl groups has been briefly described in the placentas of various mammals (Ashbel and Seligman, 1949; Wislocki, 1952), as has also the PAS reaction (Wislocki, 1950). Many histochemical observations on a variety of placentas were summarized by Starck (1945–50).

A. LIPIDS

Present information on the histochemical localization of lipids in various placentas is fragmentary. The main effort has been directed toward localizing within the placenta the type of lipid droplets which occur in the steroid-producing cells of the adrenal cortex and gonads. These droplets are acetone soluble, birefringent, exhibit greenish fluorescence, and give positive Ashbel-Seligman and Schiff reactions for carbonyl groups. As has been discussed in the section on methods, these nonspecific reactions actually reflect the degree of unsaturation in the compounds comprising the fixed lipid droplets. Certainly further work is needed to characterize more fully the various lipids of placentas, especially in relation to the storage of cholesterol and triglycerides.

In the following descriptions it will be seen that the lipid reactions characteristic of steroid-producing cells usually occur in some part of the trophoblast. In the *human* placenta, only the syncytium contains the lipid droplets characteristic of steroid-producing cells. The *cat* possesses a so-called endotheliochorial type of placenta, consisting of sinusoidal maternal capillaries and "decidual" giant cells arranged in sheets alternating with lamellae of trophoblast, the latter enclosing the fetal stroma and capillaries. The trophoblast consists of an outer syncytial and an inner cellular layer. The cellular layer contains abundant lipid droplets of variable, but relatively large size. They are sudanophilic and birefringent (Fig. 15.59), exhibit greenish fluorescence, give an Ashbel-Seligman reaction for carbonyl groups (Fig. 15.20) and stain intensely with Schiff's reagent. The syncytium is negative in these respects, except for a mild diffuse coloration by the Ashbel-

Seligman carbonyl method (Fig. 15.20) and a greyish tint with sudan black B which is attributable probably to mitochondria. The "decidual" giant cells, generally regarded as of maternal origin, and the maternal endothelium give no lipid reactions beyond a delicate sudanophilia associated with the presence of mitochondria.

In *rodents* two types of placentas, a chorio-allantois of the hemochorial type and a yolk sac placenta, function concurrently throughout gestation. Lipids occur in many placental constituents of the rat: labyrinthine trophoblast, giant cells, parietal endoderm, visceral endoderm, decidua capsularis, and mesothelium lining the exocoelom. Bridgman (1948) pointed out that in the rat the labyrinthine trophoblast contains lipid from the 12th day onward and that it diminishes shortly before term. This lipid in rats and mice is birefringent and gives an intense carbonyl reaction (Figs. 15.16, 15.17, and 15.21) (Wislocki, Deane, and Dempsey, 1946; Ashbel and Seligman, 1949; Wislocki, 1952). This cellular layer is a logical suspect as the site of steroid hormonal synthesis. However, these reactions are present also in the visceral endoderm of the yolk sac where lipid droplets occur in great abundance from 9 to 17 days (Figs. 15.74–15.77). These lipids which occur principally as large infranuclear droplets (Figs. 15.78 and 15.83) are birefringent, strongly fluorescent, and give a strong carbonyl reaction with the Schiff reagents (Wislocki, Deane and Dempsey, 1946). Further work has confirmed these observations and has also shown this acetone-soluble lipid gives a strong Ashbel-Seligman reaction and contains cholesterol. It immediately turns a brilliant blue-green in the Schultz test (Padykula, unpublished observations). One difference between the labyrinthine and endodermal lipids is the color response in the Schultz test. The labyrinthine lipid turns red-brown but never the blue-green which indicates the presence of cholesterol. Lehner (1914) reported that intranuclear lipid droplets are abundant in the visceral endoderm of the mouse. This finding is confirmed in the rat by electron microscopy (see Figs. 15.78 and 15.80). The significance of this lipid in the yolk sac is not clear, although the findings of Luse (1958), Luse, Davies and Smith (1959), Luse, Davies and Clark (1959) suggest that it is absorbed lipid. Further discussion of the lipids of the yolk sac was given in the section on yolk sac placentation.

In placentas of two species of *shrews* (*Blarina brevicauda* and *Sorex fumeus*) Wimsatt and Wislocki (1947) described numerous coarse lipid droplets in the columnar trophoblastic epithelium forming the chorionic membrane. These droplets are sudanophilic and birefringent, exhibit greenish fluorescence, and give an intense reaction with Schiff's reagent. In the chorio-allantoic placenta, minute sudanophilic particles are observed in the placental trabeculae, but birefringence and fluorescence are not evident and Schiff's reaction is feeble.

In the placenta of the *bat* (*Myotis lucifugus lucifugus*) Wimsatt (1948) observed sudanophilic lipids in nearly all placental constituents, but only those present in the columnar trophoblastic cells of the membranous chorion were birefringent, emitted a greenish-yellow fluorescence, and gave positive phenylhydrazine, Schiff's and Liebermann-Burchardt reactions. With respect to these reactions, it is apparent that the membranous chorion of shrews and bats is similar.

In the placenta of the *Virginia deer* (*Odocoileus virginianus borealis*) in midgestation, lipid droplets which are birefringent and give an Ashbel-Seligman reaction are present in a layer of epithelium lining the maternal crypts of the placentomas (Wislocki, 1952). A further interesting feature of the *deer's* placenta is an intense reaction for lipids (sudanophilia, birefringence, positive Ashbel-Seligman carbonyl reaction) in the withered, degenerating peripheral ends of the maternal septa. This reactive material is evidently attributable to degeneration of a portion of the epithelium covering the maternal septa.

In the *sheep*, the epithelial layer clothing the maternal septa consists of syncytial trophoblast derived from the chorionic villi (Wimsatt, 1950; Amoroso, 1951, 1952). Although it has not been investigated, the epithelium lining of the maternal crypts of the deer's placenta may also be of fetal origin. In the *sheep*, Wimsatt (1951) remarks briefly that lipid droplets, which are birefringent and give positive Baker's acidhematein and Liebermann-Burchardt reactions, are present in the columnar trophoblastic cells, but no mention is made of the reaction of the syncytial trophoblast lining the maternal crypts.

In view of the localization of these various lipid reactions in some part of the trophoblast, results obtained in the placenta of a *pig* (17 cm. crown to rump length) are an interesting exception (Wislocki, 1952). At this period of gestation, lipids are not encountered in the chorionic epithelium, except phospholipids of mitochondria which are demonstrable by means of sudan black B (Fig. 15.15) and Baker's acid hematein

---

PLATE 15.XII

Fig. 15.50. Human placental labyrinth at full term, stained by the periodic acid-Schiff (PAS) method after exposure of the section to saliva. Zenker's acetic acid fixative. The walls of the sinusoidal fetal capillaries and the (reticular) basement membrane upon which the syncytium rests are deeply stained. The outer zone of the syncytium is also noticeably stained. Although many of the capillaries deeply indent the syncytium producing so-called "syncytial" or "epithelial plates," a narrow rim of syncytium and the PAS-stained wall of the subjacent capillary always intervene between the intervillous space and the lumen of the capillary. Compare with Figures 15.14, 15.19, 15.25, and 15.41. × 280.

Fig. 15.51. Degenerate placental villi at 2 months of gestation, illustrating their intense metachromatic staining with toluidin blue. Basic lead acetate fixative. Compare with Figure 15.57. × 240. (Wislocki and Dempsey, 1948.)

Fig. 15.52. Human decidua vera at 2½ months of gestation, stained by the PAS method. Rossman's fixative. Observe the pronounced staining of ground substance encapsulating the poorly stained decidual cells. Two arterioles are visible near the center of the figure. Compare with Figures 15.53 and 15.58 which illustrate decidua stained by other means. × 240. (Wislocki and Dempsey, 1948.)

Fig. 15.53. Human decidua vera at 4 months of gestation, showing the acid phosphatase reaction of the decidual cells. Gomori's method, using glycerophosphate as substrate at pH 4.7. × 240. (Wislocki and Dempsey, 1948.)

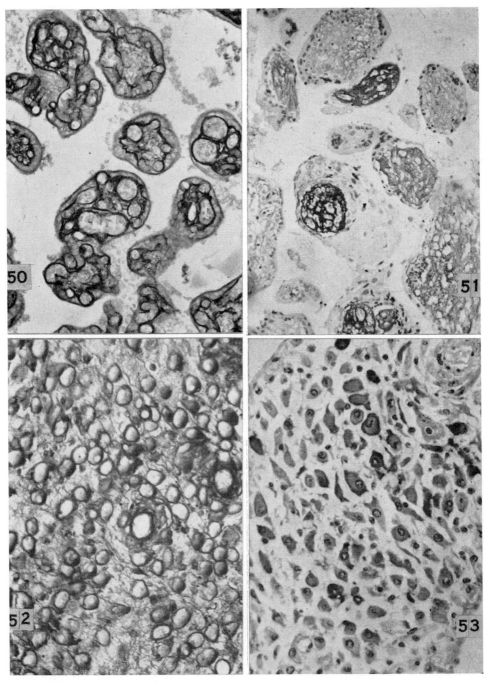

PLATE 15.XII

test. Instead, extremely minute, lipid droplets giving an Ashbel-Seligman reaction are present in the epithelium of the uterine mucosa (Figs. 15.15 and 15.22). Later in gestation, from about the 20-cm. stage on, large sudanophilic lipid droplets begin to appear in the basal ends of the columnar trophoblastic cells of the chorionic fossae (Wislocki and Dempsey, 1946b), but these have not been studied by other histochemical reactions for lipids.

B. GLYCOGEN AND CARBOHYDRATE CONTAINING MACROMOLECULES

Since Claude Bernard suggested in 1859 that the placenta may perform the glycogenic function for the embryo before the developing liver has acquired this function, considerable attention has been given to localizing this important metabolic reserve. In previous paragraphs, the localization and fluctuations in glycogen were reviewed for the human placenta. In this species, glycogen has a widespread distribution during the first 2 months, occurring in the syncytium, Langhans cells, stromal fibroblasts, Hofbauer cells, peripheral cytotrophoblasts, and decidual cells. After the second month, there is a sharp decline in glycogen storage in all these components, except in the decidual cells which retain glycogen until term. This decline has also been recorded biochemically by Villee (1953) whose measurements of glycogen content show a rapid drop after 8 weeks of gestation. Furthermore, glucose production is possible early in gestation but not at term (Villee, 1953). Concerning Bernard's hypothesis, it is interesting to note Villee's observation that the glycogenic storage function of the human fetal liver is acquired at 7 to 8 weeks of gestation. Thereafter, the glycogen content of the fetal liver rises sharply, as placental glycogen content falls.

Glycogen storage in the rat placenta is also widespread, occurring in various parts of the maternal-fetal complex (Goldman, 1912; Krehbiel, 1937; Bridgman, 1948a, b; Padykula, 1958b; Bulmer and Dickson, 1960). Early storage during the first ten days is chiefly a decidual function. However, the trophoblastic ectoplacental cone and its later derivative, the spongy zone, contain some glycogen from implantation until term, with peak storage occurring the 15th day of gestation. The vascularized trophoblast of the labyrinth and the visceral endoderm of the inverted yolk sac placenta initiate glycogen storage at 14 days, reach a peak at 18 days, and have released most

---

PLATE 15.XIII

FIG. 15.54. A portion of a human chorionic villus at 2½ months of gestation, stained by the periodic acid-Schiff (PAS) method (exposed to saliva). Orth's fixative. Observe the marked reaction of the outer zone of the syncytium, the delicate stippling of the deeper layer, the chromophobic appearance of the Langhans cells, the intense staining of the basement membrane and the strong response of the large vacuolated Hofbauer cell. Compare with Figure 15.29. × 7 ocular; × 90 objective.

FIG. 15.55. Cytotrophoblasts from a human placental septum at full term, showing the cells partially surrounded by dark red stained fibrin. Orth's fixative. PAS stain. The cytoplasm of the trophoblasts contains a delicate stippling of PAS positive material as well as accentuated staining around the nuclear membrane. Compare with Figure 15.48. × 7 ocular; × 90 objective.

FIG. 15.56. A lamella of a cat's placenta, stained by the PAS method. Orth's fixative. Treatment with saliva. Observe the intense reaction in a narrow zone located between the maternal capillaries and giant decidual cells and the trophoblastic syncytium. In the trophoblast occasional large intensely stained droplets of "colloid" are visible. Compare with Figures 15.60 and 15.61. × 7 ocular; × 60 objective.

FIG. 15.57. A degenerating placental villus at 6 months of gestation, consisting of degenerating stroma which has become intensely metachromatic (red), surrounded by a mantle of bluish green-stained, hyalinized syncytium. Basic lead acetate fixative. Toluidin blue stain. Compare with Figure 15.51. × 7 ocular; × 20 objective.

FIG. 15.58. The decidua basalis of a human placenta at 2½ months of gestation, illustrating the characteristic red metachromasia of the ground substance surrounding the decidual cells. A cleft in the decidua contains bluish green-stained fibrin. Basic lead acetate fixative. Compare with Figure 15.52, stained by PAS reagents. Toluidin blue stain. × 7 ocular; × 40 objective.

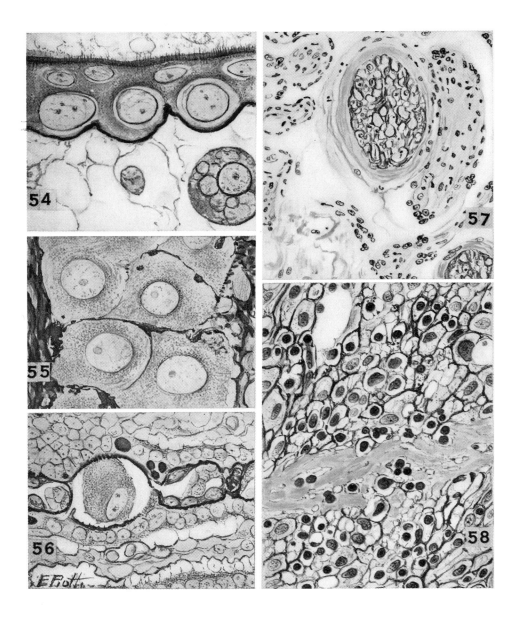

of this material by the 21st day. Concerning these fluctuations, it may be said that the glycogen content of the fetal placenta is highest immediately preceding the great terminal growth spurt of the embryo and fetal placenta. It should also be noted that, as in the human, placental glycogen content is decreasing during the period when the fetal liver is beginning to store glycogen (Padykula and Leduc, 1955).

The distribution of glycogen in the rabbit placenta is drastically different from that of the human and the rat. In this species glycogen is localized exclusively in the decidua of the maternal placenta; the fetal placental tissue, including the yolk sac, is devoid of glycogen (Bernard, 1859; Chipman, 1902; Lochhead and Cramer, 1908; Loveland, Maurer and Snyder, 1931; Tuchmann-Duplessis and Bortolami, 1954; Davies, 1956). Glycogen content reaches a peak near the 17th day of gestation, and decreases until term. Several investigators (Lochhead and Cramer, 1908; Tuchmann-Duplessis and Bortolami, 1954) have further substantiated Claude Bernard's observation that the decline in placental glycogen correlates in time with the onset of the hepatic glycogenic function in the fetus. In the guinea pig a similar temporal correlation has been made for glycogen storage in the placenta and fetal liver (DuBois and Ducommun, 1955).

Saliva-insoluble carbohydrates, such as glycoproteins and mucopolysaccharides, revealed by the PAS reaction are demonstrable in the placentas of all animals which have been examined (Wislocki, 1951). In the *pig's placenta* a positive reaction is given by minute droplets in the apical ends of the uterine gland cells, in the glandular secretion (Fig. 15.66), and in the uterine surface epithelium. An intense reaction is given by the secretion (uterine milk) in the lumens of the chorionic areolae. Numerous positively stained, delicate droplets are present in the distal cytoplasm of the columnar epithelium lining the chorionic fossae and areolae (Fig. 15.65). In the basal part of the tall columnar cells lining the chorionic fossae there are, in addition, large "colloid" droplets (Fig. 15.65) which are stained intensely red (Wislocki and Dempsey, 1946b).

In the numerous trophoblastic binucleate giant cells of the *sheep* and *cow*, Wimsatt (1951) reported the presence of many PAS-positive cytoplasmic granules. The trophoblastic giant cells of the *Virginia deer* react similarly (Wislocki, unpublished observation).

In the chorionic lamellae of the *cat's placenta*, deeply stained PAS-reactive material is present between the fetal trophoblast and the maternal vessels (Figs. 15.56 and 15.61). In addition, large, deeply stained colloid droplets are located irregularly in the trophoblastic syncytium (Fig. 15.56). In the placental "brown" border of the cat, a reaction is present in the chorionic epithelium, as well as in the secretion in the uterine lumen and in the surface and glandular uterine epithelium (Fig. 15.62).

In the *rat's placenta*, the apical cytoplasm of the uterine epithelium, amorphous material in the uterine and vitelline cavities, the substance of Reichert's membrane and the apical cytoplasm of the vitelline epithelial cells (Fig. 15.72) all react strongly (Wislocki, and Padykula, 1953). The trophoblast of the chorio-allantoic placenta gives a relatively faint reaction (Fig. 15.72).

C. METACHROMASIA

None of the structures in the placentas of the various animals cited above, which are strongly PAS positive, exhibits any metachromasia (Wislocki, 1953), except that the binucleate cells of the sheep react faintly under some conditions of staining (Wimsatt, 1951). Also the ground substance of the stroma of the chorionic rugae of the pig's placenta is moderately metachromatic.

D. PHOSPHATASES

Because the methods for alkaline and acid phosphatase were among the first histochemical procedures for localizing enzymes, many observations have been made on this type of hydrolytic activity. The absorptive surfaces of the small intestine, kidney, and placenta, which are characterized by brush borders, contain strong *alkaline phosphatase activity*. In many forms the syncytial trophoblast is rich in alkaline phosphatase activity. In the human syncytium, alkaline phosphatase activity which is low early in gestation increases greatly later. This enzymatic activity is high in the syncytial trophoblast of the cat, rodents (Figs. 15.71 and 15.73), shrews, and bats. Alkaline phosphatase occurs in the visceral endoderm of the splanchnopleuric yolk sac of rodents (Fig. 15.70) (Hard, 1946; Wislocki, Deane and Dempsey, 1946; Pritchard, 1947; Padykula, 1958a), shrews (Wislocki and Wimsatt, 1947), and bats (Wimsatt, 1949). Thus, this enzyme is located at two major placental absorptive surfaces.

In the *pig's* placenta, alkaline phosphatase activity is high in the columnar epithelial cells of the chorionic fossae (Fig. 15.67) and in the stroma and blood vessel walls of the maternal endometrium (Fig. 15.68) (Wislocki and Dempsey, 1946b; Dempsey and Wislocki, 1947). However, it is completely absent from the chorionic areolae and extremely low in the epithelium of the chorionic rugae. In the *cow* and *sheep*, binucleate trophoblastic giant cells are rich in alkaline phosphatase (Wimsatt, 1951). In the *Virginia deer* at midgestation, this enzyme was found in the binucleate giant cells, stroma and walls of the blood vessels of the maternal septa, epithelium clothing these septa, and at the surface of the trophoblast covering the chorionic villi. In the

cat, alkaline phosphatase occurs also in material surrounding the capillaries and decidual giant cells (Fig. 15.60). In the paraplacental "brown" border of the cat, there is abundant alkaline phosphatase activity in the uterine glands and surface epithelium, in the uterine secretion, and in the outer parts of the columnar epithelial cells of the membranous chorion (Fig. 15.63).

Acid phosphatase occurs in the human syncytium and also in the labyrinthine trophoblast of the rat where it increases in activity in the last week of gestation (Padykula, 1958). In the rat placenta, this enzyme appears in the cytotrophoblast of the spongy zone and in the giant cells on the 17th day and increases steadily until term. In the cat, acid phosphatase occurs in the trophoblast of the placental lamellae, in the uterine glands, in the uterine surface epithelium, and to some degree in the epithelium of the membranous chorion (Wislocki, 1953). In the pig, acid phosphatase activity is high in the uterine glands (Fig. 15.69), in the uterine milk occurring in the lumens of the chorionic areolae, and in the distal ends of the epithelial cells lining the areolae (Wislocki and Dempsey, 1946b; Dempsey and Wislocki, 1947). The activity of the uterine surface epithelium is moderate. In

PLATE 15.XIV

FIG. 15.59. Frozen section of the placental labyrinth of a cat, viewed under a polarizing microscope, to illustrate the strong birefringence encountered in the cellular trophoblast of the placental lamellae (fetal crown to rump length, 110 mm.). The birefringence is associated with numerous sudanophilic lipid droplets which exhibit greenish fluorescence and give a positive Ashbel-Seligman reaction for carbonyl groups. Compare with Figure 15.20 which illustrates the carbonyl reaction. × 280. (Wislocki and Dempsey, 1946a.)

FIG. 15.60. A placental lamella of a cat, illustrating the presence of alkaline phosphatase in the interstitial matrix around the maternal blood vessels and decidual giant cells and extending into the syncytial trophoblast (embryo length, 13 mm.). Gomori's method, using glycerophosphate as substrate at pH 9.4. × 800. (Wislocki and Dempsey, 1946a.)

FIG. 15.61. Placental lamellae of a cat (fetal crown to rump length, 45 mm.), illustrating the periodic acid-Schiff (PAS) reaction which is localized in the interstitial matrix surrounding the maternal blood vessels and decidual giant cells and intervening between them and the trophoblast. Compare with the similar localization of alkaline phosphatase in Figure 15.60 and also with Figure 15.56. Zenker's acetic acid fixative. Treatment with saliva. × 260.

FIG. 15.62. The paraplacental endometrium ("brown" border) of a pregnant cat (fetal crown to rump length, 45 mm.), illustrating the intense PAS reaction in the secretion of the uterine glands which is poured into the uterine lumen. A reaction is present also in the cytoplasm of the distal ends of the uterine epithelium. The paraplacental chorionic membrane (opposite the uterine epithelium at the extreme upper border of the photograph) consists of columnar cells the supranuclear cytoplasm of which contains PAS-stained droplets. Zenker's acetic acid fixative. Treated with saliva. × 260.

FIG. 15.63. The paraplacental "brown" border of a pregnant cat (fetal crown to rump length, 45 mm.), illustrating the intense alkaline phosphatase reaction in the endometrium (right) and lesser reaction in the chorion (left). Gomori's method, using glycerophosphate as substrate at pH 9.4. × 120.

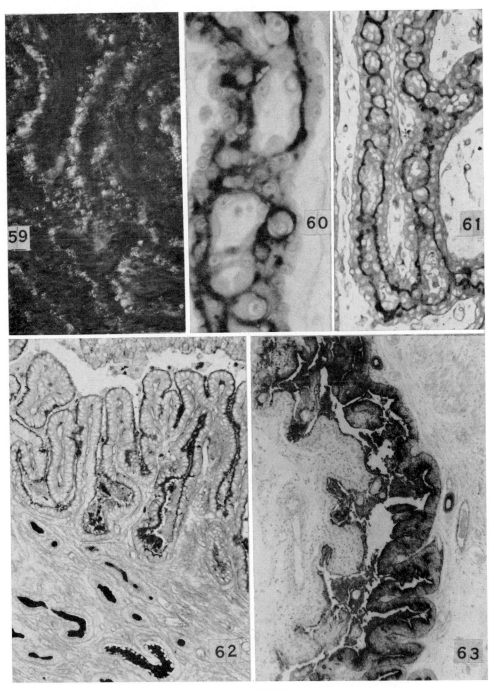

PLATE 15.XIV

the trophoblast covering the chorionic rugae, acid phosphatase activity is low or completely absent.

In the rat placenta the distribution of phosphatase activity toward *adenosine triphosphate* at alkaline pH has been described by Padykula (1958a).

VII. Evidence of the Possible Site of Production of Placental Steroid Hormones

In the section on methods, a procedure for characterizing lipids was outlined for localizing the sites of the synthesis of steroid hormones or their precursors in histologic sections. It was pointed out that none of the reactions involved in the procedure is specific for the identification of ketosteroids, but lipids possessing all of the properties enumerated have been found solely in those organs (adrenals, gonads, and placenta) in which steroid hormones are known to be produced.

In formalin-fixed, frozen sections of *human placenta*, birefringent, sudanophilic lipid droplets are abundantly present in the syncytial trophoblast throughout gestation. They are acetone soluble, react with phenylhydrazine (Wislocki and Bennett, 1943), give a positive Schiff reaction, exhibit yellowish-green fluorescence (Dempsey and Wislocki, 1944; Rockenshaub, 1952), and also react positively with the Ashbel-Seligman reagents for carbonyl groups (Ashbel and Seligman, 1949; Seligman, Ashbel and Cohen, 1951; Wislocki, 1952; Ashbel and Hertig, 1952). The lipid droplets diminish in size and relative abundance as gestation advances, but are, nevertheless, still apparent in the syncytium at full term (Wislocki and Bennett, 1943, Figs. 10 and 11). The decrease in droplet size with age may not necessarily indicate a reduction of functional activity, for in the adrenal cortex and ovaries a diminution in the size of the lipid droplets accompanies active secretion (Deane, Shaw and Greep, 1948; Barker, 1951). Furthermore, since the total volume of the syncytium must increase considerably as the placental villi grow and branch, it seems reasonable to assume that the absolute quantity of the

lipids may not actually diminish. Thus, there is possibly no discrepancy between the increase in formation and excretion of steroid compounds in the course of gestation and the total amount of lipids in the syncytium at term.

Strands of syncytium which penetrate the trophoblastic shell and junctional zone in the first trimester of pregnancy (Wislocki and Bennett, 1943) and undergo degeneration are probably responsible for the presence in these regions of occasional patches of lipids giving these reactions.

The uterine glandular epithelium contains large sudanophilic droplets which are not birefringent, but stain with Schiff's reagent (Wislocki and Dempsey, 1945) and give a hydrazide reaction (Ashbel and Hertig, 1952). Wislocki and Dempsey (1945) erroneously equated Schiff's reaction with the "plasmal" reaction and speculated on its possible significance. It now seems more probable that Schiff's reagent, under the conditions of fixation utilized by them, reveals peroxides of unsaturated lipids (Nicander, 1951). Ashbel and Hertig (1952) attributed staining of the epithelium of the endometrial glands by the carbonyl procedure to "ketosteroids," a conclusion which Atkinson, in a discussion of their paper, found difficult to believe, since he observed that all of the cellular elements of the parietal decidua give a positive reaction for carbonyl groups. This objection seems valid, inasmuch as the hydrazide will react with the oxidation products of unsaturated groups.

In mammals, other than man and the rhesus monkey, the observations cited in a previous section of this review indicate that lipid reactions characteristic of steroid-producing cells are also usually located in some part of the trophoblast (cat, shrews, bat, rodents). However, the pig's placenta is exceptional in that the sudanophilic lipid droplets giving the Ashbel-Seligman and Schiff reactions are located in the uterine epithelium. It is doubted that the reactions in the sow's uterine epithelium are indicative of steroidal synthesis, inasmuch as Wislocki and Dempsey (1945) encountered no birefringence in the epithelium. Estrogens have been detected by various means of assay in the placenta of the sow, being excreted between the 20th and 30th days of gestation and thereafter diminishing, to increase again around the 10th or 12th week and continuing to do so until term (Cowie, 1948). As a possible source of estrogens, the sudanophilic lipid droplets, present in the columnar cells of the sow's chorionic fossae in the latter half of gestation (Wislocki and Dempsey, 1946b), should be investigated further.

An histochemical method for visualizing steroid-3β-ol-dehydrogenase activity by tetrazolium salts has proved useful in identifying steroid-producing cells in the rat adrenal, ovary, and testis (Levy, Deane, and Rubin, 1959). Application of this technique to the rat placenta (Deane, Lobel, Driks, and Rubin, 1960) has localized steroid-3β-ol-dehydrogenase activity in the trophoblastic giant cells. This activity is greatest between the 8th and 15th day, becomes low by 18 days, and is nearly absent by the 21st day of gestation. Further application of this technique to other placental types should be fruitful.

VIII. Evidence of the Possible Site of Production of Placental Gonadotrophic Hormones

A. HUMAN PLACENTA

Friedheim (1929), Sengupta (1935), Gey, Jones and Hellman (1938), Jones, Gey and Gey (1943), and Stewart, Sano and Montgomery (1948) have grown human placental trophoblast in tissue cultures. It has been observed that the cytotrophoblast rather than the syncytium proliferates and that the latter, in so far as it arises, seems to be derived from the cellular form, and is small in amount and atypical in appearance. Friedheim observed no conversion of cytotrophoblast into syncytium in actively growing cultures. Furthermore, Gey, Jones and Hellman (1938), Jones, Gey and Gey (1943), and Stewart, Sano and Montgomery (1948) demonstrated that tissue cultures containing actively growing cytotrophoblast produce appreciable quantities of chorionic gonadrotrophic hormone, even after repeated transplantation over several months. These observations indicate that

the trophoblast, and more particularly the cytotrophoblast, is the source of the hormone.

Stewart, Sano and Montgomery reported their inability to grow trophoblast from mature placentas of the 8th and 9th months. Inasmuch as the syncytium does not divide mitotically and the Langhans cells are numerically much decreased at this period, the result is not surprising. However, if they had cultured tissue containing peripheral trophoblasts, obtained specifically from the placental septa or basal plate, growth might have been anticipated.

Chorionic gonadotrophic hormone is, as a rule, abundantly present in the urine of women suffering from hydatidiform moles or chorion epitheliomas (Tenney and Parker 1939, 1940; Rubin, 1941), and disappears promptly after the successful surgical removal of these tumors. Tenney and Parker noted that the amount of hormone corresponds roughly to the number of trophoblastic cells in a mole or chorion epithelioma and that a mole with cystic villi and slight trophoblastic proliferation gives a low titer. These findings also indicate that proliferating cytotrophoblast is the source of the hormone and that the syncytium is of less or of no importance.

Wislocki and Bennett (1943) emphasized that the curve of excretion of chorionic gonadotrophic hormone corresponds very well with the period of active proliferation of the trophoblastic shell. Nevertheless, a discrepancy seemed to exist in that the cytotrophoblast has generally been believed to degenerate and disappear in the last trimester, whereas the excretion of chorionic gonadotrophin continues throughout gestation (Venning, 1948). This apparent discrepancy is now understandable in the light of observations reported here which demonstrate that, although the Langhans cells which are chromophobic diminish greatly in number, the peripheral cytotrophoblasts which are chromophilic survive until full term in large numbers in the septa placentas and basal plate as viable, functional cells (Wislocki, 1951).

Baker, Hook and Severinghaus (1944) described blue granules in both the cytotrophoblast and the syncytium of the human placenta, demonstrable by a trichrome stain devised by Severinghaus (1932). According to them, these granules enlarge toward the surface of the syncytium and then seem to liquefy, forming vacuoles which liberate their contents through the brush border into the maternal blood stream. In late pregnancy, as the syncytium becomes thinner, these granules and vacuoles disappear. The investigators interpreted these findings as signifying that the trophoblast of early pregnancy performs a significant secretory function, and they emphasized that the period of activity was roughly contemporaneous with the time of greatest excretion of gonadrotrophin.

Bruner and Witschi (1947) and Bruner (1951), investigating the distribution of chorionic gonadotrophin in the human placenta by biochemical means, reported that it is found at all stages of pregnancy, the concentration being highest in the fetal portion of the placenta. It is evident, they stated, that the major part of the hormone is "released from the plasmotrophoblast into the maternal blood, whereas only a small fraction passes the inner placental barrier, the cytotrophoblast, to enter the fetal blood stream." They apparently believed that the hormone is formed by the synctium.

Similarities between the peripheral trophoblasts and the cells of the anterior lobe of the hypophysis believed to produce the hypophyseal gonadotrophic hormones, suggested to Dempsey and Wislocki (1945) that the peripheral trophoblasts produce chorionic gonadotrophin. They demonstrated that the cytoplasm of the syncytium and peripheral trophoblasts of the human placenta contains a basophilic substance similar to that in the true basophilic cells of the anterior lobe of the hypophysis, which in both instances is abolished by digestion with crystalline ribonuclease. That the hypophyseal basophilic cells contain ribonucleoprotein was first demonstrated by Desclin (1940). Since ribonucleoprotein is generally concentrated in cells in which protein synthesis is actively taking place, Wislocki, Dempsey and Fawcett (1948) suggested that its presence in the peripheral trophoblast might be related to the formation there of chorionic gonadotrophin. On the other hand, they thought that the ribonucleoprotein in the syncytium which is particularly abundant in the first months of gestation might represent the primary site of synthesis of fetal plasma proteins, a function taken over by the hepatic cells when the fetal liver becomes sufficiently differentiated. Wislocki (1951) observed that the basophilia of the peripheral trophoblasts persists until full term, coinciding with the

---

PLATE 15.XV

FIG. 15.64. Chorionic folds of a pig's placenta (fetal crown to rump length, 130 mm.), showing many intraepithelial blood capillaries (blood cells not visible), resulting in the formation of many extremely thin epithelial plates some of which appear to be quite as thin as the human "epithelial plates" seen at full term (cf. with Figure 15.50). Compare with Figures 15.23 and 15.28 which are also of pig's placenta. Zenker-formol fixative. Eosin and methylene blue stain. × 400. (Wislocki and Dempsey, 1946b.)

FIG. 15. 65. A chorionic fossa of a pig's placenta (fetal crown to rump length, 120 mm.), illustrating the presence of finely dispersed periodic acid-Schiff (PAS) positive material in the distal ends of the columnar cells and coarse PAS stained droplets in their proximal ends. Orth's fixative. × 150.

FIG. 15.66. Uterine glands in the maternal placenta of a pig (fetal crown to rump length, 120 mm.), showing the strongly PAS-reactive secretion in the lumens. Orth's fixative. × 165.

FIG. 15.67. The chorion of a pig's placenta (fetal crown to rump length, 120 mm.) to illustrate the intense reaction of alkaline phosphatase in the columnar cells of the chorionic fossae located between the chorionic rugae. Gomori's method, using nuclei acid at pH 9.6. × 200.

FIG. 15.68. The endometrium of a pig's placenta (fetal crown to rump length, 120 mm.), to illustrate the intense alkaline phosphatase reaction in the endometrial stroma and blood vessel walls. The enzyme is essentially negative in the epithelium (ep) covering the endometrial folds as well as in the epithelium lining the uterine glands (g). Gomori's method, using fructose diphosphate at pH 9.4. × 200.

FIG. 15.69. Uterine glands in a pig's placenta (fetal crown to rump length, 125 mm.), illustrating the intense acid phosphatase activity of the glandular cells. Gomori's method, using glycerophosphatase at pH 4.7. × 170. (Wislocki and Dempsey, 1946b.)

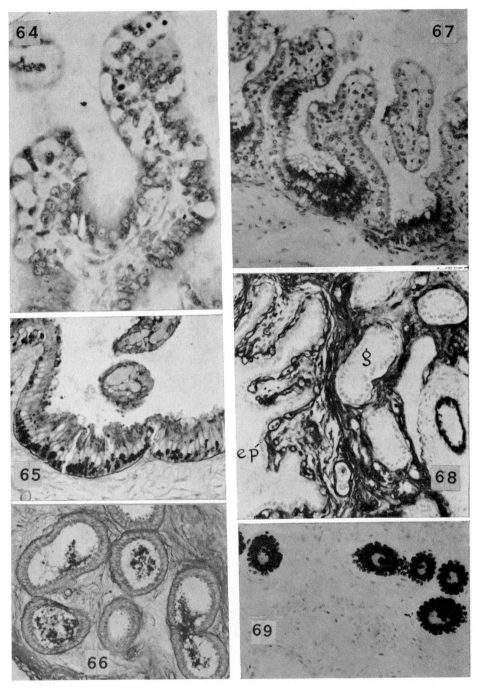

PLATE 15.XV

continued production of chorionic gonado-trophin.

The gonadotrophic hormones of both pituitary and placenta are known to be gly-coproteins (Bettelheim-Jevons, 1958). Pu-rified gonadotrophins of pituitary and pla-centa contain hexose and hexosamine. Catchpole (1949) reported that he found a glycoprotein constituent of the basophil cells of the hypophysis of the rat, demonstrable by means of the PAS stain. On the basis of the increase of this reaction after castration, as well as from other physiologic correlates, he concluded that a part of the material represents the follicle-stimulating hormone. Pearse (1949) likewise observed a positive PAS reaction in the pituitary basophils which he ascribed similarly to the gonado-trophic hormone. Moreover, he described a particular type of vesiculated chromophobe which he suggested might represent a phase in the secretory cycle of the basophils. Purves and Griesbach (1951a, b) estab-lished that there are two categories of gly-coprotein-containing basophils in the rat pi-tuitary, the gonadotrophs and thyrotrophs. (See also discussion in chapter by Purves.) These two groups of basophils can be dis-tinguished on the basis of shape, geograph-ical distribution, nature of granulation, and responses to changes in hormonal environ-ment. Pearse (1949) noticed PAS-positive material in the form of granular masses, globules, and vesicles in "the trophoblast layer of the placenta and in the Langhans cells of chorionepithelioma." Inasmuch as the granular part of this material could be removed by diastase, it seemed to consist of

glycogen. However, the globules and vesi-cles which were saliva fast he regarded as being probably of "mucoprotein nature" and as representing chorionic gonadotrophin.

Wislocki, Dempsey and Fawcett (1948) mentioned briefly that after fixation in Rossman's fluid and removal of glycogen they were unable to demonstrate any reac-tion in the cytotrophoblast by the PAS method. However, on further trials with other fixatives, including Zenker's acetic acid mixture and Orth's fluid, delicate granules were rendered visible (Wislocki, 1950) in the cytoplasm of some fraction of the periph-eral trophoblasts throughout gestation (Figs. 15.49 and 15.55). These fine, but often in-distinct, particles are more like those de-scribed in the pituitary basophils by Catch-pole (1949) than the globules and vesicles mentioned by Pearse (1949) which were not seen in these preparations. Although the re-actions observed in the peripheral cytotro-phoblast may bear a relationship to the presence of chorionic gonadotrophin, it should not be overlooked that the syncytial trophoblast also exhibits a delicately stip-pled, variable reaction and that its outer surface and brush border are quite strongly stained (Figs. 15.29 and 15.54). Further-more, it should be borne in mind that a variety of carbohydrate-containing sub-stances, including various mucopolysaccha-rides, glocoproteins glycolipids, and gly-coliproteins react with the PAS reagents and that such reactive substances are widely distributed in cells and tissues. As a result of this, the possible identification of cho-rionic gonadotrophin by this single reaction

---

PLATE 15.XVI

FIG. 15.70. The placenta of a guinea pig (fetal crown to rump length, 75 mm.), illustrating the distribution of alkaline phosphatase. The reaction is extremely intense in the placental cotyledons (fine-meshed syncytium) and diminishes abruptly in the coarse, interlobular syn-cytium. The villous portion of the yolk sac (at top of figure above the placenta) is also rich in alkaline phosphatase. The subplacenta beneath the placental labyrinth is negative, but the junctional and decidual zones are quite reactive. Gomori's method, using glycerophos-phate as substrate at pH 9.4. × 3½. (Wislocki, Deane and Dempsey, 1946.)

FIG. 15.71. The placental labyrinth of a mouse, on the 15th day of gestation illustrating the intense alkaline phosphatase reaction in the trophoblastic syncytium. Gomori's method, using glycerophosphate as substrate at pH 9.4. × 170. (Wislocki, Deane and Dempsey, 1946.)

FIG. 15.72. The chorio-allantoic placenta and yolk sac of a rat on the 21st day of gestation, illustrating the periodic acid-Schiff reaction of the epithelium of the villous portion of the yolk sac and of Reichert's membrane. Orth's fixative. Treatment with saliva. × 175. (Wis-locki and Padykula, 1953.)

FIG. 15.73. A detail of the guinea pig's placenta shown in Figure 15.70, illustrating the in-tense alkaline phosphatase reaction in the trophoblastic syncytium enclosing the maternal vascular channels. × 830. (Wislocki, Deane and Dempsey, 1946.)

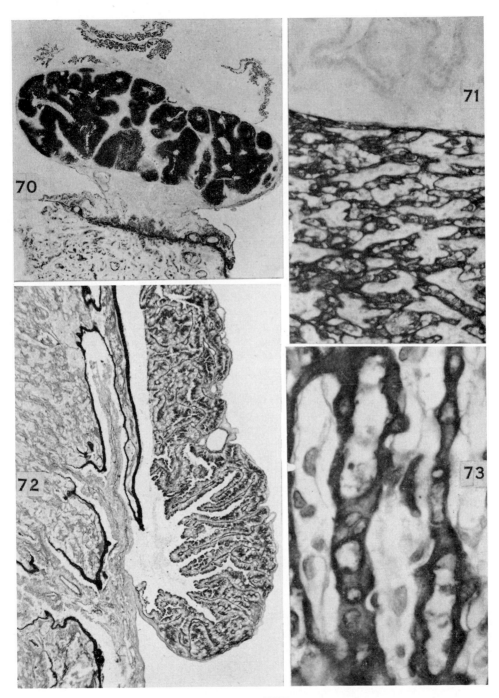

PLATE 15.XVI

must be accepted with considerable reservation.

From the foregoing summary of the evidence regarding the localization of chorionic gonadotrophic hormone, it seems probable that in the human the trophoblast is the site of its formation. However, it is not clearly established whether it is localized in the Langhans cells, syncytium, peripheral cytotrophoblast, or in several of these elements. Evidence favors the peripheral trophoblasts. The Langhans cells are a less likely site because they are chromophobic and decline perceptibly in size and number by the beginning of the last trimester, whereas chorionic gonadotrophin and the peripheral trophoblasts persist until full term. Involvement of the syncytium seems unlikely, because it is the probable site of formation of the placental steroid hormones, and because it gradually loses its cytoplasmic basophilia, whereas the production of chorionic gonadrotrophin continues until full term.

In attempting to evaluate the possible nature of granules, vacuoles, lipid droplets, mitochrondria, and other organelles in the syncytium, the entire role of the placental barrier must be kept in mind. The syncytial trophoblast is chiefly involved in the absorption and transfer of metabolites from the maternal to the fetal blood stream, besides serving as a means of excreting certain waste products. Many of the organelles which its cytoplasm contains are related in some manner to these functions, although it is not possible at present to assign specific roles to many of them. Wislocki and Streeter (1938) and Wislocki and Bennett (1943) suggested that a considerable number of the vacuoles seen in the syncytium, especially early in gestation, might be related to absorption. They based their opinion on the probability that much of the syncytial cytoplasm is in a state of motion and flux, with the likelihood that maternal plasma is absorbed by a process of pinocytosis in the manner visualized by Lewis (1931) in cells growing in tissue culture. Recent observations of the human placenta with the electron microscope (Boyd and Hughes, 1954; Wislocki and Dempsey, 1955a) bear out this interpretation. On the other hand, waste products of fetal metabolism, such as creatine, creatinine, and urea, are so readily diffusible that their excretion would in all probability not be associated with the formation of granules which liquefied and formed vacuoles. There is considerable justification for associating the formation of placental steroid hormones with the sudanophilic, birefringent, lipid droplets present in the syncytium, but there is no evidence that steroid hormones are liberated from cells, in the adrenal glands or elsewhere, in a visible sequence of liquefying granules and discharging vacuoles. In regard to placental gonadotrophin, the slight evidence which can be assembled regarding its localization tends to place it in the peripheral trophoblasts rather than in the Langhans cells and syncytium. On the other hand, early in gestation during implantation and subsequent invasion of the uterine wall by the trophoblast, cytolytic substances and enzymes are quite possibly released by the trophoblast and these probably account for some of the granules and vacuoles seen in parts of the trophoblast at that period (Wislocki and Bennett, 1943).

Considering all of the evidence, chorionic gonadotrophic hormone of the human is most likely produced by the peripheral trophoblasts. This opinion is based on the observed results of culturing trophoblast, as well as on several histochemical similarities of the basophils of the pituitary gland with the peripheral trophoblasts (cytoplasmic basophilia, PAS reaction). Of importance for this concept is the observation that, whereas the majority of the Langhans cells diminish in size and number by the 6th month of gestation, many of the peripheral trophoblasts remain viable and functional until full term (Wislocki, 1951), thus coinciding with the continued production of chorionic gonadotrophin. According to these observations, the Langhans cells, clothing the secondary villi and located in the proximal ends of the trophoblastic cell columns, represent a germinal bed composed of chromophobic trophoblasts, from which the lineages of the syncytium and the chromophilic peripheral trophoblasts are separately derived. A further parallelism with the pituitary is apparent here, in that in both organs chromophobic cells are postulated as being the precursors of the chromophilic elements.

Little is known about the site of placental gonadotrophin production in infrahuman mammals. The PAS reaction provides little information about possible sites of formation of the hormone in various animals, because the reaction occurs in many placental components. This undoubtedly reflects the presence of other carbohydrate-containing substances besides the gonadotrophic hormone. Several reports on the mare (Cole and Goss, 1943; Rowlands, 1947; Amoroso, 1952; and Clegg, Boda and Cole, 1954) indicate that the equine gonadotrophin is produced by special parts of the endometrium of the maternal placenta called endometrial cups. Observations of Clegg, Boda and Cole (1954) suggest that the glandular epithelium is the site of gonadotrophic hormone production. A recent detailed discussion of the comparative aspects of hormonal functions was presented by Amoroso (1960).

IX. Significance and Relationships of Some Placental Constituents

A. RIBONUCLEOPROTEIN

Most of the cytoplasmic basophilia encountered in the trophoblast, uterine surface epithelium, and cells of the endometrial glands is due to the presence of ribonucleoprotein. Because most embryonic or rapidly growing cells are rich in this nucleoprotein, it has been difficult to separate the ribonucleoprotein associated with growth from that related to the synthesis of specific proteins by placental cells. Intense cytoplasmic basophilia occurs in the trophoblast of the pig (Wislocki and Dempsey, 1946b), cat (Wislocki and Dempsey, 1946a), rodents (Wislocki, Bunting and Dempsey, 1947), and man. Basophilia is extremely intense in the early part of gestation and diminishes in the second half of pregnancy, except in the pig in which it remains constant and in the bat in which, according to Wimsatt (1949), it becomes more pronounced. In the human, it has been proposed (Wislocki, Dempsey and Fawcett, 1948) that one of the functions of the ribonucleoprotein of the syncytium is to synthesize the proteins of the fetal blood plasma

before the fetal liver becomes sufficiently differentiated to assume that activity, whereas the ribonucleoprotein in the peripheral trophoblasts might conceivably be related to the formation there of gonadotrophic hormone. Consonant with the former thought is the gradual decline in cytoplasmic basophilia as pregnancy progresses.

Ribonucleoprotein is closely associated with the secretory activities of uterine glands. The surface epithelium and glands of the uterus, just before and during gestation, are rich in basophilic substance, greatest in amount in the pregnant sow, intermediate in carnivores, and least in rodents and in pregnant women (Wislocki and Dempsey, 1945). In the epitheliochorial placenta of the sow, all of the nutritive substances obtained by the fetus must either traverse or be secreted by the uterine surface epithelium or the uterine glands. The glands which are rich in ribonucleoprotein release a copious secretion which reacts intensely with PAS reagents (mucopolysaccharide), but is not metachromatic. It gives a strong reaction for acid phosphatase. This secretion, designated as uterine milk, seems to be absorbed mainly by the cells of the chorionic fossae and areolae. In the cat, the markedly basophilic paraplacental uterine glands release a secretion which is rich in mucopolysaccharide, glycogen, and phosphatases and is absorbed by the columnar cells of the brown border of the chorion. The subplacental glands of the cat are strongly basophilic, but react only faintly with PAS reagents. In rodents, the uterine glands and surface epithelium also seem to secrete nutriment which is absorbed through the yolk sac placenta. These secretory cells are basophilic, and their distal cytoplasm and secretion react intensely for mucopolysaccharide with PAS reagents. In the human, at the time of implantation and for a considerable period thereafter, the paraplacental and subplacental glands are moderately basophilic and contain glycogen, PAS-reactive mucopolysaccharide, lipids, and phosphatases. Moreover, unlike the uterine glands of various animals, their secretion contains some metachromatic mucin (Wislocki and Dempsey, 1948). The secretion of the glands located in the basal decidua may supply the growing peripheral trophoblast (trophoblastic shell and cell columns) with nourishment.

B. ALKALINE PHOSPHATASE

From the study of the placentas of man, cats, pigs, and rodents, Wislocki and Dempsey (1945, 1946a, b) and Wislocki, Deane and Dempsey (1946) concluded that a layer of alkaline phosphatase intervenes between the maternal and fetal placental circulations. Wislocki and Wimsatt (1947) found this to be true also in shrews, and Wimsatt (1949) observed a layer located similarly between the maternal and fetal circulations in the placenta of the bat. In hemochorial and endotheliochorial types of placentas, the enzyme is usually present in the outermost layer of the trophoblast, whereas in the epitheliochorial placenta of the pig it is present mainly in the stroma of the maternal placenta. Dempsey and Wislocki (1945) pointed out that many substances may depend on phosphatases for their transfer across cellular boundaries, and they suggested that a layer of different phosphatases located in the placental barrier may participate in the transfer of metabolites. Wimsatt (1949) remarked that this view is consonant with a variety of metabolic processes which must be carried out at the placental barrier and accords with the interpretation of the barrier as a "selective" membrane. This distribution of phosphatase in the outer zone and brush border of the human syncytium resembles very strikingly the location of the enzyme in the epithelium of the small intestine and in the convoluted tubules of the kidney. These three absorptive surfaces also have well developed brush borders composed of numerous microvilli. Hence in the placenta, as in these latter sites, alkaline phosphatase may be associated in the microvilli with the absorption of phosphorylated compounds. Alkaline phosphatase is also a component of the barrier in the yolk sac placenta of rodents (Hard, 1946; Wislocki, Deane and Dempsey, 1946; Padykula, 1958), although it fluctuates in the vitelline epithelium at different periods of gestation. As in the human syncytium, the epithelium of the visceral layer of the yolk sac of rodents possesses a brush border.

In various parts of the endometrium and fetal placentas of lower mammals and man, Dempsey and Wislocki (1947) observed differences in alkaline phosphatase reactions following the use of a variety of substrates. Some structures reacted with many substrates whereas others reacted with only one or two. It was concluded that the observed differences could be accounted for most reasonably by the assumption that the tissues contain multiple enzymes of varying specificity which frequently do not coincide in their distribution.

In the placentas of man, cats, rodents, and shrews alkaline phosphatase increases

---

PLATE 15.XVII

Lipids of the rat yolk sac

All of the sections illustrated in Figures 15.74 to 15.77 were fixed in 10 per cent buffered formalin and stained with sudan black B.

FIG. 15.74. Parietal wall and nonvillous visceral wall of the yolk sac at 13 days of gestation. The parietal endoderm (p) contains minute lipid droplets and rests on an unstained Reichert's membrane (r). Across the yolk sac cavity larger lipid droplets occur in the nonvillous visceral endoderm (v); however, the lipid here is less abundant than in the villous portion shown in Figure 15.75. In the left border of the photograph, lipid occurs also in giant cells and decidual cells of the capsularis. × 275.

FIG. 15.75. Villous visceral splanchnopleure at 13 days of gestation. Peak storage of lipid by the visceral endoderm occurs at this time (12 to 13 days). Note that the position of the lipid droplets is principally infranuclear. Lipid is much less abundant in the mesenchyme and mesothelium of the visceral splanchnopleure. Compare with Figures 15.76 and 15.77. Higher magnification of these endodermal cells is provided in Figures 15.78 to 15.81. × 275.

FIG. 15.76. Villous visceral splanchnopleure at 17 days of gestation. By the 17th day of gestation, the villi have elongated and branched, and the lipid content of each endodermal cell has decreased. The cells toward the tip of the villus tend to have more lipid than those at the base. The droplets remain infranuclear. Compare with Figures 15.75 and 15.77. × 275.

FIG. 15.77. Villous visceral splanchnopleure at 19 days of gestation. The endodermal cells are quite free of lipid droplets. There is a background sudanophilia which is mostly concentrated in the mitochondria. Compare with Figures 15.75 and 15.76. × 275.

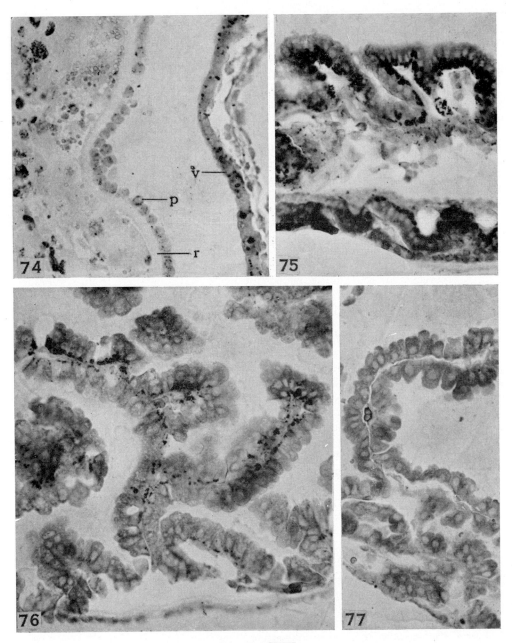

Plate 15.XVII

in the course of gestation as cytoplasmic basophilia decreases. In the human trophoblastic syncytium, alkaline phosphatase first appears in the outer eosinophilic (alkaline) zone and seems to advance into the syncytium as the basophilia recedes. In the placentas of other animals listed above alkaline phosphatase is also usually localized in regions which are acidophilic. Wimsatt (1949) reported an exception to this inverse relationship of basophilia and phosphatase, because in the bat both substances are plentiful during the first half of gestation, whereas, in the second half, phosphatase activity declines while basophilia persists.

Wislocki and Dempsey (1945) observed from study of the placentas of various animals that a layer of phosphatase intervenes between the maternal blood stream and regions where glycogen accumulates. Hard (1946) observed a similar spatial relationship in the placenta of the guinea pig between alkaline phosphatase, on the one hand, and accumulation of glycogen and lipid on the other. Wimsatt (1948, 1949) reported similar relations between the two substances in the placenta of the bat. Whether or not these two phenomena are related has been debated (Wimsatt, 1949; Pritchard, 1947). In this connection it is of interest, as more has been learned about the localization of glycogen by the use of the PAS reaction, that the cellular elements of the secondary and tertiary villi of the human placenta up to 6 weeks of gestation are moderately rich in glycogen, at a time when extremely little alkaline phosphatase has made its appearance in the placental bar-rier. And later, as alkaline phosphatase increases tremendously in amount, stainable glycogen disappears completely from the chorionic villi.

Wimsatt (1949) observed that the trophoblastic cells of the membranous chorion of the bat "contain heavy deposits of neutral fat, phospholipids, and cholesterids" and concluded that phosphatases, abundantly present in the adjacent decidua, "may be involved in the lipid metabolism and transport in this portion of the placental barrier." Regarding this he called attention to the possibility that phosphatases in the placental barrier provide a mechanism whereby ciruclating fats are phosphorylated, thereby facilitating the absorption and transmission of lipids. In this connection, it is interesting to note that Green and Meyerhof (1952) have shown that these enzymes can phosphorylate some compounds under certain circumstances.

C. ALKALINE PHOSPHATASE AND THE PERIODIC ACID-SCHIFF (PAS) REACTION

Moog and Wenger (1952) reported that neutral mucopolysaccharide, as demonstrable by the PAS reaction, occurs at sites of high alkaline phosphatase activity and they cite examples in various tissues and organs. They suggested that the mucopolysaccharide may serve as a cytoskeleton for the enzyme. They described the placental labyrinth of the mouse as an illustration of this relationship, stating that the trophoblastic syncytium is rich in both substances. However, in the similarly constructed placental

---

PLATE 15.XVIII

Visceral endoderm of the rat yolk sac

FIGS. 15.78 AND 15.79. Cytologic distribution of lipids in the visceral endoderm. Frozen section, sudan black B. In Figure 15.78 the large clear nuclei have tiny cholesterol containing droplets which are truly intranuclear. The infranuclear cytoplasm is packed with larger droplets which are also rich in cholesterol. At the surface of these cells note the delicate sudanophilia of the brush border and also the narrow sudanophobic band immediately beneath this border. The supranuclear cytoplasm contains many unstained vacuoles (Fig. 15.78) and also clusters of tiny lipid droplets (Fig. 15.79). In Figure 15.79 the plane of section runs obliquely through the apical cytoplasm. Three large lipid clusters are shown. × 1950.

FIG. 15.80. Electron micrograph of a visceral endodermal cell at 12 days of gestation. A large homogeneous cholesterol rich droplet is located in the cytoplasm near the polymorphic nucleus. Two minute droplets (*d*), which are also rich in cholesterol, occur within the nucleus. The apical cytoplasm contains vacuoles which are heterogeneous with respect to size and content. The limiting membrane of these vacuoles is usually incomplete. The free surface of this cell is formed of numerous microvilli. Beneath the surface, many small canaliculi with dense walls can be seen. × 7600.

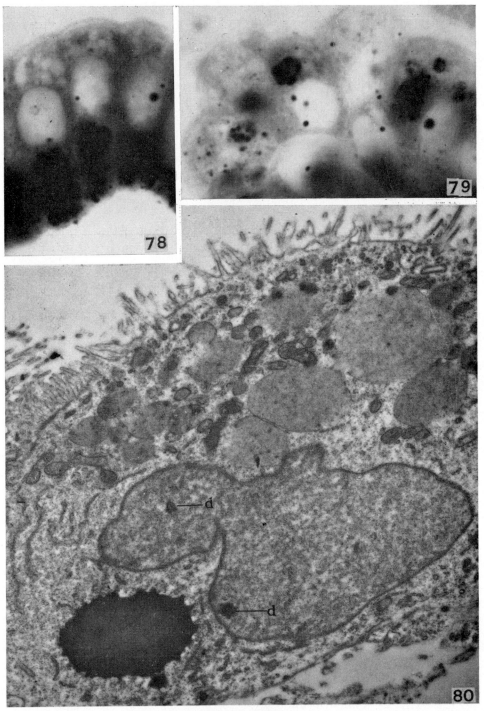

PLATE 15.XVIII

labyrinth of the rat, it has been observed that the alkaline phosphatase reaction predominates in the trophoblast, whereas the PAS reaction occurs mainly in the adjacent basement membrane which supports the syncytium and encloses the fetal capillaries. Thus, although the two reactions are closely associated, they are by no means located in the same tissue elements. Despite this discrepancy, there is no question but that in many tissues the thesis Moog and Wenger have stated holds true. Indeed, numerous examples which bear out their conclusion can be found in the placentas of various animals. Thus, in the human placenta, intense reactions for alkaline phosphatase and for PAS-positive substances occur in the outer zone and brush border of the syncytial trophoblast. In the cat's placental labyrinth, both occur together with great intensity in the perivascular sheaths intervening between the maternal blood vessels and the trophoblast, as well as in the columnar chorionic epithelium of the paraplacental brown border. In the rat and guinea pig the two reactions are encountered in the epithelium of the visceral layer of the yolk sac placenta. Finally, in the pig's placenta, the two reactions coincide in the distal ends of the columnar cells lining the chorionic fossae.

D. RELATIONSHIP OF LIPIDS TO THE PLACENTAL BARRIER

In reference to the question of lipids demonstrable in the placental barrier, Wislocki and Bennett (1943) emphasized, and Dempsey and Wislocki (1944) offered further substantiating evidence to show that, although lipids are demonstrable histologically in great abundance in the human trophoblastic syncytium, they are probably, for the most part, lipids associated with mitochondria and with the production of steroid hormones, rather than lipids in process of transmission across the placenta. Huggett and Hammond (1952) summarized the question of the manner of transmission of fat from mother to the fetus. In their opinion the chemical results do not show how the fat actually traverses the placenta; "they neither prove nor disprove the possibility of hydrolysis at the placental membrane and subsequent resynthesis in the deep syncytium." All that the results show is "that particular or labeled fatty acids, originally on the maternal side, appear later in the fetal tissues."

Regarding phospholipids, Popjak and Beeckmans (1950) concluded from a study of rabbits that the placenta does not transmit unhydrolyzed phospholipid molecules to the fetus. Similarly, glycerophosphate which is a phosphorus-containing degradation product of lecithin does not pass unhydrolyzed. In a previous investigation Popjak (1947) showed that fetal phospholipids in rats, rabbits, and guinea pigs are formed by synthesis within the fetal tissues. Popjak and Beeckman's findings offer a situation where phosphatases might serve as the dephosphorylating agents.

E. FIBRINOID

Earlier in this review the histologic properties of the ground substance of the human trophoblastic cell columns and shell were described. Grosser (1925a) called this ground substance "fibrinoid," adopting a term which had been introduced previously to describe substances occurring in a variety of pathologic lesions. Fibrinoid was defined originally as a somewhat refractile, homogeneous, intercellular substance with an affinity for acid dyes and with histologic resemblances to fibrin (Neumann, 1880). Recently, Altshuler and Angevine (1949, 1951) maintained that fibrinoid stains metachromatically with toluidin blue and reacts with the PAS reagents. From this, they concluded that fibrinoid consists of an acid mucopolysaccharide containing mucoitin sulfuric acid. On the basis of metachromatic staining, they identified placental fibrinoid in Nitabuch's membrane, the subchorial plate, and degenerating chorionic villi. Wislocki and Dempsey (1948) described metachromatic staining of the stroma of degenerating villi (Fig. 15.57) and of the ground substance of the decidua (Fig. 15.58), but they did not observe metachromasia of the ground substance of the peripheral trophoblast. However, it is specifically in the latter that Grosser (1925a) placed the placental fibrinoid, distinguishing it from fibrin and indicating that he did not believe it is related to fibrinoid elsewhere in the body. Altshuler and Angevine use the term "fibrinoid" differently from Grosser and other investigators. The staining seen by them in Nitabuch's layer is probably referable to metachromasia of the ground substance of the decidua and is most likely physiologic rather than pathologic in nature, inasmuch as similar metachromatic ground substance occurs in the endometrium during the normal menstrual cycle (Bensley, 1934; Wislocki and Dempsey, 1948).

Despite the fact that fibrin, placental fibrinoid, and collagen seem to be identical in reference to staining with acid and basic dyes and isoelectric points (Singer and Wislocki, 1948; Sokoloff, Mund and Kantor, 1951) both fibrin and collagen are distinguishable in a number of respects from placental fibrinoid. Moreover, although fibrinoid of pathologic lesions may be metachromatic, the ground substance of the peripheral trophoblast is not and the only placental substance comparable to pathologic fibrinoid is possibly the metachromatic ground substance of the stroma of degenerating chorionic villi.

X. Placental Permeability with Respect to Morphologic Types

The evidence that the placental barrier in individual species becomes more permeable to some substances as pregnancy progresses seems to be adequately established. Utilizing rabbits, it has been shown that permeability to antibodies (Rodolfo, 1934), phenolsulfonphthalein (Lell, Liber and Snyder, 1932), neoarsphenamine (Snyder, 1943), and radioactive sodium (Flexner and Pohl, 1941a) increases during the course of gestation. In the rat, a similar increase in permeability to insulin (Corey, 1932) and radioactive sodium (Flexner and Pohl, 1941b) has been demonstrated, and the same is true for sodium in the guinea pig, sow, goat, and cat (Flexner and Pohl, 1941a–d; Pohl and Flexner, 1941). A progressive increase in rate of transfer of heavy water has also been observed in the guinea pig and man (Gellhorn and Flexner, 1942; Hellman, Flexner, Wilde, Vosburgh and Proctor, 1948). Flexner and his associ-

ates related their results to the progressive thinning of the chorio-allantoic placenta of the individual species studied with respect to the reduction of the number and width of the layers in the course of gestation. This is a natural conclusion in view of the morphologic observations reported in preceding passages which show that in individual species there is a diminution in both width and number of layers of the chorio-allantoic barrier in the course of gestation. For the human, this correlation is well illustrated by a series of drawings presented by Flexner, Cowie, Hellman, Wilde and Vosburgh (1948).

Little comparative information exists with respect to the relative permeability of different types of placentas. What data are available concern mainly the over-all exchange through the fetal membranes and give few, excepting inferential, clues to the exact regions and cytologic means of transfer. Moreover, most of the substances followed have been readily diffusible ones and proteins of various kinds which afford no histochemical means for their detection. The manifold combinations of placental structures in various animals and their cytologic complexities have already been outlined to some degree. However, the majority of investigators, speculating on the comparative aspects of physiologic exchange across the placental barrier, have generally ignored all placental structures, excepting the chorio-allantois. The popularity of Grosser's morphologic scheme of the progressive differentiation of the chorio-allantoic placenta, to the almost complete exclusion of the consideration of all other routes of exchange, has been due doubtlessly to its relative simplicity and its adaptability to a concept, widely held until recently, that all placental transmission can be explained on the basis of diffusion and filtration. Moreover, the fact that little is known of the physiologic activity of the placental structures other than the chorio-allantois has also contributed to their neglect.

It has been generally held that various proteins are readily transmitted by the hemochorial placentas of man and rodents, whereas their passage is slow or entirely prevented in epitheliochorial and syndesmochorial types of placentas (Needham, 1931, Table 227). To give a well known example, immune bodies are not transmitted through placentas of ungulates, whereas in animals possessing hemochorial placentas their transfer takes place readily (Kuttner and Ratner, 1923; Ratner, Jackson and Gruehl, 1927; Ratner, 1943). However, the hemochorial placenta of the rat and rabbit is not involved in antibody transfer; the inverted yolk sac placenta handles this function exclusively in these species. In the monkey which lacks a yolk sac placenta, Bangham, Hobbs and Terry (1958) obtained experimental evidence that the hemochorial chorio-allantoic disc handles antibody transfer. Thus, the routes of antibody transfer are different in primates and rodents.

Flexner and his associates have related the variations in rates of transfer of sodium per unit weight of placenta in pigs, goats, cats, rodents, and man to the four morphologic types of Grosser. On this basis they found that approximately 320 times as much sodium passes across a unit weight of the rat's placenta per hour as across the sow's placenta, and that between the sow and the goat the difference is approximately 16 times, whereas between the goat and the cat, both of which possess syndesmochorial placentas (see Section IV C), the difference is slight (Gellhorn, 1943; Flexner, Cowie, Hellman, Wilde and Vosburgh, 1948). The inference is that the fewer the layers of tissue intervening between the circulations the greater is the rate of transfer per hour of a readily diffusible substance across a unit weight of placenta. However, these results are based on transfer *per unit weight* instead of transfer *per unit absorbing surface* of the placental barrier. Weight as a unit of measurement would be more acceptable if the placentas of different animals were essentially alike in their internal structure, so that unit weights contained approximately similar amounts of transmitting surfaces. Actually a gram of pig's placenta contains a large amount of edematous chorionic stroma and much endometrium, including uterine glands, and hence cannot be truly compared or equated with a gram of human placenta which contains relatively closely packed chorionic villi. As a consequence, any representative part of pig's placenta by weight contains little effective absorbing surface and a large amount of extraneous tissue, whereas a similar amount by weight of human placenta contains a relatively large amount of effective absorbing surface. Thus, comparisons of the relative rates of transmission of substances across various types of placental barriers based upon units of weight are relatively unsatisfactory.

Measurements based on the relative areas of the effective transmitting surface would be more significant. However, the rates of transmission of substances exchanged by diffusion would depend not alone on the surface area of the placental membrane but more exactly on the areas of contact with the maternal and fetal capillaries variously associated with the membrane. To obtain accurate measurements of these complex surfaces would be well nigh impossible and no attempts to do so have been made, with the exception of the surface area of the human placenta, for which crude measurements vary from

---

Fig. 15.81. Electron micrograph of a visceral endodermal cell of the rat yolk sac at 13 days. The junction of two endodermal cells occurs at J. Only a portion of the cell at the right is shown. Cholesterol rich lipid occurs in different forms both above and below the nucleus. A portion of a large homogeneous droplet (D) is seen in close association with the basal surface of the nucleus. Above the nucleus, lipid clusters (LC) of various sizes are conspicuous. The individual lipid units which comprise the cluster are irregular in shape and are bound together by membranes. Long filamentous mitochondria (M) are oriented roughly parallel to the long axis of this columnar cell. The perinuclear cytoplasm is rich in typical elements of the endoplasmic reticulum, which are often longitudinally oriented. A vacuole (V) similar to those seen in Figure 15.80 occurs near the free surface. The superficial cytoplasm is composed of pleomorphic, anastomosing microvilli. The plasma membrane of the microvilli (MV) is continuous with that which lines the canaliculi (C). These canaliculi which lie beneath the surface have dense walls, and they anastomose in a complicated fashion. The free surface is further enlarged in Figure 15.82. $\times$ 12,800.

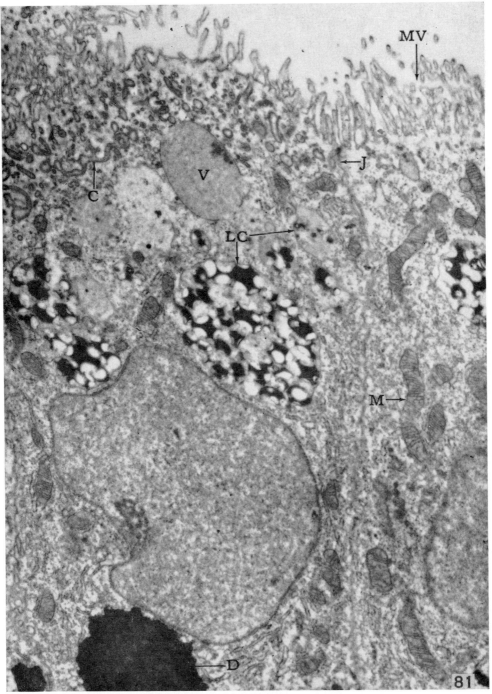

PLATE 15.XIX

six square yards (Dodds, 1924; Rech, 1924) up to twice that figure (Christoffersen, 1934). At present, there would seem to be no clear demonstration of a correlation between Grosser's four morphologic types and the relative rates at which placental exchange takes place.

It is, of course, quite probable that readily diffusible substances, such as oxygen, water, and salts, are exchanged through the thinnest parts of the placental membranes which are usually confined to the chorioallantoic placenta. However, it is probably not true, as previously generally believed, that almost all substances capable of transmission, including proteins, traverse the thinnest regions. It would seem likely that all of the substances requiring regulation, including most carbohydrates, lipids, and proteins, are exchanged through thicker and more specialized regions.

Cunningham (1920, 1922) was one of the first to discern, from experiments on the differential permeability of the placental barriers of cats and rabbits to potassium ferrocyanide and iron ammonium citrate, that substances which traverse the placenta are divisible into three categories. (1) Those which are diffusible and which meet with no mechanism in the placenta capable of acting on them. These pass by diffusion from mother to fetus, or in the reverse direction, without any mediation on the part of the placenta. (2) Those which meet with a definite preformed, regulatory mechanism. These include most of the substances which are designed for the fetal metabolism, including iron compounds. (3) Finally, those to which the maternal or fetal surfaces of the placental barrier are impermeable. These include most formed substances, such as cells and particulate matter.

From all of these considerations it would seem most likely that readily diffusible substances, such as water, oxygen, and some salts, are exchanged through the thinner parts of chorio-allantoic placentas, whereas more complex substances are transferred mainly through thicker regions, including the paraplacental borders and yolk sac placentas of animals which possess them. If it is true that readily diffusible substances traverse principally the thinner

portions of the placental barrier, then with respect to them, the sequence of the several placental types defined by Grosser would continue to be significant. Nevertheless, it is apparent, as Huggett and Hammond (1952) and others have recently emphasized, that the exchange of each substance will have to be individually investigated with reference to its mode of transfer and the factors affecting it, before a clear picture of placental physiology can be drawn.

In view of the results of Brambell and his associates which indicate that antibodies are transmitted through the yolk sac placenta of rodents rather than through the thin placental membrane of the allantoic placenta, one wonders what prevents antibodies and some other proteins from traversing the syndesmochorial and epitheliochorial placentas of ungulates. Is it so much that the placental barrier in ungulates is too thick to permit their passage, or is it perhaps mainly that the barrier lacks the particular provisions which in the rodent's yolk sac facilitate their passage?

The human placenta is interesting in that it provides only one general avenue for the transfer of substances from mother to fetus. The chorionic villi transmit both readily diffusible substances and those requiring chemical mediation of various kinds for their transfer. This raises the question as to whether, here, all substances follow the same morphologic route through the placental membrane. This cannot be answered, except to suggest that possibly they do not, because of slight histologic differences between the chorionic villi in various segments of the villous tree and of possible differences in the relationships of the segments to the maternal circulation. Similarly, the arrangement of the fetal blood vessels and the mode of circulation of the blood within them might also result in differences in permeability and functional activity in different regions of the villous trees. These are questions which should be investigated further. It seems reasonable to anticipate that future biochemical investigations will define transport mechanisms in the placenta, as they have in the kidney tubules and small intestine.

Another point of interest concerning the

placental barrier is the fact that the trophoblast of the human placenta forms a syncytial sheet completely devoid of intercellular spaces or cement. Unlike capillaries, in which diffusion and filtration of water-soluble substances are believed by some to occur solely or mainly through the intercellular spaces, this continuous sheet of cytoplasm affords the only possible route of placental transfer. In the sow, to take another example, it is interesting that the thinnest epithelium covering the chorionic rugae is syncytial in character; it is particularly through these rugae that the transmission of gases, water, and salts is believed to occur. The relative inability of leukocytes to traverse the placental barrier may possibly be related to the absence of intercellular spaces. In contrast to many chorio-allantoic placentas, yolk sac placentas are composed of discrete epithelial cells with well defined intercellular spaces which appear with great prominence under the electron microscope (Dempsey, 1953).

XI. Summarizing Reflections on Comparative Placentation and Placental Permeability

The chorion, chorio-allantois, and yolk sac of mammals become variously apposed to the uterine mucosa to give rise to the "placental barrier" which mediates the physiologic exchange between the mother and the fetus. The chorio-allantoic placenta of eutherian mammals undergoes changes in the course of gestation. This aging process is characterized by a gradual diminution in width and cytologic simplification of the various layers of the placental barrier, and by a progressive elimination of one or more of the maternal layers in most groups of mammals. This gradual diminution in width of the chorio-allantoic placental barrier is believed to account for the fact that placental transmission of some readily diffusible substances, such as oxygen, water, and various salts, increases as gestation proceeds.

In those groups of mammals possessing an inverted yolk sac placenta, an elimination of several fetal, instead of maternal, layers occurs in the course of gestation. The principal remaining layer, the visceral endodermal epithelium, undergoes some degree of cytologic aging but does not diminish in width. Some mammals possess still other structures which mediate exchange between the mother and fetus. The principal of these, the various central and paraplacental hematomas of carnivores, persist throughout gestation, without apparent cytologic changes or any reduction in width or number of layers.

In mammals possessing only a yolk sac placenta, such as some marsupials, or solely a chorio-allantoic placenta, such as man, physiologic exchange must be mediated entirely through one type of placenta. In many groups of mammals both types of placentas develop and exist concurrently for varying periods of time, in which event placental exchange seems to be divided between them. However, the respective functional roles of each of these very different placental structures in the transmission of various substances has not been extensively investigated.

Until recently it was generally assumed that nearly all substances which traverse the placenta do so by diffusion through the thinnest parts of the chorio-allantoic placenta. However, it now seems more likely that most substances are regulated in their passage through the placental barrier and that possibly only some readily diffusible substances, such as oxygen, water, and some salts whose rates of placental exchange increase during the course of gestation, are transmitted mainly through the thinner parts of the chorio-allantoic placenta. Proteins, lipids, and carbohydrates which seem to be regulated in their passage are probably transmitted in many different ways and are acted on variously by the enzymes and complex organelles present in the cytoplasm of the cells of the barrier. Recent experimental observations indicate that in the visceral endoderm of the rodent yolk sac the nucleus may be involved in some transfers. In man and monkeys, which possess only a chorio-allantoic placenta, this regulation must take place solely in the trophoblast, but in other groups of animals which possess, in addition, either a yolk sac placenta or placental hematomas, transfer of some substances evidently occurs through the latter structures. Recent investigations indicate that in the rabbit and rat some proteins and dyes, administered experimentally, are transferred by way of the yolk sac. In those marsupials which possess only a yolk sac placenta nothing is known about the mode of physiologic exchange, except that it is sufficient to support fetal development.

Grosser arranged the chorio-allantoic placentas of eutherian mammals in a phylogenic series comprising four placental types dependent on a progressive decrease in the number of layers intervening between the maternal and fetal circulations. According to his theory, the most primitive placental barrier consists of six layers whereas the most highly developed barriers have been reduced to three layers. Although Grosser recognized yolk sac placentas and hematomas as supplemental means of transfer of some nutritive materials from mother to fetus, only his chorio-allantoic placental types have been generally adopted to explain the passage of nearly all substances from mother to fetus. By the removal of a succession of three more or less functionally equivalent, maternal layers in a phylogenic sequence, the placental barrier has been envisioned as becoming progressively narrower, or thinner, and increasingly more permeable to the passage by diffusion of an increasingly larger number of substances. This scheme of the phylogenic simplification of the placental barrier seemed to be repeated in an ontogenic sense by the observed thinning of the placental barrier in the course of gestation in individual species. According to this belief, substances of larger molecular size, particularly proteins, are the last which are enabled to diffuse across the placental barrier in the postulated phylogenic and ontogenic series of stages.

With the growing recognition that the passage of a great many substances across the placental barrier is chemically regulated (Huggett and Hammond, 1952) and that the cytoplasm of the barrier contains a host of enzymes and numerous organelles, it seems increasingly evident that Grosser's doctrine must be reevaluated and modified. It has become necessary to consider each substance individually, with respect to its place of passage and the fatcors regulating its exchange. Thus, the regional cytologic and histochemical organization of the barrier, of which Grosser's doctrine takes little cognizance, should assume much greater importance; and, in addition to the relative thickness and width of the barrier, the relative extent and nature of its absorbing surfaces will have to be more carefully explored. The electron microscope should be of considerable value in ascertaining the structure of the absorbing surfaces and interior of the barrier. Studies of the human placenta in early months of gestation, recently begun with the electron microscope, have revealed a multitude of microvilli on the surface of the trophoblast and vesicles in the syncytium. This suggests that absorption from the intervillous space takes place to a considerable extent by the process of pinocytosis. Indications of absorption by pinocytosis have also been reported by means of electron microscopy in the epithelium of the yolk sac of the guinea pig and rat. A major role in placental physiologic exchange may eventually have to be assigned to pinocytosis. It seems apparent that pinocytosis is a process which predominates in the first part of human gestation but subsequently diminishes as the placental barrier becomes thinner and more simplified. It seems probable that as

PLATE 15.XX

Electronmicrographs of the rat visceral endoderm at 13 days of gestation

FIG. 15.82. Free surface of the visceral endoderm. The junction of two cells occurs at *J* which is marked also by the dense cytoplasmic condensation of the terminal bar. Note that the microvilli (*mv*) are penetrated by tiny tubules. At point *x*, the plasma membrane of the microvilli is continuous with the denser membrane which forms the walls of the canaliculi. Near the center of the photograph, the canaliculi are in the form of a figure 8, showing the anastomosis of the system of superficial canals. × 28,000.

FIG. 15.83. Basal surface of the visceral endoderm. The close association of a large lipid droplet with the concave basal surface of the nucleus is illustrated here. Two typical clusters of Golgi membranes (*g*) are located near the basal region of the nucleus. Mitochondria and elements of the endoplasmic reticulum are abundant. × 13,200.

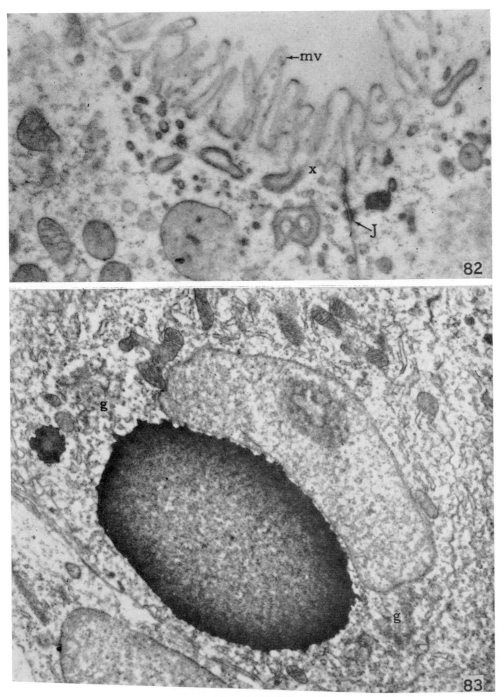

PLATE 15.XX

the rate of transfer of simple substances by diffusion across the barrier increases, the rate of absorption of more complex substances by pinocytosis declines. In rodents' placentas, on the other hand, although the trophoblastic cells of the placental labyrinth become thinner and their cytoplasm more simplified, pinocytosis seems to persist throughout gestation in the epithelium of the yolk sac thereby affording a continuous means for the absorption of substances of larger molecular size. Comparative studies of the placentas of animals with the electron microscope are just beginning, so that, although it seems that pinocytosis might play an important role in placental physiologic exchange, no broader generalizations regarding its significance can at present be offered. It is apparent that in the future more attention will have to be paid to the chemical, histochemical, and cytologic structure of every part of the barrier with respect to the mode of passage of different kinds of substances. Moreover, a comprehensive theory of placental exchange, from the comparative and phylogenic point of view, will have to take cognizance of all of the structures forming the placental barrier, instead of confining itself to the chorio-allantoic placenta as defined in terms of Grosser's four placental types.

XII. References

Acconci, G. 1912. Di alcune fini particolarita di struttura della mucosa uterina, della decidua e dell 'uovo. Folia Gynec., **7**, 25.

Altshuler, C. H., and Angevine, D. M. 1949. Histochemical studies on the pathogenesis of fibrinoid. Am. J. Path., **25**, 1061–1077.

Altshuler, C. H., and Angevine, D. M. 1951. Acid mucopolysaccharide in degenerative disease of connective tissue, with special reference to serous inflammation. Am. J. Path., **27**, 141–156.

Amoroso, E. C. 1947. The vascular relations in the placenta of the sow. Proc. Physiol. Soc., **18**, 1; 47.

Amoroso, E. C. 1951. The interaction of the trophoblast and endometrium at the time of implantation in the sheep. J. Anat. (Proc.), **85**, 428–429.

Amoroso, E. C. 1952. Placentation. In *Marshall's Physiology of Reproduction*, 3rd ed., A. S. Parkes, Ed., Vol. 2, pp. 127–311. New York: Longmans, Green and Company.

Amoroso, E. C. 1960. Comparative aspects of the hormonal functions. In *The Placenta and Fetal Membranes*, C. A. Villee, Ed., pp. 3–28. Baltimore: The Williams & Wilkins Company.

Anderson, J. W. 1959. The placental barrier to gamma-globulins in the rat. Am. J. Anat., **104**, 403–430.

Arey, L. B. 1946. *Developmental Anatomy*, 5th ed. Philadelphia: W. B. Saunders Company.

Ashbel, R., and Hertig, A. T. 1952. Histochemical demonstration of ketosteroids in normal, abnormal and neoplastic placentae. J. Nat. Cancer Inst., **13**, 221–222.

Ashbel, R., and Seligman, A. M. 1949. A new reagent for the histochemical demonstration of active carbonyl groups. A new method for staining ketonic steroids. Endocrinology, **44**, 565–583.

Baker, J. R. 1946. The histochemical recognition of lipine. Quart. J. Microscop. Sc., **87**, 441–470.

Baker, B. L., Hook, S. J., and Severinghaus, A. E. 1944. The cytological structure of the human chorionic villus and decidual parietalis. Am. J. Anat., **74**, 291–325.

Banghan, D. R., Hobbs, K. R., and Terry, R. J. 1958. Selective placental transfer of serum-proteins in the rhesus. Lancet, **2**, 351.

Barcroft, J. 1947. *Researches on Pre-natal Life*. Springfield, Ill.: Charles C Thomas.

Bargmann, W., and Knoop, A. 1959. Elektronenmikroskopische Untersuchungen an Plazentarzotten des Menschen (Bemerkungen zum Synzytiumproblem). Ztschr. Zellforsch., **50**, 472–493.

Barker, W. L. 1951. A cytochemical study of lipids in sows' ovaries during the estrous cycle. Endocrinology, **48**, 772–785.

Barrnett, R. J., and Seligman, A. M. 1952. Histochemical demonstration of protein-bound sulfhydryl groups. Science, **116**, 323–327.

Bennett, H. S. 1940. The life history and secretion of the cells of the adrenal cortex of the cat. Am. J. Anat., **67**, 151–227.

Bensley, S. H. 1934. On the presence, properties and distribution of the intercellular ground substance of loose connective tissue. Anat. Rec., **60**, 93–109.

Bergeron, J. A., and Singer, M. 1958. Metachromasy: an experimental and theoretical evaluation. J. Biophys. Biochem. Cytol., **4**, 433–458.

Bernard, C. 1859. Recherches sur l'origine de la glycogénie dans la vie embryonnaire; nouvelle fonction du placenta. Compt. rend. Soc. biol., **11**, 101–7.

Bettelheim-Jevons, F. R. 1958. Protein-carbohydrate complexes. Advances Protein Chem., **13**, 35–105.

Bienenfeld, B. 1912. Beitrag zur Kenntnis des Lipoidgehaltes der Placenta. Biochem. Ztschr., **43**, 245–255.

Bjorkman, N., and Bloom, G. 1957. On the fine structure of the foetal-maternal junction in the bovine placentome. Ztschr. Zellforsch., **45**, 649–659.

Bøe, F. 1953. Studies on the vascularization of the human placenta. Acta obst. et gynec. scandinav., Suppl., **32**, 57.

Boyd, J. D., and Hughes, A. F. W. 1954. Observations on human chorionic villi using the electron microscope. J. Anat., **88**, 356–362.

Brachet, J. 1953. The use of basic dyes and ribonuclease for cytochemical detection of ribonucleic acid. Quart. J. Microscop. Sc., **94**, 1–10.

Brambell, F. W. R., Hemmings, W. A., and Rowlands, W. T. 1948. The passage of antibodies from the maternal circulation into the embryo in rabbits. Proc. Roy. Soc., London, ser. B, **135**, 390–403.

Brambell, F. W. R., Hemmings, W. A., Henderson, M., and Rowlands, W. T. 1950. The selective admission of antibodies to the foetus by the yolk-sac splanchnopleur in rabbits. Proc. Roy. Soc., London, ser. B, **137**, 239–252.

Brambell, F. W. R., Hemmings, G. P., Hemmings, W. A., Henderson, M., and Rowlands, W. T. 1951. The route by which antibodies enter the circulation after injection of immune serum into the exocoel of foetal rabbits. Proc. Roy. Soc., London, ser. B, **138**, 188–204.

Brambell, F. W. R., and Halliday, R. 1956. The route by which passive immunity is transmitted from mother to foetus in the rat. Proc. Roy. Soc., London, ser. B, **145**, 179–185.

Brambell, F. W. R. 1957. The development of fetal immunity. Macy Foundation Conferences on Gestation, **4**, 143–201.

Bremer, J. L. 1916. The interrelations of the mesonephros, kidney, and placenta in different classes of mammals. Am. J. Anat., **19**, 179–209.

Bridgman, J. 1948a. A morphological study of the development of the placenta of the rat. I. An outline of the development of the placenta of the white rat. J. Morphol., **83**, 61–85.

Bridgman, J. 1948b. A morphological study of the development of the placenta of the rat. II. An histological and cytological study of the development of the chorioallantoic placenta of the white rat. J. Morphol., **83**, 195–223.

Bruner, J. A. 1951. Distribution of chorionic gonadotropin in mother and fetus at various stages of pregnancy. J. Clin. Endocrinol., **11**, 360–374.

Bruner, J. A., and Witschi, E. 1947. Distribution of chorionic gonadotropin. Anat. Rec. (Abstr.), **99**, 662.

Bulmer, D., and Dickson, A. D. 1960. Observations on the carbohydrate materials in the rat placenta. J. Anat., **94**, 46–58.

Buño, W., and Curi, C. R. 1945. Distribucion de la fosfatase en la placenta humana. Ciencia, **6**, 59.

Caffier, P. 1929. Die proteolytische Fähigkeit von Ei und Eibett. Zentralbl. Gynäk., **53**, 2410–2425.

Catchpole, H. R. 1949. Distribution of glycoprotein hormones in the anterior pituitary gland of the rat. J. Endocrinol., **6**, 218–225.

Chipman, W. W. 1902. Observations on the placenta of the rabbit, with special reference to the presence of glycogen, fat and iron. Studies Royal Victoria Hosp., Montreal, **1**, 1.

Christoffersen, A. K. 1934. La superficie des villosités choriales du placenta á la fin de la grossesse (étude d'histologie quantitative). Compt. rend. Soc. biol., **117**, 641–644.

Clegg, M. T., Boda, J. M., and Cole, H. H. 1954. The endometrial cups and allantochorionic pouches in the mare with emphasis on the source of equine gonadotrophin. Endocrinology. **54**, 448–463.

Cole, H. H., and Goss, H. 1943. The source of equine gonadotrophin. In *Essays in Biology*. Berkeley and Los Angeles: University of California Press.

Corey, E. L. 1932. Placental permeability to insulin in the albino rat. Physiol. Zool., **5**, 36–48.

Cowie, A. T. 1948. Pregnancy diagnosis tests: a review. Commonwealth Agricultural Bureau, Joint Publication, No 13, Great Britain.

Cunningham, R. S. 1920. Studies in placental permeability. I. The differential resistance to certain solutions offered by the placenta in the cat. Am. J. Physiol., **53**, 439–456.

Cunningham, R. S. 1922. Studies in placental permeability. II. Localization of certain physiological activities in the chorionic ectoderm in the cat. Am. J. Physiol., **60**, 448–460.

Davies, J. 1956. Histochemistry of the rabbit placenta. J. Anat., **90**, 135–142.

Deane, H. W. 1952. Histochemical observations on the ovary and oviduct of the albino rat during the estrous cycle. Am. J. Anat., **91**, 363–414.

Deane, H. W., and Greep, R. O. 1946. A morphological and histochemical study of the rat's adrenal cortex after hypophysectomy with comments on the liver. Am. J. Anat., **79**, 117–145.

Deane, H. W., Lobel, B. L., Driks, E. C., and Rubin, B. L. 1960. Études supplémentaires de l'activité de l'enzyme stéroïde-3β-ol déshydrogénase des organes reproductifs de la rate. Proceedings of the 1st International Congress of Histochemistry and Cytochemistry, p. 111. Paris: Pergamon Press.

Deane, H. W., and Morse, A. 1948. The cytological distribution of ascorbic acid in the adrenal cortex of the rat under normal and experimental conditions. Anat. Rec., **100**, 127–141.

Deane, H. W., and Seligman, A. M. 1953. Evaluation of procedures for the cytological localization of ketosteroids. Vitamins & Hormones, **11**, 173.

Deane, H. W., Shaw, J. H., and Greep, R. O. 1948. The effect of altered sodium or potassium intake on the width and cytochemistry of the zona glomerulosa of the rat's adrenal cortex. Endocrinology, **43**, 133–153.

De Duve, C. 1959. Lysosomes, a new group of cytoplasmic particles. In *Subcellular Particles*, T. Hayashi, Ed., pp. 128–159. New York: The Ronald Press Company.

Dempsey, E. W. 1953. Electron microscopy of the

visceral yolk-sac epithelium of the guinea pig. Am. J. Anat., **93**, 331–363.

DEMPSEY, E. W., AND BASSETT, D. L. 1943. Observations on the fluorescence, birefringence and histochemistry of the rat ovary during the reproductive cycle. Endocrinology, **33**, 384–401.

DEMPSEY, E. W., AND WISLOCKI, G. B. 1944. Observations on some histochemical reactions in the human placenta, with special reference to the significance of the lipoids, glycogen and iron. Endocrinology, **35**, 409–429.

DEMPSEY, E. W., AND WISLOCKI, G. B. 1945. Histochemical reactions associated with basophilia and acidophilia in the placenta and pituitary gland. Am. J. Anat., **76**, 277–301.

DEMPSEY, E. W., AND WISLOCKI, G. B. 1946. Histochemical contributions to physiology. Physiol. Rev., **26**, 1–27.

DEMPSEY, E. W., AND WISLOCKI, G. B. 1947. Further observations on the distribution of phosphatases in mammalian placentas. Am. J. Anat., **80**, 1–33.

DEMPSEY, E. W., WISLOCKI, G. B., AND AMOROSO, E. C. 1955. Electron microscopy of the pig's placenta, with especial reference to the cell membranes of the endometrium and chorion. Am. J. Anat., **96**, 65–102.

DEMPSEY, E. W., AND WISLOCKI, G. B. 1956. Electron microscopic observations on the placenta of the cat. J. Biophys. Biochem. Cytol., **2**, 743–754.

DEMPSEY, E. W., BUNTING, H., SINGER, M., AND WISLOCKI, G. B. 1947. The dye-binding capacity and other chemo-histological properties of mammalian mucopolysaccharides. Anat. Rec., **98**, 417–429.

DESCLIN, L. 1940. Détection de substances pentosenucléiques dans les cellules du lobe antérieur de l'hypophyse du rat et du cobaye. Compt. rend. Soc. biol., **133**, 457–459.

DODDS, G. S. 1924. The area of the chorionic villi in the full term placenta. Anat. Rec., **24**, 287–294.

DOYLE, W. L. 1950. The distribution of phosphatases in the rabbit appendix after x-irradiation. Am. J. Anat., **87**, 79–117.

DuBois, A. M., AND DUCOMMUN, S. 1955. Variations de la teneur en glycogène et en graisse du placenta de cobaye, au cours de la gestation. Acta Anat., **25**, 398.

DUVAL, M. 1892. *Le Placenta des Rongeurs,* Felix Alcan, Ed. Paris: Ancienne Librairie Germer Bailliere et Cie.

ENDERS, A. C. 1960. Electron microscopic observations on the villous haemochorial placenta of the nine-banded armadillo (*Dasypus novemcinctus*). J. Anat., **94**, 205–215.

EVERETT, J. W. 1935. Morphological and physiological studies of the placenta of the albino rat. J. Exper. Zool., **70**, 243–285.

FAWCETT, D. W., WISLOCKI, G. W., AND WALDO, C. M. 1947. The development of mouse ova in the anterior chamber of the eye and in the abdominal cavity. Am. J. Anat., **81**, 413–443.

FLEXNER, L. B., AND POHL, H. A. 1941a. The transfer of radioactive sodium across the placenta of the white rat. J. Cell. Comp. Physiol., **18**, 49–59.

FLEXNER, L. B., AND POHL, H. A. 1941b. The transfer of radioactive sodium across the placenta of the rabbit. Am. J. Physiol., **134**, 344–349.

FLEXNER, L. B., AND POHL, H. A. 1941c. Transfer of radioactive sodium across the placenta of the guinea pig. Am. J. Physiol., **132**, 594–611.

FLEXNER, L. B., COWIE, D. B., HELLMAN, L. M., WILDE, W. S., AND VOSBURGH, G. J. 1948. The permeability of the human placenta to sodium in normal and abnormal pregnancies and the supply of sodium to the human fetus as determined with radioactive sodium. Am. J. Obst. & Gynec., **55**, 469–480.

FRIEDHEIM, E. A. H. 1929. Die Züchtung von menschlichen Chorionepithel in vitro. Ein Beitrag zur Lehre vom Chorionepitheliom. Arch. Path. Anat., **272**, 217–244.

FUJIMURA, G. 1921. Cytological studies on the internal secretory functions in the human placenta and decidua. J. Morphol., **35**, 485.

GELLHORN, A. 1943. Placental transmission of radioactive isotopes. In *Proceedings of the Conference on Problems of Human Fertility*, E. T. Engle, Ed., pp. 158–166. Menasha, Wisc.: Banta Publishing Company.

GELLHORN, A., AND FLEXNER, L. B. 1942. Transfer of water across the placenta of the guinea pig. Am. J. Physiol., **136**, 750–756.

GELLHORN, A., FLEXNER, L. B., AND POHL, H. A. 1941. The transfer of radioactive sodium across the placenta of the sow. J. Cell. Comp. Physiol., **18**, 393–400.

GERSH, I., AND CATCHPOLE, H. R. 1949. The organization of ground substance and basement membrane and its significance in tissue injury, disease and growth. Am. J. Anat., **85**, 457–521.

GEY, G. O., JONES, G. E., AND HELLMAN, L. M. 1938. The production of a gonadotropic substance (prolan) by placental cells in tissue culture. Science, **88**, 306–307.

GOLDMANN, E. 1912. Die äussere und innere Sekretion des gesunden und kranken Organismus im Lichte der "vitalen Färbung," Teil II. Beitr. klin. Chir., **78**, 1–108.

GOMORI, G. 1941a. The distribution of phosphatase in normal organs and tissues. J. Cell. Comp. Physiol., **17**, 71–84.

GOMORI, G. 1941b. Distribution of acid phosphatase in the tissues under normal and under pathological conditions. Arch. Path., **32**, 189–199.

GOMORI, G. 1945. The microtechnical demonstration of sites of lipase activity. Proc. Soc. Exper. Biol. & Med., **58**, 362–364.

GOMORI, G. 1950. Methods of study for tissue lipase. In *Menstruation and Its Disorders*, E. T. Engle, Ed., pp. 52–60. Springfield, Ill.: Charles C Thomas.

GRÄFENBERG, E. 1909a. Der Antitrypsingehalt des mütterlichen Blutserums während der Schwangerschaft als Reaktion auf tryptische Einflüsse der Eioberfläche. München. med. Wchnschr., **56**, 702–704.

GRÄFENBERG, E. 1909b. Beiträge zur Physiologie der Eieinbettung. Ztschr. Geburtsh. Gynäk., **65**, 1–35.

GREEN, H., AND MEYERHOF, O. 1952. Synthetic action of phosphatase. III. Transphosphorylation with intestinal and semen phosphatase. J. Biol. Chem., **197**, 347–364.

GROSSER, O. 1909. *Vergleichende Anatomie und Entwicklungsgeschichte der Eihäute und der Placenta*. Wien-Leipzig: W. Braumüller.

GROSSER, O. 1925a. Über Fibrin und Fibrinoid in der Placenta. Ztschr. Anat., **76**, 304–319.

GROSSER, O. 1925b. Entwicklungsgeschichte des Menschen von der Keimzelle bis zur Ausbildung der äusseren Körperform unter Berücksichtigung ihrer vergleichend-entwicklungsgeschichtlichen Grundlagen. Vergleichende und menschliche Placentationslehre. In *Biologie und Pathologie des Weibes*, J. Halban and L. Seitz, Eds., Vol. 6, p. 1. Berlin: Urban and Schwarzenberg.

GROSSER, O. 1948. *Grundis der Entwicklungsgeschichte des Menschen*. Berlin: Springer-Verlag.

HAMILTON, W. J., AND BOYD, J. D. 1951. Observations on the human placenta. Proc. Roy. Soc. Med., **44**, 489.

HAMILTON, W. J., AND BOYD, J. D. 1960. Development of the human placenta in the first three months of gestation. J. Anat., **94**, 297–328.

HAMILTON, W. J., BOYD, J. D., AND MOSSMAN, H. W. 1952. *Human Embryology*, 2nd Ed. Baltimore: The Williams & Wilkins Company.

HARD, W. L. 1946. A histochemical and quantitative study of phosphatase in the placenta and fetal membranes of the guinea pig. Am. J. Anat., **78**, 47–77.

HELLMAN, L. M., FLEXNER, L. B., WILDE, W. W., VOSBURGH, G. J., AND PROCTOR, N. K. 1948. The permeability of the human placenta to water and the supply of water to the human foetus as determined with deuterium oxide. Am. J. Obst. & Gynec., **56**, 861–868.

HERMAN, E., AND DEANE, H. W. 1953. A comparison of the localization of alkaline glycerophosphatase, as demonstrated by the Gomori-Takamatsu method, in frozen and in paraffin sections. J. Cell Comp. Physiol., **41**, 201–224.

HERTIG, A. T., AND ROCK, J. 1941. Two human ova of the previllous stage, having an ovulation age of about 11 and 12 days respectively. Contr. Embryol., Carnegie Inst. Washington, **29**, 127–156.

HERTIG, A. T., AND ROCK, J. 1945. Two human ova of the previllous stage, having a developmental age of about 7 and 9 days respectively. Contr. Embryol., Carnegie Inst. Washington, **31**, 65–94.

HERTIG, A. T., ROCK, J., AND ADAMS, E. C. 1956. A description of 34 human ova within the first 17 days of development. Am. J. Anat., **98**, 435–494.

HILL, J. P. 1932. The developmental history of the primates (Croonian Lecture). Philos. Tr. Roy. Soc., London, **221**, 45–178.

HOFBAUER, J. 1905. *Grundzüge einer Biologie der menschlichen Plazenta*. Wien-Leipzig: W. Braumüller.

HOFBAUER, J. 1925. The function of the Hofbauer cells of the chorionic villus particularly in relation to acute infection and syphilis. Am. J. Obst. & Gynec., **10**, 1–14.

HOLZAEPFEL, J. H., AND BARNES, A. C. 1947. Placental metabolism of vitamin C. II. Histochemical analysis. Am. J. Obst. & Gynec., **53**, 864–868.

HOTCHKISS, R. D. 1948. A microchemical reaction resulting in the staining of polysaccharide structures in fixed tissue preparations. Arch. Biochem., **16**, 131–141.

HUGGETT, A. ST. G. 1944. Influence of diet on pregnancy. I. The role of the placenta in foetal nutrition. Proc. Nutrition Soc., **1**, 227–237.

HUGGETT, A. ST. G., AND HAMMOND, J. 1952. Physiology of the placenta. In *Marshall's Physiology of Reproduction*, 3rd ed., A. S. Parkes, Ed., pp. 312–397. New York: Longmans, Green and Company.

IRVING, F. C., AND HERTIG, A. T. 1937. A study of placenta accreta. Surg. Gynec. & Obst., **64**, 178–200.

JONES, G. E., GEY, G. O., AND GEY, M. K. 1943. Hormone production by placental cells maintained in continuous culture. Bull. Johns Hopkins Hosp., **72**, 26–38.

KARNOVSKY, M. L., AND DEANE, H. W. 1954. Alterations of adrenal cortical lipides by formalin fixation as determined chemically and histochemically. J. Histochem. (Abstr.), **2**, 478.

KARNOVSKY, M. L., AND DEANE, H. W. 1955. Aldehyde formation in the lipide droplets of the adrenal cortex during fixation, as demonstrated chemically and histochemically. J. Histochem., **3**, 85–102.

KREHBIEL, R. H. 1937. Cytological studies of the decidual reaction in the rat during early pregnancy and in the production of deciduomata. Physiol. Zool., **10**, 212–234.

KUTTNER, A., AND RATNER, B. 1923. The importance of colostrum to the newborn infant. Am. J. Dis. Child., **25**, 413–434.

LEBLOND, C. P. 1950. Distribution of periodic acid-reactive carbohydrates in the adult rat. Am. J. Anat., **86**, 1–49.

LEDUC, E. H., AND DEMPSEY, E. W. 1951. Activation and diffusion as factors influencing the reliability of the histochemical method for alkaline phosphatase. J. Anat., **85**, 305–314.

LEHNER, J. 1914. Dottersack der weissen Maus. Anat. Anz., **46**, 182–186.

LELL, W. A., LIBER, K. E., AND SNYDER, F. F. 1932. Quantitative study of placental transmission and the permeability of foetal membranes at various stages of pregnancy. Am. J. Physiol., **100**, 21–31.

LEVY, H., DEANE, H. W., AND RUBIN, B. L. 1959. Visualization of steroid-3β-ol dehydrogenase activity in tissues of intact and hypophysectomized rats. Endocrinology, **65**, 932–943.

LEWIS, W. H. 1924. Hofbauer cells (clasmatocytes) of the human chorionic villus. Bull. Johns Hopkins Hosp., **35**, 183–185.

LEWIS, W. H. 1931. Locomotion of lymphocytes. Bull. Johns Hopkins Hosp., **49**, 29–36.

LOCHHEAD, J., AND CRAMER, W. 1908. The glycogenic changes in the placenta and the foetus of the pregnant rabbit: a contribution to the chemistry of growth. Proc. Roy. Soc., London, ser. B, **80**, 263–284.

LOVELAND, G., MAURER, E. E., AND SNYDER, F. F. 1931. The diminution of the glycogen store of the rabbit's placenta during the last third of pregancy. Anat. Rec., **59**, 265–275.

LOW, F. N. 1953. Pulmonary alveolar epithelium of laboratory mammals and man. Anat. Rec., **117**, 241–263.

LUSE, S. A. 1957. The morphological manifestations of uptake of materials by the yolk sac of the pregnant rabbit. Macy Foundation Conferences on Gestation, **4**, 115–142.

LUSE, S., DAVIES, J., AND SMITH, M. 1959. Electron microscopy of experimental inclusions in cytoplasm and nuclei of yolk sac cells. Fed. Proc., **18**, 491.

LUSE, S., DAVIES, J., AND CLARK, S. L., JR. 1959. Electron microscopy of nuclear inclusions. Am. J. Path., **35**, 686.

MALL, F. P., AND MEYER, A. W. 1921. Hofbauer cells in normal and pathologic conceptuses. Contr. Embryol., Carnegie Inst. Washington, **12**, 301.

MARTIN, B. F., AND JACOBY, F. 1949. Diffusion phenomena complicating the histochemical reaction for alkaline phosphatase. J. Anat., **83**, 351–363

MAYERSBACH, H. 1958. Zur Frage des Proteinüberganges von der Mutter zum Foeten. I. Befunde an Rattan am Ende der Schwangerschaft. Ztschr. Zellforsch. mikroskop. Anat., **48**, 479–504.

McKAY, D. G., ADAMS, E. C., HERTIG, A. T., AND DANZIGER, S. 1955a. Histochemical horizons in human embryos. I. Five millimeter embryo —Streeter horizon XIII. Anat. Rec., **122**, 125–151.

McKAY, D. G., ADAMS, E. C., HERTIG, A. T., AND DANZIGER, S. 1955b. Histochemical horizons in human embryos. II. Six and seven millimeter embryos—Streeter horizon XIV. Anat. Rec., **126**, 433–463.

McMANUS, J. F. A. 1945. Granules of the human polymorphonuclear leucocyte. Nature, London, **156**, 173.

MICHAELIS, L. 1947. The nature of the interaction of nucleic acids and nuclei with basic dyestuffs. Cold Spring Harbor Symposia Quant. Biol., **12**, 131.

MITCHELL, A. J., AND WISLOCKI, G. B. 1944. Selective staining of glycogen by ammoniacal silver nitrate: a new method. Anat. Rec., **90**, 261–266.

MOOG, F., AND WENGER, E. L. 1952. The occurrence of a neutral mucopolysaccharide at sites of high alkaline phosphatase activity. Am. J. Anat., **90**, 339–377.

MOSSMAN, H. W. 1926. The rabbit placenta and the problem of placental transmission. Am. J. Anat., **37**, 433–497.

MOSSMAN, H. W. 1937. Comparative morphogenesis of the foetal membranes and accessory uterine structures. Contr. Embryol., Carnegie Inst. Washington, **26**, 129.

NACHLAS, M. M., AND SELIGMAN, A. M. 1949. The histochemical demonstration of esterase. J. Nat. Cancer Inst., **9**, 415–425.

NATAF, B. 1953. Evolution des activités phosphatasique alcaline et arginasique du placenta de Cobaye á différents stades de la gestation. Compt. rend Soc. biol., **147**, 1564–1565.

NEEDHAM, J. 1931. *Chemical Embryology*. Cambridge, England: The Macmillan Company.

NEUMANN, E. 1880. Die Picrocarminfärbung und ihre Anwendung auf die Entzundüngslehre. Arch. mikroskop. Anat., **18**, 130.

NEWTON, W. H. 1938. Hormones and the placenta. Physiol. Rev., **18**, 419–446.

NICANDER, L. 1951. The plasmal reaction of Feulgen and Voit with special reference to the adrenal body. Acta Anat., **12**, 174–197.

ORD, M. G., AND THOMPSON, R. H. S. 1950. Nature of placental cholinesterase. Nature, London, **165**, 927–928.

ORTMANN, R. 1949. Über Kernsekretion, Kolloid- und Vakuolenbildung in Beziehung zum Nukleinsäuregehalt in Trophoblast-riesenzellen der menschlichen Placenta. Ztschr. Zellforsch. mikrobiol. Anat., **34**, 562–583.

PADYKULA, H. A. 1952. The localization of succinic dehydrogenase in tissue sections of the rat. Am. J. Anat., **91**, 107–132.

PADYKULA, H. A., AND LEDUC, E. H. 1955. Études Histochimiques du foie prénatal et postnatal. VIᵉ Congrés Féderatif Internat. d'Anatomie, Paris.

PADYKULA, H. A. 1958a. A histochemical and quantitative study of enzymes of the rat's placenta. J. Anat., **92**, 118–129.

PADYKULA, H. A. 1958b. Histochemistry of the rat's placenta. In *Environmental Influences on Prenatal Development*, Beatrice Mintz, Ed., pp. 34–38. Chicago: University of Chicago Press.

PALADE, G. E. 1951. Intracellular localization of acid phosphatase. A comparative study of biochemical and histochemical methods. J. Exper. Med., **94**, 535.

PALADE, G., AND SIEKEVITZ, P. 1956. Liver microsomes. An integrated morphological and biochemical study. J. Biophys. Biochem. Cytol., **2**, 171–200.

PALAY, S. L., AND KARLIN, L. J. 1959a. An electron microscopic study of the intestinal villus. I. The fasting animal. J. Biophys. Biochem. Cytol., **5**, 363–372.

PALAY, S. L., AND KARLIN, L. J. 1959b. An electron microscopic study of the intestinal villus. II. The pathway of fat absorption. J. Biophys. Biochem, Cytol., **5**, 373–384.

PEASE, D. 1955. The fine structure of the kidney seen by the electron microscope. J. Histochem., **3**, 295–308.

PEARSE, A. G. 1949. The cytochemical demonstration of gonadotropic hormone in the human anterior hypophysis. J. Path. & Bact., **61**, 195–202.

PEARSE, A. G. E. 1960. *Histochemistry, Theoretical and Applied*. Boston: Little, Brown and Company.

POHL, H. A., AND FLEXNOR, L. B. 1941. Transfer of radioactive sodium across the placenta of the cat. J. Biol. Chem., **139**, 163.

POLLOCK, W. F. 1942. Histochemical studies of the interstitial cells of the testis. Anat. Rec., **84**, 23–29.

POPJAK, G. 1947. Synthesis of phospholipids in foetus. Nature, London, **160**, 841–842.

POPJAK, G., AND BEECKMANS, M. L. 1950. Are phospholipins transmitted through the placenta? Biochem. J., **46**, 99–103.

PRITCHARD, J. J. 1947. The distribution of alkaline phosphatase in the pregnant uterus of the rat. J. Anat., **81**, 352–364.

PURVES, H. D., AND GRIESBACH, W. E. 1951a. The site of thyrotrophin and gonadotrophin production in the rat pituitary studied by McManus-Hotchkiss staining for glycoprotein. Endocrinology, **49**, 244–264.

PURVES, H. D., AND GRIESBACH, W. E. 1951b. The significance of the Gomori staining of the basophiles of the rat pituitary. Endocrinology, **49**, 652–662.

RAMSEY, E. M. 1949. The vascular pattern of the endometrium of the pregnant rhesus monkey (*Macaca mulatta*). Contr. Embryol., Carnegie Inst. Washington, **33**, 113–147.

RAMSEY, E. M. 1954. Circulation in the maternal placenta of primates. Am. J. Obst. & Gynec., **67**, 1–14.

RATNER, B. 1943. The passage of native proteins through the placenta. In *Proceedings of the Conference on Problems of Human Fertility*, E. T. Engle, Ed., pp. 167–182. Menasha, Wisc.: Banta Publishing Company.

RATNER, B., JACKSON, H. C., AND GRUEHL, H. L. 1927. Transmission of protein hypersensitiveness from mother to offspring. I. Critique of placental permeability. J. Immunol., **14**, 249–265.

RAVIN, H. A., ZACKS, S. I., AND SELIGMAN, A. 1953. The histochemical localization of acetylcholinesterase in nervous tissue. J. Pharmacol. & Exper. Therap., **107**, 37–53.

REALE, E., AND PIPINO, G. 1957. Les variations de la répartition histochimique de la succinodéhydrogénase au cours de la placentation chorion-allantoidienne et vitelline étudiées dans le Mus musculus albinus. Compt. rend. A. Anat., XLIV, Réunion-Leyde.

REALE, E., AND PIPINO, G. 1959. La distribuzione della succinodeidrogenasi nella placenta di alcuni mammiferi. Studio istochimico. Arch. ital. Embriol., **64**, 318–356.

RECH, W. 1924. Untersuchungen über die Grösse der Zottenoberfläche der menschlichen Plazenta. Ztschr. Biol., **80**, 349–358.

ROCK, J., AND HERTIG, A. T. 1948. The human conceptus during the first two weeks of gestation. Am. J. Obst. & Gynec., **55**, 6–17.

ROCKENSCHAUB, A. 1952. Eigenfluoreszenze und

Hormonbildung in der Plazenta. Mikroskopie, **7**, 56.

RODOLFO, A. 1934. A study of the permeability of the placenta of the rabbit to antibodies. J. Exper. Zool., **68**, 215.

ROWLANDS, I. W. 1947. Anterior pituitary-like hormones. J. Endocrinol., **5**, xx–xxiii.

RUBIN, I. C. 1941. Two unusual cases of chorioepithelioma. Am. J. Obst. & Gynec., **41**, 1063–1068.

RUNNER, M. 1947. The development of mouse eggs in the anterior chamber of the eye. Anat. Rec., **98**, 1–17.

SCHÖNIG, A. 1929. Über den Kalktransport von Mutter und Kind und über Kalkablagerungen in der Plazenta. Ztschr. Geburtsh. Gynäk., **94**, 451–465.

SCHIEBLER, T. H., AND KNOOP, A. 1959. Histochemische und Elektronenmikroskopische Untersuchungen an der Rattenplazenta. Ztschr. Zellforsch., **50**, 494–552.

SCOTT, G. H. 1933. A critical study and review of the method of microincineration. Protoplasma, **20**, 133–151.

SELIGMAN, A. M., AND ASHBEL, R. 1951. Histochemical demonstration of ketosteroids in virilizing tumors of the adrenal cortex. Endocrinology, **49**, 110–126.

SELIGMAN, A. M., AND RUTENBURG, A. M. 1951. The histochemical demonstration of succinic dehydrogenase. Science, **113**, 317–320.

SELIGMAN, A. M., ASHBEL, R., AND COHEN, R. F. 1951. Histochemical demonstration of active carbonyl groups in normal and neoplastic tissues. J. Nat. Cancer. Inst., **12**, 226.

SENGUPTA, B. 1935. Plazenta in der Gewebekultur. Arch. exper. Zellforsch., **17**, 281.

SEVERINGHAUS, A. E. 1932. A cytological technique for the study of the anterior lobe of the hypophysis. Anat. Rec., **53**, 1–5.

SINGER, M. 1952. Factors which control the staining of tissue sections with acid and basic dyes. Internat. Rev. Cytol., **1**, 211–255.

SINGER, M., AND MORRISON, P. R. 1948. The influence of pH, dye and salt concentration on the dye binding of modified and unmodified fibrin. J. Biol. Chem., **175**, 133–145.

SINGER, M., AND WISLOCKI, G. B. 1948. The affinity of syncytium, fibrin and fibrinoid of the human placenta for acid and basic dyes under controlled conditions of staining. Anat. Rec., **102**, 175–193.

SMITH, G. V., AND SMITH, O. W. 1948. Internal secretions and toxemia of late pregnancy. Physiol. Rev., **28**, 1–22.

SNYDER, F. F. 1943. Placental transmission in relation to the stage of pregnancy. In *Proceedings of the Conference on Problems of Human Fertility*, E. T. Engle, Ed., pp. 144–157. Menasha, Wisc.: Banta Publishing Company.

SOKOLOFF, L., MUND, A., AND KANTOR, T. G. 1951. The affinity of fibrinoid substances for acid dyes. Am. J. Path., **27**, 1037–1045.

SPANNER, R. 1935a. Beitrag zur Kenntnis des Baues der Plazentarsepten, gleichzeitig ein

Versuch zur Deutung ihrer Enstehung. Morphol. Jahrb., **75**, 374.

SPANNER, R. 1935b. Mutterlicher und kindlicher Kreislauf der menschlichen Placenta und seine Strombahnen. Ztschr. Anat., **105**, 163–242.

SPANNER, R. 1940. Betrachtungen zum Placentakreislauf des Menschen. Zentralbl. Gynäk., **64**, 2002–2011.

STARCK, D. 1945–1950. Vergleichende Entwicklungeschichte der Wirbeltiere. Fortschr. Zool., **9**, 249–367.

STEWART, H. L., JR., SANO, M. E., AND MONTGOMERY, T. L. 1948. Hormone secretion by human placenta grown in tissue culture. J. Clin. Endocrinol., **8**, 175–188.

STIEVE, H. 1940. Die Entwicklung und der Bau der menschlichen Placenta. I. Zotten, Trophoblastinseln und Scheidewände in der ersten Hälfte der Schwangerschaft. Ztschr. mikro.-anat. Forsch., **48**, 287–358.

STIEVE, H. 1941. Bemerkungen uber den Blutkreislauf in der Placenta des Menschen. Zentralbl. Gynäk., **65**, 370.

STIEVE, H. 1944. Vergleichendanatomische Untersuchungen über das Zottenraumgitter in der Primatenplacenta. Ztschr. mikro.-anat. Forsch., **54**, 480–542.

STIEVE, H., AND VON DER HEIDE, I. 1941. Über die Entwicklung der Septen in der menschlichen Plazenta. Anat. Anz., **92**, 1–16.

SZENDI, B. 1933. Die Wege des Glykogens durch die hämochoriale Placenta. Ztschr. Anat., **101**, 791–798.

SZENDI, B. 1934. Experimentelle Studien über die entgiftende Funktion der Decidua. Arch. Gynäk., **157**, 389–399.

TELKKÄ, A., AND LEHTO, L. 1954. Histochemically demonstrable succinic dehydrogenase activity of placental tissues. Ann. Mëd. exper. Biol. Fenniae, **32**, 292–296.

TENNEY, B. 1936a. A clinical and pathological study of one hundred and fifty cases of tubal pregnancy. New England J. Med., **214**, 773–776.

TENNEY, B. 1936b. Syncytial degeneration in normal and pathologic placentas. Am. J. Obst. & Gynec., **31**, 1024–1028.

TENNEY, B., AND PARKER, F. 1939. Hydatidiform mole and chorionepithelioma. New England J. Med., **221**, 598–601.

TENNEY, B., AND PARKER, F. 1940. The placenta in toxemia of pregnancy. Am. J. Obst. & Gynec., **39**, 1000–1005.

TONUTTI, E., AND PLATE, E. 1937. Über das Vitamin C in der menschlichen Placenta. Arch. Gynäk., **164**, 385–397.

TORDA, C. 1942. Choline esterase content of tissues without innervation (the placenta). Proc. Soc. Exper. Biol. & Med., **51**, 398–400.

TUCHMANN-DUPLESSIS, H., AND BORTOLAMI, R. 1954. Les constituants histochimiques de l'allentoplacenta du lapin. Bull. Micro. Appl., **4**, 73–88.

VENNING, E. 1948. The excretion of various hormone metabolities in normal pregnancy. In *The Normal and Pathological Physiology of Pregnancy. Proceedings of the Conference of the Committee on Human Reproduction of the National Research Council,* Baltimore: The Williams & Wilkins Company.

VILLEE, C. A. 1953. Regulation of blood glucose in the human fetus. J. Appl. Physiol., **5**, 437.

WATANABE, H. 1923. Über die Lipoidsubstanzen der Placenta in verschiedenen Schwangerschaftsmonaten mit besonderer Berücksichtigung ihrer Mengenverhältnisse. J. Biochem. Tokyo, **2**, 369.

WEEKES, H. C. 1935. A review of placentation among reptiles with particular regard to function and evolution of the placenta. Proc. Zool. Soc., London, **2**, 625.

WEISS, L. P., AND FAWCETT, D. W. 1953. Cytochemical observations on chicken monocytes, macrophages and giant cells in tissue culture. J. Histochem. **1**, 47–65.

WEISS, L. P., TSOU, K. C., AND SELIGMAN, A. M. 1954. Histochemical demonstration of protein-bound amino groups. J. Histochem. **2**, 29–49.

WEN, I. C., CHANG, H. C., AND WONG, A. 1936. Studies on tissue acetylcholine in cytological considerations of the chorionic villous epithelium of the human placenta. Chinese J. Physiol., **10**, 559.

WIMSATT, W. A. 1948. The nature and distribution in the placenta of the bat (*Myotis lucifugus lucifugus*), with observations of the mitochondria and Golgi apparatus. Am. J. Anat., **82**, 393–467.

WIMSATT, W. A. 1949. Cytochemical observations on the fetal membranes and placenta of the bat, *Myotis lucifugus lucifugus*. Am. J. Anat., **84**, 63–141.

WIMSATT, W. A. 1950. New histological observations on the placenta of the sheep. Am. J. Anat., **87**, 391–457.

WIMSATT, W. A. 1951. Observations on the morphogenesis, cytochemistry and significance of the binucleate giant cells of the placenta of ruminants. Am. J. Anat., **89**, 233–281.

WIMSATT, W. A., AND WISLOCKI, G. B. 1947. The placentation of the American shrews, *Blarina brevicauda* and *Sorex fumeus*. Am. J. Anat., **80**, 361–435.

WISLOCKI, G. B. 1929. On the placentation of primates, with a consideration of the phylogeny of the placenta. Contr. Embryol., Carnegie Inst. Washington, **20**, 51.

WISLOCKI, G. B. 1950. Saliva-insoluble glycoproteins, stained by the periodic acid-Schiff procedure, in the placentas of pig, cat, mouse, rat and man. J. Nat. Cancer Inst., **10**, 1341.

WISLOCKI, G. B. 1951. The histology and cytochemistry of the basal plate and septa placentae of the normal human placenta delivered at full term. Anat Rec. (Abstr.), **109**, 359.

WISLOCKI, G. B. 1952. The Ashbel-Seligman reaction for carbonyl groups in the placentas of man and animals. Anat. Rec., **112**, 438.

WISLOCKI, G. B. 1953. Succinic dehydrogenase, esterases and protein-linked sulfhydryl groups in human placenta. Anat. Rec. (Abstr.), **115**, 380–381.

WISLOCKI, G. B. 1956. Morphological aspects of ageing in the placenta. Ciba Foundation Colloquia Ageing, **2,** 105–114.

WISLOCKI, G. B., AND BENNETT, H. S. 1943. The histology and cytology of the human and monkey placenta, with special reference to the trophoblast. Am. J. Anat., **73,** 335–449.

WISLOCKI, G. B., AND DEMPSEY, E. W. 1945. Histochemical reactions of the endometrium in pregnancy. Am. J. Anat., **77,** 365–403.

WISLOCKI, G. B., AND DEMPSEY, E. W. 1946a. Histochemical reactions in the placenta of the cat. Am. J. Anat., **78,** 1–45.

WISLOCKI, G. B., AND DEMPSEY, E. W. 1946b. Histochemical reactions of the placenta of the pig. Am. J. Anat., **78,** 181–225.

WISLOCKI, G. B., AND DEMPSEY, E. W. 1946c. Histochemical age-changes in normal and pathological placental villi hydatidiform mole, eclampsia). Endocrinology, **38,** 90–109.

WISLOCKI, G. B., AND DEMPSEY, F. W. 1948. The chemical histology of human placenta and decidua with reference to mucoproteins, glycogen, lipids and acid phosphatase. Am. J. Anat., **83,** 1–41.

WISLOCKI, G. B., AND DEMPSEY, E. W. 1955a. Electron microscopy of the human placenta. Anat. Rec., **123,** 133–167.

WISLOCKI, G. B., AND DEMPSEY, E. W. 1955b. Electron microscopy of the placenta of the rat. Anat. Rec., **123,** 33–63.

WISLOCKI, G. B., AND PADYKULA, H. A. 1953. Reichert's membrane and the yolk sac of the rat investigated by histochemical means. Am. J. Anat., **92,** 117–151.

WISLOCKI, G. B., AND STREETER, G. L. 1938. On the placentation of the macaque (*Macaca mulatta*), from the time of implantation until the formation of the definitive placenta. Contr. Embryol., Carnegie Inst. Washington, **27,** 1.

WISLOCKI, G. B., AND WIMSATT, W. A. 1947. Chemial cytology of the placenta to two North American shrews *(Blarina brevicauda* and *Sorex fumeus).* Am. J. Anat., **81,** 269–307.

WISLOCKI, G. B., BUNTING, H., AND DEMPSEY, E. W. 1947. Metachromasia in mammalian tissues and its relationship to mucopolysaccharides. Am. J. Anat., **81,** 1–37.

WISLOCKI, G. B., DEANE, H. W., AND DEMPSEY, E. W. 1946. The histochemistry of the rodent's placenta. Am. J. Anat., **78,** 281–345.

WISLOCKI, G. B., DEMPSEY, E. W., AND FAWCETT, D. W. 1948. Some functional activities of the placental trophoblast. Obst. & Gynec. Surv., **3,** 604–614.

WISLOCKI, G. B., WEISS, L. P., BURGOS, M. H., AND ELLIS, R. A. 1957. The cytology, histochemistry and electron microscopy of the granular cells of the metrial gland of the gravid rat. J. Anat., **91,** 130–140.

YAMADA, E. 1955. The fine structure of the renal glomerulus of the mouse. J. Biophys. Biochem. Cytol., **1,** 551–566.

ZANCLA, L. 1912. Contributo allo studio istochimico del ferro placentare. Folia Gynec., **6,** 297.

16

GESTATION[1]

M. X. Zarrow, Ph.D.

PROFESSOR OF ZOOLOGY, PURDUE UNIVERSITY, LAFAYETTE, INDIANA

I. Introduction

Reproduction in the animal kingdom is accomplished by a wide variety of methods, from simple budding and binary fission in the invertebrates to gestation in the mammal and the development of a new organ, the placenta. The development of viviparity, which covers millions of years of evolution, brought with it many new problems, and with each problem new factors came into play so that reproduction in the mammal is a highly co-ordinated series of events—a co-ordination that is both temporal and spatial, that requires certain events to occur in a proper sequential arrangement, and, above all, is dependent on the endocrine system.

It is obvious that the maintance of gestation in the mammal is a complex phenomenon. It involves directly or indirectly a major portion of the endocrine system with concomitant changes in the general metabolic state of the organism and in many of the enzymes present in the blood and the tissues. Finally, a new endocrine organ, the placenta, comes into being also to play its specific role in gestation.

II. Length of Gestation

The duration of gestation is highly variable and depends primarily on the species involved. In general, the longer the gestation, the more self-sufficient and mature are the young at the time of birth. It is obvious, however, that this is not true under all conditions. The young of the guinea pig are highly advanced at birth, although the length of gestation is approxi-

[1] Aided by grants from the Purdue Research Foundation.

mately 69 days, whereas in the primate, with a gestation period of 6 to 9 months, depending on the species, the young are helpless at birth. A partial summary of gestation length and the litter size of a representative but not inclusive list of mammals is presented in Table 16.1.

The length of gestation appears to be rather constant for each species or at least within a strain. Even where the phenomenon of delayed implantation is a natural event the length of pregnancy remains constant, although the quiescent period may vary. It is, however, possible for delayed implantation to occur in a species where this does not ordinarily appear, which could lead to a marked increase in the duration of gestation. Thus, an increase of 1 to 7 days has been reported in the rat or mouse if mated while lactating (Pincus, 1936). Recently, Bruce and East (1956) examined the effect of concurrent lactation on the number and viability of the young and the length of pregnancy in the mouse. They observed a wide variation in the delay of implantation for every size of litter studied, but, in general, the delay tended to be longer for the larger suckling litters.

Smith, Albert and Wilson (1951) reported a 310-day pregnancy period in a human female. Gestation was confirmed early by pregnancy tests and a normal child with respect to body weight was born at 30 days after the expected parturition. Such phenomena seem to be rare in primates and no explanation is possible at the present time.

Although the lengths of the gestation periods are quite constant for a given strain, the length of gestation is inversely related to the litter size. This has been demonstrated in both a genetically pure strain and a heterogeneous strain of quinea pigs (Goy, Hoar and Young, 1957). An average gestation length of 69.9 days was obtained in the pure strain of guinea pigs with a litter size of 1, as compared with a gestation length of 65.3 days for a litter size of 6.

A sex difference has also been postulated in length of gestation. Although the difference is very small, e.g., only a fraction of a day in man, the difference is signifi-

cant. Recently, McKeown and MacMahon (1956) concluded that pregnancy is longer in the cow, horse, and possibly the sheep and camel when the offspring are male, and longer in man and possibly the guinea pig when the offspring are female.

III. Normal Reproductive Potential

The reproductive potential in the primate is limited to the period from the menarche to the menopause. Hence, it is much shorter than the total life span of the female. Fertility studies as a function of age have been rather sparse for different species although it is generally agreed that fertility declines with age. A reproductive period considerably shorter than the life span of the animal has also been reported in certain strains of mice (Thung, Boot and Mühlbock, 1956) and in the rat (Ingram, Mandl and Zuckerman, 1958).

Although Slonaker (1928) showed that the rat may remain fertile for 22 months, it is known that the average size of successive litters in both rats and mice first rises to a maximum and then falls (King, 1924; Ingram, Mandl and Zuckerman, 1958). The latter have shown both a decrease in the number of fertile female rats with each successive litter and hence with age (Fig. 16.1) and a decline in the number of young with each successive litter (Fig. 16.2).

These results indicate that the reproductive potential of both the colony of rats and of the individual rat declines with age. Many factors may obviously be at work here, such as nutrition, size, and part played by the male. Ingram, Mandl and Zuckerman (1958) feel that none of the above factors is responsible for the decline in litter size and offer the following four possibilities: (1) the number of follicles which mature and ovulate declines with age, (2) the capacity of the ovum to be fertilized declines with age, (3) the number of fertilized ova that develop to term declines with age, and (4) the total number of available oocytes declines with age.

Evidence from the pig (Perry, 1954) and rat indicates that factors 2 and 3 are certainly involved. Inasmuch as the number of corpora lutea rises with age in the pig, the decline in size of litters can be

TABLE 16.1
Length of gestation and litter size in various species of mammals

Species		No. of Young	Length of Gestation	Reference[a]
Common name	Scientific name			
Armadillo	*Dasypus novemcinctus*, L.	4	150 days	(1), (2)
Baboon	*Papio hamadrys*, L.	1	183 days	(1)
Baboon, chacma	*Papio porcarius*, B.	1	7 months	(1), (2)
Bat, common European	*Vespertilio murinus*, L.	1	50 days	(1)
Bat, common pipistrello	*Pipistrellus pipistrellus*, S.	1	44 days	(3)
Bear, black	*Euarctos americanus*, P.	1–4	208 days	(1), (2)
Bush baby	*Galago senegalensis*, G.	1–2	4 months	(1)
Camel, batrachian	*Camelus bactrianus*, L.	1	370–440 days	(1)
Capuchin	*Cebus apella*, L.		160–170 days	(1)
Cat	*Felis catus*, L.	3.8 (1–8)	56–65 days	(4)
Cat, domestic	*Felis catus*, L.	4	63 days	(1)
Chimpanzee	*Pan satyrus*, L.	1	236.5 ± 13.3[b] days	(1)
Chimpanzee	*Pan satyrus*, L.	1–2	226.8 ± 13.3[b] days	(17)
Chinchilla	*Chinchilla laniger*, B.	1–4	105–111 days	(1), (2)
Chipmunk	*Tanarios striatus*, L.	3–5	31 days	(1)
Cow	*Bos taurus*, L.	1–2	277–290 days	(1)
Cow (Jersey)	*Bos taurus*, L.	1–2	282.7 ± 5.4[b] days	(5)
Cow (Holstein-Friesian)	*Bos taurus*, L.	1–2	278–280 days[c]	(6)
Coyote	*Canis latrans*, S.	5.7	60–65 days	(1)
Deer, Virginia	*Odocoileus virginianus*, B.	2	7 months	(1)
Dog	*Canis familiaris*, L.	Multiple	58–63 days	(1)
Dog	*Canis familiaris*, L.	Multiple	61 days	(4)
Echidna	*Echidna aculeata*	1	16–28 days	(1)
Elephant		1	20 months	(8)
Elephant, Indian	*Elephas maximus*, L.	1	607–641 days	(1)
Ferret	*Mustela furo*, L.	5–13	42 days	(1)
Ferret	*Mustela furo*, L.	5–13	42 days	(4)
Fox, red	*Vulpes fulfa*, D.	1–8	52 days	(1)
Goat	*Capra hircus*, L.	1–2	21 weeks	(7)
Goat, domestic	*Capra hircus*, L.	1–3	146–151 days	(1)
Gopher, pocket	*Geomys bursarius*, S.	1–6		(1)
Ground squirrel, thirteen-lined	*Citellus tridecimlineatus*, N.	5–13	28 days	(1)
Guinea pig	*Cavia porcellus*, L.	1–6	67–68 days	(1)
Guinea pig	*Cavia porcellus*, L.		65.3–70.5 days	(7)
Hamster, golden	*Cricetus auratus*, H.		16–19 days	(1)
Hamster, golden	*Cricetus auratus*, H.	5	16 days	(9)
Hare, snowshow	*Lepus americanus*, E.	1–7	38 days	(1)
Hedgehog, European	*Erinoceus europaeus*, L.	5	34–49 days	(1)
Hippopotamus	*Hippopotamus amphibius*, L.	1	237 ± 12 days	(1)
Horse	*Equus caballus*, L.	1	330 days	(1)
Hyena, spotted	*Crocuta crocuta*, E.	1–2	110 days	(1)
Kangaroo rat	*Bettongia cuniculus*, O.	1	6 weeks	(1)
Lemur	*Lemur macaco*, L.	1–2	146 days	(1)
Lion	*Felis leo*, L.	2–6	105–113 days	(1)
Macaque	*Macaca mulatta*, Z.	1	163.7 ± 8 days	(1), (10)
Macaque		1	24 weeks	(8)
Man	*Homo sapiens*, L.	1	280 ± 9.2 days	(1)
Marmoset	*Hopale jacchus*, L.	1–3	140–50 days	(1)
Marten, pine	*Martes americana*, T.	3–5	220–265 days	(1)
Mink	*Mustela vison*, S.	4–10	39–76 days	(1)
Mink	*Mustela vison*	4	51 days[d] (40–75)	(11), (12)
Mole, common American	*Scalopus aquaticus*, L.	2–5	6 weeks	(1)
Mouse	*Mus musculus*, L.		19–20 days	(4)
Mouse, field	*Microtus pennsylvanicus*, O.	6–8		(1)
Mouse, house	*Mus musculus*, L.	4–5–7.5	19 days	(1)
Mouse, wild	*Peromyscus maniculatus*		23 days	(13)
Mouse, wood	*Peromyscus leucopus*, L.	3–7	23 days	(1)

TABLE 16.1—*Continued*

Species		No. of Young	Length of Gestation	Reference[a]
Common name	Scientific name			
Opossum, Australian	*Trichosurus vulpecula*, K.	1	16 days	(1)
Opossum, Virginia	*Didelphis virginiana*, K.	8–12	12.5–13 days	(1), (2), (8)
Otter	*Lutra canadensis*, S.	1–4	60 days	(1)
Pig, domestic	*Sus scrofa*, L.	4–12	112–115 days	(1)
Pig, wild	*Sus cristatus*, W.	4–6	4 months	(1)
Porcupine	*Erethizon dorsatum*, L.	1	16 weeks	(1)
Puma	*Felis concolor*, T.	1–4	90–93 days	(1)
Rabbit, domestic	*Crycotalagus cuniculus*, L.	Multiple	30–32 days	(1)
Rabbit, domestic	*Crycotalagus cuniculus*, L.	Multiple	31 (28–36 days)	(1)
Racoon	*Procyon lotor*, L.	1–6	63 days	(1)
Rat	*Rattus rattus*, L.	6.1–9.2[c]	22 days	(1)
Rat	*Rattus rattus*, L.		21–23 days	(4)
Reindeer	*Rangifer tarandus*, L.	1–2	7–8 months	(1)
Rhinoceros		1	18 months	(8)
Rhinoceros, black	*Rhinocerus bicornuis*, L.	1	530–550 days	(1)
Seal, northern fur	*Callorhinus ursinus*, L.	1	Almost 1 year	(1)
Sheep, bighorn	*Ovis canadensis*, L.	1	180 days	(1)
Sheep, domestic	*Ovis aries*, L.	1–2	144–152 days[c]	(1)
Shrew, common	*Sorex aranus*, L.	6.45	13–19 days	(1)
Shrew, short-tailed	*Blarina brevicauda*, S.	3–7	17–20 days	(1)
Skunk	*Mephitis mephitis*, S.	4–7	62 days	(1)
Squirrel, red	*Sciurus hudsonicus*, E.	3–6	40 days	(1)
Stoat	*Mustela musleta*		6 weeks[d]	(14)
Tasmanian devil	*Sarcophilus ursinus*, K.	4	31 days	(1)
Vole	*Microtus agrestis*		20–22 days	(16)
Weasel	*Mustela nivalis*	6–7	50 weeks[d] (includes) lactation)	(15)
Whale, sperm	*Physeter catadon*, L.	1	1 year	(1)
Wolf, timber	*Canis lycoon*, S.	1–12	63 days	(1)
Woodchuck	*Marmota monox*, L.	4.07	28 days	(1)
Zebu	*Bos indicus*, L.		285 days	(1)

[a] References. (1) Asdell, 1946. (2) Kenneth, 1947. (3) Deanesly and Warwick, 1939. (4) **Farris**, 1950. (5) Rollins, Laben and Mead, 1956. (6) Norton, 1956. (7) Goy, Hoar and Young, 1957. (8) Arey, 1946. (9) Selle, 1945. (10) Hartman, 1932. (11) Pearson and Enders, 1944. (12) Enders, 1952. (13) Svihla, 1932. (14) Deanesly, 1943. (15) Deanesly, 1944. (16) Chitty, 1957. (17) Peacock and Rogers, 1959.

[b] Standard deviation.

[c] Depends on the strain.

[d] Excluding the quiescent period.

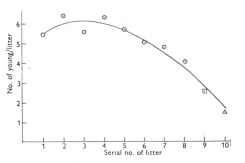

FIG. 16.1. Decline in litter size with birth of successive litters. ● mean of 35 litters; ☐ mean of 14 litters; △ mean of 4 litters. (From D. L. Ingram, A. M. Mandl and S. Zuckerman, J. Endocrinol., **17**, 280, 1958.)

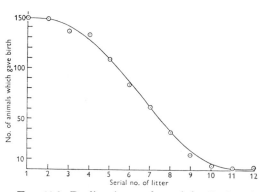

FIG. 16.2. Decline in number of fertile female rats with birth of successive litters. (From D. L. Ingram, A. M. Mandl and S. Zuckerman, J. Endocrinol., **17**, 280, 1958.)

attributed only to failure of fertilization or to fetal death. A similar increased incidence of embryonic death or failure of fertilization has been described in the aged rat, although it should be noted that the number of corpora lutea present at parturition in the rat is not an index of the number of ova released before conception because the corpora lutea in old age may persist for longer periods. Finally, a marked reduction in the number of oocytes with age has been shown in the rat, a drop from approximately 20,000 oocytes at age day 1 to approximately 2000 oocytes at age 250 to 300 days (Mandl and Zuckerman, 1951). In addition, Ingram (1958) showed that the litter size in rats declined markedly with the reduction in number of oocytes following graded doses of x-ray. This experiment tends to confirm the concept that the decline in fertility with age is due to a decline in the number of oocytes.

IV. Environment

A. CROWDING

The factors concerned in the growth and survival of a population under natural conditions may obviously involve reproduction. Variations in population level have been of great interest to the mammalogist and student of wildlife for many years. Decreased productivity in mammalian populations associated with increased density of the population has been considered a controlling factor in the regulation of wildlife population.

Experimental analysis by Christian and Lemunyan (1958) indicated that a number of factors are involved. These authors exposed mice to excessive crowding and noted the number of implantation sites, embryos, and births. All the females became pregnant but only 3 of the 10 bore litters during the period of crowding or later (Table 16.2). It would seem that the crowded females were unable to maintain normal pregnancies and that the environmental situation interfered with the endocrine balance and resulted in a marked pregnancy wastage. The data reveal that in addition to a postimplantation loss, there was also a pre-implantation loss because the number of implantation scars in the uterus was markedly less in the crowded females. This could be due to a failure of the fertilized egg to implant or to a decrease in the number of available ova. Although direct data are not available, it is of interest to speculate as to whether this effect of crowding is mediated by way of the pituitary-adrenocortical axis.

B. BODY TEMPERATURE AND HYPOXIA

Disturbances in reproduction have been noted in mammals exposed to high temperatures or chronic hypoxia. It has been known for some time that women moving to the tropics show a high rate of abortion (Castellani and Chalmers, 1919). Recently Macfarlane, Pennyamt and Thrifte (1957) reported a 30 per cent reduction in human conception rates in the summer as compared with the winter in Australia. The same authors reported a marked degree of fetal resorption in rats exposed to a temperature of 35°C. This confirmed the previous observations of Sundstroem (1927) in rats and Oegle (1934) in mice where exposure to 31°C. caused a reduction in litter size.

In a similar manner, disturbances have also been reported in reproduction following exposure to decreased oxygen tension.

TABLE 16.2

Productivity of mice crowded 10 pairs to a cage compared to their 10 control pairs

Note that all of the females became pregnant but that the crowded females exhibited a marked intra-uterine loss of young, reduction of implantation sites, reduction of litter size, and significant delay until the birth of first litters compared to the controls. Crowding produced a 75 per cent loss in the number of young born. (From J. J. Christian and C. D. Lemunyan, Endocrinology, **63**, 517, 1958.)

	No. of Pairs	No. of Litters Born	Mean No. Days to Litter Birth	Mean No. Progeny per Litter ± S.E.	No. Females with Placental Scars	Mean No. Scars per Female
Crowded females......	10	3	40 ± 1.0	7.67 ± 0.33	10	6.90 ± 1.37
Isolated females.......	10	10	26 ± 1.5	9.00 ± 0.75	10	11.00 ± 0.47

Monge (1942) reported a lack of reproduction in the Spaniards for more than 50 years after residence in certain areas of Bolivia (14,000 feet or more above sea level). Many malformations have also been observed in the progency of mice, rats, and rabbits exposed to low atmosperic pressures. Exposure of mice on the 10th day of pregnancy for 2 hours to a 6 per cent oxygen-94 per cent nitrogen mixture at normal atmospheric pressure gave malformations in the young comparable with those found after exposure to a low atmospheric pressure which was equivalent to the above with respect to the number of oxygen molecules per unit of air (Curley and Ingalls, 1957). Although these malformations involved the ribs and vertebrae, it is conceivable that more extensive malformations could result in death of the fetuses leading to resorption or abortion of the young.

Vidovic (1952, 1956) made a very complete study of the effect of lowered body temperature on gestation in the rat using the technique of Giaja (1940) in which an hypoxic hypothermia is induced by cooling under reduced oxygen tension. The animal is placed in a sealed container which is surrounded by ice for a period of approximately 10 hours. Under these conditions a hypothermia of 3 to 4 hours' duration and body temperature of 14 to 18°C. can be induced. No deleterious effects were noted in the rats cooled on or before the 13th day of pregnancy. However, the induction of hypothermia after the 13th day resulted in a marked increase in the disturbance of gestation. These disturbances consisted of an increased number of resorbed fetuses, an increased ratio between stillborn and live young in that more stillborn occurred, a decreased body weight in the progeny, and a delay in the onset of parturition. In addition, a marked increase in sensitivity to hypothermia was noted in the animals as pregnancy progressed. Courrier and Marois (1953) cooled pregnant rats by exposure to a temperature of 0°C. for 2 hours. Thereafter the rats were placed in cold water for 3 to 4 hours and a body temperature of 15.5 to 17°C. was obtained. Exposure to the above treatment on the 7th to the 11th day of preg-

nancy had no effect on the fetuses or the pregnancy. Treatment on the 12th to the 18th day of pregnancy led to resorption and abortion of the young. The authors concluded that the degree of deleterious effects following exposure to cold varied with the length of the pregnancy.

Recently, Fernandez-Cano (1958a) exposed pregnant rats for 5 hours on 2 consecutive days to one of the following three experimental procedures: (1) an environmental temperature of 103°F. that led to an increase in body temperature to 104°F.; (2) an environmental temperature of 26°F. that led to a decrease in body temperature to 94°F.; and (3) barometric pressure of 410 mm. Hg. Both temperature changes led to a marked decrease in the number of implantations and, to a lesser extent, to some embryonic degeneration after implantation (Table 16.3). Although some deleterious action was seen before implantation, hypoxia was more harmful after implantation. Whereas these results are not in full agreement with Vidovic's report, it must be remembered that Vidovic used a combination of cold and hypoxia to induce the effects that he observed. Adrenalectomy failed to increase embryonic degenerations in rats treated as above (Fernandez-Cano, 1958b). Inasmuch as adrenocorticotrophic hormone (ACTH) causes degeneration of the embryos in intact pregnant rats and not in adrenalectomized rats (Velardo, 1957), it is apparent that these results are explainable on the basis of an increased release of adrenal corticoids due to the stressor and/or a direct action of the corticoids on the development of the embryo.

V. Maternal Hormone Levels during Gestation

Proof that certain hormones are necessary for a successful pregnancy came from evidence involving ablation of the source of the hormone and replacement therapy. This was followed by quantitative analyses of the concentration of the hormone in the blood and urine throughout gestation. The increasing concentrations of the hormones as pregnancy advances can be used as a second argument for the role of hormones in the development and maintenance of pregnancy (Zarrow, 1957). Changes of this

TABLE 16.3

The effect of increase or decrease of body temperature and hypoxia on the pregnancy of the rat
(From L. Fernandez-Cano, Fertil. & Steril., **9**, 45, 1958.)

| Group | Days of Treatment | No. Rats | Total No. Corpora Lutea | Percentage of Degeneration | | | Means of Degeneration for Each Rat | Standard Error | Percentage against Control |
				Before implantation	After implantation	Total degeneration			
Control....................		16	166	2.4	0	2.4	0.2	0.11	
High body temperature.....	1–2	8	98	52	12	64	8.3	1.6	>0.01
High body temperature.....	3–4	8	117	28	3	31	4.6	2.6	>0.01
High body temperature.....	6–7	8	95	2	14	16	1.9	0.5	>0.01
High body temperature.....	10–11	8	89	2	10	12	1.3	1.8	>0.01
Low body temperature......	1–2	8	93	25	5	30	3.5	1.0	>0.01
Low body temperature......	3–4	8	98	33	4	37	4.5	1.4	>0.01
Low body temperature......	6–7	8	100	3	13	16	2.0	0.2	>0.01
Low body temperature......	10–11	8	91	2.1	12.1	14.2	1.6	0.5	>0.01
Hypoxia....................	1–2	8	103	21.3	2.9	24.2	3.1	0.4	>0.01
Hypoxia....................	3–4	8	108	25.9	3.7	29.6	3.8	0.3	>0.01
Hypoxia....................	6–7	8	97	0	25.7	25.7	3.1	1.0	>0.01
Hypoxia....................	10–11	8	94	2.1	65.9	68.0	8.0	1.4	>0.01

kind have been observed for such steroids as the estrogens, gestagens, and the 17-α-hydroxycorticoids. In addition, certain nonsteroidal hormones such as the gonadotrophins human chorionic gonadotrophin (HCG) and pregnant mare's serum (PMS) and the polypeptide, relaxin, increase during gestation. Some evidence for a possible involvement of thyroxine, prolactin, and oxytocin will be included. The maximal concentration of these hormones in the blood of the female during pregnancy is given in Table 16.4.

A. ESTROGENS

The fact that large amounts of estrogen are excreted in the urine of pregnant women and mares has been known for a long time. Additional data (reviewed by Newton, 1939) indicate that this phenomenon occurs in all species studied, such as the chimpanzee, the macaque, the cow, the pig, and the rat. In general, an increasing amount of estrogen is excreted as pregnancy progresses. The estrogenic material in the urine of the pregnant woman appears mostly in the form of estriol with lesser amounts of estrone and estradiol (Fig. 16.3). The estriol concentration increases only slightly in the urine of women for the first 100 to 125 days of pregnancy, but thereafter it increases very rapidly until parturition. Newton (1939) discussed the possible

role of estrogen in pregnancy in great detail. He first asked whether the increased urinary concentration of estrogen indicates that this hormone is acting to a lesser degree as pregnancy advances or to a greater degree. He marshaled his facts pro and con and came to the conclusion that there is an increased production of estrogen throughout pregnancy and hence an increased activity of the hormone. In his analysis of the action of estrogen, five possibilities were suggested. (1) Estrogen is involved in the growth of the uterus in pregnancy. (2) Estrogen is involved in the increased uterine contractility and sensitivity to oxytocin necessary for parturition. (3) Estrogen is concerned with the continued secretion of progesterone by way of the pituitary gland or acting directly on the corpus luteum. (4) Estrogen synergizes with progesterone. (5) Estrogen stimulates mammary gland growth. A 6th possibility is that estrogen reverses the progesterone block (Csapo, 1956a). Several of these possibilities will be considered later in conjunction with progesterone, the maintenance of pregnancy, and parturition.

B. GESTAGENS

The significance of the role of progesterone during pregnancy stemmed from the historic work of Fraenkel who proved the validity of Gustav Born's suggestion that

TABLE 16.4

Maximal hormone levels in the blood during pregnancy

Hormone	Species	Type of Assay	Hormone Amt /ml. Plasma	Reference
Estriol	Man	Chem.	0.0914 µg.	Aitkin and Preedy, 1957
Estriol	Man	Chem.	0.066 µg.	Loraine, 1957
Estrone	Man	Chem.	0.0647 µg.	Aitkin and Preedy, 1957
Estrone	Man	Chem.	0.0305 µg.	Loraine, 1957
Estradiol	Man	Chem.	0.0144 µg.	Aitkin and Preedy, 1957
Estradiol	Man	Chem.	0.0105 µg.	Loraine, 1957
Gestagen	Rabbit	Biol.	10 µg.[a]	Zarrow and Neher, 1955
Gestagen	Mouse	Biol.	8 µg.[a]	Forbes and Hooker, 1957
Gestagen	Ewe	Biol.	12 µg.[a]	Neher and Zarrow, 1954
Progesterone	Ewe	Chem.	0.0033 µg.	Short, 1957
Progesterone	Ewe (ovarian vein	Chem.	2 µg.	Edgar and Ronaldson, 1958
Progesterone	Cow	Chem.	0.0086 µg.	Short, 1958b
Gestagen	Man	Biol.	2 µg.[a]	Forbes, 1951
Gestagen	Man	Biol.	25 µg.[a]	Fujii, Hoshino, Aoki and Yao, 1956
Progesterone	Man	Chem.	0.239 µg.	Oertel, Weiss and Eik Nes, 1959
Progesterone	Man	Chem.	0.142 µg.	Zander and Simmer, 1954
Progesterone	Sow	Chem.	0.0034 µg.	Short, 1957
Progesterone	Goat	Chem.	0.0071 µg.	Short, 1957
Relaxin	Guinea pig	Biol.	0.5 G.P.U.[b]	Zarrow, 1947a
Relaxin	Rabbit	Biol.	10 G.P.U.[b]	Marder and Money, 1944
Relaxin	Man	Biol.	2 G.P.U.[b]	Zarrow, Holmstrom and Salhanick, 1955
Relaxin	Sow	Biol.	2 G.P.U.[b]	Hisaw and Zarrow, 1951
Relaxin	Cow	Biol.	4 G.P.U.[b]	Wada and Yuhara, 1955
Hydrocortisone	Man	Chem.	0.22 µg.	Gemzell, 1953
Thyroxine	Man	Chem.	0.83 µg.[c]	Peters, Man and Heinemann, 1948
STH	Rat	Biol.	3.5–7[d]	Contopoulos and Simpson, 1957
HCG	Man	Biol.	120 I.U.	Haskins and Sherman, 1952
HCG	Man	Biol.	70 I.U.	Wilson, Albert and Randall, 1949
PMS	Horse	Biol.	50 I.U.	Cole and Saunders, 1935

[a] Expressed as equivalents of progesterone.

[b] Guinea pig units.

[c] Protein-bound iodine.

[d] µg. equivalent of a purified bovine growth-promoting substance.

the corpus luteum is necessary for the maintenance of pregnancy. Fraenkel demonstrated at the turn of the century that the corpus luteum of the rabbit is essential for the maintenance of pregnancy in the rabbit (Fraenkel and Cohn, 1901; Fraenkel, 1903; Fraenkel, 1910). These observations were confirmed by Hammond and Marshall (1925) who found that castration before the 20th day of pregnancy led to the termination of pregnancy in 24 hours. Castration later in pregnancy resulted in abortion approximately 2 days after the operation. In 1928, Corner showed that an extract of the corpus luteum could induce a progestational endometrium in the castrated rabbit. This was soon followed by the demonstration that this extract could induce implantation of the fertilized egg in the rabbit and maintain pregnancy in the castrated animal (Allen and Corner, 1929; 1930). Purification of the extract of the corpus luteum led to the chemical identification of the active substance by Butenandt, Westphal and Cobler in 1934, and in the following year Allen, Butenandt, Corner and Slotta (1935) agreed to the name progesterone for this hormone of the corpus luteum.

These events were soon followed by the discovery that progesterone is excreted in the urine as the glucuronide of pregnanediol and pregnanolone, metabolites of progesterone. Studies of urinary products of progesterone were immediately undertaken and a marked increase in urinary pregnanediol was observed in the human female throughout pregnancy, especially in the second half (Fig. 16.3).

The discovery by Hooker and Forbes (1947) of a new assay for progesterone sensitive to a concentration of 0.3 μg. per ml. led to many studies on the blood levels of this hormone during gestation. Subsequent studies revealed a lack of specificity for the assay (Zarrow, Neher, Lazo-Wasem and Salhanick, 1957; Zander, Forbes, von Münstermann and Neher, 1958) and a discrepancy between the values obtained by chemical and biologic techniques. It is obvious that the bioassay data possess significance but a final evaluation can be made only when the identity of the compound or compounds measured in the blood of the animals by the Hooker-Forbes test has been established.

The concentration of gestagen in the blood of pregnant sheep (Neher and Zarrow, 1954), women (Forbes, 1951; Schultz, 1953; Fujii, Hoshino, Aoki and Yao, 1956), rabbits (Zarrow and Neher, 1955), and mice (Forbes and Hooker, 1957) has been determined by the Hooker-Forbes test and

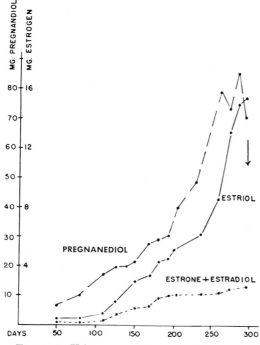

FIG. 16.3. Urinary excretion of estrogens and pregnanediol throughout gestation in the human being. (From E. Venning, Macy Foundation, Conferences on Gestation, **3,** 1957.)

expressed as μg. equivalents of progesterone. The data obtained from pregnant women by the different investigators are in marked disagreement. Whereas both Forbes (1951) and Schultz (1953) failed to observe any significant rise in blood gestagen of pregnant women throughout gestagen, Fujii, Hoshino, Aoki and Yao (1956) obtained a conspicuous rise during this period. The data reported by Forbes (1951) indicate an extremely low level for protein-bound progesterone (0.5 μg. per ml. plasma or less) and a maximum of 2 μg. per ml. free progesterone (Fig. 16.4). The concentration of the hormone in the blood showed a series of irregular peaks throughout gestation and varied from less than 0.3 μg. to 2 μg. per ml. plasma. In general, these results were confirmed by Schultz (1953) who assayed the blood from 46 women at 6 to 17 weeks of pregnancy. Again the results failed to reveal any consistent change with the length of pregnancy. Both investigators (Forbes, 1951; Schultz, 1953) were led to question the importance of progesterone during gestation in the primate. Fujii, Hoshino, Aoki and Yao (1956), on the other hand, reported a significant increase in the level of circulating progesterone throughout gestation. Again these investigators used the Hooker-Forbes assay but indicated that the plasma was not treated in any way except for dilution before the assay. The results obtained by this latter group revealed a rise from a level of 6 μg. progesterone per ml. plasma during the luteal phase of the cycle to a high of 25 μg. during the last trimester of pregnancy (Fig. 16.5). The concentration showed a steady increase from the 4th to the 24th week of pregnancy, and a plateau from the 24th week until term. A sharp drop occurred within 12 to 24 hours after parturition with zero values noted by 72 hours postpartum. Analysis of the urine for pregnanediol showed a rather good correlation between the two curves although the plasma levels rose sooner than the urinary pregnanediol.

The curve for the concentration of progesterone in the pregnant mouse is markedly different from those reported for other species (Forbes and Hooker, 1957). Again the Hooker-Forbes assay was used

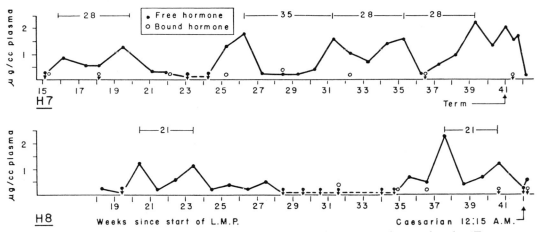

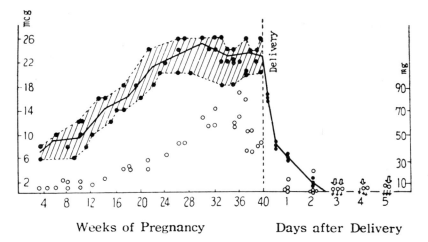

Fig. 16.4. Free and bound gestagen in the plasma of the pregnant human female. (From T. R. Forbes, Endocrinology, **49**, 218, 1951.)

Fig. 16.5. Concentration of gestagen in the blood plasma and pregnanediol in the uterine of the pregnant human female. Gestagen levels were determined by the Hooker-Forbes test. (From K. Fujii, K. Hoshino, I. Aoki and J. Yao, Bull. Tokyo Med. & Dent. Univ., **3**, 225, 1956.)

as with the other species and the values expressed as activity equivalent to progesterone. The values for the bound action were consistently low and, in general, less than 1 μg. per ml. plasma (Fig. 16.6). The concentration of the free hormone showed marked variations on the first day or so of pregnancy. Actually a variation from 1 μg. per ml. plasma to 8 μg. per ml. plasma was seen on day 0. This type of fluctuation has also been seen in the rabbit and is without explanation at the present time. However, such marked variations disappeared by the 4th day of pregnancy and the results became much more consistent. The average

curve for the concentration of gestagen in the blood of the pregnant mouse showed two peaks, one the 7th to the 9th day and a second the 15th day. The concentration increased from 2 μg. per ml. plasma the 4th day of gestation to an average of approximately 8 μg. the 7th day. This level was maintained until day 9 and fell thereafter with a second peak occurring on day 15 and an immediate drop on day 16. Thereafter the levels remained low throughout the remainder of pregnancy.

Although it may be assumed that the initial peak in the concentration of the gestagen is due to an increased activity

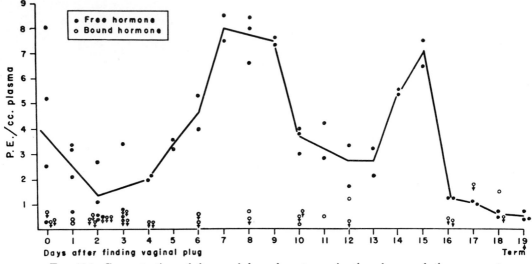

F<small>IG</small>. 16.6. Concentration of free and bound gestagen in the plasma of the pregnant mouse. Gestagen levels were determined by the Hooker-Forbes test. (From T. R. Forbes and C. W. Hooker, Endocrinology, **61**, 281, 1957.)

on the part of the corpora lutea, an explanation of the second peak and the drop between the two peaks offers more difficulty. The latter may reflect a diminished luteal activity. This could be assumed on the grounds that the corpus luteum is the only source of gestagen during this period of gestation and that the luteal cells show cytologic signs of regressive changes, although the drop in serum progestogen antidates the cytologic changes by several days. An explanation for the second peak would probably involve increased secretory activity by the placenta. Progestational activity has been found in placental extracts and progesterone has been isolated from the placentae of human beings and mares (Salhanick, Noall, Zarrow and Samuels, 1952; Pearlman and Cerceo, 1952; Zander, 1954; Short, 1956). Thus, the drop in serum gestagen seen on day 10 could be due to loss in the activity of the corpora lutea and the second rise as a contribution from the placentas. It is of interest that the low levels on days 10 to 13 and between day 16 to term appear to have no counterpart in other species. The physiologic significance of this is still unknown and will require further work on additional species and on the mouse before an explanation is forthcoming. It is of interest that the concentration of gestation in the blood dur-

ing the first 12 days of pregnancy corresponds with the intensity of the response to progesterone exhibited by the endometrium during the same period (Atkinson and Hooker, 1945). This would suggest that the serum gestagen levels reflect the physiologic state of the animal.

Serum gestagen levels in the rabbit reveal a curve of increasing concentration throughout pregnancy (Zarrow and Neher, 1955). Initial values of 0.3 to 1 μg. per ml. serum were noted at the time of mating, with a sharp rise beginning on the 4th day of gestation. The concentration rose to a level of 6 to 8 μg. per ml. by the 12th day and thereafter showed only a slight rise to a maximal concentration of 8 to 10 μg. per ml. serum at parturition (Fig. 16.7). No drop in serum hormone level was observable at parturition or 1 hour later. The first significant drop occurred at 6 to 12 hours postpartum when the gestagen level had decreased 50 per cent. It is of interest that the serum progestagen levels did not fall until after the conceptus had been expelled.

Pregnant rabbits castrated the 12th, 19th, or 24th day of gestation aborted within 1 to 3 days following removal of the ovaries (Zarrow and Neher, 1955). In all instances the serum gestagen levels fell before the abortion. Figure 16.8 shows the

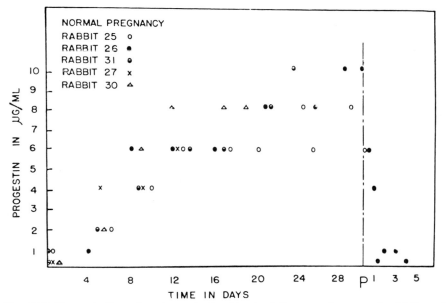

Fig. 16.7. Concentration of gestagen in the blood of the normal pregnant rabbit as determined by the Hooker-Forbes test. (From M. X. Zarrow and G. M. Neher, Endocrinology, **56**, 1, 1955.)

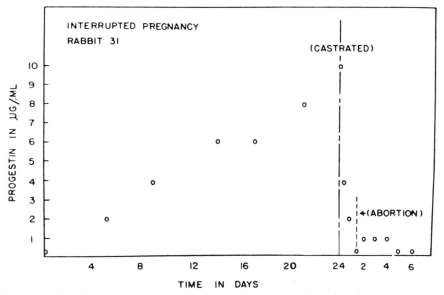

Fig. 16.8. The effect of castration on serum progestogen levels and maintenance of gestation in the rabbit. Gestagen levels were determined by the Hooker-Forbes test. (From M. X. Zarrow and G. M. Neher, Endocrinology, **56**, 1, 1955.)

changes in serum gestagen levels before and after castration of a pregnant rabbit. The concentration increased from a level of 0.3 μg. per ml. at day 0 to 10 μg. per ml. on day 24 when the rabbit was castrated. A 60 per cent drop in serum gestagen level is seen 12 hours after castration with a further drop at the 36th hour, when the animal aborted.

Studies on the concentration of serum gestagen in the pregnant ewe (Neher and Zarrow, 1954) permit a comparison with the results obtained in the rabbit. Such a comparison is extremely valuable in view

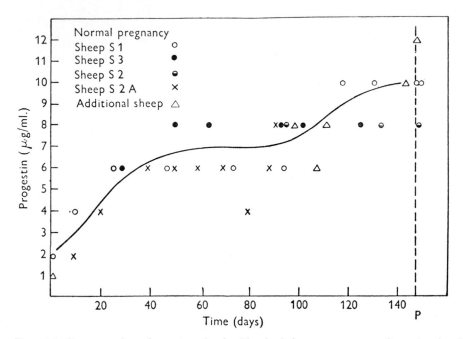

Fig. 16.9. Concentration of gestagen in the blood of the pregnant ewe. Gestation levels were determined by the Hooker-Forbes test. (From G. M. Neher and M. X. Zarrow, J. Endocrinol., **11**, 323, 1954.)

of the fact that castration of the rabbit invariably leads to abortion whereas castration of the pregnant ewe does not do so if the ovaries are removed during the second half of pregnancy. Again the progesterone determinations were carried out on untreated serum and the samples assayed by the Hooker-Forbes technique using progesterone as a standard. An initial rise in the serum gestagen level occurred soon after mating and seemed to level off at a concentration of 6 μg. per ml. approximately the 50th day of gestation (Fig. 16.9). Thereafter, the concentration remained unchanged for approximately 50 days, when a second rise to a level of 8 to 12 μg. occurred. These levels remained unchanged until at least 30 minutes after parturition was complete.

Castration at various times after the 66th day of pregnancy failed to influence the concentration of circulating gestagen or interfere with the pregnancy. The data in Figure 16.10 show a normal concentration of 8 to 10 μg. gestagen from the 114th day of gestation to parturition although the animal was ovariectomized the 114th day. Pregnancy was normal in all castrated

ewes and the expected drop in serum gestagen was observed following parturition.

It can now be stated that the human being, the monkey, the ewe, the rabbit, the mouse, and probably the guinea pig (Herrick, 1928; Ford, Webster and Young, 1951) have met the problem of a second source of progesterone supply with varying degrees of success. In the ewe, placental replacement of the ovary as a source of progesterone can be considered as complete by approximately the 66th day of pregnancy. Castration at this time will neither interfere with the pregnancy nor with the concentration of the hormone in the blood. In the monkey, castration as early as the 25th day of gestation (Hartman, 1941) does not interfere with pregnancy and in the human being castration as early as the 41st day after the last menstrual period may not interfere with pregnancy (Melinkoff, 1950; Tulsky and Koff, 1957). One may conclude, therefore, that the placenta can adequately take on the role of the ovary in this regard. On the other hand, aspects of the situation in the human female are still puzzling, especially the blood gestagen values; but despite this ambiguity

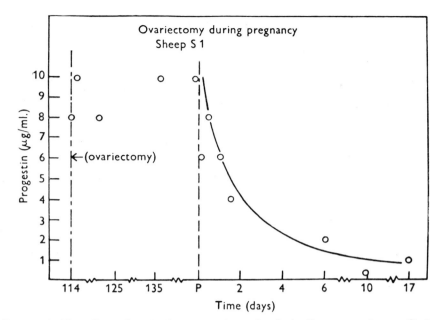

FIG. 16.10. The effect of castration on gestagen levels in the pregnant ewe. Gestagen levels were obtained by the Hooker-Forbes test. Note that castration failed to interfere with the pregnancy or the level of gestagen in the blood. (From G. M. Neher and M. X. Zarrow, J. Endocrinol., 11, 323, 1954.)

it might be concluded that here also the placenta has successfully replaced the ovary. In the rabbit, on the other hand, castration at any time during pregnancy will cause a decrease in the level of the circulating hormone and terminate the pregnancy. Hence, in this species, the placenta has failed to replace completely the ovary. The mouse is another instance in which castration leads to abortion so that one can assume a failure on the part of the placenta to replace the endocrine activity of the ovary. In this case, however, the second peak of circulating gestagen has been ascribed to the placenta and this presents the possibility of a partial replacement of the ovary by the placenta but a replacement that is not adequate since pregnancy is terminated by ovariectomy.

As indicated above, a marked discrepancy exists between the bioassays and the chemical determinations of gestagens in the blood and other tissues. The chemical determinations of progesterone invariably give results that are far lower than those obtained by bioassay methods. Edgar and Ronaldson (1958) found a maximal concentration of approximately 2 μg. progesterone per ml. ovarian venous blood during

gestation in the ewe. This concentration was no higher than that seen in the ewe during a normal estrous cycle. The maximal level reached during the estrous cycle was maintained when pregnancy supervened and remained fairly constant until the last month of pregnancy. Thereafter the concentration fell and no progesterone was detectable at 15 days prepartum (Fig. 16.11). Inasmuch as no progesterone was found in the peripheral blood of the ewe, this poses again the following question: What was being measured in the peripheral blood by the bioassay procedure? In addition, a second question is posed by the earlier discussion on the need of the ovary in the maintenance of pregnancy as to the relative contributions of the ovary and the placenta to the concentration of this hormone in the body.

That the biologic methods are measuring more than progesterone is obvious from the many reports emphasizing the high levels obtained by bioassay and the low levels obtained by chemical techniques. In addition to the above data, Short (1957, 1958a, 1958b) reported the presence of progesterone in the peripheral blood of the pregnant cow but only in the order of 0.0074 to

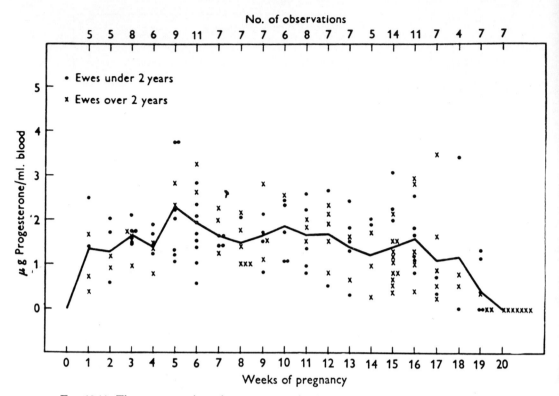

Fig. 16.11. The concentration of progesterone in the ovarian venous blood of the pregnant ewe. Progesterone was determined by chemical methods. (From D. G. Edgar and J. W. Ronaldson, J. Endocrinol., **16,** 378, 1958.)

0.0098 μg. per ml. plasma. It is of interest that the level remained constant from the 32nd to about the 256th day of pregnancy and then decreased several days before parturition. In the human being values of 0.17 to 0.44 μg. per ml. during the final trimester of pregnancy have recently been reported (Oertel, Weiss and Eik-Nes (1959).

Numerous investigators have suggested that the discrepancy between the chemical and biologic assays is due to the presence of unknown gestagens in the blood. This has been validated in part by the discovery of 2 metabolites in the blood of the pregnant human female (Zander, Forbes, Neher and Desaulles, 1957). They have been identified as 20α-hydroxypregn-4-en-3-one and 20β-hydroxypregn-4-en-3-one and have been shown to be active in both the Clauberg and Hooker-Forbes tests (Zander, Forbes, von Münstermann and Neher 1958). The 20β-epimer was twice as active as progesterone in the Hooker-Forbes test and the 20α-epimer one-fifth as active. It

is likely that more unidentified gestagens occur in the blood and other tissues.

C. SOURCES OF GESTAGENS

The second question asked above concerning the role of the placenta *versus* the ovary as a source of progesterone probably cannot be answered in a simple manner. Wide differences exist between species (1) in the need of the ovary for maintenance of pregnancy, (2) in the concentration of the hormone in peripheral blood, (3) in the activity of the placenta in secreting progesterone, and (4) in the presence of extraovarian and extraplacental sources of the hormone.

The presence of progesterone in the placenta of the human being has been confirmed (Salhanick, Noall, Zarrow and Samuels, 1952; Pearlman and Cerceo, 1952) and a high output of progesterone demonstrated. Zander and von Münstermann (1956) and Pearlman (1957) independently reported the production of approximately 250 mg. progesterone into the peripheral circulation every 24 hours. This and other evidence tends to prove that the placenta is the major source of progesterone in the human species. However, with respect to other species, progesterone has been found only in the placenta of the mare (Short, 1957) although in amounts much less than in the human being. Placentas of the cow, ewe, sow, or bitch were all negative. Although the placenta of the mare contains progesterone and castration does not lead to abortion after day 200 of gestation, no progesterone was found in the peripheral blood or uterine vein blood. The ewe offers an even more intriguing problem inasmuch as (1) a discrepancy exists between the biologic and chemical values for progesterone in the peripheral blood, (2) the placentas contain no progesterone, and (3) no progesterone is found in the uterine vein blood (Edgar, 1953). This has led to the conclusion that the maintenance of pregnancy in the ewe may be dependent on an extra-ovarian, extraplacental source of progesterone.

If such a conclusion is correct, and it must be added that the evidence is still tenuous, then the adrenal cortex must be considered as a possible source. Beall and Reichstein isolated a small amount of progesterone from the adrenal cortex in 1938 and Hechter, Zaffaroni, Jacobson, Levy, Jeanloz, Schenker and Pincus (1951) demonstrated from perfusion experiments that progesterone is an important intermediate metabolite in the synthesis of the adrenal corticoids. In addition, it has long been known that desoxycorticosterone possesses progesterone-like activity (Courrier, 1940) which is due to a conversion of the desoxycorticosterone molecule to a gestagen. This has been shown by experiments *in vivo* in the monkey (Zarrow, Hisaw and Bryans, 1950), rat, and rabbit (Lazo-Wasem and Zarrow, 1955), and by an incubation experiment with rat tissue (Lazo-Wasem and Zarrow, 1955). In addition, Zarrow and Lazo-Wasem reported the release of a gestagen from the adrenal cortex of the rat and rabbit following treatment with ACTH. The substance was obtained from the peripheral blood and measured by the Hooker-Forbes test, but it was not identified chemically. This was followed by the finding that pregnanediol is present in the urine of ovariectomized women, but not ovariectomized, adrenalectomized women (Klopper, Strong and Cook, 1957), and by the finding that progesterone is present in the adrenal venous blood of the cow, sow, and ewe (Balfour, Comline and Short, 1957). In all instances the concentration of progesterone in the adrenal venous blood was 10 to 100 times greater than the concentration in the arterial blood. Thus the total evidence that the adrenal cortex can secrete progesterone is more than adequate. The question remains as to whether the adrenal cortex contributes to the progesterone pool of the body during pregnancy and whether a species difference exists here.

D. RELAXIN

The initial discovery by Hisaw (1926, 1929) of the presence of an active substance in the blood and ovaries responsible for relaxation of the pubic symphysis of the guinea pig has led in recent years to a consideration of this substance as a hormone of pregnancy (Hisaw and Zarrow, 1951). Some doubt as to the existence of relaxin was raised in the 1930's by investigators who were able to show that pubic relaxation in the guinea pig could be obtained with estrogen alone or estrogen and progesterone (de Fremery, Kober and Tausk, 1931; Courrier, 1931; Tapfer and Haslhofer, 1935; Dessau, 1935; Haterius and Fugo, 1939). This matter was resolved by the demonstration that pubic relaxation in the guinea pig following treatment with the steroids or relaxin differed in (1) time required for relaxation to occur, (2) histologic changes in the pubic ligament, and (3) treatment with estrogen and progesterone which induced the formation of relaxin (Zarrow, 1948; Talmage, 1947a, 1947b). Subsequent discoveries of additional biologic activities possessed by relaxin and further purification of the hormone has led to the conclusion that relaxin is an active substance in the body, and that it plays a significant role during parturition. The hormone has been found in the blood or other tissues of the dog, cat, rabbit, sheep, cow, rat, and man. The specific action of this hormone varies with the species involved. Still unsolved is the question as to whether the water-soluble extract obtained from the ovary and referred to as relaxin is a single substance or a group of active substances (Frieden and Hisaw, 1933; Sher and Martin, 1956).

The concentration of relaxin in the blood increases as pregnancy progresses until a plateau is reached. This has been demonstrated in the rabbit (Marder and Money, 1944), guinea pig (Zarrow, 1947), cow (Wada and Yuhara, 1955), and human being (Zarrow, Holmstrom and Salhanick, 1955). Relaxin has also been found to increase in the ovary of the sow (Hisaw and Zarrow, 1949). In general, the shape of the curve for the concentration of relaxin in the blood as a function of the length of pregnancy has been more or less the same for all species studied. Figure 16.12 indicates that the concentration of relaxin in the blood of the pregnant rabbit rises from a level of 0.2 guinea pig unit (G.P.U.) per ml. for the first trimester of pregnancy, i.e., until day 12, to a level of 10 G.P.U. per ml.

on day 24. This concentration was then maintained until parturition. After delivery of the young, the concentration of the hormone decreased 80 per cent in 6 hours. On the 3rd day postpartum no hormone could be detected.

As indicated above, the concentration of relaxin in the blood of the pregnant cow and human being showed approximately the same type of curve. In the cow the concentration rose gradually from a level of 1 G.P.U. per ml. to a maximum of approximately 4 G.P.U. at 6 months (Fig. 16.13). Thereafter the level remained unchanged until parturition, when the level dropped at a rate comparable to that seen in the rabbit. The curve for the concentration of relaxin in the blood serum of the pregnant woman followed the general pattern described above (Fig. 16.14). The concentration rose from a level of 0.2 G.P.U. per ml. the 6th week of pregnancy to a maximum of 2 G.P.U. the 36th week. Thereafter the level remained unchanged until delivery. Again the postpartum fall was precipitous and the hormone was not detectable at 24

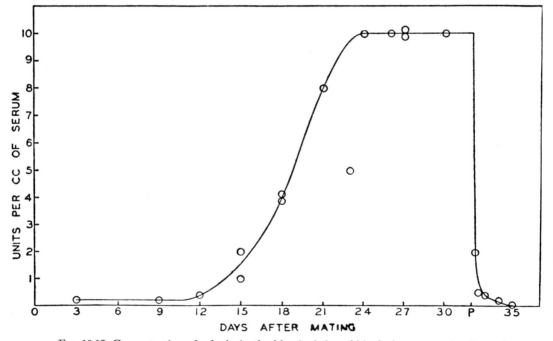

FIG. 16.12. Concentration of relaxin in the blood of the rabbit during pregnancy. Parturition (P) occurred 32 days after mating. Guinea pig units (G.P.U.) of relaxin are plotted against days pregnant. (From S. N. Marder and W. L. Money, Endocrinology, 34, 115, 1944.)

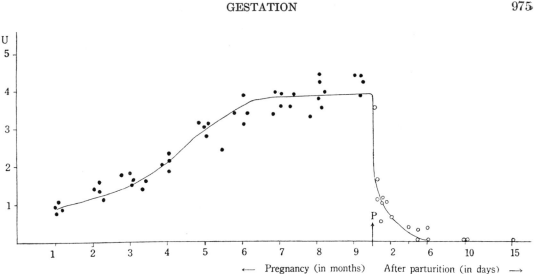

Fig. 16.13. Concentration of relaxin in the blood of the cow during pregnancy. Parturition is indicated by P. (From H. Wada and M. Yuhara, Jap. J. Zootech. Sc., **26**, 12, 1955.)

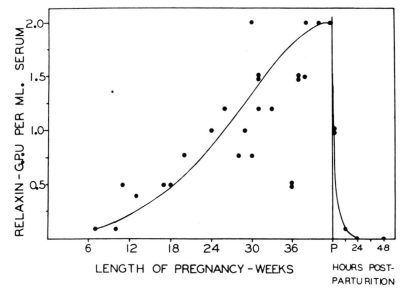

Fig. 16.14. The concentration of relaxin in the blood serum of normal pregnant women. (From M. X. Zarrow, E. G. Holmstrom and H. A. Salhanick, Endocrinology, **15**, 22, 1955.)

hours postpartum. Studies in the guinea pig revealed a marked rise in relaxin on day 21 of gestation to a maximal concentration of 0.5 G.P.U. per ml. serum on day 28 (Zarrow, 1948). Thereafter the level remained unchanged for approximately 4 weeks. Contrary to the results obtained in the rabbit, cow, and human being a drop in the concentration of the hormone in the pregnant guinea pig was noted before parturition. The concentration of relaxin fell to 0.33 G.P.U. per ml. on the 63rd day of gestation and then dropped to nondetectable levels within 48 hours postpartum.

Although no studies have been carried out on the blood levels of relaxin in the sow as a function of the length of pregnancy, analysis of the ovary for relaxin has revealed a situation comparable to that reported for the blood in other species. The concentration rose from 5 G.P.U. per gm. ovarian tissue during the luteal phase of the cycle to approximately 10,000 G.P.U. per gm. fresh ovarian tissue by the time a fetal length of 5 inches had been reached (Hisaw and Zarrow, 1949).

E. SOURCES OF RELAXIN

The ovaries, placentas, and uteri are possible sources of relaxin in different species. It seems from the extremely high concentration in the ovary of the sow during pregnancy that this organ is the major site of relaxin synthesis at this time. However, studies on other species indicate that both the placenta and uterus may be involved.

Treatment of castrated, ovariectomized rabbits with estradiol and progesterone stimulated the appearance of relaxin in the blood of the rabbit as indicated by the ability of the blood to induce relaxation of the pubic symphysis of estrogen-primed guinea pigs (Hisaw, Zarrow, Money, Talmage and Abramovitz, 1944). Similar experiments on castrated, hysterectomized rabbits failed to reveal the presence of the hormone in the blood of the treated animals. Treatment with estradiol alone also failed to stimulate the release of relaxin. It is obvious then that, if the bioassay is specific for relaxin, the uterus is a definite source of this hormone. Comparable results were also obtained in the guinea pig (Zarrow, 1948). Treatment with estradiol and progesterone caused pubic relaxation and the presence of relaxin in the blood after approximately 3 days of treatment with progesterone. In the absence of the uterus relaxin was not demonstrable in the blood.

The concentration of relaxin in the blood of the rabbit castrated the 14th day of pregnancy and maintained with progesterone remained unaffected by removal of the ovaries, provided the pregnancy was maintained (Zarrow and Rosenberg, 1953). Figure 16.15 shows a typical curve for the relaxin content of the blood of such an animal. The concentration of the hormone rose between days 12 and 24 to a maximal concentration of 10 G.P.U. per ml. and was maintained till the time of normal parturition. It is of interest that in those instances in which the placentas were not maintained in good condition, the concentration of the hormone fell. Analysis of the reproductive

tract revealed concentrations of 5 G.P.U. per gm. fresh ovarian tissue during pseudopregnancy and approximately 25 G.P.U. during the last trimester of gestation. The uterus contained 50 G.P.U. per gm. fresh tissue during pseudopregnancy and an equal concentration the first 24 days of pregnancy. The 26th day of pregnancy the concentration fell to 15 G.P.U. per gm. The highest concentration was in the placenta which contained from 200 to 350 G.P.U. per gm. Some evidence indicated that after treatment with estradiol minimal amounts of relaxin, *i.e.*, 5 G.P.U. per gm., were present in the vaginal tissue (Table 16.5).

F. ADRENAL CORTEX

1. Hydrocortisone

Initial studies on the possible role of the adrenal cortex in gestation involved the determination of the two urinary metabolites of the gland, *i.e.*, the 17-ketosteroids and the corticoids. Inasmuch as the 17-ketosteroids are believed to be associated with the androgenic activity of the adrenal cortex, bioassays for adrenogenic activity in the urine were carried out. Dingemanse, Borchart and Laqueur (1937) found no increase in urinary androgen by the 6th to the 8th month of pregnancy whereas Hain (1939) reported that pregnant women secreted even less androgen than nonpregnant women. Pincus and Pearlman (1943) found no change in the urinary 17-ketosteroids of the pregnant and nonpregnant woman although Dobriner (1943), by the use of chromatographic separation, showed a marked decrease in androsterone. Venning (1946) found no change in the urinary ketosteroids as measured by the antimony trichloride reagent described by Pincus (1943), but the ketosteroids measured by the Zimmerman reagent (dinitrobenzene) showed a significant rise in the latter part of pregnancy. The discrepancy between the two determinations can be explained by the fact that other ketonic substances besides 17-ketosteroids give a color in the Zimmerman reaction. These are the 20-ketosteroids and to a limited extent the 3-ketosteroids. Venning (1946) believes most of this in-

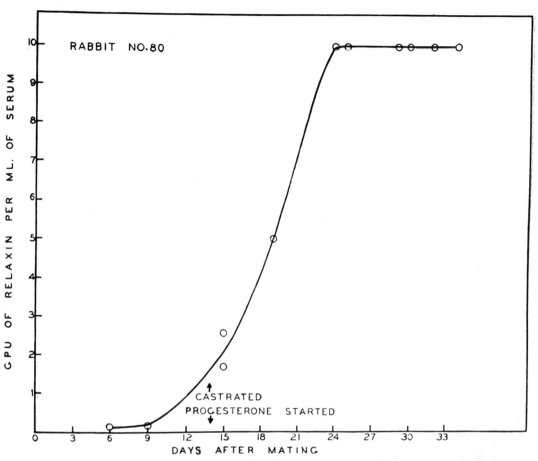

FIG. 16.15. Concentration of relaxin in the blood of a pregnant rabbit castrated the 14th day of gestation and maintained with 4 mg. progesterone daily until the 32nd day. Post-mortem examination revealed 8 placentas and 2 dead fetuses. (From M. X. Zarrow and B. Rosenberg, Endocrinology, **53**, 593, 1953.)

TABLE 16.5

Relaxin content of the blood serum and tissue of the reproductive tract of the rabbit

(From M. X. Zarrow and B. Rosenberg, Endocrinology, **53,** 593, 1953.)

Treatment	No. of Rabbits	Relaxin Concentration in G.P.U.					
		Per ml. serum	Per gm fresh tissue				
			Ovary	Uterus	Placenta whole	Placenta fetal	Placenta maternal
Pseudopregnant............	3	0.2–0.3	5	50			
Chorionic gonadotrophin...	4	0.2	5	50			
Pregnant 13 days..........	3	1.0	30	50			
Pregnant 24 days..........	2	10.0	25	50	75	10	250
Pregnant 25 days..........	2	10.0	20	30	50	20	350
Pregnant 26 days..........	2	10.0	25	15	50	25	200
Pregnant 28 days..........	1	10.0	25		75		

crease in ketosteroid excretion during pregnancy is the result of increased output of the stereoisomers of pregnanolone.

Measurement of urinary glucocorticoids by the glycogen deposition test showed an initial increase in the first trimester of pregnancy in the human being. After the initial rise, the urinary excretion level returned to normal with a second increase the 140th to 160th day of pregnancy. Values of 200 to 300 μg. equivalent of 17,hydroxy-11-dehydrocorticosterone per 24 hours of urine were obtained at days 200 to 240. In most instances the urinary output fell several weeks before parturition.

Analysis of the blood levels for 17α-hydroxycorticosterone in the pregnant wo-

man confirmed the results obtained with the urine (Gemzell, 1953; Seeman, Varangot, Guiguet and Cédard, 1955). Gemzell (1953) reported a rise from approximately 5 μg. per 100 ml. plasma to an average of approximately 22 μg. per cent (Fig. 16.16). A further rise to 36 μg. per cent was noted at the time of labor. This has been confirmed by McKay, Assali and Henley (1957) who found an average rise of approximately 40 μg. per cent during labor lasting more than 6 hours. Although McKay, Assali and Henley reported values still well above normal on the 4th to 6th day postpartum, Gemzell (1953) reported a drop to 1.99 μg. per cent on the 6th day postpartum.

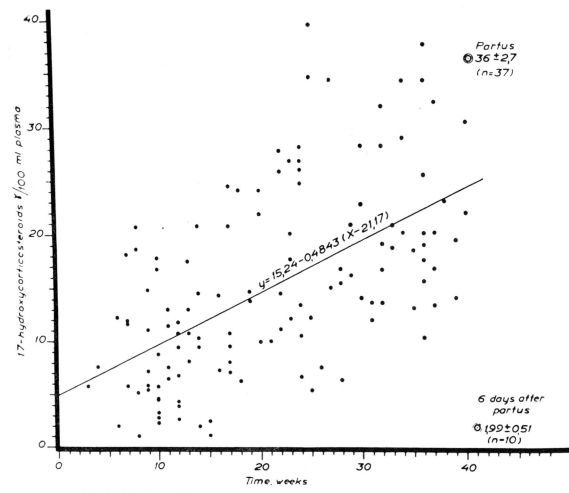

FIG. 16.16. Correlation between the concentration of 17-hydroxycorticosteroids in the blood of pregnant women and the duration of pregnancy (in weeks). Conception at zero time. (From C. A. Gemzell, J. Clin. Endocrinol.,**13,** 898, 1953.)

The mechanism whereby labor induces a marked stimulation of the adrenal cortex is still obscure. It is possible that labor is a stressful state and the stress induced by both the pain and the muscular work act to stimulate the increased release of ACTH resulting in increased adrenocortical activity. Some confirmation of this may be obtained from the fact that significant increase in plasma 17α-hydroxycorticoids is noted only if the labor lasts more than 6 hours.

Analysis of the rise in plasma levels of hydrocortisone during pregnancy has suggested that the phenomenon is not simply the result of an increased rate of secretion from the adrenal cortex, but rather the result of an increased retention and an alteration in the metabolism of the hormone (Cohen, Stiefel, Reddy and Laidlaw, 1958).

2. Aldosterone

The isolation for aldosterone by Simpson, Tait, Wettstein, Neher, von Euw, Schindler and Reichstein (1954) and its identification as the hormone regulating fluid and mineral metabolism stimulated marked interest in the role of this hormone. Among the items of interest was its significance in pregnancy and in the toxemia of pregnancy. Early studies by Chart, Shipley and Gordon (1951) revealed the presence of a sodium retention factor in the urine that increased from a normal pregnancy value of 36 to 106 μg. equivalent of desoxycorticosterone acetate (DOCA) per 24 hours to a maximum of 1008 μg. equivalent in pregnancy toxemia. These results were confirmed by Venning, Simpson and Singer (1954) and by Gordon, Chart, Hagedorn and Shipley (1954). In addition a slight increase in the sodium retaining factor was observed in gravid women as compared to nongravid women.

The discovery that the greater part of the aldosterone in urine is present in the conjugated fraction led to a repetition of the above work using both acid hydrolysis and incubation with β-glucuronidase (Venning and Dyrenfurth, 1956; Venning, Primrose, Caligaris and Dyrenfurth, 1957). The results show little change in the excretion of free aldosterone throughout pregnancy, but the glucuronidase and acid-hydrolyzed fractions increased markedly (Fig. 16.17). The urinary excretion values increased from a prepregnancy normal of 1 to 6 μg. aldosterone (average for women was 3.8 ± 14 μg. per 24 hours; Venning, Dyrenfurth and Giroud, 1956) to approximately 25 μg. per 24 hours. The first significant rise occurred about the third month of gestation and an increased concentration was obtained until after parturition, when there was a rapid fall to the nonpregnant values.

G. THYROID GLAND

Clinical data have long indicated a possible involvement of the thyroid gland in gestation (Salter, 1940). In regions where the iodine supply is low this is demonstrated by an enlargement of the thyroid during pregnancy. The formation of a goiter has been interpreted as evidence for an increased need for iodine during gestation. Scheringer (1930) and Bokelmann and Scheringer (1930) reported a rise in the iodine content of the blood of pregnant women during the first trimester of pregnancy with a peak at the seventh month. The increased concentration is maintained until shortly after parurition. In the goat, however, Leitch (1927) reported no change in serum iodine during gestation until just before parturition. Analysis of umbilical vein blood revealed values that were normal, i.e., lower than in the mother (Leipert, 1934). Increased thyroid secretion (Scheringer, 1931) and increased urinary excretion of iodine have been reported in pregnant women (Nakamura, 1932; 1933). However, Salter (1940) concluded in his review that no reliable evidence of increased thyroid hormone levels in the blood during pregnancy is available.

Peters, Man and Heinemann (1948) reported a range of 4 to 8 μg. per cent of serum-precipitable iodine in the normal, nonpregnant woman with a rise to 8.3 μg. per cent (range 6 to 11.2 μg. per cent) in the pregnant woman (Fig. 16.18). It is of interest that the elevation in the protein-bound iodine (PBI) does not follow the course of changes in the basal metabolic rate. Whereas the former is already high by the second month of pregnancy the basal metabolic rate rises gradually after approximately the 4th month of pregnancy (Rowe and Boyd, 1932; Javert, 1940). No other symptoms of hyperthyroidism are seen in pregnancy which leads to the question of the significance of the rise in protein-bound iodine. A somewhat comparable paradox exists in the guinea pig in which a rise in the rate of oxygen consumption during pregnancy is not accompanied by an increase in heart rate (Hoar and Young, 1957).

Recently, Werner (1958) reported a decrease in the I^{131} up-take after treatment with triiodothyronine in both the normal and pregnant woman. From this and other data he ruled out any abnormal pituitary-thyroid relationship or marked secretion of thyroid-stimulating hormone (TSH) by the placenta and concluded that the increased PBI in pregnancy is due to an increased binding capacity of the serum protein.

Feldman (1958) failed to find any increase in the level of serum-butanol-extracted io-

dine throughout pregnancy in the rat. Actually the values were consistently lower than in the controls and similarly the total amount of PBI in the thyroid of the pregnant rat was consistently lower. He did find an increase in the rate of excretion of I^{131}, a diminished up-take of I^{131} by the thyroid, and a decreased half-life for thyroxine in the pregnant rats. It is obvious that these results are quite dissimilar from those obtained in the pregnant women. One can only conclude at this time that pregnancy has an effect on iodine metabolism and a species difference exists.

H. GROWTH HORMONE

Although it has been possible to demonstrate the presence of growth-promoting substance (STH) in the blood plasma, there are few data bearing on the identity of the substance and few quantitative measurements. Westman and Jacobsohn (1944) first showed the presence of a growth-promoting sub-

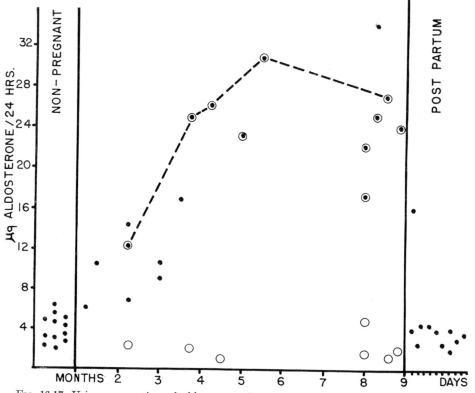

FIG. 16.17. Urinary excretion of aldosterone throughout pregnancy in the human being. ○, free fraction only; ●, free and acid-hydrolyzed fraction; ⊙, free, enzyme and acid-hydrolyzed. (From E. H. Venning and I. Dyrenfurth. J. Clin. Endocrinol., **16**, 426, 1956.)

stance in the blood by cross transfusion between a normal and hypophysectomized rat united in parabiosis. Gemzell, Heijkenskjöld and Ström (1955), using the technique of adding exogenous growth hormone to the sample of blood, failed to find any growth-promoting substance in 23-ml. equivalents of blood. However, retroplacental blood from human beings gave a positive response at a level of 7- to 15-ml. equivalents of plasma without the addition of exogenous STH. Increase in the width of the proximal tibial epiphysis of the rat was used as an end point. A comparable concentration of 650 μg. equivalent of the standard STH per 100 ml. plasma was also found in the blood from the umbilical cord.

Contopoulos and Simpson (1956, 1957) measured the STH of the plasma in the pregnant rat, using the tibial cartilage, tail length, and body weight increase. No significant increase in plasma STH was noted on the 5th day of pregnancy, however, a significant rise was observed by the 9th day. An estimated 3-fold increase in plasma STH during pregnancy was reported from calcu-

lations on both the tibial cartilage and the tail length tests. No changes were reported in the STH activity of the pituitary gland throughout pregnancy. Recently, the persistence of greater than normal amounts of growth-promoting activity was reported in the plasma of pregnant rats after hypophysectomy. Since the fetal pituitary probably does not contribute to the STH pool of the mother, at least in early pregnancy, it is likely that the placenta may be a source of the hormone.

I. PROLACTIN

Few data are available on the concentration of prolactin during gestation. This has been due, in part, to the minute amounts of the hormone present in the urine and blood and to the inadequacy of the available assays. Although Hoffmann (1936) failed to find any prolactin in the urine of women before parturition, Coppedge and Segaloff (1951) and Fujii and Schimizu (1958) reported measurable amounts of prolactin in the urine of pregnant women. Coppedge and Segaloff reported a gradual rise in the excre-

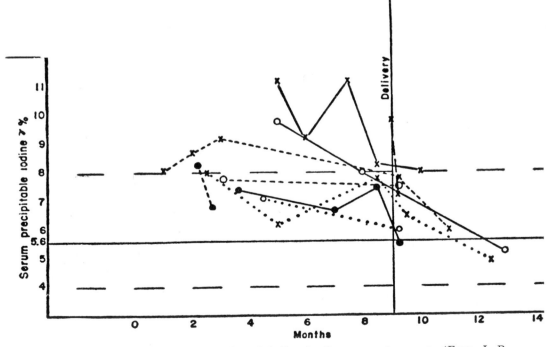

Fig. 16.18. The level of protein-bound iodine in the pregnant woman. (From J. P. Peters, E. B. Man and M. Heinemann, in *The Normal and Pathologic Physiology of Pregnancy,* The Williams & Wilkins Co., 1948.)

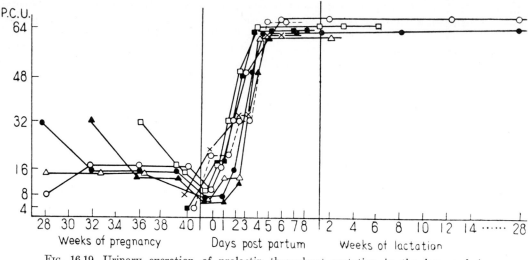

FIG. 16.19. Urinary excretion of prolactin throughout gestation in the human being. One pigeon crop unit (P.C.U.) is equivalent to 0.3 I.U. (From K. Fujii and A. Shimizu, Bull. Tokyo Med. & Dental Univ., **5**, 33, 1958.)

tion of prolactin throughout pregnancy and a gradual decline following parturition even though lactation was maintained. The number of observations, however, was limited and the authors point out that the results were equivocal. Fujii and Shimizu observed an initial drop in the prolactin output during the first month of pregnancy followed by a rise to approximately 32 P.C.U. (one pigeon crop sac unit is equivalent to 0.3 I.U.) per 24 hours during the second trimester of pregnancy in women. (Fig. 16.19). This was followed by a drop to approximately 10 P.C.U. per 24 hours between the 30th and 38th weeks of pregnancy and a marked rise to 64 P.C.U. per 24 hours during the lactation period.

J. PLACENTAL GONADOTROPHINS

Placental gonadotrophins have been found in the monkey, chimpanzee, human being, mare, and rat (Hisaw and Astwood, 1942). The physiologic activities of these placental hormones differ among the three groups of mammals and appear to represent divergent evolutionary steps in the adoption of pituitary function by the placenta. The physiologic properties of the placental gonadotrophins differ not only among themselves but also from the pituitary gonadotrophins. The gonadotrophin from the rat placenta (luteotrophin) has been shown to be leuto-

trophic with the ability to maintain a functional corpus luteum in the hypophysectomized rat (Astwood and Greep, 1938). The hormone has no effect on follicular growth or ovulation. Its function appears to be that of maintaining the secretory activity of the corpus luteum in the rat from the 10th day of pregnancy to term.

The placental hormones of the human being (HCG) and the mare (PMS) have been studied in much greater detail. These two hormones differ markedly in both chemical and physiologic properties. The presence of HCG in the urine and the absence of PMS in the urine would alone indicate a marked difference in the size of the two molecules. Physiologically, PMS is highly active in producing follicular growth and some luteinization, whereas HCG has no effect on follicular growth but will induce ovulation and a delay in the onset of menstruation. This would indicate a luteotrophic action. Although chorionic gonadotrophin has been reported in the macaque (Hamlett, 1937) between the 18th and 25th day of pregnancy, and in the chimpanzee from the 25th to the 130th day of gestation (Zuckerman, 1935; Schultz and Snyder, 1935), little work has been done on the characterization and identification of these substances except in man and horse.

It is of some interest to note that the ap-

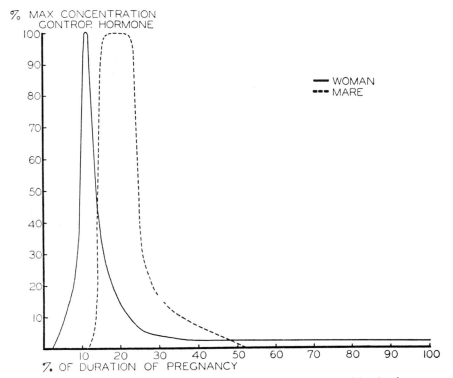

Fig. 16.20. The relative time of appearance of placental gonadotrophins in the pregnant mare and the woman. (From E. T. Engle, in *Sex and Internal Secretions*, 2nd ed., The Williams & Wilkins Company, Baltimore, 1939.)

pearance of the placental gonadotrophins in the blood and urine of horse and man occurs at approximately the same relative time in pregnancy (Fig. 16.20). The role played by these hormones in gestation is still not clear, but it is significant that their appearance corresponds with the time of implantation of the blastocyst and their disappearance roughly with the time when ovariectomy no longer interferes with the maintenance of the pregnancy.

1. Human Chorionic Gonadotrophin (HCG)

The discovery of the presence of a gonadotrophic hormone in human pregnancy urine by Aschheim and Zondek (1927) was soon followed by a description of its biologic activity and quantitative determinations of its concentration in the urine throughout pregnancy (Ascheim and Zondek, 1928). Recently a number of investigators have determined the titer of chorionic gonadotrophin in the serum of pregnant women. These curves agree very well with the values ob-

tained from the urine. Figure 16.21 is a typical curve for the concentration of chorionic gonadotrophin in the blood of pregnant women (Haskins and Sherman, 1952). A peak value of 120 I.U. per ml. of serum was obtained on the 62nd day after the last menses and a rapid decline was noted to a low of approximately 10 I.U. per ml. of serum on day 154. A subsequent rise to 20 I.U. was noted by day 200 and this was maintained until the end of pregnancy. These results are in excellent argeement with those reported by Wilson, Albert and Randall (1949) using the ovarian hyperemia test in the immature rat. These authors obtained a peak concentration of approximately 70 I.U. per ml. of serum on the 55th day after the last menses. A gradual decrease occurred thereafter to a low of approximately 20 I.U. per ml. of serum which remained unchanged from day 100 to parturition although the data indicate a slight rise towards the end of pregnancy.

The significance of the excretion pattern

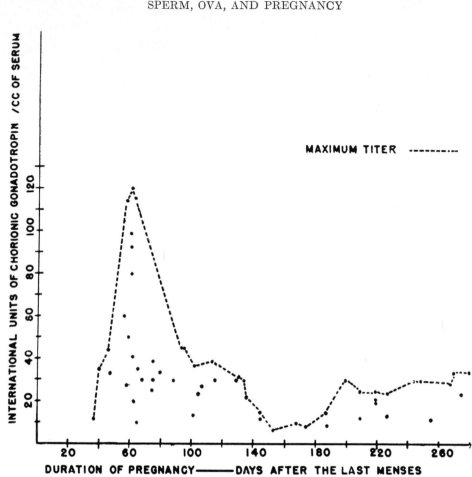

Fɪɢ. 16.21. Concentration of human chorionic gonadotrophin in the blood of the normal pregnant woman. The hormone levels were determined by the male frog test. (From A. L. Haskins and A. I. Sherman, J. Clin. Endocrinol., **12**, 385, 1952.)

and concentration of the hormone in the serum is still a matter of conjecture. Browne, Henry and Venning (1938) suggested that the peak level of chorionic gonadotrophin in the blood reflects an increased production and a physiologic need in order to maintain a functional corpus luteum during early pregnancy. Recent evidence has tended to confirm this opinion in that HCG has been found to be active in the maintenance of the secretory activity of the corpus luteum in the primate (Hisaw, 1944; Brown and Bradbury, 1947; Bryans, 1951). In addition, histologic studies reveal a direct proportion between the number of Langhans' cells and the amount of hormone excreted (Stewart, Sano and Montgomery, 1948; Wislocki, Dempsey and Fawcett, 1948).

The possibility that the kidney plays a role in the changes in the concentration of HCG was investigated by Gastineau, Albert and Randall (1948). The renal clearance was relatively constant throughout all stages of pregnancy although the urine and serum concentrations of the hormone varied as much as 20-fold. In addition, the mean, renal clearance found during pregnancy was not markedly different from that found in cases of hydatiform mole and testicular chorioma. Inasmuch as the renal elimination of the hormone remained constant, it was obvious that two possible explanations existed: these were (1) changes in the secretion rate, and (2) changes in extrarenal disposal of the hormone. Studies on the latter were contradictory. Whereas Friedman and Weinstein (1937) and Bradbury and Brown (1949) reported an excretion of 20 per cent and higher of HCG following the injection of HCG, Johnson, Albert and Wilson (1950) found an excretion of 5.8 per cent in pregnant women during the immediate postpartum period. Zondek and Sulman (1945) reported a 5 to 10 per cent elimination of HCG in the urine of animals. Thus Bradbury and Brown felt that there is relatively little destruction or utilization of the hormone in the body; Wilson, Albert and Randall (1949) believed that 94 per cent of the circulating hormone is affected by extrarenal factors and that the fluctuating character of hormonal level in serum or urine depends entirely on changes in rate of hormone production.

An analysis of the distribution of chorionic gonadotrophin in the mother and fetus led Bruner (1951) to conclude that the ratio of maternal blood to urinary gonadotrophin is not constant although the ratio of gonadotrophin in the chorion to maternal blood is constant. Consequently, she concluded that the concentration of gonadotrophin in the urine does not depend entirely on the rate of production of the hormone and that the

method of gonadotrophin elimination changes during pregnancy. She also pointed out that a significant amount of chorionic gonadotrophin is found in the fetus and that this is due to the fact that, although the chorion releases the hormone into the maternal blood, secondarily some of it passes the placental barrier and enters the fetal system across the wall of the chorionic vesicle.

2. Equine Gonadotrophin (PMS)

The presence of a gonadotrophin in the blood of the pregnant mare was first described by Cole and Hart in 1930. The hormone appears in the blood about the 40th day of pregnancy and increases rapidly to a concentration of 50 to 100 rat units (R.U.) per ml. by the 60th day of pregnancy (Cole and Saunders, 1935). This concentration is maintained for approximately 40 to 65 days. By day 170 it has fallen to a nondetectable level (Fig. 16.22).

Catchpole and Lyons (1934) suggested that the placenta is the source of the gonadotrophin and indicated that the chorionic epithelium is the probable source. Cole and

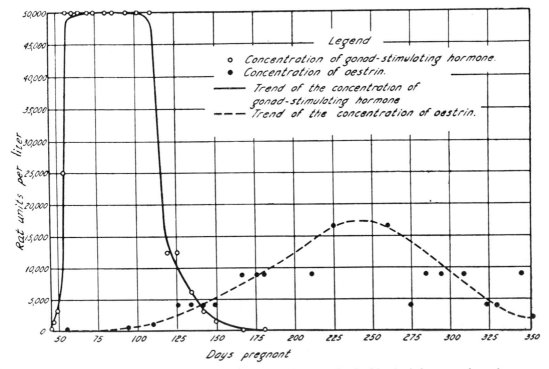

FIG. 16.22. The concentration of pregnant mare's serum in the blood of the mare throughout pregnancy. (From H. H. Cole and F. J. Saunders, Endocrinology, **19**, 199, 1935.)

Goss (1943), on the other hand, concluded that the endometrial cups are the source of the hormone. Recent evidence tends to confirm the endometrial cups as the source of the hormone (Clegg, Boda and Cole, 1954). The endometrial cups form in the endometrium opposite the chorion in the area where the allantoic blood vessels fan out. The cups develop precisely at the time when the hormone is first obtained in the serum of the pregnant mares and desquamation of the endometrial cups is complete at the time of the disappearance of the hormone from the maternal blood. Analyses of the cups for gonadotrophin content reveal a correlation between the concentration of the hormone in the maternal blood and the concentration in the endometrial cups. Finally, histochemical stains for glycoprotein indicate the presence of this substance only in the epithelial cells lining the uterine lumen and the uterine glands in the cup area (for complete discussion of the subject see the chapter by Wislocki and Padykula).

VI. Pregnancy Tests

The discovery of gonadotrophic activity in the urine of pregnant women by Aschheim and Zondek in 1927 led to introduction of the first valid test for pregnancy (Aschheim and Zondek, 1928). These investigators used the immature mouse and reported the presence of corpora hemorrhagica as indicative of the presence of a gonadotrophin in the urine and a positive reaction for pregnancy. The Aschheim-Zondek test for pregnancy was the first successful test of its kind and has been used both as a qualitative and quantitative test. In the latter instance, a serial dilution of the urine is made in order to obtain the minimal effective dose.

It is not too surprising that many tests for pregnancy have been described. In general, all of the successful tests involve the detection of chorionic gonadotrophin in the urine, and to some extent in the blood. The changes that have appeared in the development of new pregnancy tests have been those concerned with the use of different species of animals, the rapidity with which the test could be completed, and convenience to the laboratory. Thus the Friedman test (Friedman, 1929; Friedman and Lapham, 1931) followed soon after the Aschheim-Zondek test and in turn was succeeded by several newer tests.

Approximately five reliable tests are now available (Table 16.6). All are concerned with the detection of HCG and have an accuracy of 98 to 100 per cent. The Aschheim-Zondek suffers from a time requirement of 96 hours and was largely supplanted by the Friedman test that used the isolated rabbit and required only 48 hours. Within recent years several new tests have been reported using the frog, toad, and immature rat. Frank and Berman (1941) first noted the occurrence of hyperemia in the ovary of the immature rat, following the injection of HCG. Albert (1949) reported excellent results with the use of this test in 1000 cases. Comparison of the rat hyperemia test with the Friedman test was on the whole very good and revealed the same order of accuracy for both tests. The Friedman test, however, will detect about 5 I.U. of HCG which would mean a concentration of 500 I.U. of HCG per 24-hour output of urine (assuming a 24-hour urine output of 1500 ml.). Positive results in the rat test require a 24-hour output of 1000 I.U., indicating that the ovarian hyperemia test in the rat is about one-half as sensitive as the Friedman test. Nevertheless, the rat

TABLE 16.6

Pregnancy tests with an accuracy of 98 to 100 per cent

Animal	Sex	Observed End Point	Time	Reference
			hr.	
Immature mouse	F	Corpora hemorrhagica	96	Aschheim and Zondek, 1928
Isolated rabbit	F	Corpora hemorrhagica	48	Friedman and Lapham, 1931
Xenopus laevis	F	Extrusion of ova	8–12	Shapiro and Zwarenstein, 1934a
Bufo arenarum	M	Extrusion of sperm	2–4	Galli-Mainini, 1947
Immature rat	F	Hyperema of ovary	4	Frank and Berman, 1941

test requires only 4 hours and a larger number of animals can be utilized, thus decreasing the error due to use of inadequate numbers of animals. Comparison of the rat hyperemia and the Friedman tests revealed that the former is slightly more accurate but a little less sensitive (Albert, 1949).

Within two years after the publication of the Friedman test for pregnancy, Shapiro and Zwarenstein (1934a, 1934b, 1935) and Bellerby (1934) reported the use of the African toad (*Xenopus laevis*, D) in the diagnosis of pregnancy. Again the test was based on the ability of HCG to induce the extrusion of ova by the frog following the injection of the urine into the dorsal lymph sac. Extrusion of the ova occurred in 6 to 15 hours and the test was shown to compare favorably with both the Aschheim-Zondek and Friedman tests, although it did not give the graded response seen with the A-Z test (Crew, 1939). Weisman and Coates (1944) found an accuracy of 98.9 per cent with the Xenopus test over a 5-year period during which 1000 clinical cases were examined.

Galli-Mainini (1947) first reported the use of the male batrachian in the diagnosis of pregnancy and Robbins, Parker and Bianco (1947) simultaneously reported the release of sperm by Xenopus following treatments with gonadotrophins. Galli-Mainini (1948) pointed out that this reaction is not restricted to a single toad, but would probably be found in many frogs and toads. He added that care should be used to employ animals with a continuous spermatogenesis. This was immediately confirmed by reports from different countries using various species of frogs and toads endogenous to the areas. Immediate use of *Rana pipiens* was reported in the United States and this species became very popular in that country (Wiltberger and Miller, 1948).

The advantages of the sperm-release test are the time requirements, simplicity, end point, and opportunity to use many animals. On the other hand, the reaction is all or none and shows no gradation in degree of reaction. In general, the urine is injected into the dorsal lymph sac and the cloaca aspirated for sperm 1 to 3 hours later. Although this is the most recent of the pregnancy tests, many reports have appeared

and some evaluation as to accuracy may be attempted. Galli-Mainini (1948) reported an accuracy of 98 to 100 per cent in a summary of more than 3000 tests and 100 per cent accuracy for negative results in more than 2000 controls. Robbins (1951) reported an accuracy of 89.5 per cent in the first trimester of pregnancy. Pollak (1950) indicated that as many as 20 per cent of the negative tests obtained in the summer were false. This suggested the existence of a refractory state at this season. Bromberg, Brzezinski, Rozin and Sulman (1951) reported on a comparison of several tests including 700 cases. An accuracy of 85 per cent was obtained with the male frog test, 99 per cent with the rat hyperemia test, 98.5 per cent with the Friedman test and 98 per cent with the Aschheim-Zondek test. The authors indicate that the 15 per cent failures to get a positive reaction in the frog could be due in part to the poor sensitivity of the animal which could only be overcome by concentrating and detoxifying the urine. Comparison of the minimal amounts of HCG to elicit a positive reaction are $\frac{1}{3}$ I.U. for the rat hyperemia test, 1 I.U. for the Aschheim-Zondek and Hyla tests, 2 I.U. for the Rana and Bufo tests, and 5 I.U. for the Friedman test. Reinhart, Caplan and Shinowara (1951) reported an accuracy of 99 per cent with 840 urine specimens; only 3 false negatives were noted in 346 specimens from known pregnant women and no false positives noted in 125 nonpregnant women. The authors attribute the high degree of accuracy to standardization of the procedure by which extraneous factors were eliminated. These include (1) the use of 2 or more 30- to 40-gm. frogs for each test, (2) elimination of all animals suffering from red leg and other diseases, (3) adequate time for sperm release, (4) concentration of the urine, (5) maintenance of frogs at 15 to 22°C., and (6) during the summer the injection of an increased volume of urine and an increase to 4 hours in the period for sperm release. The maintenance of frogs in a hibernating state by keeping them in a refrigerator at 38°F. has been reported to insure a high degree of sensitivity regardless of the season (Allison, 1954). Although it is obvious that more data are needed, the present results are very promising for the "frog-sperm" test and if the seasonal effect can be eliminated, this test will be the equal of the other four.

VII. Water and Electrolyte Balance

The changes in the various components of the blood during pregnancy have been described in a number of species (Tables 16.7 and 16.8). It is generally agreed that a marked increase in the blood and plasma volume and a decrease in the relative amounts of erythrocytes and hemoglobin occur during the last trimester. Inasmuch as the increase in the plasma volume in man exceeds the concurrent increase in the total cell volume, the resultant hemodilution produces an anemia which has been described as the "physiologic" anemia of pregnancy.

TABLE 16.7

The average percentage of change in the constituents of the blood and in the extracellular fluid volume during normal pregnancy in man

Author	Increase					Decrease			Time of Determination in Pregnancy
	Extra-cellular space	Blood vol-ume	Plas-ma vol-ume	Cell vol-ume	Total hemo-globin	Hema-tocrit	RBC count	Gram % hemoglobin	
	%	%	%	%	%	%	%		
Adams, 1954		11	22			19			6th week antepartum
Bibb, 1941						28		25	3rd trimester
Caton, Roby, Reid and Gibson, 2nd, 1949	59		49						3rd trimester
Caton, Roby, Reid, Caswell, Maletskos, Fluharty and Gibson, 1951		45	55						60 days antepartum
Chesley, 1943	25				15				3rd trimester
Dieckmann and Wegner, 1934a, b, c, d		23	25	20	13	14	14	15	3rd trimester
Ferguson, 1950								25% in 50% of patients	
Freis and Kenny, 1948	15		32			10			3rd trimester
Friedman, Goodfriend, Berlin and Goldstein, 1951	9								At term
Ganguli, 1954							21	14	Throughout pregnancy
Gemzell, Robbe and Sjostrand, 1954		30			10				8th week antepartum
Hamilton and Higgins, 1949						12	8	10	3 months antepartum
Jarosova and Daum, 1951	49	59	78	59					9th month
Lambiotte-Escoffier, Moore and Taylor, Jr., 1953	None								10th lunar month
Lund, 1951			48		15				3rd trimester
McLennan and Corey, 1950			40						10th lunar month
McLennan and Thouin, 1948		32	41	20					At term
Miller, Keith and Rownetree, 1915		9	17			16			3rd trimester
Mukherjee and Mukherjee, 1953			16						3rd trimester
Roscoe and Donaldson, 1946		25			15				3rd trimester
Thompson, Hersheimer, Gibson and Evans, Jr., 1938		45	65	17					9th lunar month
Tysoe and Lowenstein, 1950		28	34	17		11	22		At term
White, 1950		24	35	9					3rd trimester

TABLE 16.8

The average percentage of change in the constituents of the blood and in the extracellular fluid volume during normal pregnancy in various laboratory and domestic animals

Animals	Increase				Decrease			Author
	Blood volume	Pasma volume	Cell volume	Total hemo-globin	Hema-tocrit	RBC count	Gram % hemoglobin	
	%	%	%	%	%	%		
Rat						40	20–40	Beard and Myers, 1933
	41			20	10	18	7	Bond, 1958
						30	31	Newcomer, 1947
					29	25	33	van Donk, Feldman and Steenbock, 1939
Rabbit	50						10–20	Salvesen, 1919
					17	20	17	Zarrow and Zarrow, 1953
	6	12	0	0		12	13	Horger and Zarrow, 1957
Sheep	25	22	10				Initial decrease, normal at term	Barcroft, Kennedy and Mason, 1939
Cow	Slight	Slight			0	0	0	Reynolds, 1953

Comparable changes were observed in the blood constituents and plasma volumes of the rat and rabbit during the latter third of gestation. Although there is no increase in the total cell volume, the resultant "physiologic" anemia of pregnancy in the rabbit follows the same general pattern as that reported in the human being (Horger and Zarrow, 1957).

A significant decrease in the erythrocyte number, hemoglobin concentration, and hematocrit, and an increase in the blood volume have been noted in the rat during pregnancy (Table 16.8). However, the increase in blood volume is correlated with an increase in body weight and the ratio of blood volume to body weight remains unchanged (Bond, 1948). Calculation of the total number of erythrocytes and grams of hemoglobin actually showed an increase in these constituents during gestation, indicating that the anemia of pregnancy in the rat is due to a hemodilution in which the blood volume increases proportionately faster than the number of erythrocytes.

Comparable results were also reported in the rabbit (Zarrow and Zarrow, 1953). A marked drop in the relative number of circulating erythrocytes and percentage of hemoglobin is seen invariably towards the end of gestation (Fig. 16.23). A marked

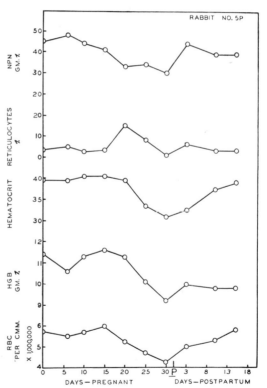

FIG. 16.23. Changes in the relative number of circulating erythrocytes, reticulocytes, percentage of hemoglobin, hematocrit, and nonprotein nitrogen of the blood of the rabbit during pregnancy and after parturition. (From M. X. Zarrow and I. G. Zarrow, Endocrinology, **52**, 424, 1953.)

fall in hematocrit occurs concomitantly with the fall in the two blood constituents along with an increase in the reticulocytes. The time of onset of the increase in reticulocytes is variable and seems to occur during the second trimester of gestation. Their number returns to normal before parturition in spite of the increasing severity of the anemia. A second rise in the reticulocytes is seen during the first week postpartum. All the other constituents return to normal values during the first or second week postpartum.

Disagreement exists as to whether there is a change in the volume of the extracellular fluid compartment during pregnancy in the human being. Whereas certain investigators have reported rather marked increases in the extracellular space (Chesley and Chesley, 1941; Chesley, 1943; Freis and Kenny, 1948; Caton, Roby, Reid and Gibson, 1949; Friedman, Goodfriend, Berlin and Goldstein, 1951; Jarosova and Daum, 1951), others have reported that the changes in this fluid compartment are proportional to changes in the body weight (Lambiotte-Escoffier, Moore and Taylor, 1953; Seitchik and Alper, 1954). The results obtained in the rabbit support the findings of the latter authors as no disproportionate increase in the thiocyanate space was observed during pregnancy in the rabbit. The slight increase that occurred during the last trimester of

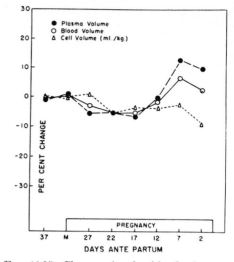

FIG. 16.25. Changes in the blood plasma and total erythrocyte volume during pregnancy. (From L. M. Horger and M. X. Zarrow, Am. J. Physiol., **189**, 407, 1957.)

gestation was in good agreement with the fluid accumulation by the developing fetus. Similarly the increase in blood volume in the rat is correlated with increase in body weight.

Thus the anemia of pregnancy as observed in the rabbit and rat is very similar to that reported for man. It can be characterized as a normochromic and normocytic anemia. Although a decrease in the relative concentrations of hemoglobin and erythrocytes occurs, the total amounts of these components of the blood remain unchanged. Consequently, the anemia of pregnancy is due to a hemodilution.

The anemia induced by treatment with estradiol is similar to the anemia of pregnancy in many respects. Witten and Bradbury (1951) treated 16 women with 5 mg. estrone or 0.4 mg. estradiol dipropionate and noted an erythrocyte drop of 14.8 per cent, a hemoglobin drop of 8.5 per cent, a hematocrit drop of 15 per cent, and a blood volume increase. Treatment of the castrated rabbit with 1 mg. estradiol daily caused a 20 per cent decrease in both erythrocyte count and hemoglobin with no significant changes in total hemoglobin or number of erythrocytes. Estradiol also caused an increase in plasma and blood volume (Fig. 16.24) which was comparable to that seen during pregnancy (Fig. 16.25), but no sig-

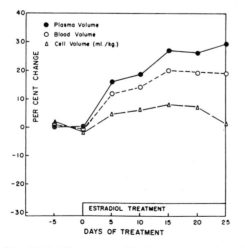

FIG. 16.24. Changes in blood plasma and total erythrocyte volume in the ovariectomized rabbit treated with 1 mg. estradiol daily. (From L. M. Horger and M. X. Zarrow, Am. J. Physiol., **189**, 407, 1957.)

nificant change in cell volume was obtained. The estradiol-induced anemia is both normochromic and normocytic and is caused by a hemodilution. However, in addition to the changes in the blood and plasma volumes, estradiol induces a significant increase in the thiocyanate space. Furthermore, only the massive dosage of 1.0 mg. estradiol per day elicits an anemia comparable to that observed in pregnancy. This dosage level is probably toxic since there is a decrease in the body weight of most rabbits which received this treatment. Thus, in spite of the similarities of these anemias, it is likely that estrogen is not the sole etiologic agent in the anemia of pregnancy.

Progesterone alone at dosages of 4 mg. daily has little effect on the plasma volume or the thiocyanate space. This steroid does exert a significant influence on the action of estradiol on the blood and plasma volume, but it is to be noted that rather large dosages of estradiol were still needed to induce a significant hypervolemia and that the effect depends on the ratio of the concentration of the two hormones. The hypervolemia induced by the treatment with 4 mg. progesterone in combination with 0.1 mg. estradiol was greater than that caused by the estradiol alone, whereas the treatment with 4 mg. progesterone in combination with 1.0 mg. estradiol resulted in an inhibition of the estrogenic activity (Fig. 16.26). Thus progesterone may play a dual role in the water metabolism of the gravid female. In the presence of low titers of estrogen, progesterone augments its action which may be a means of insuring an adequate fluid retention to provide for the fluid requirements of the fetus. However, if the titers of the estrogens and possibly of other steroids affecting salt and water metabolism became excessively high, the progesterone may provide a protective measure by inhibiting the activity of these substances. This concept is in accord with reports describing the diuretic action of progesterone in the hypophysectomized rat (Selye and Bassett, 1940) and the inhibition of the salt- and water-retaining action of DOCA and cortisone by progesterone (Landau, Bergenstal, Lugibihl and Kascht, 1955).

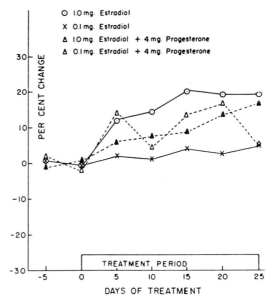

Fig. 16.26. Changes in the blood volume of the ovariectomized rabbit treated with 0.1 mg. and 1.0 mg. estradiol daily and with a combination of the two estrogen treatments and 4 mg. progesterone. (From L. M. Horger and M. X. Zarrow, Am. J. Physiol., **189**, 407, 1957.)

It is also of interest that no anemia was observed in animals treated with various combinations of estrogen and progesterone (Horger and Zarrow, 1957). Progesterone elicits an increase in the cell volume which approximates that of the plasma volume. Because no erythrocyte counts were made in this study, it is not possible to state whether this increase in the cell volume is caused by a macrocytosis or an increase in the number of erythrocytes. Vollmer and Gordon (1941) reported that progesterone caused an increase in the erythrocyte count of the rat but that the action was inconsistent. Hence it is possible that the increase in the cell volume is due to an enhancement of hematopoiesis by the progesterone. This possibility is not inconsistent with the absence of an increase in the reticulocyte count in response to these treatments since a reticulocytosis usually occurs only after an intense stimulation of the hematopoietic tissue such as by hemorrhage.

In view of the previous discussion, it is improbable that the anemia of pregnancy is due entirely to the interaction of estrogen and progesterone. These hormones appear to play an important role in the salt and water metabolism of the gravid female. Furthermore, it is noted that the cow exhibits a hypervolemia but no anemia during pregnancy (Reynolds, 1953) and that a similar condition is produced in the rabbit by the treatment with various combinations of these steroids. Hence the interaction of estrogen and progesterone may be responsible for this species difference.

Inasmuch as no antidiuretic hormone (ADH) could be detected in any of the plasma samples, it is apparent that the plasma titers of ADH did not rise above 10 μU. per ml. during the experimental period. However, in view of the increased ability of the blood to inactivate ADH during pregnancy (McCartney, Vallach and Pottinger, 1952; Croxatto, Vera and Barnafi, 1953), there may be an increased rate of turnover of ADH during gestation. Consequently the data obtained in this study neither substantiate nor eliminate ADH as an etiologic agent in the anemia of pregnancy.

A number of investigators have attributed the hypervolemia of pregnancy to structural changes in the circulatory system. Burwell (1938) observed a marked similarity between the circulatory changes observed in pregnancy and those observed in a patient with an arteriovenous fistula. He noted that in both conditions there is an increase in the blood volume, cardiac output, pulse rate, pulse pressure, and an increased venous pressure near the opening of the fistula. He concluded that the changes in the circulation of the pregnant woman are caused by an arteriovenous leak through the placenta and the obstruction of the venous return by the enlarged uterus. Bickers (1942) correlated the intensity of the edema of the right or left leg with the location of the placenta in the uterus. The edema was observed to be consistently greater on the same side as the location of the placenta whereas the edema of the legs was equal when implantation occurred on the anterior or posterior wall of the uterus. However, when the uterus was lifted off the interior vena cava, there was no precipitous drop in the venous pressure in the femoral vein. Thus this study supports the arteriovenous shunt theory of Burwell.

One objection to this theory is that it does not account for the decrease in the blood volume during the 10th lunar month of pregnancy. However, it has been reported that during the latter part of pregnancy there is an increase in the resistance to the flow of blood through the placenta. This increase is due to the increased number of villi and to the anastomizing of the villi in the placenta. Since an increase in the peripheral resistance to blood flow results in a hemoconcentration, this would account for the decrease in the blood volume during the last lunar month of gestation (Kline, 1951; McGaughey, 1952).

Other objections to the arteriovenous shunt theory were reported by Kellar (1950) who found that blood flow through the placenta is sluggish rather than rapid as in an arteriovenous shunt. He also observed that the uterine venous blood is not exceedingly rich in oxygen as is the venous return of an arteriovenous aneuryism and he concluded that, although the uterus is an area of decreased resistance to blood flow, the effect is not entirely due to the placenta. He suggested that thyroxine may be partially responsible for the expansion of the blood volume since mild thyrotoxicosis is common in pregnancy. This concept is supported by the observation that there is a tendency for vasodilation in the upper extremities during the latter months of gestation (Burt, 1950). Furthermore, the basal metabolic rate increases during this period (Sandiford and Wheeler, 1924; Rowe and Boyd, 1932). It is to be noted, however, that the changes in the blood flow in the extremities are closely correlated with the cardiovascular changes occurring during pregnancy but not with the changes in the hormonal levels in the blood (Herbert, Banner and Wakim, 1954).

Since there is no disproportionate increase in the thiocyanate space of the rabbit during pregnancy, the increase in the blood volume can best be explained on the basis of cardiovascular changes during the latter part of gestation. However, in view of the previous discussion, it is extremely improbable that this hypervolemia is induced by any one factor. Rather, it is more probable that the condition is produced by a multiplicity of factors. On the basis of the previous reports, it is evident that the placenta, due to its similarity to an arterio-venous aneuryism, is partially responsible for the hypervolemia. The marked increase in the uterine size and vascularity during pregnancy (Barcroft and Rothschild, 1932) will also account for a considerable amount of the increase in the blood volume. In addition, the tendency for dilation of the peripheral blood vessels may account for another portion of the increase in the blood volume. Thus, in general, the hypervolemia of pregnancy can be attributed primarily to structural changes in the circulatory system.

It cannot be denied, however, that the cardiovascular system is influenced by the changes in the endocrine balance during gestation. It is well known that the placenta elaborates large amounts of sex steroids and corticoids. It has also been suggested that there is an increased production of thyroxine and ADH at this time. In addition, water-soluble extracts of the pregnant sow's ovaries have been shown to cause water retention and anemia in the rabbit (Zarrow and Zarrow, 1953). The resultant hormonal balance becomes somewhat precarious as the additional secretions of the glands tend to build up the blood titers of the sex steroids and other substances which influence water metabolism. It is possible that when a proper balance of these factors is maintained, the pregnancy is normal and the various requirements of the fetus are provided without disrupting the distribution of the body fluids outside of the vascular system. However, if the balance is not maintained, the animal tends to accumulate fluid, and edema and other pathologic complications result.

VIII. Plasma Proteins

It has long been known that the plasma proteins play a significant role in the fluid balance of the organism and as such are also involved in water balance during pregnancy (Mack, 1955). In addition, the plasma proteins are of importance in many other functions, such as heat and energy source and replacement of tissue in which function they act as a protein source whenever needed and form the metabolic pool. These proteins are synthesized in general,

in the liver and reticuloendothelial system and may be classified as albumins or globulins although many different entities of these two classifications are known to exist.

The maintenance and stabilization of blood volume and the equilibrium of fluid exchange between the extravascular and intravascular compartments is a function of the albumin fraction of special significance in pregnancy, in addition to its other functions of acting as carrier for other substances and supplying of nutrients. The regulation of blood volume by albumin depends on its osmotic action and is of much greater significance than the globulins. Approximately 4.6 gm. albumin and 3.17 gm. globulin per 100 ml. of plasma are found in the normal, nonpregnant woman. At least four types of globulins are present in the plasma among which are found the lipoproteins, prothrombin, fibrinogen, antibodies, and several hormones.

Although both the plasma proteins and albumin drop during pregnancy, this does not necessarily indicate a drop in the total available albumin protein. An increase in the plasma volume compartment of 25 per cent as seen in pregnancy could easily result in an increase in the total amount of circulating protein. However, as the total circulating blood volume increases in pregnancy, the albumin fraction and γ-globulin seem to be diluted whereas the other globulins become more concentrated. Nevertheless, the globulins cannot compensate for the albumin loss and the total protein decreases. Mack (1955) has listed several possible explanations for the above paradox: (1) the small albumin molecule may diffuse more freely into tissues and across placental membrane, and (2) albumin synthesis cannot keep pace with utilization.

Innumerable studies on the plasma proteins of women during pregnancy have revealed markedly consistent changes in the albumin-globulin ratio of the plasma. The concentration of total protein and albumin decreases while the total globulin increases. The trend is apparent by the first trimester and continues throughout gestation. A return to the nonpregnant pattern is seen shortly after parturition. The total protein dropped 13 per cent and the albumin 26 per cent. The various globulin fractions showed a rise except for the γ-globulin (Mack, 1955). As a result of these changes, the albumin-globulin ratio declines throughout pregnancy and shows the well known reversal (Fig. 16.27) and recovery to normal by 6 weeks postpartum.

Although it is obvious that the albumin fraction is important in maintaining the

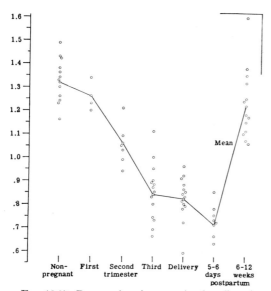

Fig. 16.27. Progressive decrease in the albumin-globulin ratio of the plasma during pregnancy in women. (From H. C. Mack, *The Plasma Proteins in Pregnancy*, Charles C Thomas, Springfield, Ill., 1955.)

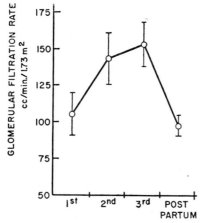

Fig. 16.28. Changes in the glomerular filtration rate throughout pregnancy in the woman. (From W. J. Dignam, P. Titus and N. S. Assali, Proc. Soc. Exper. Biol. & Med., **97, 512, 1958.**)

blood fluid compartment, the changed albumin-globulin ratio cannot solely account for the retention of water and edema present in pregnancy. Although it has been argued that the hypoalbuminemia through diminished colloid osmotic pressure is the cause of water retention in the tissues, the occurrence of the postpartum diuresis at the time when the albumin is lowest would tend to indicate some other mechanism (Dieckmann and Wegner, 1934a–d). Additional mechanisms, such as changes in the hormone level, especially the sex steroids and adrenal corticoids, may be responsible.

IX. Renal Function

Studies on renal function during pregnancy have resulted in contradictory reports. The earlier investigations failed to show any effect of pregnancy on renal function (Chesley and Chesley, 1941; Welsh, Wellen and Taylor, 1942; Dill, Isenhour, Cadden and Schaffer, 1942), whereas recent studies indicate a marked change in renal function during gestation (Bucht, 1951; Dignam, Titus and Assali, 1958). Part of the explanation for the divergent results could be the type of patient studied, the periods when studied, and the types of controls. Dignam, Titus and Assali studied both the renal plasma flow and glomerular filtration rate in various patients throughout gestation and immediately following parturition. Care was taken to select individuals without any history of cardiovascular or renal disease. Both the renal plasma flow and the glomerular filtration rate (Fig. 16.28) were increased throughout gestation. The initial rise was extremely marked during the 1st and 2nd trimesters of pregnancy. A slight rise was noted during the 3rd trimester and a return to normal by 6 to 8 weeks postpartum.

Recently, de Alvarez (1958) reported a 50 to 60 per cent rise in the glomerular filtration rate and a 60 per cent rise in the renal plasma flow during the 1st trimester of pregnancy in the human being. This is in agreement with the findings of Dignam, Titus and Assali (1958). However, de Alvarez reported, in addition, a progressive decline in both the glomerular filtration rate and renal plasma flow during the 2nd and 3rd trimesters. The filtration factor (glomerular filtration rate divided by the renal plasma flow) remained low in the first 2 trimesters and increased in the last trimester. This is evidence for an increase in tubular resorption of water and electrolyte. It can only be concluded, therefore, that kidney function is altered during pregnancy, especially the 1st trimester. Results from investigations involving the 2nd and 3rd trimesters are contradictory. De Alvarez concludes that the changes in renal hemodynamics during pregnancy are mediated by the endocrine system because the alterations in renal function seem to be related to the sodium and water retention. If the changes are progressive throughout gestation, it would be possible to correlate the phenomenon with a number of hormones that increase during pregnancy. On the other hand, if the phenomenon is transient, *i.e.*, only during the 1st trimester, then the phenomenon can only be correlated with HCG.

X. Enzymes

A. HISTAMINASE

The presence of histaminase or diamine oxidase in tissues of the body has been known for some time. As yet the enzyme has not been crystallized but is believed to be a flavoprotein (Swedin, 1943). The enzyme is not specific for histamine because it inactivates other diamines such as cadaverine and putrescine. Histaminase determinations, in general, are based on incubation of the test material with histamine dihydrochloride for a fixed period of time and the bioassay of the residual histamine carried out on an isolated strip of guinea pig intestine.

Histaminase has been found in the plasma of men and women with an increase during pregnancy from a value of between 0.003 and 0.008 μg. per ml. per hr. to a value of between 3.5 and 10 at parturition (Ahlmark, 1944, 1947). This has been confirmed by Swanberg (1950), who determined the histaminolytic activity in peripheral blood throughout pregnancy (Fig. 16.29). A marked rise is observed from the 10th to the 20th week of pregnancy, and thereafter the concentration plateaus until after parturition.

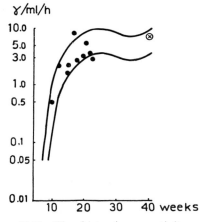

Fig. 16.29. The histaminase activity of the peripheral blood of the human female during pregnancy (●) and at parturition (⊗). (From H. Swanberg, Acta scandinav., Suppl. 79, **23,** 1950.)

Both the maternal placenta and the decidual tissue have been identified as major sites for formation of the enzyme. Danforth and Gorham (1937) reported the presence of histaminase in the placenta of a series of patients at term. This was confirmed by Swanberg (1950) who, in addition, separated the placenta by a series of slices parallel to the surface of the organ and reported that the layer adjacent to the uterine wall, consisting of practically only the thin decidual membrane, contained a mean value of 614 μg. per gm. per hr. of histaminase as compared to 38 for the fetal portion of the placenta. Confirmation of the concept that the maternal placenta is the main source of histaminolytic activity can be obtained from the finding of histaminase in decidual tissue of nonpregnant females and in the maternal placentas of animals. In cases in which maternal and fetal placentas can be separated easily, the maternal placenta contained from 14- to 100-fold the activity seen in the fetal placenta. Comparison of the histaminolytic activity in the decidual tissue of the sterile horn and the control pregnant horn of the uterus of a rabbit revealed 319 μg. per gm. per hr. and 222 μg. per gm. per hr., respectively. Treatment with progesterone or induction of pseudopregnancy caused a marked rise in the histaminase of the endometrium to upwards of 1000 μg. per gm. per hr. Nonetheless, histaminase was not observed in the blood plasma of the progesterone treated rabbits whereas progesterone treatment of two nonpregnant women caused a marked rise in plasma histaminase.

The physiologic significance of histaminase is still unknown. A consideration of this problem must take into account not only the action of the enzyme and changes in its concentration under different physiologic conditions, but also the species problem. In regard to the latter point, the data are extremely inadequate. Only two species have been studied in any detail and these are the human being and the rabbit. One can conclude from the available data that histaminase is produced by the maternal placenta, decidua, and uterine endometrium. It increases with pregnancy in these tissues and its concentration may be correlated with the progestational hormone. It increases in the blood of the human being, rat, and guinea pig during pregnancy but not in the cat or rabbit (Swanberg, 1950; Carlsten, 1950). The obvious hypothesis that histaminase protects the uterus from the stimulating action of histamine has not been confirmed. But it is somewhat paradoxical to note that urinary histamine also increases during pregnancy. Kahlson, Rosengren and Westling (1958) reported a daily 24-hour excretion of 18 to 43 μg. of histamine during the first 2 weeks of pregnancy in the human being. A marked increase was noted on the 15th day with a peak of 123 to 835 μg. per 24 hr. at the peak of excretion which occurred 1 to 2 days before parturition. As yet no role can be attributed to this substance. It is of interest that the increased histaminase present during pregnancy can serve the role of protecting the uterus from the muscle-contracting action of this substance. Because the amount of urinary histamine excreted is correlated with the number of young and no changes are apparent in the concentration of histamine in the tissues during pregnancy, it would seem that the excessive formation of histamine during the last trimester of pregnancy takes place in the uterus and its contents and the basic action of histaminase is protective.

It was shown recently that the excessive formation of histamine during the last tri-

mester of pregnancy in the rat is due to an increase in the rate of histidine decarboxylase activity (Kahlson, Rosengren, Westling and White, 1958). Inasmuch as removal of the fetuses without other interference with the pregnancy abolishes the increased urinary histamine, it can be concluded that the site of formation is in the fetus. This histamine could escape into the maternal circulation and eventually be eliminated via the kidneys.

Roberts (1954) reported that aminoguanidine leads to a general disturbance of pregnancy in the rat; large doses tended to produce death of the mother and smaller doses tended to kill all or part of the litters and some of the mothers. Again one could conclude a protective action on the part of histaminase during the latter part of pregnancy.

B. CARBONIC ANHYDRASE

Carbonic anhydrase was discovered by Meldrum and Roughton in 1933 and soon shown to catalyze the following reaction, $H_2CO_3 \rightleftarrows CO_2 + H_2O$. The enzyme was found to occur in many tissues and was generally located within the cell especially in cells possessing a secretory function. The discovery by Lutwak-Mann and Laser (1954) that carbonic anhydrase is present in the uterine mucosa led to a thorough study of the changes in the concentration of the enzyme and the factors controlling its presence (Lutwak-Mann, 1955; Lutwak-Mann and Adams, 1957). The enzyme has been found to be present in the reproductive tract of a wide variety of mammals. In general, the uterine endometrium, placenta, and Fallopian tubes are the main loci of activity although there are marked differences among different species. Carbonic anhydrase activity was found consistently in all the animals studied such as the rat, hamster, guinea pig, rabbit, pig, and ewe. No activity was noted in the uterine mucosa of the nonpregnant animal except the ewe and the rabbit. In several species, such as the cow, human being, and pig, carbonic anhydrase was also found in the Fallopian tube.

A marked rise in carbonic anhydrase of the endometrium of the rabbit was noted during the first trimester of pregnancy

(Fig. 16.30). The value rose from a pre-pregnancy level of 20 enzyme units (E.U.) per gm. of fresh tissue to a maximum of 100 E.U. per gm. at approximately the 8th day of pregnancy. This level was maintained until the 12th day and then declined to approximately the prepregnancy level by about the 20th day. Examination of the placentas at this time revealed marked activity, 68 E.U. per gm. of maternal placenta and 25 E.U. per gm. of fetal placenta. The curve for the concentration of carbonic anhydrase in the uterine mucosa during pseudopregnancy is essentially the same as that seen during pregnancy, although some minor differences exist.

It is obvious from the above data and from the evidence involving the increased concentration of carbonic anhydrase in the uterine mucosa following treatment with progesterone, that the enzyme is probably under the control of the luteoid hormone. Indeed, an excellent correlation has been shown between the degree of progestational proliferation in the uterus and the concentration of carbonic anhydrase. In the ewe, however, the carbonic anhydrase of the uterus is independent of the ovary. A possible explanation for this discrepancy between the two species has been offered on the basis of differences in the blood level of progesterone. However, no explanation is forthcoming for the failure to maintain the carbonic anhydrase level throughout pregnancy in the rabbit, even though the circulating progesterone remains high.

The significance of this enzyme in the physiology of reproduction is still unknown. From the data on the rabbit, it might be inferred that the carbonic anhydrase contributes to the maintenance of bicarbonate in the blastocyst fluid. The universal presence of the enzyme in placental tissue could also lead to the assumption that carbonic anhydrase is involved in fetal metabolism. Lutwak-Mann (1955) indicates that the enzyme might be involved in the transmission of calcium across the placenta. Whether carbonic anhydrase is essential for fetal development and successful pregnancy is still unanswered. Treatment with carbonic anhydrase inhibitors (Diamox) failed to affect adversely the pregnancy or fetuses in pregnant rats even though no

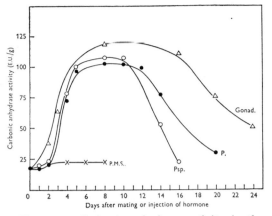

FIG. 16.30. Carbonic anhydrase activity in the uterus of the rabbit during pregnancy, pseudopregnancy, large doses of gonadotrophin, and pregnant mare's serum (PMS). Pregnancy, ●——— ; pseudopregnancy, ○——— ; gonadotrophin, □———□; PMS, ×———×. (From C. Lutwak-Mann, J. Endocrinol., **13**, 26, 1955.)

enzyme activity was present either in the maternal blood or placenta.

XI. Factors in the Maintenance of Gestation

A. THYROID GLAND

Several recent reviews have pointed out that the extract role of the thyroid gland in reproductive physiology is still in need of elucidation (Peterson, Webster, Rayner and Young, 1952; Reineke and Soliman, 1953). Numerous investigations over the past half century have definitely indicated that the thyroid gland is involved in reproduction but the site and manner of action are still not well known. In addition, contradictory reports indicate that each species and even each strain may have to be studied independently (Maqsood, 1952). Some evidence for the involvement of the thyroid gland in gestation has already been considered. The increase in PBI at the onset of pregnancy and the incidence of miscarriage in the human female when the PBI fails to rise tend to involve the thyroid hormone in the maintenance of pregnancy. Habitual abortion in women is usually associated with either hypo- or hyperthyroidism (Litzenberg, 1926). Litzenberg and Carey (1929) reported that in 70 married women with low basal metabolic rates approximately 45 per cent had one or more abortions or stillbirths. If one eliminates the sterile woman from the group, the figure for women showing abortion or stillborn rises to approximately 35 per cent. However, the results are still controversial both with regard to data obtained within a single species and from different species.

Hypothyroidism in the rat induced by the prolonged administration of thiouracil resulted in a resorption of the fetus in 100 per cent of the cases (Jones, Delfs and Foote, 1946). Rogers (1947) reported a reduction in litter size following sulfaguanidine and Krohn and White (1950) reported a reduction in litter size following thyroidectomy in the rat. Thyroidectomy early in pregnancy caused a resorption of the fetuses and if performed at a later stage in pregnancy resulted in the birth of stillborn young (Chu, 1945). Following the induction of pregnancy in thyroidectomized rabbits, either a resorption of the young or abortion or prolongation of gestation was noted and the newborn young were usually dead. Chu concluded that the thyroid hormone was concerned with the vitality and growth of the embryos during gestation. In the pig the average duration of pregnancy was 114 days for normal gilts and 124.5 days for thiouracil-treated animals. In addition, the controls farrowed an average of 8.67 pigs per litter compared with 3.25 per litter for the thiouracil-treated sows (Lucas, Brunstad and Fowler, 1958). The difference was significant in both instances. Bruce and

Sloviter (1957) pointed out that part of the conflicting reports on the role of the thyroid in gestation might be due to the different methods used in producing a thyroid-deficient state. Surgical removal of the gland generally results in the loss of the parathyroids which may be also important in the maintenance of gestation (Krichesky, 1939), although adequate information is lacking. The use of antithyroidal substances offers more serious objections because these drugs not only pass through the placenta but they are nonspecific and interfere with other glands such as the adrenal cortex (Zarrow and Money, 1949; McCarthy, Corley and Zarrow, 1958), with nutrition, and with the general status of the animal. Consequently, Bruce and Sloviter preferred to establish a thyroidectomized state in mice by the use of radioactive iodine after establishing the dose necessary to induce total destruction of the thyroid without damage to the parathyroid or gametes.

Although Gorbman (1950) reported a complete loss of reproductive activity in the mouse following treatment with I^{131}, Bruce and Sloviter (1957) reported no effect on the ability of the mouse to conceive or bear young. This discrepancy could be due in part to the strain differences in the sensitivity of the ovary to the I^{131}. Bruce and Sloviter (1957), however, noted a decrease in the average litter size of thyroid-deficient mice (Fig. 16.31). The data indicate a maximum of 6 young per litter in thyroid-deficient mice *versus* 10 young per litter for the normal mice. It is apparent that the entire curve for the litter size of thyroid-deficient mice is shifted toward a smaller size. This has also been observed in the rat following thyroidectomy (Nelson and Tobin, 1937). The thyroid-deficient mice also showed a prolongation of gestation as reported in rats, guinea pigs, and sows. Of the thyroid-deficient rats, 46 per cent showed a gestation period of more than 19 days whereas only 15 per cent of the normal controls showed a gestation period of more than 19 days whereas only 15 per cent of the normal controls showed a gestation period of more than 19 days (Table 16.9). Analysis of the data based on grouping according to litter size showed clearly an

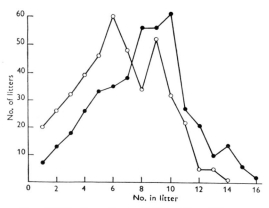

FIG. 16.31. The effect of thyroid deficiency on litter size. ○, 422 litters from thyroid-deficient mice; ●, 423 litters from normal control mothers. (From H. M. Bruce and H. A. Sloviter, J. Endocrinol., **15**, 72, 1957.)

effect of litter size on length of gestation. The smaller litter size gave a higher incidence of prolonged gestation.

Studies on oxygen consumption in the guinea pig revealed a slight but significant rise of 8 per cent at the end of gestation (Hoar and Young 1957). The increase in oxygen consumption is consistent but slight for the first 60 days of pregnancy after which the significant increase occurs (Fig. 16.32). The rise continued until 5 days postpartum and then fell rapidly. In a second set of experiments oxygen consumption was measured in control, thyroidectomized, and thyroxine-injected, pregnant guinea pigs. Measurements were taken at the time of mating and at parturition. In all three instances, an increase in the oxygen consumption was noted at parturition as compared with the values at the time of

mating (Fig. 16.33). Again the control guinea pigs showed a 7.9 per cent gain in oxygen consumption by the end of pregnancy, but both the thyroidectomized pregnant guinea pigs and the thyroxine-treated guinea pigs also showed an increase in oxygen consumption of 11.9 and 16.2 per cent, respectively. The increase in oxygen consumption was not paralleled by increases in heart rate; actually the heart rate decreased in several instances. In addition, neither the weight of the thyroid gland nor the histology of the gland was changed during pregnancy. It is obvious then that an explanation for the rise in oxygen consumption during pregnancy may not involve the thyroid gland. On the basis of changes in its appearance, Hoar and Young (1957) suggested the possibility that the adrenal cortex is involved and that the increased oxygen consumption is due to an increased release of adrenal corticoids. More evidence is needed before this suggestion can be fully accepted.

Further work from the same laboratory has led to the concept that one locus of action of thyroxine during pregnancy is at parturition (Hoar, Goy and Young, 1957). These investigators used an inbred strain of guinea pigs that is characteristically hypothyroid and a genetically heterogeneous stock in which the level of thyroid activity is presumed to be higher. It had been previously shown that pregnancy wastage was high in the hypothyroid guinea pigs. Treatment with thyroxine reduced the percentage of stillborn from 40 to 13.6 in the hypothy-

TABLE 16.9

Effect of thyroid-deficiency and litter size on length of gestation in mice

(From H. M. Bruce and H. A. Sloviter, J. Endocrinol., **15**, 72, 1957.)

No. of Young in Litter	Thyroid-deficient			Control		
	No. of pregnancies	>19 days		No. of pregnancies	>19 days	
		No.	Per cent		No.	Per cent
1–5	36	24	67	16	7	44
6–9	40	13	33	38	3	7
10–14	20	7	35	28	2	8
	—	—	—	—	—	—
Totals	96	44	46	82	12	15

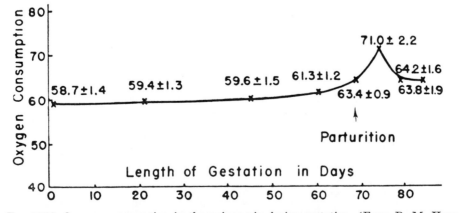

Fig. 16.32. Oxygen consumption in the guinea pig during gestation. (From R. M. Hoar and W. C. Young, Am. J. Physiol., **190**, 425, 1957.)

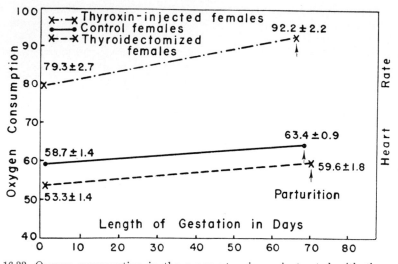

FIG. 16.33. Oxygen consumption in the pregnant guinea pig treated with thyroxine or thyroidectomized before mating. (From R. M. Hoar and W. C. Young, Am. J. Physiol., **190**, 425, 1957.)

roid guinea pigs, *i.e.*, to a level seen in the untreated heterogeneous group. Treatment of the heterogeneous group with thyroxine not only failed to reduce the percentage of stillborn but actually increased the abortion rate particularly in the 2nd and 3rd trimesters. The most consistent result, however, was a decrease in length of gestation following treatment with thyroxine, and an increase following thyroidectomy. From these experiments it was concluded that the thyroid hormone facilitates parturition and need be present only late in gestation to exert its action.

It is apparent that in some species the thyroid hormone is involved directly in pregnancy. In the absence of the hormone, certain species tend to resorb or to abort; or if pregnancy is maintained gestation tends to be lengthened. This is probably due to an interference with the mechanism of parturition. In certain species such as the guinea pig only a parturitional problem has been demonstrated; in others an entire galaxy of symptoms may be present. Reduction in the size, number, and viability of the young give added emphasis to an essential role for thyroxine in the phenomenon of gestation.

B. ADRENAL CORTEX

Removal of the adrenal cortex without further treatment invariably leads to dis-

turbances in reproductive physiology and the termination of pregnancy. Although the early results were controversial in that some investigators reported that adrenalectomy failed to affect gestation in the rat (Lewis, 1923; Ingle and Fisher, 1938), others reported that adrenalectomy led to abortion (Wyman, 1928; Dessau, 1937) or to some other disturbance of gestation (McKeown and Spurrel, 1940). Davis and Plotz (1954) adrenalectomized two groups of pregnant rats on the 4th to 6th and the 14th to 16th day of pregnancy. Abortion occurred in all 12 rats adrenalectomized during the first half of pregnancy whereas only 1 of the 12 adrenalectomized during the second half of pregnancy aborted. However, even in those adrenalectomized during the second half of gestation, an effect on pregnancy was observed. A significantly higher incidence of stillborn and sickly young (14.4 per cent) and a marked decrease in the weight of the fetuses were noted (Table 16.10).

Early results indicated that extracts of the adrenal cortex could readily replace the absent adrenal gland and maintain successful pregnancies. Within recent years it has been demonstrated that many steroids such as cortisone and 9α-chlorohydrocortisone at 10 μg. per day (Llaurado, 1955) permit fecundation and successful maintenance of pregnancy. Successful maintenance

TABLE 16.10

Effects of adrenalectomy on the character of the litter, and on fetal body weight and adrenal weight

(From M. E. Davis and E. J. Plotz, Endocrinology, **54**, 384, 1954.)

	Pregnant Controls	Adrenalectomy 2nd Half of Pregnancy	Percentage *versus* Pregnant Controls
No. of litters....	21	11	
Dead and "sickly" young.	5	13	
Vigorous young...	182	78	<0.01
Fetal body weight (gm.)..........	6.13 (±0.10)[a]	5.22 (±0.30)[a]	<0.01
Fetal adrenal weight (mg.)....	0.496 (±0.017)[a]	0.554 (±0.041)[a]	>0.3
Fetal body weight/ fetal adrenal weight × 1000...	12.35 (0.34±)[a]	9.42 (±0.31)[a]	<0.01

[a] Calculation of standard error of the mean:

$$S.E. = \sqrt{\frac{Ed^2}{n(n-1)}}$$

of a pregnancy has also been reported in an adrenalectomized human female maintained on hydrocortisone 9α-fluorohydrocortisone (Laidlaw, Cohen and Gornal, 1958). In this instance measurements of urine excretion of aldosterone revealed an increase to 4.4 μg. per 24 hours during the last trimester of pregnancy and a postpartum value of 0.5 μg. Inasmuch as the value is only 1/10 of that seen in a normal pregnancy the authors concluded that the adrenal cortex of the mother is the major source of aldosterone during pregnancy and that a high output is not a major prerequisite for a normal pregnancy.

Treatment with either 0.9 per cent saline drinking water or with cortisone increased the number of successful pregnancies following adrenalectomy during the first half of gestation. Pregnancy was normal in 8 of 11 adrenalectomized rats (Davis and Plotz, 1954). Treatment with 2 mg. of cortisone acetate resulted in successful pregnancies in 13 of 14 rats adrenalectomized on the 4th to 6th day of gestation and 12 of 12 rats adrenalectomized on the 14th to 16th day of gestation. However, complete main-

tenance was not obtained. The body weight of the mothers and the weight of the fetuses were significantly lower than in the controls, and the number of stillborn and sickly young was increased.

A comparison of the pregnancy-maintenance activity in a number of adrenal corticoids indicated that a combination of a glucocorticoid and mineralocorticoid provides the best protection in the adrenalectomized rat (Cupps, 1955). Nulliparous rats were adrenalectomized, placed on treatment, and mated. Under these conditions the adrenalectomized controls and the rats treated with desoxycorticosterone acetate failed to become pregnant inasmuch as no implantation sites were obtained (Table

TABLE 16.11

Effect of adrenal steroids on reproduction in adrenalectomized female rats

(From P. T. Cupps, Endocrinology, **57**, 1, 1955.)

Daily Treatment	No. of Rats	No. Born Alive (average)	Implantation Sites (average)	Weight Change during Pregnancy (average)[a]
				gm.
Control...........	7	8.2	11.0	46.4
Cortisone acetate ¼ mg...........	6	3.5[b]	5.6[c]	−30.8[c]
Cortisone acetate ½ mg...........	6	3.6[b]	6.2[c]	−1.5[c]
Cortisone acetate 1¼ mg...........	5	3.5	8.6[b]	17.2[c]
Cortisone acetate 2½ mg...........	5	5.8	10.0	12.8[c]
Hydrocortisone acetate 1¼ mg....	7	5.0	8.5[b]	30.7
Cortisone acetate 1¼ mg. plus...... Desoxycorticosterone acetate ½ mg.............	5	9.0	9.6	44.6
Desoxycorticosterone acetate ¼ mg..............	4	0	0	
Desoxycorticosterone acetate ½ mg..............	5	0	0	
Desoxycorticosterone acetate 1 mg.	4	0	0	
Adrenalectomized control.........	5	0		

[a] Weight change of mother from day of breeding to day after parturition.
[b] Significant at 0.05 level.
[c] Significant at 0.01 level.

16.11). Treatment with 2.5 mg. cortisone acetate per day was partially effective in restoring reproductive capacity. Injections of 1.25 mg. hydrocortisone acetate per day gave results comparable with those obtained when cortisone was given, although the ratio of young born alive to implantation sites indicated that hydrocortisone acetate was more effective. It was definitely more effective than cortisone acetate in maintaining the body weight of the mother. However, reproduction was completely restored to normal in the adrenalectomized rat following treatment with desoxycorticosterone acetate and cortisone acetate.

Interference with gestation in the normal animal has been reported by several investigators following treatment with ACTH or adrenal corticoids (Courrier and Colonge, 1951; Robson and Sharaf, 1952; Velardo, 1957). This is taken to indicate that there is a finely balanced requirement for adrenocortical hormones during gestation; and that suboptimal or supra-optimal amounts of the hormone interfere with pregnancy. Courrier and Colonge found that cortisone administered to intact rabbits in the second half of pregnancy interfered with gestation. Robson and Sharaf treated both pregnant rabbits and mice with ACTH and reported a marked effect on gestation. Abortion or resorption occurred in 8 of 9 mice and in 8 of 11 rabbits. Contamination by posterior pituitary hormones or gonadotrophins can be excluded. A subsequent experiment with cortisone also caused marked interference with pregnancy in the rabbit when 20 mg. were given; 10 mg. were without effect. Administration of cortisone to castrated or hypophysectomized pregnant rabbits maintained with progesterone also caused damage to the pregnancy. Since the hormone was not acting by way of the ovary or pituitary gland, the authors felt that cortisone was acting directly on the uterus and the uterine contents.

In the rat, however, Meunier, Duluc and Mayer (1955) observed an effect on pregnancy only when cortisone acetate was injected at the time of mating. Rats injected with 10 to 25 mg. cortisone acetate daily for 5 to 6 days beginning on day 12 or day 14 of gestation had a normal pregnancy.

Velardo (1957) reinvestigated the problem in the rat and reported a marked reduction in litter size and an increase in the number of stillborn following ACTH treatment. Although quantitative differences appeared, a significant decrease in litter size was observed only when the hormone was given (1) before mating, (2) immediately after mating, or (3) between the 11th and 15th day after mating. However, the greatest effect was noted when the ACTH was administered immediately after mating. Surprisingly enough, litter size was markedly reduced only if adrenalectomy was performed on day 7 of gestation. Adrenalectomy on day 8 to 14 of gestation had no effect on live litter size. However, a total of 6, 9, and 13 stillbirths were obtained following adrenalectomy on days 8, 9, and 11. It is interesting that the number of stillbirths decreased from 21 following adrenalectomy on day 7 to none following adrenalectomy on day 14. It is apparent that the adverse effects of adrenalectomy on gestation decrease as pregnancy progresses. It is also apparent from these and other experiments that the action of ACTH is mediated by the adrenal cortex. From these results and others described above, it seems likely that the adrenal corticoids may be acting on the uterus.

Mayer and Duluc (1955) found that adrenalectomy of the rat on the 14th to the 16th day of pregnancy led to variable results. In 17 pregnant adrenalectomized rats, gestation was terminated in 8, but no interference was observed in 9. The rats that failed to maintain pregnancy died within 2 to 3 days. Again it would appear that delicate hormonal balances are involved. In a further investigation of this problem Aschkenasy-Lelu and Aschkenasy (1957) reported that a diet adequate in salt and proteins would prevent interference with pregnancy in rats adrenalectomized before mating. On a low protein diet, pregnancy could be maintained only in the intact rat (80 per cent) and then only if daily injections of progesterone were given. These authors believe that the role of the adrenal corticoids in pregnancy is concerned with stimulation of appetite and mobilization and degradation of proteins to amino acids. The latter action would permit the replacement of body protein in the absence of a normal protein intake.

C. PANCREAS

The impact of diabetes mellitus on the course of pregnancy has been of interest to the clinician for many years. In a recent review of the subject, Reis, DeCosta and Allweiss (1952) came to the conclusion that "the carefully controlled diabetic aborts no more frequently than the nondiabetic." On the other hand, it has been well known for many years that uncontrolled diabetes and pregnancy are basically incompatible (Eastman, 1946).

Studies in the rat have given controversial results with regard to the influence of insulin on pregnancy. Davis, Fugo and Lawrence (1947) reported that in the alloxan diabetic rat pregnancy was normal for the first 12 days. Thereafter death of the fetuses occurred followed by resorption. Sinden and Longwell (1949) and Levi and Weinberg (1949) reported no detrimental effect from diabetes on the course of pregnancy. The latter group obtained 12 pregnancies from 25 rats made permanently diabetic with alloxan. Eleven of the 12 rats went to term and delivered normal fetuses and 1 died during pregnancy. Recently, Wells, Kim, Runge and Lazarow (1957) reported a 14 per cent loss in fetal weight, an increase in gestation length from a normal of 538 to 563 hours, and an increase in fetal or neonatal mortality in the pregnant rat made diabetic by pancreatectomy or treatment with alloxan.

In general, the clinical data indicate that uncontrolled diabetes has a detrimental effect on pregnancy, but that the abortion rate in the controlled diabetics approaches that seen in the "normal" population. Since the crux of the matter seems to hinge on the severity of the diabetes, one might conclude that the effect of insulin is an indirect one by virtue of its action in maintaining a good metabolic state. The conflicting reports from animal experimentation may be due to the differences resulting from uncontrolled environmental and dietary factors.

D. OVARY: PROGESTERONE, ESTRADIOL, AND RELAXIN

Marshall and Jolly (1905) were probably the first to point out that ovariectomy during pregnancy leads to abortion or resorption of the fetuses in the rat. Subsequently, a number of investigators repeated these experiments and confirmed the findings in all species tested thus far, provided ovariectomy is performed before implantation. Removal of the ovaries after gestation is well under way, however, does not disturb the course of pregnancy in all species. The human being, monkey, horse, ewe, and cow are examples of species not dependent on the ovary for the maintenance of pregnancy once it has been well established. Species such as the rabbit and the rat require the presence of the ovary throughout pregnancy.

The importance of progesterone for pregnancy was established by Allen and Corner (1929) who first showed that an extract of the corpus luteum will maintain pregnancy in the castrated rabbit. Identification of the active substance in the extract as progesterone led to the use of the hormone in many other species. Allen (1937) reported that crystalline progesterone was inferior to the crude luteal extract in the maintenance of pregnancy in the castrated rabbit. From these and other data, such as the enhancing action of estrogen on the progesterone-induced progestational reaction, he inferred that a combination of estrogen and progesterone should be superior to progesterone alone in the maintenance of pregnancy. However, he pointed out with proper caution that the dosages would have to be carefully regulated because estrogen could also antagonize progesterone. Although Robson (1936) failed to enhance the action of progesterone with estrone in the pregnant hypophysectomized rabbit, Pincus and Werthessen (1938) obtained enhancement with both the androgens and estrogen. Whereas the early work indicated that a pregnancy maintenance dose of progesterone varied from 0.5 to 2 mg. (Allen and Corner, 1930), later experimentation indicated that the dosage varied with the stage of pregnancy. An adequate dose of approximately 1 mg. progesterone in the early stages of pregnancy needs to be increased to 5 mg. in the later stages (Allen and Heckel, 1939; Courrier and Kehl, 1938a, b). These investigators also revealed that an optimal effect could be obtained by using a progesterone-estrogen combination in the ratio of 750 to 1. Chang (1951) transferred ova to nonovulated intact rabbits and noted that massive doses in the order of 25 mg. macrocrystalline progesterone injected for three times were required to obtain a 50 per cent maintenance of pregnancy. He also reported that under the conditions of his experiment an initially high dose was needed for the passage of the ova, implantation, and early maintenance. Since then, further experimentation, especially on other species, has revealed a significant role by estrogen in enhancing the pregnancy-maintaining action of progesterone.

A vast literature exists for the human being on the prevention of threatened abortion by progesterone which is beyond the scope of this review. Variation from negative results to excellent maintenance is reported. It is obvious that a great deal of variability exists here and, to some extent, this is explained by a need for more objective criteria in evaluating threatened abortion and the therapy (Guterman and Tulsky, 1949). It is obvious that if the

TABLE 16.12

Maintenance of pregnancy in the rat castrated on the 12th day of gestation

(From J. Yochim and M. X. Zarrow, Fed. Proc., **18**, 174, 1959.)

No. Rats	Progesterone		Estradiol Daily	Implantation Site	No. of Fetuses	No. of Fetuses Alive	Pregnancy Index
	Daily dose	No. daily ℞					
	mg.		µg.				
4				40	37	37	0.925
4	2	1		47	32	27	0.574
7	1	2		76	12	2	0.026
9	1.5	2		99	61	49	0.495
7	2	2		85	65	63	0.741
6	1	2	0.1	69	50	48	0.696
5	1.5	2	0.1	51	48	46	0.900
5	2	2	0.1	60	55	54	0.900

threatened abortion were the result of some disturbance other than progesterone, that progesterone therapy might be without success. Indirect evidence for the need for progesterone to maintain a successful pregnancy in the human being and for the lack of need for the corpus luteum once pregnancy is established has been presented by Tulsky and Koff (1957). Corpora lutea were removed from day 35 to day 77 of pregnancy in 14 women. Two of the women exhibited spontaneous abortion and a marked drop in pregnanediol excretion. The remaining 12 maintained a normal pregnancy and pregnanediol excretion. The data can be interpreted to indicate a need for progesterone during pregnancy and that this need can be met by a nonovarian source, *i.e.*, the placenta.

In both the rat and mouse, successful maintenance of pregnancy after castration has been obtained with progesterone or a combination of progesterone and estrogen. However, partial maintenance following castration can be obtained in the rat under special circumstances. Haterius (1936) removed all the fetuses except one and left all placentas intact. Under these conditions the remaining fetus was carried beyond term. Alexander, Fraser and Lee (1955) found that castration of the rat on the 9th day resulted in 100 per cent abortion, whereas 60 per cent of the fetuses were retained until term if castration was on the 17th day. Dosage of progesterone as high as 5 to 10 mg. daily following castration the 9th day gave only partial maintenance. It is possible that better results would have followed multiple daily injections. Yochim and Zarrow (1959) castrated rats on day 12 of gestation and obtained a pregnancy index (no. of fetuses alive at day 20 ÷ no. of implantation sites at day 12) of 0.741 when 2 mg. progesterone were given in two divided daily doses and 0.495 when 1.5 mg. progesterone was given (Table 16.12). However, the addition of 0.1 µg. estradiol daily markedly enhanced the action of the progesterone so that a pregnancy index of 0.9, *i.e.*, equivalent to the normal controls, was obtained with 1.5 mg. progesterone.

Finally, Hall (1957) has indicated that relaxin synergizes with estradiol and progesterone in the maintenance of pregnancy in the castrated mouse. One mg. progesterone per day maintained pregnancy in 83 per cent of the mice castrated on day 14 of gestation, but 0.5 mg. maintained pregnancy in only 30 per cent of the animals. The addition of 1.5 μg. estradiol per day was without effect. On the other hand, the addition of relaxin to the estradiol and 0.5 mg. progesterone gave pregnancy maintenance in over 80 per cent of the mice as compared with 30 per cent when progesterone alone was given.

Smithberg and Runner (1956) induced ovulation and mating in prepubertal mice (age 30 to 35 days) and obtained 100 per cent implantation with 0.5 to 1 mg. progesterone daily and approximately 90 per cent successful pregnancies when 2 mg. progesterone were given. A comparison of the amount of progesterone required for maintenance of pregnancy in the normal and castrated prepubertal mouse is given in Figure 16.34. In an interesting application of the information available on the induction of ovulation and maintenance of pregnancy, Smithberg and Runner (1957) were able to obtain successful pregnancies in genetically sterile, obese mice.

Haterius (1936) observed that distortion of the fetus occurred following ovariectomy in the rat. This has been confirmed by Zeiner (1943) in the rat and by Courrier and Colonge (1950) in the rat and rabbit. It was noted that castration greatly compressed the fetuses and eventually caused death. Courrier and Colonge (1950) in very elegant experiments showed that removal of the rabbit fetus into the peritoneal cavity prevented the distortion and death which ordinarily followed castration. Frazer (1955) obtained similar results in the rat and concluded that fetal death after castration of the mother follows a rise in intrauterine pressure which is associated with an increased tone of the circular uterine muscle fibers. Consequently the increased survival of the extra-uterine fetuses following ovariectomy in the mother is the result of the removal of this pressure by the circular muscle of the uterus.

Many investigators have demonstrated that gestation can be prolonged by inhibiting parturition. Both the injection of large doses of progesterone or the formation of

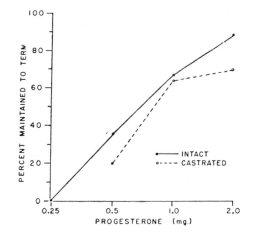

FIG. 16.34. Daily dose of progesterone required to maintain pregnancy in the normal and castrated prepubertal mouse. (From M. Smithberg and M. N. Runner, J. Exper. Zool., **133**, 441, 1956.)

a new set of functional corpora lutea during pregnancy will prevent parturition. The injection of an ovulating dose of HCG on the 25th day of pregnancy in the rabbit delayed parturition for 15 days after the injection, i.e., until the 40th day of gestation (Snyder, 1934). The fetuses survived in utero for only 3 days and grew to greater than normal size during this period. The placentas persisted until day 41 of gestation. Comparable results were obtained following daily injections of progesterone into pregnant rabbits (Zarrow, 1947a). Haterius (1936) obtained prolongation of pregnancy in the castrated rat by removing all the fetuses except one, leaving all placentas intact. Recently a comparable experiment was performed in the rabbit with intact ovaries (Hafez, Zarrow and Pincus, 1959). In 2 of 10 rabbits, live fetuses were obtained by cesarean section on day 36. However, in 8 of the 10, delivery was delayed beyond day 36, although some degree of fetal resorption was present in all instances. Prolongation of pregnancy in the rat was obtained by the injection of prolactin (Meites and Shelesnyak, 1957), but only if the ovaries were present.

E. PITUITARY GLAND

In general, hypophysectomy before midpregnancy leads to resorption. This is especially true of the rat and mouse. On the other hand, hypophysectomy at midpregnancy or later does not interfere in the maintenance of gestation in these species (Pencharz and Long, 1933; Selye, Collip and Thompson, 1933a, b; Pencharz and Lyons, 1934). In the dog, ferret, and rabbit, hypophysectomy leads to abortion (Aschner, 1912; McPhail, 1935a; White, 1932), whereas the results in the cat seem contradictory (Allan and Wiles, 1932; McPhail, 1935b).

Hypophysectomy of the rhesus monkey does not always interfere with pregnancy. Smith (1954) obtained normal pregnancies in 10 of 20 hypophysectomized rhesus monkeys. The remaining animals aborted. Although more data are needed, it seems that the pituitary gland can be removed very early in gestation without disturbing the pregnancy. Whereas hypophysectomy before midterm invariably leads to abortion or resorption in the rat or mouse, 1 of the 4 monkeys hypophysectomized between the 29th and 34th day of gestation carried its young to term. Inasmuch as Hartman and Corner (1947) showed that the placenta secretes sufficient progesterone by the 25th day of gestation to maintain pregnancy, it is apparent that the placenta in the monkey is able to maintain its endocrine secretory activity independent of the pituitary and at a sufficiently high level to replace the ovary.

Little, Smith, Jessiman, Selenkow, van't Hoff, Eglin and Moore (1958) reported a successful pregnancy in the 37-year-old woman hypophysectomized the 25th week of pregnancy. The mother was maintained on thyroid, cortisone, and pitressin tannate replacement therapy. The excretion of chorionic gonadotropin and pregnandiol was not markedly different from that seen in normal gestation. Estrogen excretion was slightly reduced and the 17-hydroxycorticosteroids dropped to zero when cortisone therapy was discontinued. It would seem that this phase of adrenocortical activity was reduced and that ACTH or corticoidlike substances from the placenta were inadequate. No interference in aldosterone output was observed.

Hypophysectomy on the 10th day of gestation in mice terminated the pregnancy in only 3 of 19 animals (Gardner and Allen, 1942). Sixteen mice carried their litters to term although 7 of the 16 had a difficult and prolonged parturition. Body weight curves were normal and the corpora lutea appeared unaffected by the loss of the pituitary gland, indicating either the independence of the corpus luteum or the presence of a placental luteotrophin. Marked involution of the adrenal cortex was noted in all instances.

Simultaneous measurements of the concentration of cholesterol in the adrenal gland and ACTH in the pituitary of the rat revealed a drop in adrenal cholesterol and pituitary ACTH on the 15th day of gestation (Poulton and Reece, 1957). This was followed by a marked increase of both substances on the 21st day of pregnancy and a sharp drop at parturition. The authors concluded that a gradual increase occurs in the secretory activity of the adrenal cortex which reaches a peak on the 15th day of pregnancy in the rat. Thereafter the activity decreased until parturition when a marked increase was observed. The initial decrease in pituitary ACTH potency followed by an increase after day 15 is interpreted as an initial increase in ACTH release followed by a decreased release. The decrease in pituitary ACTH potency at parturition is compatible with the marked increase in adrenocortical activity at this time if the decreased pituitary ACTH activity is interpreted as indicative of ACTH release.

Maintenance of pregnancy in rats hypophysectomized early in pregnancy was obtained with prolactin by Cutuly (1942), although Lyons, Simpson and Evans (1943) reported negative results with a purified prolactin. However, a partial maintenance of pregnancy was obtained with purified prolactin and estrone.

F. PLACENTA

The placenta is not only involved in the synthesis of hormones during pregnancy but also in the transfer of substances between mother and fetus. It is obvious that the transfer of substances is limited and the placenta does offer a barrier. This problem bears not only on the matter of fetal nutrition, but also on the fetal environment and as such is important in the sexual development of the fetus (see chapter by Burns).

The presence of estriol in the urine of newborn male infants has led to the conclusion that estrogens can pass through the placenta because of their low molecular weight (Diczfalusy, Tillinger and Westman, 1957). Studies on the transfer of estrogens across the placental barrier in the guinea pig with C^{14}-labeled estradiol revealed an extremely rapid disappearance of radioactivity from the maternal blood following intravenous injection of the hormone into the mother, and the appearance of large amounts of water-soluble radioactivity in the fetal plasma (Dancis, Money, Condon and Levitz, 1958). However, no estradiol was found in the fetal plasma. Replacement of fetal circulation with a perfusion system indicated that estradiol did not pass the placenta although estriol was readily transferred in both directions. These authors reported that the placenta was relatively impermeable to the water-soluble estrogens found in the urine, which are essentially glucuronides.

The discovery in 1927 of large amounts of estrogens and gonadotrophins in the blood and urine of pregnant women led to the question as to whether the placenta is a gland of internal secretion. This can be answered with an unequivocal yes. Nevertheless, several questions are still unanswered: (1) the number of hormones produced by the placenta, (2) the quantities, and (3) the secretory activity of the placenta in different species.

Data on the presence of gonadotrophins in the placenta have already been discussed. At least three different types of gonadotrophins have been extracted from the placentas of the human being, mare, and rat. These have been defined physiologically and appear to be different in the three species. Cole and his co-workers have identified the endometrial cups as the source of PMS in the mare, whereas the elegant experiments of Stewart, Sano and Montgomery (1948) indicate that HCG in the human being is secreted by the Langhans cells. These investigators grew human placental cells in

tissue culture and obtained gonadotrophin in the culture. They also noted a direct correlation between the growth of the Langhans cells and the production of gonadotrophic hormone (see also the discussion of this subject in the chapter by Wislocki and Padykula).

The initial discovery of a progressive rise in the secretion of adrenal corticoids in pregnancy (Venning, 1946) has been confirmed by numerous investigators. Gemzell (1953) attributed the steady rise to a stimulation of the adrenal glands by excessive amounts of estrogen present during pregnancy and to hyperactivity of the fetal adrenals. The hypertrophy of the fetal adrenal cortex in the rat following adrenalectomy of the pregnant mother was first reported by Ingle and Fisher in 1938 and confirmed by Walaas and Walaas (1944), and Knobil and Briggs (1955). However, the 17-ketosteroid and corticoid level of fetal urine is very low (Day, 1948; Jailer and Knowlton, 1950) as are the 17-hydroxycorticosteroids in the blood of the newborn infant (Klein, Fortunato and Papados, 1953). ACTH-like activity has been found in extracts of the placenta (Jailer and Knowlton, 1950; Tarantino, 1951; Opsahl and Long, 1951) and corticoid activity has been found in the placenta of horses and human beings, as demonstrated by the glycogen deposition and growth-survival test in adrenalectomized rats (Johnson and Haines, 1952). Berliner, Jones and Salhanick (1956) isolated 17α-hydroxycorticoids from the human placenta.

Pincus (1956) reported that ACTH can stimulate steroidocorticogenesis in the perfused placenta. Using the ascorbic acid depletion test, Assali and Hamermesz (1954) assayed the blood in the intervillous space and the chorionic villous tissue for ACTH. Good activity was observed in the blood from the intervillous spaces and in the tissue of the chorionic villi. Corticotrophic activity was also obtained by Lundin and Holmdahl (1957) from placentas obtained at full term, but the activity was small compared with that obtained from the pituitary gland.

The possible role of the fetal pituitary was investigated by Knobil and Briggs

(1955) who noted that hypophysectomy of the mother prevented the fetal adrenal weight increase observed following adrenalectomy of the pregnant mother. However, complete atrophy of the adrenal gland was not observed in the pregnant mother if the conceptus was present. It was concluded that ACTH can cross the placental barrier and that the fetus or placenta or both produce a sufficient amount of ACTH, to influence the maternal adrenal gland in the absence of the maternal hypophysis. It is still questionable, however, whether these sources, i.e., placenta and fetal pituitary, are of sufficient magnitude to account for the increased release of adrenal corticoids. Hofmann, Knobil and Caton (1954) showed that the ability of the hypophysectomized nonpregnant rat to secrete a water load is not greater than that of the hypophysectomized pregnant rat. Hence the contribution of the fetal pituitary or placenta to the corticoid pool is not of sufficient magnitude to influence water balance.

As with the gonadotrophins, the increased amounts of estrogen and pregnanediol during pregnancy were thought to be derived from the placenta. In 1933, Selye, Collip and Thompson presented evidence to indicate that the placentas of rats produce both estrogen and gestagen. Many physiologic data have been accumulated to prove this point, but completely convincing evidence was obtained only when these hormones were identified in placental extracts and in fluid perfused through the placenta. Diczfalusy and Lindkvist (1956) identified estradiol in the placenta and the presence of progesterone was described by Salhanick, Noall, Zarrow and Samuels (1952) and by Pearlman and Cerceo (1952).

Perfusion experiments on human placentas have revealed that this organ secretes a number of steroids (Pincus, 1956). These include progesterone, desoxycorticosterone cortisol, and a number of unidentified steroids. Addition of ACTH to the perfusate had no effect on the concentration of cortisol, but it did increase the concentration of the reduced corticosteroids, namely, the tetrahydro derivatives of cortisone and cortisol. This was interpreted as a stimulation of the placenta by ACTH resulting in an increased release of the corticoid as demonstrated by the increase in the degradation products.

The identification of the placenta as a source of both sex steroids and certain gonadotrophins clarifies the manner by which pregnancy can be maintained in certain species in the absence of the pituitary gland or ovary (see sections above on ovary and pituitary gland). Newton and Beck (1939) and others showed the hypophysectomy of the pregnant mouse does not precipitate abortion. Studies of the ovary reveal that, if the placentas are retained, the corpora lutea remain normal but removal of the placentas causes immediate degeneration of the corpora lutea (Deanesly and Newton, 1940). A comparable situation appears to exist in the rabbit and rat; it is assumed, therefore, that the placenta takes over control of the corpus luteum in pregnancy in those species that require the ovary for successful gestation. In other species, such as man, sheep, cattle, and guinea pig, it seems that the placenta can supplant the ovary after pregnancy has progressed to a certain stage.

G. PELVIC ADAPTATION

The discovery that pelvic changes are under hormonal control in certain species was the result of extensive studies on pelvic adaptations associated with parturition (see reviews by Allen, Hisaw and Gardner, 1939; Hisaw and Zarrow, 1951). It has been argued that, in general, a narrow pelvis is present in mammals living in burrows. This would have the advantage of permitting an animal to turn within narrow confines, but a narrow pelvis would also interfere with the delivery of the young at parturition. As Hisaw pointed out in his extensive studies, this problem has been met by special adaptations on the part of different species. This has varied from a resorption of the cartilaginous pubic arch in the male and female mole (Scalopus aquaticus machrinus, Raf.) which is independent of the endocrine system (Hisaw and Zilley, 1927) to elongation of the pubic ligament which is directly under hormonal control (Hisaw and Zarrow, 1951).

The symphysis pubis of the pocket gopher, Geomys bursarius (Shaw), behaves as a female secondary sexual character so that a sex dimorphism exists in this species. The pubic cartilages ossify in both sexes and unite to form a complete pelvis with a rigid symphysis pubis. At this stage, the pelvis is too small for the passage of the young, but with the first estrus in the female, the pubic bones are gradually resorbed, leaving the pelvis open ventrally. The pelvis in the male remains intact (Hisaw, 1925). Treatment with estrogen alone can readily bring about the resorption of the pubic bones.

A third type of adaptive mechanism has been described in great detail in the guinea pig and led to the discovery of the hormone, relaxin. A sex dimorphism of the pelvis exists in the guinea pig, as in the pocket gopher, but in addition parturition is further facilitated by marked relaxation of the pubic ligaments and of the sacroiliac joint. Thus far extensive pelvic relaxation has been described in the guinea pig (Hisaw, 1926, 1929), mouse (Gardner, 1936; Newton and Lits, 1938; Hall and Newton, 1946a), women (see review by Hisaw and Zarrow, 1951), and rhesus monkey (Straus, 1932; Hartman and Straus, 1939). No relaxation of the pubic symphysis has been reported in the ewe but a relaxation of the sacroiliac joint and an elongation of the sacrosciatic ligament was noted the 2nd to 3rd month of gestation. These changes increased as pregnancy progressed (Bassett and Phillips, 1955). Treatment with stilbestrol alone caused a marked loosening of the sacroiliac joint and the sacrosciatic ligament. The addition of relaxin to the treatment was without effect (Bassett and Phillips, 1954).

The role of relaxin in the relaxation of the pubic symphysis has been studied most extensively in the guinea pig and mouse. The work before 1950 was reviewed by Hisaw and Zarrow in 1951. The controversies (de Fremery, Kober and Tausk, 1931; Haterius and Fugo, 1939) as to whether such a hormone exists need not be discussed here, in detail, except to point out that the evidence supporting this opinion is more than adequate. Zarrow (1946, 1948) showed that pubic relaxation could be induced by estradiol alone, by a combination of estradiol and progesterone, or by relaxin in an estrogen primed animal (Table 16.13). The difference in the time required to induce relaxation, i.e., 23 days for estrogen alone, 13 days for estrogen and progesterone, and 6 hours for relaxin, and data indicating that progesterone caused the presence of relaxin in the blood of guinea pig only if a uterus was present led to the concept that pubic relaxation may be produced independ-

TABLE 16.13

Relaxation of the symphysis pubis and relaxin content of blood, urine, and uteri of castrated and castrated, hysterectomized guinea pigs after treatment with moderate doses of estradiol and progesterone

(From M. X. Zarrow, Endocrinology, **42**, 129, 1948.)

No. of Guinea Pigs	Treatment, Daily		Average Relaxation Time		Relaxin Content		
	Estradiol	Progesterone	Total	After progesterone treatment	Blood serum	Urine	Uterus
	μg.	*mg.*	*days*	*days*	*G.P.U./ml.*	*G.P.U./ml.*	*G.P.U./gm.*
Castrated							
9[a]	10	1 from day 11	13.5 (13–14)	3.5	0.5	0.3	10
10	10	2 from day 11	13.0 (12–14)	3	0.5	0.5	10
10	10		23.7 (16.31)		Negative at 4 ml.	Negative at 5 ml.	Negative
Castrated, hysterectomized							
11	10	1 from day 11	23.7 (17–30)	13.7	Negative at 4 ml.	Negative at 8 ml.	
10	10		25.6 (18–32)		Negative at 4 ml.	Negative at 4 ml.	

[a] One guinea pig not included in the table required 22 days of treatment for pubic relaxation.

ently by estradiol (prolonged treatment) or relaxin (single injection). It is also possible to conclude that the action of progesterone is indirect and due to the formation of relaxin in the uterus (Zarrow, 1948; Hisaw, Zarrow, Money, Talmage and Abramovitz, 1944). In the mouse, however, progesterone inhibits the action of relaxin on the pubic symphysis (Hall, 1949).

Further evidence that two hormones are involved in pubic relaxation was provided by histologic examination of the pubic ligament. Symphyseal relaxation following estrogen appeared to be due to a resorption of bone and a proliferation of loose fibrous connective tissue with an increase in mucoid alkaline phosphatase and water content (Talmage, 1947a, 1947b, 1950; Heringa and van der Meer, 1948). Relaxin produced a breakdown and splitting of the collagenous fibers into thin threads and a similar change was noted with progesterone (Talmage, 1947a, 1950).

Histochemical and biochemical studies of the pubic symphysis have recently been reviewed (Frieden and Hisaw, 1933) and tend to show that relaxin produces specific changes. These include loss of metachromasia (Heringa and van der Meer, 1948), accumulation of Evans blue in vivo, and increased solubility of the glycoproteins in the McManus-Hotchkiss reaction, all of which indicate that a depolymerization of the ground substance and basement membrane glycoproteins had occurred (Perl and Catchpole, 1950). Frieden and Hisaw (1951) found an increase in water content of the symphyseal tissue, but failed to find a decrease in the water-soluble hexose and hexoseamine following a single injection of relaxin. On the basis of a depolymerization of ground substance, a decrease should have occurred. However, repeated injections of relaxin led to a decrease in the insoluble hexoses and hexoseamines. In addition, consistent decreases in collagen content and trypsin-resistant protein content were noted. No hyaluronidase was found, but β-glucuronidase was increased during relaxation. Gersh and Catchpole (1949) reported the presence of a collagenase from histochemical studies, but no confirmation has been forthcoming. Relaxin also has a protein anabolic effect which occurs in the absence of pubic relaxation (Frieden, 1956). This action was demonstrated by the increased up-take of labeled glycine by the connective tissue proteins of the pubic symphysis. Recent experiments indicate that relaxin not only acts in conjunction with the female sex steroids but can also act alone (Brennan and Zarrow, 1959). However, it is apparent that the available data are still inadequate for a clear understanding of the mechanism of action of relaxin.

Relaxation of the pubic symphysis of the mouse has been studied in great detail by Hall. In a series of reports she showed that pubic relaxation occurs in the mouse during pregnancy and following treatment with estradiol and relaxin (Hall and Newton, 1946a, b). This was later confirmed by Kliman, Salhanick and Zarrow (1953). Contrary to the results reported following work on the guinea pig, progesterone not only failed to influence the effect of estrone on the pubic symphysis of the mouse, but progesterone also inhibited the action of relaxin. It was suggested that this inhibition is the result of an antagonism by progesterone on the action of relaxin and that a true species difference exists (Hall, 1949, 1955). Histologic studies revealed that changes in the pubic symphysis during pregnancy and after treatment with relaxin and estradiol are similar (Hall, 1947). These changes consist of proliferation of articular hyaline cartilage, resorption of the medial ends of the pubes, lengthening of the pubic ligament by formation of new cartilage, and reversion of the cartilage to collagenous connective tissue. Hall (1956) suggested that estradiol causes a depolymerization of the mucopolysaccharides through enzymatic action resulting in a matrix sufficiently pliable to respond to the tensions set up by relaxin. Evidence presented in support of this concept was the loss of metachromasia and the increase in water. In addition, a two-step effect was seen with relaxin: (1) complete degradation of the matrix, and (2) the appearance of a gap in the cranial part of the cartilage produced by stretching of the symphyseal cleft. Some data in support of the latter part of this concept were presented by van der Meer (1954) who showed that inhibition of pelvic muscle tension inhibited relaxation in the guinea pig. In a similar type of experiment Crelin (1954) tied together the innominate bones of a mouse before pregnancy and obtained some dorsoventral displacement of the pubic symphysis but normal relaxation was inhibited.

H. DILATION OF THE UTERINE CERVIX

Dilation or softening of the uterine cervix in the pregnant woman at the time of labor has been known for a long time. This reaction has been used to determine whether delivery can be anticipated. Within recent years this phenomenon has been described in a number of animals and some analysis of the hormonal control of the reaction has been attempted.

Relaxation of the uterine cervix of the rat during pregnancy was first reported by de Vaal in 1946 and confirmed by Uyldert and de Vaal in 1947. Relaxation was measured by the insertion of a gauging pin into a cervix that had been removed and the diameter determined at the point where resistance is first felt. The measurements revealed a marked rise from approximately 3.5 mm. on the 17th day of pregnancy to 10 mm. at parturition. Recently, both Harkness and Harkness (1956) and Yochim and Zarrow (1959) have taken in vitro measurements of the relaxation of the uterine cervix of the rat and observed marked relaxation during the latter part of gestation and at parturition. Yochim and Zarrow (1959) removed the cervix, suspended it from a rod and measured the stretch due to weights added at fixed intervals until the cervix broke. The amount of relaxation of the cervix was determined by the amount of stretch obtained with a weight of 50 gm. Under these conditions, the curve for relaxation of the cervix showed two slopes as pregnancy progressed (Fig. 16.35). The initial slope between day 12 and day 20 showed a rise of approximately 4 mm., with an extremely abrupt rise of 14 mm. on day 21. By 24 hours after parturition the degree of dilation had fallen to 3 mm. It is of interest that the curve for the tensile strength of the cervix (expressed in grams force necessary to tear 1 mg. cervical tissue in a rat weighing 100 gm.) was the opposite to that seen for cervical dilation. The tensile strength fell from approximately 50 gm. force to a low of 3 gm. at parturition and then rose during the postpartum period. The drop in tensile strength preceded the changes in the dilation of the cervix and was essentially completed 5 to 6 days before parturition or when the abrupt increase in dilatability of the cervix occurred.

Similar changes have been described in the dilatability of the cervix of the mouse (Steinetz, Beach and Kroc, 1957) with increased dilatability progressed beyond the 15th day (Fig. 16.36). The diameter of the cervix increased from approximately 2 mm. to about 5 mm. at delivery. It is apparent that the rate of the reaction, i.e., dilation, is much more rapid in the rat, although it is possible that the method of measurement is responsible for the differences.

The induction of cervical dilation by relaxin was reported by Graham and Dracy (1953) in the cow, and by Zarrow, Sikes and Neher (1954) in the sow and the heifer. Treatment with stilbestrol followed by relaxin caused a dilation of the uterine cervix of the gilt from 2/8 or 3/8 inch to 1 inch (Zarrow, Neher, Sikes, Brennan and Bullard, 1956). Measurements were made by the passage of aluminum rods, and, although the technique is not too exact, the differences are significant. Stilbestrol given alone or in combination with progesterone had no effect on the cervical dilation. On the other hand, Smith and Nalbandov (1958) have recently reported that estrogen treatment constricted the uterine cervix of the sow and that relaxin was without effect. A cue with respect to the mechanism of action of relaxin is given by the similarity of the action of relaxin on the pubic symphyseal ligament and the uterine cervix. In both instances, an increase in water content and a marked depolymerization occurs.

Cullen and Harkness (1958) observed relaxation of the uterine cervix of the rat with estradiol alone, or with estradiol and progesterone, or with estradiol and relaxin, but maximal dilation was obtained only with a combination of estradiol, progesterone, and relaxin. In general Kroc, Steinetz and Beach (1959b) obtained comparable results in the rat. Estrogen alone caused some in-

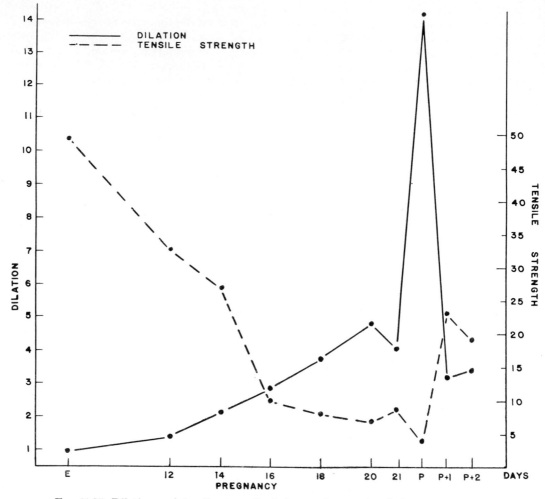

Fig. 16.35. Dilation and tensile strength of the uterine cervix of the rat during estrus, pregnancy, and 2 days postpartum. The dilation of the cervix in mm. of stretch per 50 gm. of added weight. The tensile strength is expressed in grams force necessary to tear 1 mg. cervical tissue in a rat weighing 100 gm. E = estrus; P = parturition. (From J. Yochim and M. X. Zarrow, Fed. Proc., **18,** 174, 1959.)

crease in dilatability when 5 μg. estradiol cyclopentylpropionate were given, and a decrease when 50 μg. were given. Progesterone had no consistent effect either alone or in estrogen-primed animals. Relaxin alone caused some softening of the cervix, but gave a maximal effect only when given with progesterone in estrogen-primed animals. Normal cervical dilation was also obtained in pregnant rats castrated the 15th day of gestation and maintained with progesterone, estradiol, and relaxin (Kroc, Steinetz and Beach, 1959; Yochim and Zarrow, 1959). Data on dilation of the uterine cervix of the

mouse are rather sparse; nevertheless, softening of the cervix with relaxin has been reported (Kroc, Steinetz and Beach, 1959).

It is not the purpose of this review to evaluate the data on cervical softening in the human female. The nature of the action of relaxin in the human female is controversial. Nevertheless, softening of the cervix following treatment with relaxin has been reported (Eichner, Waltner, Goodman and Post, 1956; Stone, Sedlis and Zuckerman, 1958) although McGaughey, Corey and Thornton (1958) reported no effect on the cervix following relaxin.

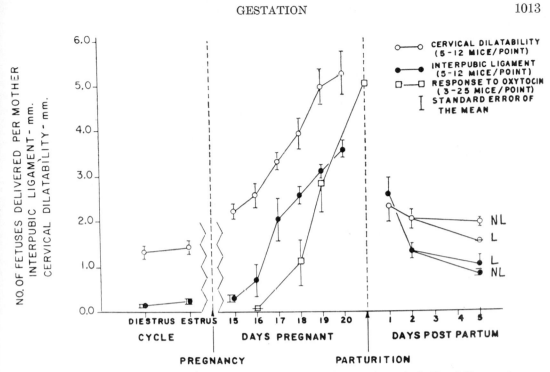

FIG. 16.36. Increased length of the pubic ligament, increased cervical dilatability, and increased responsiveness to oxytocin with the length of pregnancy in the mouse. L = lactating; NL = not lactating. (From B. G. Steinetz, V. L. Beach and R. L. Kroc, Endocrinology, **61**, 271, 1957.)

XII. Uterine Myometrial Activity

The classical and well known description of uterine muscular activity has been more than adequately reviewed by Reynolds (1949). Since then Csapo and his colleagues have reported a series of elegant experiments involving the action of estrogen and progesterone on the uterine myometrium and have evolved the concept of "progesterone block" in the control of uterine activity (1956a, 1956b). It has been shown that the ovarian steroid hormones regulate myometrial activity and that the uterine contractions are dependent on the relative amounts of the two hormones. Contractility is dependent basically on the concentration of the high energy phosphates which are maintained by estrogen which in turn is involved in the synthesis of these substances (Csapo, 1950; Menkes and Csapo, 1952). Discovery of the staircase phenomenon in the uterine myometrium similar to that exhibited by cardiac muscle led to a marked difference between the action of estrogen and progesterone (Csapo and Corner, 1952).

With decreasing frequency of electrical stimulation in an isometric arrangement, tension decreased if the uterus was dominated by estrogen and increased if it was dominated by progesterone. Uteri from castrated rabbits were insensitive to the frequency of electrical stimulation. Thus estrogen induced a "positive staircase" response and progesterone a "negative staircase" response, although in the latter instance some estrogen is also present. These staircase responses have been used successfully as a measure of hormone domination and have been shown to be a function of the Na^+ and K^+ gradients across the myometrial cell membrane.

Uterine motility during estrus, the diestrum, and pregnancy has been described by many investigators in great detail (for a review see Reynolds, 1949). The diestrous uterus shows extremely slow, feeble, uncoordinated movements. The contractions may arise in any part of the uterus and extend in any direction. At estrus, the uterine contractions become rhythmic and sweep over

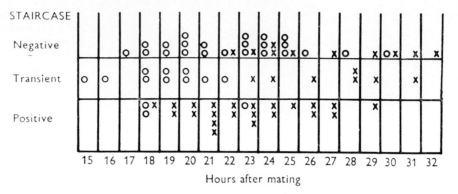

FIG. 16.37. Change from a positive to a negative staircase as the hormone dominance of the myometrium moves from the estrus to the progestational state after mating. × and O indicate the two strains of rabbits used. (From B. M. Schofield, J. Physiol., **138**, 1, 1957.)

the uterine horn in a wave starting at the tubal end. Both amplitude and rate are increased. During pregnancy the uterus becomes relatively quiescent. In general this pattern of myometrial activity has been reproduced with both hormones, estradiol and progesterone.

Recently Schofield (1957), using the Csapo technique, has studied, *in vivo*, myometrial activity in the rabbit. In a series of experiments she was able to show in several strains of rabbits that, when mating occurs during estrus, the uterine myometrium is dominated by estrogen. Within 20 to 28 hours after mating, the positive staircase effect passes through a transient effect to a negative effect indicating the development of progesterone dominance (Fig. 16.37). This condition remained in effect throughout pregnancy until 24 hours before parturition when a reversion to estrogen domination was indicated by the positive staircase response (Fig. 16.38). Thus the progesterone-dominated uterus is maintained throughout pregnancy and the uterus is nonreactive to oxytocin. Csapo (1956a) and others have shown that labor cannot be induced by oxytocin in the rabbit before day 30 of gestation, but 24 hours later, on removal of the progesterone block, 96 per cent of the rabbits delivered following treatment with oxytocin. He believes that the specific action of progesterone involves a blocking of the excitation-contraction coupling which is a consequence of the disturbed ionic balance in the myometrial cell. Thus a block is set up to the propagation of the contraction wave which can be removed only by a decrease in the level of progesterone.

The role of the water-soluble extract, relaxin in myometrial activity, is still uncertain. That an inhibition of estrogen-induced uterine contractions is obtained in certain species, such as the rat, mouse, and guinea pig, with relaxin preparations is unquestionable. However, we still have not answered the questions as to whether this hormone plays a role in uterine contractions under normal physiologic conditions and whether the uterine contraction-inhibiting

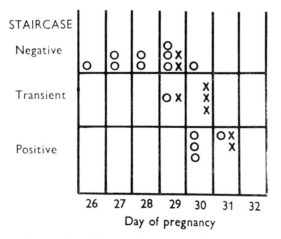

FIG. 16.38. Change from negative through transient to positive staircase as the hormone dominance reverses at the end of pregnancy, indicating estrogen dominance. × and O indicate the two strains of rabbits used. (From B. M. Schofield, J. Physiol. **138**, 1, 1957.)

substance is relaxin or a contaminant of the relaxin extract.

Krantz, Bryant and Carr (1950) reported than an aqueous extract of the corpus luteum would produce an inhibition or decrease of uterine activity in the guinea pig and rabbit previously primed with estrone. This has been amply confirmed with both *in vivo* and *in vitro* preparations involving spontaneous contractions measured isometrically in the guinea pig (Felton, Frieden and Bryant, 1953; Wada and Yuhara, 1956; Miller, Kisley and Murray, 1957), rat (Sawyer, Frieden and Martin, 1953; Wada and Yuhara, 1956; Bloom, Paul and Wiqvist, 1958), and mouse (Kroc, Steinetz and Beach, 1959). However, Miller, Kisley and Murray (1957) failed to show any action of relaxin on uterine motility in the rabbit and the human being *in vitro*. Thus, the information on the rabbit is contradictory and a similar situation exists with regard to the human female for whom both positive and negative results have been reported following treatment with relaxin for threatened abortion (McGaughey, Corey and Thornton, 1958; Stone, Sedlis and Zuckerman, 1958; Eichner, Herman, Kritzer, Platock and Rubinstein, 1959). In briefly summarizing the action of relaxin on the uterine myometrium it should be pointed out that (1) relaxin inhibits uterine motility in an estrogen-primed animal, (2) the action may be species-limited, and (3) relaxin treatment does not interfere with the action of pitocin.

XIII. Parturition

A. PROGESTERONE

A number of theories have been suggested to explain the hormonal control of parturition. The most popular is that parturition is due to a decrease in the level of progesterone which allows oxytocin to exert its effect on the uterus. Evidence has already been presented indicating that pregnancy can be maintained in the castrated rabbit by an extract of corpora lutea, or progesterone, and even prolonged in rats (Nelson, Pfiffner and Haterius, 1930; Miklos, 1930), mice (Mandelstamm and Tschaikowsky, 1931), and rabbits (Zarrow, 1947a). Snyder

(1934) and Koff and Davis (1937) prolonged gestation in rabbits by inducing the formation of new corpora lutea during the last trimester of pregnancy.

Knaus (1930) originally noted a marked antagonism between posterior pituitary extract and the corpus luteum hormone and Koff and Davis (1937) reported that in prolonged gestation induced by progesterone, posterior pituitary extract was ineffective until two days after the last injection. Csapo (1956a) performed a series of elegant experiments and concluded that progesterone blocks the uterine contractions, and that premature labor could not be induced with oxytocin before the 30th day of gestation in the rabbit except for a very small percentage of animals. This has been confirmed by Fuchs and Fuchs (1958).

Zarrow and Neher (1955) found the serum gestagen levels in the pregnant rabbit fell only after parturition was under way. Hence the problem arose as to how parturition could begin while a high blood concentration of gestagen was present. A partial answer was obtained in experiments by Csapo (1956b) and Schofield (1957) who showed that the progesterone-dominated uterus of the pregnant rabbit becomes estrogen-dominated and responsive to oxytocin 24 hours before parturition. Hence the concentration of progesterone in the serum is meaningless by itself and it could be theorized that the significant point is the ratio of estrogen to progesterone. Csapo (1956a), however, offered an alternative solution. He observed a local effect of placental progesterone on the myometrium so that the myometrium closest to the placenta is under a greater progesterone-dominance than that portion of the myometrium lying more distant. Hence the local level of progesterone would be the significant factor in the onset of parturition and not the systemic level.

B. OXYTOCIN

It is now generally believed that parturition is the result of the action of the posterior pituitary hormone on the myometrium of the uterus sensitized by estrogen. The development of this hypothesis followed from the well known fact that oxytocin produces uterine contractions and induces labor and delivery of the young. It is apparent, however, that a mass of contradictory data exist and the hypothesis is still in need of better evidence before it can be fully accepted (for review of early literature see Reynolds, 1949).

Some of the evidence supporting the above hypothesis is the fact of the presence, to a limited degree, of a deficiency syndrome in parturition following removal of the posterior pituitary gland. The data, however, are still equivocal. Labor is apparently prolonged in the monkey (Smith, 1946) and guinea pig (Dey, Fisher and Ranson, 1941) after total hypophysectomy. Nevertheless, parturition will occur normally after removal of the pituitary gland in the rabbit (Robson, 1936), cat (Allen and Wiles, 1932), mouse (Gardner and Allen, 1942), and rat (Smith, 1932). Even where there is some indication of interference with labor, delivery occurs. However, the lack of consistent results and species differences may be due to the recent finding that the posterior pituitary hormones are synthesized in the hypothalamus and that removal of the posterior pituitary is only effective under limited conditions because the source of the hormone is still present. These experiments have also been criticized on the ground that the anterior pituitary was also removed and hence interference with many other hormones occurred.

Additional evidence in favor of a role for the neurohypophysis in the delivery of the young is the increase in uterine motility following stimuli that bring about release of the posterior pituitary hormones, and the lack of an effect on the uterus when release of the hormone is blocked.

Positive evidence for the release of oxytocin at the time of parturition is still lacking as are measurements of the concentration in the blood. Fitzpatrick (1957) takes the view that oxytocin is liberated as an essential part of normal parturition and cites the following evidence. (1) A superficial similarity exists between spontaneous labor and that induced by oxytocin. Harris (1955) also stresses the similarity in the uterine response to oxytocin and to electrical stimulation of the supraoptic hypophyseal nucleus. (2) Mechanical dilation of the uterus or cervix evokes an increase in uterine contractions presumably by way of a nervous reflex release of oxytocin (Ferguson, 1941). (3) Oxytocin is decreased in the posterior pituitary gland of the rat and the dog after labor (Dicker and Tyler, 1953).

Evidence from the attempts to measure the concentration of oxytocin in body fluids at the time of parturition is inadequate. The early reports of higher concentrations in the urine (Cockrill, Miller and Kurzrok, 1934) and blood (Bell and Morris, 1934; Bell and Robson, 1935) during parturition are questioned because of the inadequate methods of extraction and lack of specificity in the assay. Recently, Hawker and Robertson (1957, 1958) reinvestigated the problem and concluded that two oxytocic substances are present in the blood and hypothalamus of cats, cows, and rats and blood of women. However, they found that the concentration of oxytocin in the blood fell during labor from a high during pregnancy. It is apparent that this presents a paradoxical situation in view of the fact that the concentration of oxytocin is low at the time of parturition; a time when the hormone is supposedly exerting its greatest effect. The situation is further complicated by the presence of two oxytocic factors and the presence of an oxytocinase in the blood and placenta (von Fekete, 1930; Page, 1946; Woodbury, Ahlquist, Abreu, Torpin and Watson, 1946; Hawker, 1956). Although more work is required on this problem and especially with regard to the specificity and concentration of the oxytocinase, there is some indication of a fall in enzyme level before parturition. Tyler (1955) reported a decrease in the blood level of the enzyme towards the end of pregnancy and Sawyer (1954) reported a decrease in oxytocinase activity in rat tissues at the end of pregnancy.

C. RELAXIN

Recently, the discovery of the action of relaxin on the pubic symphysis, uterine cervix, and uterine motility has raised the question of the role of this hormone in parturition. Certainly in the species that normally show pubic relaxation, relaxin would appear to play a significant role. However, this phenomenon is a special adaptation and the question of cervical dilatability becomes more important because it seems to occur in all species examined thus far. It would seem that relaxin can induce cervical dilatability in conjunction with the sex steroids and that cervical dilation is a necessary event in parturition, but whether relaxin controls this event under physiologic conditions is still unknown and direct evidence is unavailable. It is also apparent in some species that relaxin can inhibit uterine contractions without interfering with the action of oxytocin. Kroc, Steinetz and Beach (1959) reported that relaxin actually restored responsiveness to oxytocin in mice treated with progesterone. Again the question is raised as to whether this is merely a good experiment or a part of the normal physiologic events.

D. LABOR

In a general way the events leading to labor may be summarized as follows. As pregnancy approaches term, the uterus becomes subject to increasing pressure from within, due to a differential change in the growth rates of the fetus and the uterus (Woodbury, Hamilton and Torpin, 1938). Concurrently, a reversal from progesterone to estrogen domination occurs, which also contributes to an increase in uterine tonus. As intra-uterine tension increases, spontaneous contractions acquire a greater efficiency and forcefulness. Because the radius of curvature in the human uterus is greater at the fundus than at the cervix, and because the myometrium is thicker at the upper pole (by a factor of 2) the contractile force is stronger at the fundus than at the cervical end. This contractile gradient produces a thrust toward the cervix.

Utilization of a type of strain gauge, the tokodynamometer, has afforded information on the rate and strength of contraction of the various parts of the parturient uterus simultaneously (Reynolds, Heard, Bruns and Hellman, 1948). These measurements have indicated that, during the first stage of labor, the fundus exerts strong contractions of rather long duration. The corpus exhibits less intense contractions, usually of shorter duration, which frequently diminish in force as labor advances. The lower uterine segment is almost inactive throughout the first

stage of parturition. According to Reynolds (1949), both the fundus and the midportion contract at the same time, but the fundus remains contracted for a longer period of time than the corpus beneath, thus building up a force downward. If cervical dilation has not occurred, the three areas of the uterus will continue to contract. As cervical dilation begins, the contractions in the midportion of the uterus decrease in intensity and the contractions in the lower segment disappear. Cervical dilation has been observed only when there is a preponderance of rhythmic activity of the fundus over the rest of the uterus.

When amniotic fluid is lost after the rupture of the membranes, the absolute tension within the wall of the uterus is reduced so that the ratio of force between fundus and cervix is increased. Thus rupture of the membranes decreases the tension in the cervix more than the fundus and the net effect is an increased force from the fundus. This change tends to precipitate the parturition more rapidly.

As pregnancy nears term, both increased tonus of the myometrium and rapid growth of the fetus cause a rise in intra-uterine pressure. This rise results in a decrease of effective arterial blood pressure in the placenta. During this period also, thrombosis is observed in many of the venous sinuses of the placenta and many of the blood vessels become more or less obstructed by giant cells. During parturition, the systemic blood pressure of the mother rises with each contraction, but, due to the increased intra-uterine pressure produced by the contractions, the effective maternal arterial blood pressure in the placenta decreases to zero. Thus maternal circulation is cut off from the fetus.

Measurements of intra-uterine pressure at term show that the human uterus contracts with a pressure wave which varies from 25 to 95 mm. Hg (Woodbury, Hamilton and Torpin, 1938). The uterine wall is subjected to an average tension of 500 gm. per cm.^{2} and, during delivery of the head, may, with the aid of abdominal musculature, develop as much as 15 kg. force.

In animals giving birth to multiple young (rat and mouse) evacuation of the horn proceeds in an orderly fashion beginning at the cervical end. As evacuation of the lowest implantation site starts, changes occur in the periods of contractions of segments of uterine artery near its entrance into the uterine wall (Knisely, 1934; Keiffer, 1919). Gradually the constriction phase becomes proportionately longer than the dilation phase until the arterial lumen is obliterated. The myometrium in the area of the constricting segments becofes more active and, after long intense local contractions of the uterine muscle, the fetuses and the placentas separate and are discharged through the dilated cervix. After evacuation, a relaxation of the contracted segment of uterus occurs and the process is repeated at the next implantation site.

Recently, Cross (1958) re-examined the problem of labor in the rabbit. He concluded that (1) oxytocin in physiologic amounts can induce labor that is comparable to the events normally seen, (2) oxytocin is released during a normal labor, and (3) oxytocin can induce delivery without supplementary mechanisms. He noted that straining movements involving reflex abdominal contractions initiated by distention of the vagina and cervix aided in expulsion of the fetus. It is also possible that this might cause reflexly an increased secretion of oxytocin. Other reflex mechanisms have been suggested, but evidence is inadequate. Cross cites a report by Kurdinowski published in 1904 in which the entire process of labor and delivery in an isolated full-term rabbit uterus perfused with Locke's solution is described. In these experiments orderly delivery of the viable fetuses was affected by the contractile efforts of the uterus and vagina in absence of any hormonal or nervous stimuli.

XIV. Conclusion

Although we have garnered much information, no major conclusions can be drawn at this time concerning gestation in the mammal. This is probably true because of the vastness of the subject and the lack of sufficient data, especially that of a comparative nature. It is probably fitting to close this chapter with the final statement written by Newton in the second edition of Sex and Internal Secretion, "It seems rather

that the investigation of endocrine relationships during pregnancy is still in the exploratory stage and that the time is not ripe for systematization."

It is true that many data have been accumulated in the last two decades since the publication of the second edition of this book. It is also probably true that some systematization can now be started. But above all we need more data on different species in order to systematize fully the role of the various hormones and glands in pregnancy and to evaluate the metabolic and other changes that occur at this time.

XV. References

ADAMS, J. Q. 1954. Cardiovascular physiology in normal pregnancy: studies with the dye dilution technique. Am. J. Obst. & Gynec., **67,** 741.

AHLMARK, A. 1944. Studies on the histaminolytic power of plasma with special reference to pregnancy. Acta physiol. scandinav., **9,** suppl. 28.

AHLMARK, A. 1947. The histaminolytic power of plasma with special reference to pregnancy. In *17th International Physiological Congress,* p. 127. Oxford.

AITKEN, E. H., AND PREEDY, J. R. K. 1957. The determination of plasma estrogen levels in late pregnancy. Ciba Foundation Colloquia Endocrinol., **11,** 331.

ALBERT, A. 1949. Evaluation of the hypermia test for pregnancy as a routine clinical laboratory procedure: comparison of results with those of 1000 consecutive Friedman tests. Proc. Staff Meet. Mayo Clin., **24,** 259.

ALEXANDER, D. A., FRAZER, J. F. D., AND LEE, J. 1955. The effect of steroids on the maintenance of pregnancy in the spayed rat. J. Physiol., **130,** 148.

ALLAN, H., AND WILES, P. 1932. The role of the pituitary gland in pregnancy and parturition, hypophysectomy in the cat. J. Physiol., **75,** 23.

ALLEN, E., HISAW, F. L., AND GARDNER, W. U. 1939. The endocrine function of the ovaries. In *Sex and Internal Secretions,* 1st ed., E. Allen, Ed. Baltimore: The Williams & Wilkins Company.

ALLEN, W. M. 1937. Some effects of estrin and progestin in the rabbit. Cold Spring Harbor Symposia Quant. Biol., **5,** 104.

ALLEN, W. M., BUTENANDT, A., CORNER, G. W., AND SLOTTA, K. H. 1935. Nomenclature of corpus luteum hormone. Science, **82,** 153.

ALLEN, W. M., AND CORNER, G. W. 1929. Physiology of corpus luteum. III. Normal growth and implantation of embryos after early ablation of ovaries, under the influence of extracts of the corpus luteum. Am. J. Physiol., **88,** 340.

ALLEN, W. M. AND CORNER, G. W. 1930. Physiology of corpus luteum. VII. Maintenance of pregnancy in rabbit after very early castration, by corpus luteum extracts. Proc. Soc. Exper. Biol. & Med., **27**, 403.

ALLEN, W. M., AND HECKEL, G. P. 1939. Maintenance of pregnancy by progesterone in rabbits castrated on the 11th day. Am. J. Physiol., **125**, 31.

ALLISON, R. M. 1954. Reduced maintenance of frogs used for pregnancy diagnosis by enforced hibernation. J. Endocrinol., **11**, 377.

AREY, L. B. 1946. *Developmental Anatomy*, 5th ed. Philadelphia: W. B. Saunders Company.

ASCHHEIM, S., AND ZONDEK, B. 1927. Ei und Hormon. Klin. Wchnschr., **6**, 1321.

ASCHHEIM, S., AND ZONDEK, B. 1928. Die Schwangerschaftsdiagnose aus dem Harm durch Nochweis des Hyphysenvorderlappenhormons. Klin. Wchnschr., **7**, 1453.

ASCHKENASY-LELU, P., AND ASCHKENASY, A. 1957. Intervention des surrénales dans le gestation en fonction de la teneur du régime en proteins. Arch. Sc. Physiol., **11**, 125.

ASCHNER, B. 1912. Über die Funktion der Hypophyse. Arch. ges. Physiol., **65**, 341.

ASDELL, S. A. 1946. *Patterns of Mammalian Reproduction*. Ithaca, N. Y.: Comstock Publishing Company, Inc.

ASSALI, N. S., AND HAMERMESZ, J. 1954. Adrenocorticotrophic substances from human placenta. Endocrinology, **55**, 561.

ASTWOOD, E. B., AND GREEP, R. O. 1938. A corpus-stimulating substance in the rat placenta. Proc. Soc. Exper. Biol. & Med., **38**, 713.

ATKINSON, W. B., AND HOOKER, C. W. 1945. Day day level of estrogen and progestin throughout pregnancy and pseudopregnancy in mouse. Anat. Rec., **93**, 75.

BALFOUR, W. E., COMLINE, R. S., AND SHORT, R. V. 1957. Secretion of progesterone by the adrenal gland. Nature, London, **180**, 1480.

BARCROFT, J., KENNEDY, A., AND MASON, M. F. 1939. The blood volume and kindred properties in pregnant sheep. J. Physiol., **95**, 159.

BARCROFT, J., AND ROTHSCHILD, P. 1932. The volume of blood in the uterus during pregnancy. J. Physiol., **76**, 447.

BASSETT, E. G., AND PHILLIPS, D. S. M. 1954. Pelvic relaxation in sheep. Nature, London, **174**, 1020.

BASSETT, E. G., AND PHILLIPS, D. S. M. 1955. Changes in the pelvic region of the ewe during pregnancy and parturition. New Zealand Vet. J., **3**, 20.

BEALL, D., AND REICHSTEIN, T. 1938. Isolation of progesterone and allopregnanolone from the adrenal. Nature, London, **142**, 479.

BEARD, H. H., AND MYERS, V. C. 1933. Studies in the nutritional anemia of the rat. IX. Observations on the anemia of pregnancy. Am. J. Physiol., **106**, 449.

BELL, G. H., AND MORRIS, S. 1934. The oxytocic property of the blood of the cow. J. Physiol., **81**, 63.

BELL, G. H., AND ROBSON, J. M. 1935. Oxytocic properties of blood extracts and their physiologic significance. J. Physiol., **84**, 351.

BELLERBY, C. W. 1934. A rapid test for the diagnosis of pregnancy. Nature, London, **133**, 194.

BERLINER, D. L., JONES, J. E., AND SALHANICK, H. A. 1956. The isolation of adrenal-like steroids from the human placenta. J. Biol. Chem., **223**, 1043.

BIBB, J. D. 1941. Protein and hemoglobin in normal and toxic pregnancies. Am. J. Obst. & Gynec., **42**, 103.

BICKERS, W. 1942. The placenta: a modified arterio-venous fistula. South. Med. J., **35**, 593.

BLOOM, G., PAUL, K. G., AND WIQVIST, N. 1958. A uterine-relaxing factor in the pregnant rat. Acta Endocrinol., **28**, 112.

BOKELMANN, O., AND SCHERINGER, W. 1930. Beitrag zur Kenntnis der Schilddrüsenfunktion und des Jodstoffwechsels in der gestation. Arch. Gynäk., **143**, 512.

BOND, C. F. 1948. The nature of the anemia of pregnancy in the rat. Endocrinology, **43**, 180.

BRADBURY, J. T., AND BROWN, W. E. 1949. Absorption and excretion of chorionic gonadotrophin administered intramuscularly in women. J. Clin. Endocrinol., **8**, 1037.

BRENNAN, D. M., AND ZARROW, M. X. 1959. Water and electrolyte content of the uterus of the intact and adrenalectomized rat treated with relaxin and various steroid hormones. Endocrinology, **64**, 907.

BROMBERG, Y. M., BRZEZINSKI, A., ROZIN, S., AND SULMAN, F. G. 1951. Reliability of pregnancy tests with male batrachia and female rodents. Acta endocrinol., **7**, 31.

BROWN, W. E., AND BRADBURY, J. T. 1947. A study of the physiologic action of human chorionic hormone. Am. J. Obst. & Gynec., **53**, 749.

BROWNE, J. S. L., HENRY, J. S., AND VENNING, E. H. 1938. The urinary excretion of prolan, estrin and pregnanediol in normal pregnancy. J. Clin. Invest., **17**, 503.

BRUCE, H. M., AND EAST, J. 1956. Number and viability of young from pregnancies concurrent with lactation in the mouse. J. Endocrinol., **14**, 19.

BRUCE, H. M., AND SLOVITER, H. A. 1957. Effect of destruction of thyroid tissue by radioactive iodine on reproduction in mice. J. Endocrinol., **15**, 72.

BRUNER, J. A. 1951. Distribution of chorionic gonadotrophin in mother and fetus at various stages of pregnancy. J. Clin. Endocrinol., **11**, 360.

BRYANS, F. E. 1951. Progesterone of the blood in the menstrual cycle of the monkey. Endocrinology, **48**, 733.

BUCHT, H. 1951. Studies on renal function in man. Scandinav. J. Clin. & Lab. Invest., **3**, suppl. 3, 5.

BURT, C. C. 1950. Symposium on haemodynamics in pregnancy. IV. The peripheral circulation in pregnancy. Edinburgh Med. J., **57**, 18.

BURWELL, C. S. 1938. The placenta as a modified arteriovenous fistula, considered in relation to the circulatory adjustments to pregnancy. Am. J. Med. Sc., **195,** 1.

BUTENANDT, A., WESTPHAL, U., AND COBLER, H. 1934. Über einen Abbau des Stigmasterius zu Corpus-Luteumwirksamen Stoffen; ein Beitrag zier Konstitution des Corpus-Luteum Hormons (Vorläuf. mitteil). Ber. deutsch. chem. Gesellsch., **67,** 1611.

CARLSTEN, A. 1950. No change in the histaminase content of lymph and plasma in cats during pregnancy. Acta physiol. scandinav., **20,** suppl. 70, 27.

CASTELLANI, A., AND CHALMERS, A. S. 1919. *Manual of Tropical Medicine*, 3rd ed. New York: William Wood & Company.

CATCHPOLE, H. R., AND LYONS, W. R. 1934. The gonad-stimulating hormone of pregnant mares. Am. J. Anat., **55,** 167.

CATON, W. L., ROBY, C. C., REID, D. E., AND GIBSON, J. G., 2nd. 1949. Plasma volume and extravascular fluid volume during pregnancy and the puerperium. Am. J. Obst. & Gynec., **57,** 471.

CATON, W. L., ROBY, C. C., REID, D. E., CASWELL, C. J., MELETSKOS, C. J., FLUHARTY, R. G., AND GIBSON, J. G. 1951. The circulating red cell volume and body hematocrit in normal pregnancy and the puerperium. Am. J. Obst. & Gynec., **61,** 1207.

CHANG, M. C. 1951. Maintenance of pregnancy in intact rabbits in the absence of corpora lutea. Endocrinology, **48,** 17.

CHART, J. J., SHIPLEY, E. G., AND GORDON, E. S. 1951. Evidence for a sodium retaining factor in toxemia of pregnancy. Proc. Soc. Exper. Biol. & Med., **78,** 244.

CHESLEY, L. C. 1943. Study of extracellular water changes in pregnancy. Surg. Gynec. & Obst., **76,** 589.

CHESLEY, L. C., AND CHESLEY, E. R. 1941. Extracellular water in late pregnancy and its relation to the development of toxemia. Am. J. Obst. & Gynec., **42,** 976.

CHITTY, H. 1957. The estrous cycle and gestation period in the lactating field vole, *Microtus agrestis*. J. Endocrinol., **15,** 279.

CHRISTIAN, J. J., AND LEMUNYAN, C. D. 1958. Adverse effects of crowding on lactation and reproduction of mice and two generations of their progeny. Endocrinology, **63,** 517.

CHU, J. P. 1945. The influence of the thyroid on pregnancy and parturition in the rabbit. J. Endocrinol., **4,** 109.

CLEGG, M. T., BODA, J. M., AND COLE, H. H. 1954. The endometrial cups and allantochorionic pouches in the mare with emphasis on the source of equine gonadotrophin. Endocrinology, **54,** 448.

COCKRILL, J. R., MILLER, E. G., AND KURZROK, R. 1934. Presence of oxytocic substance in urine

during labor. Proc. Soc. Exper. Biol. & Med., **31,** 527.

COHEN, M., STIEFEL, M., REDDY, W. J., AND LAIDLAW, J. C. 1958. The secretion and disposition of cortisol during pregnancy. J. Clin. Endocrinol., **18,** 1076.

COLE, H. H., AND GOSS, H. 1943. The source of equine gonadotrophin. In *Essays in Biology in Honor of Herbert H. Evans*, p. 107. San Francisco: University of California Press.

COLE, H. H., AND HART, G. H. 1930. The potency of blood serum of mares in progessive stages of pregnancy in effecting the sexual maturity of the immature rat. Am. J. Physiol., **93,** 57.

COLE, H. H., AND SAUNDERS, F. J. 1935. The concentration of gonad-stimulating hormone in blood serum and of estrin in the urine throughout pregnancy in the mare. Endocrinology, **19,** 199.

CONTOPOULOS, A. N., AND SIMPSON, M. E. 1956. Increased FSH and ICSH content in the pituitary of pregnant rats. Anat. Rec., **124,** 276.

CONTOPOULOS, A. N., AND SIMPSON, M. E. 1957. Increased growth promoting substance in the plasma of pregnant rats. Endocrinology, **61,** 765.

CONTOPOULOS, A. N., AND SIMPSON, M. E. 1959. Growth-promoting activity of pregnant rat plasma after hypophysectomy and after thyroidectomy. Endocrinology, **64,** 1023.

COPPEDGE, R. L., AND SEGALOFF, A. 1951. Urinary prolactin excretion in man. J. Clin. Endocrinol., **11,** 465.

CORNER, G. W. 1929. Physiology of the corpus luteum. II. Production of a special uterine reaction (progestational proliferation) by extracts of corpus luteum. Am. J. Physiol., **88,** 326.

COURRIER, R. 1931. Recherches sur le Mechanisme de la Crise Génital du Nouveau-Né. In *Proceedings Second International Congress for Sex Research*, p. 355. Edinburgh: Oliver & Boyd.

COURRIER, R. 1940. La désoxycorticosterone est Capable de Maintenir la Grossesse on de Provoquer l'avortement. Presse méd., **48,** 658.

COURRIER, R., AND COLONGE, R. A. 1950. Nouvelles remarques concernant l'effet de l'ovariectomie sur la gestation. Compt. rend. Siances, Acad. Sc., **230,** 1438.

COURRIER, R., AND COLONGE, R. A. 1951. Cortisone et gestation chez la lapine. Compt. rend. Acad. Sc., **232,** 1164.

COURRIER, R., AND KEHL, R. 1938a. Données préliminaires sur le besoin quantitatifen progestine chez la lapine gestante castrie. Realisation de grossesses partielles. Compt. rend. Soc. biol., **127,** 529.

COURRIER, R., AND KEHL, R. 1938b. Sur le besoin hormonal quantitatif chez la lapine gestante castrée. Compt. rend. Soc. biol., **128,** 188.

COURRIER, R., AND MAROIS, M. 1953. Action de l'hypothermie experimental sur la gestation chez le rat. Compt. rend. Soc. biol., **23,** 1922.

CRELIN, E. S. 1954. Prevention of innominate

bone separation during pregnancy in the mouse. Proc. Soc. Exper. Biol. & Med., **86**, 22.

CREW, F. A. E. 1939. Biological pregnancy diagnosis tests: a comparison of the rabbit, the mouse and the "clawed toad" (*Xenopus laevus*) as experimental animal. Brit. M. J., **1**, 766.

CROSS, B. A. 1958. On the mechanism of labor in the rabbit. J. Endocrinol., **16**, 261.

CROXATTO, H., VERA, C., AND BARNAFI, L. 1953. Inactivation of antidiuretic hormone by blood serum of the pregnant woman. Proc. Soc. Exper. Biol. & Med., **83**, 784.

CSAPO, A. 1950. Actomyosin of the uterus. Am. J. Physiol., **160**, 46.

CSAPO, A. 1956a. Progesterone "block." Am. J. Anat., **98**, 273.

CSAPO, A. 1956b. The mechanism of effect of the ovarian steroids. Recent Progr. Hormone Res., **12**, 405.

CSAPO, A., AND CORNER, G. 1952. The antagonistic effects of estrogen and progesterone on the staircase phenomenon in uterine muscle. Endocrinology, **51**, 378.

CULLEN, B. M., AND HARKNESS, R. D. 1958. Effect of estradiol, progesterone and relaxin on the physical properties of uterine cervix. J. Physiol., **140**, 46P.

CUPPS, P. T. 1955. The ability of certain adrenal steroids to restore reproduction in adrenalectomized female rats. Endocrinology, **57**, 1.

CURLEY, F. J., AND INGALLS, T. H. 1957. Hypoxia at normal atmospheric pressure as a cause of congenital malformations in mice. Proc. Soc. Exper. Biol. & Med., **94**, 87.

CUTULY, E. 1942. Effects of lactogenic and gonadotrophic hormones on hypophysectomized pregnant rats. Endocrinology, **31**, 13.

DANCIS, J., MONEY, W. L., CONDON, G. P., AND LEVITZ, M. 1958. The relative transfer of estrogens and their glucuronides across the placenta in the guinea pig. J. Clin. Invest., **37**, 1373.

DANFORTH, D. N., AND GORHAM, F. 1937. Placental histaminase. Am. J. Physiol., **119**, 294.

DAVIS, M. E., FUGO, N. W., AND LAWRENCE, K. G. 1947. Effect of alloxan diabetes on reproduction in the rat. Proc. Soc. Exper. Biol. & Med., **66**, 638.

DAVIS, M. E., AND PLOTZ, E. J. 1954. The effects of cortisone acetate on intact and adrenalectomized rats during pregnancy. Endocrinology, **54**, 384.

DAY, E. M. A. 1948. The urinary excretion of 17-ketosteroids and of corticosteroid-like hormones by the newborn infant. M. J. Australia, **2**, 122.

DE ALVAREZ, R. R. 1958. Renal glomerulotubular mechanisms during normal pregnancy. I. Glomerular filtration rate, plasma flow and creatine clearance. Am. J. Obst. & Gynec., **75**, 931.

DEANESLY, R. 1943. Delayed implantation in the stoat. Nature, London, **151**, 365.

DEANESLY, R. 1944. The reproductive cycle of the female weasel (*Mustela nivalis*). Proc. Zool. Soc., Part III, **114**, 339.

DEANESLY, R., AND NEWTON, W. H. 1940. The influence of the placenta on the corpus luteum of pregnancy in the mouse. J. Endocrinol., **2**, 317.

DEANESLY, R., AND WARWICK, T. 1939. Observations on pregnancy in the common bat (*Pipistrellus pipistrellus*). Proc. Zool. Soc. London, ser. A, **109**, 57.

DE FREMERY, P., KOBER, S., AND TAUSK, M. 1931. Errveiterung der Symphysis pubis des weiblichen Meerschweinchens durch Mentorman. Acta. brev. neerl. Physiol., **1**, 146.

DESSAU, F. 1935. Effect of crystalline female sex hormones on the pelvic ligaments of the guinea pig. Acta brev. neerl. Physiol., **5**, 1.

DESSAU, F. 1937. Observations on adrenalectomized pregnant rats. Acta brev. neerl. Physiol., **7**, 55.

DE VAAL, O. M. 1946. Extensibility of the ostium uteri in the rat. Acta brev. neerl. Physiol., **14**, 79.

DEY, F. L., FISHER, C., AND RANSON, S. W. 1941. Disturbances in pregnancy and labor in guinea pigs with hypothalamic lesions. Am. J. Obst. & Gynec., **42**, 459.

DICKER, S. E., AND TYLER, C. M. 1953. Vasopressor and oxytocic activities of the pituitary glands of rats, guinea pigs and cats and of human fetuses. J. Physiol., **121**, 206.

DICZFALUSY, E., AND LINDKVIST, P. 1956. Isolation and estimation of "free" estrogens in human placentae. Acta endocrinol., **22**, 203.

DICZFALUSY, E., TILLINGER, K. G., AND WESTMAN, A. 1957. Studies on estrogen metabolism in newborn boys. 1. Excretion of estrone estradiol 17β and estriol during the first few days of life. Acta endocrinol., **26**, 307.

DIECKMANN, W. J., AND WEGNER, C. R. 1934a. Studies of the blood in normal pregnancy. I. Blood and plasma volumes. Arch. Int. Med., **53**, 71.

DIECKMANN, W. J., AND WEGNER, C. R. 1934b. Studies of the blood in normal pregnancy. II. Hemoglobin, hematocrit and erythrocyte determinations and total amount of variations of each. Arch. Int. Med., **53**, 188.

DIECKMANN, W. J., AND WEGNER, C. R. 1934c. Studies of the blood in normal pregnancy. III. Hemoglobin and cell volume coefficients; erythrocyte volume; hemoglobin content and concentration; color; volume and saturation indexes. Arch. Int. Med., **53**, 345.

DIECKMANN, W. J., AND WEGNER, C. R. 1934d. Studies of the blood in normal pregnancy. IV. Percentages and grams per kilogram of serum protein and fibrin and variations in the total amount of each. Arch. Int. Med., **53**, 353.

DIGNAM, W. J., TITUS, P., AND ASSALI, N. S. 1958. Renal function in human pregnancy. I. Changes in glomerular filtration rate and renal plasma flow. Proc. Soc. Exper. Biol. & Med., **97**, 512.

DILL, L. V., ISENHOUR, C. E., CADDEN, J. F., AND SCHAFFER, N. K. 1942. Glomerular filtration and renal blood flow in the toxemias of pregnancy. Am. J. Obst. & Gynec., **43**, 32.

DINGEMANSE, E., BORCHARDT, H., AND LAQUEUR, E. 1937. Capon conab growth-promoting substances ("male hormones") in human urine of males and females of varying age. Biochem. J., **31**, 500.

DOBRINER, K. 1943. Qualitative and quantitative determinations of urinary steroid hormone metabolites in normal persons, in patients with cancer, adrenal disorders, pregnancy and mycoid and lymphatic leukemia; and its subjects receiving testosterone medication. Macy Foundation Conferences on Metabolic Disorders of Convalescence, **3**, 211.

EASTMAN, N. J. 1946. Diabetes mellitus and pregnancy; a review. Obst. & Gynec. Surv., **1**, 3.

EDGAR, D. G. 1953. The progesterone content of body fluids and tissues. J. Endocrinol., **10**, 54.

EDGAR, D. G., AND RONALDSON, J. W. 1958. Blood levels of progesterone in the ewe. J. Endocrinol., **16**, 378.

EICHNER, E., HERMAN, I., KRITZER, L., PLATOCK, G. M., AND RUBINSTEIN, L. 1959. The effects of relaxin on term and premature labor. Ann. New York Acad. Sc., **75**, 1023.

EICHNER, E., WALTNER, C., GOODMAN, M., AND POST, S. 1956. Relaxin, the third ovarian hormone: its experimental use in women. Am. J. Obst. & Gynec., **71**, 1935.

ENDERS, R. K. 1952. Reproduction in the mink (*Mustela vison*). Proc. Am. Phil. Soc., **96**, 691.

ENGLE, E. T. 1939. Gonadotrophic substance of blood urine and other body fluids. In *Sex and Internal Secretion*, 2nd ed., E. Allen, C. H. Danforth and E. A. Doisy, Eds., Baltimore: The Williams & Wilkins Company.

FARRIS, E. J. 1950. *The Care and Breeding of Laboratory Animals*. New York: John Wiley & Sons, Inc.

FELDMAN, J. D. 1958. Iodine metabolism in pregnancy. Am. J. Physiol., **192**, 273.

FELTON, L. C., FRIEDEN, E. H., AND BRYANT, H. H. 1953. The effects of ovarian extracts upon activity of the guinea pig uterus *in situ*. J. Pharmacol. & Exper. Therap., **107**, 160.

FERGUSON, J. H. 1950. Pregnancy hemoglobin levels in the rural south. Am. J. Obst. & Gynec., **60**, 411.

FERGUSON, J. K. W. 1941. A study of the motility of the intact uterus at term. Surg. Gynec. & Obst., **73**, 359.

FERNANDEZ-CANO, L. 1958a. Effect of increase or decrease of body temperature and hypoxia on pregnancy in the rat. Fertil. & Steril., **9**, 455.

FERNANDEZ-CANO, L. 1958b. Effects of changes in body temperature and hypoxia on pregnancy in adrenalectomized rats. Fertil. & Steril., **9**, 461.

FITZPATRICK, R. J. 1957. On oxytocin and uterine function. In *The Neurohypophysis*. New York: Academic Press, Inc.

FORBES, T. R. 1951. Systemic levels of plasma progesterone during pregnancy in women and monkeys. Endocrinology, **49**, 218.

FORBES, T. R., AND HOOKER, C. W. 1957. Plasma levels of progestin during pregnancy in the mouse. Endocrinology, **61**, 281.

FORD, D. H., WEBSTER, R. C., AND YOUNG, W. C. 1951. Rupture of the vaginal closure membrane during pregnancy in the guinea pig. Anat. Rec., **109**, 707.

FRAENKEL, L. 1903. Die function des corpus luteum. Arch. Gynäk., **68**, 583.

FRAENKEL, L. 1910. Neue experimenté zur function des corpus luteum. Arch. Gynäk., **91**, 705.

FRAENKEL, L., AND COHN, F. 1901. Experimentalle unterschung über den einfluss des corpus luteum auf die insertion des eies. Anat. Anz., **20**, 294.

FRANK, R. T., AND BERMAN, R. L. 1941. A twenty-four hour pregnancy test. Am. J. Obst. & Gynec., **42**, 492.

FRAZER, J. F. T. 1955. The mechanism of fetal loss after pregnant rats are spayed. J. Physiol., **130**, 253.

FREIS, E. D., AND KENNY, J. F. 1948. Plasma volume, total circulating protein and "available fluid" abnormalities in preeclampsia and eclampsia. J. Clin. Invest., **27**, 283.

FRIEDEN, E. H. 1956. The effects of estrogen and relaxin upon the uptake of glycine-1-C^{14} by connective tissue *in vivo*. Endocrinology, **59**, 69.

FRIEDEN, E. H., AND HISAW, F. L. 1933. The biochemistry of relaxin. Recent Progr. Hormone Res., **8**, 333.

FRIEDEN, E. H., AND HISAW, F. L. 1951. The mechanism of symphyseal relaxation. The distribution of deducing groups, hexoseamine, and proteins in symphyses of normal and relaxed guinea pigs. Endocrinology, **48**, 88.

FRIEDMAN, M. H. 1929. Effect of injections of urine from pregnant women on ovary of rabbit. Proc. Soc. Exper. Biol. & Med., **26**, 720.

FRIEDMAN, M. H., AND LAPHAM, M. E. 1931. A simple, rapid procedure for the laboratory diagnosis of early pregnancies. Am. J. Obst. & Gynec., **21**, 405.

FRIEDMAN, M. H., AND WEINSTEIN, G. L. 1937. The excretion of gonadotrophin by normal human males after ingestion and injection of extracts of pregnancy urine. Endocrinology, **21**, 489.

FRIEDMAN, M. M., GOODFRIEND, M. J., BERLIN, P. F., AND GOLDSTEIN, T. 1951. Extracellular fluid in normal pregnancy. Am. J. Obst. & Gynec., **61**, 609.

FUCHS, F., AND FUCHS, A. R. 1958. Induction and inhibition of labor in the rabbit. Acta Endocrinol., **29**, 615.

FUJII, K., HOSHINO, K., AOKI, I., AND YAO, J. 1956. Plasma progesterone level during human gestation. Bull. Tokyo Med. & Dent. Univ., **3**, 225.

FUJII, K., AND SHIMIZU, A. 1958. Prolactin excretion in urine of women. Bull. Tokyo Med. & Dent. Univ., **5**, 33.

GALLI-MAININI, C. 1947. Pregnancy test using the male toad. J. Clin. Endocrinol., **7**, 653.

GALLI-MAININI, C. 1948. Pregnancy test with male batrachia. Endocrinology, **43**, 349.

GANGULI, N. C. 1954. Observations on the blood picture during normal pregnancy. J. Indian Med. A., Calcutta, **23**, 332.

GARDNER, W. U. 1936. Sexual dimorphism of the pelvis of the mouse, the effect of estrogenic hormones upon the pelvis and upon the development of scrotal hernias. Am. J. Anat., **59**, 459.

GARDNER, W. U., AND ALLEN, E. 1942. Effects of hypophysectomy at midpregnancy in mouse. Anat. Rec., **83**, 75.

GASTINEAU, C. F., ALBERT, A., AND RANDALL, L. M. 1948. The renal clearance of chorionic gonadotrophin hormone in pregnancy and in neoplasm of the testes. J. Clin. Endocrinol., **8**, 599.

GEMZELL, C. A. 1953. Blood levels of 17-hydroxycorticosteroids in normal pregnancy. J. Clin. Endocrinol., **13**, 898.

GEMZELL, C. A., HEIJKENSKJÖLD, F., AND STRÖM, L. 1955. A method for demonstrating growth hormone activity in human plasma. J. Clin. Endocrinol., **15**, 537.

GEMZELL, C. A., ROBBE, H., AND SJOSTRAND, R. 1954. Blood volume and total amount of hemoglobin in normal pregnancy and the puerperium. Acta obst. et gynec. scandinav., **33**, 289.

GERSH, I., AND CATCHPOLE, H. R. 1949. The organization of ground substance and basement membrane and its significance in tissue injury, disease, and growth. Am. J. Anat., **85**, 457.

GIAJA, J. 1940. Lethargie obtenue chez la rat par la depression barometrique. Compt. rend. Acad. Sc., **210**, 80.

GORBMAN, A. 1950. Functional and structural changes consequent to high dosages of radioactive iodine. J. Clin. Endocrinol., **10**, 1177.

GORDON, E. S., CHART, J. J., HAGEDORN, D., AND SHIPLEY, E. 1954. Mechanism of sodium retention in preeclamptic toxemia. Obst. & Gynec., **4**, 39.

GOY, R. W., HOAR, R. M., AND YOUNG, W. C. 1957. Length of gestation in the guinea pig with data on the frequency and time of abortion and stillbirth. Anat. Rec., **128**, 747.

GRAHAM, E. F., AND DRACY, A. E. 1953. The effect of relaxin and mechanical dilation on the bovine cervix. J. Dairy Sc., **36**, 772.

GUTERMAN, H. S., AND TULSKY, A. S. 1949. Observations on the use of progesterone in threatened abortion. Am. J. Obst. & Gynec., **58**, 495.

HAFEZ, E. S. E., ZARROW, M. X., AND PINCUS, G. 1959. Experimental attempts to prolong gestation in the rabbit. Fertil. & Steril., **10**, 150.

HAIN, A. M. 1939. Estrogenic and androgenic substances in advanced pregnancy. Quart. J. Exper. Physiol., **29**, 139.

HALL, K. 1947. The effects of pregnancy and relaxin on the histology of the pubic symphysis in the mouse. J. Endocrinol., **5**, 174.

HALL, K. 1949. The role of progesterone in the mechanism of pelvic relaxation in the mouse. Quart. J. Exper. Physiol., **35**, 65.

HALL, K. 1955. The effect of various combinations of progesterone and estrogen on the symphysis pubis of ovariectomized mice. J. Endocrinol., **12**, 247.

HALL, K. 1956. An evaluation of the roles of estrogen, progesterone and relaxin in producing relaxation of the symphysis pubis of the ovariectomized mouse using the technique of metachromatic staining with toluidine blue. J. Endocrinol., **13**, 384.

HALL, K. 1957. The effect of relaxin extracts progesterone and estradiol on maintenance of pregnancy parturition and rearing of young after ovariectomy in mice. J. Endocrinol., **15**, 108.

HALL, K., AND NEWTON, W. H. 1946a. The normal course of separation of the pubes in pregnant mice. J. Physiol., **104**, 346.

HALL, K., AND NEWTON, W. H. 1946b. The action of "relaxin" in the mouse. Lancet, 54.

HAMILTON, H. G., AND HIGGINS, R. S. 1949. A correlated study of serum protein, erythrocyte count, leukocyte count, hemoglobin and hematocrit in normal pregnancy. Am. J. Obst. & Gynec., **58**, 345.

HAMLETT, G. W. 1937. Positive Friedman tests in the pregnant rhesus monkey, *Macaca mulatta*. Am. J. Physiol., **118**, 664.

HAMMOND, J., AND MARSHALL, F. H. A. 1925. *Reproduction in the Rabbit*. London: Oliver & Boyd, Ltd.

HARKNESS, M. L. R., AND HARKNESS, R. D. 1956. Changes in the properties of the uterine cervix of the rat in pregnancy. J. Physiol., **131**, 19P.

HARRIS, G. W. 1955. *Neural Control of the Pituitary Gland*. London: Edward Arnold & Company.

HARTMAN, C. G. 1932. Studies in the reproduction of the monkey Macacus (*Pithecus rhesus*) with special reference to menstruation and pregnancy. Contr. Embryol., Carnegie Inst. Washington, **33**, 1–173.

HARTMAN, C. G. 1941. Noneffect of ovariectomy on the 25th day of pregnancy in the rhesus monkey. Proc. Soc. Exper. Biol. & Med., **48**, 221.

HARTMAN, C. G., AND CORNER, G. W. 1947. Removal of the corpus luteum and of the ovaries of the rhesus monkey during pregnancy: observations and cautions. Anat. Rec., **98**, 539.

HARTMAN, C. G., AND STRAUS, W. L. 1939. Relaxation of the pelvic ligaments in pregnant monkeys. Am. J. Obst. & Gynec., **37**, 498.

HASKINS, A. L., AND SHERMAN, A. I. 1952. The quantitative assay of serum chorionic gonatrophin in pregnancy using the modified male frog technique. J. Clin. Endocrinol., **12**, 385.

HATERIUS, H. O. 1936. Reduction of litter size and maintenance of pregnancy in the oophorectomized rat: Evidence concerning the endocrine role of the placenta. Am. J. Physiol., **114**, 399.

HATERIUS, H. O., AND FUGO, N. W. 1939. Relaxation of the pelvic ligaments of the guinea pig induced by progesterone. Proc. Soc. Exper. Biol. & Med., **42**, 155.

HAWKER, R. W. 1956. Inactivation of antidiuretic hormone and oxytocin during pregnancy. Quart. J. Exper. Physiol., **41**, 301.

HAWKER, R. W., AND ROBERTSON, P. A. 1957. Oxytocin in human female blood. Endocrinology, **60**, 652.

HAWKER, R. W., AND ROBERTSON, P. A. 1958. Are there two oxytocic hormones? Med. J. Australia, **1**, 671.

HECHTER, O., ZAFFARONI, A., JACOBSON, R. P., LEVY, H., JEANLOZ, R. M., SCHENKER, V., AND PINCUS, G. 1951. The nature and the biogenesis of the adrenal secretory product. Recent Progr. Hormone Res., **6**, 215.

HERBERT, C. M., BANNER, E. A., AND WAKIM, K. G. 1954. Circulatory manifestations during pregnancy and nonpregnancy. Am. J. Obst. & Gynec., **68**, 1553.

HERINGA, G. C., AND VAN DER MEER, C. 1948. Bekkenverwijding tijdens zwangerschap en baring bij knoagdieren. Vlaamsche Acad. Geneesk. Belgie, **10**, 416.

HERRICK, E. H. 1928. The duration of pregnancy in guinea pigs after removal and also after transplantation of the ovaries. Anat. Rec., **39**, 193.

HISAW, F. L. 1925. The influence of the ovary on the resorption of the pubic bones of the pocket-gopher, *Geomys bursarius*. J. Exper. Zool., **42**, 411.

HISAW, F. L. 1926. Experimental relaxation of the pubic ligament of the guinea pig. Proc. Soc. Exper. Biol. & Med., **23**, 66.

HISAW, F. L. 1929. The corpus luteum hormone. I. Experimental relaxation of the pelvic ligaments of the guinea pig. Physiol. Zool., **2**, 59.

HISAW, F. L. 1944. The placental gonadotrophin and luteal function in monkeys (*Macaca mulatta*). Yale J. Biol. & Med., **17**, 121.

HISAW, F. L., AND ASTWOOD, E. B. 1942. The physiology of reproduction. Ann. Rev. Physiol., **4**, 503.

HISAW, F. L., AND ZARROW, M. X. 1949. Relaxin in the ovary of the domestic scow (*Sus scrofa* L.). Proc. Soc. Exper. Biol. & Med., **69**, 395.

HISAW, F. L., AND ZARROW, M. X. 1951. The physiology of relaxin. Vitamins & Hormones, **8**, 151.

HISAW, F. L., ZARROW, M. X., MONEY, W. L., TALMAGE, R. V. N., AND ABRAMOVITZ, A. A. 1944. Importance of the female reproductive tract in the formation of relaxin. Endocrinology, **34**, 122.

HISAW, F. L., AND ZILLEY, M. L. 1927. A study

of the pelvic girdle of 20-mm. embryos of the mole *Scalopus aquaticus machrinus* (Raf.). J. Mammol., **8**, 115.

HOAR, R. M., AND YOUNG, W. C. 1957. Respiratory metabolism during pregnancy in the guinea pig. Am. J. Physiol., **190**, 425.

HOAR, R. M., GOY, R. W., AND YOUNG, W. C. 1957. Loci of action of thyroid hormone on reproduction in the female guinea pig. Endocrinology, **60**, 337.

HOFFMANN, F. 1936. Über die Entstehung der Laktation. Zentralbl. Gynäk., **60**, 2882.

HOFMANN, F. G., KNOBIL, E., AND CATON, W. L. 1954. The effect of pregnancy on the excretion of water loads by rats. Endocrinology, **55**, 114.

HOOKER, C. W., AND FORBES, T. R. 1947. A bioassay for minute amounts of progesterone. Endocrinology, **41**, 158.

HORGER, L. M., AND ZARROW, M. X. 1957. Certain endocrine aspects of the anemia of pregnancy in the rabbit. Am. J. Physiol., **189**, 407.

INGLE, D. J., AND FISHER, G. T. 1938. Effect of adrenalectomy during gestation on the size of the adrenal glands of newborn rats. Proc. Soc. Exper. Biol. & Med., **39**, 149.

INGRAM, D. L. 1958. Fertility and oocyte numbers after x-irradiation of ovary. J. Endocrinol., **17**, 81.

INGRAM, D. L., MANDL, A. M., AND ZUCKERMAN, S. 1958. The influence of age on litter-size. J. Endocrinol., **17**, 280.

JAILER, J. W., AND KNOWLTON, A. I. 1950. Simulated adrenocortical activity during pregnancy in an addisonian patient. J. Clin. Invest., **29**, 1430.

JAROSOVA, V., AND DAUM, S. 1951. Objem plasmy, krve a mimobunecnè tekutiny v prubehu normalniho tehotenstvi. Ceskoslov Gynaek., **16**, 36.

JAVERT, C. T. 1940. Hyperthyroidism and pregnancy. Am. J. Obst. & Gynec., **39**, 954.

JOHNSON, C. E., ALBERT, A., AND WILSON, R. B. 1950. Renal and extrarenal disposal of chorionic gonadotrophin in the immediate postpartum period. J. Clin. Endocrinol., **10**, 371.

JOHNSON, R. H., AND HAINES, W. J. 1952. Extraction of adrenal cortex hormone activity from placental tissue. Science, **116**, 456.

JONES, G. E. S., DELFS, E., AND FOOTE, E. C. 1946. The effect of thiouracil hypothyroidism on reproduction in the rat. Endocrinology, **38**, 337.

KAHLSON, G., ROSENGREN, E., AND WESTLING, H. 1958. Increased formation of histamine in the pregnant rat. J. Physiol., **143**, 91.

KAHLSON, G., ROSENGREN, E., WESTLING, H., AND WHITE, T. 1958. The site of increased formation of histamine in the pregnant rat. J. Physiol., **144**, 337.

KEIFFER, M. H. 1919. Recherches sur l'appareil hemostatique de l'uterus de femme. Bull. Acad. Med. Paris, **81**, 650.

KELLAR, R. J. 1950. Symposium on haemodynamics in pregnancy. V. Haemodynamics in pregnancy. Edinburgh Med. J., **57**, 27.

KENNETH, J. H. 1947. Gestation periods. Imperial Bureau of Animal Breeding and Genetics, Technical Communication No. 5, Edinburgh.

KING, H. D. 1924. Litter production and the sex ratio in various strains of rats. Anat. Rec., 27, 337.

KLEIN, R., FORTUNATO, J., AND PAPADOS, C. 1953. Free blood corticoids in the newborn infant. J. Clin. Invest., 33, 35.

KLIMAN, B., SALHANICK, H. A., AND ZARROW, M. X. 1953. The response of the pubic symphysis of the mouse to extracts of pregnant rabbit serum and pregnant sow ovaries and its application as an assay method. Endocrinology, 53, 391.

KLINE, B. S. 1951. Microscopic observations of the development of the human placenta. Am. J. Obst. & Gynec., 61, 1065.

KLOPPER, A., STRONG, J. A., AND COOK, L. R. 1957. The excretion of pregnanediol and adrenocortical activity. J. Endocrinol., 15, 180.

KNAUS, H. H. 1930. Zur Frage der Standardisation des Corpus Luteum-Extraktes. Arch. exper. Path. u. Pharmakol., 151, 371.

KNISELY, M. H. 1934. Microscopic observations on circulatory systems of living transilluminated mammalian spleens and parturient uteri. Proc. Soc. Exper. Biol. & Med., 32, 212.

KNOBIL, E., AND BRIGGS, F. N. 1955. Fetal-maternal endocrine interrelations: the hypophyseal-adrenal system. Endocrinology, 57, 147.

KOFF, A. K., AND DAVIS, M. E. 1937. The mechanism of prolongation of pregnancy in the rabbit. Am. J. Obst. & Gynec., 34, 26.

KRANTZ, J. C., BRYANT, H. H., AND CARR, C. J. 1950. The action of aqueous corpus luteum extract upon uterine activity. Surg. Gynec. & Obst., 90, 327.

KRICHESKY, B. 1939. The influence of thyroidectomy on the period of gestation in the rabbit. Am. J. Physiol., 126, 234.

KROC, R. L., STEINETZ, B. G., AND BEACH, V. L. 1959. The effects of estrogen, progestogens and relaxin in pregnant and nonpregnant laboratory rodents. Ann. New York Acad. Sc., 75, 942.

KROHN, P. L., AND WHITE, H. C. 1950. The effect of hypothyroidism on reproduction in the female albino rat. J. Endocrinol., 6, 375.

LAIDLAW, J. C., COHEN, M., AND GORNAL, A. G. 1958. Studies on the origin of aldosterone during human pregnancy. J. Clin. Endocrinol., 18, 222.

LAMBIOTTE-ESCOFFIER, C., MOORE, D. B., AND TAYLOR, H. C., JR. 1953. The volume of distribution of insulin, antipyrine and radiosodium during normal and toxemic pregnancy and during the puerperium. Am. J. Obst. & Gynec., 66, 18.

LANDAU, R. L., BERGENSTAL, D. M., LUGIBIHL, K., AND KASCHT, M. E. 1955. The metabolic effects of progesterone in man. J. Clin. Endocrinol., 15, 1194.

LAZO-WASEM, E. A., AND ZARROW, M. X. 1955. The conversion of desoxycorticosterone acetate to a progesterone-like substance. Endocrinology, 56, 511.

LEIPERT, T. 1934. Zur kenntnis des physiologisehen blutjodspiegels. Biochem. Ztschr., 270, 448.

LEITCH, I. 1927. The estimation of iodine in foodstuffs and body fluids. Biochem. J., 20, 1003.

LEVI, J. E., AND WEINBERG, T. 1949. Pregnancy in alloxan diabetic rats. Proc. Soc. Exper. Biol. & Med., 72, 658.

LEWIS, J. T. 1923. Extirpation of adrenal glands in albino rats. Am. J. Physiol., 64, 503.

LITTLE, B., SMITH, O. W., JESSIMAN, A. G., SELENKOW, H. A., VAN'T HOFF, W., EGLIN, J. M., AND MOORE, F. D. 1958. Hypophysectomy during pregnancy in a patient with cancer of the breast. J. Clin. Endocrinol., 18, 425.

LITZENBERG, J. C. 1926. Relation of basal metabolism to sterility. Am. J. Obst. & Gynec., 12, 706.

LITZENBERG, J. C., AND CAREY, J. B. 1929. The relation of basal metabolism to gestation. Am. J. Obst. & Gynec., 17, 550.

LLAURADO, J. G. 1955. Successful pregnancy in adrenalectomized rats given small doses of 9α-halohydrocortisones. Endocrinology, 57, 516.

LORAINE, J. A. 1957. General discussion. Ciba Foundation Colloquia Endocrinol., 2, 19.

LUCAS, J. J., BRUNSTAD, G. E., AND FOWLER, S. H. 1958. The relationship of altered thyroid activity to various reproductive phenomena in gilts. J. Endocrinol., 17, 54.

LUND, C. J. 1951. The iron deficiency anemia of pregnancy including plasma volume, total hemoglobin, erythrocyte protoporphyrin in treated and untreated normal and anemic patients. Am. J. Obst. & Gynec., 62, 947.

LUNDIN, P. M., AND HOLMDAHL, S. 1957. Corticotrophic activity of human placenta. Acta Endocrinol., 26, 388.

LUTWAK-MANN, C. 1955. Carbonic anhydrase in the female reproductive tract: occurrence, distribution and hormonal dependence. J. Endocrinol., 13, 26.

LUTWAK-MANN, C., AND ADAMS, C. E. 1957. Carbonic anhydrase in the female reproductive tract. II. Endometrial carbonic anhydrase as indicator of luteoid potency: correlation with progestational proliferation, J. Endocrinol., 15, 43.

LUTWAK-MANN, C., AND LASER, H. 1954. Bicarbonate content of the blastocyst fluid and carbonic anhydrase in the pregnant rabbit uterus. Nature, London, 173, 268.

LYONS, W. R., SIMPSON, M. E., AND EVANS, H. M. 1943. Hormonal requirements for pregnancy and mammary development in hypophysectomized rats. Proc. Soc. Exper. Biol. & Med., 52, 134.

MACFARLANE, W. V., PENNYAMT, P. R., AND THRIFTE, E. 1957. Resorption and loss of fetuses in rats living at 35°C. J. Physiol., 135, 451.

MACK, H. C. 1955. The Plasma Proteins in Pregnancy. Springfield, Ill.: Charles C Thomas.

MAN, E. B., HEINEMANN, M., JOHNSON, C. E., LEARY, D. C., AND PETERS, J. P. 1951. The precipitable iodine of serum in normal pregnancy and its relation to abortions. J. Clin. Invest., **30**, 137.

MANDELSTAMM, A., AND TSCHAIKOWSKY, W. K. 1931. Hormonale Sterilisierung des weiblichen Säugetiers. I. Mitteilung Zentralbl. Gynäk., **55**, 3004.

MANDL, A. M., AND ZUCKERMAN, S. 1951. The relation of age to numbers of oocytes. J. Endocrinol., **7**, 190.

MAQSOOD, M. 1952. Thyroid functions in relation to reproduction of mammals and birds. Biol. Rev., **27**, 281.

MARDER, S. N., AND MONEY, W. L. 1944. Concentration of relaxin in the blood serum of pregnant and postpartum rabbits. Endocrinology, **34**, 115.

MARSHALL, F. H. A., AND JOLLY, W. A. 1905. Contributions to the physiology of mammalian reproduction. II. The ovary as an organ of internal secretion. Philos. Tr., ser. B, **198**, 123.

MAYER, G., AND DULUC, A.-J. 1955. Surrenales et corps jaunes on cours de la gestation et de la lactation. Arch. Sc. Physiol., **9**, 97.

McCARTHY, J. L., CORLEY, R. C., AND ZARROW, M. X. 1958. Effect of goitrogens on the adrenal gland. Fed. Proc., **17**, 424.

McCARTNEY, C. P., VALLACH, F. J., AND POTTINGER, R. E. 1952. Further studies on the inactivation of pitressin antidiuretic effect by the blood of pregnant women. Am. J. Obst. & Gynec., **63**, 847.

McDONALD, L. E., McNUTT, S. H., AND NICHOLS, R. E. 1953. On the essentiality of the bovine corpus luteum of pregnancy. Am. J. Vet. Res., **14**, 539.

McGAUGHEY, H. S. 1952. The cause of the blood and vascular alterations of normal pregnancy and pre-eclampsia-eclampsia. Am. J. Obst. & Gynec., **64**, 1268.

McGAUGHEY, H. S., COREY, E. L., AND THORNTON, W. N. 1958. An evaluation of the action of relaxin on isolated human uterine muscle and cervical tissues *in vitro*. Am. J. Obst. & Gynec., **75**, 23.

McKAY, E., ASSALI, N. S., AND HENLEY, M. 1957. Blood levels of 17-hydroxycorticosteroids (17-OHCS) during labor of human pregnancy. Proc. Soc. Exper. Biol. & Med., **95**, 653.

McKEOWN, T., AND MacMAHON, B. 1956. Sex differences in length of gestation in mammals. J. Endocrinol., **13**, 309.

McKEOWN, T., AND SPURREL, W. R. 1940. The results of adrenalectomy in the pregnant albino rat. J. Physiol., **98**, 255.

McLENNAN, C. E., AND COREY, D. L. 1950. Plasma volume late in pregnancy. Am. J. Obst. & Gynec., **59**, 662.

McLENNAN, C. E., AND THOUIN, L. G. 1948. Blood volume in pregnancy. Am. J. Obst. & Gynec., **55**, 189.

McPHAIL, M. K. 1935a. Studies on the hypophysectomized ferret. IX. The effect of hypophysectomy on pregnancy and lactation. Proc. Roy. Soc., London, ser. B, **117**, 34.

McPHAIL, M. K. 1935b. Hypophysectomy of the cat. Proc. Roy. Soc., London, ser. B, **117**, 45.

MEITES, J., AND SHELESNYAK, M. C. 1957. Effects of prolactin on duration of pregnancy viability of young and lactation in rats. Proc. Soc. Exper. Biol. & Med., **94**, 746.

MELDRUM, N. U., AND ROUGHTON, F. J. W. 1933. Carbonic anhydrase: its preparation and properties. J. Physiol., **80**, 113.

MELINKOFF, E. 1950. Questionable necessity of the corpus luteum. Am. J. Obst. & Gynec., **60**, 437.

MENKES, J. H., AND CSAPO, A. 1952. Changes in the adenosine triphosphate and creatine phosphate content of the rabbit uterus throughout sexual maturation and after ovulation. Endocrinology, **50**, 37.

MEUNIER, J. M., DULUC, A. J., AND MAYER, G. 1955. Action de la cortisone sur l'équilibre hormonal de la progestation et de la gestation. Compt. rend. Soc. biol., **149**, 366.

MIKLOS, L. 1930. Experimentelle Verlängerung der Schwangerschaft mittels Corpus Luteum-Extrakten. Zentralbl. Gynäk., **54**, 1755.

MILLER, J. R., KEITH, N. M., AND ROWNETREE, L. G. 1915. Plasma and blood volume in pregnancy. J. A. M. A., **65**, 779.

MILLER, J. W., KISLEY, A., AND MURRAY, W. J. 1957. The effects of relaxin-containing ovarian extracts on various types of smooth muscle. J. Pharmacol. & Exper. Therap., **120**, 426.

MONGE, C. 1942. Chronic mountain sickness. Physiol. Rev., **23**, 166.

MUKHERJEE, C., AND MUKHERJEE, S. K. 1953. Studies in iron metabolism in anaemias in pregnancy. II. Iron binding capacity and iron saturation of plasma. J. Indian M. A., **23**, 1.

NAKAMURA, U. 1932. Experimental study of the thyroid function during pregnancy, parturition and the puerpurium. Japan. J. Obst. & Gynec., **15**, 114.

NAKAMURA, U. 1933. Experimental study of the thyroid function during pregnancy, parturition, and puerpurium. Japan. J. Obst. & Gynec., **16**, 244.

NEHER, G. M., AND ZARROW, M. X. 1954. Concentration of progestin in the serum of the nonpregnant, pregnant and postpartum ewe. J. Endocrinol., **11**, 323.

NELSON, W. O., PFIFFNER, J. J., AND HATERIUS, H. O. 1930. The prolongation of pregnancy by extracts of corpus luteum. Am. J. Physiol., **91**, 690.

NELSON, W. O., AND TOBIN, C. E. 1937. Studies on the physiology of lactation. VII. Lactation in thyroidectomized rats and guinea pigs. Endocrinology, **21**, 670.

NEWCOMER, J. S. 1947. The relation of the hypophysis, ovary, placenta and fetus to the development of anemia during the last half of pregnancy in the rat. Endocrinology, **40**, 182.

NEWTON, W. H. 1939. Some problems of endocrine function in pregnancy. In *Sex and In-*

ternal Secretions, 2nd ed., E. Allen, C. H. Danforth and E. A. Doisy, Eds. Baltimore: The Williams & Wilkins Company.

NEWTON, W. H., AND BECK, N. 1939. Placental activity in the mouse in the absence of the pituitary gland. J. Endocrinol., **1,** 65.

NEWTON, W. H., AND LITS, F. J. 1938. Criteria of placental endocrine activity in the mouse. Anat. Rec., **72,** 333.

NOBLE, N. J. D., AND ROWLAND, S. 1953. The utilization of radioiodine during pregnancy. J. Obst. & Gynaec. Brit. Emp., **60,** 892.

NORTON, H. W. 1956. Gestation period for Holstein-Friesian cows. J. Dairy Sc., **39,** 1619.

OEGLE, C. 1934. Adaptation of sexual activity to environmental stimulation. Am. J. Physiol., **107,** 628.

OERTEL, G. W., WEISS, S. P., AND EIK-NES, K. B. 1959. Determination of progesterone in human blood plasma. J. Clin. Endocrinol., **19,** 213.

OPSAHL, J. C., AND LONG, C. N. 1951. Identification of ACTH in human placental tissue. Yale J. Biol. & Med., **24,** 199.

PAGE, E. W. 1946. The value of plasma pitocinase determinations in obstetrics. Am. J. Obst. & Gynec., **52,** 1014.

PEACOCK, L. J., AND ROGERS, C. M. 1959. Gestation period and twinning in chimpanzees. Science, **129,** 959.

PEARLMAN, W. H. 1957. A comparative study of [16-³H] progesterone metabolism in pregnant and nonpregnant women. Biochem. J., **65,** 7P.

PEARLMAN, W. H., AND CERCEO, E. 1952. The isolation of progesterone from human placenta. J. Biol. Chem., **198,** 79.

PEARSON, O. P., AND ENDERS, R. K. 1944. Duration of pregnancy in certain mustelids. J. Exper. Zool., **95,** 21.

PENCHARZ, R. I., AND LONG, J. A. 1933. Hypophysectomy in the pregnant rat. Am. J. Anat., **53,** 117.

PENCHARZ, R. I., AND LYONS, W. R. 1934. Hypophysectomy in the pregnant guinea pig. Proc. Soc. Exper. Biol. & Med., **31,** 1131.

PERL, E., AND CATCHPOLE, H. R. 1950. Changes induced in the connective tissue of the pubic symphysis of the guinea pig with estrogen and relaxin. Arch. Path., **50,** 233.

PERRY, J. S. 1954. Fecundity and embryonic mortality in pigs. J. Embryol. & Exper. Morphol., **2,** 308.

PETERS, J. P., MAN, E. B., AND HEINEMANN, M. 1948. Pregnancy and the thyroid gland. In *The Normal and Pathologic Physiology of Pregnancy.* Baltimore: The Williams & Wilkins Company.

PETERSON, R. R., WEBSTER, R. C., RAYNER, B., AND YOUNG, W. C. 1952. The thyroid and reproductive performance in the adult female guinea pig. Endocrinology, **51,** 504.

PINCUS, G. 1936. *The Eggs of Mammals.* New York: The Macmillan Company.

PINCUS, G. 1943. New color reaction for certain urinary 17-ketosteroids. Endocrinology, **32,** 176.

PINCUS, G. 1956. Steroidogenesis in perfused human placentas. Macy Foundation Conferences on Gestation, **3,** 9.

PINCUS, G., AND PEARLMAN, W. H. 1943. The intermediate metabolism of the sex hormones. Vitamins & Hormones, **1,** 294.

PINCUS, G., AND WERTHESSEN, N. T. 1938. The maintenance of embryo life in ovariectomized rabbits. Am. J. Physiol., **124,** 484.

POCHIN, E. E. 1952. The iodine uptake of the human thyroid throughout the menstrual cycle and in pregnancy. Clin. Sc., **11,** 441.

POLLAK, O. J. 1950. Limited usefulness of male amphibia for pregnancy tests. J. Lab. & Clin. Med., **36,** 127.

POULTON, B. R., AND REECE, R. P. 1957. The activity of the pituitary-adrenal cortex axis during pregnancy and lactation. Endocrinology, **61,** 217.

REINEKE, E. P., AND SOLIMAN, F. A. 1953. Role of thyroid hormone in reproductive physiology of the female. Iowa State Coll., J. Sc., **28,** 67.

REINHART, H. L., CAPLAN, I. J., AND SHINOWARA, G. Y. 1951. Factors influencing the male frog test. Am. J. Clin. Path., **21,** 624.

REIS, R. A., DECOSTA, E. J., AND ALLWEISS, M. D. 1952. *Diabetes and Pregnancy.* Springfield, Ill.: Charles C Thomas.

REYNOLDS, M. 1953. Measurement of bovine plasma and blood volume during pregnancy and lactation. Am. J. Physiol., **175,** 118.

REYNOLDS, S. R. M. 1949. *Physiology of the Uterus.* New York: Paul B. Hoeber, Inc.

REYNOLDS, S. R. M., HEARD, O. O., BRUNS, P., AND HELLMAN, L. M. 1948. A multichannel strain gage tokodynamometer: an instrument for studying patterns of uterine contractions in pregnant women. Bull. Johns Hopkins Hosp., **82,** 446.

ROBBINS, S. L. 1951. Observations on the use of the male North American frog (*Rana pipiens*) in pregnancy diagnosis. J. Clin. Endocrinol., **11,** 213.

ROBBINS, S. L., AND PARKER, F., JR. 1948. The use of the male North American frog (*Rana pipiens*) in the diagnosis of pregnancy. Endocrinology, **42,** 237.

ROBBINS, S. L., PARKER, F., JR., AND BIANCO, P. D. 1947. The reaction of the male South African clawed frog (*Xenopus laevis*) to gonadotrophins. Endocrinology, **40,** 227.

ROBERTS, M. 1954. The effect of a histaminase inhibitor (aminoguanidine) on pregnancy in the rat. J. Endocrinol., **11,** 338.

ROBSON, J. M. 1936. Maintenance of pregnancy in the hypophysectomized rabbit with progestin. J. Physiol., **86,** 415.

ROBSON, J. M., AND SHARAF, A. A. 1952. Effect of adrenocorticotrophic hormone (ACTH) and cortisone on pregnancy. J. Physiol., **116,** 236.

ROGERS, P. V. 1947. The effect of sulfaguanidine on reproduction in the rat. Anat. Rec., **97,** 48.

ROLLINS, W. C., LABEN, R. C., AND MEAD, S. W. 1956. Gestation length in an inbred Jersey herd. J. Dairy Sc., **39**, 1578.

ROSAHN, P. D., GREENE, H. S. N., AND HU, C. K. 1934. Hereditary variations in the gestation period of the rabbit. Science, **79**, 526.

ROSCOE, N. H., AND DONALDSON, A. M. M. 1946. The blood in pregnancy. II. The blood volume, cell volume, and hemoglobin mass. J. Obst. & Gynaec. Brit. Emp., **53**, 527.

ROWE, A. W., AND BOYD, W. C. 1932. The metabolism in pregnancy. IX. The fetal influence on the basal rate. J. Nutrition, **5**, 551.

SALHANICK, H. A., NOALL, M. W., ZARROW, M. X., AND SAMUELS, L. T. 1952. The isolation of progesterone from human placentas. Science, **115**, 708.

SALTER, W. T. 1940. *The Endocrine Function of Iodine*. Cambridge, Mass.: Harvard University Press.

SALVESEN, H. A. 1919. The determination of blood volume by the carbon monoxide method. J. Biol. Chem., **40**, 109.

SANDIFORD, I., AND WHEELER, T. 1924. The basal metabolism before, during, and after pregnancy. J. Biol. Chem., **62**, 329.

SAWYER, W. H. 1954. Inactivation of oxytocinase by homogenates of uteri and other tissues from normal and pregnant rats. Proc. Soc. Exper. Biol. & Med., **87**, 463.

SAWYER, W. H., FRIEDEN, E. H., AND MARTIN, A. C. 1953. *In vitro* inhibition of spontaneous contractions of the rat uterus by relaxin-containing extracts of sow ovaries. Am. J. Physiol., **172**, 547.

SCHERINGER, W. 1930. Beitrag zur kenntnis des blutjodspeigets bein weibe unter physiologischen bedingungen. Arch. Gynäk., **143**, 319.

SCHERINGER, W. 1931. Die jodausscheidung im harm der schwangeren unter physiologischen und experimentellen bedingungen. Arch. Gynäk., **145**, 701.

SCHOFIELD, B. M. 1957. The hormonal control of myometrial function during pregnancy. J. Physiol., **138**, 1.

SCHULTZ, A. H., AND SNYDER, F. F. 1935. Observations on reproduction in the chimpanzee. Bull. Johns Hopkins Hosp., **57**, 193.

SCHULTZ, D. H. 1953. Levels of progesterone in systemic plasma during the first trimester of human pregnancy. Am. J. Obst. & Gynec., **66**, 1260.

SEEMAN, A., VARANGOT, J., GUIGUET, C., AND CÉDARD, L. 1955. Sur les valeurs du taux plasmatique des 17-hydroxycorticostéroides libres chez la femme au cours de grossesse, de l'accouchement et dans le sang du cordon. Compt. rend. Soc. biol., **149**, 637.

SEITCHIK, J., AND ALPER, C. 1954. The body compartments of normal pregnant, edematous pregnant, and pre-eclamptic women. Am. J. Obst. & Gynec., **68**, 1540.

SELLE, R. M. 1945. Hamster sexually mature at 28 days of age. Science, **102**, 485.

SELYE, H., AND BASSETT, L. 1940. Diuretic effect of progesterone. Proc. Soc. Exper. Biol. & Med., **44**, 502.

SELYE, H., COLLIP, J. B., AND THOMPSON, D. L. 1933a. Effect of hypophysectomy upon pregnancy and lactation. Proc. Soc. Exper. Biol. & Med., **30**, 589.

SELYE, H., COLLIP, J. B., AND THOMPSON, D. L. 1933b. Effect of hypophysectomy upon pregnancy and lactation in mice. Proc. Soc. Exper. Biol. & Med., **31**, 82.

SHAPIRO, H. A., AND ZWARENSTEIN, H. A. 1934a. A rapid test for pregnancy on *Xenopus laevis*. Tr. Roy. Soc. South Africa, **22**, 75.

SHAPIRO, H. A., AND ZWARENSTEIN, H. A. 1934b. A rapid test for pregnancy on *Xenopus laevis*. Nature, London, **133**, 762.

SHAPIRO, H. A., AND ZWARENSTEIN, H. A. 1935. A test for the early diagnosis of pregnancy on the South African clawed toad (*Xenopus laevis*). South African M. J., **9**, 202.

SHER, I. H., AND MARTIN, G. J. 1956. Relaxin, a review. Exper. Med. & Surg., **14**, 89.

SHORT, R. V. 1956. Progesterone in the placentae of domestic animals. Nature, London, **178**, 743.

SHORT, R. V. 1957. Progesterone and related steroids in the blood of domestic animals. Ciba Foundation Colloquia Endocrinol., **11**, 362.

SHORT, R. V. 1958a. Progesterone in blood. I. The chemical determination of progesterone in peripheral blood. J. Endocrinol., **16**, 415.

SHORT, R. V. 1958b. Progesterone in blood. II. Progesterone in the peripheral blood of pregnant cows. J. Endocrinol., **16**, 426.

SIMPSON, S. A., TAIT, J. F., WETTSTEIN, A., NEHER, R., VON EUW, J., SCHINDLER, O., AND REICHSTEIN, T. 1954. Konstitution des Aldosterons, des neuen Mineralcorticoids. Experiential, **10**, 132.

SINDEN, J. A., AND LONGWELL, B. B. 1949. Effect of alloxan diabetes on fertility and gestation in the rat. Proc. Soc. Exper. Biol. & Med., **70**, 607.

SLONAKER, J. R. 1928. The effect of different amounts of sexual indulgence in the albino rat. IV. Length of sexual life. Am. J. Physiol., **84**, 192.

SMITH, J. C., AND NALBANDOV, A. V. 1958. The role of hormones in the relaxation of the uterine portion of the cervix in swine. Am. J. Vet. Res., **19**, 15.

SMITH, P. E. 1932. Nonessentiality of the posterior hypophysis for parturition in the rat. Am. J. Physiol., **99**, 345.

SMITH, P. E. 1946. Nonessentiality of hypophysis for maintenance of pregnancy in rhesus monkey. Anat. Rec., **94**, 497.

SMITH, P. E. 1954. Continuation of pregnancy in rhesus monkeys (*Macaca mulatta*) following hypophysectomy. Endocrinology, **55**, 655.

SMITH, R. A., ALBERT, A., AND WILSON, R. B. 1951. A confirmed 310-day period of human gestation. Am. J. Obst. & Gynec., **62**, 458.

SMITHBERG, M., AND RUNNER, M. N. 1956. The

induction and maintenance of pregnancy in prepuberal mice. J. Exper. Zool., **133**, 441.

SMITHBERG, M., AND RUNNER, M. N. 1957. Pregnancy induced in genetically sterile mice. J. Hered., **48**, 97.

SNYDER, F. F. 1934. Prolongation of pregnancy and complications of parturition in the rabbit following induction of ovulation near term. Bull. Johns Hopkins Hosp., **54**, 1.

STEINETZ, B. G., BEACH, V. L., AND KROC, R. L. 1957a. The influence of progesterone, relaxin and estrogen on some structural and functional changes in the preparturient mouse. Endocrinology, **61**, 271.

STEINETZ, B. G., BEACH, V. L., AND KROC, R. L. 1959b. The physiology of relaxin in laboratory animals. In *Recent Progress in the Endocrinology of Reproduction*, C. W. Lloyd, Ed. New York: Academic Press, Inc.

STEWART, L. H., JR., SANO, M. E., AND MONTGOMERY, T. L. 1948. Hormone secretion by human placenta grown in tissue culture. J. Clin. Endocrinol., **8**, 175.

STONE, M. L., SEDLIS, A., AND ZUCKERMAN, M. 1958. Relaxin: a critical evaluation. Am. J. Obst. & Gynec., **76**, 544.

STRAUS, W. A. 1932. Pelvic relaxation in the pregnant rhesus monkey. Anat. Rec., **52**, suppl. 1, 38.

SUNDSTROEM, E. S. 1927. The physiologic effects of tropical climate. Physiol. Rev., **7**, 320.

SVIHLA, A. 1932. A comparative life history study of the mice of the genus Peromyscus. Univ. Michigan Museum Zool. Publication No. 24.

SWANBERG, H. 1950. Histaminase in pregnancy. Acta physiol. scandinav., **23**, suppl. 79.

SWEDIN, B. 1943. Unterschungen über da Diaminoxydaseferment (Histaminase). Acta med. scandinav., **114**, 210.

TALMAGE, R. V. 1947a. Changes produced in the symphysis pubis of the guinea pig by sex steroids and relaxin. Anat. Rec., **99**, 91.

TALMAGE, R. V. 1947b. A histologic study of the effects of relaxin on the symphysis pubis of the guinea pig. J. Exper. Zool., **106**, 281.

TALMAGE, R. V. 1950. The role of estrogen in the estrogen-relaxin relationship in symphyseal relaxation. Endocrinology, **47**, 75.

TAPFER, S., AND HASLHOFER, L. 1935. Hormonale Weiterstellung des Beckens in Tierversuch. Arch. Gynäk., **159**, 313.

TARANTINO, C. 1951. Sulla presenza di ACTH nella placenta. Folia endocrinol., **5**, 197.

THOMPSON, K. J., HIRSHEIMER, A., GIBSON, J. B., AND EVANS, W. A., JR. 1938. Studies on the circulation in pregnancy. III. Blood volume changes in normal pregnant women. Am. J. Obst. & Gynec., **36**, 48.

THUNG, P. J., BOOT, L. M., AND MÜHLBOCK, O. 1956. Senile changes in the estrous cycle and in ovarian structure in some inbred strains of mice. Acta endocrinol., **23**, 8.

TULSKY, A. S., AND KOFF, A. K. 1957. Some observations on the role of the corpus luteum in early pregnancy. Fertil. & Steril., **8**, 118.

TYLER, C. M. 1955. The elaboration and utilization of posterior pituitary hormones. Ph.D. Thesis, University of London.

TYSOE, F. W., AND LOWENSTEIN, L. 1950. Blood volume and hematologic studies in pregnancy and the puerperium. Am. J. Obst. & Gynec., **60**, 1187.

UYLDERT, I. E., AND DE VAAL, O. M. 1947. Relaxation of the rat's uterine ostium during pregnancy. Acta brev. neerl. Physiol., **15**, 49.

VAN DER MEER, C. 1954. Experiments on the mechanism of action of relaxin. Acta endocrinol., **4**, 325.

VAN DONK, E. C., FELDMAN, H., AND STEENBOCK, H. 1939. An analysis of the anemia of pregnancy in the rat. Am. J. Physiol., **107**, 616.

VELARDO, J. T. 1957. Action of adrenocorticotrophin on pregnancy and litter size in rats. Am. J. Physiol., **191**, 319.

VENNING, E. H. 1946. Adrenal function in pregnancy. Endocrinology, **39**, 203.

VENNING, E. H. 1957. The secretion of various hormones and the activity of the adrenal cortex in pregnancy. Macy Foundation Conferences on Gestation, **3**, 71.

VENNING, E. H., AND DYRENFURTH, I. 1956. Aldosterone excretion in pregnancy. J. Clin. Endocrinol., **16**, 426.

VENNING, E. H., DYRENFURTH, I., AND GIROUD, C. J. P. 1956. Aldosterone excretion in healthy persons. J. Clin. Endocrinol., **16**, 1326.

VENNING, E. H., PRIMROSE, T., CALIGARIS, L. C. S., AND DYRENFURTH, I. 1957. Aldosterone excretion in pregnancy. J. Clin. Endocrinol., **17**, 473.

VENNING, E. H., SIMPSON, G. A., AND SINGER, B. 1954. Adrenocortical function in toxemia of pregnancy. Am. J. Obst. & Gynec., **67**, 542.

VIDOVIC, V. L. 1952. Kälte-und hypoxitoleranz von Rattenembryonen. Experientia, **8**, 304.

VIDOVIC, V. L. 1956. Effect of hypothermia on the estrus cycle, the mature egg, pregnancy and lactation of the white rat. Thesis, University of Belgrade, Belgrade, Jugoslavia.

VOLLMER, E. P., AND GORDON, A. S. 1941. Effect of sex and gonadotrophic hormones upon the blood picture of the rat. Endocrinology, **29**, 828.

VON FEKETE, K. 1930. Beitrage zur Physiologie der Graviditate. Endokrinologie, **7**, 367.

WADA, H., AND YUHARA, M. 1955. Studies on relaxin in ruminants. I. Relaxin content in the blood serum of pregnant and postpartum dairy cows. Japan. J. Zootech. Sc., **26**, 12.

WADA, H., AND YUHARA, M. 1956. Inhibitory effect of relaxin preparation upon spontaneous uterine contractions of the rat and guinea pig *in vitro*. Sc. Rept. Fac. Agric., Okayama Univ., **9**, 11.

WALAAS, E., AND WALAAS, O. 1944. Studies on the compensatory hypertrophy of the fetal adrenal glands in the albino rat produced by adrenalectomy during pregnancy. Acta path. et microbiol. scandinav., **21**, 640.

WEISMAN, A. I., AND COATES, C. W. 1944. *The South African Frog (Xenopus laevis) in*

Pregnancy Diagnosis. New York: Clark & Fritts.

WELLS, L. J., KIM, J. N., RUNGE, W., AND LAZAROW, A. 1957. Gestation period in diabetic rats and body weights in fetuses and new born. Physiologist, **1**, 85.

WELSH, C. A., WELLEN, I., AND TAYLOR, H. C., JR. 1942. The filtration rate, effective renal blood flow, tubular excretory mass and phenol red clearance in normal pregnancy. J. Clin. Invest., **21**, 57.

WESTMAN, A., AND JACOBSOHN, D. 1944. Über die Nebennieren-funktion bei parabiosen zwischen Hypophysektomierten und nebennierenlosen Ratten. Acta path. et microbiol. scandinav., suppl., **54**, 191.

WERNER, S. C. 1958. The effect of triiodothyronine administration on the elevated protein-bound iodine level in human pregnancy. Am. J. Obst. & Gynec., **75**, 1193.

WHITE, R. 1950. Blood volume in pregnancy. Edinburgh M. J., **57**, 14.

WHITE, W. E. 1932. The effect on ovulation and pregnancy of blocking the pituitary circulation in the rabbit. Am. J. Physiol., **102**, 505.

WILSON, R. B., ALBERT, A., AND RANDALL, L. M. 1949. Quantitative studies on the production, destruction, and elimination of chorionic gonadotrophin in normal pregnancy. Am. J. Obst. & Gynec., **58**, 1.

WILTBERGER, P. D., AND MILLER, D. F. 1948. The male frog, *Rana pipiens*, as a new test animal for early pregnancy. Science, **107**, 198.

WISLOCKI, G. B., DEMPSEY, E. W., AND FAWCETT, D. W. 1948. Some functional activities of the placental trophoblast. Obst. & Gynec. Surv., **3**, 604.

WITTEN, C. L., AND BRADBURY, J. T. 1951. Hemodilution as a result of estrogen therapy: estrogenic effect in the human female. Proc. Soc. Exper. Biol. & Med., **78**, 626.

WOODBURY, R. A., AHLQUIST, R. P., ABREU, B., TORPIN, R., AND WATSON, W. G. 1946. The inactivation of pitocin and pitressin by human pregnancy blood. J. Pharmacol. & Exper. Therap., **86**, 359.

WOODBURY, R. A., HAMILTON, W. F., AND TORPIN, R. 1938. The relationship between abdominal, uterine, and arterial pressures during labor. Am. J. Physiol., **121**, 640.

WYMAN, L. C. 1928. Studies on suprarenal insufficiency. I. The effect of suprarenal insufficiency on reproduction and the estrous cycle in the albino rat. Am. J. Physiol., **86**, 528.

YOCHIM, J., AND ZARROW, M. X. 1959. Relaxation of the uterine cervix of the rat. Fed. Proc., **18**, 174.

ZANDER, J. 1954. Progesterone in human blood and tissue. Nature, London, **174**, 406.

ZANDER, J., FORBES, T. R., NEHER, R., AND DESAULLES, P. 1957. Über biologisch aktive Progesteronmetaboliten im menschlichen Organismus. Klin. Wchnschr., **35**, 143.

ZANDER, J., FORBES, T. R., VON MÜNSTERMANN, A. M., AND NEHER, R. 1958. Δ⁴-3-Ketopregnene-20α-ol and Δ⁴-3-ketopregnene-20-β-ol, two naturally occurring metabolites of progesterone: isolation identification, biologic activity and concentration in human tissues. J. Clin. Endocrinol., **18**, 337.

ZANDER, J., AND SIMMER, H. 1954. Die chemische Bestimmung von Progesterone in Organischen substraten. Klin. Wchnschr., **32**, 529.

ZANDER, J., AND VON MÜNSTERMANN, A. M. 1956. Progesteron in menschlichen Blut und Geweben. III. Progesteron in der Plazenta, in der Ulerusschleimhaut und im Fruchtwasser. Klin. Wchnschr., **34**, 494.

ZARROW, M. X. 1946. Relaxation in the symphysis pubis of the guinea pig produced by estradiol and progesterone. Anat. Rec., **96**, 32.

ZARROW, M. X. 1947a. The physiology and pharmacology of relaxin. Ph.D. Thesis, Harvard University, Cambridge, Mass.

ZARROW, M. X. 1947b. Relaxin content of blood, urine and other tissues of pregnant and postpartum guinea pigs. Proc. Soc. Exper. Biol. & Med., **66**, 488.

ZARROW, M. X. 1948. The role of the steroid hormones in the relaxation of the symphysis pubis of the guinea pig. Endocrinology, **42**, 120.

ZARROW, M. X. 1957. Maternal hormones in pregnancy, in gestation. Macy Foundation Conferences on Gestation, **3**, 17.

ZARROW, M. X., HISAW, F. L., AND BRYANS, F. 1950. Conversion of desoxycorticosterone acetate to progesterone *in vivo*. Endocrinology, **46**, 403.

ZARROW, M. X., HOLMSTROM, E. G., AND SALHANICK, H. A. 1955. The concentration of relaxin in the blood serum and other tissues of women during pregnancy. J. Clin. Endocrinol., **15**, 22.

ZARROW, M. X., AND LAZO-WASEM, E. A. 1955. The release of a progesterone-like substance from the adrenal gland. Acta endocrinol., **18**, 273.

ZARROW, M. X., AND MONEY, W. L. 1949. Involution of the adrenal cortex of rats treated with thiouracil. Endocrinology, **44**, 345.

ZARROW, M. X., AND NEHER, G. M. 1955. Concentration of progestin in the serum of the rabbit during pregnancy, the puerpurium and following castration. Endocrinology, **56**, 1.

ZARROW, M. X., NEHER, G. M., LAZO-WASEM, E. A., AND SALHANICK, H. A. 1957. Biological activity of certain progesterone-like compounds as determined by the Hooker-Forbes bioassay. J. Clin. Endocrinol., **17**, 658.

ZARROW, M. X., NEHER, G. M., SIKES, D., BRENNAN, D. M., AND BULLARD, J. F. 1956. Dilation of the uterine cervix of the sow following treatment with relaxin. Am. J. Obst. & Gynec., **72**, 260.

ZARROW, M. X., AND ROSENBERG, B. 1953. Sources of relaxin in the rabbit. Endocrinology, **53**, 593.

ZARROW, M. X., SIKES, D., AND NEHER, G. M. 1954. Effect of relaxin on the uterine cervix and vulva of young castrated sows and heifers. Am. J. Physiol., **179**, 684.

ZARROW, M. X., AND ZARROW, I. G. 1953. Anemia in the rabbit during pregnancy and following treatment with water soluble ovarian extracts. Endocrinology, **52,** 424.

ZEINER, F. N. 1943. Studies on the maintenance of pregnancy in the white rat. Endocrinology, **33,** 239.

ZONDEK, B., AND SULMAN, F. 1945. The mechanism of action and metabolism of gonadotrophic hormones in the organism. Vitamins & Hormones, **3,** 297.

ZUCKERMAN, S. 1935. The Aschheim-Zondek diagnosis of pregnancy in the chimpanzee. Am. J. Physiol., **110,** 597.

Addendum

Several reports on an exteroceptive block to pregnancy in mice appeared since this manuscript was completed. In a series of three articles, Bruce (Nature, London, **184,** 105, 1959; Science, **131,** 1526, 1960; and J. Reprod. Fertil., **1,** 96, 1960) has shown that exposure of newly mated, female mice to strange males caused an inhibition of pregnancy that ran as high as 80 per cent. Prior removal of the olfactory bulbs abolished the reaction. The pregnancy block in this instance consisted in a failure of the blastocysts to implant.

Physiology of Reproduction in Submammalian Vertebrates

17

ENDOCRINOLOGY OF REPRODUCTION IN COLD-BLOODED VERTEBRATES

Thomas R. Forbes, Ph.D.

SCHOOL OF MEDICINE, YALE UNIVERSITY,
NEW HAVEN, CONNECTICUT

I. Introduction

The cold-blooded vertebrates, particularly fish and reptiles, are forms studied by relatively few investigators of reproductive endocrinology. Even so, enough information has accumulated to emphasize that problems in the biology of reproduction of the lower vertebrates are varied, phylogenetically significant, and altogether fascinating.

This chapter resulted from an effort to bring together some of this information. In general, the approach has been to discuss aspects of the structure and function of the reproductive tract and later to outline what is known regarding their endocrine control. The attempt has been both to correlate what is known and to indicate what must still be explored. Several possible topics have been omitted, either because they are dealt with elsewhere in this volume (see chapters by Greep, Burns, Guhl, Blandau, Bishop, Young) or because, arbitrarily, they were considered to be outside the scope of this review. References in most cases have been cited on a representative but not total basis. Generic names since superseded are retained, although usually in parentheses, to assist the reader who seeks out the original paper.

Special attention is directed to the particularly useful discussions and reviews of Cunningham (1900), Bridge (1910), Noble (1931), Régnier (1938), Volsøe (1944), Bretschneider and Duyvené de Wit (1947), Ponse (1949), Hoar (1955, 1957a), Marshall (1956), Harrison Matthews and Marshall (1956), and Pickford and Atz (1957). To these and many other sources and to the wise critics of his manuscript the author is profoundly indebted.

II. Testis and Spermatogenesis

Fish

The spermatogenetic process is seasonal in some fish and more or less continuous in others. The testis of the perch is smallest from late June to late August (northern hemisphere). Spermatogenesis then proceeds rapidly enough so that by early November the gonad has reached its greatest size (Turner, 1919). In the stickleback, *Gasterosteus pungitius*, spermatogenesis occurs in the winter and spring (van Oordt, 1924), but it extends through the autumn, winter, and spring in *G. aculeatus* (Courrier, 1921c, 1922a, b; Craig-Bennett, 1931). Testicular volume, an indicator of spermatogenetic rate, in the top-minnow, *Gambusia affinis*, in summer is eight times as great as in winter (Geiser, 1922). In *Fundulus* spermatogenesis is at its height in late May, June, and July (Matthews, 1938). The process begins in June or July in the salmon parr, *Salmo salar*, and ripe sperm have accumulated by October or November (Jones, 1940; Jones and Orton, 1940). (A parr is a young salmon which has not yet migrated to the sea.) This fish, incidentally, may be paedogenetic, *i.e.*, it may spawn before becoming adult (Jones and Orton, 1940). In *Brachyraphis episcopi*, related to *Gambusia*, on the other hand, reproductive cycles may occur in any month (Turner, 1938a).

In higher orders of fish spermatogenesis occurs in testicular lobules which are the homologues of the seminiferous tubules of the amniotes (Oslund, 1928). It is common for the ripe sperm to form balls or cysts within the testes (Conel, 1917; Turner, 1919; Okkelberg, 1921; Geiser, 1922; Oslund, 1928; Vaupel, 1929; Matthews, 1938). In the basking shark, *Cetorhinus maximus*, cilia rotate the masses of sperm into balls while testicular epithelial cells secrete concentric layers of investing material. The resulting spermatophore is 2 to 3 cm. or more in diameter (Harrison Matthews, 1950). The sperm ball of *Lebistes reticulatus* contains thousands of germ cells; their tails are directed toward the center and intertwine to hold the ball together (Vaupel, 1929). The cephalic end of the mesonephros of the elasmobranch *Chimaera* secretes a substance which similarly agglutinates the sperm into a spermatophore (Parker and Burlend, 1909).

Sperm storage in the male has been reported in *Gambusia*. This fish breeds from spring until September, and again in November, spermatozoa remaining in the testis for release the following spring (Self, 1940).

Spawning occurs in the early spring in the three-spined stickleback, *Gasterosteus aculeatus aculeatus* (Ikeda, 1933), and in the spring and early summer in the carp and goldfish (Scruggs, 1951), top-minnow (Carranza and Winn, 1954), perch (Turner, 1919), and striped bass (Pearson, 1938). In *Fundulus*, sperm are shed in June, July, and even August (Matthews, 1938). Fertilization is internal in the basking shark, *Cetorhinus maximus*, the clasper being used as an intromittent organ; mating occurs in late spring and early summer (Harrison Matthews, 1950). Eels spawn in the spring and summer. The wonderful story of their migration from as far away as Europe to the breeding grounds in the western Atlantic Ocean and of the eventual return of the young, sometimes again to rivers 3000 feet above sea level in Switzerland, is one of the most remarkable known to naturalists. The eel's migration was described by the Danish biologist, Johs. Schmidt (1922); the reader is urged to consult his paper.

Gerbil'skii's (1955) studies of sturgeons (*Acipenser güldenstädti*, *A. stellatus*, and *Huso huso*) reveal that within each species there may be several "biologic races." The time of spawning of the race depends on the river system in which the race lives and may vary by several months from the spawning time of other races of the same species. Temperature is believed to be one of the factors involved.

Atrophy of the testis in old age has been reported in the myxinoids *Bdellostoma* and *Myxine* (Conel, 1917) and in a teleost, *Astyanax mexicanus* (Rasquin and Hafter, 1951).

Amphibians

In *Salamandra*, the female may be inseminated at any time between February and October (Baylis, 1939). Spermatogenesis occurs in *Triturus* in summer and early fall. The testes reach their maximal size in July and August. Actual mating, however, is deferred until the period from April through June, the mature sperm being stored over the winter (Adams, 1940). *Eurycea* breeds in late March and the first part of April. By the latter date, the store of mature sperm is exhausted. In June the masses of spermatogonia in the testicular lobules have begun to transform into primary spermatocytes. Spermatids are seen in late July, and mature spermatozoa are present before the first of September (Weichert, 1945). Spermatogenesis in *Necturus* extends from April through August, with shedding of sperm from late August to early October. Thereafter the testes are inactive until the following spring (Aplington, 1942).

The toad, *Bufo bufo*, breeds in the spring, and the testes are largest then. Spermatogenesis begins in the summer in preparation for the next spring (Ting and Boring, 1939). Sperm production is also cyclic in *Rana* (Aron, 1926; van Oordt and van Oordt, 1955).

Control of spermatogenesis has been proven to be largely through the pituitary gland (see chapter by Greep). Release of spermatozoa has also been effected in *Rana* by the injection of epinephrine, even after hypophysectomy or total section of the spinal cord. *Bufo*, however, did not make this response to the administration of epinephrine (Li and Chang, 1949).

Except for two primitive families, all salamanders enclose masses of their spermatozoa in sacs called spermatophores. The latter are formed by specialized male cloacal glands (Dunn, 1923; Noble, 1931) which presumably are under endocrine control.

Reptiles

The organization of the reptilian testis is in general like that of higher vertebrates. True seminiferous tubules are present. The period of active spermatogenesis is evident on macroscopic examination, because the testis increases in size as the germ cells multiply and accumulate. In *Testudo orbicularis*, the musk turtle, *Sternotherus odoratus*, the box turtle, *Terrapene carolinensis*, and the Algerian *Emys leprosa*, spermatogenesis begins late in the spring and continues until early in the fall (Pellegrini, 1925; Risley, 1938; Hansen, 1939; Altland, 1951; Combescot, 1954a). These turtles mate in the spring, whereas the musk turtle mates in the spring and fall (Risley, 1938;

Combescot, 1954b). In lizards, active spermatogenesis may, depending on the species, take place at almost any time of year, with a peak of spermiogenic activity, followed by mating, appearing perhaps most commonly in the spring and early summer.[1] In the snake, *Thamnophis*, spermatogenesis begins late in the spring and is most active in June and July. Spermiogenesis is conspicuous in August and October, and mating occurs in the spring (Cieslak, 1945; Fox, 1952). Spermatogenesis is continuous in *Vipera berus* except during hibernation, and mating begins in late April or early May (Volsøe, 1944). The alligator apparently breeds in the spring (Reese, 1915), but information on the mating activities and spermatogenesis in the Crocodilia is surprisingly scanty.

III. Sources of Male Hormone

Fish

Fish testes produce androgen. Hazleton and Goodrich (1937) and Potter and Hoar (1954) prepared extracts of salmon testes which when bioassayed showed male hormone activity. (The effects of castration will be described later.) Which testicular cells produce androgen is controversial. In the higher vertebrates, the interstitial cells (Leydig cells) are usually believed to secrete male hormone, and it was natural to search for these cells in fish. Champy (1923a, b) and van Oordt (1923, 1924, 1925) concluded that male hormone does not come from interstitial cells in *Tinca vulgaris*, *Phoxinus laevis*, *Gasterosteus pungitius* L., and *Xiphophorus helleri*. Courrier (1921b) and Weisel (1949) did not find interstitial cells either in primitive elasmobranchs or in two teleost species. Such cells have, however, been noted in the testes of other species (Courrier, 1921b, 1922c; Kolmer and Scheminzky, 1922a). Furthermore, interstitial cells undergo maximal development (thus seeming to signal secretory activity) just before and during the breeding period; their presence may be

---

[1] Pellegrini, 1925; Frankenberger, 1928; Courrier, 1929; Altland, 1941; Breckenridge, 1943; Reynolds, 1943; Dutta, 1944; Kehl, 1944b; Woodbury and Woodbury, 1945; Miller, 1948, 1951; Kitada, 1951; Dessauer, 1955; Fox, 1958.

partly obscured, before spawning, by the crowding and distention of the testis with sperm.[2] Follenius (1953) showed that if prepubertal *Lebistes* are exposed to x-rays the testes become completely sterile and Sertoli cells are also destroyed, but secondary sex characters nevertheless develop on schedule. Since the interstitial cells are the only functional tissue remaining, this experiment is strong evidence for origin of androgen from these cells. In several teleosts in which intersitial cells are not seen, there are specially developed cells in the wall of the testicular lobule or crypt (Hoar, 1957b; Marshall and Lofts, 1956). When the spawning season approaches, these "lobule boundary cells" acquire fat inclusions, give a positive test for cholesterol, and generally resemble the interstitial cells of higher vertebrates.

Amphibians

There are conflicting opinions as to whether androgen is produced by the interstitial cells of the amphibian testis. Indeed, it is likely that the term "interstitial" is not appropriate in this case. The urodele testis does not have seminiferous tubules, but rather seminiferous lobules or cysts (Pérez, 1921). Between the lobules there are only thin layers of connective tissue which, according to Pérez, is not at all homologous with the interstitial tissue seen between the seminiferous tubules of higher vertebrates.

Aron (1924a, 1926), on the other hand, refers to testicular interstitial tissue in *Rana* and says that its cyclic evolution is correlated directly with the seasonal development of secondary sex characters, particularly the growth of glands in the callosity of the thumb. This has been confirmed in *Discoglossus*, another anuran, in which interstitial tissue is said to be abundant (Benoit, Kehl, and Leportois, 1941; Kehl, 1944a). Because the administration of testosterone also induces development of the callosity of *Discoglossus*, it is concluded that the interstitial cells produce androgen. The male secondary sex characters of

Triturus, a newt, are highly developed during the fall, winter, and spring; at the same time a variety of mature cells—sperm, interstitial cells, and Sertoli cells—is also abundant (Adams, 1940).

Noble (1931) has much support for his conclusion that in the amphibian testis male hormone is derived from sperm or Sertoli cells rather than from interstitial cells. In the urodele some of the testicular stromal cells develop into interstitial cells, but only *after* the breeding season, when, of course, the secondary sex characters have regressed. Thus, although the interstitial cells increase in number, size, and lipid content, thereby coming to resemble mammalian interstitial cells, there is no direct evidence for their endocrine function, and the reason for their development is unexplained. In addition, these cells are entirely undeveloped at the time when the sex characters indicate by their prominence that male hormone is being released.[3] Further research on the source of testicular androgen is required.

Reptiles

The reptilian testis produces male hormone, as shown by the results of castration. Valle and Valle (1943) extracted the testes of the rattlesnake, *Crotalus t. terrificus*, and of the related viper, *Bothrops jararaca*; 10 mg. testicular tissue contained enough androgen for positive results in two nonquantitative biologic tests.

The role, if any, of interstitial cells in the production of androgen in reptiles has not been established. Interstitial cells have been seen in turtles of the genera *Emys*, *Terrapene* (*Cistudo*), and *Testudo*; the cells increase in size and lipid content before and during the breeding season.[4] Since interstitial cell volume decreases in June when the epididymis is undergoing seasonal development, the interstitial cells are probably not responsible for epididymal changes (Dornesco, 1926a). In *Terrapene* the increase in cell size may be related to the se-

---

[2] Courrier, 1921a, c, 1922a, b; Craig-Bennett, 1931; Stephan and Clavert, 1938; Potter and Hoar, 1954; Marshall and Lofts, 1956.

[3] Humphrey, 1921, 1925; Champy, 1922a, b, 1923c, 1924, 1932; Harms, 1926a; Oslund, 1928.
[4] Ganfini, 1902; Pellegrini, 1925; Dornesco, 1926a; Stieve, 1933; Altland, 1951; Combescot, 1954a.

cretion of male hormone (Altland, 1951). In the musk turtle, *Sternotherus*, on the other hand, interstitial cells are present but show no seasonal variation (Risley, 1938).

Franz von Leydig (1821–1908), the German anatomist and zoologist whose name enters into the eponym for the interstitial cells, observed them (1857) in the testis of a lizard, *Lacerta agilis*. Since then, the cells have been seen in the testes of several lacertilians.[5] Herlant (1933) and Regamey (1935) state unequivocally that in the lizards they studied the development of the interstitial gland and of the secondary sex characters is correlated. Interstitial cells have also been noted in the testes of several snakes.[6] Herlant (1933) reported no seasonal variation in number, size, etc., of the interstitial cells in *Vipera* and *Tropidonotus*, but Volsøe (1944) observed maximal development of the cells in *Vipera* in the early spring, shortly before the mating season. Fox (1952), reviewing the situation for reptiles generally, concluded that "the maximal interstitial cell size occurs during the breeding period although in certain species the cells may be relatively large during other seasons as well." Since secondary sex characters become conspicuous during the breeding season and the interstitial cells give indication of activity at this period or a little earlier, the presumption is strong that the two phenomena are related.

Interstitial cells are absent from the testis of the immature alligator (Forbes, 1940a). There seems to be no information on whether interstitial tissue occurs in adult Crocodilia.

[5] *Anolis* (Fox, 1958), *Phrynosoma* (Blount, 1929), *Uromastix* (Kehl, 1935, 1944b), *Hemidactylus* (Dutta, 1944), *Xantusia* (Miller, 1948), *Scincus* (Kehl, 1935, 1944b), *Acanthodactylus* (Kehl, 1935, 1944b), *Takydromus* (Takewaki and Fukuda, 1935a), *Lacerta* (Frankenberger, 1922; Reiss, 1923a, b; Pellegrini, 1925; Herlant, 1933; Stieve, 1933; van den Broek, 1933; Regamey, 1935), *Anguis* (Ganfini, 1902; Dalcq, 1920; Herlant, 1933), *Heloderma* (Pesce, 1935), and *Varanus* (Heberer, 1930; Kehl, 1935, 1944b).

[6] *Boa* (Ganfini, 1902), *Natrix* (*Tropidonotus*) (Herlant, 1933), *Coluber* (*Zamenis*) (Ganfini, 1902; Pesce, 1935), *Thamnophis* (*Eutenia*) (Cieslak, 1945; Fox, 1952), and *Vipera* (Herlant, 1933; Volsøe, 1944).

IV. Excurrent Pathways for Sperm

Fish

In cyclostomes the testicular cysts rupture and release mature sperm into the coelom, from whence they escape to the exterior by way of a genital papilla (Conel, 1917; Hoar, 1957a). In higher forms sperm are carried in "vasa deferentia," but these, according to Eggert (1931), are not homologous with the structures of the same name in amniotes. "Vasa deferentia" and testes may be paired or single (Geiser, 1922; Oslund, 1928; Matthews, 1938; Chavin and Gordon, 1951).

Courrier (1922b) observed seminal vesicles in the stickleback, as did Eggert (1931) in *Periophthalmus*, but the latter believes that the seminal vesicles are not homologous with those of mammals. In *Gillichthys* the vesicles are large structures caudal to the testes proper. Their function is uncertain, but may simply be to store sperm. They do not change their appearance seasonally, are not affected by the administration of testosterone, and presumably are not under endocrine control (Weisel, 1949). The sperm ducts are secretory in the teleost, *Astyanax* (Rasquin and Hafter, 1951). The goby and the blenny have *glandes annexes* at the caudal ends of the testes; when the interstitial tissue of the testis is increased in volume, the tubes of the *glandes annexes* are dilated with colloid secretion. These are glands of external secretion; their product has been compared to that of the prostate, but the function of the secretion is uncertain (Vivien, 1938; Coujard, 1941a, b).

Amphibians

The duct systems whereby sperm are collected and conveyed to the exterior have been comprehensively described by Noble (1931) in his admirable book on the amphibians. Several fine tubules, the vasa efferentia, join the testis directly or indirectly to the mesonephros, which in amphibians is also the functional kidney. In most genera the vasa efferentia empty into glomerular capsules. The sperm then traverse the urinary collecting tubules and the mesonephric (Wolffian) duct to reach the cloaca.

This pattern is somewhat modified in different genera. In *Rana* and *Alytes* (Noble, 1931), and in *Eurycea* (Weichert, 1945) and *Triton* (Aron, 1924b), the terminal part of the mesonephric duct is distended by accumulated sperm and thus functions as a kind of seminal vesicle.

Reptiles

In all the amniotes, the mesonephros is eventually supplanted as a urinary organ by the metanephros, or permanent kidney. The mesonephros, however, is immediately adjacent to the gonad and in the adult male serves as a collecting and conveying mechanism for the mature germ cells. In reptiles a few rete tubules or canals join the terminal ends of the seminiferous tubules to some of the mesonephric glomerular capsules; in many lizard species the rete canals are reduced to one (Alverdes, 1926, 1928; Regamey, 1935). The glomeruli themselves disappear after they cease to function, but the excurrent pathway provided by the mesonephric tubules and the mesonephric duct persists, affording the sperm a continuous route into the cloaca. In the adult reptile, as in higher vertebrates, the mesonephros is often referred to as the epididymis, and the mesonephric duct as the vas deferens.

V. Secretory Specializations of the Mesonephros and Metanephros

Fish

Fishes lack the metanephros of the amniotes. Instead, most of the mesonephros continues to function as a kidney. The anterior end of the mesonephros may be modified in the male as a collecting organ for the sperm. In various species of stickleback (*Gasterosteus*) a further and very interesting specialization has occurred. The male cares for the young. One of his functions is to build a nest, collecting and assembling plant debris, and sticking it together with a special secretion, a kind of waterproof cement. In the spring, as the time for nest-building approaches, the diameter of the tubules in the secretory portion of the mesonephros increases considerably. The epithelial cells of the tubules become three or four times as tall as before and fill with eosinophilic secretory granules which liquefy to produce the glutinous cementing substance for nest-building. This specialization does not occur in the female.[7]

Amphibians

Elevated, granule-filled epithelial cells lining the mesonephric collecting tubules and duct are a male sex character in *Triton alpestris* and *T. cristatus* (Aron, 1924b). Their function is not apparent.

Reptiles

Cyclic changes in the height and apparent secretory activity of the epithelium investing the epididymal tubules have been noted repeatedly (van den Broek, 1933). In the turtle *Terrapene* (*Cistudo*), epithelial cell height rises steadily from 14.5 μ in February to 37.6 μ in July, declining thereafter to 11.8 μ in October. The increase in cell height correspondingly reduces the internal diameter of the tubule (Dornesco, 1926b).

Van der Stricht (1893) apparently was the first to note the glandular nature of the epididymal epithelium of a lizard, *Lacerta vivipara*, and of the legless lacertilian, *Anguis fragilis*. In *Lacerta*, *Hemidactylus*, and *Anguis* there are four well defined seasonal periods for the epithelium lining the epididymal tubules: repose (autumn and winter), presecretion (February and March), secretion (April to June), and reconstruction (late June and early July). During the secretory phase the tubules are distended with a milky liquid containing sperm (Henry, 1900; Reiss, 1923b; Regamey, 1935). Secretory activity has been observed during the breeding season in the epididymides of lizards.[8] When an epididymis of *Takydromus* was surgically isolated, the contained sperm retained their activity for at least 70 days. This finding implies the possibility of prolonged epididymal sperm

[7] Möbius, 1885; Borcea, 1904; Hess, 1918; Courrier, 1921c, 1922a, b; van Oordt, 1924; Craig-Bennett, 1931; Ikeda, 1933; van den Broek, van Oordt, and Hirsch, 1938.

[8] *Anolis* (Fox, 1958), *Eumeces* (Reynolds, 1943), *Hemidactylus* (Dutta, 1946), and *Takydromus* (Takewaki and Fukuda, 1935a).

storage. Readers interested in the detailed anatomy of the lizard epididymis are referred to the accounts of Alverdes (1926, 1928).

There are no true seasonal changes in the ductuli efferentes (tubules connecting testis and epididymis) of the viper, *Vipera berus* (Volsøe, 1944). Each epididymal tubule has high, secretory epithelial cells in one portion and low, nonsecretory epithelial cells in the other. Chromophilic secretion granules accumulate in the apices of the secretory cells at all seasons and are eventually released into the lumen of the tubule. There seems to be no seasonal variation in the quantity of granules. Epithelial cells of the ductus epididymidis show considerable seasonal variation in height (low in summer, high in winter) but little or no secretory activity at any time. The ductus deferens also lacks secretory activity. In the garter snake, *Thamnophis*, epithelial cells are low in April and May and high in summer, fall, and winter (Fox, 1952).

Gampert (1866) first described what later came to be called the *sexual segment* of the metanephros. In the nephron of the common water snake, *Tropidonotus natrix*, a special segment is interposed between the distal convoluted tubule and the collecting tubule. Tribondeau (1902) described a *tube intermédaire* in the kidneys of *T. viperinus* and in *Vipera aspis*. He called attention to the segment's distinctive secretory granules and speculated as to its function. Later it was determined that in *Tropidonotus*, *Coluber* (*Zamenis*), and *Vipera*, the segment in question is not the last but next to the last, or preterminal, preceding the final portion of the nephron which in turn empties into the collecting tubule (Regaud and Policard, 1903a, b, c, d). Cells from the segment could be kept alive *in vitro* for 3 days in salt solution and could be stained supravitally. In some tubes, the cells were accumulating granules, whereas elsewhere granules were being discharged. It was further noted that a large preterminal segment occurs in male but not in female *Lacerta* and *Anguis*. The term *segment sexuel* was therefore applied to the structure. Finally, it was discovered that the sexual segment shows seasonal variations at the same time as does the testis, bespeaking androgenic control.

Many studies have since been made of the sexual segment in lizards. General agreement emerges that its epithelial cells in the adult male become so tall during the breeding season that the segment is macroscopically hypertrophied. The apices of the cells are crowded with protein-like secretion granules which push the small round nucleus to the base of the cell.[9] In *Takydromus*, not only the sexual segment but the terminal segment, collecting tubules, and even the ureters of the adult male are lined with epithelial cells showing conspicuous secretory activity during the breeding period (Takewaki and Fukuda, 1935a).

Among adult male snakes, the preterminal segment lacks seasonal variation in *Natrix* (*Tropidonotus*) and *Thamnophis* (*Eutenia*) *sirtalis* but does show seasonal secretory activity in *T. r. radix*, *T. elegans terrestris*, and *Vipera*.[10]

Curiously enough, the sexual segment has not been found in turtles (Regaud and Policard, 1903c, d; Herlant, 1933). Information is lacking to as to a possible sexual segment in the Crocodilia.

VI. Intromittent Organ

Fish

In viviparous fish, sperm are transferred to the female, at least in some species, with the aid of an intromittent organ. Male elasmobranchs have modified pelvic fins which are used as "claspers" during copulation. The further modification of the clasper as a phallus-like organ for internal fertilization has been described in *Scyllium*, *Acanthias*, *Raia* (Leigh-Sharpe, 1920), and *Cetorhinus* (Harrison Matthews, 1950). The specialization of this organ in the frilled shark, *Chlamydoselachus anguineus*, is remarkable. The male discharges into a groove on the medial side of the clasper a mixture of sperm from the urogenital papilla and sea water from the siphon sacs.

[9] Zarnik, 1910; Reiss, 1923b; Dornesco, 1925; Cordier, 1928; Courrier, 1929; Matthey, 1929; Kehl, 1935, 1944b; Regamey, 1935; Forbes, 1941; Reynolds, 1943; Fox, 1958.

[10] Cordier, 1928; Waters, 1940; Takewaki and Hatta, 1941; Volsøe, 1944; Fox, 1952.

At copulation the mixture is ejected into the oviducts of the female (Gilbert, 1943).

The anal fin of species of *Xiphophorus, Molliensia, Gambusia,* and *Fundulus* becomes specialized after puberty into a gonopodium which is used as an intromittent organ (van Oordt, 1925; Vaupel, 1929; Turner, 1941a, b; Cummings, 1943a). In some poeciliids this fin, although elongated, is not used for intromission, but instead is employed to "fan" the ejected sperm toward eggs which also have just been discharged (Newman, 1907).

The male's anal fin is employed for internal fertilization by at least one oviparous fish, *Apogon imberbis.* The fertilized eggs are then deposited in a clump which the male picks up, carrying the mass in his mouth during most of their incubation (Garnaud, 1950). One wonders how hungry the father becomes and how he resists temptation.

Amphibians

The majority of urodeles fertilize their eggs externally in the water, whereas nearly all female salamanders obtain sperm for internal fertilization by picking up spermatophores with their cloacal labia. According to Noble (1931), both *Ascaphus,* a very primitive frog, and the *Gymnophiona,* an order of limbless, burrowing amphibians, practice internal fertilization with the aid of an intromittent organ which is simply a muscular, highly vascular extension of the cloaca. The rectus abdominis muscles of *Ascaphus* draw this copulatory tube anteriorly so that it can be thrust into the cloaca of the female. Since *Nectophrynoïdes occidentalis* is viviparous (see below) it must also practice internal fertilization, but the mechanism is unknown (Angel and Lamotte, 1944).

Reptiles

In lizards and snakes the paired penial sacs are posterior diverticula of the cloaca and lie caudal to it in pouches under the skin of the tail. Before mating the sacs are drawn by muscle action into the cloaca and then, as they become erect, evert themselves like the fingers of a glove through the cloacal outlet. The semen passes through a

spiral furrow in each penis. The latter is then withdrawn into its recess by an elongated retractor muscle.

In turtles and crocodilians the single, arched phallus is a solid, cavernous structure. It is attached to the ventral wall of the proctodeum (the terminal chamber of the cloaca), from which it is everted on erection. The semen is carried in a deep groove along the convex penial surface, the groove being converted into a canal during erection.[11] In these reptiles the phallus of the female is morphologically similar to, but much smaller than, that of the male.

VII. Other Specialized Structures in Males

Fish

Evidence will be presented later that the dimorphism in size and color seen in many species is at least partly under the control of the sex hormones. Sometimes the dimorphism is extreme. For example, late in his life the male pink salmon, *Oncorhynchus gorbuscha,* grows a huge hump on his back, and his head becomes large and bizarre in appearance (Davidson, 1935). The adult male sockeye salmon, *O. nerka,* develops the dorsal hump, an elongated jaw, and a thickened skin (Weisel, 1943). The "sword," a greatly elongated portion of the caudal fin which gives *Xiphophorus* its name, is another conspicuous male secondary sex character (van Oordt, 1925).

Amphibians

Many male frogs and toads have wartlike excrescences on their fore limbs in the breeding season. These "nuptial callosities" help the male to cling to the female during amplexus. Bles (1905) described the "nuptial asperities" (a delightfully ambiguous phrase) of *Xenopus laevis,* an African toad. Other species have similar structures, often spiny. Braun (1878) reported "large, round, black-colored warts" on the hind limbs of male *Triton viridescens* and erroneously supposed that these growths also made possible a firm grip on the female during mat-

[11] Wiedersheim, 1886; Gadow, 1887, 1923; Coe and Kunkel, 1905; Moens, 1912; Reese, 1915; Nicholson and Risley, 1941.

ing, although he admits that he never observed this process. Similar structures have been described on the medial surfaces of the hind limbs of *Diemectylus* (*Triturus*) (Jordan, 1891).

A dorsal crest or skin fold is common on adult male urodeles during the breeding season. The crest usually extends along the back and tail and in profile makes the animal look much larger. Special masculine skin pigmentation may occur. Secretions from hedonic glands on the chin and adjacent areas in *Eurycea* and *Triturus* perhaps attract females; these glands begin to accumulate their product in November and are distended by the start of the breeding season in March. Cloacal glands are a distinctive male characteristic of *Desmognathus, Triturus,* and other salamanders. Seasonally, the epithelial cells of these glands become tall and accumulate granules. Possibly the glandular secretion of *Desmognathus* may form the spermatophores.[12]

The male *D. fuscus* has a monocuspid premaxillary tooth which differs from that of the female (Noble, 1926).

The *linea masculina* is a curious and distinctive band of connective tissue lying at the dorsal and ventral edges of the obliquus abdominis muscles in various adult male ranid frogs, but not in toads (Liu, 1935; Davis and Law, 1935; Schmidt, 1938). Fore limb muscles (flexor carpi radialis, extensor carpi radialis, abductor pollicis longus) are much larger in adult male than in female toads such as *Bufo a. americanus,* apparently aiding the powerful and prolonged grasping of the female during amplexus. As Howell (1935), who described this interesting specialization, has remarked, it would be desirable to study the effects of gonadectomy and gonad transplant on these muscles.

Reptiles

The lizard's cloaca shows sexual specialization. It is divided into an anterior coprodeum, receiving the small intestine, an intermediate urodeum, and a posterior proctodeum. Adjoining chambers are separated by sphincter muscles. From the urodeum arises a dorsal urogenital diverticulum of varying size; into this diverticulum or fossa usually open conjointly the ureter and vas deferens in the male and, separately, the ureter and oviduct in the female (Gadow, 1887; Regamey, 1935; Forbes, 1941).

In the male *Lacerta agilis* (Regamey, 1933, 1935) the urogenital diverticulum, urodeum, and anterior proctodeum are lined in the spring with tall, columnar, stratified (two or three layers) epithelium containing many mucous cells. The total depth of the epithelium is 35 μ. In June and July, during the breeding season, the epithelium thickens to 40 to 45 μ. The urodeum, anterior proctodeum, and terminal portion of vas deferens (a urogenital fossa is lacking) of the adult male *Sceloporus spinosus floridanus* has a bilaminar epithelium (Forbes, 1941). Its inner stratum is formed of a single layer of columnar cells. Peripheral to them is a second layer, in most areas one cell thick, of cuboidal and low columnar cells. The regularly arranged nuclei of the two layers present a striking appearance.

Opening into the anal vestibule, or terminal portion of the proctodeum, in male *Lacerta* and *Sceloporus* are cloacal glands. One pair lies anterior and ventral, the others (a single gland in *Lacerta,* a pair in *Sceloporus*) lie posterior and dorsal, to the proctodeum. The glands lack definitive capsules and consist of numerous lobules separated by thin but dense connective tissue septa. Each lobule forms an acinus-like epithelial pouch, sometimes containing a little secretion.

Several lizard genera have femoral glands which are developed as male accessory sex structures.[13] In *Lacerta* there are 16 to 21 glands on the anterior surface of each thigh. The glands lie just under the skin and open by way of a short duct which penetrates a conical elevation of the skin. The duct openings are visible macroscopically. The golden-yellow secretion of the glands is abundant during the breeding season.[14]

---

[12] Jordan, 1891; Bresca, 1910; Aron, 1924b; Humphrey, 1925; Noble, 1926, 1931; Adams, 1940; Weichert, 1945.

[13] von Leydig, 1872; Braun, 1877; Schaefer, 1901, 1902; Cohn, 1904; Tölg, 1905; Mahendra, 1936, 1953; Forbes, 1941.

[14] Felizet, 1911; Reiss, 1923b; Matthey, 1929; Suchow, 1929; Padoa, 1933; Regamey, 1935.

Few species of turtle show external sexual dimorphism. An exception is *Terrapene carolina*, in which the eye of the male is red whereas that of the female is brown (Blake, 1921).

The male tuatara, *Sphenodon punctatum*, the sole living representative of the order Rhynchocephalia, is much larger than the female and has a conspicuous dorsal crest with white spines. In the breeding season the male's crest may become erect and swollen (Thomas, 1890). Remarkably little is known about the reproductive system and its function in this fascinating reptile.

The gular skin fold which the lizard *Anolis* can erect from its throat is a striking masculine characteristic. Male lizards of some species distinguish themselves by dorsal crests and bright colors.

Among the snakes, certain scales or scaly tubercles near the anus may show sexual dimorphism, and, as in the lizards, the slight bulging of the penial sacs on external examination distinguishes the male from the female (Blanchard, 1931; Noble, 1934; Lederer, 1942). The tip of the tail of the male fer-de-lance, *Bothrops atrox*, may be a bright yellow. There is reason to think that this wriggling, twisting tail-tip may lure lizards, toads, and other food within striking distance (Burger and Smith, 1950). The male Paraguayan anaconda is smaller than the female, and his pelvic spurs are better developed (Lederer, 1942). Males of *Engyrus carinatus*, a New Guinea boid snake, have pelvic spurs, whereas these structures are missing in most adult and all juvenile females (Stickel and Stickel, 1946). Male boas and pythons use their spurs to scratch the body of the female during mating (Davis, 1936). Tubercles on the chins of some colubrid snakes are tactile organs; if the tubercles are covered with tape, the male will not court the female (Noble, 1934). Davis (1936) has reviewed the role of spurs, tubercles, etc., in the courting behavior of snakes.

Although evidence will be presented later for endocrine control of the adult development of some accessory sex structures, it must be remembered that genetic factors also play their role. Relative degrees of control exercised by genes and hormones constitute a significant area for research.

VIII. Effects of Orchiectomy

Fish

Ablation of gonads helps to disclose the structures, physiologic processes, and behavior which are partly or completely under the control of testicular or ovarian hormones (see Pickford and Atz, 1957, for review). The most frequently observed result of the castration of male fish has been a loss of the special, occasionally brilliant, skin color in those species with color dimorphism. Sometimes there is a seasonal pigmentary change in the chromatophores, or pigment-bearing cells. Such change is associated with the time of spawning, and is referred to as *Hochzeitskleid*, or nuptial coloration. If castration is performed before the breeding season, the nuptial coloration fails to appear; if during the season, the color may rapidly fade. Removal of only one testis has little or no effect; apparently the remaining gonad can release enough androgen to maintain normal coloration. Loss of male coloration due to castration has been demonstrated in several genera.[15]

The male Japanese bitterling also has pearl organs, 5 to 10 small dermal excrescences like white warts on the anterior part of the head. Orchiectomy interferes with their development (Tozawa, 1929), as it does with the growth of the gonopodium in *Gambusia* (St. Amant, 1941; Turner, 1941a).

Amphibians

Orchiectomy has shown that many male secondary sex characters are under the control of testicular hormones. Steinach (1894) found removal of the *Samenbläschen*, a saclike appendage of the mesonephric duct, from a frog had no effect on the sex characters, but castration before the breeding season resulted in the failure of amplexus to occur. Among the urodeles, orchiectomy in *Discoglossus* is followed by prompt regres-

---

[15] The stickleback, *Gasterosteus* (Bock, 1928; Becker and Lehmensick, 1933; Ikeda, 1933), the bitterling, *Acheilognathus* (Tozawa, 1929), and *Phoxinus* (Kopeć, 1927), *Halichoeres* (Kinoshita, 1935), *Oryzias* (Niwa, 1955), and *Amia* (Zahl and Davis, 1932).

sion of the nuptial pad (Kehl, 1944a) and in male *Xenopus* by a much delayed drop in serum calcium (Shapiro and Zwarenstein, 1933). Removal of the testes is succeeded by regression of sexual accessories in *Bufo*, but removal of Bidder's organ does not have this effect (Ponse, 1922a, b). Nuptial excrescences and other sex structures regress after orchiectomy in *Bombinator* (Moszkowska, 1932). In *Rana*, removal of the testes results in diminution in size of seminal vesicles and thumb pads and in failure of nuptial coloring and other sex characters to appear (Aron, 1926; Christensen, 1931; Kinoshita, 1932), but the *linea masculina* is not affected (Davis and Law, 1935). It is suggested that once the latter is established it does not require hormonal support from the testis.

In *Triton* (*Triturus*) and *Desmognathus*, two familiar genera of *Salientia*, orchiectomy of adults results in regression or disappearance of the dorsal crest, of the specialized epithelium of the Wolffian duct and cloaca, and of male skin coloration. The masculine premaxillary tooth is replaced by a tooth like that seen in the female (Bresca, 1910; Aron, 1924b; Noble and Davis, 1928; Noble and Pope, 1929).

Reptiles

Castration of the box turtle, *Terrapene carolina*, caused great reduction in the size of the epididymis. Motile sperm could still be obtained from the epididymis 74 days after orchiectomy (Hansen, 1939). (The ability of the surgically isolated epididymis of the lizard to store sperm has already been mentioned.) Sanfelice (1888) removed part of a testis from one snake, *Natrix* (*Tropidonotus*) *natrix*, and one lizard, *Lacerta agilis*, and observed some testicular regeneration. The latter phenomenon perhaps represents early evidence of sorts for a gonadotrophic hormone in these reptiles. In the blindworm, *Anguis fragilis*, seasonal development of the renal sexual segment and of other sexual accessories was prevented if the castration was performed before the breeding season. If done during this season, atrophy of the accessories followed in about 15 days (Herlant, 1933). Orchiectomy of *Lacerta* caused increase in the size of the fat bodies, disappearance of the green body color, persistence of the femoral glands in the quiescent phase, involution of the epididymis, and absence of epididymal and femoral gland secretion. The sexual segment of the kidney remained in the nonsecretory phase, and the epithelium of the urogenital fossa was low and nonglandular (Matthey, 1929; Regamey, 1935; Padoa, 1929, 1933). Seasonal development of sex accessories was prevented by castration of *Takydromus* (Takewaki and Fukuda, 1935a). Sperm viability in the epididymis was much less than in normal lizards (Takewaki and Fukuda, 1935b; *cf.* Hansen's results, above, in the box turtle). Involution of sexual accessories after orchiectomy also occurred in *Eumeces* (Reynolds, 1943) and *Uromastix* (Kehl, 1935, 1944b).

Removal of the testes had no effect on the renal sexual segment in the snake *Thamnophis r. radix* (Waters, 1940) but did in *Natrix* (Takewaki and Hatta, 1941).

IX. Effects of Androgens

Sex hormones have been given experimentally in a variety of ways. These hormones are freely soluble in certain vegetable fats such as sesame oil and in alcohols and are slightly soluble in water. Solutions can be injected subcutaneously, intramuscularly, or intraperitoneally. Solid pellets made by compressing the crystalline hormone can be implanted in various body sites for slow, continuous absorption. Sex hormones can even be fed. Solutions can be applied to the skin; in fish and amphibians, percutaneous absorption can be achieved if the hormone is dissolved in the aquarium water. Finally, in one of the oldest techniques, testes or ovaries can be grafted into experimental animals.

Fish

Administration of testicular hormone to intact carp and of testosterone propionate to hypophysectomized killifish accelerated the rate of spermatogenesis (Castelnuovo, 1937; Burger, 1942). Intraperitoneal injection of androgens in *Fundulus heteroclitus* stimulated increase in weight of the testis even after hypophysectomy (Pickford and Atz, 1957). Pregneninolone (ethinyl testosterone) when fed to *Lebistes* interfered with normal body growth in both sexes (Scott, 1944). The liver of *Oryzias* is sexually dimorphic during the breeding season; if a testosterone propionate pellet is implanted in the female at this time, her liver acquires a typical male appearance (Egami, 1955a).

It has already been shown that skin color may be under the control of androgens, and it is therefore not surprising that administered male sex hormone may conspicuously affect coloration. Thus, the injection of testosterone propionate into hypophysectomized *Fundulus* or into *Fundulus* during the nonbreeding period evoked the yellow body color typical of the spawning season (Burger, 1942). Nuptial coloration was produced in *Rhodeus, Acheilognathus, Oryzias*, and an unspecified genus of bitterling by administration of male hormone in various forms; the androgen was given during the nonbreeding season, or to castrated males, or to females.[16] The addition of pregneninolone to aquarium water induced the appearance of male coloration, and also caused the disappearance of the black "gravid spot" from the tail fin of the female, in *Lebistes* (Eversole, 1941; Régnier, 1941).

Gonopodia and other male secondary sex characters have also been studied as indicators of androgen action. Gonopodia have been produced in female *Platypoecilus, Lebistes, Gambusia*, and *Molliensia* by injections of testosterone propionate or by the addition to the aquarium water of pregneninolone (in some cases, 1 mg. in 14,000,000 ml. water) or methyl testosterone (1 mg. in as much as 25,000,000 ml.)[17] Treatment of castrated male *Gambusia* with pregneninolone or with testis grafts permits the normal development of the gonopodium (St. Amant, 1941). If the anal fin, the female homologue of the gonopodium of adult female *Platypoecilus maculatus*, is amputated and if any of several androgens (androsterone and testosterone propionate are most effective) is then injected, a male-like but atypical go-

nopodium is regenerated (Grobstein, 1940, 1942a, b, 1947).

When adult lampreys become sexually mature, ducts develop for the escape of mature germ cells from the mesonephros to the exterior, and the cloacal labia undergo vascular distention. Administration of either testosterone or of estrone, a female sex hormone, to adult but sexually immature lampreys will evoke the same changes (Knowles, 1939).

Further evidence for the control of sexual accessory structures by androgens is summarized by Pickford and Atz (1957).

Amphibians

Androgen has been supplied experimentally by injection and by the transplantation of testes. Testicular homotransplants failed to restore male sex accessories in castrate *Rana* in an early experiment (Smith and Schuster, 1912), perhaps because the grafts did not survive. Amplexus occurred promptly after injection of a suspension of dried bull testes into the dorsal lymph sacs of adult male frogs (Brossard and Gley, 1929). Ponse (1922a, b, 1930) restored male sex characters by testis grafting in castrate *Bufo vulgaris*, as did Moszkowska (1932) in *Bombinator*. The injection of androgens caused development of the nuptial pads in *Discoglossus* (Kehl, 1944a) but not in *Xenopus* (Berk, 1939). Curiously, ovulation could be induced in the latter genus both by injecting the intact animal with any of several androgens or other steroids (Shapiro, 1939) or by adding testosterone and androstenedione to a frog Ringer solution in which an *excised* ovary was suspended (Shapiro and Zwarenstein, 1937). Implantation of testosterone propionate tablets into castrate male and female toads (*Bufo vulgaris*) resulted in the development of male accessories in both sexes (Harms, 1950). Similar treatment before the breeding season of both male and female cricket frogs (*Acris gryllus*) evoked male skin coloration and hypertrophy of Wolffian ducts (both sexes), oviducts, and seminal vesicles (Greenberg, 1942). Injections of the same hormone into castrate male *Rana pipiens* resulted in growth of the nuptial pads and vestigial oviducts (Wolf, 1939).

Bresca (1910) made an interesting ob-

[16] Gläser and Haempel, 1932; Owen, 1937; Gläser and Ranftl, 1938; Havas, 1939; Niwa, 1955.

[17] Eversole, 1941; Régnier, 1941; Turner, 1941b, 1942a, b, c; Cummings, 1943b; Hamon, 1945; Gallien, 1948; Hopper, 1949; Tavolga, 1949; Egami, 1954a.

servation in *Triturus* (*Triton*). Transplantation of testes to females was not followed by masculinization of accessory sex organs, but if a secondary female sex structure was itself transplanted to a normal male, the sexually appropriate transformation occurred, *e.g.*, the middorsal skin stripe of the female became a dorsal crest when grafted on the male. In later experiments with *Triton*, castration and successful re-implantation of testes (autotransplantation), and the injection of testosterone in oil into adults during the nonbreeding season both resulted in the development of male accessory structures (Aron, 1924b; Fleischmann and Kann, 1936). In *Desmognathus*, testis transplants into spayed females evoked the development of masculine premaxillary and maxillary teeth and of abdominal, pelvic, and cloacal glands (Noble, 1926; Noble and Davis, 1928; Noble and Pope, 1929).

Reptiles

In the juvenile box tortoise, *Terrapene carolina*, testosterone propionate pellets stimulated the growth of claws almost as large as those of adult males (Evans, 1951a). The administration of androgens to immature *Chelydra* and to two species of *Pseudemys* resulted in acceleration of claw growth and growth of the penis (Evans, 1946, 1951b, 1952a, b).

The first successful effort to graft testes into lizards seems to have been that of Regamey (1935) in castrate *Lacerta*. His grafts did not survive in males but were successful in 3 of 25 females; in these 3 the mesonephric rudiment was transformed into an epididymis-like structure, and the mesonephric duct became a vas deferens. Kehl (1944b) injected androsterone benzoate into female *Uromastix* during the sexually quiescent period. This resulted in conspicuous growth and glandular development of the oviducts. (Other evidence will be presented below for a "bisexual" action of the androgens in some cases.) A second result (Kehl, 1938) was the development of the renal sexual segment to a stage resembling that of the male's sexual segment at the height of the breeding season. Treatment of *Sceloporus* with testosterone and testosterone propionate stimulated slight development of the mesonephric rest and duct in females and conspicuous enlargement of the male epididymis, femoral glands, and hemipenes. Both the oviduct and the male Müllerian duct segments also grew remarkably (Gorbman, 1939; Forbes, 1941; Altland, 1943). The administration of androgens caused growth of the epididymis and sexual segment of the kidney of *Eumeces* (Reynolds, 1943) and of the dorsonuchal crest of *Anolis* (Evans, 1948).

In the snake, *Thamnophis*, injections of testosterone propionate stimulated pronounced development of the sexual segments in castrate adult males and females and in intact immature snakes of both sexes (Waters, 1940).

Administration of testosterone to the immature alligator, *Alligator mississippiensis*, evoked striking growth of the oviducts in the females and of the penis in the single experimental male. The mesonephroi and Wolffian ducts in both sexes and the phalluses of the females did not respond (Forbes, 1938b). Injection of older but still immature alligators with testosterone propionate caused conspicuous development of the oviduct and of the male and female phallus (Forbes, 1939).

Other effects of administered androgens in embryonic and immature reptiles are discussed in the section on "Experimental Sex Reversal."

X. External Transport of Eggs and Young

Fish

Most fish appear to be indifferent to their eggs and offspring. However, male pipefish and seahorses carry the developing eggs in skin pouches, whereas the eggs adhere to the surface of the belly of a catfish, *Platystacus*. The male sea catfish *Galeichthys* and *Conorhynchos* protect the developing eggs by carrying them in their mouths (Jordan, 1905; Strawn, 1958). The transport period lasts 60 to 80 days in *Galeichthys* (Ward, 1957).

Amphibians

In general, amphibians abandon their eggs after they are laid. It is an interesting vagary of nature, however, that a number of species do transport their eggs and larvae by one means or another. In most cases, this is a matter not only of specialized behavior but of some morphologic modification. *Alytes obstetricans*, a European form, is popularly called the midwife toad. Actually, it is the male of this species which manages to wind about his hind legs the strings of eggs which the female has laid. Here they stay, encased in their sticky jelly, until they hatch. The female *Hyla goeldii*, a South American frog, carries a mass of incubating eggs on her back with the aid of a low skin fold which helps to form a kind of shallow receptacle (Boulenger, 1895). At least four other genera of South American tree frogs similarly transport incubating eggs as a mass, partly or completely covered by a flap of dorsal skin, or individually, each egg in a separate pocket of skin on the back (Noble, 1931). Bartlett (1896) reported to the Zoological Society of London how the eggs are placed on the back of the Surinam toad, *Pipa americana*. He and a keeper observed the process in the reptile house at the Zoological Gardens. Late in April two pairs of the frogs were seen in amplexus. The male had firmly grasped the lower abdomen of the female, his body extending caudal to hers. Her "oviduct" was protruded more than an inch, arching between the belly of the male and the back of the female. (Subsequent dissection by Boulenger of a female which died during oviposition showed that the "oviduct" was actually an "ovipositor, formed by the cloaca.") The male squeezed the sac-like ovipositor and moved it about, thus directing the even placement of the eggs. The latter stuck to the back, and the ovipositor later was retracted. It is known (Parker and Haswell, 1921) that the eggs eventually sink into cavities which develop in the spongy dorsal skin, that lid-like structures form over the cavities, and that the larvae remain in these convenient, individual containers until they metamorphose. What regulates the modification of the dorsal skin so that, at the proper time, each egg can "implant" in this strange site?

Tadpoles of the genera *Dendrobates* and *Phyllobates* attach themselves by buccal suckers to the back of an adult male (Boulenger, 1895). The larvae of *Arthroleptis*

seychellensis, a frog found in the Seychelles Islands of the Indian Ocean, swim to the back of the adult. Here they attach themselves, not by buccal suckers but by a sticky ectodermal secretion. Contact is always between the ventral skin of the larva and the dorsal skin of the adult (Brauer, 1898).

Reptiles

There appear to be no reports of morphologic specialization for the external transport of reptilian eggs or young.

XI. Ovary; Ovogenesis; Ovulation

Fish

The ovaries of fish range from primitive structures to rather complex organs which may combine functions of the mammalian ovary, oviducts, uterus, and even, to an extent, the mammary gland. On the other hand, detailed knowledge regarding the genital systems of most species of fish is surprisingly scanty, particularly in terms of histologic detail. Surely this is an important and fascinating area for research.

The brook lamprey, *Entosphenus wilderi*, which has been carefully studied by Okkelberg (1921), attains its full body length while still a larva. Then it metamorphoses. Now, in August or September, comes the climactic stage of its life. The gonads mature, growing swiftly to the point where they occupy all the body cavity. The digestive tract atrophies. Thereafter the lamprey eats nothing. It breeds the following April, and then dies. There is a single testis or ovary in the sexually mature animal. The eggs are enclosed in follicles; the latter are believed by Okkelberg to be homologous with the cysts of the testis. The mature ova are, as in cyclostomes generally (Hoar, 1957a), shed into the coelomic cavity and then escape to the exterior by way of abdominal pores, urogenital sinus, and urogenital papilla.

In the basking shark, an elasmobranch, only the right ovary develops (Harrison Matthews, 1950). It may contain about 6,000,000 ova, 0.5 mm. or more in diameter and possessing some yolk. When the ripe follicles rupture, the ova escape into a pouch inside the ovary, then are propelled into the oviduct and uterus. In the dogfish, *Scyliorhinus canicula*, abdominal cilia, present only in the adult female, move the ova from the ovary to the oviduct (Metten, 1939).

The varieties of female reproductive tract in the bony fish were long ago categorized by Brock (1878) on the basis of his study of 57 species in almost as many genera. In one class the solid ovary has no excurrent duct, eggs being discharged into the coelomic space and escaping by way of the abdominal pore. The ovary may consist of a single layer, as in the eel *Anguilla*, or of several layers, as in the *Salmonidae*. In a second category of fish the ovary is a sac, closed anteriorly and ending posteriorly in an oviduct. Only a little of the ovarian wall may contain eggs, as in *Scorpaena*, *Lepadogaster*, and *Ophidium*, or most of the wall may be filled with eggs carried in masses which are knob-shaped in cross section, as in *Lophobranchis* and *Blennius*, or in lamellae. MacLeod (1881) also recognized these two classes of ovary. He pointed out that in the first, or solid, type the medial surface (*face vasculaire*) is smooth, invested with endothelium, and lacks germinal epithelium. The lateral surface, or *face germinative*, is covered with egg-bearing folds and germinal epithelium. The solid type of ovary is seen in salmonid and murenid fish. In all other bony fish, the paired ovaries are hollow; their external surface is vascular, whereas the interior is invested with germinal epithelium. The ovarian sac ends posteriorly in an oviduct. Right and left oviducts join to form a common canal which opens through the body wall between anus and urinary orifice. Part or all of the internal, or ovigerous, surface of the ovary is folded in a variety of patterns.

The ovary of *Fundulus* as described by Matthews (1938) belongs in the second category. This ovary is single but bilobed anteriorly. Ovigerous lamellae project into its central cavity. Follicles may begin to mature at any time of year. The ovary is smallest in July, increases slowly in size until April, then grows rapidly until ovulation in June. The ovaries of *Neotoca* and *Oryzias* also belong in this class (Mendoza, 1940; Robinson and Rugh, 1943).

Oviposition necessarily coincides with the shedding of sperm by the male in those fish in which fertilization is external.

Amphibians

Ovulation and fertilization occur during the spring in most amphibians (Smith, 1955). In *Rana pipiens* the the cyst-like follicle bulges as it matures (Rugh, 1935). Eventually it ruptures at the stigma, not abruptly but in less than a minute. The ovum slowly emerges, being forced through an aperture smaller than the egg itself. The follicles of the frog's ovary can be ruptured artificially by pressure or by the application of a pepsin-hydrochloric acid mixture (Rugh, 1935; Kraus, 1947). Smooth muscle fibers are a normal component of the amphibian ovary. Kraus and others have noted that the muscle fibers are larger in the mature than in the immature ovary. The fibers contract rhythmically, not only during ovulation but at other times. Their role, if any, is not clear. Rugh believes that normal follicular rupture follows, and is due to local changes induced earlier by pituitary hormones. It is interesting that if ripe follicles are excised they still may ovulate up to 12 hours later. Thus the final release of the ovum would seem to be an autonomous process.

Reptiles

Important early descriptions of the adult reptilian ovary include those of von Leydig (1853, 1872), Waldeyer (1870), Braun (1877), and Loyez (1905–1906). In turtles and lizards the ovaries are round and plump; in snakes, elongated; in the immature alligator, flat and rather long (Reese, 1915; van den Broek, 1933; Forbes, 1937).

The musk turtle, *Sternotherus odoratus*, breeds in April and early May and ovulates usually between May 15 and 20. The eggs are carried in the oviducts for 20 to 35 days, then laid (Risley, 1933a). The box turtle, *Terrapene carolina*, ovulates in June and July and lays its eggs soon afterward (Altland, 1951). Munson (1904) says that the ovaries of the tortoise, *Clemmys marmorata*, fill most of the abdominal cavity when the eggs have acquired all of their yolk. In an Algerian tortoise, *Emys leprosa*, the eggs apparently reach their maximal size and are ovulated in June (Combescot, 1954b).

Waldeyer (1870) mentions an investing layer of germinal epithelium on the ovary of *Lacerta* and the numerous layers of epithelium in the mature follicle. Regamey (1935) adds details. The ovary is supported by a mesovarium developed from the dorsal abdominal wall. Young ovocytes lie close to the hilus. The ovary is invested with cuboidal epithelium, but only the epithelium close to the hilus is considered to be germinative. Ovogenesis continues throughout the year. Ripe follicles are seen in April and May, and ovulation occurs at this time. *Uromastix* follows the same schedule (Kehl, 1935), as do *Eumeces* (Breckenridge, 1943), *Hemidactylus* (Dutta, 1944), and *Sceloporus* (Woodbury and Woodbury, 1945). It is believed that *Anolis* ovulates alternately from the right and left ovaries (Noble and Greenberg, 1941); the ovaries are largest between March and September (Dessauer, 1955). This lizard produces single eggs at intervals of about two weeks during a breeding season lasting from midspring until the end of summer (Hamlett, 1952). Usually only one ovum matures at a time in *Xantusia vigilis* (Miller, 1948).

It seems that the snake *Tropidonotus viperinus* mates in October or November and ovulates in the following June or July, whereas *Coronella laevis* mates in August and September and ovulates in May and June (Rollinat, 1898). The viviparous prairie rattler, *Crotalus v. viridis*, ovulates late in the spring or early in the summer. The young are born in August or September. The evidence is strong that the snake does not ovulate the next year, but only in the spring two years after the previous ovulation (Rahn, 1942).

Alligators lay their numerous (100 to 200) eggs in April or May after maturing to a length of at least six feet (Cope, 1900; McIlhenny, 1935). The immature alligator ovary is lobulated (Reese, 1915). It consists of a well defined cortex and a medulla (Forbes, 1937, 1940a). The cortex is invested with germinal epithelium and contains numerous immature follicles with eggs of various sizes. The underlying medulla consists chiefly of connective tissue strands (the remains of the medullary cords), between which are large lacunae. The posterior third of the ovary is composed of solid medullary tissue. This is a "medullary rest"; it persists with little change from the embryonic period, lacks germinal epithelium, and resembles primitive testicular tissue.

XII. Sources of Estrogens

Fish

A few investigators have searched for estrogens in fish gonads. Assay of an extract of 10 pounds of swordfish, *Xiphias gladius*, ovaries showed less than 6 rabbit units of estrogen (Weisman, Mishkind, Kleiner and Coates, 1937). Ovaries of the flounder, *Pseudopleuronectes americanus*, contain small amounts of estrogen, as indicated by assay of extracts in rats (Donahue, 1941). Chemical assay of 420 cc. pooled urine from 25 male and female *Lophius piscatorius*, the angler fish, revealed 0.7 mg. folliculin, 1.5 mg. total phenolic steroids, 0.055 mg. 11-oxysteroids, and 0.35 mg. 17-ketosteroids (Brull and Cuypers, 1954). The mature ova of the dogfish, *Mustelus canis*, contain a large amount of estrogen (Hisaw and Abramowitz, cited by Pickford and Atz, 1957).

The production of estrogens by fish ovaries deserves vigorous study. The results might well shed light not only on morphologic changes but on reproductive behavior. Perhaps migration itself is stimulated in part by sex hormones.

Amphibians

The writer has found only one pertinent report (Grant, 1937), and that without details: an "estrogenic substance can be extracted from amphibian ovaries." Further research is desirable, but no doubt has been impeded by the problem of obtaining enough ovarian tissue to yield detectable amounts of sex hormone.

Reptiles

Injection daily for four days of 0.1 cc. follicular fluid from the ovaries of *Crotalus terrificus* provoked vaginal estrus in castrate mice (Fraenkel and Martins, 1938). Alcoholic extracts of the ovaries of crotalid snakes on bio-assay contained the equivalent of 200 estrone units per kilogram of fresh ovaries (Valle and Valle, 1943).

XIII. Oviduct; Egg Transport

Fish

According to Stromsten (1931), Rathke (1824) discovered the oviduct of the fish. This renowned old anatomist and embryologist also recognized that the oviduct is absent in the lamprey, *Petromyzon*, in the eel, and in some salmonid fish, a deficiency since noted in additional species (Brock, 1878; MacLeod, 1881). In such fish the eggs are released into the coelom and then reach the exterior through an abdominal pore. As already stated, in most bony fish the ovary is hollow, and the eggs or young pass successively into the ovarian cavity, oviduct, and (in some viviparous forms) uterus. Information is needed as to how the inert eggs are moved. Eggert (1931) has concluded that the oviduct is not homologous with the Müllerian duct of higher vertebrates.

The oviduct of the Japanese medaka, *Oryzias latipes*, has been described in some detail (Robinson and Rugh, 1943), but there is little information on seasonal variation in the fish oviduct and on the role, if any, of sex hormones in oviducal development.

Amphibians

In most and perhaps all adult females, but not in males or in immature females, the ventral and lateral coelomic peritoneum is ciliated (Donahue, 1934; Rugh, 1935). The cilia roll the liberated eggs into the ostium of the oviduct, about two hours being required for the journey. If transplanted eggs or even buckshot are introduced into any part of the coelom, ciliary action will eventually deliver them to the oviduct, although as Rugh remarks, the heavy buckshot are moved very slowly.

The amphibian oviduct may increase in size during the breeding season, then regress (de Allende, 1939). The jelly-like coating characteristic of extruded amphibian eggs is contributed by oviducal glands. After oviposition this coating takes up water and swells (Noble, 1931) to form a sticky layer which protects the egg and often attaches the egg mass to underwater debris or even to the adults in those species which transport the eggs externally.

Reptiles

Lataste described in 1876 the histology of the oviduct of a turtle, *Cistudo* (*Terrapene*) *europaea*. The three layers of the ostium consist of partly ciliated mucosa, connective tissue, and investing peritoneum. The middle portion of the duct also has glandular and muscular layers. In the final, or cloacal, portion there are two muscle layers, and the gland cells contain chromophilic granules. Argaud (1920) saw both granule-producing and mucin-producing gland cells in the oviduct of an unidentified turtle. The oviduct of the immature *Testudo* is lined with nonciliated cuboidal epithelium, and the epithelium is also low in the sexually inactive adult. During the breeding season the oviduct is enlarged and the mucosa contains muciparous cells interspersed among cells in which the cytoplasm is crowded with large secretion granules (Argaud, 1920; Kehl, 1930).

A classic study of the oviduct, including that of the turtle *Chrysemys*, was made by Parker (1931). He described longitudinal pro-ovarian bands of cilia which sweep the sperm toward the ovary. Abovarian bands of cilia beat in the opposite direction. If the oviduct were opened longitudinally and particles of coal dust were scattered on it, both types of band demonstrated their ciliary action. Eggs, on the other hand, were believed to be moved down the oviducts by peristalsis. Van den Broek (1933) confirmed Parker's observations regarding the regular longitudinal folds of the mucosa. The former states that the albumen of the egg is produced by the oviduct proper, whereas the egg shell, the final investment, is secreted by the "uterus" or last part of the oviducal tube. Seasonal development of the mucosal cells of the ostium occurs in *Terrapene* (Hansen and Riley, 1941). In adult *Emys*, on the other hand, the mucosal cells do not change throughout the year (Combescot, 1954b, 1955).

The mucosa of the oviduct of *Hatteria* (*Sphenodon*) is folded and during pregnancy is glandular in its terminal portion (Osawa,

1898). Ciliated cells and goblet cells are also present (van den Broek, 1933). For the lizards, the general picture which emerges is of seasonal development of the oviducal mucosa in most forms, of a specialized area for the secretion of albumen, and of a "uterus" or "incubation chamber" for the oviparous species.[18] Crowell (1932) has seen in *Phrynosoma* and *Sceloporus*, as has Dutta (1946) in *Hemidactylus*, a tract of pro-ovarian cilia like that described by Parker for the turtle. Specialization of the uterus for viviparity is discussed below.

In April to July the oviducal glands of the snake *Natrix t. tigrina* are conspicuous and their cells are crowded with secretion granules (Takewaki and Hatta, 1941). Seasonal development of the uterine portion of the prairie rattler's oviduct also occurs (Rahn, 1942).

The immature alligator's oviduct has been described (Reese, 1915; Forbes, 1937, 1940a), but information on the adult structure seems to be lacking.

XIV. Other Specializations in Females

Reptiles

During the period of sexual inactivity the stratified epithelium lining the urogenital fossa of female *Lacerta* is about 30 μ in thickness. In the spring breeding period, however, due to a remarkable increase in stratification the epithelium becomes 210 to 260 μ thick. Opening through the stratified epithelium are long, sinuous tubules producing an amorphous secretion. Regression of the stratified layer starts in July, continues gradually, and is not yet complete when hibernation begins in November. As Regamey (1933, 1935) points out, the glands at the height of their development remind one of the uterine glands of mammals. Dantchakoff (1938) remarked that the highly developed

[18] *Phrynosoma* and *Sceloporus* (Crowell, 1932), *Uromastix* (Kehl, 1935), *Hoplodactylus* (Boyd, 1942), *Hemidactylus* (Dutta, 1946; Mahendra, 1953), *Xantusia* (Heimlich and Heimlich, 1950), *Lygosoma* (Weekes, 1927b), *Lacerta* (Sacchi, 1888; Regamey, 1935; Jacobi, 1936), *Anguis* (Coe and Kunkel, 1905; Jacobi, 1936), *Anniella* (Coe and Kunkel, 1905), *Amphisbaena, Anops,* and *Trogonophis* (Coe and Kunkel, 1905), unspecified genus (Giersberg, 1922).

stratified epithelium of the urogenital fossa and cloaca in the lizard has a good deal of resemblance to the stratified vaginal epithelium of a rodent in estrus.

In male, immature, and nonestrous female colubrid snakes of a viviparous species of *Natrix,* calcium, magnesium, and protein levels in the plasma were relatively low and showed little variation throughout the year. The same was true in *Thamnophis.* However, concentrations of all three substances rose very conspicuously while females of both genera were in estrus, with the highest values of all being attained in *Thamnophis* just after ovulation (Dessauer, Fox, and Gilbert, 1956).

XV. Effects of Ovariectomy

Fish

Ovariectomy has little effect on female coloration in the bowfin, *Amia calva* (Zahl and Davis, 1932) in *Halichoeres poecilopterus* (Kinoshita, 1935), or in the stickleback, *Gasterosteus aculeatus* (Bock, 1928).

Amphibians

If *Rana pipiens* is ovariectomized in September, the oviducts degenerate by December (Wolf, 1928). The glandular cells decrease in size, and few secretory granules are observed. This is said to be the only species of frog in which the Müllerian ducts (corresponding to the oviducts of the female) are quite well formed in the male (Christensen, 1931). In immature animals of both sexes the ducts are similar and small; with the onset of sexual maturity, the oviducts grow further in females. That this is due to ovarian hormones was proved by ovariectomy. Removal of the ovaries from adult *Bufo arenarum* also results in oviducal atrophy (Galli-Maïnini, 1950).

In the female, as in the male, of *Xenopus laevis* castration causes a drop in the serum calcium level (Shapiro and Zwarenstein, 1933).

Reptiles

Male and female *Lacerta* castrates are indistinguishable externally. The oviduct atrophies to the nonbreeding stage (evidence that ovarian hormones are secreted chiefly or only during the breeding season), as does the epithelium of the urogenital fossa, and seasonal development of all structures thereafter, of course, fails to occur (Regamey, 1935). Ovariectomy of the snake *Natrix* causes rapid oviducal atrophy (Takewaki and Hatta, 1941).

XVI. Effects of Estrogens and Progesterone

Female sex hormones when experimentally administered are usually very effective in modifying the reproductive systems of fish, amphibians, and reptiles.

Fish

Estrogen is reported to have stimulated spermatogenesis when injected into immature male carp (Castelnuovo, 1937) but to have suppressed spermatogenesis in *Platypoecilus* (Cohen, 1946). In the loach, *Misgurnus*, the injection of estrone or estradiol benzoate caused discharge of sperm and inhibition of spermatogenesis in the male, whereas ovarian development was inhibited in the female. Suppression of the release of gonadotrophin from the pituitary was suggested as the underlying mechanism (Egami, 1954b, c). The liver of *Oryzias* and *Gasterosteus* during the breeding season is sexually dimorphic in structure, color, and weight. Administration of estrogen to males at this time results in transformation of their livers to the female type (Egami, 1955a; Oguro, 1956). Curiously, in *Platypoecilus* estradiol and estradiol benzoate had opposite effects. In males less than 18 mm. long, estradiol did not affect the testes but the anal fin grew slightly. In older males, large gonopodia developed and the testes were stimulated. The same hormone caused ovarian degeneration and growth of gonopodia in females. Estradiol benzoate, however, inhibited testes and ovaries and caused no gonopodial development (Tavolga, 1949).

Pregneninolone, sometimes regarded as a "bisexual" hormone, induced partial masculinization of immature female *Platypoecilus*, and evoked typical female body size and body index in immature males (Cohen, 1946).

In the years before World War II much interest centered on some experiments on the bitterling, *Rhodeus amarus*. At breeding time the urogenital papilla of the European cyprinid hypertrophies into a rather lengthy ovipositor; with the latter, eggs are deposited in fresh water mussels (Bretschneider and Duyvené de Wit, 1947). In 1932 Fleischmann and Kann reported that the injection of follicular hormone into the female bitterling during the nonbreeding period resulted in lengthening of the ovipositor. Injections of salt solution or anterior lobe hormone did not give this result. Further, implantation of the bitterling ovary in a castrate female mouse, it was stated, produced estrus. This seemed to show that ovipositor growth was due to estrogen from the fish's ovaries. Ehrhardt and Kühn (1933, 1934) found that the addition to 1 liter aquarium water of 5 ml. pregnancy urine, one tablet (150 mouse units) ovarian hormone, or urine extracts also caused ovipositor lengthening. Injection, or addition to aquarium water, of Progynon (estradiol) produced ovipositor growth in females outside the breeding season and in castrate males (Fleischmann and Kann, 1934). The idea developed that the response might be sensitive and specific enough to provide the basis for a bio-assay for estrogens or progesterone. There is little doubt that the ovipositor responds to rather small amounts of these hormones.[19] However, it was discovered that ovipositor growth may also be evoked by adrenal cortical hormones, purified male hormones, and male urine, as well as by various alcohols and other solvents and at least one inorganic compound.[20] de Groot and Duyvené de Wit (1949), who have vividly described the oviposition of *Rhodeus*, found that the ovipositor rapidly elongates in response to copulin, a male hormone which, they postulated, is released into the aquarium water by the male bitterling. The bitterling assay

[19] Fleischmann and Kann, 1935; Duyvené de Wit, 1940; Bretschneider and Duyvené de Wit, 1947; van der Veen and Duyvené de Wit, 1951.

[20] Szüsz, 1934; Barnes, Kanter and Klawans, 1936; Kleiner, Weisman and Mishkind, 1936; Duyvené de Wit, 1938, 1939; Gläser and Ranftl, 1938; Fleischmann and Kann, 1938; van Koersveld, 1948.

appears not to have been used in recent years.

Amphibians

Diethylstilbestrol provoked hypertrophy of the rudimentary oviducts and atrophy of the Wolffian ducts in adult normal and castrated *Triturus* (Adams, 1946). Injection of mammalian follicular extract or of estrone into ovariectomized *Rana pipiens* prevented atrophy of the oviducts and sometimes caused oviducal hypertrophy (Wolf, 1928; March, 1937). Estrone had little effect on the oviducts of normal toads (de Allende, 1940), but estradiol helped to prevent oviducal castration atrophy (Galli-Maïnini, 1950). The injection of estrone into male toads caused growth in the summer but not in the winter of the vestigial Müllerian ducts; growth was due to development of mucus-secreting glands (van Oordt and Klomp, 1946). Penhos and Nallar (1956) determined the rate of oviducal secretion in *Bufo arenarum* by ligating both ends of the oviduct, treating the toad, then removing and weighing the oviduct and accumulated secretion. Progesterone administration stimulated secretion; this action of the hormone was enhanced by concurrent administration of estradiol benzoate and testosterone propionate, but not by desoxycorticosterone and folic acid, whereas preliminary treatment with hydrocortisone had an inhibitory effect. Progesterone, on the other hand, had little or no effect on the accessory sex structures of tadpoles of *Bufo bufo* (Lugli, 1955).

Although peritoneal cilia do not normally occur in male *Rana pipiens*, the intraperitoneal injection of theelin (estrone) into males for 30 days resulted in the appearance of patches of cilia on the coelomic peritoneum (Donahue, 1934). In the toad *Xenopus* the hyperemia of the cloacal labia which is typical in females during the breeding season could be produced at other times by the administration of pituitary hormones, methyl testosterone, testosterone propionate, or progesterone. These steroids also produced oviducal hyperemia (Berk and Shapiro, 1939).

Reptiles

The injection of folliculin, an estrogen, into immature female *Testudo iberica*, a turtle, every other day for 3 or 4 weeks resulted in oviducal hypertrophy to more than normal adult size. The mucosal cells became columnar, and some acquired cilia (Kehl, 1930). Estrogens and testosterone propionate both caused moderate growth of foreclaws in immature *Pseudemys elegans* (Evans, 1946, 1952a). It is surprising that estrogens should have the same effect as an androgen on this accessory sex structure.

Theelin injections provoked conspicuous growth of the oviduct of the female, reduced epididymal diameter in males, and increased the number of mitotic figures in the male vas deferens in *Sceloporus* (Gorbman, 1939). In another lizard, *Anolis*, administration of the same estrogen resulted in major atrophy of the testis, lesser atrophy of the ovary, and hypertrophy of oviducts, ductus deferens, and cloacal epithelium in both males and females (Evans and Clapp, 1940). Treatment of male *Eumeces* with estradiol benzoate had little effect (Reynolds, 1943), but injection of estradiol diproprionate into sexually quiescent female *Uromastix* caused development of the reproductive tract equal to that seen in the breeding season (Kehl, Leportois and Benoit, 1941; Kehl, 1944b). Progesterone caused conspicuous growth of the oviduct in *Uromastix* (Kehl, 1941, 1944b).

XVII. Fertilization; Sperm Storage in Females

Fish

External fertilization, of course, takes place in the water. Internal fertilization occurs in various sites. Sometimes the eggs are shed into the ovarian cavity and there encounter the sperm (Stuhlman, 1887; Turner, 1938c). In the poeciliids *Lebistes*, *Xiphophorus*, *Heterandria*, and *Glaridichthys* and in *Neotoca* and *Jenynsia* the ovum is fertilized while still in the follicle. Shortly before arrival of the sperm the follicular cells separating the mature ovum from the central ovarian cavity thin out to form a funnel-shaped invagination or *delle*. At the apex of the latter there is a minute pore or *propyle* that permits entrance of the sperm. The embryo develops in the follicle, which eventually ruptures at the site of the propyle and releases the young fish for birth.[21]

Some female fish are able to store sperm in the oviduct or ovary for long periods, making possible the fertilization of the eggs months after contact with the male. Sperm storage is reported for sharks and rays (Lo Bianco, 1908–1909), and is common in the *Embiotocidae* and *Poeciliidae*.[22]

Nothing is known regarding the endocrine control of fertilization and sperm storage.

Amphibians

Salamander sperm are transported in spermatophores (Noble, 1931). Spallanzani knew in 1785 (Jordan, 1891) that several European salamanders somehow practice internal fertilization, although he was not aware that the female usually picks up with her cloacal labia the spermatophores which the male has just shed. Among the urodeles, *Cryptobranchoidea* and *Siren* are exceptional in that the males do not form spermatophores, the females lack spermathecae (see below), and fertilization is external (Dunn, 1923).

Most female urodeles have special seminal receptacles, or spermathecae, in which the sperm are stored after the spermatophores disintegrate within the cloaca (Dunn, 1923; Noble, 1931). The spermathecae are actually cloacal glands, in the depths of which the sperm congregate. As Noble points out, de Beaumont (1928) proved the homology of these glands with the cloacal glands of the male. He transplanted testes into female *Triton* (*Triturus*) *cristatus*, and 6 to 10 months later found that the cloacal glands had assumed the secretory appearance characteristic of the male. (It will be recalled that the homologous male glands form the spermatophores.) Noble (1931) has traced the phylogeny of the spermatheca.

Baylis (1939) kept a female *S. salamandra* in an aquarium, isolated from all other salamanders. In 2 weeks she produced a brood of motile larvae, and did so again almost 2 years later. Baylis feels that it is usual for the female to store sperms in her spermathecae from impregnation in the summer at least until after a brood is born the next spring. The stored sperm then fertilize internally the next batch of eggs. The long "gestation period" for this brood includes, incidentally, several months of hibernation. Adams (1940) found sperm in the spermathecae of the newt, *Triturus viridescens*, during every month of the year, but in greatest quantity in the fall and spring.

Reptiles

Female reptiles may store sperm which retain their fertilizing capacity for months or even years, possibly an advantage in that members of some species are slow moving and relatively scanty, with consequent reduction in the opportunities for mating. Isolated diamond back terrapins, *Malaclemmys centrata*, have been known to lay fertile eggs (as indicated by the presence of an embryo) as long as 4 years after the last mating (Barney, 1922; Hildebrand, 1929). A similar record has been established by the box turtle, *Terrapene c. carolina* (Ewing, 1943).

An instance of sperm storage in a chameleon, *Microsaura p. pumila* has been reported (Atsatt, 1953)

Prolonged sperm storage has been observed most frequently in female snakes, some of which have been proven capable of keeping sperm alive and functional for up to 5 years (see Fox's review, 1956, for all reptiles).[23]

[21] Wyman, 1854; Philippi, 1908; Scott, 1928; Bailey, 1933; Purser, 1938; Fraser and Renton, 1940; Mendoza, 1940.

[22] *Cymatogaster* (Eigenmann, 1892a; Turner, 1938b), *Amphigonopterus* (Hubbs, 1921), *Xiphophorus* (Vallowe, 1953), *Platypoecilus* (Tavolga and Rugh, 1947), *Glaridichthys* (Philippi, 1908; Winge, 1937), *Lebistes* (Vaupel, 1929; Purser, 1937; Clark and Aronson, 1951), *Gambusia* (Dulzetto, 1928), and *Heterandria* (Fraser and Renton, 1940).

[23] *Agkistrodon contortrix*, 11 days (Gloyd, 1933); *Causus rhombeatus*, 5 months (Woodward, 1933); *Crotalus v. viridis*, throughout winter (Rahn, 1942; Ludwig and Rahn, 1943); *Vipera aspis*, throughout winter (Rollinat, 1946); *Boiga multimaculata*, 1 year (Kopstein, 1938); *Coronella austriaca*, throughout winter (Rollinat, 1946); *Drymarchon corais couperi*, 4 years and 4 months (Carson, 1945); *Leimadophis viridis*, delayed fertilization (Mertens, 1940); *Leptodeira albofusca*, 1 year (Kluth, 1936); *L. annulata polysticta*, 5 years (Haines, 1940); *Natrix natrix*, throughout winter (Rollinat, 1946; Petter-Rousseaux, 1953); *N. subminiata*, 5 months (Kopstein, 1938); *N. vittata*, 1½ years (Kopstein, 1938); *Storeria dekayi*, 4

The prairie rattler's reproductive system includes, in anteroposterior succession, ovary, oviduct, uterus, and vaginal pouch, all of these being paired, and finally the single cloaca. A careful study of sperm distribution during their storage in winter hibernation showed that the germ cells are concentrated in the anterior extremity of the vagina and in the posterior end of the uterus. It is believed that in the spring the sperm migrate into the oviduct in order to fertilize the eggs (Rahn, 1942; Ludwig and Rahn, 1943).

Live sperm can be demonstrated in a uterine smear from the garter snake for a month or more after mating (Rahn, 1940a). The female garter snake stores sperm between the uterus and the most anterior portion of the oviduct (designated the infundibulum) in a short, thick segment with specialized alveolar glands. The latter communicate with the oviducal cavity by branched, ciliated ducts. In this species sperm from a fall mating spend most of the winter in disorganized masses in the oviducal cavity. In February or March the germ cells move into the lumina of the alveolar glands. Here in striking fashion the sperm are ranked side by side, their heads against the alveolar epithelium and their tails projecting into the lumen. Finally, at ovulation, the sperm move on to fertilize the eggs (Fox, 1956).

Very little seems to have been published on physiologic aspects of sperm storage in reptiles. One wonders how the metabolic requirements of the sperm are met for months or years, how the sperm are guided to the storage site, and how they are "released" at the proper time. It seems safe to assume that these processes are at least partly under the control of sex hormones. This is an area much in need of study.

XVIII. Oviparity and Ovoviviparity

Oviparous animals release their eggs to develop outside the body. In ovoviviparous animals, fertilization is internal, and the embryo undergoes at least part of its development within the mother. However, in this

months (Trapido, 1940); *Thamnophis sirtalis,* several months (Rahn, 1940a; Blanchard, 1942); *Tropidoclonion lineatum,* probably throughout winter (Gloyd, 1928; Force, 1931); *Xenodon merremi,* 1 year (Graber, 1940).

case the fertilized ovum acquires a definite investing membrane or shell. There is enough yolk for the nutrition of the growing embryo so that no food materials need be supplied by the mother. In viviparity at least part of the embryo's nourishment is of maternal origin. Intermediate stages also exist. The evolution of viviparity is ably discussed by Harrison Matthews (1955).

Fish

Oviparity of course is common. Ovoviviparity also occurs (see, for example, Turner, 1937a; Hisaw and Albert, 1947); in poeciliid fish the embryos develop within the follicles and maintain gas exchange with the mother. Because more than one (sometimes up to nine!) brood, each of a different age, may develop in the same ovary, a kind of superfetation exists (Turner, 1937a, 1947).

Amphibians

Nearly all amphibians are oviparous. A few salamanders, including *Oedipus, Hydromantes* (Noble, 1931), and *Salamandra* (Baylis, 1939), bring forth living young and are regarded as ovoviviparous.

Reptiles

Reptiles, depending on species, may be oviparous, ovoviviparous, or viviparous. Oviparity has been reported, for example, for lizards of the genera *Amphibolurus, Lygosoma,* and *Egernia* (Weekes, 1934). *Phrynosoma cornutum,* the horned toad, is oviparous, whereas *P. douglassi* is viviparous (Edwards, 1903). *Hemidactylus flaviviridis,* the Indian house gecko (Mahendra, 1936), and *Anniella pulchra,* the American legless lizard (Coe and Kunkel, 1905) are ovoviviparous. Jacobi (1936) has described in detail the reproductive anatomy of the ovoviviparous lacertilians *Lacerta agilis* and *Anguis fragilis.*

Some snakes, the turtles, and the crocodilians bury their eggs or lay them in nests for extended incubation. Other snakes appear to be ovoviviparous, *i.e.,* the egg is well supplied with yolk and acquires a shell, but is retained in the oviduct for at least part of the incubation period. Examples are *Trachyboa* (Barbour, 1937), the colubrid snakes *Natrix* and *Thamnophis* (Bragdon, 1946), and the sea snakes *Aipysurus, Enhydrina, Hydrophis, Lapemis, Laticauda,* and *Thalassophis* (Smith, 1930; Smedley, 1930, 1931; Bergman, 1943).

XIX. Viviparity

Fish

Viviparity in some fish and in mammals has, it will be seen, much in common. Hormones from the glands of internal secretion initiate and regulate many aspects of reproduction in the higher vertebrates, and there is reason to believe that similar controls are important in fish. Although actual evidence for such endocrine regulation is scanty, some phenomena of gestation in this class should be briefly reviewed. For details, see Turner (1933, 1940c, 1947), Mendoza (1937), and Needham (1942).

The finding of an embryo within an egg case in a specimen of *Rhineodon typus,* the whale shark (this adult exceeded 65 feet in length), was taken as strong presumptive evidence that this species is oviparous (Baughman, 1955). However, specializations of the uterus of the basking shark, *Cetorhinus maximus,* suggest that it is viviparous (Harrison Matthews, 1950), as is *Spinax* (Wallace, 1903) and the dogfish, *Mustelus* (Te Winkel, 1950). It is thought that ovarian tissue and immature eggs in another shark, *Lamna,* disintegrate into the oviduct, are passed into the uterus, and are swallowed as food by the embryo. The gut of the embryo becomes greatly distended with this yolk-like material; the actual yolk sac is separate and very small (Shann, 1923). In three genera of ray, *Myliobatis, Pteroplataea* and *Trygon,* the uterine mucous membrane gives off long papillae, or trophonemata, which secrete a fluid rich in albumen. The secretion escapes into the uterine cavity and is swallowed by the fetus, as proven by finding the same material in the fetal intestine. In *Pteroplataea* the uterine papillae extend into the fetal spiracle, actually a kind of suckling. The fetuses are not otherwise attached to the mother (Wood-Mason and Alcock, 1891; Alcock, 1892).

Viviparity in teleosts was known to Aristotle (Thompson, 1910) and has interested biologists ever since. Embryos develop within the ovarian follicles in representa-

tives of the *Poeciliidae, Anablepidae,* and *Goodeidae.*[24] In the *Embiotocidae, Zoarcidae, Goodeidae,* and *Jenynsiidae* the fertilized ovum is released promptly into the ovarian cavity and develops there.[25]

The ovary may contribute to the food supply of the embryo by the secretion of nutritive fluid into the follicular or ovarian cavity; the embryo is bathed in and swallows or absorbs this fluid through the skin.[26] The food in addition may consist of dead sperm, dead embryos, and disintegrated ova. Absorption is facilitated in *Anablepidae, Goodeidae,* and *Poeciliidae* by villi (trophotaeniae) extending from the yolk sac or gut opening, by specialization of the tips of the embryonic fins, by ovarian wall processes which extend into the branchial chamber of the embryo, or by development of the pericardial membrane as an absorptive surface.[27] In certain *Anablepidae* and *Poeciliidae* there is actually a pseudoplacenta (Fraser and Renton, 1940; Turner, 1940a, b). Respiratory exchange and the removal of waste are effected by the same mechanisms as is nutrition.

Mendoza (1940) noted that epithelium of the ovary of the *Goodeidae* secretes not only when embryos requiring nutrition are present but also in virgin females; he concluded that these changes are cyclic and independent of the presence of embryos. The analogy with the uterine epithelium of mammals is evident. Turner (1937a, 1940c, 1947), commenting on the regulation of successive broods in those poeciliid fish in which superfetation occurs, hypothesizes that follicle-stimulating hormone from the pituitary may be responsible. In *Lebistes* an increase in thyroid activity is correlated with the period of rapid growth and differentiation of the embryo (Stolk, 1951a).

Amphibians

Viviparity has been described for the African frog *Nectophrynoïdes.* Internal ferti-

[24] Kuntz, 1913; Turner, 1933, 1937a, 1940a, c; Purser, 1938.

[25] Stuhlman, 1887; Eigenmann, 1892b; Scott, 1928; Mendoza, 1936, 1937, 1940; Turner, 1937b.

[26] Eigenmann, 1892a, b; Hubbs, 1921; Scott, 1928; Turner, 1933, 1938c, 1940a, c, 1947; Mendoza, 1936, 1937, 1940; Fraser and Renton, 1940.

[27] Turner, 1933, 1937b, 1938c; Mendoza, 1937, 1940, 1956; Tavolga and Rugh, 1947.

lization is somehow accomplished without an intromittent organ. In *N. vivipara* as many as one hundred larvae may develop in the bicornuate uterus. The larvae have long, vascular tails which possibly maintain contact with the uterine wall to permit respiratory exchange (Noble, 1931). In *N. occidentalis* (Angel and Lamotte, 1944; Lamotte and Tuchmann-Duplessis, 1948), each slim oviduct is dilated posteriorly to form a uterine horn. The two horns, which join caudally, are muscular, well vascularized, and lined with columnar epithelium. In pregnancy the oviduct does not change, but the horn enlarges as its one to ten embryos grow. There is no placenta; the fluid in which the embryos rest may supply nourishment and oxygen. The young are retained until after metamorphosis. When born, they may be two-fifths the length of the mother.

N. occidentalis has been found only at an elevation of 1200 meters, in fields on top of Mount Nimba in French Guinea. The gestation period is from September to June (Lamotte and Rey, 1954). During the dry season (December to February) no specimens were found, and it is believed that the adults may aestivate at this time. It may be that viviparity represents an adjustment to an environment which not only lacks bodies of water for incubation of eggs but which has the added hazard of a dry season. This frog is also typically viviparous in that only 10 to 30 ova are found in an animal and that the eggs have almost no yolk (Lamotte, Rey and Vilter, 1956).

Reptiles

Many snakes and lizards are viviparous. Several types of placentae occur, and placental exchange takes place.[28] Fraser and Renton (1940) call attention to the similarity between the uterine epithelium underlying the allantoplacenta in the lizard *Lygosoma ocellatum*, as described by Weekes (1930), and the expanded pericardium through which respiratory and nutritional exchange take place in the embryo of the viviparous fish, *Heterandria formosa*.

[28] Flynn, 1923; Harrison and Weekes, 1925; Weekes, 1927a, 1929, 1930, 1935; Rahn, 1939; Boyd, 1942; Dutta, 1946; Heimlich and Heimlich, 1950; Kasturirangan, 1951; Bellairs, Griffiths and Bellairs, 1955; Clark, Florio, and Hurowitz, 1955.

XX. Corpus Luteum

Fish

Structures resembling corpora lutea occur in widely divergent types of fish—the myxinoids *Bdellostoma* and *Myxine* (Conel, 1917), the elasmobranchs *Spinax* (Wallace, 1903), *Squalus* (Hisaw and Albert, 1947), *Cetorhinus* (Harrison Matthews, 1950), *Myliobatis* (Giacomini, 1896a), and several teleosts, including *Lebistes* (Stolk, 1951b), *Rhodeus* (Bretschneider and Duyvené de Wit, 1947), and *Fundulus* (Matthews, 1938). The corpora persist during pregnancy in viviparous species. Mendoza (1943), however, feels that the corpus luteum of *Neotoca*, because it lacks any indication of endocrine activity, cannot be compared to the mammalian corpus luteum. Physicochemical assay of blood drawn from carp, *Cyprinus carpio*, in October, after the spawning season, did not reveal the presence of progesterone (Bondy, Upton and Pickford, 1957). Hisaw and Abramowitz (cited by Pickford and Atz, 1957) failed to find progesterone in the corpora lutea of the dogfish, *Mustelus canis*, and removal of the corpora lutea during pregnancy did not affect the embryos. It is possible, as suggested by various authors, that acquisition of an endocrine function by the corpus luteum was a somewhat belated evolutionary development. This area deserves further investigations.

Amphibians

Corpora lutea have been reported in *Rana, Nectophrynoides, Bufo, Triton, Salamandrina,* and *Salamandra* (Giacomini, 1896b; Hett, 1923; Lamotte and Rey, 1954), although Duschak (1924) denies that corpora occur in *Rana.*

Reptiles

Altland (1951) has described the corpus luteum of the box turtle, *Terrapene c. carolina,* and Rahn (1938), that of the snapping turtle. In general, the corpora resemble those of mammals. A curious feature of the reptilian corpus luteum is the absence of blood vessels in the central epithelial portion. The box turtle's corpora are present in June, the month when the eggs are retained in the oviduct, and atrophy after oviposition.

Corpora lutea occur in both oviparous and viviparous lizards.[29] The suggestion that a hormone from the corpus luteum prevents further follicular growth and ovulation was made by Cunningham and Smart (1934) and Panigel (1951b). Boyd (1940), calling attention to the corpora lutea of oviparous reptiles, offers the hypothesis that in this vertebrate class the corpus luteum may have evolved before the placenta and only subsequently acquired an endocrine function related to viviparity (cf. discussion of corpus luteum function in fish and amphibians). The gestation period in *Xantusia* lasts about three months; by histologic criteria the corpus luteum appears functional for the first two months (Miller, 1948, 1951). Bilateral ovariectomy or destruction of the corpora lutea at the beginning of pregnancy in *Lacerta vivipara* does not interrupt gestation or embryonic development (Panigel, 1953, 1956). Hypophysectomy also fails to affect embryonic growth, but both this operation and ovariectomy make parturition difficult, as does the administration of progesterone (Panigel, 1956).

Corpora lutea have been found in the ovaries of many genera of snakes.[30] Corpora may persist during part or all of gestation. Ovariectomy during early and middle preg-

nancy of various species of the colubrid snakes *Natrix, Thamnophis,* and *Storeria* was followed by resorption of the embryos or the birth of dead embryos. The injection of progesterone after ovariectomy did not prevent death of the embryos. Ovariectomy late in pregnancy seemed to have no effect. Hypophysectomy interfered with pregnancy at any stage. Injection of posterior pituitary extract did not influence early or middle pregnancy, but induced delivery thereafter (Clausen, 1940). Removal of all corpora lutea from pregnant *Bothrops* and *Crotalus* resulted in cessation of embryonic development (Fraenkel, Martins and Mello, 1940), but, as Bragdon (1951) suggests, the high postoperative mortality leaves some doubt whether embryonic death was due to loss of the corpora lutea or to other factors. On the other hand, Rahn (1939, 1940b) castrated 23 pregnant *Thamnophis* and *Natrix* at various stages of pregnancy and found live young at autopsy up to 25 days later. In *Natrix* and *Thamnophis* neither hypophysectomy as early as the first week after ovulation nor ovariectomy interfered with pregnancy (Bragdon, 1942, 1946, 1951, 1952). Both operations did interfere with parturition. Bragdon concludes that in these snakes corpora lutea are not essential for the maintenance of pregnancy. Panigel's extensive study of the viviparous lizard (*Zootoca vivipara*) (1956) supports this opinion.

Bio-assay of alcoholic extracts of the corpora lutea of *Bothrops* and *Crotalus* revealed progestin (Porto, 1941), as did bio-assays of plasma from *Natrix* and *Thamnophis* (Bragdon, Lazo-Wasem, Zarrow and Hisaw, 1954). In the latter study, the results, expressed in Progesterone Equivalents, were as follows. In two donors with inactive ovaries and two with pre-ovulatory follicles, plasma levels were 0.3, 1.0, 0.3, and 0.3 µg./ml. Other assays showed, at early ovulation, 2.0 µg./ml.; end of first third of pregnancy, 4.0 and 4.0 µg./ml.; end of second third of pregnancy, 4.0 and 6.0 µg./ml.; full term, 8.0 µg./ml.

It is also of interest that bio-assay of plasma from two snakes with testes in full development gave Progesterone Equivalent values of 0.3 and 1.0 µg./ml. (Bragdon, Lazo-Wasem, Zarrow and Hisaw, 1954).

[29] Oviparous: *Amphibolurus* (Weekes, 1934), *Hemidactylus* (Dutta, 1944), and *Lacerta viridis* (Cunningham and Smart, 1934). Viviparous: *Hoplodactylus* (Boyd, 1940), *Xantusia* (Miller, 1948, 1951, 1954), *Egernia, Lygosoma,* and *Tiliqua* (Weekes, 1927a, 1934), *Lacerta (Zootoca) vivipara* (Hett, 1924; Regamey, 1935; Panigel, 1951a), and *Anguis* (Lucien, 1903; Cunningham and Smart, 1934).

[30] Oviparous: *Xenodon* (Fraenkel and Martins, 1939). Ovoviviparous: *Coronella* (Rollinat, 1898) and *Dryophylax* and *Tomodon* (Valle and Souza, 1942). Viviparous: *Natrix (Tropidonotus)* (Rollinat, 1898; Rahn, 1939, 1940b; Bragdon, 1946, 1951; Bragdon, Lazo-Wasem, Zarrow and Hisaw, 1954), *Potamophis* (Rahn, 1939), *Storeria* (Rahn, 1939), *Thamnophis* (Rahn, 1939, 1940a, b; Cieslak, 1945; Bragdon, 1946, 1951, 1952; Bragdon, Lazo-Wasem, Zarrow and Hisaw, 1954), *Enhydrina* (Samuel, 1944; Kasturirangan, 1951), *Hydrophis* (Samuel, 1944), *Bothrops* and *Crotalus* (Fraenkel and Martins, 1938, 1939; Fraenkel, Martins and Mello, 1940; Porto, 1941; Rahn, 1939; Valle and Valle, 1943). *Natrix, Thamnophis,* and *Crotalus* are regarded as ovoviviparous by some investigators.

This may be compared to the observation that progestin can be detected in the blood of roosters but not of capons (Fraps, Hooker and Forbes, 1949).

XXI. Developmental Basis for Sexual Dimorphism

Fish

Most embryologists believe that in amphibians and amniotes the functional ovarian cortex develops from the primitive cortex of the fetal gonad and that the testis is derived from the embryonic medulla. Ponse (1949), in an extensive and careful discussion of the embryology of the gonad, concludes that a cortex and medulla cannot be distinguished in the developing gonad of the fish. D'Ancona (1950) shares this opinion. Studies of the brook lamprey, *Entosphenus wilderi* (Okkelberg, 1914, 1921), and of the closely related *Petromyzon* (Lubosch, 1903) reveal that male and female gonads are at first indistinguishable morphologically (undifferentiated gonad stage). Later (bisexual stage) a distinction can be made on the basis of the relative numbers of spermatocytes and oocytes; both kinds of germ cells appear in both sexes. Prolonged juvenile bisexuality resulting from arrest of sexual development at the end of the second stage is probably the basis for much of the hermaphroditism in fish. In a third phase (stage of sexual differentiation), the heterosexual germ cells disappear from the lamprey gonad or persist in rudimentary form, and the sex of the lamprey finally becomes apparent. D'Ancona (1950) summarizes evidence for similar development of the gonad in several other plagiostomes.

Much, or even all, of the development of the ovary and testis in both lower orders of fish and teleosteans may occur after hatching or birth. In *Gobius* the gonads are said not even to appear until 15 days after birth (MacLeod, 1881).

Knowledge of the development of the reproductive system of the teleosts, as of the cyclostomes, is fragmentary. D'Ancona (1950) divides the teleosteans which have been studied into two groups. In the first, the gonads gradually differentiate from an indifferent to a bisexual stage and then into ovaries or testes. The viviparous teleost *Cymatogaster* is an example (Eigenmann, 1897). The gonadal anlage in the 8-mm. larva is a simple fold of peritoneum on either side of the mesentery. Each fold acquires a core of germ cells and stromal cells, and the two folds, or germinal ridges, fuse posteriorly. In 15- to 17-mm. larvae the ovaries can be distinguished because they are shorter than the testes and have a longitudinal groove which will later invaginate further to form the central cavity of the ovary. The testes develop internal lobules and a central, branched collecting tubule. At 22 mm. the ovaries have become tubular; the walls are thick superiorly and medially where "oviferous folds" will develop, and are thin inferiorly and laterally. Later the two ovarian cavities join posteriorly. The oviducts develop much as in higher vertebrates: a plate is grooved into two parallel ridges, and the latter bridge over the intervening space to form a tube which is then extended caudally. Ovaries and oviducts are continuous. The vas deferens, which is not homologous with the oviduct, is lined with stromal cells from the testis.

Johnston (1951) gives a similar description for another acanthopterygian, *Micropterus*, the black bass. He adds that the testis also becomes tubular; the cavity proper, or testocoel, functions as a primary collecting duct. Branches from the testocoel complete the collecting system. A similar development of the gonads and gonoducts appears to occur in several other genera.[31]

D'Ancona's (1950) second group of teleost fish includes representatives of the *Sparidae* and *Serranidae* (Dantchakoff, 1936; Kinoshita, 1936; Lavenda, 1949; D'Ancona, 1950). Although these are also acanthopterygian families (see above) the embryonic gonads are persistently ovotestes. Both ovarian lamellae and testicular lobules may protrude into the central cavity of the same gonad. In *Sparus longispinis*

---

[31] *Amia* (D'Ancona, 1955), eel (Grassi, 1919), the trout (Mršić, 1923, 1930; Ashby, 1952), *Xiphophorus* (Essenberg 1923; Régnier, 1938; Vallowe, 1957), pipe fish, sea horse, and goby (MacLeod, 1881), goldfish (Stromsten, 1931), guppy (Dildine, 1936), and *Cottus* (Hann, 1927).

there are two oviducts and two vasa deferentia. When a body length of 100 mm. is reached, either the testicular component and vasa deferentia degenerate, or the ovarian component and the oviducts disappear (Kinoshita, 1936).

Amphibians

See chapter by Burns.

Reptiles

Probably the first published observations on the embryology of the reproductive system in the turtle were those of Rathke (1848). Risley has summarized the subsequent literature on the subject and has carefully analyzed the origin of the germ cells (1933b) and the embryology of the reproductive system (1933c) in *Sternotherus odoratus,* the musk turtle. He recognized three stages in gonadal development — indifferent, bisexual, and differentiated. During the indifferent phase the primitive germinal epithelium, a specialized area of peritoneum investing the ventromedial surface of each mesonephros, dorsally proliferates sex cords containing germ cells. Stromal elements grow between the epithelial sex cords. The gradually thickening mass of tissue thus formed is known as the genital ridge. Extension of the epithelial elements of the sex cord beyond the gonad and to a nearby Malpighian corpuscle in the mesonephros marks the establishment of the rete cord connection.

In the bisexual period there is a further proliferation of the germinal epithelium and its germ cells to form an investing cortex. Internal to the latter is a medulla composed of the original sex cords and their gametes. Cortex and medulla are both well developed, and all embryos at this stage also have mesonephroi (potential epididymides), mesonephric ducts (potential vasa deferentia), Müllerian ducts, and phalluses. This bisexual condition, sometimes referred to as juvenile or rudimentary hermaphroditism, persists for a relatively long time. Late in embryonic development, morphologic sex differentiation ensues as a third stage. In the male, the medullary cords begin to acquire lumina and to become seminiferous tubules and the cortex and

Müllerian duct begin to regress. In the female, the cortex develops further, the medullary cords regress to connective tissue strands, and the growth of the phallus is checked. It must be emphasized, however, that at hatching heterosexual vestiges are still conspicuous.

The development of the reproductive tract in most other reptiles is also relatively slow as compared to that of higher vertebrates. The process may in fact never really be completed, so that the adult frequently or regularly retains definite heterosexual remnants, *e.g.,* a vestigial mesonephros in the female and a part of the Müllerian duct in the male.

Risley's account for the turtle in general confirms Braun's early (1877) account of the development of the reproductive system in lizards and snakes (chiefly *Lacerta, Anguis, Tropidonotus,* and *Coronella*). Mihálkovics' (1885) excellent study (chiefly of the lizard) added important information. He reminds his readers, for example, that Braun "was struck by the proximity of the adrenal anlage to that of the gonad in reptiles ... so that one would be led to think of a relationship between the two structures." This is in reference to the fact that the adrenal cortex takes origin from specialized epithelium lying between the root of the mesentery and the germinal epithelium. The anlage of the adrenal cortex (medial) and the anlage of the genital ridge (lateral) proliferate epithelial cords dorsally at about the same time. Actually, it is difficult to determine the dividing line between the two anlagen at this early stage except on the basis that the germ cells normally are confined to the developing gonad. This physical continuity in the embryo is sometimes overlooked, but is of interest in view of the demonstrated ability of the adult mammalian adrenal cortex to produce sex hormones, an ability which may well be shared by some of the lower vertebrates. Other accounts are those of Hoffmann (1889), Peter (1904), Simkins and Asana (1930), and Forbes (1956).

Regamey (1935) mentions a male *Lacerta* embryo of advanced development which retained both oviducts. Dantchakoff (1938) describes male and female lizard embryos at hatching. The testis, clearly recognizable as such, contains sex cords with numerous germ cells and is invested with a thin coelomic epithelium. The ovary is also well differentiated, consisting of outer cortex and central medulla. The two components are clearly delimited. Most of the germ cells are in the cortex. The metanephros is well developed. Both sexes have mesonephric ducts, but Müllerian ducts are present only in the female. The development of the reproductive tract in *Anolis* is similar, although in this genus the Müllerian ducts may persist after hatching in the male (Forbes, 1956).

Probably the earliest study of the embryology of the snake's gonads was that of Rathke (1839). Hartley's modern (1945) account calls attention to the brief and early (16th to 19th day) period of sexual differentiation in the garter snake and to the relative scarcity of heterosexual vestiges at birth. Both phenomena apparently are unique for the snake among reptiles.

The writer (Forbes, 1940a) has described the embryology and post-hatching development of the gonads, adrenal cortex, and Müllerian duct of the alligator, *Alligator mississippiensis*. Prolonged indifferent, bisexual, and sexually differentiated stages much like those reported in the turtle by Risley (see above) were observed. A period of pronounced bisexuality is succeeded by sexual differentiation, but heterosexual structures regularly persist until well after hatching. The degree of adult bisexuality is unknown, but the male alligator 18 months after hatching still has irregular patches of cortex (potential ovarian tissue) on his testis. The male Müllerian ducts are fully formed at hatching, and their anterior extremities may still be present 18 months later. Females at this age and earlier have in the posterior third of each gonad a solid mass of medullary cords (potential seminiferous tubules) similar to those seen in the embryonic testis, but lacking germ cells. A mesonephros and mesonephric duct are always present. Thus again there is a considerable retention of heterosexual structures.

XXII. Spontaneous Adult Hermaphroditism and Sex Reversal

Fish

Aristotle recognized hermaphroditism in the *channe*, a perch-like form, and in two other varieties (Thompson, 1910), as did Ovid (Ovidius Naso, 1911). All three fish are thought to have been serranids (Dufossé, 1856; Thompson, 1910). The classical writers apparently shared the popular belief that the fish are hermaphroditic because all specimens caught contained eggs, *i.e.*, no males were ever seen. A chapter title in a book by Guilaume Rondelet (1558) concerns fish "which give birth without the assistance of the male," evidently a reference (the text is not enlightening) either to hermaphroditism or to parthenogenesis. Dufossé (1856) states flatly that in three serranid species the same fish which lays the eggs also fertilizes them.

Cavolini (1792) found ovotestes in the *Patsch* and *Blutstrieme*; there is reason to think that these were two of the fish about which Aristotle had commented. Yarrell exhibited to the Zoological Society of London in 1845 a herring "having a lobe of female, or hard roe, on one side, and a lobe of male, or soft roe, on the other." The note adds that the same phenomenon had been seen in several other kinds of fish. In the 1880's a friend of Carl Vogt, the German naturalist, was about to eat a smoked herring when he noticed that the reproductive tract was abnormal. The friend carefully removed the tract, sent it to Vogt with a letter, and, one hopes, ate the rest of the herring. In spite of the unconventional fixation of the tissues it was possible to confirm histologically that both gonads were ovotestes; in addition, an excretory duct on each side was so arranged as to carry off both sperm and ova (Vogt, 1882).

A number of examples of adult hermaphroditism are summarized in Table 17.1. Additional references and details may be found in books by Gemmill (1912) and Dean (1923) and in D'Ancona's article (1956). Two types of adult hermaphroditism can be recognized. The basis for the first lies

TABLE 17.1

Spontaneous adult pseudohermaphroditism and hermaphroditism in fish

Genus	Gonads	Accessory Structures	Reference
Myxine..............	Ovotestis		Cunningham, 1886a; Nansen, 1887; Cole, 1905
Bdellostoma..........	Ovotestis		Cunningham, 1886b
(Scyllium)*..........	Ovotestis	Gonopodium, oviducts	Vayssière and Quintaret, 1914
Scyliorhinus..........	Ovotestis	Gonopodium, oviducts	Murray and Baker, 1924; Arthur, 1950
Squalus..............	Testis and ovary	Oviducts, male pelvic fins	Rowan, 1929
Raia.................	Testes	Oviduct	Matthews, 1885
Acipenser............	Testes	Oviduct	Maschkowzeff, 1934
Pseudoscaphirhynchus..	Testes	Oviduct	Maschkowzeff, 1934
Clupea..............	Testis and ovary; ovotestes	Oviduct, vas deferens	Smith, 1870; Smitt, 1882; Vogt, 1882; Southwell, 1902; Grimpe, 1922–1925; Gäbler, 1930; Bullough, 1940a
Sardina.............	Ovotestes		Andreu, 1955
Alosa...............	Ovotestis; testis and ovary		Fowler, 1912
Salmo...............	Ovotestes	Male genital ducts	Stewart, 1894a; Gibbs, 1956
"Trout".............	Testis and ovary; ovotestes		de Beer, 1924; Mršić, 1930
Oncorhynchus........	Testis and ovary		Crawford, 1927
Esox................	Ovotestis		Kolmer and Scheminzky, 1922b
Phoxinus............	Ovotestes	Male gonoducts and pigmentation	Bullough, 1940b
Notropis............	Testis and ovary	Oviduct, vas deferens	Reed, 1954
Carassius............	Ovotestis		Kinoshita, 1933
Lefua...............	Ovotestes	Female external appearance	Kobayashi, 1955
Anguilla............	Ovotestis		Grassi, 1911, 1919
(Morrhua)*..........	Ovotestes	Vas deferens	Smith, 1870
Gadus...............	Testis and ovary		Howes, 1891
Fundulus............	Ovotestis	Oviduct, male coloration	Newman, 1908; Chidester, 1917
Lebistes.............	Ovotestis	Female coloration, gonopod	Blacher, 1926; Spurway, 1957
Xiphophorus.........	Ovotestis	Intersexual accessories	Essenberg, 1926; Harms, 1926b; Friess, 1933; Régnier, 1938
Glaridichthys.........	Testes	Male to female type anal fin	Philippi, 1904
Monopterus..........	Ovotestes		Bullough, 1947
Serranus.............	Ovotestes		Dufossé, 1856; van Oordt, 1930; van den Broek, 1933; Dantchakoff, 1936
Centropristes.........	Ovotestes		Lavenda, 1949
Morone..............	Ovotestes		Bishop, 1920
Roccus..............	Testis and ovary		Schultz, 1931
Huro................	Testis and ovary; ovotestes		James, 1946
"Perch".............	Ovotestis		Turner, 1927
Boleosoma...........	Ovotestes		Lagler and Chin, 1951
Sargus..............	Ovotestes		Stephan, 1901; van Oordt, 1930
Pagellus............	Ovotestes		Gómez Larrañeta, 1953
Taius...............	Ovotestes		Aoyama, 1955
Coris...............	Ovotestes		Bacci and Razzauti, 1958
Scomber.............	Ovotestes		Stewart, 1894b

* Synonymous with following genus.

in the fact that, as has been stated, the developing gonads of most fish pass through an indifferent and then a bisexual stage. In the latter phase, both ovarian and testicular elements are present and there is, in effect, a transient and juvenile hermaphroditism. Subsequently, the gonad usually becomes a testis or ovary. In exceptional cases, functional gonadal tissue of both sexes persists into adulthood (Table 17.1). In *Sargus* and *Serranus* such hermaphroditism appears to be normal and frequent. In many individuals of these genera, gross and microscopic study has proven the co-existence of normal ova and sperm (van Oordt, 1930; van den Broek, 1933; Dantchakoff, 1936; D'Ancona, 1950).

Hermaphroditism in *Lebistes* is not regular. However, functional bisexuality was observed in 1 fish and in 18 of its young; parent and offspring, although virgin and individually isolated, bore young (Spurway, 1957). Parthenogenesis was discarded as an explanation in view of the co-existence of functional testicular and ovarian tissue and the likelihood of self-fertilization. The occurrence of the latter, although claimed in other cases, seems not previously to have been supported by the evidence; in Spurway's series self-fertilization seems probable. The offspring of the 18 fish, incidentally, were almost all females.

In a second type of hermaphroditism the adult fish at first is morphologically of one sex but subsequently undergoes spontaneous reversal to the other. If the testis develops first, the condition is known as protandry. Cunningham (1886a) and Nansen (1887) believed that *Myxine* is usually a protandrous hermaphrodite, but Cole (1905) and Conel (1917) were not convinced. Cole was of the opinion that every adult *Myxine* has "either a mature testis and a rudimentary ovary, or a mature ovary and a rudimentary testis." Hermaphroditism due to sex reversal does occur during adulthood in widely divergent teleostean genera (Table 17.1). It is significant that, with the exception of the doubtful case mentioned above, all instances of spontaneous sex reversal seem to be protogynous (ovary first, testis later) rather than protandrous.

Bullough (1947) has reviewed Liu's almost inaccessible report (1944) on the Oriental species *Monopterus javanensis*, which regularly "functions as a female during the first half of its life and as a male during the second." The same phenomenon is reported for *Pagellus* (Gómez Larrañeta, 1953) and for *Coris* (Bacci and Razzauti, 1958). In *Centropristes* the males retain ovarian, and the females testicular, tissue. Age can be determined by examination of the scales. The females are more numerous in the younger age groups, but disappear by the tenth year, whereas all fish surviving during the next 10 years are males. On the basis of this evidence, Lavenda (1949) believes that there may regularly be spontaneous female to male sex reversal after the fifth year. Aoyama (1955) found that 22 of 3291 individuals of the yellow sea bream, *Taius tumifrons*, had hermaphroditic gonads in which a transition from ovary to testis was in progress. Similar transformation was observed in 10 of 414 minnows (Bullough, 1940b).

Although exceptional, female to male sex reversal has been described repeatedly and in full detail for *Xiphophorus* (Essenberg, 1926; Harms, 1926b; Friess, 1933; Régnier, 1938). Before sex reversal the females give birth to young; after reversal the newly formed males demonstrate the completeness of their transformation by successfully impregnating virgin females. The oviduct is converted to a sperm duct, male coloration replaces that of the female, and the gonopodium and characteristic "sword" develop. No pathologic tissues have been found, a point of possible significance, as development of a testis in a hen, for example, is known to follow tubercular destruction of the functional ovary. Oviposition is arrested and the female's characteristic "pregnancy spot" (*Trächtigkeitsfleck*) between the pelvic and anal fins fades. Then, as the gonopodium and sword begin to grow, the ova disappear, the follicles become atretic, and most of the ovary disintegrates, leaving the epithelium of the ovarian cavity. Leukocytes eventually dispose of the masses of ovarian debris. From the residual epithelium radial sex cords rapidly proliferate to form a testis, and germ cells multiply quickly. Eventually the new testis is indistinguishable in morphology, location, and function from the testis of a typical male. The process of reversal may require 3 or 4 months.

It is possible that *complete* adult sex reversal is more common than is realized. Unless by observation or autopsy it were detected while in progress, or unless subsequent genetical studies could prove that sex reversal had occurred, the phenomenon might easily be unrecognized.

The difficult question of the role, if any, of the chromosomes in regulating sex reversal appears to be very imperfectly understood. Consideration of this and related genetical problems is outside the scope of this chapter.

Amphibians

See chapter by Burns.

Reptiles

Cases of postembryonic retention of heterosexual accessory structures and of hermaphroditism in reptiles are summarized in Table 17.2. The conditions described for *Hatteria* (*Sphenodon*) (Osawa, 1897) apparently, and for *Malaclemmys* (Risley, 1941b) and *Alligator* (Forbes, 1938b, 1940b) definitely, are normal rather than exceptional.

One of the most remarkable cases was that of Hansen's (1943) turtle. Histologic sections showed two ovotestes. The anterior and posterior extremities of each gonad were testicular and contained seminiferous tubules. The central ovarian portion contained mature and immature eggs. Vasa efferentia joined the testicular areas to the epididymides. The latter contained sperm, and were connected by vasa deferentia to the cloaca. There were two normal and apparently functional oviducts and a normal penis. External characteristics were masculine.

Tayler's hermaphroditic lizard (1918) had bilateral ovotestes with ova, seminiferous tubules, and interstitial tissue. Epididymides were normal except for the absence of sperm and of vasa efferentia. Oviducts were incomplete, and there was a penis.

The writer (Forbes, 1940b) has described the medullary "rest" at the posterior end of each ovary in the immature alligator. The rest is composed of medullary cords containing germ cells. The cords may have lumina. Rete canals join the medullary tubules to a persistent mesonephros, the duct of which extends to the cloaca. The female thus seems to have potential testicular tissue served by a complete excurrent system. The medullary rest is bilateral but is quite similar to the vestigial right gonad of the hen (Brode, 1928); the latter contains germ cells for three weeks after hatching. Rete tubules and a right mesonephros and mesonephric duct also occur in the hen.

Retention of heterosexual gonoducts is not unusual. For an unknown reason, in such cases all or nearly all of the mesonephric duct persists, whereas only part of the Müllerian duct is retained.

XXIII. Experimental Sex Reversal

Fish

Some effects of androgens and estrogens on gonoducts, coloration, and other accessory sex structures have been described. Attention will now be directed primarily to the effects of administered sex hormones on the gonads themselves and to the sex-reversing action of castration.

When the fighting fish, *Betta splendens*, was ovariectomized, a testis regenerated from the severed end of the oviduct in 7 of 150 spayed fish (Noble and Kumpf, 1937). In time the 7 fish showed male fins, spermatogenesis, male behavior, spawning, and fertilization of eggs. Nine males and 12 females from these matings grew to maturity. If males, on the other hand, were castrated, they always regenerated testes.

Testosterone propionate influenced the genital ridge and accessory sex structures in the elasmobranch *Scyliorhinus* to develop in the female condition (Chieffi, 1954). The same compound when given to female *Phoxinus* minnows caused ovarian disintegration and the appearance of masculinization pigment (Bullough, 1940b). In *Xiphophorus* feeding (by adding it to aquarium water) of testis powder or testosterone propionate to pregnant females and to the young when they were born had the result that all the young which grew to

TABLE 17.2
Spontaneous postembryonic pseudohermaphroditism and hermaphroditism in reptiles

Genus	Gonads	Accessory Structures	Reference
Chelonia		Mesonephros and duct in female	Evans, 1939
Chrysemys	Ovotestes, epididymides, oviducts		Risley, 1941a
Malaclemmys	Masculinizing (?) medullary tumor of ovary		Risley, 1941a
		Male Müllerian ducts; mesonephros and ducts in females*	Risley, 1941b
Pseudemys	Ovotestes	Oviducts, vasa deferentia, epididymides, male claws, penis	Hansen, 1943
Emys		Mesonephric ducts in female; oviducts in male	van Wijhe, 1881; Wiedersheim, 1886; Hoffmann, 1890
	Ovotestis, testis	Mesonephric duct and oviduct	Matthey, 1927
		Müllerian ducts in male	Nicholson and Risley, 1940
		Female had penis. Male had Müllerian duct.	Combescot, 1954b
Testudo		Male had Müllerian duct	Gadow, 1887
	Ovotestis, testis	Oviduct	Fantham, 1905
		Müllerian ducts in male	van den Broek, 1933
		Mesonephric ducts in female	Alverdes, 1928
Chelonia		Female had vs defaerens	van Wijhe, 1881
		Male had Müllerian duct. Mesonephric duct in female	Hoffmann, 1890
Trionyx		Mesonephric duct in female	van Wijhe, 1881
Rhynchocephalia			
Hatteria (Sphenodon)		Müllerian ducts in male*	Osawa, 1897
Lacertilia			
Sceloporus		Müllerian ducts in male	Forbes, 1941
Amphibolurus		Müllerian ducts in male	Hill, 1893
Stellio		Müllerian ducts in male	Schoof, 1888
Uromastix		Mesonephros and duct in female	Schoof, 1888
Chamaeleo		Mesonephros and duct in female	Schoof, 1888
Hemidactylus		Mesonephros and duct in female	Mahendra, 1953
Platydactylus		Mesonephric duct in female	Braun, 1877
Gongylus		Mesonephros and duct in female	Schoof, 1888
Lacerta		Müllerian duct in male; mesonephros and duct in female	von Leydig, 1853, 1872; Braun, 1877; Howes, 1887; Schoof, 1888; Jacquet, 1895; Lantz, 1923; Regamey, 1931
	Ovotestes	Penial sacs, oviducts, epididymides	Tayler, 1918
Anguis		Müllerian duct in male; mesonephros and duct in female	Leydig, 1853, 1872; Braun, 1877
Anniella		Mesonephric ducts in females	Coe and Kunkel, 1905
Ophidia			
Callopeltis		Mesonephric ducts in females	Braun, 1877
Coronella		Mesonephric ducts in females	Braun, 1877
Tropidonotus		Mesonephric ducts in females	Braun, 1877
Zamenis		Mesonephric ducts in females	Braun, 1877
Pelias		Mesonephric ducts in females	Braun, 1877

TABLE 17.2—*Continued*

Genus	Gonads	Accessory Structures	Reference
Crocodilia *Alligator*	Ovarian medullary rest; testicular cortex	Müllerian ducts in males; mesonephric ducts in females Rete system, mesonephros and duct in females; Müllerian ducts in males.*	Gadow, 1887 Forbes, 1940b

* Occur regularly.

maturity were males. Intramuscular injections of testosterone propionate into pregnant females, immature fish, and adult nonpregnant females caused complete masculinization of some but not all fish. Male sex characters were conspicuously developed in all cases (Régnier, 1938, 1939). Baldwin and Goldin (1939), Querner (1956), and Vallowe (1957) in carefully controlled experiments carried out a somewhat similar series of injections and obtained masculinization, in some cases with spermatogenesis, of about half the experimental fish. Treatment of female *Lebistes* and *Platypoecilus* with androgens had little or no effect on the ovaries except to suppress ovogenesis but did stimulate the growth of male accessory sex structures such as the gonopodium (Eversole, 1939; Régnier, 1939, 1942; Taylor, 1948; Querner, 1956). Mohsen (1958) more recently, however, gave relatively low doses (0.015 or 0.03 mg. thrice weekly) of pregneninolone to *Lebistes* for 6 months after hatching and observed not only the development of gonopodia in all treated fish but the transformation of ovaries to ovotestes. Testes of treated males were normal, except that the higher dose stimulated spermatogenesis. Testosterone propionate, paradoxically, elicited the appearance of ova at the base of an otherwise normal testis in adult male *Oryzias* (Egami, 1955c).

Not only androgen but estradiol benzoate, progesterone, and desoxycorticosterone acetate, if injected into the embryonic yolk sac, feminized the genital ridges of *Scyliorhinus* (Chieffi, 1954). Immature trout were partially feminized by keeping them in water to which estrogen had been added (Padoa, 1939a). Injection of estrin into the body cavity of the minnow *Phoxinus laevis* caused breakdown of the tests and assumption of female coloration (Bullough, 1940b). Administration of female sex hormones to *Lebistes* males transformed the testes to ovotestes and feminized the secondary sex characters of immature, but not of mature, males. Estrogen had no effect in females (Berkowitz, 1938, 1941; Querner, 1956). Various estrogens when given to *Oryzias* caused the appearance of testis-ova (Egami, 1955b, c; Okada, 1943). Similar treatment apparently had the same result in immature but not in mature male *Xiphophorus* (Vallowe, 1957). In *Hepatus* (*Serranus*) *hepatus*, treatment with estrogen stimulated the growth of the hermaphroditic gonad (Padoa, 1939b).

Thus, the accessory sex structures of fish apparently may be influenced by administration of heterosexual sex hormones, particularly androgens, at any time, and the sex of gonads of embryonic, immature, and sometimes mature fish may be partially or completely reversed by the same agents. Further experiments with special attention to the histologic details of each stage of reversal would be valuable, as would the measurement of endogenous sex hormone levels in blood and gonads.

Amphibians

See chapter by Burns.

Reptiles

Risley (1940) injected 0.25 mg. testosterone propionate in oily solution into the eggs of the turtle, *Chrysemys marginata belli*. The embryos were in the gastrula stage. The mortality rate was high, and only one injected male embryo survived. Of the five surviving injected female embryos, two had gonads with slight and three with more advanced modification toward testes in that the ovarian cortex was thinner, and the medullary cords were larger and more numerous, than in the controls. No accessory structures were affected.

Juvenile diamond-back terrapins, *Malaclemmys centrata*, were also injected with testosterone propionate (Risley, 1941b). In the males there resulted cavitation of the medullary cords and slight growth of Müllerian ducts. In the females ovarian and follicular size were less than normal, and Müllerian ducts grew conspicuously. Wolffian ducts and ureters hypertrophied in both sexes. Estradiol dipropionate injections caused reduction of testis size but growth of its cortical remnant and of Müllerian ducts, Wolffian ducts, and ureters in both sexes.

Classic studies on sex reversal in lizard embryos of an unidentified species have been made by Dantchakoff (1938). Fertile eggs were removed surgically from the mother, 8 to 12 being obtained at each operation. An injection of 0.05 to 0.15 mg. folliculin (an estrogen) in sesame oil was made into the egg under the blastoderm. Treated eggs and their controls were opened and examined 2 weeks after injection, approximately 2 weeks before hatching, 1 week before hatching, or 3 to 5 days after hatching. Estrogen treatment converted the testes to "hypo-ovaries." The medulla was inhibited, and a true cortex was developed, although it was thinner than in a normal female. In treated females the ovarian cortex and medulla were hypertrophied. In experimental embryos of both sexes large Müllerian ducts were present, although the ducts were often incomplete in the males. (Müllerian ducts were always absent at hatching in control males.) Estrogen did not appear to affect the mesonephric ducts. The cloacal epithelium of treated males and females was transformed, as Dantchakoff points out, very much in the manner described by Allen and Doisy (1923) for the vaginal epithelium of rodents in estrus. The epithelium had increased from 2 or 3 to 25 or 30 cell layers in thickness. The ureters were unaffected, but the cloacal extremities of the Wolffian ducts and the bladder-like diverticulum of the cloaca showed epithelial hypertrophy and metaplasia. Dantchakoff concluded that folliculin helps to control the normal development of the female reproductive system in the lizard, particularly in regulating Müllerian duct growth and in the "feminine orientation" of the indifferent gonad. From this she reasoned that folliculin is not present in the normal male embryo.

Implantation of testosterone propionate pellets into gonadectomized and intact, immature and adult *Anolis* of both sexes (Noble and Greenberg, 1940, 1941) resulted in oviduct hypertrophy in all females as compared to untreated controls.

Pellets of testosterone propionate or estradiol dipropionate were implanted subcutaneously in gonadectomized and intact, male and female, immature and adult *Anolis* (Noble and Greenberg, 1940, 1941). In the females both hormones caused conspicuous oviduct hypertrophy and extreme keratinization of urodeal cloacal epithelium. The androgen also produced hypertrophy of the ovaries, Wolffian ducts, and "sexual segments" of the kidneys. Both hormones caused a similar keratinization of the cloaca in males, whereas androgen evoked hypertrophy of the Wolffian duct and sexual segment and maintained in normal condition the epididymis and vas deferens of adult castrate males. Forbes (1941) implanted either testosterone or estrone in adult male *Sceloporus*. Treatment was followed by some reduction in testicular volume, acceleration of spermatogenesis, hypertrophy, and mucosal hyperplasia of persisting segments of Müllerian duct, apparent stimulation of the femoral glands, and hypertrophy of the epididymides and vasa deferentia. Absorption of estrone resulted in reduction of testicular volume, and spermatogenesis almost ceased. Seminiferous and epididymal tubules and femoral and cloacal glands became atrophic, as did the cells of the sexual segments. On the other hand, there was great hypertrophy of the Müllerian duct vestiges and stratification and cornification of the urodeal and proctodeal mucosa. It is believed that in mammals the administration of either sex hormone depresses the release of pituitary gonadotrophin, thus removing endocrine support for the gonad, but that testosterone also acts directly to stimulate both spermatogenesis and accessory sex structures. Such an interpretation would seem applicable as well to the results obtained in *Sceloporus.*

In the garter snake (Hartley, 1945) sex differentiation, as previously stated, normally occurs between the 16th and 19th day of pregnancy. To study the effect of sex hormones, testosterone propionate or estradiol dipropionate was injected during the first month of pregnancy, either into the peritoneal cavity of the mother or into the amniotic sacs. For some reason, intraperitoneal injections had no effect on the young. Intra-amniotic androgen increased the rate of spermatogonial mitoses and growth of seminiferous tubules. This hormone prevented regression of the ovarian medulla but checked development of the ovarian follicles. Estrogens reduced the size of the seminiferous tubules but caused no change in the ovary. Müllerian duct hypertrophy was seen during the last month of gestation in females injected with estrogen and androgen. Parturition did not occur if estrogen had been injected; the reason for this failure was not clear.

Sex hormones have also been injected into the immature alligator (Forbes, 1938a, b, 1939). Estrone injections for 80 days evoked conspicuous hypertrophy not only of the ovarian cortex but also of the cortical vestiges on the testis. The oviducts of the treated females became so huge as to occupy most of the abdominal cavity, and persistent Müllerian duct segments in the injected males also showed much growth. Treatment with testosterone and testosterone propionate was followed by hypertrophy of the oviducts, penes, and clitorides. Curiously enough, neither hormone affected the mesonephroi or their ducts.

As Dantchakoff (1938) points out, sex hormones may play an important role in the differentiation and development of the reproductive system of reptiles, both during and after embryonic life. Whereas experimental treatment by no means duplicates the normal release of endogenous sex hormones, it is likely that the latter are produced in significant quantity during development. This hypothesis should be investigated in the reptile, perhaps by techniques which have already shown their

value in comparable studies of other vertebrate classes. Discovery of the mechanisms of sex reversal and of normal morphologic sex differentiation still challenges the biologist.

XXIV. Addendum

Fish

Seasonal development of the gonads of the Japanese cyprinodont *Oryzias* reaches its peak in June and July, and spawning ensues; by September the gonads are of minimal size, recovering during the winter (Egami, 1956). Spawning occurs in late September to early March in the sea garfish, *Reporhampus,* of southern Australia; neither sex usually attains maturity until the age of three years (Ling, 1958). The sea horse, *Hippocampus,* breeds off the Florida coast from February to October on days having more than eleven hours of sunshine (Strawn, 1958). The Black Sea merling, *Odontogadus,* spawns the year around (Burdak, 1955). In the whiting (*Gadus merlangus* L.) and Norway pout (*G. esmarkii* Nilsson), seasonal development of the gonads occurs from January to May, and spawning takes place in May and June. Cells resembling interstitial cells can be seen in the spent testis, and a corpus luteum-like structure has been detected in the ovary (Gokhale, 1957). The selachian corpus luteum appears to be functional (Chieffi and Rattazzi, 1957).

Administration of methyl testosterone to juvenile male *Lebistes* provokes early maturation of the testis, promptly followed by its degeneration. In adults this compound causes hypertrophy of the sperm duct, inhibition of ovogenesis, and enlargement of the lumen of the ovarian excurrent duct (Geske, 1956). Testosterone treatment promotes growth of the vas deferens and of the dorsal fin rays of both sexes of the file fish, *Monocanthus* (Ishii and Egami, 1957). Implantation of testosterone propionate pellets into females, or of estrone pellets into males, of *Oryzias* promotes growth of male or female type, respectively, in the interneural and interhemal spines and the basipterygium (Egami and Ishii, 1956).

Unhatched eggs of *Fundulus confluentus,*

stranded in moist plant debris three months after flooded lowlands had dried up, were placed in tap water. Normal hatchlings emerged from the eggs in 15 to 30 minutes (Harrington and Haeger, 1958), another instance of successful adaptation of the embryo to an unfavorable environment. Ovarian eggs of the dogfish, *Squalus suckleyi*, contain estradiol-17β (Wotiz, Botticelli, Hisaw, Jr., and Ringler, 1958). Estrogen administration to *Lebistes* damages the testis, inhibits ovogenesis, and is associated with reduction in height of the epithelium of the sperm duct and with enlargement of the lumen of the ovarian excurrent duct (Geske, 1956). Treatment of the goldfish with estradiol was followed by a rise in the serum level of total protein and of non-ultrafilterable phosphorus and calcium, but not, as in the bird, by concomitant hyperossification (Bailey, 1957).

In the selachians *Torpedo* and *Scyliorhinus* the primitive gonad consists of both cortex and medulla. During development, the germ cells remain in the cortex if the gonad is to become an ovary; if it is to be a testis, they migrate to the medulla. In either case, the gonad of the female is briefly bisexual in appearance. The interrenal body and gonadal medulla have a common origin. As in birds, ovarian asymmetry appears to be genetically fixed (Chieffi, 1950, 1952, 1955). Embryos of both sexes of *Scyliorhinus* have Müllerian ducts, but they persist only in females (Thiebold, 1954).

Two adult female *Lebistes reticulatus* and one adult female *Xiphophorus helleri*, individually and continuously isolated from birth, gave birth to litters of 22, 14, and 28 young, all females. The mothers showed the characteristic "pregnancy spot," a pigmented area near the base of the tail. Microscopic study of the gonads showed them to be entirely ovarian and revealed the total absence of sperm, ruling out the possibility of self-fertilization by gametes from testicular tissue. Parthenogenesis seems the only other explanation. It is suggested that parthenogenesis may have resulted from stimulation of the mature ova by the toxin of a phycomycete with which all three mothers were infected (Stolk, 1958). Ova were observed in a testis of *Barbus stigma* (Sath-

yanesan, 1957). True hermaphroditism has been reported for the cutthroat trout (Turner, 1946; Benson, 1958).

Injection of testosterone propionate into *Scyliorhinus* embryos was followed by hypertrophy of the Wolffian ducts of females and testicular inhibition in males. Treatment of male embryos with estradiol benzoate resulted in persistence and hypertrophy of the Müllerian duct and conversion of the testis to an ovotestis. In a strain of the medaka, *Oryzias*, the female is white due to a recessive, sex-linked color gene (X^rX^r), whereas the male is orange-red due to a dominant color gene linked to the Y chromosome (X^rY^R). Thus color reveals the genetic sex. If the third-generation offspring of such fish were reared from hatching to 8 months on a diet containing estrone or stilbestrol, both the white and the red fish were morphologically females. (An exceptional red fish had both ovarian and testicular tissue.) The red fish, genotypic males, clearly had undergone sex reversal. Normal diet had no effect on sex. If the sex-reversed fish were mated to normal males, they had normal offspring (Yamamoto, 1953, 1957). If methyl testosterone were fed, beginning at hatching, to the offspring of normal parents, development of both testes and ovaries was inhibited. At certain dosage levels of this androgen, female to male sex reversal also occurred (Yamamoto, 1958).

Reptiles

Stefan (1958) studied immature male and female tortoises, *Emys leprosa*. Even after hatching, testes still retained cortical rests, medullary cords persisted in the ovaries, and Müllerian ducts were present in both sexes. Treatment with androgens and estrogens had little effect on the gonads, presumably because their differentiation was already too advanced. Both types of hormone stimulated Müllerian duct growth, and androgens caused phallic hypertrophy in both sexes.

XXV. References

ADAMS, A. E. 1940. Sexual conditions in *Triturus viridescens*. III. The reproductive cycle of the adult aquatic form of both sexes. Am. J. Anat., **66**, 235–273.

ADAMS, A. E. 1946. Sexual conditions in *Triturus viridescens*. IV. The effects of the administration of diethylstilbestrol on adult normal and castrated males. J. Exper. Zool., **101**, 1–39.

ALCOCK, A. 1892. On utero-gestation in *Trygon bleekeri*. Ann. Nat. Hist., ser. 6, **9**, 417–427.

ALLEN, E., AND DOISY, E. A. 1923. An ovarian hormone: a preliminary report on its localization, extraction, and partial purification, and action in test animals. J. A. M. A., **81**, 819–821.

ALTLAND, P. D. 1941. Annual reproductive cycle of the male fence lizard. J. Elisha Mitchell Sc. Soc., **57**, 73–83.

ALTLAND, P. D. 1943. Hypertrophy of hemipenes in lizards treated with androgen during period of sexual rest. Proc. Pennsylvania Acad. Sc., **17**, 81–83.

ALTLAND, P. D. 1951. Observations on the structure of the reproductive organs of the box turtle. J. Morphol., **89**, 599–621.

ALVERDES, K. 1926. Die Samenableitungswege der Eidechsen. Ztschr. mikroskop. anat. Forsch., **6**, 420–442.

ALVERDES, K. 1928. Die Epididymis der Sauropsiden im Vergleich zu Säugetier und Mensch. Ztschr. mikroskop. anat. Forsch., **15**, 405–471.

ANDREU, B. 1955. Un nuevo caso de hermafroditismo en *Sardina pilchardus* Walb. de la ría de Vigo. Invest. Pesq., **2**, 3–7.

ANGEL, F., AND LAMOTTE, M. 1944. Un crapaud vivipare d'Afrique occidentale, *Nectophrynoïdes occidentalis* Angel. Ann. Sc. Natur. (Zool.), **6**, 63–89.

AOYAMA, T. 1955. On the hermaphroditism in the yellow sea bream, Taius tumifrons. Japan. J. Ichthyol., **4**, 119–129.

APLINGTON, H. W., JR. 1942. Correlative cyclical changes in the hypophysis and gonads of *Necturus maculosus* Rafinesque. I. The male. Am. J. Anat., **70**, 201–249.

ARGAUD, R. 1920. Sur les glandes de l'oviducte chez les cheloniens. Compt. rend. Soc. biol., **83**, 828–829.

ARON, M. 1924a. Cycle séminal, cycle interstitiel et caractères sexuels secondaires chez *Rana esculenta*. Compt. rend. Soc. biol., **90**, 797–799.

ARON, M. 1924b. Recherches morphologiques et expérimentales sur le déterminisme des caractères sexuels mâles chez les urodèles. Arch. Biol., **34**, 1–166.

ARON, M. 1926. Recherches morphologiques et experiméntales sur le déterminisme des caractères sexuels secondaires mâles chez les Anoures (*Rana esculenta* L. et *Rana temporaria* L.). Arch. Biol., **36**, 1–97.

ARTHUR, D. R. 1950. Abnormalities in the sexual apparatus of the common dogfish (*Scyliorhynus caniculus*). Proc. Linnean Soc., London, **162**, 52–56.

ASHBY, K. R. 1952. Sviluppo del sistema riproduttivo di *Salmo trutta* L., in condizioni normali e sotto l'influenza di ormoni steroidi. Riv. Biol., **44**, 1–19.

ATSATT, S. R. 1953. Storage of sperm in the female chameleon *Microsaura pumila pumila*. Copeia, 59.

BACCI, G., AND RAZZAUTI, A. 1958. Protogynous hermaphroditism in *Coris julis* L. Nature, London, **181**, 432–433.

BAILEY, R. E. 1957. The effect of estradiol on serum calcium, phosphorus, and protein of goldfish. J. Exper. Zool., **136**, 455–469.

BAILEY, R. J. 1933. The ovarian cycle in the viviparous teleost *Xiphophorus helleri*. Biol. Bull., **64**, 206–225.

BALDWIN, F. M., AND GOLDIN, H. S. 1939. Effects of testosterone propionate on the female viviparous teleost, *Xiphophorus helleri* Heckel. Proc. Soc. Exper. Biol. & Med., **42**, 813–819.

BARBOUR, T. 1937. Ovoviviparity in *Trachyboa*. Copeia, 139.

BARNES, B. O., KANTER, A. E., AND KLAWANS, A. H. 1936. Bitterling ovipositor lengthening produced by adrenal extracts. Science, **84**, 310.

BARNEY, R. L. 1922. Further notes on the natural history and artificial propagation of the diamond back terrapin. Bull. U. S. Bureau Fisheries, **38**, 91–111.

BARTLETT, A. D. 1896. Notes on the breeding of the Surinam water toad (*Pipa americana*) in the Society's Gardens. Proc. Zool. Soc., London, 595–597.

BAUGHMAN, J. L. 1955. The oviparity of the whale shark, *Rhineodon typus*, with records of this and other fishes in Texas waters. Copeia, 54–55.

BAYLIS, H. A. 1939. Delayed reproduction in the spotted salamander. Proc. Zool. Soc., London, ser. A, **109**, 243–246.

BECKER, J., AND LEHMENSICK, R. 1933. Kastrationsversuche an in Brunst befindlichen männlichen Stichlingen. Klin. Wchnschr., **12**, 387–388.

BELLAIRS, R., GRIFFITHS, I., AND BELLAIRS, A. D'A. 1955. Placentation in the adder, *Vipera berus*. Nature, London, **176**, 657–658.

BENOIT, J., KEHL, R., AND LEPORTOIS, M. 1941. Sur l'interstitielle du testicule chez le Discloglosse. Compt. rend. Soc. biol., **136**, 522–524.

BENSON, N. G. 1958. Hermaphroditism in the cutthroat trout. Copeia, 239–240.

BERGMAN, A. M. 1943. The breeding habits of sea snakes. Copeia, 156–160.

BERK, L. 1939. Studies in the reproduction of *Xenopus laevis*. III. The secondary sex characters of the male *Xenopus*: the pads. South African J. M. Sc., **4**, 47–60.

BERK, L., AND SHAPIRO, H. A. 1939. Studies in the reproduction of *Xenopus laevis*. II. The histologic changes in the accessory sex organs of female *Xenopus* induced by the administration of endocrine preparations. South African J. M. Sc., suppl., **4**, 13–17.

BERKOWITZ, P. 1938. The effects of estrogenic substances in *Lebistes reticulatus* (guppy). Anat. Rec., **71**, 161–175.

BERKOWITZ, P. 1941. The effects of estrogenic substances in the fish (*Lebistes reticulatus*). J. Exper. Zool., **87**, 233–243.

BISHOP, S. C. 1920. A case of hermaphroditism in the white perch, *Morone americana* (Gmelin). Copeia, 20–21.

BLACHER, L. J. 1926. The dependence of secondary sex-characters upon testicular hormones in *Lebistes reticulatus*. Biol. Bull., **50**, 374–381.

BLAKE, S. F. 1921. Sexual differences in coloration in the spotted turtle, *Clemmys guttata*. Proc. U. S. Nat. Museum, **59**, 463–469.

BLANCHARD, F. C. 1942. A test of fecundity of the garter snake *Thamnophis sirtalis sirtalis* (Linnaeus) in the year following the year of insemination. Papers Michigan Acad. Sc., Arts and Letters, **28**, part II, 313–316.

BLANCHARD, F. N. 1931. Secondary sex characters of certain snakes. Bull. Antivenin Inst. Am., **4**, 95.

BLES, E. J. 1905. The life-history of *Xenopus laevis* Daud. Tr. Roy. Soc. Edinburgh, **41**, 789–821.

BLOUNT, R. F. 1929. Seasonal cycles of the interstitial cells in the testis of the horned toad (*Phrynosoma solare*): seasonal variations in the number and morphology of the interstitial cells and volume of the interstitial tissue. J. Morphol., **48**, 317–343.

BOCK, F. 1928. Kastration und sekundäre Geschlechtsmerkmale bei Teleostiern. Ztschr. wiss. Zool., **130**, 455–468.

BONDY, P. K., UPTON, G. V., AND PICKFORD, G. E. 1957. Demonstration of cortisol in fish blood. Nature, London, **179**, 1354–1355.

BORCEA, I. 1904. Quelques observations sur une Epinoche: *Gasterosteus aculeatus*, provenant d'une rivière se déversant au fond de la baie Aber, près du laboratoire de Roscoff. Bull. Soc. Zool. France, 24 mai, 140.

BOULENGER, G. A. 1895. On the nursing-habits of two South American frogs. Proc. Zool. Soc., London, 209–210.

BOYD, M. M. M. 1940. The structure of the ovary and the formation of the corpus luteum in *Hoplodactylus maculatus*, Gray. Quart. J. Microscop. Sc., **82**, 337–376.

BOYD, M. M. M. 1942. The oviduct, foetal membranes, and placentation in *Hoplodactylus maculatus* Gray. Proc. Zool. Soc., London, ser. A, **112**, 65–104.

BRAGDON, D. E. 1942. Studies on the reproduction of viviparous snakes. Anat. Rec., **84**, 453–454.

BRAGDON, D. E. 1946. Follicular atresia in ovoviviparous snakes. Anat. Rec., suppl., **96**, 542–543.

BRAGDON, D. E. 1951. The nonessentiality of the corpora lutea for the maintenance of gestation in certain live-bearing snakes. J. Exper. Zool., **118**, 419–435.

BRAGDON, D. E. 1952. Corpus luteum formation and follicular atresia in the common garter snake, *Thamnophis sirtalis*. J. Morphol., **91**, 413–445.

BRAGDON, D. E., LAZO-WASEM, E. A., ZARROW, M. X., AND HISAW, F. L. 1954. Progesterone-like activity in the plasma of ovoviviparous snakes. Proc. Soc. Exper. Biol. & Med., **86**, 477–480.

BRAUER, A. 1898. Ein neuer Fall von Brutpflege bei Froschen. Zool. Jahrb., Abt. System., Geog., u. Biol. Thiere, **12**, 89–94.

BRAUN, M. 1877. Das Urogenitalsystem der einheimischen Reptilien. Arb. zool.-zootom. Inst. Würzburg, **4**, 113–228.

BRAUN, M. 1878. Über äussere Hülfsorgane bei der Begattung von *Triton viridescens* Raf. Zool. Anz., **1**, 124–126.

BRECKENRIDGE, W. J. 1943. The life history of the black-banded skink *Eumeces septentrionalis septentrionalis* (Baird). Am. Midland Naturalist, **29**, 591–606.

BRESCA, G. 1910. Experimentelle Untersuchungen über die sekundären Sexual-charaktere der Tritonen. Roux' Arch. Entwicklungsmech. Organ., **29**, 403–431.

BRETSCHNEIDER, L. H., AND DUYVENÉ DE WIT, J. J. 1947. *Sexual Endocrinology of Nonmammalian Vertebrates*. New York: Elsevier Publishing Company.

BRIDGE, T. W. 1910. Fishes. In *The Cambridge Natural History*. S. F. Harmer and A. E. Shipley, Eds. London: Macmillan Company.

BROCK, J. 1878. Beiträge zur Anatomie und Histologie der Geschlechtsorgane der Knochenfische. Morphol. Jahrb., **4**, 505–572.

BRODE, M. D. 1928. The significance of the asymmetry of the ovaries of the fowl. J. Morphol. & Physiol., **46**, 1–57.

BROSSARD, G., AND GLEY, P. 1929. Production expérimentale du reflexe d'embrassement de la Grenouille. Compt. rend. Soc. biol., **101**, 757–758.

BRULL, L., AND CUYPERS, Y. 1954. Quelques caractéristiques biologiques de *Lophius piscatorius* L. Arch. Int. Physiol., **62**, 70–75.

BULLOUGH, W. S. 1940a. A case of hermaphroditism in the herring (*Clupea harengus*, Linn.). Proc. Leeds Philos. & Lit. Soc., **3**, 638–641.

BULLOUGH, W. S. 1940b. A study of sex reversal in the minnow (*Phoxinus laevis*, L.). J. Exper. Zool., **85**, 475–501.

BULLOUGH, W. S. 1947. Hermaphroditism in the lower vertebrates. Nature, London, **160**, 9–11.

BURDAK, V. D. 1955. Ob osobennostyakh polovogo tsikla v nerestechernomorskogo merlanga (*Odontogadus merlangus euxinus* (Nordmann). [The characteristics of the sexual cycle in the spawning Black Sea merling.] Doklady Akad. Nauk, SSSR., **104**, 657–659.

BURGER, J. W. 1942. Some effects of androgens on the adult male Fundulus. Biol. Bull., **82**, 233–242.

BURGER, W. L., AND SMITH, P. W. 1950. The coloration of the tail tip of young fer-de lances: sexual dimorphism rather than adaptive coloration. Science, **112**, 431–433.

CARRANZA, J., AND WINN, H. E. 1954. Reproductive behavior of the blackstripe topminnow, *Fundulus notatus*. Copeia, 273–278.

CARSON, H. L. 1945. Delayed fertilization in a captive indigo snake with notes on feeding and shedding. Copeia, 222–225.

CASTELNUOVO, G. 1937. Effetti di alcuni ormoni sulla maturazione delle Carpe. Riv. Biol., **23**, 365–372.

CAVOLINI, P. 1792. *Abhandlung über die Erzeu-*

gung der Fische und der Krebse, pp. 83–84. Berlin: Vossichen Buchhandlung.

CHAMPY, C. 1922a. Sur le determinisme des caracteres sexuels chez les Tritons. Compt. rend. Acad. Sc., **174**, 192–194.

CHAMPY, C. 1922b. Sur les conditions de la genèse de l'harmozone sexuelle chez les Batraciens anoures. Compt. rend. Acad. Sc., **174**, 497–500.

CHAMPY, C. 1923a. Observations sur les caractères sexuels chez les Poissons. Compt. rend. Soc. biol., **88**, 414–416.

CHAMPY, C. 1923b. Sur la "source de l'hormone sexuelle" chez les Poissons et en général. Compt. rend. Soc. biol., **88**, 1127–1129.

CHAMPY, C. 1923c. Sur les caractères sexuels annexes chez les Amphibiens. Compt. rend. Soc. biol., **88**, 55–57.

CHAMPY, C. 1924. A propos des caractères sexuels des Anoures. Compt. rend. Soc. biol., **90**, 838–840.

CHAMPY, C. 1932. Observations sur les caractères sexuels de la Grenouille. Arch. Zool. expér. et gén., **74**, 399–409.

CHAVIN, W., AND GORDON, M. 1951. Sex determination in *Platypoecilus maculatus*. I. Differentiation of the gonads in members of all-male broods. Zoologica, **36**, 135–145.

CHIDESTER, F. E. 1917. Hermaphroditism in *Fundulus heteroclitus*. Anat. Rec., **12**, 389–396.

CHIEFFI, G. 1950. Il differenziamento dei sessi nei Selaci. Experientia, **6**, 465.

CHIEFFI, G. 1952. Sull' organogenesi dell'interrenale e della medulla della gonade in *Torpedo ocellata* e in *Scylliorhinus canicula*. Pubbl. Staz. Zool. Napoli, **23**, 186–200.

CHIEFFI, G. 1954. L'inversione del sesso ottenuta con gli ormoni sessuali e corticosurrenale in *Scylliorhinus canicula*. Pubbl. Staz. Zool. Napoli, **25**, 477–498.

CHIEFFI, G. 1955. Sull' origine dell'asimmetria dell'ovario negli embrioni di *Scylliorhinus canicula*. Monitore zool. ital., **43**, 31–41.

CHIEFFI, G., AND RATTAZZI, M. 1957. Il contenuto in lipidi e steroidi del corpo luteo di alcuni Selaci. Boll. Zool., **25**, 1–7.

CHRISTENSEN, K. 1931. Effect of castration on the secondary sex characters of males and females of *Rana pipiens*. Anat. Rec., **48**, 241–250.

CIESLAK, E. S. 1945. Relations between the reproductive cycle and the pituitary gland in the snake, *Thamnophis radix*. Physiol. Zool., **18**, 299–328.

CLARK, E., AND ARONSON, L. R. 1951. Sexual behavior in the guppy, *Lebistes reticulatus* (Peters). Zoologica, **36**, 49–65.

CLARK, H., FLORIO, B., AND HUROWITZ, R. 1955. Embryonic growth of *Thamnophis s. sirtalis* in relation to fertilization date and placental function. Copeia, 9–13.

CLAUSEN, H. J. 1940. Studies on the effect of ovariotomy and hypophysectomy on gestation in snakes. Endocrinology, **27**, 700–704.

COE, W. R., AND KUNKEL, B. W. 1905. The female

urogenital organs of the limbless lizard Anniella. Anat. Anz., **26**, 219–222.

COHEN, H. 1946. Effects of sex hormones on the development of the platyfish, *Platypoecilus maculatus*. Zoologica, **31**, 121–128.

COHN, L. 1904. Die Schenkeldrüsen des *Cnemidophorus lemniscatus* Daud. Zool. Anz., **27**, 185–192.

COLE, F. J. 1905. Notes on Myxine. Anat. Anz., **27**, 323–326.

COMBESCOT, C. 1954a. Sur le cycle sexuel mâle, et notamment la spermatogénèse, chez la Tortue d'eau algérienne (*Emys leprosa* Schw.). Compt. rend. Soc. biol., **148**, 2021–2023.

COMBESCOT, C. 1954b. Sexualité et cycle génital de la Tortue d'eau algérienne, *Emys leprosa* Schw. Bull. Soc. Hist. Nat. Afrique Nord, **45**, 366–377.

COMBESCOT, C. 1955. Données histophysiologiques sur l'oviducte de la Tortue d'eau algérienne (*Emys leprosa* Schw.). Compt. rend. Soc. biol., **149**, 93–95.

CONEL, J. L. 1917. The urogenital system of Myxinoids. J. Morphol., **29**, 75–163.

COPE, E. D. 1900. The crocodilians, lizards, and snakes of North America. Rept. U. S. National Museum for 1898, pp. 155–1270. Washington: Government Printing Office.

CORDIER, R. 1928. Études histophysiologiques sur le tube urinaire des Reptiles. Arch. Biol., Paris, **38**, 111–171.

COUJARD, R. 1941a. L'évolution de la glande testiculaire des Bleniides. Compt. rend. Soc. biol., **135**, 371–373.

COUJARD, R. 1941b. Sur l'existence d'une glande testiculaire et d'une glande génitale annexe chez les Gobies. Compt. rend. Soc. biol., **135**, 570–574.

COURRIER, R. 1921a. Glande interstitielle du testicule et caractères sexuels secondaires chez les Poissons. Compt. rend. Acad. Sc., **172**, 1316–1317.

COURRIER, R. 1921b. Sur l'existence d'une glande interstitielle dans le testicule des Poissons. Compt. rend. Soc. biol., **85**, 939–941.

COURRIER, R. 1921c. Sur le conditionnement des caractères sexuels secondaires chez les Poissons. Compt. rend. Soc. biol., **85**, 486–488.

COURRIER, R. 1922a. Étude préliminaire du déterminisme des caractères sexuels secondaires chez les Poissons. Arch. Anat., Hist., et Embryol., **1**, 115–144.

COURRIER, R. 1922b. Sur l'indépendence de la glande séminale et des caractères sexuels secondaires chez les Poissons. Compt. rend. Acad. Sc., **174**, 70–72.

COURRIER, R. 1922c. Sur l'existence d'une glande interstitielle dans le testicule des Blennies. Bull. Soc. Zool., France, **47**, 458–462.

COURRIER, R. 1929. Les modifications saisonnières de l'appareil urogénital chez *Uromastix acanthinurus* (Bell). Arch. anat. microscop., **25**, 388–413.

CRAIG-BENNETT, A. 1931. The reproductive cycle of the three-spined stickleback, *Gasterosteus aculeatus*, Linn. Phil. Tr. Roy. Soc., ser. B. **219**, 197–279.

CRAWFORD, D. R. 1927. Notice of hermaphroditism in silver salmon, *Oncorhynchus kisutch*. Copeia, 34.

CROWELL, P. S. 1932. The ciliation of the oviducts of reptiles. Proc. Nat. Acad. Sc., U. S. A., **18**, 372–373.

CUMMINGS, J. B. 1943a. Morphogenesis of the gonopodium in *Molliensia latipinna*. J. Morphol., **73**, 1–17.

CUMMINGS, J. B. 1943b. Quantitative studies on the induction of gonopodia in females of *Molliensia latipinna*. J. Exper. Zool., **94**, 351–385.

CUNNINGHAM, J. T. 1886a. On the structure and development of the reproductive elements in *Myxine glutinosa*. Quart. J. Microscop. Sc., N. S., **27**, 49–76.

CUNNINGHAM, J. T. 1886b. The reproductive organs of Bdellostoma, and a teleostean ovum from the west coast of Africa. Tr. Roy. Soc., Edinburgh, **33**, 247–250.

CUNNINGHAM, J. T. 1900. *Sexual Dimorphism in the Animal Kingdom*. London: Adam and Charles Black, Ltd.

CUNNINGHAM, J. T. AND SMART, W. A. M. 1934. The structure and origin of corpora lutea in some of the lower Vertebrata. Proc. Roy. Soc., ser. B, **116**, 258–281.

DALCQ, A. 1920. Le cycle saisonnier du testicule de l'Orvet. Compt. rend. Soc. biol., **83**, 820–821.

D'ANCONA, U. 1950. Détermination et différenciation du sexe chez les Poissons. Arch. Anat. microscop. et Morphol. expér., **39**, 274–294.

D'ANCONA, U. 1955. Osservazioni sulle gonadi giovanili di Amia calva. Arch. ital. anat. e embriol., **60**, 201–225.

D'ANCONA, U. 1956. Inversions spontanèes et expérimentales dans les gonades des Téléostéens. L'Année biol., 3ème sér., **32**, 89–99.

DANTCHAKOFF, V. 1936. Sur les facteurs de l'histogenèse chez des hermaphrodites. Compt. rend. Soc. biol., **123**, 856–858.

DANTCHAKOFF, V. 1938. Über chemische Werkzeuge bei der Realisation normal bestimmter embryonaler geschlechtlicher Histogenese bei Reptilien. Roux' Arch. Entwicklungsmech. Organ., **138**, 465–521.

DAVIDSON, F. A. 1935. The development of the secondary sexual characters in the pink salmon (*Oncorhynchus gorbuscha*). J. Morphol., **57**, 169–183.

DAVIS, D. D., AND LAW, C. R. 1935. Gonadectomy and a new secondary sexual character in frogs. Science, **81**, 562–564.

DAVIS, D. D. 1936. Courtship and mating behavior in snakes. Field Museum Nat. Hist., Zool., **21**, 257–290.

DE ALLENDE, I. L. C. 1939. Cycle sexuel du crapaud *Bufo arenarum* femelle. Compt. rend. Soc. biol., **130**, 676–679.

DE ALLENDE, I. L. C. 1940. Action de l'oestrone sur l'oviducte du crapaud, *Bufo arenarum* Hens. Compt. rend. Soc. biol., **133**, 313–315.

DEAN, B. 1923. *A Bibliography of Fishes*. 3 vols. New York: American Museum of Natural History.

DE BEAUMONT, J. 1928. Modifications de l'appareil uro-génital du *Triton cristatus* femelle après greffe de testicules. Compt. rend. Soc. biol., **98**, 655–656.

DE BEER, G. R. 1924. Note on a hermaphrodite trout. Anat. Rec., **27**, 61–62.

DE GROOT, B., AND DUYVENÉ DE WIT, J. J. 1949. Copulin and ovopositor growth in the female bitterling (*Rhodeus amarus* Bl.). Acta Endocrinol., **3**, 129–136.

DESSAUER, H. C. 1955. Seasonal changes in the gross organ composition of the lizard, *Anolis carolinensis*. J. Exper. Zool., **128**, 1–12.

DESSAUER, H. C., FOX, W., AND GILBERT, N. L. 1956. Plasma calcium, magnesium and protein of viviparous colubrid snakes during estrous cycle. Proc. Soc. Exper. Biol. & Med., **92**, 299–301.

DILDINE, G. C. 1936. Studies in teleostean reproduction. I. Embryonic hermaphroditism in *Lebistes reticulatus*. J. Morphol., **60**, 261–277.

DONAHUE, J. K. 1934. Sex-limitation of cilia in body cavity of the frog (*Rana pipiens*). Proc. Soc. Exper. Biol. & Med., **31**, 1166–1168.

DONAHUE, J. K. 1941. Occurrence of estrogens in the ovaries of the winter flounder. Endocrinology, **28**, 519–520.

DORNESCO, G.-T. 1925. Sur l'existence d'un segment sexuel dans le tube urinifère du rein des *Lacerta* impubères. Compt. rend. Soc. biol., **93**, 1620–1621.

DORNESCO, G.-T. 1926a. Sur le déterminisme de la sécrétion du canal épididymaire chez *Cistudo europaea* Dum. et Bibr. Compt. rend. Soc. biol., **95**, 1585–1586.

DORNESCO, G.-T. 1926b. Évolution annuelle de l'épididyme chez *Cistudo europaea* Dum. et Bibr. Compt. rend. Soc. biol., **95**, 1583–1585.

DUFOSSÉ. 1856. De l'hermaphrodisme chez certains vertébrés. Ann. Sc. nat., 4ème sér., Zool., **5**, 295–332.

DULZETTO, F. 1928. Osservazioni sulla vita sessuale della *Gambusia holbrooki* (Grd.). Atti R. Acad. Naz. Lincei Rend. Cl. Sci. Fis. Mat. e Nat., **8**, 96–101.

DUNN, E. R. 1923. The breeding habits of salamanders and their bearing on phylogeny. Copeia, 25–28.

DUSCHAK, F. 1924. Zur Corpus luteum-Frage bei den Anuren. Ztschr. Anat., **74**, 608–613.

DUTTA, S. K. 1944. Studies of the sexual cycle in the lizard, *Hemidactylus flaviviridis* (Ruppel). Allahabad Univ. Stud. Zool. Sect., 57–153.

DUTTA, S. K. 1946. Cyclical changes in the genital ducts of the lizard, *Hemidactylus flaviviridis* (Ruppel). Allahabad Univ. Stud. Zool. Sect., 1–44.

DUYVENÉ DE WIT, J. J. 1938. Die Reaktion des weiblichen und männlichen Bitterlings auf einige reine Sexualhormone. Klin. Wchnschr., **17**, 376–378.

DUYVENÉ DE WIT, J. J. 1939. Ovipositor lengthening of the female bitterling produced by administration of progesterone. Endocrinology, **24**, 580–582.

DUYVENÉ DE WIT, J. J. 1940. A quantitative and qualitative test for steroid hormones based on the ovipositor reaction of the female bitterling (*Rhodeus amarus* Bloch). J. Endocrinol., **2**, 141–156.

EDWARDS, C. L. 1903. A note on *Phrynosoma*. Science, **17**, 826–827.

EGAMI, N. 1954a. Appearance of the male character in the regenerating and transplanted rays of the anal fin in females of the fish, *Oryzias latipes*, following treatment with methyldihydrotestosterone. J. Fac. Sc. Tokyo Imp. Univ., Sect. IV, **7**, 271–280.

EGAMI, N. 1954b. Effects of estrogen on testis of the loach, *Misgurnus anguillicaudatus*. J. Fac. Sc. Tokyo Imp. Univ., Sec. IV, **7**, 121–130.

EGAMI, N. 1954c. Inhibitory effect of estrone benzoate on ovarian growth in the loach, *Misgurnus anguillicaudatus*. J. Fac. Sc. Tokyo Imp. Univ., Sect. IV, **7**, 113–119.

EGAMI, N. 1955a. Effect of estrogen and androgen on the weight and structure of the liver of the fish, *Oryzias latipes*. Annot. Zool. Japon., **28**, 79–85.

EGAMI, N. 1955b. Production of testis-ova in the males of *Oryzias latipes*. I. Testis-ova in the fish receiving estrogens. Japan. J. Zool., **11**, 353–365.

EGAMI, N. 1955c. Production of testis-ova in adult males of *Oryzias latipes*. II. Effect on testis-ova production of nonestrogenic steroids given singly or simultaneously with estradiol. Japan. J. Zool., **11**, 367–371.

EGAMI, N. 1956. Production of testis-ova in adult males of *Oryzias latipes*. VII. Seasonal changes of frequency of testis-ovum production. Japan. J. Zool., **12**, 71–79.

EGAMI, N., AND ISHII, S. 1956. Sexual differences in the shape of some bones in the fish, *Oryzias latipes*. J. Fac. Sc. Tokyo Univ., IV, Zool., **7**, 563–571.

EGGERT, B. 1931. Die Geschlechtsorgane der *Gobiiformes* und *Blenniiformes*. Ztschr. wiss. Zool., **139**, 249–558.

EHRHARDT, K., AND KÜHN, K. 1933. Ein bisher unbekannte biologische Wirkung des weiblichen Sexualhormons. (Künstliches Wachstum der Legerohre bei Bitterlingen.) Monatsschr. Gebürts. Gynäk., **94**, 1–4.

EHRHARDT, K., AND KÜHN, K. 1934. Weitere Untersuchungen über kunstliches (hormonales) Wachstum der Legerohre bei weiblichen Bitterlingen. Endokrinologie, **15**, 1–14.

EIGENMANN, C. H. 1892a. On the viviparous fishes of the Pacific Coast of North America. Bull. U. S. Fish Commission, **12**, 381–478.

EIGENMANN, C. H. 1892b. *Cymatogaster aggregatus* Gibbons; a contribution to the ontogeny of viviparous fishes. Bull. U. S. Fish Commission, **12**, 401–479. (Cited by Turner, 1933.)

EIGENMANN, C. H. 1897. Sex-differentiation in the viviparous teleost *Cymatogaster*. Roux' Arch. Entwicklungsmech. Organ., **4**, 125–179.

ESSENBERG, J. M. 1923. Sex differentiation in the viviparous teleost *Xiphophorus helleri* Heckel. Biol. Bull., **45**, 46–96.

ESSENBERG, J. M. 1926. Complete sex-reversal in the viviparous teleost *Xiphophorus helleri*. Biol. Bull., **51**, 98–111.

EVANS, L. T. 1939. Rudiments of epididymis and vas efferens in female turtles. Anat. Rec., suppl., **75**, 56.

EVANS, L. T. 1946. Endocrine effects upon the claws of immature turtles, *Pseudemys elegans*. Anat. Rec., **94**, 406.

EVANS, L. T. 1948. The effects of gonadotropic and androgenic hormones upon dorsonuchal crest of the lizard. Anat. Rec., **100**, 657–658.

EVANS, L. T. 1951a. Male hormone effects upon the claws of juvenile box tortoises. Anat. Rec., suppl., **109**, 370.

EVANS, L. T. 1951b. Effects of male hormone upon the tail of the slider turtle, *Pseudemys scripta Troostii*. Science, **114**, 277–279.

EVANS, L. T. 1952a. Endocrine relationships in turtles. II. Claw growth in the slider, *Pseudemys scripta Troostii*. Anat. Rec., **112**, 251–263.

EVANS, L. T. 1952b. Endocrine relationships in turtles. III. Some effects of male hormone in turtles. Herpetologica, **8**, 11–14.

EVANS, L. T., AND CLAPP, M. L. 1940. The effects of ovarian hormones and seasons on *Anolis carolinensis*. II. The genital system. Anat. Rec., **77**, 57–75.

EVERSOLE, W. J. 1939. The effects of androgens upon the fish (*Lebistes reticulatus*). Endocrinology, **25**, 328–330.

EVERSOLE, W. J. 1941. The effects of pregneninolone and related steroids on sexual development in fish (*Lebistes reticulatus*). Endocrinology, **28**, 603–610.

EWING, E. H. 1943. Continued fertility in female box turtles following mating. Copeia, 112–114.

FANTHAM, H. B. 1905. On hermaphroditism and vestigial structure in the reproductive organs of *Testudo graeca*. Ann. Mag. Nat. Hist., ser. 7, **16**, 120–126.

FELIZET, J. 1911. Recherches sur les glandes fémorales de *Lacerta muralis*. J. anat., Paris, **47**, 333–370.

FLEISCHMANN, W., AND KANN, S. 1932. Über eine Funktion des weiblichen Sexualhormons bei Fischen (Wachstum der Legeröhre des Bitterlings). Arch. ges. Physiol., **230**, 662–667.

FLEISCHMANN, W., AND KANN, S. 1934. Über das Wachstum der Legeröhre des Bitterlings unter den Einfluss des weiblichen Sexualhormons. II. Arch. ges. Physiol., **234**, 130–136.

FLEISCHMANN, W., AND KANN, S. 1935. Zur Frage des Spezifizität des Legerohrentestes für Follikelhormon. Klin. Wchnschr., **14**, 644.

FLEISCHMANN, W., AND KANN, S. 1936. Wirkung des Testosterons auf das Wachstum des Kammes von Triton cristatus. Arch. ges. Physiol., **237**, 517–518.

FLEISCHMANN, W., AND KANN, S. 1938. The bitterling ovipositor reaction to corticosterone. Science, **87**, 305–306.

FLYNN, T. T. 1923. On the occurrence of a true allantoplacenta of the conjoint type in an Australian lizard. Rec. Australian Museum, **14**, 72–77.

FOLLENIUS, E. 1953. Contribution à l'étude du déterminisme de la différenciation des caractères sexuels chez les Cyprinodontes. Action des rayons X sur les gonades de *Lebistes reticulatus* Regan. Bull. biol., **87**, 68–91.

FORBES, T. R. 1937. Studies on the reproductive system of the alligator. I. The effects of prolonged injections of pituitary whole gland extract in the immature alligator. Anat. Rec., **70**, 113–133.

FORBES, T. R. 1938a. Studies on the reproductive system of the alligator. II. The effects of prolonged injections of oestrone in the immature alligator. J. Exper. Zool., **78**, 335–367.

FORBES, T. R. 1938b. Studies on the reproductive system of the alligator. III. The action of testosterone on the accessory sex structures of recently hatched female alligators. Anat. Rec., **72**, 87–95.

FORBES, T. R. 1939. Studies on the reproductive system of the alligator. V. The effects of injections of testosterone propionate in immature alligators. Anat. Rec., **75**, 51–57.

FORBES, T. R. 1940a. Studies on the reproductive system of the alligator. IV. Observations on the development of the gonad, the adrenal cortex, and the Müllerian duct. Contr. Embryol. Carnegie Inst. Washington, **174**, 129–155.

FORBES, T. R. 1940b. Studies on the reproductive system of the alligator. VI. Further observations on heterosexual structures in the female alligator. Anat. Rec., **77**, 343–365.

FORBES, T. R. 1941. Observations on the urogenital anatomy of the adult male lizard, *Sceloporus,* and on the action of implanted pellets of testosterone and of estrone. J. Morphol., **68**, 31–69.

FORBES, T. R. 1956. The development of the reproductive system of a lizard, *Anolis carolinensis.* Am. J. Anat., **98**, 139–158.

FORCE, E. 1931. Habits and birth of young of the lined snake, *Tropidoclonion lineatum* (Hallowell). Copeia, 51–53.

FOWLER, H. W. 1912. Hermaphrodite shad in the Delaware. Science, **36**, 18–19.

FOX, W. 1952. Seasonal variation in the male reproductive system of Pacific Coast garter snakes. J. Morphol., **90**, 481–554.

FOX, W. 1956. Seminal receptacles of snakes. Anat. Rec., **124**, 519–540.

FOX, W. 1958. Sexual cycle of the male lizard, *Anolis carolinensis.* Copeia, 22–29.

FRAENKEL, L., AND MARTINS, T. 1938. Sur le corps jaune des serpents vivipares. Compt. rend. Soc. biol., **127**, 466–468.

FRAENKEL, L., AND MARTINS, T. 1939. Estudos sobre a fisiologia sexual das serpentes. Mem. Inst. Butantan, **13**, 393–398.

FRAENKEL, L., MARTINS, T., AND MELLO, R. F. 1940. Studies on the pregnancy of viviparous snakes. Endocrinology, **27**, 836–837.

FRANKENBERGER, Z. 1922. Zur Frage der funktionellen Bedeutung der Hodenzwischenzellen. Anat. Anz., **55**, 545–550.

FRANKENBERGER, Z. 1928. Études sur la spermatogenèse des Reptiles. Compt. rend. A. anat., Prague, **23**, 163.

FRAPS, R. M., HOOKER, C. W., AND FORBES, T. R. 1949. Progesterone in blood plasma of cocks and nonovulating hens. Science, **109**, 493.

FRASER, E. A., AND RENTON, R. M. 1940. Observations on the breeding and development of the viviparous fish, *Heterandria formosa.* Quart. J. Microscop. Sc., **81**, 479–520.

FRIESS, E. 1933. Untersuchungen über die Geschlechtsumkehr bei *Xiphophorus helleri* Heckel. Roux' Arch. Entwicklungsmech. Organ., **129**, 255–355.

GÄBLER, H. 1930. Zwei Fälle von Zwittergonaden bei *Clupea harengus* L. Zool. Anz., **91**, 72–75.

GADOW, H. 1887. Remarks on the cloaca and on the copulatory organs of the Amniota. Philos. Tr. Roy. Soc., London, ser. B, **178**, 5–37.

GADOW, H. 1923. Amphibia and reptiles. In *Cambridge Natural History,* vol. 8. Macmillan Company, London.

GALLIEN, L. 1948. Sur la structure des nageoires chez les femelles de *Lebistes reticulatus* Regan, masculinisées par la pregnéninolone. Compt. rend. Acad. Sc., **226**, 1749–1751.

GALLI-MAÏNINI, C. 1950. Action de l'ovaire et des oestrogènes sur l'oviducte du crapaud. Compt. rend. Soc. biol., **145**, 133–134.

GAMPERT, O. 1866. Über die Niere von Tropidonotus natrix. Ztschr. wiss. Zool., **16**. (Cited by Volsøe, 1944.)

GANFINI, C. 1902. Struttura e sviluppo della cellule interstiziali del testicolo. Arch. ital. di anat. e embriol., **1**, 233–294.

GARNAUD, J. 1950. La reproduction et l'incubation branchiale chez *Apogon imberbis* G. et L. Bull. Inst. Océanograph., **977**, 1–10.

GEISER, S. W. 1922. Seasonal changes in the testis of Gambusia affinis, the top-minnow. Anat. Rec., **23**, 104–105.

GEMMILL, J. F. 1912. *The Teratology of Fishes.* Glasgow: James Maclehose.

GERBIL'SKII, N. L. 1955. Biologic races of Caspian sturgeons. Systematic Zool., **4**, 82–92.

GESKE, G. 1956. Untersuchungen über den Einfluss von *p*-oxy-Propiophenon, Methyl Testosteron, und Äthinyl-Oestradiol auf die innersekretorischen Organe von Lebistes reticulatus Peters. Roux' Arch. Entwicklungsmech. Organ., **148**, 263–310.

GIACOMINI, E. 1896a. Contributo all'istologia

dell'ovario dei Selaci con speciale riguardo sopra ad alcune particolarite di struttura riscontrati nell'ovario di *Myliobatis bovina* Geoff. St. Hil. Ric. Lab. Anat. norm. Univ. Roma, **5**, 221. (Cited by Matthews and Marshall, 1956.)

GIACOMINI, E. 1896b. Sui corpi lutei veri degli Anfibi con una breve appendice sui corpi lutei veri degli Uccelli "Gallus domesticus." Monitore zool. ital. **7**, 214–230, 249–266.

GIBBS, E. D. 1956. A bisexual steelhead. California Fish & Game, **42**, 229–231.

GIERSBERG, H. 1922. Untersuchungen über Physiologie und Histologie des Eileiters der Reptilien und Vögel; nebst einem Beitrag zur Fasergenese. Ztschr. wiss. Zool., **120**, 1–97.

GILBERT, P. W. 1943. The morphology of the male urogenital system of the frilled shark, *Chlamydoselachus anguineus*. J. Morphol., **73**, 507–528.

GLÄSER, E., AND HAEMPEL, O. 1932. Der Nachweis des männlichen Sexualhormons mit dem Fischtest. Deutsche med. Wchnschr., **58**, 1247–1248.

GLÄSER, E., AND RANFTL, F. 1938. Die Bitterlingsteste auf männliche und weibliche Sexualhormone. Klin. Wchnschr., **17**, 1120–1124.

GLOYD, H. K. 1928. The amphibians and reptiles of Franklin County, Kansas. Tr. Kansas Acad. Sc. **31**, 115–141. (Cited by Fox, 1956.)

GLOYD, H. K. 1933. Studies on the breeding habits and young of the copperhead, *Agkistrodon mokasen* Beauvois. Papers Michigan Acad. Sc., Arts and Letters, **19**, 587–604. (Cited by Fox, 1956.)

GOKHALE, S. V. 1957. Seasonal histologic changes in the gonads of the whiting (*Gadus merlangus* L.) and the Norway pout (*G. esmarkii* Nilsson). Indian J. Fish, **4**, 92–112.

GÓMEZ LARRAÑETA, M. 1953. Observaciones sobre la sexualidad de *Pagellus erythrinus* L. Publ. Inst. Biol. Aplicada, **13**, 83–101.

GORBMAN, A. 1939. Action of mammalian sex hormones in the lizard, *Sceloporus occidentalis*. Proc. Soc. Exper. Biol. & Med., **42**, 811–813.

GRABER, R. 1940. Beobachtungen an *Ophis* (syn. *Xenodon*) *merremi* und *O. severus*. Wchnschr. Aquar.- und Terrark., **37**, 291–292. (Cited by Fox, 1956.)

GRANT, R. 1937. Effect of estrone on the oviducts of *Triturus viridescens*. Anat. Rec., Suppl., **67**, 20.

GRASSI, B. 1911. Richerche sulle Anguille argentina allevate forzatamente in vasche d'acqua dolce. Atti acad. Lincu rend., **5**, **21**, 675–677. (Cited by Chidester, 1917.)

GRASSI, B. 1919. Nuove richerche sulla storia naturale dell'Anguilla. R. Com. Talass. ital., Mem., **67**, 1. (Cited by Hann, 1927.)

GREENBERG, B. 1942. Some effects of testosterone on the sexual pigmentation and other sex characters of the cricket frog (*Acris gryllus*). J. Exper. Zool., **91**, 435–451.

GRIMPE, G. 1922–1925. Über eine merkwürdige Zwittergonade des Herings (*Clupea harengus*

L.). Sitzungsb. naturforsch. Gesells. Leipzig., **49–52**, 60–70.

GROBSTEIN, C. 1940. Effect of testosterone propionate on regenerating anal fin of adult *Platypoecilus maculatus* females. Proc. Soc. Exper. Biol. & Med., **45**, 484–486.

GROBSTEIN, C. 1942a. Effect of various androgens on regenerating anal fin of adult *Platypoecilus maculatus* females. Proc. Soc. Exper. Biol. & Med. **49**, 477–478.

GROBSTEIN, C. 1942b. Endocrine and developmental studies of gonopod differentiation in certain poeciliid fishes. II. Effect of testosterone propionate on the normal and regenerating anal fin of adult *Platypoecilus maculatus* females. J. Exper. Zool., **89**, 305–328.

GROBSTEIN, C. 1947. The role of androgen in declining regenerative capacity during morphogenesis of the *Platypoecilus maculatus* gonopodium. J. Exper. Zool., **106**, 313–344.

HAINES, T. P. 1940. Delayed fertilization in *Leptodeira annulata polysticta*. Copeia, 116–118.

HAMLETT, G. W. D. 1952. Notes on breeding and reproduction in the lizard *Anolis carolinensis*. Copeia, 183–185.

HAMON, M. 1945. Effets morphologiques du propionate de testostérone sur la femelle de *Gambusia holbrooki* Gir. Compt. rend. Soc. biol., **139**, 110–111.

HANN, H. W. 1927. The history of the germ cells of *Cottus bairdii* Girard. J. Morphol., **43**, 427–497.

HANSEN, I. B. 1939. Castration of the box turtle, *Terrapene carolinensis*. Bull. Mt. Desert Island Biol. Lab., 24–25.

HANSEN, I. B. 1943. Hermaphroditism in a turtle of the genus *Pseudemys*. Copeia, 7–9.

HANSEN, I. B., AND RILEY, A. S. 1941. Seasonal changes in the oviduct of the turtle, *Terrapene carolina*. Anat. Rec., suppl., **81**, 116.

HARMS, J. W. 1926a. *Körper und Keimzellen*, Vol. I, pp. 130–138. Berlin: Springer-Verlag.

HARMS, J. W. 1926b. Beobachtungen über Geschlechtsumwandlungen reifer Tiere und deren F₁ Generation. Zool. Anz., **67**, 67–79.

HARMS, J. W. 1950. Zur Geschlechtsbestimmung mit Testosteron bei Erdkröten. Ztschr. Naturforsch., **5b**, 173.

HARRINGTON, R. W., JR., AND HAEGER, J. S. 1958. Prolonged natural deferment of hatching in killifish. Science, **128**, 1511.

HARRISON, L., AND WEEKES, H. C. 1925. On the occurrence of placentation in the scincid lizard *Lygosoma entrecasteauxi*. Proc. Linnean Soc. New South Wales., **50**, 470–486.

HARRISON MATTHEWS, L. 1950. Reproduction in the basking shark, *Cetorhinus maximus* (Gunner). Philos. Tr. Roy. Soc., ser. B, **234**, 247–316.

HARRISON MATTHEWS, L. 1955. The evolution of viviparity in vertebrates. In *Comparative Physiology of Reproduction and the Effects of Sex Hormones in Vertebrates*, I. Chester Jones and P. Eckstein, Eds., p. 129–144. Cambridge, University Press.

HARRISON MATTHEWS, L., AND MARSHALL, F. H. A. 1956. Cyclical changes in the reproductive organs of the lower vertebrates. In *Marshall's Physiology of Reproduction*, A. S. Parkes, Ed., Vol. I, p. 156–225. London: Longmans, Green and Company.

HARTLEY, R. T. 1945. Effects of sex hormones on the development of the urogenital system in the garter snake. J. Morphol., **76**, 115–137.

HAVAS, L. 1939. Influence of colchicine on the sexually induced colour change of *Rhodeus amarus*. Nature, London, **143**, 809–810.

HAZLETON, L. W., AND GOODRICH, F. J. 1937. Note on the presence of male sex hormone in fish testes. J. Am. Pharmacol. A. **26**, 420–421.

HEBERER, G. 1930. Das Hodeninterstitium von *Varanus komodoensis* Ouwens. Ztschr. mikroskop.-anat. Forsch., **20**, 388–416.

HEIMLICH, E. M., AND HEIMLICH, M. G. 1950. Uterine changes and placentation in the yucca night lizard. J. Entomol. & Zool., **42**, 5–12.

HENRY, A. 1900. Étude histologique de la fonction sécrétoire de l'épididyme chez les Vertébrés supérieurs. Arch. anat. microscop., **3**, 229–292.

HERLANT, M. 1933. Recherches histologiques et expérimentales sur les variations cycliques du Testicule et des caractères sexuels secondaires chez les Reptiles. Arch. Biol., **44**, 347–468.

HESS, W. N. 1918. A seasonal study of the kidney of the five-spined stickleback, *Eucalia inconstans cayuga* Jordan. Anat. Rec., **14**, 141–163.

HETT, J. 1923. Das Corpus luteum des Molches (*Triton vulgaris*). Ztschr. Anat. Entwicklungsges., **68**, 243–271.

HETT, J. 1924. Das Corpus luteum der Zauneidechse (*Lacerta agilis*). Ztschr. mikroskop.-anat. Forsch., **1**, 41–84.

HILDEBRAND, S. F. 1929. Review of experiments on artificial culture of diamond-back terrapin. U. S. Bureau Fisheries Bull., **45**, 25–70.

HILL, J. P. 1893. Note on the presence of vestigial Müllerian ducts in a full-grown male lizard (*Amphibolurus muricatus*). Proc. Linnean Soc. New South Wales, ser. 2, **8**, 325–326.

HISAW, F. L., AND ALBERT, A. 1947. Observations on the reproduction of the spiny dogfish, *Squalus acanthias*. Biol. Bull, **92**, 187–199.

HOAR, W. S. 1955. Reproduction in teleost fish. In *The Comparative Physiology of Reproduction and the Effects of Sex Hormones in Vertebrates*, I. Chester Jones and P. Eckstein, Eds., pp. 5–22. Cambridge: University Press.

HOAR, W. S. 1957a. The gonads and reproduction. In *The Physiology of Fishes*. M. E. Brown, Ed., Vol. I. New York: Academic Press, Inc.

HOAR, W. S. 1957b. Endocrine organs. In *The Physiology of Fishes*. M. E. Brown, Ed. Vol. I. New York: Academic Press, Inc.

HOFFMANN, C. K. 1889. Zur Entwicklungsgeschichte der Urogenitalsorgane bei den Reptilien. Ztschr. wiss. Zool., **48**, 260–300.

HOFFMANN, C. K. 1890. Reptilien. In *Bronn's Klassen und Ordnungen des Thier-Reichs*, Vol. 6, Section III. Leipzig: Winter.

HOPPER, A. F., JR. 1941. The early embryology of Platypoecilus maculatus. Copeia, 218–224.

HOPPER, A. F. 1949. The effect of ethynyl testosterone on the intact and regenerating anal fins of normal and castrated females and normal males of Lebistes reticulatus. J. Exper. Zool., **111**, 393–414.

HOWELL, A. B. 1935. Sexual difference in the muscles of Salientia. Copeia, 188–189.

HOWES, G. B. 1887. On the vestigial structures of the reproductive apparatus in the male of the green lizard. J. Anat. & Physiol., **21**, 185–189.

HOWES, G. B. 1891. On some hermaphrodite genitalia of the codfish (*Gadus morrhua*), with remarks upon the morphology and phylogeny of the vertebrate reproductive system. J. Linnean Soc., **23**, 539–558.

HUBBS, C. L. 1921. The ecology and life-history of *Amphigonopterus aurora* and of other viviparous perches of California. Biol. Bull., **40**, 181–209.

HUMPHREY, R. R. 1921. The interstitial cells of the urodele testis. Am. J. Anat., **29**, 213–279.

HUMPHREY, R. R. 1925. The development of the temporary sexual characters in *Diemyctylus viridescens* in relation to changes within the testis. Anat. Rec., suppl., **29**, 362.

IKEDA, K. 1933. Effect of castration on the secondary sexual characters of anadromous three-spined stickleback, *Gasterosteus aculeatus aculeatus* L. Japan. J. Zool., **5**, 135–157.

ISHII, S., AND EGAMI, N. 1957. Effect of testosterone on the dorsal fin of the file fish, *Monocanthus cirrhifer*. Annot. Zool. Japon., **30**, 77–82.

JACQUET, M. 1895. Note sur un cas d'hermaphroditisme incomplet chez le Lacerta agilis. Bibliog. Anat., **3**, 267.

JACOBI, L. 1936. Ovoviviparie bei einheimischen Eidechsen. Vergleichende Untersuchungen an den Eiern und am Ovidukt von Lacerta agilis und Anguis fragilis. Ztschr. wiss. Zool., **148**, 401–464.

JAMES, M. F. 1946. Hermaphroditism in the largemouth bass. J. Morphol., **79**, 93–95.

JOHNSTON, P. M. 1951. The embryonic history of the germ cells of the largemouth black bass, *Micropterus salmoides salmoides* (Lacépède). J. Morphol., **88**, 471–542.

JONES, J. W. 1940. Histologic changes in the testis in the sexual cycle of male salmon parr (*Salmo salar* L. juv.). Proc. Roy. Soc. London, ser. B, **128**, 499–509.

JONES, J. W., AND ORTON, J. H. 1940. The paedogenetic male cycle in *Salmo salar* L. Proc. Roy. Soc. London, ser. B., **128**, 485–499.

JORDAN, D. S. 1905. *A Guide to the Study of Fishes*, Vol. I, p. 128. New York: Henry Holt & Company, Inc.

JORDAN, E. O. 1891. The spermatophores of Diemectylus. J. Morphol., **5**, 263–270.

KASTURIRANGAN, L. R. 1951. Placentation in the sea-snake, *Enhydrina schistosa* (Daudin). Proc. Indian Acad. Sc. **34B**, 1–32.

KEHL, R. 1930. Action de la folliculine de mammifère sur l'oviducte de la Tortue. Compt. rend. Soc. biol., **105**, 512–513.

KEHL, R. 1935. Note préliminaire sur le cycle génital chez quelques reptiles sahariens. Compt. rend. Soc. biol., **118**, 1077–1079.

KEHL, R. 1938. Action de l'androstérone sur le "segment sexuel" urinaire de l'Uromastix femelle. Compt. rend. Soc. biol., **127**, 142–144.

KEHL, R. 1941. Nouvelles recherches sur l'action des hormones sexuelles sur l'oviducte des Reptiles. Compt. rend. Soc. biol., **135**, 1475–1476.

KEHL, R. 1944a. Études de quelques problèmes d'endocrinologie génitale chez un batracien nord-africain (discoglosse). Rev. Canad. Biol., **3**, 29–95.

KEHL, R. 1944b. Étude de quelques problèmes d'endocrinologie génitale chez certains reptiles du sud-algérien. Rev. Canad. Biol., **3**, 131–219.

KEHL, R. M., LEPORTOIS, M., AND BENOIT, J. 1941. Biométrie du cycle génital normal et expérimental de l'*Uromastix* femelle. Compt. rend. Soc. biol., **136**, 520–522.

KINOSHITA, T. 1933. A new case of hermaphroditism in *Carassius auratus* L. J. Sc. Hiroshima Univ., ser. B 1, **2**, 206–210.

KINOSHITA, Y. 1932. Influence of castration on the secondary sexual characters of *Rana limnocharis*. J. Sc. Hiroshima Univ., ser. B 1, **2**, 21–31.

KINOSHITA, Y. 1935. Effects of gonadectomies on the secondary sexual characters in *Halichoeres poecilopterus* (Temminck and Schlegel). J. Sc. Hiroshima Univ., ser. B 1, **4**, 1–14.

KINOSHITA, Y. 1936. On the conversion of sex in *Sparus longispinis* (Temminck and Schlegel), (Teleostei). J. Sc. Hiroshima Univ., ser. B 1, **4**, 69–79.

KITADA, J. I. 1951. Histologic observations on the seasonal changes in the testis of a lizard (*Eumeces latiscutatus*). Japan. J. Genet., **26**, 195–197.

KLEINER, I. S., WEISMAN, A. I., AND MISHKIND, D. I. 1936. Use of the female bitterling as a test for male hormone. J. A. M. A., **106**, 1643–1644.

KLUTH, F. 1936. Ungewöhnlich späte Eiablage bei Schlangen. Bl. Aquar.- und Terrark., **47**, 20. (Cited by Fox, 1956.)

KNOWLES, F. G. W. 1939. The influence of anterior-pituitary and testicular hormones on the sexual maturation of lampreys. J. Exper. Biol., **16**, 535–547.

KOBAYASHI, H. 1955. On an hermaphroditic loach, *Lefusa nikkonis* (Jordan et Fowler). Annot. Zool. Japon., **28**, 17–18.

KOLMER, W., AND SCHEMINZKY, F. 1922a. Finden sich Zwischenzellen nur bei den höheren Wirbeltieren? Arch. ges. Physiol., **194**, 352–361.

KOLMER, W., AND SCHEMINZKY, K. 1922b. Zwei Fälle von Hermaphroditismus verus. Arch. ges. Physiol., **194**, 362–364.

KOPEĆ, S. 1927. Experiments on the dependence of the nuptial hue on the gonads in fish. Biologica Generalis, **3**, 259–280.

KOPSTEIN, F. 1938. Ein Beitrag zur Eierkunde und zur Fortpflanzung der Malaiischen Reptilien. Bull. Raffles Museum, **14**, 81–167.

KRAUS, S. D. 1947. Observations on the mechanism of ovulation in the frog, hen, and rabbit. West. J. Surg., Gynec. & Obst., **55**, 424–437.

KUNTZ, A. 1913. Notes on the habits, morphology of the reproductive organs, and embryology of the viviparous fish, *Gambusia affinis*. Bull. U. S. Bureau Fisheries, **33**, 181–190.

LAGLER, K. F., AND CHIN, M. B. 1951. Ova-testes in the percid fish *Boleosoma n. nigrum* (Rafinesque). Copeia, 99–100.

LAMOTTE, M., AND REY, P. 1954. Existence de Corpora lutea chez un Batracien anoure vivipare, *Nectophrynoïdes occidentalis* Angel; leur évolution morphologique. Compt. rend. Acad. Sc., **238**, 393–395.

LAMOTTE, M., AND TUCHMANN-DUPLESSIS, H. 1948. Structure et transformations gravidiques du tractus génital femelle chez un Anoure vivipare (*Nectophrynoïdes occidentalis* Angel). Compt. rend. Acad. Sc., **226**, 597–599.

LAMOTTE, M., REY, P., AND VILTER, V. 1956. Evolution ovarienne au cours de la gravidité chez un Batracien vivipare (*Nectophrynoïdes occidentalis*). Compt. rend. Soc. biol., **150**, 393–396.

LANTZ, L.-A. 1923. Hermaphroditisme partiel chez *Lacerta saxicola*. Bull. Soc. Zool. France, **48**, 289–290.

LATASTE, F. 1876. Anatomie microscopique de l'oviducte de la cistude d'Europe. Arch. Phys., ser. 2, **3**, 185–196.

LAVENDA, N. 1949. Sexual differences and normal protogynous hermaphroditism in the Atlantic sea bass, *Centropristes striatus*. Copeia, 185–194.

LEDERER, G. 1942. Fortpflanzung und Entwicklung von *Eunectes notaeus* Cope (Boidae). Zool. Anz., **139**, 162–176.

LEIGH-SHARPE, W. H. 1920. The comparative morphology of the secondary sexual characters of elasmobranch fishes. The claspers, clasper siphons, and clasper glands. J. Morphol., **34**, 245–265.

LI, M.-H., AND CHANG, H.-C. 1949. On the release of spermatozoa in male frogs with adrenaline. Chinese J. Physiol., **17**, 201–206.

LING, J. K. 1958. The sea garfish, *Reporhamphus melanochir* (Cuvier and Valenciennes) (Hemiramphidae) in South Australia: breeding, age determination, and growth rate. Australian J. Marine & Freshwater Res., **9**, 60–110.

LIU, C. C. 1935. "The linea masculina," a new secondary sex character in Salientia. J. Morphol., **57**, 131–145.

Liu, C. K. 1944. Sinensia, **15**, 1. (Cited by Bullough, 1947.)

LoBianco. 1908–1909. Notizie biologiche riguardanti specialmente il periodo di maturita sessuale degli animali del golfo di Napoli. Mitt. zool. Sta. Neapel., **19**, 513. (Cited by Hartman, 1934.)

Loyez, M. 1905–1906. Recherches sur le développemente ovarien des oeufs méroblastiques à vitellus nutritif abondant. Arch. anat. microbiol., **8**, 69–397.

Lubosch, W. 1903. Über die Geschlechtsdifferenzierung bei Ammocoetes. Verhandl. Anat. Gesellsch. Vers., 17. (Cited by Okkelberg, 1921.)

Lucien. 1903. Note préliminaire sur les premiers phases de la formation des corps jaunes chez certaines reptiles. Compt. rend. Soc. biol., **55**, 1116–1117.

Ludwig, M., and Rahn, H. 1943. Sperm storage and copulatory adjustment in the prairie rattlesnake. Copeia, 15–18.

Lugli, L. 1955. Azioni sperimentali del progesterone sullo sviluppo delle gonadi e degli organi di Bidder in girini di *Bufo bufo* (L.). Monitore zool. Ital., **63**, 316–330.

MacLeod, J. 1881. Recherches sur la structure et le développement de l'appareil reproducteur femelle des téléostéens. Arch. Biol., **2**, 497–532.

Mahendra, B. C. 1936. Contributions to the bionomics, anatomy, reproduction and development of the Indian house-gecko, *Hemidactylus flaviviridis* Rüppel. I. Proc. Indian Acad. Sc., ser. B, **4**, 250–281.

Mahendra, B. C. 1953. Contributions to the bionomics, anatomy, reproduction and development of the Indian house-gecko, *Hemidactylus flaviviridis* Rüppel. V. The urinogenital system. Proc. Indian Acad. Sc., ser. B, **38**, 215–230.

March, F. 1937. Some hormone effects in Amphibia. Proc. Zool. Soc. London, ser. A, **107**, 603–665.

Marshall, A. J., and Lofts, B. 1956. The Leydig-cell homologue in certain teleost fishes. Nature, London, **177**, 704–705.

Marshall, F. H. A. 1956. The breeding season. In *Marshall's Physiology of Reproduction*, A. S. Parkes, Ed., Vol. I, Part I, pp. 1–42. London: Longmans, Green and Company.

Maschkowzeff, A. 1934. Der Genitalapparat der Acipenseridae. Zool. Jahrb., Abt. Anat. u. Ontog., **58**, 397–414.

Matthews, J. D. 1885. Oviduct in an adult male skate. J. Anat. & Physiol., **19**, 144–149.

Matthews, S. A. 1938. The seasonal cycle in the gonads of Fundulus. Biol. Bull., **75**, 66–74.

Matthey, R. 1927. Intersexualité chez un Tortue (*Emys europaea*). Compt. rend. Soc. biol., **97**, 369.

Matthey, R. 1929. Caractères sexuels secondaires du Lézard mâle (*Lacerta agilis*). Bull. Soc. vaud. Sc. nat., **57**, 71–81.

McIlhenny, E. A. 1935. *The Alligator's Life History*. Boston: Christopher Publishing House.

Mendoza, G. 1936. The ovarian cycle of the viviparous teleost, *Skiffia bilineata*, a member of the family Goodeidae. Anat. Rec., Suppl., **67**, 62.

Mendoza, G. 1937. Structural and vascular changes accompanying the resorption of the proctodaeal processes after birth in the embryos of the Goodeidae, a family of viviparous fishes. J. Morphol., **61**, 95–125.

Mendoza, G. 1940. The reproductive cycle of the viviparous teleost, *Neotoca bilineata*, a member of the family Goodeidae. II. The cyclic changes in the ovarian soma during gestation. Biol. Bull., **78**, 349–365.

Mendoza, G. 1943. The reproductive cycle of the viviparous teleost, *Neotoca bilineata*, a member of the family Goodeidae. IV. The germinal tissue. Biol. Bull., **84**, 87–97.

Mendoza, B. 1956. Adaptations during gestation in the viviparous cyprinodont teleost, *Hubbsina turneri*. J. Morphol., **99**, 73–95.

Mertens, R. 1940. Neuere Beobachtungen über die Fortpflanzung der Schlangen. Wchnschr. Aquar.-Terrark., **37**. (Cited by Volsøe, 1944.)

Metten, H. 1939 Reproduction of the dogfish. Nature, London, **143**, 121–122.

Miller, M. R. 1948. The seasonal histological changes occurring in the ovary, corpus luteum, and testis of the viviparous lizard, *Xantusia vigilis*. Univ. California Publ. Zool., **47**, 197–224.

Miller, M. R. 1951. Some aspects of the life history of the yucca night lizard, *Xantusia vigilis*. Copeia, 114–120.

Miller, M. R. 1954. Further observations on reproduction in the lizard, *Xantusia vigilis*. Copeia, 38–40.

Möbius, K. 1885. Über die Eigenschaften und den Ursprung der Schleimfäden des Seestichlingsnestes. Arch. mikroskop. Anat., **25**, 554–563.

Moens, N. L. I. 1912. Die Peritonealkanäle der Schildkröten und Krokodile. Morphol. Jahrb., **44**, 1–80.

Mohsen, T. 1958. Masculinizing action of pregneninolone on female gonads in the cyprinodont, *Lebistes reticulatus* R. Nature, London, **181**, 1074.

Moszkowska, A. 1932. Etudes endocrinologiques (testicule et hypophyse) chez le *Bombinator*. Bull. biol. France et Belge, **66**, 502–552.

Mršić, W. 1923. Die Spätbefruchtung und deren Einfluss auf Entwicklung und Geschlechtsbildung, experimentell nachgeprüft an der Regenbogenforelle. Arch. mikroskop. Anat. u. Entwicklungsmech., **98**, 129–207.

Mršić, W. 1930. Über das Auftreten intermediärer Stadien bei der Geschlechtsdifferenzierung der Forelle. Arch. Entwicklungsmech. Organ., **123**, 301–332.

Munson, J. P. 1904. Researches on the oogenesis

of the tortoise, *Clemmys marmorata*. Am. J. Anat., **3**, 311–347.

MURRAY, P. D. F., AND BAKER, J. R. 1924. An hermaphrodite dogfish (*Scyliorhinus canicula*). J. Anat. & Physiol., **58**, 335–339.

NANSEN, F. 1887. A protandric hermaphrodite (*Myxine glutinosa*) amongst the vertebrates. Bergens Mus. Aarsb. (Cited by Witschi, 1934.)

NEEDHAM, J. G. 1942. *Biochemistry and Morphogenesis*. Cambridge: University Press.

NEWMAN, H. H. 1907. Spawning behavior and sexual dimorphism in *Fundulus heteroclitus* and allied fish. Biol. Bull., **12**, 314–348.

NEWMAN, H. H. 1908. A significant case of hermaphroditism in fish. Biol. Bull., **15**, 207–214.

NICHOLSON, F. A., AND RISLEY, P. L. 1941. A study of the urogenital systems of *Emys blandingii*, with observations on the occurrence of Mullerian ducts in males. Proc. Iowa Acad. Sc., **47**, 343–360.

NIWA, H. 1955. Effects of castration and administration of methyltestosterone on the nuptial coloration of the medaka, *Oryzias latipes*. Japan. J. Ichthyol., **4**, 193–200.

NOBLE, G. K. 1926. The production of cloacal glands in the adult female *Desmognathus fuscus* by testicular transplants; the change of tooth form in the adult male by castration. Anat. Rec., **34**, 140.

NOBLE, G. K. 1931. *The Biology of the Amphibia*. New York and London: McGraw-Hill Book Company.

NOBLE, G. K. 1934. The hypertrophy of the tactile organs of snakes in correlation with sexual functions. Anat. Rec., suppl., **58**, 3–4.

NOBLE, G. K., AND DAVIS, S. H. 1928. The effect on the dentition and cloaca of testicular transplants in the adult female salamander, *Desmognathus*; the effect of castration on the male. Anat. Rec., **38**, 24.

NOBLE, G. K., AND GREENBERG, B. 1940. Testosterone propionate, a bisexual hormone in the American chameleon. Proc. Soc. Exper. Biol. & Med., **44**, 460–462.

NOBLE, G. K., AND GREENBERG, B. 1941. Effects of seasons, castration and crystalline sex hormones upon the urogenital system and sexual behavior of the lizard (*Anolis carolinensis*). J. Exper. Zool., **88**, 451–479.

NOBLE, G. K., AND KUMPF, K. F. 1937. Sex reversal in the fighting fish, *Betta splendens*. Anat. Rec., Suppl., **70**, 97.

NOBLE, G. K., AND POPE, S. H. 1929. The modification of the cloaca and teeth of the adult salamander, *Desmognathus*, by testicular transplants and by castration. J. Exper. Biol., **6**, 399–411.

OGURO, C. 1956. Some observations on the effect of estrogen upon the liver of the three-spined stickleback, *Gasterosteus aculeatus aculeatus* L. Annot. Zool. Japon., **29**, 19–22.

OKADA, Y. K. 1943. Production of testis-ova in *Oryzias latipes* by estrogenic substances. Proc. Imperial Acad., Tokyo, **19**, 501–504.

OKKELBERG, P. 1914. Hermaphroditism in the brook lamprey. Science, **39**, 478.

OKKELBERG, P. 1921. The early history of the germ cells in the brook lamprey, *Entosphenus wilderi* (Gage), up to and including the period of sex differentiation. J. Morphol., **35**, 1–151.

OSAWA, G. 1897. Beiträge zur Lehre von den Eingeweiden der *Hatteria punctata*. Arch. mikroskop. Anat., **49**, 113–226.

OSAWA, G. 1898. Nachtrag zur Lehre von den Eingeweiden der *Hatteria punctata*. Die weiblichen Geschlechtsorgane. Arch. mikroskop. Anat., **51**, 764–794.

OSLUND, R. M. 1928. Seasonal modifications in testes of vertebrates. Quart. Rev. Biol., **3**, 254–270.

OVIDIUS NASO, P. 1911. Ovidi Halievticon Libri I Fragmentum. Lines 107–108. Lipsiae: Tevbnervs.

OWEN, S. F. 1937. The bitterling fish response to male sex hormones. Endocrinology, **21**, 689–690.

PADOA, E. 1929. Prime osservazioni sugli effetti della lesione sperimentale del testicolo nei Rettilli. Atti Soc. ital. Anat. Monitore Zool., **40**, 444–447.

PADOA, E. 1933. Ricerche sperimentali sui pori femorali e sull'epididimo della lucertola (*Lacerta muralis* Laur.) considerati come caratteri sessuali secondari. Arch. ital. anat. e embriol., **31**, 205–210.

PADOA, E. 1939a. Observations ultérieures sur la différenciation du sexe, normale et modifiée par l'administration d'hormone folliculaire, chez la Truite iridée (*Salmo irideus*). Biomorphosis, **1**, 337–354.

PADOA, E. 1939b. Prime osservazioni sulle gonadi di un Teleosteo ermafrodita (*Hepatus hepatus* L.) trattato con ormone femminile. Monitore Zool. Ital., **50**, 129–132.

PANIGEL, M. 1951a. L'évolution du corps jaune au cours de la gestation chez le lézard *Zootoca vivipara* W. (*Lacerta vivipara*). Ann. Endocrinol., **12**, 206–212.

PANIGEL, M. 1951b. Étude anatomohistologique des corps atrétiques pendant la gestation, chez le lézard *Zootoca vivipara* W. (*Lacerta vivipara* J.). Bull. Soc. Zool. France, **76**, 75–78.

PANIGEL, M. 1953. Rôle des corps jaunes au cours de la gestation chez le Lézard vivipare, *Zootoca vivipara*. Compt. rend. Acad. Sc., **236**, 849–851.

PANIGEL, M. 1956. Contribution à l'étude de l'ovoviviparité chez les reptiles; gestation et parturition chez le lézard vivipare, *Zootoca vivipara*. Ann. Sc. Nat. Zool., **18**, 569–668.

PARKER, G. H. 1931. The passage of sperms and of eggs through the oviducts in terrestrial vertebrates. Philos. Tr. Roy. Soc., ser. B, **219**, 381–419.

PARKER, T. J., AND HASWELL, W. A. 1921. *A Textbook of Zoology*, Vol. II. London: Macmillan Company.

PARKER, W. N., AND BURLEND, T. H. 1909. On

the efferent ducts of the testis in *Chimaera monstrosa*. Anat. Anz., **34**, 331–336.

PEARSON, J. C. 1938. The life history of the striped bass, or rockfish, *Roccus saxatilis* (Walbaum). Bull. Bureau Fisheries, **49**, 825–851.

PELLEGRINI, G. 1925. Sulle modificazione degli elementi interstiziali del testicolo negli animali ad attivita sessuale periodica. Arch. ital. anat. e embriol., **22**, 550–585.

PENHOS, J. C., AND NALLAR, R. 1956. Modification hormonale de la sécrétion de l'oviducte du Crapaud produite par la progestérone. Compt. rend. Soc. biol., **150**, 2023–2024.

PÉREZ, C. 1921. Sur un prétendu tissu interstitiel dans le testicule des Batraciens Urodèles. Compt. rend. Acad. Sc., **172**, 1443–1445.

PESCE, G. 1935. Contributo alla conoscenza del testicolo nei rettili. Boll. Museum Zool. Anat. comp. Genova, **15**. (Cited by Volsøe, 1933.)

PETER, K. 1904. Normentafel zur Entwicklungsgeschichte der Zauneidechse (*Lacerta agilis*). In *Normentafeln zur Entwicklungsgeschichte der Wirbeltiere*, Franz Keibel, Ed., Vol. 4. Jena: Gustav Fischer.

PETTER-ROUSSEAUX, A. 1953. Recherches sur la croissance et le cycle d'activité testiculaire de *Natrix natrix helvetica* (Lacépède). Terre et Vie, 175–223. (Cited by Fox, 1956.)

PHILIPPI, E. 1904. Ein neuer Fall von *Arrhenoidie*. S. B. Naturf. Berlin: Freunde. (Cited by Harms, 1926.)

PHILIPPI, E. 1908. Fortpflanzungsgeschichte der viviparen Teleosteer *Glaridichthys januarius* und *G. decem-maculatus* in ihrem Einfluss auf Lebensweise, makroskopische und mikroskopische Anatomie. Zool. Jahrb., **27**, 1–94.

PICKFORD, G. E., AND ATZ, J. W. 1957. *The Physiology of the Pituitary Gland of Fishes*. New York: New York Zoological Society,

PONSE, K. 1922a. Disparition et récupération des caractères sexuels secondaires mâles par castration et greffe chez Bufo vulgaris. Compt. rend. Soc. physique et hist. nat. Genève, **39**, 144–147.

PONSE, K. 1922b. L'organe de Bidder joue-t-il un rôle dans le déterminisme des caractères sexuels secondaires du crapaud? Compt. rend. Soc. Physique et hist. nat. Genève, **39**, 147–150.

PONSE, K. 1930. La notion de territoire et les excroissances digitales du crapaud. Arch. Entwicklungsmech. Organ., **121**, 755–769.

PONSE, K. 1949. *La Différenciation du Sexe et L'intersexualité chez les Vertébrés*. Lausanne: F. Rouge.

PORTO, A. 1941. Sôbre a presença de progesterona no corpo amarelo de serpentes ovovivíparas. Mem. Inst. Butantan, **15**, 27–30.

POTTER, G. D., AND HOAR, W. S. 1954. The presence of androgens in chum salmon (*Oncorhynchus keta* Walbaum). J. Fisheries Res. Bd. Canada, **11**, 63–68.

PURSER, G. L. 1937. Succession of broods of *Lebistes*. Nature, London, **140**, 155.

PURSER, G. L. 1938. Reproduction in *Lebistes reticulatus*. Quart. J. Microscop. Sc., n. ser., **81**, 151–157.

QUERNER, H. 1956. Der Einfluss von Steroidhormonen auf die Gonaden juveniler Poeciliiden. Biol. Zentralbl., **75**, 28–51.

RAHN, H. 1938. The corpus luteum of reptiles. Anat. Rec., suppl., **72**, 55.

RAHN, H. 1939. Structure and function of placenta and corpus luteum in viviparous snakes. Proc. Soc. Exper. Biol. & Med., **40**, 381–382.

RAHN, H. 1940a. Sperm viability in the uterus of the garter snake, *Thamnophis*. Copeia, 109–115.

RAHN, H. 1940b. The physiology of gestation in viviparous snakes. J. Colorado-Wyoming Acad. Sc., **2**, 45–46.

RAHN, H. 1942. The reproductive cycle of the prairie rattler. Copeia, 233–240.

RASQUIN, P., AND HAFTER, E. 1951. Age changes in the testis of the teleost, *Astyanax mexicanus*. J. Morphol., **89**, 397–407.

RATHKE, H. 1824. Über die Geschlechtstheile der Fische. Neueste Schriften Naturf. ges. Danzig, **1**. (Cited by Stromsten, 1931.)

RATHKE, H. 1839. *Entwicklungsgeschichte der Natter*. Königsberg.

RATHKE, H. 1848. *Über die Entwicklung der Schildkröten*. Braunschweig. (Cited by Braun, 1877).

REED, R. J. 1954. Hermaphroditism in the rosyface shiner, *Notropis rubellus*. Copeia, 293–294.

REESE, A. M. 1915. *The Alligator and Its Allies*. New York and London: G. P. Putnam's Sons.

REGAMEY, J. 1931. Un cas d'intersexualité chez le lézard vert (*Lacerta viridis*, Daudin). Bull. Soc. vaud. Sc. nat., **57**, 311–312.

REGAMEY, J. 1933. Les différences sexuelles du cloaque chez le lézard *Lacerta agilis* Linné. Bull. Soc. vaud. Sc. nat., **58**, 185–186.

REGAMEY, J. 1935. Les caractères sexuels du Lézard (*Lacerta agilis* L.). Rev. Suisse Zool., **42**, 87–168.

REGAUD, C., AND POLICARD, A. 1903a. Sur l'alternance fonctionnelle et sur les phénomènes histologiques de la sécrétion, dans le deuxième segment du tube urinipare, chez les Serpents. Compt. rend. Soc. biol., **55**, 894–896.

REGAUD, C., AND POLICARD, A. 1903b. Variations sexuelles de structure dans le segment préterminal du tube urinifère de quelques Ophidiens. Compt. rend. Soc. biol., **55**, 216–218.

REGAUD, C., AND POLICARD, A. 1903c. Sur variations sexuelles de structures dans le rein des Reptiles. Compt. rend. Soc. biol., **55**, 973–974.

REGAUD, C., AND POLICARD, A. 1903d. Recherches sur la structure du rein de quelques Ophidiens. Arch. anat. microscop., **6**, 191–282.

RÉGNIER, M.-T. 1938. Contribution à l'étude de la sexualité des cyprinodontes vivipares (*Xiphophorus helleri*, *Lebistes reticulatus*). Bull. biol., **72**, 385–493.

RÉGNIER, M.-T. 1939. Action du propionate du

testostérone sur les gonades de quelques Cyprinodontes vivipares. Compt. rend. Acad. Sc., **208**, 2109–2110.

RÉGNIER, M.-T. 1941. Action androgène de la prégnéninolone sur les caractères sexuels secondaires du *Lebistes reticulatus*. Compt. rend. Acad. Sc., **213**, 537–538.

RÉGNIER, M.-T. 1942. Masculinization des femelles de *Lebistes reticulatus* sous l'influence de la prégnéninolone. Compt. rend. Soc. biol., **136**, 202–203.

REISS, P. 1923a. Le cycle testiculaire du lézard. Compt. rend. Soc. biol., **88**, 447–448.

REISS, P. 1923b. Sur les caractères sexuels secondaires chez le Lézard mâle. Compt. rend. Soc. biol., **88**, 445–447.

REYNOLDS, A. E. 1943. The normal seasonal reproductive cycle in the male *Eumeces fasciatus* together with some observations on the effects of castration and hormone administration. J. Morphol., **72**, 331–377.

RISLEY, P. L. 1933a. Observations on the natural history of the common musk turtle, *Sternotherus odoratus* (Latreille). Papers Michigan Acad. Sc., **17**, 685–711.

RISLEY, P. L. 1933b. Contributions on the development of the reproductive system in the musk turtle, *Sternotherus odoratus* (Latreille). I. The embryonic origin and migration of the primordial germ cells. Ztschr. Zellforsch. mikroskop. Anat., **18**, 459–492.

RISLEY, P. L. 1933c. Contributions on the development of the reproductive system in the musk turtle, *Sternotherus odoratus* (Latreille). II. Gonadogenesis and sex differentiation. Ztschr. Zellforsch. mikroskop. Anat., **18**, 493–543.

RISLEY, P. L. 1938. Seasonal changes in the testis of the musk turtle, *Sternotherus odoratus* L. J. Morphol., **63**, 301–317.

RISLEY, P. L. 1940. Intersexual gonads of turtle embryos following injection of male sex hormone. J. Morphol., **67**, 439–453.

RISLEY, P. L. 1941a. Some observations on hermaphroditism in turtles. J. Morphol., **68**, 101–121.

RISLEY, P. L. 1941b. A comparison of effects of gonadotropic and sex hormones on the urogenital systems of juvenile terrapins. J. Exper. Zool., **87**, 477–515.

ROBINSON, E. J., AND RUGH, R. 1943. The reproductive processes of the fish, *Oryzias latipes*. Biol. Bull., **84**, 115–125.

ROLLINAT, R. 1898. Sur l'accouplement des Ophidiens d'Europe à la fin de l'été ou au commencement de l'automne. Compt. rend. Soc. biol., **50**, 56–57.

ROLLINAT, R. 1946. *La Vie des Reptiles de la France Centrale*. Paris: Delagrave. (Cited by Fox, 1956.)

RONDELET, G. 1558. *L'histoire entière des Poissons*. Lion: Bonhome.

ROWAN, W. 1929. A hermaphrodite spiny dogfish (*Squalus sucklei*). Proc. Zool. Soc. London, 441–443.

RUGH, R. 1935. Ovulation in the frog. II. Follicular rupture to fertilization. J. Exper. Zool., **71**, 163–193.

SACCHI, M. 1888. Contribution à l'histologie de l'oviducte des Sauropsides. Arch. ital. biol., **9**, 267–285.

SAMUEL, M. 1944. Studies on the corpus luteum in *Enhydrina schistosa* (Daudin) and *Hydrophis cyanocinctus* (Daudin) of the Madras Coast. Indian Acad. Sc. Proc., ser. B, **20**, 143–174.

SANFELICE, F. 1888. Intorno alla rigenerazione del testicolo. Boll. Soc. naturalisti, Napoli, **2**, 232–247.

SATHYANESAN, A. G. 1957. Occurrence of oocyte in adult testis [of] fish *Barbua stigma* (Cur. and Val.). Sc. & Culture, **23**, 203.

SCHAEFER, F. 1901. Über die Schenkelporen der Lacertilier. Zool. Anz., **24**, 308–309.

SCHAEFER, F. 1902. Über die Schenkeldrüsen der Eidechsen. Arch. Naturgesch., **1**, 27–64.

SCHMIDT, J. 1922. The breeding places of the eel. Philos. Tr. Roy. Soc., ser. B, **211**, 179–208.

SCHMIDT, K. P. 1938. A note on the linea masculina of frogs. Copeia, 199.

SCHOOF, F. 1888. Zur Kenntniss des Urogenitalsystems der Saurier. Arch. Naturgesch., **1**, 62–80.

SCHULTZ, L. P. 1931. Hermaphroditism in the striped bass. Copeia, 64.

SCOTT, J. L. 1944. The effects of steroids on the skeleton of the poeciliid fish *Lebistes reticulatus*. Zoologica, **29**, 49–52.

SCOTT, M. I. H. 1928. Sobre el Desarrollo Intraovarial de *Fitzroyia lineata* (Jen) Berg. Anal. Museo. Hist. Nat. Buenos Aires, 34. (Cited by Turner, 1933.)

SCRUGGS, W. M. 1951. The epithelial components and their seasonal changes in the pituitary gland of the carp (*Cyprinus carpio*, L.) and goldfish (*Carassius auratus*, L.). J. Morphol., **88**, 441–469.

SELF, J. T. 1940. Notes on the sex cycle of *Gambusia affinis affinis*, and on its habits and relation to mosquito control. Am. Midland Naturalist, **23**, 393–398.

SHANN, E. W. 1923. The embryonic development of the porbeagle shark *Lamna cornubica*. Proc. Zool. Soc. London, **1**, 161–171.

SHAPIRO, H. A. 1939. Ovulation in *Xenopus laevis* induced by certain steroids. South African J. M. Sc., **4**, 21–31.

SHAPIRO, H. A., AND ZWARENSTEIN, H. 1933. Metabolic changes associated with endocrine activity and the reproductive cycle in *Xenopus laevis*. I. The effects of gonadectomy and hypophysectomy on the calcium content of the serum. J. Exper. Biol., **10**, 186–195.

SHAPIRO, H. A., AND ZWARENSTEIN, H. 1937. Effects of progesterone and testosterone on Xenopus and on its excised ovary. J. Physiol., **89**, 38.

SIMKINS, C. S., AND ASANA, J. 1930. Development of the sex glands in *Calotes*. I. Cytology and growth of the gonads prior to hatching. Quart. J. Microscop. Sc., **74**, 133–149.

SMEDLEY, N. 1930. Oviparity in a sea-snake (*Laticauda colubrina*). Nature, London, **126**, 312–313.

SMEDLEY, N. 1931. Ovoviviparity in sea snakes. Nature, London, **127**, 13.

SMITH, C. L. 1955. Reproduction in female Amphibia. In *Comparative Physiology of Reproduction*, I. Chester Jones and P. Eckstein, Eds. pp. 39–55. Cambridge: University Press.

SMITH, G., AND SCHUSTER, E. 1912. Studies in the experimental analysis of sex. VIII. On the effects of the removal and transplantation of the gonad in the frog (*Rana fusca*). Quart. J. Microscop. Sc., **57**, 439–471.

SMITH, J. A. 1870. Notice of true hermaphroditism in the codfish (*Morrhua vulgaris*), and in the herring (*Clupea harengus*). J. Anat. & Physiol., **4**, 256–258.

SMITH, M. 1930. Ovoviviparity in sea snakes. Nature, London, **126**, 568.

SMITT, F. A. 1882. Description d'un Hareng hermaphrodite. Arch. Biol., **3**, 259–274.

SOUTHWELL, T. 1902. On a hermaphrodite example of the herring (*Clupea harengus*). Ann. Nat. Hist., ser. 7, **9**, 195–196.

SPURWAY, H. 1957. Hermaphroditism with self-fertilization, and the monthly extrusion of unfertilized eggs, in the viviparous fish *Lebistes reticulatus*. Nature, London, **180**, 1248–1251.

ST. AMANT, L. 1941. The effect of castration upon the development of the gonopodium in *Gambusia*. Ph.D. thesis, Northwestern University. (Cited by Turner, 1942.)

STEFAN, Y. 1958. Étude préliminaire de l'action de quelques oestrogènes et androgènes sur le tractus génital de la jeune tortue d'eau *Emys leprosa* S. Ann. Endocrinol., **19**, 481–506.

STEINACH, E. 1894. Untersuchungen zur vergleichenden Physiologie der männlichen Geschlechtsorgane insbesondere der accessorischen Geschlechtsdrüsen. Arch. ges. Physiol., **56**, 304–338.

STEPHAN, F., AND CLAVERT, J. 1938. Sur la structure du testicule du poisson *Lebistes reticulatus* en rapport avec le déterminisme de ses caractères sexuels secondaires. Compt. rend. Soc. biol., **127**, 438–440.

STEPHAN, P. 1901. À propos de l'hermaphroditisme de certains Poissons. In *Association français pour l'Avancement des Sciences*, 30ᵉ Session, Vol. I, p. 142; Vol. II, pp. 554–570.

STEWART, C. 1894a. On a hermaphrodite trout, *Salmo fario*. Proc. Linnean Soc., Zool., London, **24**, 69–70.

STEWART, C. 1894b. On a hermaphrodite mackerel, *Scomber scomber*. Proc. Linnean Soc., Zool., London, **24**, 70–71.

STICKEL, W. H., AND STICKEL, L. F. 1946. Sexual dimorphism in the pelvic spurs of *Engyrus*. Copeia, 10–12.

STIEVE, H. 1933. Zwischenzellen. In *Handbuch der vergleichenden Anatomie der Wirbeltiere*, L. Bolk, Ed., Vol. VI. Berlin and Vienna: Urban & Schwarzenburg.

STOLK, A. 1951a. Histo-endocrinological analysis of gestation phenomena in the cyprinodont *Lebistes reticulatus* Peters. I. Thyroid activity during pregnancy. Konink. Nederl. Akad. Wetensch., ser. C, **54**, 550–557.

STOLK, A. 1951b. Histo-endocrinological analysis of gestation phenomena in the cyprinodont *Lebistes reticulatus* Peters. II. The corpus luteum cycle during pregnancy. Konink. Nederl. Akad. Wetensch., **54**, 558–565.

STOLK, A. 1958. Pathological parthenogenesis in viviparous toothcarps. Nature, London, **181**, 1660.

STRAWN, K. 1958. Life history of the pygmy seahorse, *Hippocampus zosterae* Jordan and Gilbert, at Cedar Key, Florida. Copeia, 16–22.

STROMSTEN, F. A. 1931. The development of the gonads in the gold fish, *Carassius auratus* (L.). Univ. Iowa Studies Nat. Hist., **13**, 1–45.

STUHLMAN, F. L. 1887. Zur Kenntnis des Ovariums der Aalmutter (*Zoarces viviparus* Cuv.). Abh. Naturwiss. Ver. Hamburg, **10**, 1. (Cited by Turner, 1933.)

SUCHOW, G. F. 1929. Untersuchungen über die Anzahl der Schenkelporen bei *Lacerta agilis*. Zool. Anz., **71**, 53–56.

SZÜSZ, F. 1934. Untersuchungen mit Bitterlingen zur Erkennung der Schwangerschaft. Monatsschr. Geburtsh. u. Gynäk., **96**, 292–296.

TAKEWAKI, K., AND FUKUDA, S. 1935a. Effect of gonadectomy and testicular transplantation on the kidney and epididymis of a lizard, *Takydromus tachydromoides*. Fac. Sc., Imp. Univ. Tokyo, Sec. IV, **4**, 63–76.

TAKEWAKI, K., AND FUKUDA, S. 1935b. Viability of epididymal spermatozoa in unilaterally and bilaterally castrated lizards. Fac. Sc., Imp. Univ. Tokyo, Sec. IV, **4**, 77–81.

TAKEWAKI, K., AND HATTA, K. 1941. Effect of gonadectomy and hypophysectomy on the kidney and genital tract of a snake, *Natrix tigrina tigrina*. Annot. Zool. Japon., **20**, 4–8.

TAVOLGA, M. C. 1949. Differential effects of estradiol, estradiol benzoate and pregneninolone on *Platypoecilus maculatus*. Zoologica, **34**, 215–237.

TAVOLGA, W. N., AND RUGH, R. 1947. Development of the platyfish, *Platypoecilus maculatus*. Zoologica, **32**, 1–15.

TAYLER, N. 1918. A case of hermaphroditism in a lizard, *Lacerta viridis*. Proc. Zool. Soc. London, 223–230.

TAYLOR, A. B. 1948. Experimental sex reversal in the red swordtail hybrid *Xiphophorus-Platypoecilus*. Tr. Am. Microscop. Soc., **67**, 155–164.

TE WINKEL, L. E. 1950. Notes on ovulation, ova, and early development in the smooth dogfish, *Mustelus canis*. Biol. Bull., **99**, 474–486.

THIEBOLD, J. J. 1954. Étude préliminaire de l'action des hormones sexuelles sur la morphogenèse des voies génitales chez *Scylliorhinus canicula* L. Bull. Biol. France et Belge, **88**, 130–145.

THOMAS, A. P. W. 1890. Preliminary note on the development of the tuatara (*Sphenodon punctatum*). Proc. Roy. Soc. London, **48**, 152–156.

Thompson, D. W. (translator). 1910. Historia animalium. In *The Works of Aristotle*, J. A. Smith and W. D. Ross, Eds. Vol. IV, Book IV, II, 538a; Book VI, XIII, 567a. Oxford: Clarendon Press.

Ting, H.-P., and Boring, A. M. 1939. The seasonal cycle in the reproductive organs of the Chinese toad *Bufo bufo* and the pond frog *Rana nigromaculata*. Peking Nat. Hist. Bull., **14**, 49–80.

Tölg, F. 1905. Beiträge zur Kenntniss drüsenartiger Epidermoidal-Organe der Eidechsen. Arb. Zool. Inst. Wien., 15. (Cited by Regamey, 1935).

Tozawa, T. 1929. Experiments on the development of the nuptial coloration and pearl organs of the Japanese bitterling. Folia Anat. Japon., **7**, 407–417.

Trapido, H. 1940. Mating time and sperm viability in *Storeria*. Copeia, 107–109.

Tribondeau. 1902. Le tube urinifère des serpents contient trois espèces distinctes d'épithélium sécrétoire. Compt. rend. Soc. biol., **54**, 677–679.

Turner, C. L. 1919. The seasonal cycle in the spermary of the perch. J. Morphol., **32**, 681–711.

Turner, C. L. 1927. A case of hermaphroditism in the perch. Anat. Rec., **37**, 186.

Turner, C. L. 1933. Viviparity superimposed upon ovoviviparity in the Goodeidae, a family of cyprinodont teleost fishes of the Mexican plateau. J. Morphol., **55**, 207–251.

Turner, C. L. 1937a. Reproductive cycles and superfetation in poeciliid fishes. Biol. Bull., **72**, 145–164.

Turner, C. L. 1937b. The trophotaeniae of the Goodeidae, a family of viviparous cyprinodont fishes. J. Morphol., **61**, 495–523.

Turner, C. L. 1938a. The reproductive cycle of *Brachyraphis episcopi*, an ovoviviparous poeciliid fish, in the natural tropical habitat. Biol. Bull., **75**, 56–65.

Turner, C. L. 1938b. Histological and cytological changes in the ovary of *Cymatogaster aggregatus* during gestation. J. Morphol., **62**, 351–373.

Turner, C. L. 1938c. Adaptation for viviparity in embryos and ovary of *Anableps anableps*. J. Morphol., **62**, 323–349.

Turner, C. L. 1940a. Pseudoamnion, pseudochorion, and follicular pseudoplacenta in poeciliid fishes. J. Morphol., **67**, 59–89.

Turner, C. L. 1940b. Follicular pseudoplacenta and gut modifications in anablepid fishes. J. Morphol., **67**, 91–105.

Turner, C. L. 1940c. Superfetation in viviparous cyprinodont fishes. Copeia, 88–91.

Turner, C. L. 1941a. Morphogenesis of the gonopodium in *Gambusia affinis affinis*. J. Morphol., **69**, 161–185.

Turner, C. L. 1941b. Gonopodial characteristics produced in the anal fins of females of *Gambusia affinis affinis* by treatment with ethinyl testosterone. Biol. Bull., **80**, 371–383.

Turner, C. L. 1942a. Sexual dimorphism in the pectoral fin of Gambusia and the induction of the male character in the female by androgenic hormones. Biol. Bull., **83**, 389–400.

Turner, C. L. 1942b. A quantitative study of the effects of different concentrations of ethynyl testosterone and methyl testosterone in the production of gonopodia in females of *Gambusia affinis*. Physiol. Zool., **15**, 263–280.

Turner, C. L. 1942c. Morphogenesis of the gonopodial suspensorium in *Gambusia affinis* and the induction of male suspensorial characters in the female by androgenic hormones. J. Exper. Zool., **91**, 167–193.

Turner, C. L. 1946. A case of hermaphroditism in the cutthroat trout. Nat. Hist. Miscellanea, Chicago Acad. Sc., 1–2.

Turner, C. L. 1947. Viviparity in teleost fishes. Scient. Monthly, **65**, 508–518.

Valle, J. R., and Souza, P. R. 1942. Observações sôbre o sistema endócrino dos Ofídios. O corpo amarelo nas serpentes ovovivíparas não venenosas. Rev. Brasil. Biol., **2**, 81–88.

Valle, J. R., and Valle, L. A. R. 1943. Gonadal hormones in snakes. Science, **97**, 400.

Vallowe, H. H. 1953. Some physiological aspects of reproduction in *Xiphophorus maculatus*. Biol. Bull., **104**, 240–249.

Vallowe, H. H. 1957. Sexual differentiation in the teleost fish, *Xiphophorus helleri*, as modified by experimental treatment. Biol. Bull., **112**, 422–429.

van den Broek, A. J. P. 1933. Gonaden und Ausführungsgänge. In *Handbuch der vergleichenden Anatomie der Wirbeltiere*, L. Bolk, Ed. Vol. 6, pp. 1–154. Berlin & Vienna: Urban & Schwarzenberg.

van den Broek, A. J. P., van Oordt, G. J., and Hirsch, G. C. 1938. Harnorgane. In *Handbuch der vergleichenden Anatomie der Wirbeltiere*, L. Bolk, Ed., Vol. 5, pp. 683–894. Berlin and Vienna: Urban & Schwarzenberg.

Van der Stricht, O. 1893. La signification des cellules épithéliales de l'épididyme de *Lacerta vivipara*. Compt. rend. Soc. biol., **45**, 799–801.

van der Veen, H. E., and Duyvené de Wit, J. J. 1951. On the artificial induction of ovipositor growth in the bitterling (*Rhodeus amarus* Bl.). IV. The influence of body-fluids in the response of the ovipositor to progesterone. Acta endocrinol., **6**, 341–350.

van Koersveld, E. 1948. The value of the bitterling test for the estimation of steroid hormones. Acta brev. neerl. Physiol., **16**, 66–69.

van Oordt, G. J. 1923. Secondary sex characters and testis of the ten-spined stickleback (*Gasterosteus pungitius* L.). Konink. Nederl. Acad. Wetensch., **26**, 309–314.

van Oordt, G. J. 1924. Die Veränderungen des Hodens während des Auftretens der sekundären Geschlechtsmerkmale bei Fischen. I. *Gasterosteus pungitius* L. Arch. mikroskop. Anat. Entwicklungsmech., **102**, 379–405.

van Oordt, G. J. 1925. The relation between the development of the secondary sex characters and the structure of the testis in the teleost

Xiphophorus helleri Heckel. Brit. J. Exper. Biol., **3**, 43–59.

VAN OORDT, G. J. 1930. Zur mikroskopischen Anatomie der Ovariotestes von Serranus und Sargus (Teleostei). Ztschr. mikroskop.-anat. Forsch., **19**, 1–17.

VAN OORDT, G. J., AND KLOMP, H. 1946. Effects of oestrone and gonadotrophin administration in the male toad (*Bufo bufo*). Konink. Nederl. Akad. Wetensch., **49**, 565–570.

VAN OORDT, G. J., AND VAN OORDT, P. G. W. J. 1955. The regulation of spermatogenesis in the frog. In *The Comparative Physiology of Reproduction and the Effects of Sex Hormones in Vertebrates*, I. Chester Jones and P. Eckstein, Eds., Cambridge: University Press.

VAN WIJHE, J. W. 1881. Bijdragen tot de kennis van het Urogenitaalsysteem der Reptilien. Tijdschr. Nederl. Dierkund. Vereen., **5**, 111–120.

VAUPEL, J. 1929. The spermatogenesis of *Lebistes reticulatus*. J. Morphol., **47**, 555–587.

VAYSSIÈRE, A., AND QUINTARET, G. 1914. Sur un cas d'hermaphrodisme d'un *Scyllium stellare* L. Compt. rend. Acad. Sc., **158**, 2013–2014.

VIVIEN, J. H. 1938. Sur l'existence de glandes annexes du tractus génital chez le mâle de *Gobius paganellus* L. Compt. rend. Acad. Sc., **206**, 938–940.

VOGT, C. 1882. Notice sur un hareng hermaphrodite. Arch. Biol., **3**, 255–258.

VOLSØE, H. 1944. Structure and seasonal variation of the male reproductive organs of *Vipera berus* (L.). Spolia Zool. Mus. Hauniensis, **5**, 6–172.

VON LEYDIG, F. 1853. *Anatomisch-histologische Untersuchungen über Fische und Reptilien*. Berlin. (Cited by Braun, 1877.)

VON LEYDIG, F. 1857. *Lehrbuch der Histologie der Menschen und der Wirbeltiere*. Frankfurt am Main. (Cited by Stieve, 1933.)

VON LEYDIG, F. 1872. *Die in Deutschland lebenden Arten der Saurier*. Tübingen: H. Laupp.

VON MIHÁLKOVICS, G. 1885. Untersuchungen über die Entwicklung des Harn- und Geschlechtsapparates der Amnioten. Internat. Mschr. Anat. Physiol., **2**, 41–62, 65–106, 284–339, 347–385, 387–433, 435–485.

WALDEYER, W. 1870. Eierstock und Ei. Ein Beitrag zur Anatomie und Entwicklungsgeschichte der Sexualorgane. Leipzig: Wilhelm Engelmann.

WALLACE, W. 1903. Observations on ovarian ova and follicles in certain teleostean and elasmobranch fishes. Quart. J. Microscop. Sc., **47**, 161–213.

WARD, J. W. 1957. The reproduction and early development of the sea catfish, *Galeichthys felis*, in the Biloxi (Mississippi) Bay. Copeia, 295–298.

WATERS, A. J. 1940. Some hormonal effects on the sexually dimorphic kidneys of *Thamnophis r. radix*. J. Tennessee Acad. Sc., **15**, 412.

WEEKES, H. C. 1927a. A note on reproductive phenomena in some lizards. Proc. Linnean Soc. New South Wales, **52**, 25–32.

WEEKES, H. C. 1927b. Placentation and other phenomena in the scincid lizard *Lygosoma* (*Hinulia*) *quoyi*. Proc. Linnean Soc. New South Wales, **52**, 499–554.

WEEKES, H. C. 1929. On placentation in reptiles. I. Proc. Linnean Soc. New South Wales, **54**, 34–60.

WEEKES, H. C. 1930. On placentation in reptiles. II. Proc. Linnean Soc. New South Wales, **55**, 550–576.

WEEKES, H. C. 1934. The corpus luteum in certain oviparous and viviparous reptiles. Proc. Linnean Soc. New South Wales, **59**, 380–391.

WEEKES, H. C. 1935. A review of placentation among reptiles with particular regard to the function and evolution of the placenta. Proc. Zool. Soc. London, 625–645.

WEICHERT, C. K. 1945. Seasonal variation in the mental gland and reproductive organs of the male *Eurycea bislineata*. Copeia, 78–84.

WEISEL, G. F. 1943. A histological study of the testes of the sockeye salmon (*Oncorhynchus nerka*). J. Morphol., **73**, 207–229.

WEISEL, G. F. 1949. The seminal vesicles and testes of *Gillichthys*, a marine teleost. Copeia, 101–110.

WEISMAN, A. I., MISHKIND, D. I., KLEINER, I. S., AND COATES, C. W. 1937. Estrogenic hormones in the ovaries of swordfish. Endocrinology, **21**, 413–414.

WIEDERSHEIM, R. 1886. *Elements of the Comparative Anatomy of Vertebrates*. London: Macmillan Company.

WINGE, Ö. 1937. Succession of broods in *Lebistes*. Nature, London, **140**, 467.

WOLF, O. M. 1928. The effect of mammalian follicular extract on the oviducts of the frog (*Rana pipiens* Shreber). Anat. Rec., suppl., **41**, 41.

WOLF, O. M. 1939. The effect of testosterone propionate injections into castrate male frogs, *Rana pipiens*. Anat. Rec., suppl., **75**, 55.

WOODBURY, M., AND WOODBURY, A. M. 1945. Life-history studies of the sagebrush lizard *Sceloporus g. graciosus* with special reference to cycles in reproduction. Herpetologica, **2**, 175–196.

WOOD-MASON, J., AND ALCOCK, A. 1891. Further observations on the gestation of Indian rays; being natural history notes from H. M. Indian Marine Survey Steamer "Investigator," Commander R. F. Hoskyn, R. N., Commanding. Proc. Roy. Soc. London, **50**, 202–209.

WOODWARD, S. F. 1933. A few notes on the persistence of active spermatozoa in the African night-adder, *Causus rhombeatus*. Proc. Zool. Soc. London, 189–190.

WOTIZ, H. H., BOTTICELLI, C., HISAW, F. L., JR., AND RINGLER, I. 1958. Identification of estradiol-17β from dogfish ova (*Squalus suckleyi*). J. Biol. Chem., **231**, 589–592.

WYMAN, J. 1854. Observation on the development of *Anableps gronovii*, a viviparous fish from

Surinam. Boston J. Nat. Hist., **6,** 432–443. (Cited by Turner, 1933.)

YAMAMOTO, T. 1953. Artificially induced sex-reversal in genotypic males of the medaka (*Oryzias latipes*). J. Exper. Zool., **123,** 571–594.

YAMAMOTO, T. 1957. Estrone-induced intersex of genetic male in the medaka, *Oryzias latipes*. J. Fac. Sc. Hokkaido Univ., ser. VI, Zool., **13,** 440–444.

YAMAMOTO, T. 1958. Artificial induction of functional sex-reversal in genotypic females of the medaka (*Oryzias latipes*). J. Exper. Zool., **137,** 227–263.

YARRELL, W. 1845. Note on the herring (*Clupea Harengus*). Proc. Zool. Soc. London, **13,** 91.

ZAHL, P. A., AND DAVIS, D. D. 1932. Effects of gonadectomy on the secondary sexual characters in the ganoid fish, *Amia calva*. J. Exper. Zool., **63,** 291–309.

ZARNIK, B. 1910. Vergleichende Studien über den Bau der Niere von Echidna und der Reptilienniere. Jena Ztschr. Naturwiss., **46,** 113–224.

18

ENDOCRINOLOGY OF REPRODUCTION IN BIRDS

Ari van Tienhoven, Ph.D.

ASSOCIATE PROFESSOR OF AVIAN PHYSIOLOGY, DEPARTMENT OF
POULTRY HUSBANDRY, NEW YORK STATE COLLEGE OF AGRICULTURE,
CORNELL UNIVERSITY, ITHACA, NEW YORK

I. Introduction

The fascination of avian reproduction with the accompanying migration over great distances, the majestic flight of a flock of geese, the reproduction of penguins at low temperatures in uninhabitable wastes of the antarctic, all these justify a consideration of the endocrinology of avian reproduction. So little is known, however, about the factors controlling the migrations and of the maturation of the gonads of wild birds. Most of the author's experience has been gained by the study of the chicken, which by selection has become almost a zoologic monstrosity, but nevertheless has been a useful experimental animal. In writing this chapter, the author has tried to consider the literature on the subject of avian-sexual-endocrinology both for domestic and nondomestic birds. His aim has been to give both their fair due. The absence of considerations of the behavioral aspects of reproduction has been deliberate in view of the chapters in this book devoted to that subject.

II. The Male

A. THE TESTIS

1. Anatomy

Aristotle made the observation that the avian testis has a remarkable capacity for growth, as may be deduced from his statement: "So also the testicles of birds are either small or entirely invisible when not excited, but when urged by desire they become very large; this is so remarkable in pigeons and partridges that some persons have supposed that they had no testicles during winter."

Unlike most female birds, the avian male has two well developed gonads, of which the left is usually the larger one. This fact was observed in 1789 by Tannenberg and later confirmed for the sparrow, *Passer domesticus* (Etzold, 1891), and many other species (Domm, 1939). Exceptions are the pigeon, *Columba livia* (Riddle, 1918), and the turkey, *Meleagris gallopavo* (Law and Kosin, 1958), in which the right testis is larger. The difference in testicular size is not a reflection of lesser activity, for Macartney (1942) established that the number of mitotic divisions was larger in the right than in the left testis of the fowl.

The testes are suspended in the body cavity from the body wall by the short mesorchium. The exposure to the high internal temperature (40.5 to 41.6°C. according to Williams, 1958a) does not affect spermatogenesis adversely, although in mammals such temperatures would cause degeneration of the seminiferous tubules (Moore, 1939). In order to account for this phenomenon Cowles and Nordstrom (1946) proposed, without experimental evidence, that the abdominal air sacs might act as a cooling mechanism for the testes. However, Williams (1958a) found that the surface temperature of the testes (41.30°C.) was the same as the mean body temperature, and, what was new, that the exposure of the testis to lower temperatures (38.60° to 40.26°C.), by transplantation under the skin, caused an acceleration in spermatogenesis in the testes of young cockerels. On the other hand, if pieces of testes were transferred to saline with temperatures of 44.4° and 43.3°C., before transplantation, destruction of the germinal epithelium occurred (Williams, 1958b), the destruction being roughly proportional to the degree of heat used. Exposure to saline of body temperature had no effect. These results seem to indicate that lower-than-body temperatures are beneficial for spermato-

genesis, as in the mammal, but that the threshold at which higher temperatures interfere with spermatogenesis is higher in birds. Indirect evidence for the beneficial effect on spermatogenesis of lower temperature is also found in Riley's (1937) investigation of the diurnal rhythm of mitotic activity in the testes of the house sparrow. Maximal mitotic activity coincided with the lowest body temperature. Macartney (1942) could, however, not confirm these observations for the domestic fowl. The more direct experimental evidence of Williams (1958a, b) seems to confirm Riley's hypothesis.

The testis is surrounded by the *tunica albuginea*. In seasonally breeding birds this is replaced at the end of each breeding season by a new *tunica* which forms under the old one. Enclosed by the *tunica albuginea* are the seminiferous tubules and in the spaces between them the interstitial cells.

2. The Interstitium and Its Secretions

The cells of Leydig originate in the sexual cords of the embryonic gonad and migrate to the intertubular spaces (Benoit, 1950a). Several lines of evidence show that the Leydig cells secrete the androgenic hormone. In brief the evidence is that: (1) In hypophysectomized cocks the comb can be maintained only when the Leydig cells are histologically active (Nalbandov, Meyer and McShan, 1946, 1951). (2) Selective destruction of the germinal epithelium by x-rays does not affect comb size (Benoit, 1950a). (3) When parts of testes regenerate after castration, one sometimes finds tissue without Leydig cells but with Sertoli cells; in other cases Leydig cells are encountered but there are no tubules. On the basis of such dissociation, Benoit (1950a) concluded that Sertoli cells do not secrete androgens, whereas Leydig cells do. (4) Kumaran and Turner (1949a) observed the presence of birefringent crystals in the Leydig cells, suggesting the production of the hormone or its precursor in these cells. The concentration of the birefringent material increased with increasing age of young cockerels. Such observations are consistent with the increased rate of secretion of the hormone as shown by gradually increasing comb size.

Breneman and Mason (1951) estimated the cumulative androgen secretion of White Leghorn cockerels between the age of 10 and 40 days as equivalent to 614.90 μg. testosterone propionate (TP) for the 30-day period. Such a high rate of secretion in an immature male indicates early secretory activity of the Leydig cells and supports the observations of Kumaran and Turner (1949a).

The response of the comb to androgen administration is influenced by a number of variables:

1. Dorfman (1950) investigated the sensitivity of the comb of baby chicks to various doses of androgen and found that, if the sensitivity of the White Leghorn is taken as 100 per cent, the Rhode Island Red had a sensitivity of 10 per cent and the Barred Rock of 1.8 per cent. Jaap and Robertson (1953) established that inbred lines within a breed may vary in their comb response to androgen. Campos and Shaffner (1952) selected males and females from a nonpedigreed stock and established that the offspring of such matings differed between sire families as well as between dam families within sire families. It is thus important to randomize thoroughly any chicks used for androgen bioassay.

2. Forced exercise of cockerels reduced the response of the comb to a given dose of testosterone without affecting body or adrenal weight (Wong, Lavenda and Hawthorne, 1954). This experiment suggests that differences in the results of the bioassay between laboratories might in some cases be explainable by differences in the voluntary exercise the birds obtain.

3. As in other bioassays, the route of administration of the hormone is important. Generally intraperitoneal injections result in a smaller response than do those given subcutaneously (Bernstorf, 1957). The difference may be explainable by inactivation of the hormone after intraperitoneal administration (Bernstorf, 1957). When the hormone is applied locally on the comb, special care should be taken to use the same volume, for Jaap and Robertson (1953) showed that the concentration of

the hormone is more important than the total amount.

4. Light has been reported to inhibit the response of the capon or the immature cockerel comb to a given dose of androgen (Womack, Koch, Domm and Juhn, 1931; Koch and Gallagher, 1934; Caridroit and Régnier, 1944; Wong and Hawthorne, 1954). However, in the experiments of Womack, Koch, Domm and Juhn (1931) the results ascribed to differences in light can also be explained on the basis of differences in temperature, whereas in Koch and Gallagher's experiment, there was no difference in comb response of capons kept in the dark or under light. Inhibition of response occurred only if birds were first kept in the dark and then subjected to light. As Lamoreux (1943) pointed out, birds under these conditions show increased activity, which, as was indicated above, may inhibit the response of the comb to exogenous androgen. Caridroit and Régnier (1944) used only 3 capons and no controls; it was assumed, however, that comb size had equilibrated during the previous several months of treatment. Their hypothesis that thyroid activity increased in the dark, and in turn caused a greater response to exogenous androgen, was not substantiated by measurements of thyroid activity before or after exposure to darkness. In the experiment of Wong and Hawthorne (1954), investigation showed that light inhibited response at only 1 of 4 levels of androgen tested. An analysis of variance for the total experiment, instead of the reported series of individual "t" tests for each level of androgen, reveals that light did not affect the assay; neither the main effect of light nor the androgen-light interaction was significant ($p > 0.05$). On the basis of the evidence cited, the claim for an effect of light on the androgen bioassay should be given the Scottish verdict "not proven."

Lamoreux (1943) showed in a carefully conducted experiment in which temperature and light were controlled variables, that neither visible nor ultraviolet light affected comb size significantly, but that increased temperature caused an increase of the comb size. In contrast Leroy (1956, 1958) found that combs of birds raised in darkness were very much enlarged, but Leroy (1958) was also able to obtain these large combs by enclosing the comb in a cloth cover which would interfere with heat dissipation from the comb surface; this suggests that temperature may have been an important factor in his experiments.

Attempts have been made to use the size of the comb or the rate of comb growth within a breed of chickens as an aid in selection of more fertile or of genetically superior males. Although the lines producing fertile males earlier can be selected successfully by choosing the cockerels with the larger combs, no selection can be made in this manner for superior subsequent fertility (Parker, 1956). Goodwin, Cole, Hutt and Rasmusen (1955) found that their strain with larger combs, larger testes, and earlier spermatogenic activity was also the strain with the lower fertility. The lower fertility was not caused by the interference of the large comb with mating activity, for all males were dubbed at 9 weeks of age.

Pasvogel (1952) tested the hypothesis that comb growth of cockerels might aid in predicting the egg-laying performance of their offspring. In 3 out of 4 trials a selection of males on the basis of their comb growth resulted in higher egg production of the next generation. Unfortunately, this hypothesis has not been confirmed by more extensive tests.

As might be expected, androgens play an important role in the regulation of the activity and size of the secondary sex organs; the seminal vesicles in a number of passerine birds (Wolfson, 1954a), the *vas deferens* in the starling (Witschi and Fugo, 1940), the cloacal gland of *Coturnix c. japonica* (Nagra, Meyer and Bilstad, 1959), the phallus of the fowl (Nishiyama, 1954), and the penis of the drake and gander. The synchronization of spermatogenic activity and the activity of these secondary sex organs, in birds as in mammals, involves the regulation of spermatogenic activity directly by the pituitary and of the secondary sex organs by androgens, which in turn are under the control of pituitary secretions. This synchronization fits well into the hypothesis that the gonadotrophic complex is secreted and released as one complex, as

has been proposed from different lines of evidence by Nalbandov (1959a) and van Tienhoven (1959).

Other developments influenced by androgen secretion which do not seem to be directly involved in reproduction are: the normal development of the uropygial gland (Kar, 1947a), regression of the *Bursa fabricii* (Glick, 1957), the head furnishings of the turkey (Herrick, 1951), and increased resistance to lymphomatosis (Burmester and Nelson, 1945). Beak color, which may play a role in species recognition and mate selection, is regulated by androgen secretion in some species. Examples are: the black bills of the sparrow, *Passer domesticus*, African weaver finches, *Euplectes orix*, and the indigo bunting, *Passerina cyanea*; also the yellow bill of the starling, *Sturnus vulgaris*, and the crimson bill of the blackheaded gull, *Larus ridibundus* (Benoit, 1950a; Dorfman and Shipley, 1956).

In studies of blood chemistry of chickens, Sturkie (1955) obtained a decrease in the blood sugar after androgen administration. However, on reinvestigation of this problem Tapper and Kare (1956) found that although the glucose content per volume of blood was decreased, the glucose content per volume of serum was not affected. These investigations established the fact that the change in blood glucose was caused by an increase in the number of red blood cells. In view of this increase it is not surprising that Tanaka and Rosenberg (1955) found an increased hemoglobin content as a result of androgen administration to capons. In roosters, however, the differences were not always significant.

Some external characters, such as development of spurs and sexual dimorphism of plumage color, characters which at first sight might be suspected of being under the influence of androgen secretions, are not the result of the presence of androgen but rather of the absence of estrogen. For instance, castration of the mallard duck, *Anas platyrhynchos*, results in the colorful drake feather pattern (Benoit, 1950a). An exception to the above generalization are certain feathers of the ruff, *Philomachus pugnax*. The development of spurs has been reviewed by Hutt (1949); growth of larger spurs in capons than in roosters indicates that androgen inhibits spur growth. Unilateral ovariectomy of the hen leads to spur development, suggesting that estrogen suppresses spur development to a larger extent than does androgen. Transplantation experiments have indicated that the male spur has a greater potential for growth than the female spur. According to Hutt (1949), this is because of greater natural and artificial selection for this character in the male.

The role of androgens in regulation of behavior and its importance in the reproductive cycle is discussed in other chapters.

3. Seminiferous Tubules

The seminiferous tubules, in which spermatogenesis takes place, may reach a length

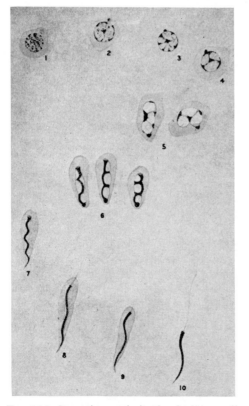

FIG. 18.1. Spermiogenesis in the duck according to Clermont (1958). The dark black dot in No. 2 represents the acrosome. This acrosomal material attaches to the nucleus which is represented in black and dark grey. (From Y. Clermont, Arch. Anat. microscop. et Morphol. expér., **47**, 47–66, 1958.)

of as much as 250 meters in an adult rooster (Kumaran and Turner, 1949a). As might be expected, the onset of spermatogenesis in domestic fowl depends on the breed and strain. The seminiferous tubules are lined by the germinal epithelium in which occasional Sertoli cells are found. Whether or not the Sertoli cells have an endocrine function in birds has not been established. The evidence concerning estrogen production in man (reviewed by Leach, Maddock, Tokuyama, Paulsen and Nelson, 1956) seems to indicate that they are not the source of estrogen. As will be discussed later, the Sertoli cells probably play an important role in the release of sperm into the lumen of the seminiferous tubules. Other functions of the Sertoli cells are not well established, but Ortavant (1959) lists as possible functions the protection of certain germ cells and aid in the maturation of spermatids.

Spermatogenesis has been studied in detail for the Pekin duck testis by Clermont (1958). The following account has been taken from his publication. The spermatogenic process can be divided into 3 periods: (1) the period of spermatogonial multiplication, during which new spermatogonia are formed continuously and during which spermatocytes are formed; (2) the period of spermatocyte division which results in spermatid formation; (3) the period of spermiogenesis, i.e., the period during which spermatids are transformed to spermatozoa.

The transformations occurring during spermiogenesis are best illustrated in Figure 18.1. The number of each figure corresponds to the different stages which Clermont (1958) distinguishes. Figure 18.2 illustrates the different cell associations formed during the spermatogenic cycle; these findings are summarized in Table 18.1.

By the use of colchicine injections to stop mitotic division, it was possible to count the number of mitoses in each stage of the cycle listed above. Clermont (1958) concluded that the scheme illustrated in Figure 18.3 was the most probable one. Lake (1956) made the very interesting observation that in fowl testes two secondary spermatocytes may remain together to form a binucleate cell. This cell becomes a four nuclear cell after the second meiotic division. After frequent multiplication within such cells they become spermatids, thus yielding many spermatids from what started as one cell. He postulated that this phenomenon may explain the formation of sperm clusters. This explanation, indeed, would seem more plausible than the formation of sperm clusters as the result of a chemotactic effect of the Sertoli cells.

After the spermatozoa have been formed they seem to "bury" their heads in the Sertoli cells. Injection of gonadotrophins into a sexually mature sparrow causes a release of sperm into the tubular lumen. Such a release of sperm coincides with the appearance of voided Sertoli cells. Similar changes can be induced in such testes by immersion in hypotonic solution suggesting that sperm release may be due to diffusion of water into the Sertoli cell (Frantz, 1958).

The seminiferous tubules may have an endocrine function, at least in some birds. The testes of seasonally producing birds show a marked regression at the end of the breeding season, a regression preceded or accompanied by a marked steatogenesis of the tubules. The lipoid material in the tubules shows a positive Schultz test reaction for cholesterol (Marshall, 1955). A similar histologic and histochemical appearance can be created by hypophysectomy of pigeons (Coombs and Marshall, 1956; Lofts and Marshall, 1959), or by the injection of prolactin in sparrows, chaffinches (*Fringilla coelebs*), and greenfinches (*Chloris chloris*) (Lofts and Marshall, 1956). Chromatographic assay of testes extracts of intact, photostimulated pigeons with bunched sperm in the seminiferous tubules, revealed no detectable progesterone, whereas the testes of the hypophysectomized pigeons with extensive steatogenesis of the tubules contained this hormone.

A bioassay of the blood for progesterone (Hooker-Forbes test) gave negative results for intact pigeons but positive results for 5 out of 6 hypophysectomized pigeons (Lofts and Marshall, 1959). This evidence strongly indicates an endocrine function for the testicular tubules of the pigeon. In pigeons progesterone plays a regulatory function in the induction of incubation behavior (Lehrman, 1958, and his chapter in this

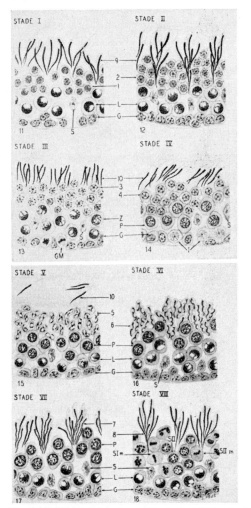

FIG. 18.2. The spermatogenetic cycle of the duck according to Clermont (1958). (S = Sertoli cell; G = spermatogonium; GM = spermatogonium in mitosis; I = primary spermatocyte in interphase; L = spermatocyte in leptotene stage; Z = spermatocyte in zygotene stage; P = spermatocyte in pachytene stage; SIm = primary spermatocyte in metaphase; SII = secondary spermatocyte; $SIIm$ = secondary spermatocyte in metaphase. The numbers indicate the stages of the cycle. (From Y. Clermont, Arch. Anat. microscop. et Morphol. expér., **47**, 47–66, 1958.)

book). Thus the secretion of progesterone by the testicular tubules may have evolved in this group of birds, whereas in species in which the male does not incubate the eggs or in which progesterone does not induce incubation behavior, this adaptation may be absent. One is reminded of this by the fact that, contrary to Lofts and Marshall

TABLE 18.1

The cellular composition during the different stages of the spermatogenic cycle of the drake
(From Y. Clermont, Arch. Anat. microscop. et Morphol. expér., 47, 47–66, 1958.)

	Stage of Cycle							
	I	II	III	IV	V	VI	VII	VIII
Spermatogonia, G	G	G	G	G	G	G	G	G
Spermatogonia in mitosis, M			M		M			M
Primary spermatocytes								
Interphase, I				I	L	L	L	L
Leptotene, L	L, Z	L, Z	Z					
Zygotene, Z								
Pachytene, P				→P	P	P	P, D	D, S, Im
Diakenesis, D								
Metaphase, SIm								
Secondary spermatocytes, SII								SII
Dividing spermatocytes, SIIm								SIIm
Spermitid. Spermiogenesis steps, 1–10	1	2	3	4	5	6	7	8
	9	9	10	10				

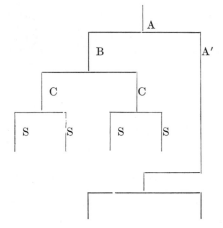

Fig. 18.3. Schematic presentation of renewal of spermatogonia in the drake (Clermont, 1958). *A, A′* = stem cells, *B, C* = differentiated spermatogonia, *S* = spermatocytes. (From Y. Clermont, Arch. Anat. microscop. et Morphol. expér., **47**, 47–66, 1958.)

(1959), Fraps, Hooker and Forbes (1949) detected progesterone in the blood of intact roosters but not in the blood of capons, indicating secretion of progesterone by testes with presumably normal spermatogenetic activity. Progesterone bioassays of the blood of hypophysectomized roosters treated with either avian luteinizing hormone (LH) or follicle-stimulating hormone (FSH) and with a combination of these two hormones should reveal whether or not tubules are the source of progesterone in the rooster.

After the sperm are released into the lumina of the seminiferous tubules they have to pass through a duct system. The latter has been described in detail by Lake (1957). On leaving the seminiferous tubules the sperm pass first through the *tubuli recti*, structures characterized by the absence of germinal epithelium and the presence of Sertoli cells. These Sertoli cells apparently secrete a lipoidal material into the lumen. After passage through the *tubuli recti* the sperm reach the *rete testis* which are lined by a cuboidal or squamous epithelium. The *rete testis* converges into the efferent ducts which are convoluted and which form cone-like structures comprising the head of the epididymis. The ducts are lined by alternating groups of tall and low cells with intense holocrine secretion. The basement membrane is surrounded by a circular smooth muscle. The ductus epididymis, which connects the efferent tubules to the vas deferens, has a tall, pseudostratified, columnar epithelium with nonmotile stereocilia. The relationship between these duct systems is illustrated in Figure 18.4.

In the epididymis, which is quite small compared with the epididymides of mammals, sperm undergo a maturation process which increases their fertilizing ability

(Munro, 1938a). Munro found that sperm obtained from the testes fertilized 3 of 69 hens, epididymal sperm fertilized 5 of 39 hens, and sperm from the *vas deferens* 57 of 77 hens. The differences between testicular and epididymal sperm are statistically not significant, but, in view of the lack of secretions in *vas deferens*, it seems probable that sperm maturation starts in the epididymis. It is not known whether epididymal sperm of chickens show a lower endogenous respiration rate and a greater Pasteur effect than do ejaculated sperm, as is the case for epididymal and ejaculated bull sperm (Mann, 1954). Munro (1938b) also showed that the change in the fertilization capacity is not affected by androgen. Different parts of the *vas deferens* were tied off, the birds caponized, and sperm collected at various intervals and tested for fertilizing capacity. Androgen treatment of these capons was without effect on the fertilizing capacity of sperm from different parts of the genital tract. This lack of effect of androgen in the caponized rooster contrasts with the effect of castration and replacement therapy in the rat (see chapter by Bishop).

The *vasa deferentia*, which become highly convoluted with approaching sexual maturity, are lined with columnal pseudostratified epithelium and have three muscle layers, an internal longitudinal, an intermediate circular, and an exterior longitudinal layer. At the distal end of the vas deferens in the fowl, at the junction with the ejaculatory duct, there is a small storage space, whereas in many passerine birds large "seminal vesicles" are present (Wolfson, 1954a). These seminal vesicles may be organs for storing sperm at lower-than-body temperatures (Wolfson, 1954b).

4. Vasa Deferentia

The vasa deferentia end in the ejaculatory ducts which have numerous subepithelial sinuses and tortuous arterioles and venules in the submucosa. These structures make the ejaculatory ducts erectile organs; together with lymph folds, the vascular body and the phallus, they form the copulatory organ (see Fig. 18.5). The phallus is formed by a combination of two round folds and the "white body." Dur-

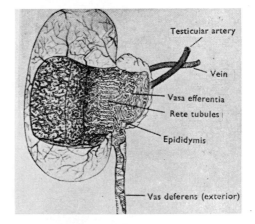

FIG. 18.4. The connections between seminiferous tubules and *vas deferens* according to Lake (1947). (From P. F. Lake, J. Anat., **91**, 116–129, 1057.)

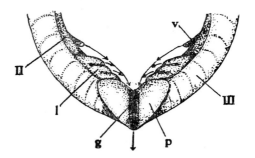

FIG. 18.5. Diagram of semen ejaculation in the rooster (according to Nishiyama, 1955). g = longitudinal groove of erected phallus; l = swelled lymphfold; p = erected phallus; v = papillary process of vas deferens; II = 2nd fold of cloaca; III = 3rd fold of cloaca, i.e., anus; ↓ ejection of semen from vas deferens (v) and outflow of transparent fluid from l, as well as ejaculation of the semen (mixture of vas deferens semen with transparent fluid along g) to the outside of the anus. (From H. Nishiyama, J. Fac. Agric. Kyushu Univ., **10**, 277–305, 1955.)

ing erection the phallus becomes engorged with lymph from the vascular body, whereas the posterior retractor penis muscle relaxes and allows the phallus to protrude. After mating, the lymph can drain back into the vascular bodies. The copulatory organ of the turkey is distinguished from that of the rooster by its lack of a midventral white body and by the presence of a separate white body on the tip of each round fold. In colored varieties of turkeys, these white bodies are highly pigmented (Lorenz, 1959). An intromittent organ, a so-called penis,

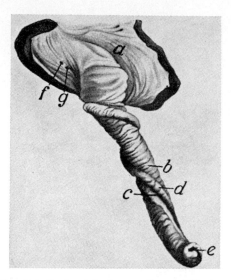

FIG. 18.6. Penis of duck according to Ellenberger and Baum (1932). a = cloaca; b = penis; c = seminal groove; d = ridge of seminal groove; e = opening of glandular tube; f = opening of vas deferens; g = opening of ureter. (From W. Ellenberger and H. Baum, in *Handbuch der Vergleichenden Anatomie der Haustiere*, 17th ed., Julius Springer Verlag, 1932.)

is found in *Anseres, Cracidae, Crypturi* and *Ratitae* (Domm, 1939). Figure 18.6 illustrates the "penis" of a drake. The semen is transported along the seminal grooves. Stimulation of the nerves originating from the sympathetic plexus and going to the lymph folds has resulted in erection of the penis of drakes (Domm, 1939). The time sperm require to traverse the duct system from testis to phallus has been estimated as 24 hours in an active rooster and 2 to 3 days in a sexually inactive one (Munro, 1938a).

The enormous variation of the morphology of sperm from different species is illustrated in Figure 18.7. The various factors which may affect sperm morphology after ejaculation will be discussed later.

The finer structure of the fowl spermatozoon has been investigated with the aid of the electron microscope (Grigg and Hodge, 1949; Bonadonna, 1954). The results can be summarized as follows: At the anterior tip of the head there is a small acrosomal spine which is embedded in the head proper. This spine is 1.5 × 0.1 μ in size and is covered by an acrosome cap. The head of

the sperm has dimensions of 14 × 0.5 μ, and is slightly curved. After eosin-nigrosin staining a crescent-shaped proximal centriole can be seen at the posterior end of the head (Lake, 1954). This centriole does not stain in fresh semen regardless of the morphology of the sperm, but after storage of sperm at 5°C. all abnormally shaped sperm show a deeply stained proximal centriole even when the head has not taken up the stain. Occasionally a normally shaped sperm will also show a stained proximal centriole (El Zayat, 1960). The midpiece, between the head and tail, measures 4 × 0.5 μ and is bounded anteriorly by the anterior distal centriole, posteriorly by the posterior distal centriole. Fibrils of the tail filament arise from the anterior distal centriole, pass medially through the midpiece, and pass through the posterior distal centriole. The tail, which starts at the midpiece tail junc-

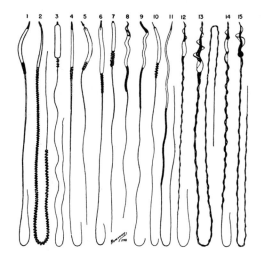

FIG. 18.7. Spermatozoa of different species of birds (according to Romanoff, 1959). *1* = Chicken (*Gallus gallus*); *2* = pigeon (*Columba livia*); *3* = turkey (*Meleagris gallopavo*); *4* = duck (*Anus platyrhynchos*); *5* = sea duck (*Aythinae*); *6* = ring-necked parrot (*Psittacus torcuatus*); *7* = black-headed gull (*Larus fuscus*); *8* = red-backed sandpiper (*Calidris alpina*); *9* = European woodcock (*Scolopax rusticula*); *10* = European coot (*Fulica atra*); *11* = European ruff (*Philomachus pugnax*); *12* = sparrow (*Passer domesticus*); *13* = greenfinch (*Chloris chloris*); *14* = songthrush (*Turdus philomelos*); *15* = chaffinch (*Fringilla coelebs*). Magnification 600 ×. (From A. L. Romanoff, *The Avian Embryo*, Macmillan Company, 1960.)

tion where the posterior distal centriole is located, is over 100 μ long. The tail has a smooth appearance except for the last two μ. It consists of an axial filament surrounded by a thin sheath, which, however, seems absent for the last 2 μ, and shows the fibrils caused by the absence of the thin sheath which surrounds the rest of the axial filament. The axial filament itself consists of 11 fibrils. Nine of these fibrils, the L fibrils, are about 450 Å in diameter and are not easily destroyed by distilled water. Two M fibrils are easily destroyed so that no estimate could be made of their diameter. Grigg and Hodge (1949) have speculated that the L fibrils might be the motor elements for the sperm whereas the M fibrils might act as controls for the L fibrils. An extensive review of the problem of sperm motility is contained in the chapter by Bishop.

B. ENDOCRINE REGULATION OF TESTICULAR ACTIVITY

1. The Pituitary Gland

The general concepts of the morphology of the pituitary gland with respect to function and of the physiology of the pituitary gland have been discussed in detail in the chapters by Purves and Greep. It seems thus desirable to discuss here only those aspects which substantiate general principles found

to be true also for the avian pituitary and to mention in what respects the avian pituitary differs from the mammalian pituitary. A large part of the description of morphology has been taken from the excellent comparative account of avian pituitaries by Wingstrand (1951).

The avian pituitary (Fig. 18.8) lacks an intermediate lobe in all species investigated. The epithelial stalk, a vestige of the connection between *adenohypophysis* and its point of origin in the oral epithelium, is more prominent in some species than in others, but it lacks glandular activity in all the species. Within the *pars distalis* a distinction can be made between caudal and cephalic lobes. The A_1 cells or dark-staining acidophils (dark red with azocarmine) are restricted to the caudal lobe (Rahn and Painter, 1941; Wingstrand, 1951; Matsuo, 1954; Mikami, 1954), whereas the A_2 cells are restricted to the cephalic lobe (Rahn and Painter, 1941; Wingstrand, 1951; Matsuo, 1954).

According to Wingstrand (1951), A_1 cells and chromophobes are sometimes difficult to distinguish. Mikami (1955) states that the thyrotrophs, which he distinguishes by their positive periodic acid-Schiff (PAS) reaction are also restricted to the cephalic lobe. Wingstrand (1951) concluded that the following avian-mammalian homologies exist: the

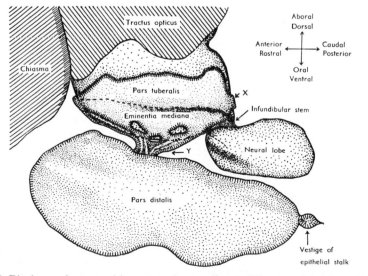

Fig. 18.8. Pituitary of a goose (*Anser anser*) according to Wingstrand (1951). (From K. G. Wingstrand, *The Structure and Development of the Avian Pituitary*. CWK Gleerup, 1951.)

TABLE 18.2

The relationship between anterior pituitary cells and their hormonal association in the fowl

Cell Type	Hormone	Reference
1. Acidophil.....................	Prolactin	Schooley, 1937; Saeki, 1955
2. Small acidophil with large nucleus......................	Prolactin	Payne, 1943
3. Basophils.....................		
a. Basophilic cytoplasm nucleus like in acidophil.....	TSH	Payne, 1944
b. Small PAS + cell...........	TSH	Perek, Eckstein and Sobel, 1957
c. β-Cell: PAS+; AF+.......	TSH	Brown and Knigge, 1958; Legait and Legait, 1955
d. β-Cell blue with Kresazan...	TSH	Legait and Legait, 1955
e. Large basophil.............	Gonadotrophin	Payne, 1940, 1944, 1947; Herrick and Finerty, 1940
f. Basophil...................	Gonadotrophin	Schooley, 1937
g. Large basophil PAS+.......	Gonadotrophin	Perek, Eckstein and Sobel, 1957
h. δ-Cell PAS+; AF−.........	Gonadotrophin	Brown and Knigge, 1958; Legait and Legait, 1955
i. Violet with Kresazan.......	Gonadotrophin	Legait and Legait, 1955.
4. Acidophilic granules in basophilic gonadotrophs.........	Luteinizing hormone?	Payne, 1955.

caudal lobe of the avian pituitary corresponds with the entire epithelial gland of the mammalian pituitary with exception of the *pars tuberalis*. The *pars tuberalis* of the avian and mammalian pituitary are homologous. A very restricted vestigial portion of the mammalian epithelial gland lying near the rostral end of the pituitary corresponds with the cephalic lobe of the avian pituitary.

Attempts have been made to establish the relationships of some of the cells of the avian pituitary with specific secretions. The techniques used are generally the same as those used for mammals (see chapter by Purves). The differences in terminology used by the different authors sometimes make it difficult to summarize the data, but an attempt to do so has been made in Table 18.2.

In studies of these relationships castration of mammals has resulted in the formation of "signet-ring" cells. In the pigeon (Schooley, 1937), and the fowl (Payne, 1940) this does not occur. However, signet-ring cells were observed in young control male and female chicks although never in older chicks. The function of these avian signet-ring cells is not known.

Some apparent discrepancies between cytologic evidence and hormone assays on pituitaries in other experiments should be mentioned. Nakajo and Tanaka (1956)

found that the bioassay of caudal and cephalic lobes of chicken pituitaries showed the presence of prolactin in both lobes. The caudal lobe showed a change in potency when broodiness of the hens was interrupted by electric shock or by a strong illumination, whereas the potency of the cephalic lobe remained unchanged. If the prolactin is produced exclusively by the acidophils or A_1 cells, and if these are limited to the caudal lobe, then one would not expect to find prolactin in the cephalic lobe. Nevertheless, the potency of the cephalic lobe was higher than that of the caudal lobe in all bioassays reported by Nakajo and Tanaka (1956).

To prevent confusion in the discussion of the relationship between the nervous system and the pituitary, a brief description of the vascularization and innervation of the avian pituitary is given here. Branches of the internal carotid artery supply the pituitary. After the internal carotid artery has given off the sphenomaxillaris artery and the vidiana artery, the carotids bend *dorsomedially* and enter the posterior end of the *sella turcica* where an intercarotic anastomoses occurs (Wingstrand, 1951; Green, 1951). Near this point the inferior hypophyseal artery is given off to the neural lobe. After the carotid arteries have separated again, several arteries branch off, but only the infundibular arteries supply the pituitary. They supply a very dense plexus of capillaries which covers the median eminence and surface of the infundibular stem. The capillaries of this primary plexus fuse in the central zone of the median eminence to form larger vessels, the so-called portal vessels. These vessels are often embedded in the epithelium of the portal zone of the *pars tuberalis*, but some vessels run directly into the *pars distalis*. No other arteries supply the *pars distalis*. In the *pars distalis* the portal vessels send their blood through the sinusoids and then drain into the sinus cavernosus or flattened veins connecting with it. In his extensive material Wingstrand found no case in which an artery or its branches penetrated the hypophyseal capsule, and in only one pigeon, did he find an artery going from the neural lobe to the *pars distalis*. The walls of the sinus cavernosus are formed by the periosteum of the *sella turcica*, the capsule of the pituitary, and the connective tissue septa and adventitia of the carotid veins. Blood from the sinus drains into the carotid veins.

The neural lobe of *Pica, Corvus, Columba, Apus*, and others is supplied by blood from the inferior hypophyseal arteries, whereas in passerine birds (*Regulus, Parus, Emberiza, Riparia, Phylloscopus*) and the fowl the blood supply comes from the infundibular arteries (Wingstrand, 1951). The blood drains into the sinus cavernosus from the capillaries of the neural lobe tissue.

In addition to this main blood supply of the pituitary, small blood vessel connections sometimes occur between the primary plexus of the median eminence and the capillary bed of the neural lobe, and occasionally single blood vessels are found between the hypothalamic vascular bed and the primary capillary bed of the median eminence. The rarity of such connections makes functional connection between these various capillary beds unlikely. This condition is different from the considerable anastomosis between the vascular beds of posterior lobe and *pars distalis* in the rat (Landsmeer, 1951).

The lack of vascular connections between *pars distalis* and neurohypophysis plus the presence of a layer of connective tissue between anterior and posterior lobes of the

pituitary (Legait, 1959) makes the transport of hormones from one lobe to the other extremely improbable. On the basis of the blood supply of the avian pituitary, Wingstrand (1951) concluded that the blood flows from median eminence to portal vessels. This conclusion has been confirmed by direct observation of the blood flow in the duck (Assenmacher, 1958).

Studies of the *pars distalis* of the avian pituitary by Drager (1945) and Green (1951) showed that the nerve fibers never penetrate the glandular part of the *pars distalis*. Metuzals (1955) claimed that a few nerve fibers penetrate into the *pars distalis* of ducks, but the origin of the fibers could not be established. Wingstrand (1951) wrote, "The *pars distalis* also contains a few scattered fibres in most preparations of pigeons and also in the geese and the ducks. The fibres are, however, so rare that large areas in a section must be examined before a single fibre is found." He continued, "It has been seen several times that fibres in the *pars distalis* are continuous with the autonomic fibre bundles in the capsule of the organ, and the nervous character of the fibres can therefore hardly be doubted. The fibres in the *pars distalis* are, however, so few that they cannot be able to influence the function of the gland."

The posterior pituitary is innervated by the *tractus hypophyseus anterior*, the *tractus supra opticohypophyseus*, the *tractus tuberohypophyseus*, and the *tractus hypophyseus posterior*, which originate in the lateral and inferior hypothalamic nuclei, the *nucleus tuberis* (Kuhlenbeck, 1937), and the *nucleus subdecussationis* (Wingstrand, 1951). According to Green (1951), the medial forebrain bundle may contribute fibers to the *tractus hypophyseus*, but Wingstrand (1951) is not as definite on this. The *tuberohypophyseal* tract shows some special adaptations, in that fibers form "loops" into the glandular layer of the median eminence where the blood supply is most prominent. In this manner the blood vessels can transport neurosecretory material to the *pars distalis* and thus affect its function (Wingstrand, 1951). A similar mechanism was proposed for some fine fibers of the *tractus hypophyseus anterior*. Because the *nucleus tuberis* is connected with a large number of nonmedullated fibers from the preoptic region, the possibility exists that areas of the preoptic region influence the anterior pituitary by way of the *nucleus tuberis*. Experimental evidence indicating that the nervous system can influence the avian anterior pituitary will be discussed later.

The evidence summarized in Table 18.2 makes it seem logical that the avian pituitary exercises the same control over the general reproductive processes that the reptilian, amphibian, and mammalian pituitaries do. Only a few of the numerous experiments offering proof of this assumption will be mentioned here.

The endocrine function of the avian anterior pituitary has been investigated by the classical methods such as ablation of the gland, replacement therapy, bioassays of the gland, and purification of the hormones. The aspects which concern the male will be discussed here whereas those pertaining to the female will be discussed in another section of this chapter.

Removal of the anterior pituitary leads to a sharp decrease in testicular size (Benoit and Aron, 1934a; Chu, 1940; Chu and You, 1946; Nalbandov, Meyer and McShan, 1946, 1951; Coombs and Marshall, 1956; Assenmacher, 1958; Lofts and Marshall, 1959), to a decrease in tubule diameter (Chu, 1940; Chu and You, 1946; Nalbandov, Meyer and McShan, 1946, 1951; Coombs and Marshall, 1956; Assenmacher, 1958; Lofts and Marshall, 1959), to a decrease in tubule diameter (Chu, 1940; Chu and You, 1946; Nalbandov, Meyer and McShan, 1946; Coombs and Marshall, 1956; Lofts and Marshall, 1956), to steatogenesis of the tubules (Coombs and Marshall, 1956, Lofts and Marshall, 1959), and, as a consequence of decreased Leydig cell activity, to a decrease in comb size (Nalbandov, Meyer and McShan, 1946, 1951), and to atrophy of the *vas deferens* (Chu, 1940).

The effect of hypophysectomy on the histology of the Leydig cells is somewhat controversial. Chu (1940) remarked that the Leydig cells of hypophysectomized pigeons were healthy in appearance but poor in staining reaction, whereas Coombs and Marshall (1956) stated that the interstitium

of hypophysectomized roosters became exhausted but that a new generation of Leydig cells with a sudanophilic and a cholesterol-positive staining reaction arose in the absence of the pituitary. This observation seems particularly puzzling in view of the experiments (Nalbandov, Meyer and McShan, 1951) in which it was found that the combs of hypophysectomized roosters could only be maintained for a limited time with mammalian gonadotrophins. This was not due to antihormone production. The comb of such roosters could respond, however, for an indefinitely long time to avian pituitary extracts. Histologic examination of the interstitium during these experimental treatments revealed two types of Leydig cells, a nonsecretory type which could be converted into the secretory type by avian gonadotrophin, and a secretory type which could be stimulated to secrete androgen by avian or mammalian LH. These experiments led Nalbandov, Meyer and McShan (1951) to the conclusion that a "third gonadotrophic hormone" may be secreted by the avian pituitary or that avian and mammalian LH are qualitatively different. In any event the experiments support the hypothesis that replacement therapy stimulates the Leydig cells. The observation of cyclic phenomena in the Leydig cells by Coombs and Marshall (1956) does not seem reconcilable with the histologic studies made by Nalbandov, Meyer and McShan (1951). The following observation by Coombs and Marshall (1956) may offer an explanation. ". . . the hypophysectomized bird was killed after only 17 days and *before there was any reduction in comb size,* so as to examine an early stage of metamorphosis" (italics mine). According to Nalbandov and Card (1943b), the reduction in comb size is obvious 6 days after hypophysectomy. The cyclic phenomena of the Leydig cells observed by Coombs and Marshall (1956) may thus be the result of traces of anterior pituitary left during the operation.

Various gonadotrophic hormone preparations, all containing FSH, have proven to be effective in causing an increase in diameter of the seminiferous tubules, re-initiation of spermatogenesis, loss of cholesterol-positive material from the lumen of the tubules, and an increase of testicular size in hypophysectomized birds (Chu, 1940; Nalbandov, Meyer and McShan, 1946; Lofts and Marshall, 1956).

Bioassays of avian pituitaries have shown that the different gonadotrophic hormones found in mammals are also present in avian pituitaries. FSH and LH were shown to be present by Witschi, Stanley and Riley (1937) and by Leonard (1937), and Burrows and Byerly (1936) demonstrated the presence of prolactin in the pituitaries of the fowl, particularly in the pituitary of broody hens. The experiments which proved that the avian pituitary contains these three gonadotrophic hormones have been confirmed many times. The response of the avian gonads to the purified hormones has already been discussed in connection with replacement therapy experiments. The application of this response in bioassay methods will be discussed in a separate section.

The LH portion of the gonadotrophic complex seems to be the only hormone which can restore the function of the Leydig cells. The restoration or the resumption of spermatogenesis in an inactive testis can be induced in hypophysectomized and in intact individuals of certain avian species by hormones other than gonadotrophins. Chu (1940) demonstrated that the germinal epithelium of the hypophysectomized pigeon can be maintained by testosterone injections, whereas Chu and You (1944) showed that spermatogenesis can be induced in such pigeons after the germinal epithelium has degenerated and the tubules contain spermatogonia and Sertoli cells only. Pfeiffer (1947) subsequently observed that testosterone will enhance further spermatogenesis in sparrows, *Passer domesticus*, provided spermatocytes were present. Wolfson and Harris (1959) could maintain gonadal activity of slate-colored juncos, *Junco hyemalis*, and white-throated sparrows, *Zonotrichia albicollis*, when illumination was reduced from 16 to 8 hours per day. In the controls gonadal activity decreased. Clermont and Benoit (1955) could not increase the size of the testes of either juvenile or adult drakes during the sexual rest period, nor could testicular size be maintained when the drakes were subjected to a sharp decrease in daily illumination. The species differences which seem to exist in intact birds do not prove that such differences will exist in hypophysectomized birds. Chu and You (1944), for instance, demonstrated that testosterone does not stimulate the testes of immature or of adult but sexually quiescent male pigeons. The hypothesis that androgen stimulates the testes of hypophysectomized ducks needs to be tested.

Doses of androgen capable of inducing spermatogenesis in hypophysectomized male pigeons cause degeneration of the germinal epithelium and a decrease in testicular size when given to intact males (Chu, 1940). Breneman and Mason (1951) found that physiologic doses of androgen are followed by a reduction of gonadotrophic potency. This inhibition was implied in the statement by Kumaran and Turner (1949c) that the same dose of androgen acts as an inhibitor of spermatogenesis at one age but stimulates it at a later age. They suggested that, in the fowl, androgen stimulates only the transformation of secondary spermatocytes; higher doses of androgen inhibit the FSH required for the transformation of spermatogonia to spermatocytes, and no spermatocytes are available when androgen is given at too early an age. Pfeiffer's data (1947) for the sparrow and Chu's data (1940) for intact young and adult pigeons also support this concept, but the concept is not consistent with the action of androgen in the hypophysectomized pigeon in which only spermatogonia are present. Further investigation as to what distinguishes the immature testis from the testis of the hypophysectomized pigeon is needed to resolve this question.

The testis is also under control of the third hormone found in the avian pituitary, prolactin. This hormone reaches its highest concentration during incubation of the eggs by the parents. It has been found in the pituitaries of the domestic fowl (Burrows and Byerly, 1936; Saeki and Tanabe, 1955), pigeons (Schooley and Riddle, 1938), the California gull, *Larus californicus* (Bailey, 1952), and pheasants, *Phasianus colchicus* (Breitenbach and Meyer, 1959). Its physiologic effects are many. In the male it causes a decrease in comb size, a decrease in testicular size, a decrease in tubule diameter, and steatogenesis of the tubules (Riddle and Bates, 1939; Breneman, 1942; Nalbandov, 1945; Lofts and Marshall, 1956). It also prevents the response of the testes to light in the white-crowned sparrow, *Zonotrichia leucophrys pugetensis* (Bailey, 1950). Prolactin does not affect testicular activity in mammals (Riddle and Bates, 1939; Lofts and Marshall, 1956). The action of prolactin on avian testes is probably caused by an inhibition of pituitary gonadotrophin secretion because small doses of FSH, given simultaneously with prolactin, prevent the decrease in testicular activity (Bates, Riddle and Lahr, 1937; Nalbandov, 1945). Breneman (1942) also observed that prolactin causes a decrease in the number of basophil cells which are implicated in the secretion of the gonadotrophic hormone.

Prolactin also is apparently required for the formation of the incubation patch, because in hypophysectomized passerines the incubation patch can only be formed after combined estrogen-prolactin treatment (Bailey, 1952). Further, the prolactin content of the California gull pituitary was correlated with the presence of the incubation patch. The occurrence of the incubation patch in both sexes is well correlated with the incubation behavior of the two sexes. If it is present in a species, it occurs in the sex or sexes which incubate (Bailey, 1952).

Prolactin injection causes molting in the fowl. This is probably the result of a direct effect on the feather follicle, because the hormone is equally as effective in roosters as in capons (Juhn and Harris, 1958).

Finally, prolactin is probably concerned with incubation behavior in the fowl (Saeki and Tanabe, 1955), although it seems that progesterone regulates incubation behavior in the ringdove, *Streptopelia risoria* (Lehrman, 1958, and his chapter in this book). The fact that hypophysectomy of the pigeon may lead to progesterone secretion by the testes (Lofts and Marshall, 1959) makes such an animal an excellent tool for establishing whether or not progesterone acts directly or by way of prolactin secretion in the pigeon.

The following hypothetical series of events may take place in the regulation of the male's breeding cycle of birds in which both sexes incubate the eggs. In the spring under the influence of increasing daylight and provided that other ecologic factors are favorable, the testes of the male reach full activity before the ovaries of the females are fully developed (Benoit, 1956). The courtship activities and vocalizations may stimulate the females' ovaries by way of the nervous-pituitary system so that the follicles mature and ovulation and oviposition can occur. At the time when about half of the clutch has been laid, estrogen secretion is at its peak and the first signs of vascularization of the incubation patch become visible (Bailey, 1952). Visual stimuli from his incubating mate may cause secretion of prolactin by the pituitary of the male, in pigeons at least (Patel, 1936). This release of prolactin could serve a triple purpose of inducing the formation of the incubation patch (Bailey, 1952), precipitating incubation behavior, and causing the functional collapse of the testes. This collapse through withdrawal of androgen might then end sexual activities which would divert the male from incubating.

Evidence exists that the mechanisms proposed above operate in birds as a group, but, as far as the author is aware, this sequence of events has not been proven for any single species. One problem in need of investigation in the male is the source of the estrogen required for the formation of the incubation patch. This sequence of events would also account for the progesterone secretion by the testes of the pigeon. (The assumption is made that the changes in the testes are the same after prolactin secretion as after hypophysectomy. Such an assumption seems to be warranted on the basis of the similarities in the histology of the testes after these treatments.) The progesterone, in turn, would cause incubation behavior. More research is required to determine which secretion starts first in the pigeon, prolactin or progesterone. Seeing his mate incubate and finish incubation may release prolactin and so explain the eclipse molt of the mallard drake, which occurs about 3 weeks sooner in mated than in unmated drakes (Hochbaum, 1944).

In species in which the male is polygamous and not concerned with incubation and care of the young, testicular collapse does not seem to occur until the end of the breeding season. An example of this is found in the pheasant (Greeley and Meyer, 1953).

The effects of other anterior pituitary hormones on avian testes are difficult to evaluate because possible contamination by gonadotrophins has not always been excluded. For example, adrenocorticotrophic hormone (ACTH) injections to roosters and capons were observed to be followed by an increase in comb size of roosters but not of capons. No atrophy similar to that in mammalian testes after ACTH administration (Dulin, 1953) was observed. Dulin (1953) assayed the ACTH preparation for gonadotrophin but used an assay method (chick testicular size as end point) which is not particularly sensitive for LH, the hormone which stimulates androgen secretion. Dulin explained the effect of ACTH by assuming increased endogenous gonadotrophin secretion by the ACTH-treated roosters. This assumption was based on the increased pituitary weights of the treated roosters. In view of assay methods used, we feel that LH contamination has not been excluded and that further experimentation is required before the described increase in comb size is assigned to ACTH *per se*.

Discussion of the effects of nongonadotrophic anterior pituitary hormones on gonads does not seem fruitful in view of the above mentioned possibility of gonadotrophin contamination.

2. The Pineal Body

Of the several endocrine organs which may affect testicular activity, the pineal body has been a most controversial one. It is fortunate that one of the experiments, in which the classical endocrine approach of ablation and replacement therapy was used, was carried out in the fowl.

Shellabarger (1953) demonstrated that ablation of the pineal body at an early age caused an increase in testes and comb weight, and a simultaneous increase in gonadotrophic potency of the pituitary. On the other hand, injection of a pineal-body extract caused a decrease in testicular weight, although a brain extract did not have this effect. Pituitary potency was not affected by either treatment. Pineal extract injections into pinealectomized cockerels reduced testicular size to that of nonoperated or sham-operated controls. Miller (1955) observed that the onset of sexual maturity in two strains of chickens, differing widely in the age at which sexual maturity is reached, coincided with the change in the pineal body from the follicular (active) to the lobular (inactive) stage. *In vitro* studies by Moszkowska (1958) established that the gonadotrophic potency of chick pituitaries cultured *in vitro* was higher when the pituitaries were cultured alone than when they were cultured in the presence of pineal body. This evidence strongly suggests that the pineal body may act as an inhibitor of pituitary activity. Moszkowska's experiments indicate that this inhibition is probably direct.

3. The Adrenal Gland

The role of the adrenal in reproduction is more difficult to evaluate in birds than in mammals. Part of this difficulty is the result of the intermingling of cortical and chromaffin cells so that the effect of cortex and medulla cannot be separated. The greater difficulty lies in the problem of complete surgical removal of the adrenals and in the high mortality after adrenalectomy (Parkes and Selye, 1936; Bülbring, 1937, 1940; Taber, Salley and Knight, 1956). Leroy and Benoit (1956) observed no mortality after adrenalectomy of drakes, *Anas platyrhynchos*, observations which do not agree with those of other workers. Bülbring (1940) emphasized that in her work with drakes every case of good survival was correlated with the presence of adrenal tissue. Efforts to sustain life of the adrenalectomized drakes, *Anas platyrhynchos?*, with desoxycorticosterone acetate (DCA) were successful only as long as injections were given. A correlation was found between the size of the testes at the time of surgery and the dose of DCA required to keep adrenalectomized drakes alive. This correlation was not a result of higher androgen secretion by the larger testes, because testosterone injections did not affect the amount of cortical extract required to keep castrated-adrenalectomized drakes alive (Bülbring, 1940).

After adrenalectomy, roosters maintained

by salt therapy show atrophy of the testes (Herrick and Torstveit, 1938; Herrick and Finerty, 1940). The atrophy may be caused by the general metabolic disturbances resulting from the adrenalectomy. Taber, Salley and Knight (1956) prevented development of the rudimentary gonad of sinistrally ovariectomized hens (poulards) by pair feeding them with adrenalectomized poulards. Both groups showed similar rudimentary gonad development. Leroy and Benoit (1954), who maintained their adrenalectomized drakes without special measures, found no testicular atrophy. This observation supports the view that testicular atrophy is correlated with the general metabolic disturbances resulting from adrenalectomy.

Chester Jones (1957) has reviewed the literature on the interrelation between testes and testicular hormones and size of the adrenal. The data suggest that long-term castration effects (8 to 11 months after operation) may result in a decrease in adrenal size, whereas short term effects (42 days after operation) result in an increase in adrenal size, which can be prevented by testosterone injections.

Administration of adrenal hormones has resulted in contradictory results. Desoxycorticosterone acetate (Link and Nalbandov, 1955; Boas, 1958) caused atrophy of the germinal epithelium, edema, and decrease in comb size of the fowl. Corticosterone increased testicular size and stimulated spermatogenesis in domestic mallard drakes (Leroy, 1952) and roosters (Conner, 1959) and an increase in comb size in the latter (Leroy, 1952). Dulin (1955), on the other hand, used three different doses of corticosterone and failed to find stimulation of testes or comb, but he observed decreased testes and comb size at the highest dose used. Cortisone caused a slight but significant increase in comb size of capons. The dose used by Leroy (1952) and the highest dose used by Dulin (1955) are essentially the same, but the length of treatment was shorter in Leroy's experiment. The most important difference between the two sets of experiments was probably in the age of the birds used. In Leroy's experiment the cockerels were 4 months old, whereas Conner (1959) used

6-week-old cockerels, and Dulin's cockerels were from 20 to 40 days of age. One is reminded of the similarity between these results and those of the experiments of Kumaran and Turner (1949c) in which androgen did not stimulate spermatogenesis at the younger age, but did stimulate it after the formation of spermatocytes had occurred. It seems possible, therefore, that cortisone stimulates the transformation of one type of germ cells (spermatocytes?) to another (spermatids?). This interpretation is not consistent with Leroy's conclusion (1953) that cortisone promotes testicular maturation in young cockerels. Unfortunately, Leroy gave no evidence to support his statement. Cortisone (Leroy, 1953), like androgen (Kumaran and Turner, 1949b), fails to prevent estrogen-induced inhibition of the testes and of comb size in the fowl.

An observation by Chester Jones (1957) on the relationship between testes and adrenals should be noted. He observed that the survival of adrenalectomized drakes was inversely related to testicular size at the time of operation. Castrated drakes required lower doses of corticosteroids for survival than did intact drakes. The explanation given was that testosterone secretions, by increasing the metabolism of the birds, might increase the requirement for the corticosteroids.

The effect of epinephrine on the gonads has not been studied in great detail. Wheeler, Searcy and Andrews (1942) observed that the injection of epinephrine into sexually mature fowl interfered with spermatogenesis and caused damage to the nuclei of the germ cells. In English sparrows adrenaline caused regression of the testes and disappearance of the black pigment from the beak. Adrenaline also prevented the gonad stimulation by gonadotrophins (Perry, 1941) but Wolfson (1945) could not confirm this finding for juncos, *Junco oreganus*, nor could Lyman (1942) for pigeons.

4. The Thyroid Gland

The thyroid gland is required for normal development of the testes and for the normal response of secondary sex organs and secondary sex characteristics to androgen.

After thyroidectomy sexual maturity is delayed temporarily and in some cases indefinitely (Benoit and Aron, 1934b; Benoit, 1936, 1937a; Greenwood and Chu, 1939; Payne, 1944; Blivaiss, 1947). The development of the penis of the Pekin drake (Benoit, 1937b) and of the comb of the rooster (Greenwood and Chu, 1939; Payne, 1944; Blivaiss, 1947) is inhibited after thyroidectomy. The lack of development of these organs, which are under androgen control, may be the result either of a lack of androgen secretion by the testes of thyroidectomized birds or of a diminished tissue responsiveness to androgen in the absence of thyroid hormone. Evidence that the last hypothesis may explain a large part of the smaller combs in thyroidectomized fowl was found in experiments conducted by Morris (1951). In these experiments with intact and thyroidectomized capons, androgen elicited a smaller response in the absence of thyroid hormone than in its presence.

Administration of thyroid hormone caused precocious sexual maturity of the drake (Jaap, 1933; Aron and Benoit, 1934) and chicken (Kumaran and Turner, 1949d) with an accompanying increase in comb size. Vaugien (1954) reported that administration of thyroxine to house sparrows during the sexual rest period resulted in recrudescence of the testes and spermatogenesis. Thus all the evidence seems to indicate that severe hypothyroidism interferes with testicular development whereas mild hyperthyroidism promotes spermatogenesis. The work of Woitkewitch, cited by Höhn (1950), showing that thyroidectomy of starlings in the summer prevents the degeneration of the testes in the fall, seems rather surprising. Such work should be confirmed before it is accepted, because it is contrary to observations made in all other species of birds on which data are available.

The effect of mild hypothyroidism induced by feeding thiouracil indicated that, at certain stages of development of the testes, hypothyroidism promotes earlier spermatogenesis (Kumaran and Turner, 1949d). However, the fact that the experimental groups sometimes contained only two birds and the well known great variability of testicular size during the stage of rapid testicular development makes it doubtful that the differences were significant. This great variability in testicular size should always be carefully considered in the design of experiments, because it means that large numbers of birds are required to demonstrate significant differences. An illustration of the relative variability of testicular size and stage of spermatogenesis can be found in the following coefficients of variability obtained in two experiments with 6-week-old White Leghorn roosters kept on experiment for 10 weeks. Groups were killed at 2-week intervals and body and endocrine organ weights recorded. Weights were expressed as milligrams per 100 grams and stage of spermatogenesis as scores 1 through 7. The following average coefficients of variability were found for 2 experiments: testicular weight, 80 per cent; comb weight, 38 per cent; thyroid weight, 24 per cent; adrenal weight, 31 per cent; body weight, 13 per cent; spermatogenesis, 40 per cent (van Tienhoven, Thomas and Dreesen, 1956). These coefficients are in excellent agreement with the figures published by Fox (1956) from experiments in which the testes had not yet undergone their great increase in size (the average testes weight was about 10 mg. in one experiment and 2.8 mg. in the other). Fox (1956) found that the coefficient of variability for body weight ranged between 4.8 to 14.1 per cent, for comb index between 14.0 to 40.1 per cent, and for testes weight between 27.6 to 160.0 per cent.

The results obtained by feeding of iodinated casein to different breeds of chickens at a variety of ages are somewhat contradictory. A review of these results has been published recently (Turner, 1959) and its repetition seems unnecessary.

5. Progesterone

Progesterone administration to cockerels reduces testicular size (Fox, 1955; Herrick and Adams, 1955), inhibits spermatogenesis (Herrick and Adams, 1956), and reduces comb size (Libby, Schaible, Meites and Reineke, 1953; Fox, 1955; Herrick and Adams, 1956). These effects are comparable with the inhibition of egg laying observed when progesterone is given in large doses to laying hens. Apparently there exists a species difference with respect to the effect of progesterone for Kar (1949) reported an increase of more than 75 per cent in testicular size when he administered 0.5 mg. progesterone per day for 30 days. Histologic examination showed that both tubules and Leydig cells were stimulated by the hormone. In this case, we might have an example of a hormone which stimulates the organ which secretes it, for Lofts and Marshall (1959) showed that progesterone is present in the tubules of hypophysectomized pigeons. Whether or not progesterone has a role in the regulation of the male pigeon's breeding cycle needs to be determined. If progesterone can stimulate the testes in the absence of the pituitary, as is the case for androgens (Chu and You, 1946), one might observe "cycles" in the absence of the anterior pituitary.

6. Estrogen

Two lines of indirect evidence suggest that estrogen is secreted by the avian male. (1) In some birds, as for instance in *Colymbiformes*, *Piciformes*, *Phalaropodidae*, and *Jacamidae* in which the male incubates the eggs, an incubation patch is formed just before incubation starts. Experimentally this incubation patch will only form under the combined effect of estrogen and prolactin (Bailey, 1952). (2) Estrogens have been isolated from the feces of roosters (Hurst, Kuksis and Bendell, 1957).

As far as the author is aware no evidence has been published in which the presence of estrogen in the blood was demonstrated. The indirect evidence, although presumptive, may have to be accepted to explain some phenomenon in the reproduction of birds.

The effects of estrogen administration have been studied extensively, both from an endocrinologic point of view and from the angle of practical applications in improving the quality and efficiency of poultry production. This subject has been reviewed expertly by Lorenz (1954). Therefore, only the aspects which involve the reproductive system will be mentioned here.

In young cockerels physiologic doses of estrogen will inhibit comb size, testicular size, and gonadotrophin secretion (Breneman, 1953). The same author demonstrated that comb growth is more sensitive to estrogen inhibition than testicular size. The latter in turn is more sensitive than gonadotrophin content of the pituitary. The difference in sensitivity between comb and testes has been confirmed (Bird, Pugsley and Klotz, 1947; Nalbandov and Baum, 1948; Boas and Ludwig, 1950). Lorenz (1959) mentions that the pituitary becomes less sensitive to estrogen-inhibition with increasing age. Other effects of estrogen, *e.g.*, lipemia, still manifest themselves at doses of estrogen which do not inhibit the pituitary. The inhibition of the comb by estrogen may be mediated also by an additional mechanism not involving the pituitary. Martin, Graves and Dohan (1955) surgically divided combs of capons in halves. All half combs received 2 μg. testosterone propionate and the other half of each comb received, in addition, 0, 80, 100, 160, or 200 μg. estrone. The results showed that the 100- and 200-μg. levels inhibited comb growth significantly. The lack of effect of the 160-μg. dose is puzzling, but the local effect of estrogen seems a real one. These experiments may mean that in adult hens, in which the pituitary apparently has become relatively insensitive to estrogen inhibition, large amounts of estrogen are required to inhibit the comb by local effect. Apparently, the estrogen-androgen ratio in the laying hen is not high enough to cause such a regression.

The question has been raised whether a temporary estrogen inhibition of the pituitary at a young age would have a "carryover" effect at older age, manifesting itself in delayed maturity, damage to testes, small comb, and decreased fertility. Reports in the literature (Akpinar and Shaffner, 1953; Eaton, Carson and Beall, 1955; Fraps, Sohn and Olsen, 1956) seem to indicate that estrogen inhibition may have a carry-over effect. However, in these cases estrogen pellets were implanted and the possibility exists that the pellets were not completely absorbed before sexual maturity. This suggestion receives support from the observation that estrogen administered as a paste did not show any carry-over effects (Eaton, Carson and Beall, 1955). Whether or not estrogen plays a role in the regulation of some of the reproductive functions of males cannot be stated definitely until evidence of estrogen secretion during various parts of the reproductive cycle has been obtained.

7. Nutrition

The importance of various nutrients for the normal development of the reproductive tract is hardly in doubt. Unfortunately, as Lutwak-Mann (1958) pointed out, few experiments have been carried out on the effects of nutritional deficiencies on reproduction of male birds, and in these the data presented were not statistically analyzed and do not lend themselves to such analysis. The conclusions reported here, therefore, may have to be accepted with reservations.

The lack of statistical analysis leads to a criticism of the design of some of the experiments, in which it was impossible to distinguish the effect of a specific deficiency from general inanition. The latter has been shown to be a cause of atrophy of the testes (Portier, 1920; Parker and McSpadden, 1943; Mason, 1949; chapter by Leathem).

Some of the studies on the effect of nutrition on reproduction in male birds have been directed to the problem of vitamin deficiencies. Of the fat-soluble vitamins, only A, D, and E have been studied in relation to their influence on male reproductive performance. Vitamin A deficiency leads to atrophy of the testes of roosters although body weight is not affected (Lowe, Morton, Cunningham and Vernon, 1957). This effect, therefore, is probably a specific deficiency symptom rather than a symptom of inanition. Feeding a vitamin A-deficient ration to mature cockerels resulted in a sharp decrease in the number of spermatozoa per ejaculate, whereas the incidence of morphologically abnormal and of nonmotile sperm increased. These symptoms all proved to be reversible when vitamin A was fed (Paredes and Garcia, 1959).

Vitamin E deficiency resulted in abnormal spermatozoa (Adamstone and Card, 1935) and atrophy of the testes (Adamstone and Card, 1934; Herrick, Eide and Snow,

1952). This atrophy may have been the result of a decrease of gonadotrophin secretion by the anterior pituitary (Herrick, Eide and Snow, 1952). Unfortunately, no data were given on body weights, so that it is not certain whether or not the observed effect was the result of starvation. In our laboratory, vitamin E deficiency has often resulted in a decrease in body weight, and thus it seems possible that, in the experiments cited, inanition may have been a contributing factor in causing testicular atrophy.

Feeding of vitamin D-deficient diets from 6 weeks of age caused a decreased testicular weight in cockerels 14 and 16 weeks of age. (Buckner, Insko, Henry and Wachs, 1951). Body weights of the vitamin-deficient birds were less than half those of the controls, thus indicating that inanition was a contributing factor.

Investigations of vitamin B deficiencies have been carried out by Haque, Lillie, Shaffner and Briggs (1949). Unfortunately, no statistical analysis of the data was reported nor do the published data lend themselves to analysis. An increase or decrease in testicular weight even at 50 per cent may not be significant, for under normal conditions testicular weight shows great variability. A vitamin deficiency may increase this variability even more, because some birds may have a genetically lower requirement than others. The latter statement finds support in the observations by Howes and Hutt (1952) and Lamoreux and Hutt (1939, 1948) that breeds differ in their nutritional requirements. On the basis of data available in the literature and after careful consideration of the possible effects of inanition Mason (1939) concluded that thiamine deficiency per se caused testicular dysfunction.

Haque, Lillie, Shaffner and Briggs (1949) determined the response of the comb to a standard dose of androgen in birds fed diets deficient in various vitamins. With the reservation that statistical analysis might prove them incorrect, the tentative conclusions may be drawn that deficiency of vitamin E, nicotinic acid, or riboflavin results in a greater than normal response of the comb. The explanation for this effect of nicotinic acid and of riboflavin may be that testosterone is not inactivated in the liver of these deficient birds. Evidence that these two vitamins are involved in the inactivation of estrogen (Singher, Kensler, Taylor, Rhoads and Unna, 1944; DeMeio, Rakoff, Cantarow and Paschkis, 1948) suggests that they may also be involved in the inactivation of testosterone. Such impairment of inactivation would result in high circulating testosterone levels. Evidence that would indicate whether or not vitamin E deficiency impairs liver function of chickens is not available, as far as I have been able to find, nor is evidence that vitamin E is involved in steroid hormone inactivation. Thus, the increased comb response to androgen in vitamin E deficiency may not with certainty be ascribed to effects of the vitamin on liver enzyme systems.

The effect of folic acid deficiency on testicular development and on the comb response to androgen has been investigated in experiments in which inanition effects were separated from specific folic acid effects by the paired feeding technique (Zarrow, Koretsky and Zarrow, 1951). The conclusion was that folic acid deficiency did not affect testes size of cockerels but that it did increase comb response to a standard dose of androgen. The latter was postulated to be the result of impaired inactivation of the testosterone by the liver.

8. Drugs

Brief mention has to be made of the effect of different drugs on testicular development. Some of these effects were first noted when the drugs were incorporated in poultry feeds to combat various diseases. Enheptin (2-amino,5-nitrothiazole) inhibits testicular and comb development, probably by inhibiting pituitary gonadotrophin secretion (Pino, Rosenblatt and Hudson, 1954). This conclusion is based on the lowered gonadotrophin content found in the pituitary of Enheptin-treated cockerels and also on the normal testicular development obtained after gonadotrophin treatment of Enheptin-fed cockerels. The related drug, 2-acetylamino-5-nitrothiazole, caused only slight, localized areas of atrophy of the seminiferous tubules and an accompanying decrease in semen volume without an effect on fertility (Cooper and Skulski, 1957).

Sulfamethazine, a coccidiostat, causes precocious testicular and comb development of cockerels (Asplin and Boyland, 1947) probably by way of an effect on the thyroid. Increased thyroid size with normal histology and normal I^{131} uptake per mg. thyroid led to the conclusion that sulfamethazine feeding caused slight hyperthyroidism (van Tienhoven, Thomas and Dreesen, 1956).

Nicarbazin, another coccidiostat which inhibits egg production (Baker, Hill, van Tienhoven and Bruckner, 1957), has no apparent effect on testicular size, semen characteristics, or fertility (van Tienhoven, Crawford and Duchaine, 1957).

Furazolidone N-(5-nitro-2-furfurylidene) -3-amino-2-oxazolidone, fed at a level of 0.011 per cent of the feed to combat Salmonella and Histomonas infections, delayed sexual maturity of turkey males. Apparently there is great variability in the response to this drug, for 4 of 30 males had not yielded any semen at 296 days of age, whereas the average age for the first ejaculate for the other 26 toms was 208 days, only one week later than the controls (Redman and Smyth, 1957). Cooper and Skulski (1955) noted that feeding of this drug (0.022 per cent of the feed) caused a marked decrease in testicular size at 12 weeks of age. The lack of an effect noted when either 0.011 or 0.022 per cent furazolidone was fed to 0- to 4-week-old cockerels (Francis and Shaffner, 1956) may have been a result of the younger age. If this drug interferes with the later stages of spermatogenesis, no difference would be noticeable at 4 weeks of age.

The mode of action, whereby the drug interferes with male reproduction, has not been established.

In general, our knowledge of the effect of nutrition and of pharmacologic agents on avian male reproduction is fragmentary compared with our knowledge of the same subject in mammals, although the rooster should be a good experimental animal for studying the interaction between metabolic factors and the functioning of the testis.

C. FERTILIZATION AND SPERM PHYSIOLOGY

1. In Vivo

Unlike most mammalian sperm, avian spermatozoa retain their fertilizing capacity for a long time *in vivo*. Exceptions are the sperm of bats and of *Armadillum vulgare* (Mann, 1954). The long functional survival of the sperm is correlated with an interesting anatomic adaptation of the infundibulum of the oviduct. Van Drimmelen (1951) found "sperm nests," small crypts, in the oviduct with groups of sperm in them. The heads of the sperm were oriented towards the oviducal wall and the tails towards the lumen (Fig. 18.9). Their location corresponds to the site of fertilization experimentally established by Olsen and Neher (1948). According to Grigg (1957), who passed a cellophane bag filled with Ringer's solution through the oviduct and found many sperm in the oviducal lumen, the sperm are apparently released into the lumen of the oviduct by the passage of the egg.

The sperm nest may serve three purposes: (1) to ensure the presence of large numbers of sperm when required; (2) to supply nutrients to the sperm; (3) to remove the waste products of sperm metabolism. Unfortunately, too little is known about avian sperm metabolism to permit a reasonable estimate of the importance of these nests.

After their release into the oviducal lumen, the sperm can penetrate the vitelline membrane and effect fertilization. Penetration of the vitelline membrane by more than one sperm was noted in *Aves* by Olsen (1942). These extra sperm are called the supernumerary sperm, and special significance has been given to them by Kushner (1954). When the sperm, which fuses with the female pronucleus, and the supernumerary sperm are from different males, the resulting chicks are alleged to have increased vigor, to have increased hemoglobin content, and, in some cases, to have characters from both sires (Kushner, 1954). The suggestion of bipaternity in birds had been made earlier by Hollander (1949) to account for some mosaics in which sex-linked color patterns were involved in pigeons. The

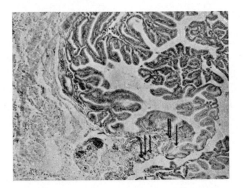

FIG. 18.9. Sperm nests in the infundibulum of the oviduct of the fowl (van Drimmelen, 1951). (From G. C. van Drimmelen, J. Vet. Res., Suppl. 1, 1951.)

hypothesis of bipaternity was tested by Alterkirch, Hoffmann and Schaaf (1955) for fowl. Male breeds with definite genetic markers were used. In 57 offspring obtained from hens mated in short succession to such males, no evidence of bipaternity was found.

Nalbandov and Card (1943a) pointed out that sperm, during their sojourn in the oviduct, may undergo changes which cause abnormal development of the embryo. The aging of spermatozoa in the oviduct not only decreased fertilizing capacity, but also increased embryonic mortality. Dharmarajan (1950) confirmed these results and established that most of the abnormalities were in the nervous and vascular system. McCartney (1951) and Hale (1955) made similar observations of increased embryonic mortality in turkeys. Lorenz (1959), who reviewed the literature which appeared before as well as after Nalbandov's and Card's publication, concluded that the available data were consistent with this concept of increased embryonic mortality as a result of fertilization by "stale" sperm. The observed deleterious effect of aging of gametes has also been observed in mammals. In them the aging of ova, but not of sperm, has also led to abnormalities in embryos. This interesting phenomenon is discussed in the chapter by Blandau and in a review by Young (1953).

It seems logical to assume that abnormal embryonic development after fertilization by stale sperm is the result of nuclear damage. Experiments with sperm subjected to x-ray irradiation have yielded results paralleling those obtained with stale sperm. Kosin (1944) established that embryonic mortality after fertilization with irradiated sperm occurred mostly during the first 4 or 5 days of incubation. This time of maximal mortality is the same as found by Nalbandov and Card (1943a) for aged sperm. Not enough data are available in the papers of Kosin (1944) and Dharmarajan (1950) to compare the kinds of abnormalities found. The effect of fertilization by sperm stored *in vitro* on embryonic development has not been studied extensively, largely because of the lack of fertility obtained with stored semen. Wilcox and Shorb (1958) were able to obtain good fertility with semen stored 26.5 hours. No effect on embryonic mortality was observed. Lake, Schindler and Wilcox (1959), in experiments which involved storing rooster semen for 37 to 38 hours, found a decrease in hatchability of fertile eggs and a statistical analysis of their

TABLE 18.3

Comparison of the composition of bull and rooster seminal plasma

All values expressed as mg. per 100 ml.

	Bull	Ref.	Rooster	Ref.
Na	289	5	378–428	6
K	155	5	39–49	6
Ca	39	5	6.9–9.3	6
Mg	11.6	4	8.4	6
B	1.48	4		
Cu	1.36	4	0.145	6
Zn	0.02	4	0.18	6
Cl	154	5	197–212	6
Glucose	0	2	41	2
Fructose	540	2	4	2
Lactic acid	35	2	0	8
Total phosphorus	55	2		
Glutamate	7.75	1	890–1340	7
Nonprotein N			142.8	7
Freezing point	.53	2	0.64	3

References:
1. Sarkar, Luecke and Duncan, 1947.
2. Mann, 1954.
3. Schindler, Weinstein, Moses and Gabriel, 1955.
4. Cragle, Salisbury and Muntz, 1958.
5. Cragle, Salisbury and VanDemark, 1958.
6. Lake, Butler, McCallum and MacIntyre, 1958.
7. Lake and McIndoe, 1959.
8. Personal observations, 1959.

data by me showed that storage of the semen resulted in increased embryonic mortality ($p < 0.01$). (In the analysis all the data were pooled for stored semen and for fresh semen.) Moravec, Mussehl and Pace (1954) observed a sharp increase in embryonic mortality after insemination of turkeys with semen stored 24, 48, and 72 hours. The data from these two experiments are not conclusive, but there is an indication that aging of fowl semen *in vitro* may have the same effects as aging *in vivo*. Nalbandov (1958) has stated, without presenting the evidence, that such was the case.

2. In Vitro

The long functional survival of the avian sperm *in vivo* stands in sharp contrast to the low fertility obtained after storage of fowl and turkey spermatozoa *in vitro*. Mammalian sperm, on the other hand, have been stored *in vitro* with relatively little loss in fertilizing capacity. It seems, therefore, fruitful to compare the various metabolic and physiologic characteristics of avian and mammalian sperm. A detailed review of the composition of cock semen and the metabolic behavior of fowl and turkey sperm *in vitro* has been published recently (Lorenz, 1959). Some observations made in our laboratory will be added here and a comparison of some aspects of the physiology of avian and mammalian sperm will be made. Bovine semen and rooster semen have been selected as representatives of the mammalian and avian classes. The selection was largely based on the amount of data available on the sperm physiology of these species. From Table 18.3 a comparison can be made of the differences in composition of the seminal plasma. One of the most striking differences is in the glutamate content. *In vitro* studies in our laboratory showed that dilution of semen with seminal plasma or Tyrode solution, 1 part semen to 4 parts diluent, did not affect respiration rate (van Tienhoven, 1960). However, it was noted that storage of avian semen in Tyrode solution decreased respiration rate and rate of fructolysis, and increased abnormal sperm (El Zayat and van Tienhoven, 1959). These effects were found to be caused by chloride ions, for the

TABLE 18.4

Comparison of the in vitro metabolism of bull and rooster spermatozoa under various experimental conditions

Factor Investigated	Bull Semen	Rooster Semen
Glucose	Metabolized to lactic acid (2)	As bull semen (9)
		Conversion to fructose (7)
Fructose	Metabolized to lactic acid (2)	As bull semen (9)
	Glucose metabolized preferentially to fructose (7)	As bull semen (9)
	Metabolized at same rate as glucose	Metabolized slower than glucose (9)
Phosphate	Depresses respiration (5)	Depresses respiration (9)
	Increase fructolysis (5)	Depresses fructolysis (9)
Glycine	Increases respiration rate (6)	Decreases respiration rate (9)
	Decreases lactate gain (6)	Same as bull semen (9)
	Reduces fructose loss in synthetic media (6)	Same as bull semen (9)
	Metabolized to CO_2 (4)	Not metabolized to CO_2 (8)
Dilution	Increases respiration (3)	Decreases respiration (9)

References,
1. van Tienhoven, Salisbury, VanDemark and Hansen, 1952.
2. Mann, 1954.
3. Bishop and Salisbury, 1955.
4. Flipse, 1956.
5. Blackshaw, Salisbury and VanDemark, 1957.
6. Flipse and Almquist, 1958.
7. Lorenz, 1959.
8. van Tienhoven, unpublished, 1959.
9. van Tienhoven, 1960.

incidence of abnormalities was linearly proportional to the concentration of chloride ions. Replacement of chloride ions by phosphate or glutamate prevented the sperm abnormalities and partly prevented the decrease in metabolic rates (El Zayat, 1960). On further investigation, it was found that phosphate decreased the initial metabolic rates, whereas glutamate did not. Glutamate was found to "spare" the utilization of fructose; apparently, glutamate itself was metabolized to yield CO_2. In many of the experiments in which efforts were made to store semen *in vitro*, the diluents contained chloride ions which from our observations clearly seem to damage the sperm. Replacing chloride with glutamate in a diluent might prevent the loss of fertilizing capacity during storage. Lake (1958) has shown that a diluent high in glutamate can support the maintenance of the fertilizing capacity of sperm for at least 24 hours. Thus, one of the main differences between bull and rooster semen may lie in a difference in sensitivity to chloride ions. Foote (1950) has shown that a Tyrode solution supported bull sperm viability better than any other synthetic diluent. It remains to be determined whether glutamate would improve sperm viability in a bovine semen diluent.

Some other differences between bull and rooster sperm are tabulated in Table 18.4. At the moment the significance of these differences is not known, partly because not enough data are available for rooster sperm to correlate *in vitro* findings with fertilizing capacity.

III. The Female

A. THE GONADS

1. The Right (Rudimentary) Gonad

With few exceptions such as *Accipitrinae, Falconinae, Buteoninae, Cathartidae*, birds normally have only one functional (left) ovary, the right gonad is either absent or very small (Domm, 1939; Stanley and Witschi, 1940). This asymmetry of gonadal development is already noticeable during embryonic development. In the duck (*Anas platyrhynchos*) primordial germ cells migrate to the left and right gonad primordium in equal numbers until the 28 to 37-somite stage is reached (75 to 85 hours of incubation). After this, more primordial germ cells migrate to the left, and after about 125 hours of incubation a difference in the asymmetry between different embryos led van Limborgh (1957) to deduce that an embryo was female if less than 41 per cent of the total number of primordial germ cells was present in the right gonad, whereas it was male if more than 45 per cent were present in the right gonad. Simon (1960) on the basis of an extensive study concluded that van Limborgh's conclusions were erroneous and that the ratio of primordial germ cells in left and right gonad of the 25 to 32-somite stage chick embryo cannot be used to determine the sex of the embryo. As both authors base their conclusions on statistical considerations of normal and abnormal sex ratios further work using cytologic techniques needs to be performed. Kosin and Ishizaki (1959) established that the presence or absence of sex chromatin in the nucleus permits sex identification of chicks. The sex chromatin is found in birds in the cells of females as it is in mammals, in spite of the fact that in birds the female is the heterogametic sex. Ohno, Kaplan and Kinosita (1960) have proposed that the sex chromatin of chickens represents a single Z chromosome in positive heteropycnosis.

Stanley and Witschi (1940) compared the asymmetric gonads of embryonic chicks with the symmetric gonads in *Accipiter cooperii, Buteo amiansis borealis,* and *Circus cyaneus hudsonius*. They found that the distribution of primordial germ cells between the left and right gonads in these latter species was still essentially symmetric at a stage of development when asymmetry already had developed in the chick. They offered the explanation that, in the chick, primordial germ cells migrate from the right to left, thus disturbing the initial symmetric arrangement. Van Limborgh (1957) tested this hypothesis by dividing the duck embryo medially and thus destroying all vascular and other connections between the left and right side. In the surviving embryos the asymmetry was not different from untreated controls. On the basis of other experiments van Limborgh came to the conclusion that the asymmetric distribution of primordial germ cells could not be explained by the fact that the embryo lies with its left side towards the yolk so that the left gonad may be better vascularized (an explanation proposed by Dantschakoff and Guelin-Sche-

drina (1933) nor could it be explained by the secretion of hormones by the gonads which inhibit or stimulate the asymmetric migration of the primordial germ cells.

The riddle of the asymmetrical distribution of the primordial germ cells still remains unsolved and no real explanation can be given for the difference between the hawks and other birds. The right ovary of the hawks is apparently functional, for no histologic differences between it and the left ovary have been found (von Faber, 1958). Domm (1939) states that yolks can be ovulated from these right ovaries; he postulated that such yolks might be transported through the left oviduct, for the right oviduct is either missing or vestigial (Stanley and Witschi, 1940; von Faber, 1958). Domm based his hypothesis on the absence of yolk material in the body cavity. It has since been shown that yolk can be absorbed from the body cavity in less than 24 hours (Sturkie, 1955a). An additional reason for believing that Domm's hypothesis is probably incorrect is that the dorsal mesentery makes it impossible for a yolk to move from the right to the left side of the body cavity. This anatomic arrangement occurs in chickens and it probably is the same in hawks. It is rather difficult to understand the evolutionary significance of the presence of two ovaries with only one oviduct and the occurrence of this arrangement in only one order.

The postembryonic development of the fowl's right gonad after sinistral ovariectomy has been investigated in different laboratories. Domm (1939) reviewed the literature which had been published to that time. Only the salient features pointed out by Domm and new evidence obtained since then will be presented here.

Ovariectomy before 30 days of age results in the development of the right gonad into a testis or an ovotestis, either of which may exhibit active spermatogenesis (Domm, 1939; Kornfeld and Nalbandov, 1954; Kornfeld, 1957) sometimes even at an earlier age than in cockerels of the same breed (Taber, Claytor, Knight, Flowers, Gambrell and Ayers, 1958). Later ovariectomy results in a greater incidence of ovotestes and ovaries than does ovariectomy before 30 days of age. Some of these right ovaries resulting from sinistral ovariectomy have follicles which can be ovulated (Nalbandov, 1959a). A number of observations indicate that the apparent effect of the age at which ovariectomy is performed on the type of development of the rudiment has an endocrinologic basis. (1) The 20-day-old chick secretes detectable amounts of estrogen as determined by bioassay of the blood (Kornfeld and Nalbandov, 1954). (2) Small doses of estrogen (2 μg. per 100 gm.) inhibit the development of the rudimentary gonad of ovariectomized pullets (Kornfeld and Nalbandov, 1957; Kornfeld, 1958). These doses are too small to affect oviduct weight significantly and may, thus, be in the range of the amounts secreted by the immature ovary. (3) If the rudiment develops in spite of estrogen treatment, the incidence of ovaries and ovotestes is greater than that of testes (Taber and Salley, 1954; Kornfeld and Nalbandov, 1954). Histologic examinations show also that estrogen inhibits medullary tissue more than cortical tissue (Taber, Claytor, Knight, Flowers, Gambrell and Ayers, 1958).

The following explanation of the age effect is thus in agreement with the experimental evidence. Estrogen secretion by the left ovary inhibits the development of the medullary tissue of the right gonad. If this inhibition is removed before 30 days, the medulla can still proliferate. By 30 days of age the estrogen inhibition has apparently destroyed the potential of the medulla to develop and thus no proliferation occurs even when the inhibition is removed. It is understood, of course, that this critical point may vary between individuals within a strain and even more so from strain to strain.

The possible stimulation of cortical tissue development by estrogen is not as clear-cut. Taber and Salley's (1954) and Kornfeld and Nalbandov's (1954) experiments indicate that estrogen favors the development of cortical tissue. However, in a series of experiments by Taber, Claytor, Knight, Flowers, Gambrell and Ayers (1958) involving large numbers of birds, no evidence was obtained that would support such a conclusion.

The development of the rudimentary gonad seems to be under the control of the anterior pituitary. Hypophysectomy (Kornfeld and Nalbandov, 1954), prolactin injections (Kornfeld and Nalbandov, 1954), and estrogen administration (Taber and Salley, 1954; Kornfeld and Nalbandov, 1954; Kornfeld, 1958; Taber, Claytor, Knight, Flowers, Gambrell and Ayers, 1958) inhibit its development. However, replacement therapy in the case of hypophysectomized birds (Kornfeld and Nalbandov, 1954) or in the case of estrogen-inhibited birds (Kornfeld and Nalbandov, 1954; Kornfeld, 1958; Taber, Claytor, Knight, Flowers, Gambrell and Ayers, 1958) does not stimulate the rudiment, nor do mammalian or avian gonadotrophins in poulards (sinistrally ovariectomized hens) (Kornfeld and Nalbandov, 1954; Kornfeld, 1958; Taber, Claytor, Knight, Flowers, Gambrell and Ayers, 1958). The lack of development in the rudiment cannot be explained by the lack of the "third gonadotrophin," because, in some of these investigations, chicken pituitary preparations were used (Kornfeld, 1958; Taber, Claytor, Knight, Flowers, Gambrell and Ayers, 1958). It seems that the estrogen inhibits the rudiment by a direct action, as proposed by Kornfeld (1958). Recently, Kornfeld (1960) obtained additional evidence that estrogen is the main agent preventing development of the rudiment. Injections of 17α-ethyl-19-nortestosterone, an anti-estrogen, resulted in its development to four times the control size in 100-day-old chickens. The lack of development after hypophysectomy in the poulard may be the result of deficiency of thyroid or adrenal hormones or of generalized metabolic disturbances caused by the hypophysectomy. It is known that adrenalectomy (Hewitt, 1947) or inanition (Taber, Salley and Knight, 1956) inhibits rudimentary gonad development, and hypophysectomy causes a sharp decrease in thyroid weight (Baum and Meyer, 1956). As has already been shown in this chapter, reduced thyroid activity severely restricts gonadal development. The inhibitory effect of prolactin on rudiment development may be explained by a direct inhibitory effect of prolactin on the rudiment or by possible side effects of prolactin which cause metabolic disturbances that interfere with development of the rudiment.

Miller (1938) utilized the occurrence of spermatogenesis in the rudimentary gonad in an ingenious procedure for identifying the sex chromosome. Study of actively dividing spermatocytes in a normal testes and in a rudimentary gonad revealed that the 5th largest chromosome, a V-shaped one, was not paired in the rudiments, but was paired in the testes from a normal male, thereby proving that this chromosome is the sex chromosome.

Development of the rudimentary gonad after ovariectomy occurs in ducks and songbirds (Nalbandov, 1958) but not in turkeys (Domm, 1939). In addition to those that can be attributed to the activity of the rudiment, other sex abnormalities sometimes occur. Crew (1923) documented a case in which a bird laid eggs and subsequently "sired" offspring. The bird had two testes with *vasa deferentia* and a diseased ovary and thus was a true hermaphrodite. Hutt (1937) reported a case in which a chicken was first more like a pullet, later showed male characteristics and produced spermatozoa (incapable of fertilization), and later looked more like a female. The bird on autopsy had a testis and *vas deferens* on the right and an ovary and oviduct on the left side. This bird was a gynandromorph, as was evident from the feather pattern which was light on the left side (one sex chromosome), dark on the right (two sex chromosomes), and from the fact that the right side exceeded the left in size. The cases reported by Crew (1923) and Hutt (1937) show that "sex reversals" can occur without involvement of the rudimentary female gonad. Benoit (1950a) listed other instances in which the same phenomenon occurred.

2. The Ovary

The ovary is attached to the body wall by a short mesovarium. In the quiescent state the ovary is a small, flat, yellow organ with small (< 1 mm.) follicles. In the active state it is a large organ composed of 5 to 6 large follicles filled with yellow yolk and a larger number of smaller follicles filled with white yolk. The large follicles are graded in size whereas the smaller follicles are more uniform. In addition to these follicles one may find atretic follicles; in the early stages of atresia they look somewhat like a shriveled balloon but later may become small, dark yellow, flabby masses. After ovulations the ovary also contains ruptured follicles. These ruptured follicles disappear rapidly in the fowl and the rook, *Corvus f. frugilegus* L. (Marshall and Coombs, 1957), but they persist until the end of the breeding season in pheasants. Counts have been made of these follicles to determine the egg production of pheasants (Kabat, Buss and Meyer, 1948; Buss, Meyer and Kabat, 1951).

The ovary is innervated by the nerves from the abdominal and pelvic plexuses and from the posterior continuation of the sympathetic trunk (Bradley, 1950). It receives its blood from the ovarian artery which is usually a branch of the left renolumbar artery but occasionally is a branch of the dorsal aorta (Nalbandov and James, 1949). The ovarian artery divides and sends 2 to 4 branches to each follicular stalk. Spiral arteries provide the main blood supply in the wall of the follicle; these spiral arteries constrict when the ruptured follicle collapses and thus little if any bleeding occurs at ovulation. The ovarian venous system is much more extensively developed than the arterial system. Nalbandov and James (1949) classified the venous system of the follicles in 3 layers: (1) a capillary network in the theca of the follicle that drains by venules into (2) a complex network peripheral to the first layer that drains into (3) a third venous layer consisting mainly of a few large veins that drain into the follicular stalk. The large veins from different follicles anastomose and drain into either the anterior or the posterior ovarian vein both of which empty into the *vena cava*.

Histologic examination of the ovary reveals the presence of the left adrenal and the epoophoron embedded in the stroma (Biswal, 1954). The large follicles (Fig. 18.10) consist of the very vascular *theca folliculi*, the basement membrane, the granulosa, and the vitelline membrane which surrounds the yolk. An area which macroscopically seems free of blood vessels stands out sharply in the follicular wall. This area, the stigma, is the place where the follicle ruptures. On microscopic examination, small blood vessels are found to cross the stigma (Nalbandov and James, 1949). In the *theca interna* of the rook Marshall and Coombs (1957) found large glandular cells whose cytoplasm contains lipid droplets, similar to those in the Leydig cells of the male. The cells are considered by Marshall and Coombs to be the source of estrogen. In addition to the thecal gland cells, Marshall and Coombs distinguished exfollicular gland cells which may arise from fibroblasts that migrate from the theca into the lumen of atretic follicles. After collapse of such follicles the cells are freed into the stroma. Although they resemble the Leydig cells histologically these cells are not homologous with them, because they arise from follicles and not from stromal tissue. The female Leydig cells, which may be considered homologous with the male Leydig cells, arise from connective tissue cells and may be the source of androgen in the female. After rupture of the mature follicle the thecal gland cells disappear and the empty follicles are invaded by erythrocytes, lymphocytes, and a very large number of fibroblasts. In birds there is no structure that may be regarded as homologous with the mammalian *corpus luteum*. The references to the ruptured follicles as an avian *corpus luteum* by Pearl and Boring (1918), Novak and Duschak (1923), and Bradley (1950) are erroneous.

3. Function of the Ovary

The avian ovary produces gametes and hormones which play an integral role in the production of the egg.

GAMETOGENESIS. Gametogenesis starts in the embryo, so primary oocytes with chromosomes in the bivalent state (Hutt, 1949) at the time of hatching are present in the ovary. During the long interval between the time of hatching and about 4 to 5 hours before ovulation, little activity takes place in the nucleus. In sharp contrast, large amounts of yolk are deposited in the follicle in the 8 to 9 days before ovulation.

About 24 hours before ovulation, the breakdown of the germinal vesicle starts (Olsen, 1942), but nuclear changes are not yet noticeable. The reduction division is

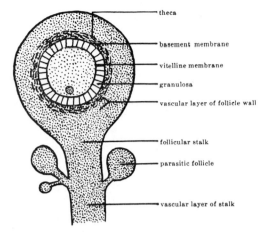

FIG. 18.10. Histology of ovarian follicle of the chicken according to Nalbandov and James (1949). (From A. V. Nalbandov and M. F. James, Am. J. Anat., **85**, 347–378, 1949.)

completed about 2 hours before ovulation in both the fowl and the turkey (Olsen and Fraps, 1944, 1950). Thus the sex of the future embryo is determined at ovulation and not at fertilization, as it is in mammals. Investigations to determine the primary sex ratio on fowl, possible only in hatches with 100 per cent fertility and no embryonic death before sex differentiation, have shown it to be unity (Hays, 1945; Landauer, 1957). The nuclear changes in the primary oocyte leading to extrusion of the first polar body and formation of the secondary oocyte are apparently under the control of LH, because LH injections produce such changes prematurely (Olsen and Fraps, 1950). The secondary oocyte extrudes the second polar body after sperm penetration of the vitelline membrane (Olsen, 1942; Olsen and Fraps, 1944).

During gametogenesis aberrations can occur which lead to parthenogenetic embryos. In certain strains of turkeys the incidence of parthenogenesis may be as high as 100 per cent (Poole and Olsen, 1958). The occurrence of parthenogenesis in birds may have been discovered as early as 1872, as was pointed out by Fraps (1955). Parthenogenesis occurs in turkeys (Olsen and Marsden, 1953, 1954, 1956; Olsen, 1956) and chickens (Olsen, 1956; Poole and Olsen, 1958). Only a small fraction of the eggs showing parthenogenetic development developed into normal embryos and only a few poults have ever been hatched from these. Such poults have always been males and so have the embryos that died but could be sexed (Poole and Olsen, 1957). The embryos have the diploid chromosome number (Yao and Olsen, 1955; Poole, 1959). Poole (1959) has classified the possibilities whereby parthenogenetic turkeys with 2N chromosomes could be formed as: (1) suppression of meiosis I or reentry of the first polar body followed by reduction division; (2) suppression of meiosis II or reentry of the second polar body; (3) nuclear but not cytoplasmic division of the mature haploid ovum.

The observation that all parthenogenetic embryos from turkeys have been males makes it probable that the explanation (1) is not correct, because it would lead one to expect some female offspring. In birds the second polar body is not extruded until the sperm penetrates the egg, so the second mechanism is probably the correct one because the possibility for the two nuclei of the ovum and the second polar body to fuse would exist in this case.

Linkage studies with males obtained from parthenogenetic development are needed to provide the answer whether possibly 2 or 3 is the correct one (Poole, 1959). Attempts to increase the incidence of parthenogenesis have been made in order to find the possible cause of parthenogenesis, and the following factors have been mentioned as causes of parthenogenesis.

1. Olsen and Marsden (1953) suggested on the basis of experiments in which turkey hens were housed such that they could see and hear or not see and hear turkey toms, that sound and sight of other turkeys would increase the incidence of parthenogenetic development. The explanation was suggested on the assumption that a neural mechanism would cause the release of a pituitary hormone involved in triggering parthenogenetic changes in the oocyte. The hypothesis that such a hormone might exist was founded on evidence that LH injections and also "spontaneous" LH release cause maturation changes in the nucleus of the ovum and cause extrusion of the first polar body (Olsen and Fraps, 1950). Unfortunately, in the experiments of Olsen and Marsden cited above, the effect of sound and sight of other turkeys cannot be separated from the effect of confinement in cages *versus* confinement in larger pens and from the effect of artificial light *versus* natural daylight. In other words, the effect assigned to sound and sight of other turkeys might have been caused also by differences in confinement or differences in light. In a second experiment by Olsen and Marsden (1956) the results were reversed: birds that could hear and see other males laid fewer eggs showing more parthenogenetic development than those hens that could not see, but might have been able to hear the males. From these experiments one might conclude that environment may play a role in increasing the incidence of parthenogenesis; however, to determine which part of the environment plays this role will require a better design such as factorial designs.

2. Olsen (1956) made the interesting observation that vaccination with fowl pox vaccine increased the incidence of parthenogenesis in a strain of turkeys in which this trait already occurred. The mechanism whereby this vaccine might act has not been determined.

During the period between hatching of the chick and ovulation, many changes take place in the follicle. The major change is the deposition of yolk which occurs usually in three phases.

1. The phase of slow yolk deposition which starts in the embryo and continues for several months or years depending on the species. During this period of yolk deposition, the follicle is formed around the vitelline membrane.

2. The intermediate phase of yolk formation during which transparent vacuoles appear and during which yolk is formed inside the vacuoles (Marza and Marza, 1935). This phase lasts about 60 days.

3. The phase of rapid yolk formation. During this phase initially white yolk and later yellow yolk is formed and the latebra becomes distinguishable. This period starts 10 to 14 days before ovulation and ends at ovulation. This phase is very rapid, and yolk formation accounts almost entirely for the enormous gain in weight which the ovary undergoes during the 10 to 12 days before ovulation starts. Data of Nalbandov

and James (1949) show that the chicken ovary may weigh 2 gm. at 150 days of age and 20 gm. at 180 days. A single follicle may increase in weight from 1 to 16 gm. in 9 days. The yellow yolk deposited during this phase is rich in lipids (50 per cent of the dry matter); it contains large amounts of cholesterol and is rich in vitellin.

The mechanism of yolk deposition is poorly understood, especially the apparent change in the selective permeability of the follicular membranes during the three phases of follicular growth and yolk formation. Although changes in the blood chemistry under the influence of estrogen in all probability play a role in mobilizing the yolk precursors, these changes do not guarantee the deposition of yolk in the follicle. Undoubtedly, the anterior pituitary hormones influence the permeability of the follicular membranes, but how they do so is not known.

ENDOCRINE ACTIVITY OF THE OVARY AND THE EFFECTS OF HORMONES. Adequate evidence exists to show that the avian ovary secretes three hormones, estrogen, androgen, and progesterone. Evidence for the secretion of each of these hormones will be presented together with the physiologic effects of the hormones as they pertain to reproduction.

1. Estrogen. Estrogen secretion by the ovary was demonstrated by Marlow and Richert (1940) by extraction procedures followed by bioassay of the extract. Subsequent chemical analyses demonstrated that the ovary of the laying hen contains estradiol, estrone, and estriol (Layne, Common, Maw and Fraps, 1958). Estrone is present in the blood in the conjugated fraction. Kornfeld and Nalbandov (1954) had previously demonstrated the presence of a biologically active estrogen in the blood of 16- to 20-day-old pullets. The evidence strongly favors the concept that estrogen is secreted by the ovary and that secretion starts during embryonic development (see chapter by Burns). The thecal gland cells are considered to be the source of estrogen (Marshall and Coombs, 1957).

Estrogens have many effects on the physiologic processes of birds. Extensive reviews have been published on various aspects of the effects of estrogens (Nalbandov, 1953;

Lorenz, 1954; Sturkie, 1954; Stammler, Katz, Pick and Rodbard, 1955; Urist, 1959), so only the most salient features will be mentioned here.

Estrogen administration causes an enlargement of the oviducts and its ligaments, an effect which will be discussed more extensively later in this chapter. In addition to this effect on a secondary sex organ, estrogens cause marked changes in the composition of the blood which are summarized in Table 18.5. The substantial agreement with respect to their nature makes it unnecessary to include all the publications on this subject. Extensive further documentation can be found in the reviews.

Investigations have been conducted in order to determine the mechanisms involved in the production of some of the changes in blood composition. The lipid and phospholipid responses can be obtained in chickens on a fat-free diet and in hypophysectomized chickens (Baum and Meyer, 1956). The responses require the normal functioning of the liver (Ranney and Chaikoff, 1951; Vanstone, Dale, Oliver and Common, 1957). The increases in plasma protein and phosphoprotein are also dependent on normal functioning of the liver (Vanstone, Dale, Oliver and Common, 1957). Thyroid hormone administration together with estrogen abolishes the estrogen-induced lipemia (Fleischmann and Fried, 1945; Hertz, Schricker and Tullner, 1951), proteinemia (Sturkie, 1951), increase in serum vitellin (Hosoda, Kaneko, Mogi and Abe, 1954), increase in biotin (Hertz, Dhyse and Tullner, 1949), and calcemia (Fleischmann and Fried, 1945). The mechanism of this inhibition is not clear, but it seems to involve a different mechanism of action of estrogen from that which produces oviducal growth, for estrogen-induced oviducal development is not affected by simultaneous thyroxine treatment (Fleischmann and Fried, 1945; Hertz, Schricker and Tullner, 1949; Hosoda, Kaneko, Mogi and Abe, 1954).

Intensive studies have been made of the effect of estrogen on calcium metabolism; Urist (1959) has given a detailed account. He established that administration of 100 mg. estrone per week to either roosters or laying hens caused the deposition of large

TABLE 18.5
Changes in blood composition after estrogen administration

Component	Sex	Control	Estrogen	Reference
Total lipids, mg. per 100 ml........	M	1100	14210	Urist, 1959
Phospolipids, mg. per cent plasma..	M	162	934	Ranney, Entenman and Chaikoff, 1949
Sphingomyelin, mg. per cent plasma	M	22	54	Ranney, Entenman and Chaikoff, 1949
Cephalin, mg. per cent plasma....	M	34	214	Ranney, Entenman and Chaikoff, 1949
Cholesterol, mg. per cent plasma...	M	235	1136	Stammler, Katz, Pick and Rodbard, 1955
Total protein, gm. per 100 ml. serum..........................	M	3.90	7.40	Urist, 1959
Albumen, gm. per 100 ml. serum...	M	1.00	0.60	Urist, 1959
Globulin, gm. per 100 ml. serum...	M	2.90	6.80	Urist, 1959
Vitellin (dilution detected)........	F	0	40	Hosoda, Kaneko, Mogi and Abe, 1955
Hemoglobin gm. per 100 ml........	F	9	5.6	Ramsay and Campbell, 1956
Total vitamin A, μg. per 100 ml...	F	5.1	46.8	Gardiner, Phillips, Maw and Common, 1952
Vitamin A ester, μg. per 100 ml....	F	0.9	42.8	Gardiner, Phillips, Maw and Common, 1952
Vitamin A alcohol, μg. per 100 ml...	F	4.2	4.0	Gardiner, Phillips, Maw and Common, 1952
Riboflavin, p.p.m.................	F	Trace?	1.22	Common and Bolton, 1946
Biotin (water sol.), mμg. per ml......	F	1.3 ± 0.22	8.3 ± 1.8	Hertz, Dhyse and Tullner, 1949
Ca, mg. per 100 ml................	M	10	97	Urist, 1959
U.F. Ca, mg. per 100 ml..........	M	6.50	8.00	Urist, 1959
Mn, μg. per 100 ml..............	F	None*	13.8	Bolton, 1955
Inorganic phosphate, mg. per 100 ml.............................	M	6.20	20.00	Urist, 1959
Total sulfate, mg. per 100 ml.......	M	5.80	1.70	Urist, 1959
Iron, μg. per 100 ml. plasma......	F	100	700	Ramsay and Campbell, 1956

* Controls were nonlaying hens, treated were 11-week-old pullets.

amounts of intramedullary bone whether the birds were on a diet with enough calcium or on one completely deficient in calcium.

The Ca-deficient diet was also deficient in vitamin D in order to further reduce the intestinal absorption of Ca. Birds fed the Ca-deficient diet deposited somewhat more medullary bone after estrogen treatment than did the estrogenized birds fed a Ca-adequate diet. The bone cortex of the Ca-deficient estrogen-treated birds showed resorption cavities and osteoporosis (Urist, 1959). Apparently, the intramedullary bone deposition occurs at the expense of the calcium from the flat bones. Estrogen treatment results in an increase in blood calcium, mainly in nondiffusible Ca (Polin and Sturkie, 1958; Urist, 1959). Discussion of this increase in blood calcium levels requires

consideration of the role of the parathyroids on Ca metabolism. Estrogen administration causes an increase in size of the parathyroids (Landauer, 1954) and of activity, as measured histologically (Benoit, 1950b; von Faber, 1954). Is this increase coincidental or physiologic? The following observations may allow the formulation of a tentative explanation for the interaction between estrogen and the parathyroid hormone.

a. Parathyroid hormone administration results in greater increase in total blood calcium in hens than in roosters (Polin, Sturkie and Hunsaker, 1957).

b. Parathyroidectomy results in a decrease in total calcium (Clavert, 1948; Polin and Sturkie, 1957) diffusible and nondiffusible; the decrease in nondiffusible

Ca is probably partly, if not completely, the result of postoperative starvation (Polin and Sturkie, 1957).

c. Parathyroidectomy of estrogen-treated capons or roosters reduces the estrogen-induced increase of diffusible calcium to about 58 per cent of the pre-operative level, whereas the nondiffusible Ca is only slightly affected. The diffusible calcium levels obtained after this treatment were similar to those obtained in parathyroidectomized birds without estrogen treatment (Polin and Sturkie, 1958).

d. Estrogen treatment after parathyroidectomy results in an increase of the nondiffusible Ca in cocks and capons, depending on the level of diffusible Ca present. The higher the latter the greater the increase in nondiffusible Ca after estrogen administration. These data indicate that estrogen can cause an increase in blood calcium when the parathyroids are functional or when enough diffusible Ca is present in the blood. Polin and Sturkie (1957) proposed that the level of diffusible Ca in the blood regulates the activity of the parathyroids. The hormone from this gland must maintain a certain level of diffusible Ca in order to make the estrogen-induced increase in nondiffusible Ca possible (Polin and Sturkie, 1958). Thus estrogen-induced high nondiffusible Ca levels coincide with deposition of the resorbed substance. The discontinuation of estrogen administration produces resorption of the intramedullary bone (Urist, 1959). This resorbate may be transported as diffusible Ca, because, after estrogen treatment, the nondiffusible Ca as well as the phosphoprotein levels decrease. Nondiffusible Ca seems to be closely associated with the phosphoprotein. According to Urist, Schjeide and McLean (1958), the phosphoprotein deposited in the yolk is deposited with the full complement of Ca that it carried in the serum. In none of the hypotheses made has an explanation been given for the increased parathyroid size and activity observed after estrogen administration. This may mean that the increased parathyroid activity is coincidental or that the parathyroid is involved in a manner not yet accounted for.

The mechanisms by which estrogen mobilizes the various components which are deposited in yolk are still largely unknown, although the site of action seems to be the liver. The importance of mobilizing the yolk precursors will be discussed under the endocrine regulation of ovarian activity.

Increased appetite has been observed after the administration of "artificial" estrogens (Lorenz, 1954; Baum and Meyer, 1956; Hill, Carew and van Tienhoven, 1958). Such stimulation of appetite may be an important adaptive mechanism in birds to provide for the deposition of large amounts of high energy materials in the yolk. It has, however, not been determined whether or not natural estrogens have the same appetite-stimulating effect in birds as the artificial estrogens. In experiments which the author was able to find in the literature, in which naturally occurring estrogens were used in birds, pair feeding was practiced. Thus, the possible appetite stimulating effect could not be evaluated. The possibility of a difference in effect on appetite regulation by naturally occurring and artificial estrogens was revealed in experiments with rats by Meites (1949). This author found that diethylstilbestrol (DES) inhibited food consumption in rats whereas estrone had no effect.

Whether the appetite-stimulating effect of artificial estrogens in chickens is the result of a direct stimulation of appetite centers in the hypothalamus or an indirect effect mediated by a change in the blood or in fat deposition has not been established.

The influence of estrogen on feather development has been extensively reviewed by Domm (1939) and by Benoit (1950a); little needs to be added to their conclusions. In most species in which sexual dimorphism occurs and in which the male has the more ornamental plumage, estrogens are responsible for the female type of feathering (so-called hen feathering). It is apparently true for the chicken, turkey, mallard, ostrich, pheasant (*Phasianus colchicus* and *Phasianus colchicus* X *gennaeus nyethemerus, Phasianus colchicus torquatus*) and bobwhite quail (*Colinus virginianus*) that the male or cock feathering is due to the absence of estrogen. In all these birds (sinistral) ovariectomy results in male type feathering, the feather type also in those cases in which no right rudimentary gonad develops (Domm, 1939). Parkes (1952) has pointed out that the feather development of the Brown Leghorn capon may be used successfully to measure the duration of action of different estrogens.

Witschi (1955 for review) has analyzed a peculiar phenomenon of determination of feather coloring which exists in certain species. During the nonbreeding season males and females of the genera *Euplectes, Steganura* and *Quelea* have the hen plumage. Just before the breeding season the male passes through a partial molt, and the new plumage is the brightly colored cock plumage. Castration of the male does not affect the changing of the plumage from eclipse to nuptial plumage, whereas ovariectomy of the female causes her to go through the same phases as the male or the castrated male. These experiments proved that plumage color was independent of androgens but, nevertheless, showed cyclic changes. Experimentally, Witschi demonstrated that LH injections will cause color changes of newly formed feathers in these species. The response is specific and sensitive enough to be used for bioassays of LH (see addendum). In intact *Euplectes*, color changes in plumage and bill occur together under normal conditions. The feather color is a reflection of the LH directly, whereas the bill color is a reflection of androgen secretion by the testes under influence of LH. In wydahs (*Steganura paradisea*), LH determines bill color directly. The lack of cock plumage in normal females is the result of estrogen inhibition of male plumage as Witschi (1937) demonstrated experimentally.

2. Androgen. Evidence for the secretion of androgen by the avian ovary can be found in the red vascular comb of the chicken before and during egg production, in the yellow bill and the stimulated *vasa deferentia* of the female starling (*Sturnus v. vulgaris*) during her reproductive season (Witschi and Fugo, 1940). These characters of the starling are stimulated by androgens only and not by estrogen or progesterone (Fugo and Witschi, 1940).

Benoit (1950a), Taber (1951), and Marshall and Coombs (1957) have suggested that the interstitial cells of the ovary (Benoit, 1950a; Taber, 1951), or, more specifically, the ovarian interstitial cells arising from the connective tissue cells of the ovarian stroma (Marshall and Coombs, 1957) are the source of androgen in female birds.

Some of the effects that androgens can have on blood composition have been discussed in a previous section of this chapter. Their main function in female birds may be to act synergistically with estrogen in the stimulation of the oviduct. In chickens androgen acts synergistically with estrogen to increase calcium retention (Common, Maw and Jowsey, 1953) and to increase endosteal bone formation (Jowsey, Oliver, Maw and Common, 1953); the interaction may be caused by increased Ca absorption from the gut caused by androgen combined with the increased formation of endosteal bone caused by estrogen (Jowsey, Oliver, Maw and Common, 1953).

3. Progesterone. Evidence that the avian ovary secretes progesterone is provided by the detection of a biologically active progestin in the blood of laying and nonlaying hens (Fraps, Hooker and Forbes, 1948, 1949) and by the chemical identification of progesterone in extracts from ovaries of laying hens (Layne, Common, Maw and Fraps, 1957). Progesterone (5 μg. per 100 ml.) as such was detected in the blood of laying hens when loss of progesterone in the peripheral tissue was circumvented (Lytle and Lorenz, 1958). The source of progesterone in the ovary has not been established. In all probability it is not the ruptured follicle, because the amount of progesterone in it is small. Fraps (1955a) proposed that the maturing follicle is a possible, but not the exclusive, source of progesterone, whereas Marshall and Coombs (1957) favored certain amorphous noncellular aggregations of cells of cholesterol-positive lipid in atretic follicles. Neither of these tissues has been proven (or disproven) to be the source of progesterone.

Whatever the source of progesterone may be, it seems to function largely in regulating the ovulatory cycle, at least in the chicken (a topic discussed under endocrine regulation of ovarian activity); progesterone acts synergistically with estrogen to stimulate oviducal development and secretory activity (discussed under oviduct development), and it may play a role in regulating incubation behavior in the ring dove (*Streptopelia risoria*) (Lehrman, 1958, and his chapter in this book). Progesterone, in doses which also cause ovarian atresia, causes molting of chickens and seems to stimulate the feather papilla (Shaffner, 1954; Juhn and Harris, 1956, 1958). Juhn and Harris (1955) defeathered birds, then gave progesterone intradermally. No stimulating effect of progesterone was observed, although thyroxine treatment under similar conditions was effective in stimulating the feather papilla. Juhn and Harris (1955) used the structure of the new feathers as an "internal assay" to detect possible stimulation of the thyroid by the injected progesterone. No evidence of thyroid stimulation was found and the hypothesis that progesterone causes molt by stimulating the thyroid was rejected. Himeno and Tanabe (1957) arrived at a similar conclusion after determination of thyroid activity with I^{131}. These authors suggested that the molt is precipitated when the ovary becomes atretic under the influence of progesterone, the consequent reduction in circulating estrogens would then allow the feather follicles to become active. In addition, progesterone would stimulate the feather papillae to form new feathers. This hypothesis does not account for the fact that testosterone causes cessation of laying (and thus atresia?) but does not induce molting, nor does it account for the precipitation of molting after pregnant mare's serum (PMS) or FSH injections (Juhn and Harris, 1956) which cause atresia but do not reduce estrogen secretion (Bates, Lahr and Riddle, 1935). The endocrine regulation of molting may well be different depending on the species. Harris and Shaffner (1956) noted that progesterone fails to induce molting in pigeons whereas similar doses induce molting in chickens. Kobayashi (1958) subsequently investigated the effect of 17 α-oxyprogesterone-7-caproate (PC) on molting of 19 avian species. He found that birds which breed all year can be induced to molt by PC injections, but in seasonal breeders the molt fails to occur. In birds of the former type complete thyroidectomy prevented the molt response to PC, but gonadectomy had no effect. Kobayashi proposed that the following mechanisms might be involved in the PC-induced molt: (1) increased sensitivity of the feather papillae to thyroid hormone, which can induce molt alone; (2) a synergistic action between PC and thyroid hormone; (3) a combination of 1 and 2. In view of the results of Juhn and Harris (1958) implicating prolactin as a hormone involved in molting, it seems that factorial experiments with hypophysectomized-gonadectomized birds should be carried out as a means of establishing the relationships between prolactin, progesterone, thyroid hormone, and estrogen on molting. An excellent review on the endocrine factors involved in molting has been published by Assenmacher (1958).

4. Ruptured follicle hormone? Rothchild and Fraps (1944a, b) noted that removal of the recently ruptured follicle caused retention of the egg in the oviduct from 9 hours to 3 days longer than normal. Removal of the largest mature follicle caused only a slight delay in oviposition, but when both the recently ruptured and the largest follicle were removed the egg was retained for from 1 to 7 days. Subsequent investigations by Conner and Fraps (1954) demonstrated a rather curious quantitative relationship between the ruptured follicle and oviposition. When half of the ruptured follicle is removed some birds show no effect, others retain the egg, and a small number lay the eggs prematurely. The smaller the portion removed, the greater the incidence of premature ovipositions. The time of removal, apparently, also played a part, for a maximal incidence of premature ovipositions occurred when the operation was performed about 9 hours after ovulation. Although the endocrine function of the ruptured follicle has not been demonstrated by replacement therapy, the evidence strongly suggests that the recently ruptured follicle has a rather short-lived endocrine activity. The short duration of its function is indicated by its rapid degeneration and by the lack of effect when the next to last ruptured follicle is removed (Rothchild and Fraps, 1944a).

4. The Oviduct

A discussion of the effects of the ovarian hormones on the development and function of the avian oviduct requires a brief anatomic description of this organ. The secondary sex organ of female birds usually consists of a single fully developed, left oviduct which has developed from the Müllerian ducts. Even in species in which the incidence of two ovaries is high, only one oviduct is developed (Witschi and Fugo, 1940; Nelson and Stabler, 1940; von Faber, 1958). In chickens the incidence of right oviducts varies between different strains, but, in a large number (80 to 85 per cent), some evidence of a right oviduct is encountered (Winter, 1958). Morgan and Kohlmeyer (1957) reported that the incidence of fully developed right oviducts was quite high in one inbred strain of chickens. Usually, however, the right oviducts are thin membranous cysts or short tubes (Winter, 1958). Development of right oviducts can be induced by estrogen treatment of the embryo, a topic discussed in the chapter by Burns. It is, thus, possible that the higher incidence of fully developed right oviducts in certain strains is the result of a higher estrogen deposition in the yolk and the consequent presence of abnormal quantities of estrogen in the developing embryo. This explanation is speculative, but may be worth further investigation.

The left oviduct is suspended from the body wall by the dorsal and ventral ligaments. The ventral ligament, at its caudal end, consists of muscle fibers radiating towards the vagina. The left dorsal oviducal ligament, the left abdominal air sac, and the body wall together form the "ovarian pocket" (Surface, 1912) into which the yolk falls after ovulation. The oviduct subsequently engulfs the yolk and transports it to the cloaca.

The oviduct can be divided into 5 anatomically distinct regions which will be described from an anatomic and functional point of view.

1. The *infundibulum* is about 7 cm. long and consists of a thin funnel. Its lips are continuous with the ventral and dorsal ligaments (Surface, 1912); the chalaziferous region is tubular in shape (Richardson, 1935; Winter, 1958). The infundibular walls are composed of the peritoneum, a thin layer of longitudinal muscles, and a nonciliated columnar epithelium. In the funnel the epithelium consists of nonciliated and ciliated cells; in the chalaziferous region goblet cells filled with mucin are also present (Richardson, 1935; Winter, 1958). The mucin cells stain with mucicarmine, thionin, hematoxylin, and Bismarck brown. Although the main function of the funnel is to engulf the egg, some mucin is deposited around the yolk while it descends the oviduct. Van Drimmelen (1951) identified the "sperm nests" in the infundibulum. Although a part of the infundibulum has been named the chalaziferous region, the chalazae are not formed there nor is the material from which they are formed secreted there. Burmester and Card (1939) resected this region of the oviduct and found no significant decrease in chalazae weight as a result of the resection.

2. The infundibulum gradually changes into the *magnum* which is about 34 cm. long in an active oviduct. It has thicker walls than the infundibulum, mainly because of enormously developed tubular glands which secrete albumen. The magnum is characterized by mucosal ridges with secondary and tertiary folds, and by an epithelium consisting of ciliated cells and of nonciliated goblet cells filled with mucin. The staining affinities of the goblet cells are similar to those of the infundibulum. The function of the magnum is mainly the secretion of the thick albumen around the yolk. This process is completed in the relatively short time of 3 to 4 hours (Warren and Scott, 1935).

3. The transition of magnum to *isthmus* is marked by a sharp band visible to the naked eye. This band is free of tubular glands and is covered by a cuboidal epithelium. The isthmus is about 8 cm. long and has a thin tubular gland layer resulting in a thinner wall than the magnum. These glands of the isthmus secrete ovokeratin for the formation of the shell membranes, a process which occurs during the 1-hour sojourn of the egg in the oviduct (Warren and Scott, 1935). Histologic examination reveals a circular muscle layer

which is better developed than that in the magnum. The epithelium consists of ciliated and nonciliated cells and of goblet cells with little or no affinity for mucin-staining dyes (Richardson, 1935). The transition from isthmus to shell gland is gradual. The area is characterized histologically by the presence of special glandular cells which show a distinct vacuolization, a pale cytoplasm, and a scarcity of granules. In this area tubular glands of the isthmus and of the shell gland apparently do not mix (Richardson, 1935). The change in epithelium is gradual.

4. The *shell gland* is about 8 cm. long and has a larger diameter than the isthmus or magnum. The longitudinal muscle layer is well developed. The mucosal folds have diagonal and transverse secondary folds. The tubular gland cells of the shell gland are smaller than those of the isthmus. The epithelium consists of a single layer of cells with apical and basal nuclei (Richardson, 1935) and of some goblet cells which lack affinity for mucin stains. In the shell gland the egg receives the thin albumen in 4 to 8 hours. The shell is deposited around the membranes, and indications are that shell formation continues as long as the egg stays in the shell gland which is about 20 hours on the average (Warren and Scott, 1935).

5. A sphincter separates the shell gland from the *vagina*. In birds which are not secreting sufficient estrogen to have caused its breakdown (Greenwood, 1935; Kar, 1947a) the occluding plate which is probably homologous with the mammalian hymen can also be found. The vagina is characterized by its highly developed, circular muscle layer and a mucosa with flat, longitudinal folds. The vaginal epithelium consists of nonciliated and ciliated cells, and of tall goblet cells. The latter stain with the same dyes as do the goblet cells of the magnum. The principal function of the vagina is its participation in the expulsion of the egg.

The infundibulum of the oviduct of the fowl is innervated by nerve fibers originating in the ovarian plexus; these nerves transverse the dorsal ligament before reaching the oviduct. The more posterior parts of the oviduct receive nerve fibers from various autonomic plexuses along the abdominal aorta (Mauger, 1941).

The pigeon's oviduct receives blood from the genital artery and from the pelvic artery, a branch of the iliac artery (Bhaduri, Biswas and Das, 1957). The anterior portion of the oviduct of the fowl receives blood from a branch of the renal artery. The magnum is supplied by a branch of the left sciatic artery and the shell gland by a branch of the *arteria pundendal communes*. The blood from the oviduct drains into the common iliac vein and from this into the vena cava.

In the adult bird, the ovarian hormones mainly control structural changes and the secretory activity of the oviduct. The administration of estrogen to immature pullets dramatically increases the size of the oviduct (Juhn and Gustavson, 1930; Kar, 1947a; Brant and Nalbandov, 1956) and of the dorsal and ventral ligaments (Kar, 1947a). It also initiates the breakdown of the occluding plate (Kar, 1947b). Although 1.00 mg. of estradiol benzoate per day may induce a 20-fold increase in oviduct size, it fails to induce development of the tubular glands of the oviduct or to induce albumen secretion by the magnum. The development of the tubular glands and the secretion of albumen can be induced by a combination of estrogen and either progesterone or androgen, whereas neither of these hormones alone produces this effect (Brant and Nalbandov, 1956). Estrogen administration induces riboflavin secretion in the magnum, but the secretion increases 18 to 35 per cent if the estrogen is given in combination with progesterone or testosterone or with both (Bolton, 1953). The secretion of avidin by the oviduct is also a synergistic response to combinations of estrogen and progesterone, and to estrogen-desoxycorticosterone acetate (DOCA) combinations. However, DOCA, progesterone, or testosterone when given alone can induce avidin secretion by the oviduct (Hertz, Fraps and Sebrell, 1943, 1944). A curious phenomenon is that estrogen and progesterone act synergistically to cause avidin secretion, but, at the same time, progesterone inhibits the estrogen-induced increase in oviduct size (Hertz, Dhyse and Tullner,

TABLE 18.6

Effect of progesterone on estrogen-induced increase in oviduct weight of immature fowl

Body Weight	Estrogen	Dose per Day	Progesterone Dose per Day	Oviduct Weight as Percentage of Oviduct with		Author
				Estrogen	Progesterone	
gm.						
580*	Estradiol benzoate	2.0 mg.	1.0 mg.	91.5		Bolton, 1953
150–200†	Stilbestrol	20 µg.	50 µg.	108.4		Mason, 1952
		20 µg.	500 µg.	176.1	508.9	
		200 µg.	50 µg.	143.2		
		200 µg.	500 µg.	61.4	2029	
	Estradiol benzoate	20 µg.	500 µg.	360.2	1246	
		200 µg.	500 µg.	82.1	3394	
100–150†	Diethyl stilbestrol	250 µg.	50 µg.	104.6		Hertz, Larsen and Tullner, 1947
		250 µg.	100 µg.	85.1		
		250 µg.	150 µg.	62.6		
		250 µg.	200 µg.	47.3		
		250 µg.	250 µg.	54.4		
		250 µg.	300 µg.	43.0		
1000†	Diethyl stilbestrol	13 mg. pellet	500 µg.	128.6	1516	Brant and Nalbandov, 1956
			1000 µg.	281.8	2284	
			2000 µg.	314.4	2835	
			4000 µg.	240.7	2474	
180*	Diethyl stilbestrol	15 mg. pellet	0.57 mg.	169.0	1127	Adams and Herrick, 1955
550*	Diethyl stilbestrol	25 µg.	50 µg.	125.8		van Tienhoven, unpublished
		25 µg.	500 µg.	158.1		
		250 µg.	50 µg.	148.2		
		250 µg.	500 µg.	188.2		
500†	Estradiol	25 µg.	5 µg.	599	373	Breneman, 1956
			25 µg.	70	463	

* Average body weight of groups.

† Weight estimated from age of birds from Table 9, Nutritional Requirements of Poultry, Nat. Res. Council, Publ. 301, 1954.

1949a). The observation that progesterone alone can inhibit this response to estrogen has been confirmed by some workers, but others have noted a definite synergistic action. Some of these experiments have been summarized in Table 18.6. The list of experiments is not complete, for in some cases no quantitative data were published (Gardiner, Phillips, Maw and Common, 1952). The different results are difficult to evaluate because of differences in body weight and the uncertainty concerning the amount of estrogen absorbed from implanted pellets. It is possible, however, that an antagonism occurs at the higher doses of estrogen. This is somewhat similar to the inhibition observed between some combinations of estradiol, estriol, and estrone in immature rats. At lower doses, estrone + estradiol and estradiol + estriol acted synergistically in stimulating uterine weight, but estradiol inhibited the effect of estriol when estradiol + estriol were given in higher doses (Grauer, Saier, Strickler and Cutuly, 1958). More detailed studies on the dose relationship and the ratio of estrogens to progesterone are required in order to determine whether the present variations in results can be explained by competitive inhibition.

It is noteworthy that Brant and Nalbandov (1956) observed no antagonism between estrogen and progesterone when oviduct weight, tubular gland development, and albumen secretion were measured. When estrogen plus 2 to 3 mg. of testosterone were administered, an optical stimulation occurred, but when a larger amount of testosterone (4 mg. per day) was given with estrogen an antagonism was indicated by the lower oviduct weight, the lesser development of the tubular glands and the smaller amount of albumen secreted. Oviducts were still larger than those of birds treated with estrogen only. However, this inhibitory effect of the higher dose of testosterone is surprising in view of the oviduct stimulation obtained with even higher doses (per unit of body weight) of androgen in the black-crowned night heron, *Nycticorax nycticorax* (Noble and Wurm, 1940), the starling, *Sturnus v. vulgaris* (Witschi and Fugo, 1940), the sparrow hawk, *Falco s. sparverius* (Nelson and Stabler, 1940), the house sparrow, *Passer domesticus* (Ringoen, 1943), and the fowl (Kline and Dorfman, 1951). Ringoen (1943) made particular note of the full development of the tubular glands of the oviduct and stated that this might be due to the secretion of estrogen by the ovary, inasmuch as large follicles had developed under the influence of the exogenous testosterone.

The question as to which hormones, androgen or progesterone, synergize with estrogen to give full oviduct development in birds may be answerable only if specified for species, and even then the possibility exists that all three hormones act together. In the fowl, ovary, oviduct, and comb development occur about the same time; the comb growth is evidence that androgen is secreted in considerable quantities. Similarly, female starlings secrete large amounts of androgen which stimulate the *vasa deferentia* and cause the yellow coloring of the bill (Witschi and Fugo, 1940). Lehrman and Brody (1957) proposed that progesterone, which acts synergistically with estrogen to cause oviduct development of ringdoves (*Streptopelia risoria*), may be the hormone which is secreted and is responsible for the synergism. This hypothesis was suggested by the onset of incubation behavior after progesterone administration (Lehrman, 1958). In this case, progesterone might stimulate the physiologic development of the oviduct and simultaneously induce parental behavior. In none of the birds investigated is there any evidence against an hypothesis which assumes that estrogen interacts with both, androgens and progesterone, to stimulate the oviduct.

Nalbandov (1959a) presented evidence

that carbonic anhydrase activity in the shell gland of the fowl may involve the pituitary, but the manner in which the pituitary is involved awaits clarification.

A brief summary of various other factors involved in the normal development of the oviduct and in the response of the oviduct to exogenous gonadal hormones concludes the discussion of the oviduct.

1. Campos and Shaffner (1952) demonstrated that different sire and dam families show differences in the magnitude of response of the oviduct to a standard dose of estrogen and androgen.

2. The exposure to infectious bronchitis when the birds are 1 to 14 days old causes development of incomplete oviducts in which a great decrease in size occurs in the magnum and shell gland (Broadfoot, Pomeroy and Smith, 1956). The older the birds at the time of exposure, the less was the incidence of incomplete oviducts.

3. The presence of a well developed right oviduct, induced by estrogen treatment of the embryo, was highly correlated with a decrease in length of the left oviduct in sexually mature hens. The hypothesis proposed to explain this phenomenon was that not enough estrogen is secreted by the ovary of the adult hen to stimulate both oviducts (van Tienhoven, 1957). It may explain also the presence of two completely developed oviducts in certain inbred lines (Morgan and Kohlmeyer, 1957). If the presence of the right oviducts were the result of larger than normal amounts of estrogen deposited in the yolk, one might expect larger than normal estrogen secretion by the hens of these strains, so that sufficient estrogen would be present to stimulate both oviducts.

4. It has been established that nutritional deficiencies can affect the response of the oviduct to exogenous estrogens. From these investigations it seems that a paradoxical situation exists in that certain deficiencies such as the thiamine (Kline and Dorfman, 1951), nicotinic acid (Haque, Lillie, Shaffner and Briggs, 1949; Kline and Dorfman, 1951), riboflavin, pantothenic acid, choline, and vitamin D deficiency (Haque, Lillie, Shaffner and Briggs, 1949) result in a greater than normal response, whereas folic acid deficiency (Hertz and Sebrell, 1944;

Hertz, 1945, 1948a, b; Haque, Lillie, Shaffner and Briggs, 1949; Kline, 1955; Kline and Dorfman, 1951b) or vitamin B_{12} deficiency reduces the oviduct response, with folic acid deficiency resulting in the greatest reduction.

The increased response of the oviduct after nicotinic acid or thiamine deficiency may be the result of a decreased inactivation of estrogen by the liver, which would in effect increase the levels of estrogen reaching the oviduct. Nicotinic acid is part of the coenzyme involved in estrogen inactivation by the liver (DeMeio, Rakoff, Cantarow and Paschkis, 1948). Whether or not the deficiencies of the other vitamins mentioned causes an increased oviduct response by affecting liver function has not been established. Riboflavin according to Singher, Kensler, Taylor, Rhoads and Unna (1944) is involved in estrogen inactivation by the liver; however, Kline and Dorfman (1951b) could not confirm the effect of increased oviduct response observed by Haque, Lillie, Shaffner and Briggs (1949).

The failure of weight to increase after estrogen administration to birds in which folic acid is deficient is probably the result of the lack of nucleic acid synthesis. Brown (1953) found that feeding of desoxypentose nucleic acid (DNA) to folic acid-deficient chicks partially restored the oviduct response to estrogen. The synthesis of DNA requires in turn the synthesis of considerable amounts of purines. Folic acid is required for synthesis of purines (Stokstad, 1954), whereas vitamin B_{12} is implicated in the metabolism of 1-carbon fragments. On the other hand, the precise role that vitamin B_{12} plays in the oviduct response to estrogen is not known. Folic acid is also required for the increase in size of the oviduct in response to large doses of testosterone (Kline and Dorfman, 1951). The observation that folic acid is not required for the comb response (Zarrow, Koretsky and Zarrow, 1951) to testosterone may be explained by the differences in the nature of the two organs. The oviduct response involves synthesis of proteins and purines, whereas the comb response involves the deposition of substantial amounts of hyaluronic acid (Boas, 1949; Boas and Ludwig, 1950).

B. ENDOCRINE REGULATION OF OVARIAN ACTIVITY

1. Anterior Pituitary

After hypophysectomy the avian ovary shows extensive atresia of the follicles and regression of the medullary tissue, especially of the interstitium (Hill and Parkes, 1934; Schooley, Riddle and Bates, 1941; Nalbandov, 1953, 1959b, c; Opel and Nalbandov, 1958). Replacement therapy with mammalian gonadotrophins is apparently successful in the pigeon, *Columba livia* (Chu and You, 1946), but only partially successful in chickens (Nalbandov, 1953). It is not clear from the published papers whether or not avian gonadotrophins are completely successful. According to Opel and Nalbandov (1958), some ovulations were induced (and thus some follicles were maintained?) a few days after hypophysectomy, but some atresia of follicles occurred. It appears that for a few hours after the withdrawal of endogenous gonadotrophins by hypophysectomy the large ovarian follicles are more susceptible to exogenous LH, because a dose of LH, which does not cause multiple ovulations in an intact laying hen, will cause their occurrence if injected into a hypophysectomized hen between 6 to 12 hours after the operation. Within this time range, the ovary becomes more and more sensitive as the time after surgery increases. In intact hens multiple ovulations can be obtained with exogenous LH provided that the hens have been pretreated for about 10 days with PMS (Fraps, Riley and Olsen, 1942) or FSH (Nalbandov and Card, 1946). Progressive changes take place in the hypophysectomized and the PMS- or FSH-treated bird, which also result in atresia of the follicles (Fraps, Riley and Olsen, 1942; Phillips, 1943). It seems, thus, that atretic changes in the follicle wall will predispose the follicle to ovulate (Nalbandov, 1959b), but that after atresia has caused breakdown of the vitelline membrane, ovulation can no longer be induced (van Tienhoven, 1955). According to Nalbandov (1958), ovulation is preceded by local ischemia of the follicular wall, particularly in the region of the stigma, which causes local necrosis. Whether or not this necrosis is the sole local precipitating factor in ovulation remains to be determined. The occurrence of ovulation *in vitro* (Neher, Olsen and Fraps, 1950), provided the follicle is not removed from the ovary until about 2 hours before expected ovulation, suggests that changes other than ischemia also must occur. Removal of the ovary earlier than the designated time might be expected to cause ischemia of the stigma as soon as the blood vessels are cut; nevertheless, no ovulation occurs when this is done.

Replacement therapy in hypophysectomized chickens (Opel and Nalbandov, 1958; Nalbandov, 1959c) or the injection of gonadotrophin into intact laying hens (Fraps, Riley and Olsen, 1942; Phillips, 1943) does not result in maintenance or formation of the follicles of graded size observed in the normal ovary. Rather, the effect of injected hormones has been akin to an all-or-none effect: either many follicles are stimulated to grow to about the same size, or no stimulation occurs (Opel and Nalbandov, 1958; Nalbandov, 1959c). The mechanisms involved in the gradation of the follicles in the normal ovary awaits further elucidation.

Gonadotrophin administration to intact chickens has different effects depending on the maturity of the birds. Until about 120 days of age, the response of the chicken ovary to mammalian gonadotrophin consists mainly of increases in estrogen and androgen secretions and of hypertrophy of the ovarian medulla. Evidence for the increase in estrogen production was hypertrophy of the oviduct (Domm, 1937; Domm and Van Dyke, 1930; Asmundson and Wolfe, 1935; Asmundson, Gunn and Klose, 1937; Lorenz, 1939; Nalbandov and Card, 1946), and increased blood lipids (Lorenz, 1939). Increased androgen secretion was indicated by growth of the comb (Domm and Van Dyke, 1930; Domm, 1937; Asmundson, Gunn and Klose, 1937; Nalbandov and Card, 1946; Taber, 1948; and Das and Nalbandov, 1955). The hypertrophy of the medulla accounts almost entirely for the increase in ovarian weight. None of the workers who injected mammalian gonadotrophins found normal development of the follicles. This lack of response of the follicles was not entirely due to the absence of the "third gonadotrophic hormone," for even implants of avian pituitaries (Domm, 1931) or daily injections of chicken anterior pituitary powder (CAP) did not result in large follicles until the birds were about 100 to 110 days old (Das and Nalbandov, 1955; Taber, Claytor, Knight, Gambrell, Flowers and Ayers, 1958). There are, however, differences in the response of the immature ovary to mammalian and avian gonadotrophins. Taber, Claytor, Knight, Gambrell, Flowers and Ayers (1958) noted the following: (1) mammalian gonadotrophins fail to induce precocious follicular development, whereas CAP can induce such development; (2) mammalian gonadotrophins cause medullary distension and consequently increase ovarian weight by about 400 per cent, whereas CAP causes no medullary distension and only a small (27 per cent) increase in ovarian weight; (3) after 12 days of PMS treatment the combs of immature pullets, which were stimulated by the PMS, start to regress, whereas with CAP treatment the combs continue to grow, a result similar to that obtained when the combs of hypophysectomized and of estrogen-treated roosters were being studied (Nalbandov, Meyer and McShan, 1951).

Both mammalian and avian gonadotrophins increase the incidence of polyovular follicles (Taber, 1948; Taber, Claytor, Knight, Gambrell, Flowers and Ayers, 1958), indicating that there is some response of the cortex of the ovary to mammalian hormones. The changes which make the ovary more responsive to avian gonadotrophins with increasing age are not known. It is known that the immature ovary responds to FSH by increased respiration (Nalbandov and Nalbandov, 1949), but whether this response changes with age has not been established.

The lack of response of the follicles in the immature ovary stands in striking contrast to the enormous development of ovarian follicles in the mature hen after either mammalian or avian gonadotrophin administration (Fraps, Riley and Olsen, 1942; Phillips, 1943). The response, however, requires the presence of the "third gonadotrophin," because in hypophysectomized hens mammalian gonadotrophins fail to elicit the response, whereas avian gonadotrophins can elicit it at least temporarily (Nalbandov,

1953; Das and Nalbandov, 1955; Opel and Nalbandov, 1958). Whether or not the avian pituitary is required for this "maturation" of the ovary has not been determined and not enough data are available for a comparison of birds hypophysectomized at different ages and given similar treatments. In all cases in which ovarian development has been obtained in chickens, large amounts of gonadotrophins, equivalent to 10 to 20 pituitaries from 12- 14-week-old "broilers," had to be used. If one assumes that the pituitaries came half from males and half from females, and that female pituitaries have half the potency of male pituitaries (comparison of data of Breneman and Mason, 1951; and Breneman, 1955), then the 18 to 20 avian pituitaries per day are equivalent to 270 to 300 I.U. gonadotrophin per day because according to Phillips (1959), 1 pituitary of a "broiler" rooster = 1 mg. dried powder = 20 I.U. PMS. Mammalian gonadotrophin injections, equivalent to 500 rat units of FSH (Nalbandov and Card, 1946) or to 100 to 200 rat units PMS (Fraps, Riley and Olsen, 1942) were needed to stimulate follicles in adult intact hens. In contrast to the rather low sensitivity of the ovary with respect to follicular growth, stands the extreme sensitivity to LH for induction of ovulation. Fraps, Fevold and Neher (1947) showed that 1 μg. LH prepared from chicken pituitaries was capable of inducing premature ovulations in 50 per cent of the hens.

The effect of gonadotrophin injections into intact female birds other than chickens seems to depend on the species used. Red-billed weavers (Witschi, 1935), European gold finches, *Carduelis elegans* (Vaugien, 1956), green finches, *Chloris chloris*, buntings and canaries, *Serinus canaria* (Vaugien, 1957), and house sparrows, *Passer domesticus* (Riley and Witschi, 1938; Witschi and Riley, 1940; Vaugien, 1954) can be stimulated to lay eggs during the nonbreeding season by injections of about 100 to 150 I.U. PMS every 3 days for 3 weeks. In contrast to those of chickens, the follicles of these birds show normal gradations in size (Riley and Witschi, 1938; Witschi and Riley, 1940), and no separate LH injections are required for ovulation (Witschi, 1935; Vaugien, 1954, 1957). The lack of ovarian

response in the robin, *Erithacus r. rubecula*, observed by Schildmacher (1939), may be explained by the low dosage used. If one excludes possible differences between species with respect to the dosage required to obtain ovarian stimulation, the generalization can be made that intact songbirds differ from chickens in their response in the following ways.

1. Regular gradation of follicular size is obtained even with rather massive doses of PMS.

2. Ovulations occur "spontaneously" and do not require separate LH injections. It seems, thus, that a comparative approach to the problem of follicle-size gradation might prove to be profitable, as might an investigation of the endocrine regulation of ovulation in song birds.

Administration of the third gonadotrophic hormone, prolactin (the luteotrophic hormone of mammals), inhibits FSH secretion and results in cessation of laying and in atresia of the follicles (Bates, Lahr and Riddle, 1935; Bates, Riddle and Lahr, 1937). Juhn and Harris (1956) reported, however, that prolactin counteracts the inhibition of laying by exogenous progesterone. This effect is rather surprising for it would assign to prolactin a true gonadotrophic function which is contrary to its effects in roosters and female pigeons (Bates, Lahr and Riddle, 1935; Bates, Riddle and Lahr, 1937). Further investigations are needed to establish whether prolactin affects male and female chickens differently.

Assays of the pituitaries from chickens (Burrows and Byerly, 1936; Saeki and Tanabe, 1956; Nakajo and Tanaka, 1956), pheasants, *Phasianus colchicus* Breitenbach and Meyer, 1959), and California gulls (Bailey, 1952) reveal that the prolactin content is maximal when the eggs are being incubated. Prolactin content decreases when the chicks are hatched, although the hen is still caring for the young. Strong lights or electric shocks to the head interrupted broodiness and decreased the prolactin content of the anterior pituitary, especially of the caudal lobe (Nakajo and Tanaka, 1956). As we noted in the section on the male, the data from a limited number of species suggest that prolactin may be required for incubation in species which have an incubation patch, whereas in ring doves (*Streptopelia risoria*), which do not have an incubation patch, incubation is not correlated with an increase in prolactin secretion (Lehrman, 1958, and his chapter in this book).

Gonadotrophin assays of pituitaries from the time of hatching into adulthood when reproductive activity is cyclic seem to have been made only on chickens. The results obtained by two groups of workers are summarized in Table 18.7. Their results are expressed in the common standard of chick units as defined by Breneman (1955). The results obtained by Riley and Fraps (1942a, b) are in essential agreement with those in the table with respect to the ratio of gonadotrophic potency of pituitaries from roosters and laying and nonlaying hens. They were not included because of the difficulty in converting mouse uterine units into chick units.

As a part of the survey of the data contained in Table 18.7, it should be noted that the amount of gonadotrophin in the pituitaries of young birds is closely correlated with ovarian weight (r = 0.898). This correlation provides an argument for the concept that the secretion of gonadotrophic hormone can be estimated from assays of the pituitary, in immature pullets as well as in adult hens. Just before ovulation begins in young hens pituitary gonadotrophin potency (and secretion?) reaches its peak. It is at a much lower level in older laying hens. This decreased gonadotrophic potency (and decreased gonadotrophin secretion?) is probably due to estrogens which are secreted in large amounts by the ovary. The lower gonadotrophin secretion would be sufficient to maintain follicles already present and to stimulate new ones to grow to ovulatory size. This concept that less gonadotrophin is required for maintenance and stimulation of follicles already present than is required for stimulation of an immature or an inactive ovary finds support in the following experimental evidence:

1. Vaugien (1957) stated on the basis of a rather small number of experiments that in song birds the ovary is more sensitive to exogenous gonadotrophin when one or more medium-sized follicles are present than

TABLE 18.7

Gonadotrophic potency of pullet and hen pituitaries in the domestic fowl

Age	Ovarian Weight of Donor	AP Assay	Authority
	mean ± S.D. mg.	chick units*	
20 days....	39.4 ± 11.3	0.4	Breneman, 1955
40 days....	99.1 ± 15.3	1.1	Breneman, 1955
60 days....	167.9 ± 32.1	3.1	Breneman, 1955
80 days	292.1 ± 62.7	4.6	Breneman, 1955
100 days....	466.3 ± 198.6	6.4	Breneman, 1955
110 days....	401.5 ± 68.1	6.4	Breneman, 1955
126 days....	5781 ± 2445.0	14.4	Breneman, 1955
Adult.......	39.1 gm.	1.0†	Saeki, Himeno, Tanabe and Katsuragi, 1956
Adult.......	3.1 gm.	2.3	Saeki, Himeno, Tanabe and Katsuragi, 1956
Adult cock..	7.6 gm. (testes)	4.10	Saeki, Himeno, Tanabe and Katsuragi, 1956

* Chick unit is equivalent to 35 per cent increase over control assay.

† Calculated (AvT) from data of Saeki *et al.*, 1956.

when the ovary contains only small follicles.

2. In order to obtain follicles of about 17-mm. diameter Taber, Claytor, Knight, Gambrell, Flowers and Ayers (1958) had to inject 18 to 20 broiler pituitaries (equivalent to 270 to 300 I.U.) per day, whereas when laying hens were injected with 80 to 160 rat units of PMS enormous stimulation of the follicles was obtained in a few days (Fraps, 1955b). to be sure, the ratios between these levels of exogenous gonado-

trophins are not as great as the ratio between gonadotrophic potency of pullets of about 126 days and laying hens, but, on the other hand, the extents of stimulation obtained with the exogenous gonadotrophins in the chickens of the two ages were not directly comparable (the laying hens were overstimulated, the immature pullets not completely stimulated).

3. On exogenous gonadotrophin administration the ovary is more sensitive when estrogen is administered before gonadotrophin injection or when administered simultaneously with gonadotrophins (Phillips, 1959). A more complete understanding of the regulation of follicular growth during the reproductive cycle will require more quantitative data on the gonadotrophic potency of pituitaries, especially during the period between the end of laying and the emergence of the new crop of follicles, more data on the sensitivity of the follicles to exogenous gonadotrophins, and pure gonadotrophic hormones (see chapters by Greep and by Young on the ovary).

2. Estrogen

Breneman (1955, 1956) investigated the effects of injection of 0.5, 1.0, 5.0 and 25.0 μg. estradiol per day for 10 days on the ovary of 30-day-old pullets and found no significant difference from control ovarian weight. Histochemically, there was evidence that 1 μg. estradiol caused increased cholesterol deposition in the follicle. Phillips (1959) injected 12.5 mg. DES per week into 6-week-old pullets and obtained a 32 per cent increase in ovarian weight ($p < 0.01$). Similarly, 10 mg. DES per day, given to adult, nonbreeding black ducks (*Anas platyrhynchos*), resulted in a 95 per cent increase in ovarian weight ($p < 0.01$). In neither of the experiments was there any yellow yolk deposition. Chu and You (1946) also failed to induce maturation of follicles by estrogen injections in hypophysectomized pigeons. It is not clear from their paper whether any stimulation of ovarian weight occurred. Schönberg and Ghoneim (1946) reported that feeding of stilbene to pullets 100 days of age resulted in egg production at 114 days of age, whereas egg production in DES-fed pullets did not start until 162

days and egg production in control pullets did not start until 146 days of age. These results suggest that there may be differences in effect between estrogens and it also suggests that stilbene feeding just before pullets reach sexual maturity may cause earlier egg production. The difference between the two estrogens may be caused, for instance, by differences in inhibition of the pituitary gonadotrophin secretion. Experimental evidence that estrogens may synergize with exogenous gonadotrophins suggests that an estrogen which does not inhibit gonadotrophin secretion but mobilizes yolk precursors could cause a somewhat earlier egg production. Clavert (1958) has, largely on theoretical grounds, defended the proposition that estrogens should augment the action of exogenous gonadotrophins with respect to stimulation of follicular growth. Clavert's hypothesis was that estrogen would mobilize yolk precursors immediately and thus facilitate yolk deposition in the follicles under the influence of gonadotrophin. If gonadotrophins were given alone, estrogen would have to be secreted under the influence of gonadotrophin and yolk mobilization could occur subsequently. This hypothesis was tested with nonbreeding black ducks by Phillips (1959). In one experiment 4 out of 6 birds treated with the combination of CAP and DES had large follicles with yellow yolk, whereas none of the birds treated with either hormone alone had yellow yolk. In the second experiment 3 out of 5 birds on the combined treatment had yellow yolk in the follicles, whereas none of the CAP-treated birds contained yellow yolk (there were no DES-treated birds in this experiment). It should be noted that similar experiments with 6-week-old pullets failed to show any large follicle formation with either CAP, DES, or the combination. This may be the result of the unresponsiveness of the immature ovary, a factor which was discussed previously.

The administration of estrogen causes delay of the next ovulation by suppressing LH release (Fraps, 1954). Progesterone administration under identical conditions results in LH release and premature ovulation. The significance of these findings will be discussed under regulation of the laying and ovulation cycle of the fowl. In the meantime the indirect evidence suggesting that estrogen has its depressing effect on gonadotrophin release by way of a neural mechanism will be cited: (1) estrogen administration to chickens causes changes in the neurosecretory cells of the paraventricular nucleus of the hyopthalamus (Legait, 1959); (2) estrogen causes gonadotrophin inhibition by way of the hypothalamus in mammals (Flerkó, 1957); this is discussed in detail in the chapter by Everett; (3) progesterone, another steroid hormone, causes release of gonadotrophins from the anterior pituitary by way of a neural mechanism. This possibility is discussed in the present chapter and, for mammals, in the chapter by Everett.

3. Androgen

Androgens, apparently, have an effect on the ovaries of hypophysectomized pigeons which corresponds to that on the testes. Chu and You (1946) obtained 4 to 6 mm. follicles filled with yolk in androgen-treated hypophysectomized pigeons. A stimulating effect on the ovary was found also in intact immature pigeons, although the testes of immature males failed to respond (Chu and You, 1946). A similar situation exists in sparrows in which injections of testosterone (0.5 to 1.0 mg. per day) stimulated the ovarian follicles to such a degree that their diameters were approximately 75 per cent larger than the average in the controls (Ringoen, 1943). Androgen administration also resulted in a modification of the follicular epithelium from simple to stratified (Ringoen, 1943).

Breneman (1955, 1956) studied the effect of androgen on the ovaries and follicular development in intact, 30-day-old chickens. Five μg. TP given daily increased ovarian weight, but administration of either 1.0 or 25 μg. did not have this effect (Breneman, 1956). Doses of 0.1, 1.0, 10.0, 50, and 100 μg. TP increased follicle area of the ovary significantly, but after a maximum was reached with the 0.1- and 10-μg. levels, the response tended to decrease. After the administration of 100 μg., the follicular area was less than when the smaller amounts were given, but it was still larger than in the controls. The increase in follicle area may well be the result of inhibition of the interstitium combined with stimulation of the follicles. Breneman (1955) emphasized that androgen administration increases the height of the follicular epithelium. Analysis of variance of Breneman's data (by me) showed that only the comparison of control *versus* all androgen levels combined was significant ($p < 0.05$). The lack of a dose-response relationship over such a wide range of doses suggests that the difference between controls and androgen-treated pullets was the result of a sampling error, unless the assumption of an all-or-none response is made with respect to increases of follicular epithelial height. Androgen, apparently, did not affect pituitary gonadotrophin assays. Breneman's (1955) statement that low doses of estradiol and testosterone facilitate the ovarian response to PMS is not supported by evidence, because no data are given on the effect of PMS alone. Nelson and Stabler (1940) injected large doses of TP (140 mg. in 30 days) into young female sparrow hawks (*Falco s. sparverius*) and found no effect on either left or right ovary. The limited data available on different species suggest the following provisional generalization: if androgens stimulate the testes of a species (sparrows, pigeons), then androgens will, under similar conditions, also stimulate the ovaries of the females.

Testosterone can cause the anterior pituitary to release LH, which results in ovulation. The incidence of premature ovulations after testosterone injection is about 41 per cent compared with 95 per cent after progesterone injection. Testosterone-induced LH release is mediated by a neural mechanism which will be discussed more fully under progesterone effects in the regulation of ovarian activity.

Testosterone, thus, seems to be capable of affecting ovarian activity in two ways. One is by a direct effect on the ovary, as in hypophysectomized pigeons, and the other is by an effect on the neural components which regulate anterior pituitary activity.

4. Progesterone

Progesterone probably plays a very important role in the regulation of ovarian activity, especially during the period of full reproductive activity, but before discussing this phase of the subject, the experimental evidence that the hormone affects ovarian activity will be reviewed.

Nalbandov (1956), in a preliminary note, presented evidence that progesterone pellets implanted into immature pullets hastened maturation of the ovarian follicles with a consequent precocious egg production. This result is consistent with the data obtained by Fraps (1950) with turkeys showing that PMS-stimulated follicles could be maintained by progesterone injections. It also agrees with the results obtained by van Tienhoven (1958) suggesting that after a broody period, egg production is somewhat enhanced by progesterone pellet implants. On the other hand, Duchaine, Driggers and Warnick (1957) observed that injections of 6 mg. progesterone every other day delayed rather than enhanced the onset of sexual maturity in 16-week-old pullets.

Broodiness of turkeys was inhibited by progesterone given in a readily absorbable form (van Tienhoven, 1958; Haller and Cherms, 1959), but no effect on subsequent egg production was observed. It seems, therefore, that the level of progesterone already in the blood may determine whether the action of exogenous hormone will be stimulating or inhibitory. This may explain the difference between the results of Nalbandov (1956) and those of Duchaine, Driggers and Warnick (1957). Apparently, no experiments were carried out in which the effect of combined treatments of gonadotrophins and progesterone on the inactive ovary were compared with the effect of single treatments.

Large doses of progesterone, administered to laying hens in paste or pellet form, interrupt egg production (Adams, 1955, 1956; Juhn and Harris, 1956; Shaffner, 1954, 1955; Harris and Shaffner, 1956), presumably by causing follicular atresia. These results obtained with forms of progesterone which are relatively long acting can be explained in terms of the timing of the high progesterone levels with respect to the ovulation cycle of the chicken. Rothchild and Fraps (1949b) demonstrated that progesterone injections about 36 to 38 hours before expected ovula-

tion result in atresia of the ovarian follicles. Atresia can be the result of an inhibition of all gonadotrophin secretion or of the release of too small an amount of LH to cause ovulation. Which of these two occurs after the progesterone administration is a matter of speculation. If one accepts the evidence that FSH and LH are secreted as one gonadotrophic complex, then the two interpretations are essentially the same and differ only quantitatively. Recently, van Tienhoven (1959) and Nalbandov (1959a) have defended the position that the FSH and LH are released as one complex. If their idea is correct, the question whether progesterone causes a partial or complete inhibition of gonadotrophins could be answered by determining the total gonadotrophic potencies of the pituitaries of the progesterone-treated hens. On the other hand, if FSH and LH are secreted as separate entities, the two interpretations for the atresia are qualitatively different, and separate assays for FSH and LH in the pituitaries of progesterone-inhibited birds should be made. In contrast to the atresia which occurs when progesterone is given 36 to 38 hours before ovulation, premature ovulations result when progesterone is given 2 to 24 hours before the expected ovulation (Fraps, 1955b, for review).

Considerable evidence has accumulated indicating that progesterone acts through a neural mechanism to cause the release from the pituitary of the gonadotrophin which induces ovulation. This evidence can be summarized as follows:

1. Progesterone-induced ovulation in the hen can be prevented by the simultaneous or previous administration of such adrenergic blocking agents as SKF 501 (Zarrow and Bastian, 1953), Dibenamine (van Tienhoven, Nalbandov and Norton, 1954), Dibenzyline (van Tienhoven, 1955), and the anticholinergic agent, atropine (Zarrow and Bastian, 1953; van Tienhoven, 1955). Recently, Moore (1958) questioned the validity of the argument that large amounts of such agents block ovulation by blocking a neural mechanism. As Everett has pointed out in his chapter, "blocking" agents must be given between 2:00 and 4:00 p.m. on the day of the proestrum if they are to block ovulation in rats. Moore (1958) adminis-

tered Dibenamine or Dibenzyline to rats for 12 days after 5:00 p.m. After this period regular cycles were resumed. Injections of either drug at the "critical period" during the proestrum failed to block ovulation in 80 per cent of the cases. Moore interpreted the blockade of ovulation observed in rats not pretreated with Dibenamine or Dibenzyline as the result of a shift in the pituitary from gonadotrophin to adrenocorticotrophin production and not to a "neural blockade." This interpretation would cast doubt on the hypothesis that progesterone acts by way of a neural mechanism were it not for rather abundant supportive evidence that this is indeed the case.

Fraps and Case (1953) found that diallyl barbituric acid (Dial), Nembutal, and calcium ethylisopropylbarbiturate (Ipral) cause premature ovulation of the follicle when given 12 to 16 hours before the expected time of ovulation. The incidence of premature ovulations was 15 to 30 per cent compared with 95 per cent when progesterone was given. Dial and Nembutal acted synergistically with subovulatory doses of progesterone to cause an incidence of 57 per cent and 30 per cent premature ovulations, respectively; the same doses of progesterone alone were followed by 5.5 per cent premature ovulations. These findings can be interpreted (Fraps, 1955b) by assuming that, after the period of depression, a period of excitation follows which lowers the threshold for the stimuli which cause the release of gonadotrophin from the pituitary. Fraps (1955b) demonstrated that phenobarbital administration blocks progesterone-induced ovulations. No explanation can be given for this opposite effect of phenobarbital unless it is that it is longer acting than Dial or Nembutal.

2. Lesions placed in the ventromedian region of the preoptic hypothalamus within about 2 hours after the injection of progesterone prevent premature ovulation (Ralph and Fraps, 1959).

3. Injections of small amounts of progesterone (5 to 10 μg.) into the diencephalon result in premature ovulations only when they are placed in the preoptic region of the hypothalamus (Ralph and Fraps, 1960). Injections into the caudal extensions of the

forebrain are also effective (Ralph and Fraps, 1960). Systemic injections of 10 μg. progesterone were ineffective as were injections of 10 μg. progesterone into the anterior pituitary. Taken together, these observations indicate that progesterone causes premature ovulation by way of a neural mechanism, but the possibility that other mechanisms are involved has not been excluded.

5. Corticosteroids

Studies on the effects of corticosteroid administration on the avian ovary have been rather limited. Fraps (1955b) reported that DOCA was as effective as progesterone in inducing premature ovulations in chickens, and the effect of either can be blocked effectively by phenobarbital. Daily injections of 5 mg. of DOCA caused inhibition of egg production in chickens (Höhn, 1960). Cortisone acetate (2.0 mg. per day) had no effect on egg production.

6. Epinephrine

Perry (1941) found that injections of epinephrine daily for 15 to 20 days after sparrows had been exposed to 15 hours of light for 30 days caused regression of the slightly stimulated ovaries and oviduct. The mechanism whereby this occurred was not established.

7. Thyroid Hormone

Early thyroidectomy (Blivaiss, 1947) or destruction of the thyroid by large doses of I[131] (Winchester, Comar and Davis, 1949) results in total lack of ovarian development. Replacement therapy with thyroxine of such chickens results in follicular maturation and egg laying (Winchester, Comar and Davis, 1949). Greenwood and Chu (1939) thyroidectomized 5 pullets and found that 2 started to lay eggs at the same average age as the control flock. Winchester (1939) observed that thyroidectomy decreased egg production of 7 hens from 3.77 to 0.42 eggs per week. Whether this difference in results between the experiments of Blivaiss (1947) and Winchester, Comar and Davis (1949) on the one hand, and of Greenwood and Chu (1939) and Winchester (1939) on the other hand, are the result of the difference in age at which the thyroid was removed or the result of incomplete removal of all thyroid tissue (especially because ectopic thyroid tissue seems to occur sometimes) cannot be judged from the few data now available. It is interesting to note that, in certain families of White Leghorn chickens, birds without any apparent thyroid tissue or with thyroids consisting of one abnormal follicle occur. In the most severe cases of hypothyroidism ovaries are immature at an age when normal hens of the same strain are in full production. Thyroxine injections will bring such hypothyroid birds into production in 7 to 21 days (the information on these hypothyroid hens was communicated to the author by Dr. R. K. Cole). The balance between gonadotrophin and thyroid hormone is apparently rather important. Clavert (1958) noted, for instance, that the ovarian response to PMS was reduced by simultaneous thyroxine injections of pigeons. Such an inhibition seems understandable in view of the inhibition of estrogen-induced lipemia and proteinemia. In effect, thyroxine decreased the concentration of yolk precursors and thus lowered the response to PMS. In view of this effect of thyroid hormone, it is not surprising that thyroid hormone feeding (mainly as iodinated casein) has given opposite results in different experiments. These results have been reviewed recently (Turner, 1959; van Tienhoven, 1959) and do not need to be discussed here.

8. Nutrition

The specific effect of nutrition on ovarian activity has not been studied in great detail; this is in contrast to the many studies on the effect of nutrition of the hen on the hatchability and embryonic development (Cravens, 1949; Landauer, 1951). Restriction of energy intake delays sexual maturity (Bruckner and Hill, 1959). Pullets, after being reared on a restricted diet, when fed *ad libitum* at the approach of sexual maturity, produced more eggs during the rest of the year than pullets reared and maintained on an unrestricted diet. The mechanisms involved in these relationships have not been studied. It seems probable that restricted energy intake results in later

gonadotrophin secretion, thus delaying sexual maturity.

Withdrawal of feed from laying hens results in atresia of the follicles and a simultaneous decrease in serum vitellin (Hosoda, Kaneko, Mogi and Abe, 1955b). These effects can be prevented by injections of FSH or PMS (Hosoda, Kaneko, Mogi and Abe, 1955a), and follicles so maintained can be ovulated (Hosoda, Kaneko, Mogi and Abe, 1956). The results suggest that starvation prevents production of gonadotrophin, a suggestion supported by bioassays of the pituitaries. Phillips (1959) found that the testes of chicks injected with pituitaries from starved hens with atretic follicles weighed 7.6 mg. compared with 10.11 mg. for the testes from chicks injected with pituitaries from well fed, laying hens. The difference was not statistically significant, but shows a trend in the expected direction. No data seem to have been published on the specific effect of the separate nutrients on ovarian activity. In most studies egg production was measured and no efforts seem to have been made to separate the effects of inanition from the specific nutrient effect.

C. REGULATION OF BREEDING CYCLES OF SEASONALLY REPRODUCING BIRDS

Aristotle's observation that the testes are small during the nonbreeding season and large during the breeding season bears witness to the accurate observations that have been made throughout history. It does not require much imagination to visualize that man must have observed the effect of environment on reproduction. The regular flight north of flocks of geese every year must have impressed the hunting tribes. But only recently some understanding has been obtained of the pathways by which the environment can affect reproduction.

1. Hypothalamic-Pituitary System

In order to understand the explanations proposed here, a review of the control of the anterior pituitary is required. The discussion is purposely limited to birds, because the relationships for other vertebrate classes are described in the chapters by Greep and Purves.

It seems that the only manner in which environmental stimuli, especially those such as light, could influence the activity of the pituitary is by way of the nervous system. Considerable evidence from different kinds of experiments implicates the hypothalamus as the structure that is specifically involved in the transmission of the stimuli to the anterior pituitary. The hypothesis has been proposed (Scharrer and Scharrer, 1954; Benoit and Assenmacher, 1955, 1959; Assenmacher and Benoit, 1958) that environmental factors cause changes in the activity of specialized hypothalamic cells, the so-called neurosecretory cells. These cells can be identified by a variety of stains (Assenmacher, 1958; Legait, 1959). They may be considered, on one hand, as nerve cells, on the other, as endocrine cells. Material produced by these cells is transported along their axons to the posterior pituitary. However, loops of these axons in the median eminence come into close contact with the capillary bed of the portal vessels of the hypothalamus where some of the neurosecretory material (NSM) is picked up by portal vessels which transport it to the anterior pituitary whose cells it stimulates. The evidence in support of this hypothesis will be presented together with the counter argument by Zuckerman (1955), who questioned the validity of this hypothesis. For convenience, the available evidence will be divided into somewhat arbitrary categories. Inasmuch as many details of findings have been published recently in the review papers and chapters of this book cited above, references will be limited largely to these reviews. Discussion will be limited to the results obtained with birds.

Anatomic evidence shows that few, if any, nerves reach the glandular tissue of the anterior pituitary. Even the few fibers found by Metuzals (1955) do not seem to have significance, because their origin could not be established. On the other hand, NSM has been observed in the hypothalamico-hypophyseal tract of ducks (Assenmacher, 1958; Legait, 1959; Benoit and Assenmacher, 1959), chickens, although rarely (Legait, 1959), and the white-crowned sparrow, *Zonotrichia leucophrys gambellii* (Oksche, Laws, Kamemoto and Farner, 1959). The axons of these neurosecretory cells form "loops" which are in close contact with the portal vessels in the *stratum glandulare* of

the "special zone" of the median eminence (Assenmacher, 1958; Oksche, Laws, Kamemoto and Farner, 1959). The median eminence can be divided into three layers: (a) *stratum ependymale*, (b) *stratum fibrosum*, (c) *stratum glandulare*. The tracts from the hypothalamus to the neurohypophysis are part of the *stratum fibrosum*, and NSM can be found here, often in such amounts that the individual fibers of the tracts can be distinguished because of the content of NSM (Oksche, Laws, Kamemoto and Farner, 1959). The *stratum glandulare* also contains large amounts of NSM arranged in arcades (Wingstrand, 1951; Legait, 1959). In this area the hypophyseal portal vessels make contact with the loops of NSM. The demonstration that the blood flow is *from* the median eminence *to* the anterior pituitary in ducks (Assenmacher, 1958), together with all the other anatomic evidence cited above, is certainly in accord with the hypothesis that the neurosecretory material from the hypothalamus is the link between the nervous system and the anterior pituitary. Zuckerman (1955) has stressed that nerve fibers such as those found by Metuzals (1955) may form the functional connection between the hypothalamus and the pituitary. However, it seems to this author that Zuckerman's argument cannot be accepted for birds until it has been established that the fibers come from the hypothalamus.

Further evidence is provided by interruptions of the connections between hypothalamus and anterior pituitary.

1. Lesions in a medial region of the ventral portion of the paraventricular nucleus in chickens caused a long lasting interruption of ovulation (Ralph, 1959). Lesions in the same area also prevented progesterone-induced ovulations (Ralph and Fraps, 1959). In other parts of the hypothalamus lesions did not consistently interrupt either "spontaneous" or progesterone-induced ovulations, and when they did, the interruption of "spontaneous" ovulations was temporary rather than long lasting. In drakes (*Anas platyrhynchos*), fairly large lesions of the anterior hypothalamus prevented the normal light-induced increase in testicular activity (Assenmacher, 1958).

2. Complete interruption of the hypophyseal portal system of laying hens re-

sulted in complete atrophy of the ovaries without any apparent effect on ACTH or thyroid-stimulating hormone (TSH) secretion as judged from adrenal and thyroid weights and histology (Shirley and Nalbandov, 1956b). Thus the ovaries resembled those of hypophysectomized hens. The thyroids and adrenals were not affected by interruption of the portal vessels, whereas their weights were drastically reduced in hypophysectomized birds.

Assenmacher (1958) reported that sectioning the portal vessels caused testicular atrophy and prevented compensatory hypertrophy after hemicastration, light-induced increase in testicular size, and cyclic activity such as that found in drakes even when kept in total darkness. His data do not indicate that thyroid weight or histology were affected, but the adrenal weights were slightly lower than in the controls. The evidence from the experiments with these two species can be interpreted in two ways. One is that destruction of the portal vessels prevents the transmission of the NSM to the anterior pituitary. The second interpretation is that sectioning the portal vessels interrupts the blood supply to the anterior pituitary, and thus causes ischemia. This latter interpretation deserves emphasis in view of Wingstrand's (1951) statement that the *pars distalis* has no blood supply other than the portal vessels. Indeed, sectioning of the hypophyseal stalk resulted in "a profound increase in fibrotic tissue as well as a decrease in the number of the usual cell types" (Shirley and Nalbondov, 1956b). Assenmacher (1958) stated that sectioning portal vessels caused atrophy of the central part of the caudal lobe but did not affect the cephalic lobe (the cephalic lobe may still have received some blood from the few anterior portal vessels that are indicated in Assenmacher's drawings). Zuckerman (1955) has emphasized the importance of the second interpretation in view of the observed infarcts in the pituitary. Benoit and Assenmacher (1959) have presented evidence that the infarct *per se* is not the factor causing testicular atrophy, but that sectioning the portal vessels causes a qualitative difference in the vascularity of the anterior pituitary. First, similar infarcts, obtained when the portal vessels regenerated or were incompletely cut, did not impede testicular response to light nor did they cause atrophy of the testes. Second, the lack of infarcts in the cephalic lobe should allow production of enough gonadotrophin to stimulate the testes, inasmuch as in intact drakes the cephalic and caudal lobes have equal gonadotrophic potencies. Third, the infarcts observed after sectioning of the portal vessels leave more than 20 per cent of the gland intact. Previous experiments had shown that, even when 80 per cent of the pituitary was removed during attempted hypophysectomies, testicular degeneration did not occur, therefore 20 per cent of the gland was sufficient to maintain the testes.

3. Sectioning the hypothalamico-hypophyseal tract in the median eminence without damage to the portal system results in genital atrophy and lack of gonadal stimulation by light (Assenmacher, 1958; Assenmacher and Benoit, 1958; Benoit and Assenmacher, 1959).

Another line of evidence stems from the correlations between activity of the neurosecretory cells and the experimentally induced gonadal activity observed by Oksche, Laws, Kamemoto and Farner (1959). An increase in daily illumination from 8 to 20 hours increased body and testicular weight of white crowned sparrows. Simultaneously, the amount of NSM in the hypothalamic nuclei and the median eminence decreased. During the dark hours of the day, NSM reaccumulates in these areas. This evidence seems rather convincing, but it should be pointed out that a variety of treatments affect the activity of the neurosecretory cells and the accumulation of NSM (Legait, 1959). The findings obtained with the white crowned sparrows are suggestive, but they cannot be regarded as proof.

Finally, anticholinergic and antiadrenergic drugs can block "spontaneous" (Zarrow and Bastain, 1953; van Tienhoven, Nalbandov and Norton, 1954) as well as progesterone-induced ovulations (Zarrow and Bastian, 1953; van Tienhoven, Nalbandov and Norton, 1954; van Tienhoven, 1955), although Zuckerman (1955) and Moore (1958) have questioned the interpretation that these drugs act specifically by blocking adrenergic or cholinergic stimuli. One might also interpret the different effects of different barbiturates on "spontaneous" and progesterone-induced ovulation (Fraps and Case, 1953; Fraps, 1955b) as not providing very direct evidence for the neural control of ovulation. Zuckerman (1955) mentioned especially the unpredictability of the effects of drugs on pituitary activity as an argument against the neurohumoral control of the pituitary.

In evaluating all the evidence one has to concede that for each line of evidence marshaled in support of the hypothesis of neurohumoral pituitary control, another hypothesis can be offered to explain the same phenomenon. It also has to be conceded that, so far, no extract has been obtained which counteracts the effects of lesions of the hypothalamic nuclei or the effects of sectioning of the portal vessels; in other words, there is no evidence available demonstrating that replacement therapy is effective in birds. However, no experiments done with birds have disproved the neurohumoral pituitary control hypothesis. As all the evidence seems to support the hypothesis and as no evidence is categorically contradictory, it seems to be the most acceptable as a working hypothesis with birds.

For the sake of convenience, the various stimuli which have been shown experimentally to affect avian reproduction will be discussed separately.

2. Light

For centuries the Japanese and Dutch have made use of additional illumination to induce out-of-season singing by song birds (Damste, 1947; Hendricks, 1956). The Japanese, presumably because they enjoyed the singing, the Dutch because they wanted to use the singing birds as decoys (Damste, 1947). The first experimental evidence that light stimulated the gonads and induced the urge for migration was obtained by Rowan (1925). Many research papers have since been published on this phenomenon, and extensive documentation can be found in the reviews by Hammond (1954), Yeates (1954), Benoit and Assenmacher (1955, 1959), Fraps (1955b, 1959), and Wolfson (1959a, b). Benoit and Assenmacher (1955)

and Farner (1959) list the species in which reproductive activity has been induced successfully by additional illumination. Male birds of the temperate zones can generally be brought into a reproductive state by increased day length. The light stimulus can be broken down into several components which may effect the response.

The effect of intensity was studied in starlings (Bissonnette, 1931), house sparrows (Bartholomew, 1949), and bobwhite quail (Kirkpatrick, 1955). It is apparent from these studies that a trend exists for greater stimulation as intensity increases. However, the numbers of birds used were small as were the observed differences, consequently the differences may have been sampling errors rather than experimentally induced effects. In Farner's equation

$$\log W_t = \log W_o + kt \qquad 1$$

in which W_t = testes weight at time t, W_o = testes weight at time 0, k = rate constant, t = time, the rate constant k was higher at an intensity of 3.0 ft.-candles than at 1.0 ft.-candles for white crowned sparrows (Farner, 1959). No further change in the rate constant was observed between 3 ft.-candles and 37.5 ft.-candles. The time of appearance of nuptial plumage in response to light of intensities between 3.67 ft.-candles and 21.6 ft.-candles showed a graded response to increasing intensities for *Euplectes pyromelana* (Rollo and Domm, 1943). Egg production of chickens is not affected by light intensity between 0.5 and 38.0 ft.-candles (Nicholas, Callenbach and Murphy, 1944) or between 1.0 and 35.0 ft.-candles (Dobie, Carver and Roberts, 1946). From these limited data it seems that gonadal response can be obtained as long as the threshold of the stimulus is reached and that an intensity-response relationship exists over a limited range only. The relationship approaches that of an all-or-none response.

Only light with a wavelength between 4000 and 8000 Å causes a testicular response in drakes (Benoit and Assenmacher, 1959), starlings (Bissonnette, 1932; Burger, 1943), chickens (Carson, Junila and Bacon, 1958), turkeys (Scott and Payne, 1937), and sparrows (Ringoen, 1942). In a series of ingenious experiments Benoit and Ott (1944) investigated the relationship between wavelength and response. They established that red and orange light, which were more effective in intact birds than was blue, penetrated deeper into the tissues of the brain than the blue. These observations have been confirmed by more refined techniques (Benoit and Assenmacher, 1959). Subsequently, a quartz rod was used to shine the light directly on the hypophyseal-hypothalamus area; under these conditions, blue light was more effective than red (Benoit and Ott, 1944).

Benoit and his co-workers have made a careful analysis of the receptors for the light stimulus. In drakes, sectioning the optic nerve reduced, but did not abolish, the gonadal response to increased light (Benoit and Assenmacher, 1955, 1959). However, when the drake heads were covered with black cloth no stimulation occurred except when the eyes were left uncovered, indicating that two sets of receptors might exist which allow photostimulation to stimulate the pituitary. Further investigations showed that light applied directly on the hypothalamus or the rhinencephalon, by means of a quartz rod was effective in gonadal stimulation (Benoit and Assenmacher, 1959). Therefore, a set of receptors connected with the optic nerve and a set of deep receptors may be involved in the stimulation of the hypothalamus. In mammals, Knoche (1956, 1957) has demonstrated unmyelinated nerve fibers which originate in the optic chiasma and, coursing through the *lamina terminalis,* reach the *ependyma* of the third ventricle as well as the *para ventricular nucleus* and the *nucleus tuberis infundibularis.* These fibers would provide a connection between the retina and hypothalamus. Whether or not similar nerve fibers are present in the avian brain is unknown.

The concept presented by Rowan (1938a, b), that light causes gonadal stimulation by inducing wakefulness, which, in turn, affects the physiology of the entire body, seems erroneous in view of the evidence now available. Bissonnette (1930) was unable to induce gonadal development by forced exercise. As a matter of fact, when starlings were exposed to light, forced exercise had a slight inhibitory effect, which may, however, not have been statistically significant in view of the variability in testes size and the small number of birds used. Benoit (1935) approached the problem by immobilizing drakes and exposing them to light. No difference in response was obtained between free-roaming and immobilized drakes to increased photoperiods. The present concept of the manner in which light induces gonadal stimulation is that it causes an increase in the secretory activity of the neurosecretory cells; the NSM is subsequently transported down the axons and is picked up by the portal vessels in the special zone of the median eminence and transported to the anterior pituitary where it can have its effect.

The duration of the photoperiod required to obtain a gonadal response has been studied in detail by Marshall (1959) and by Wolfson (1959a, b). The regulation of the gonadal cycles of birds in the Northern zone seems to be largely, but not entirely, regulated by the photoperiod. A short summary of the events in the natural breeding cycle will clarify the experimental approach used in studies of regulation of the breeding cycle. In the spring the testes and ovaries mature, and, under good conditions, breeding starts. At the end of spring or in early summer, the gonads regress. The testes show steatogenesis of the tubules, the tunica albuginea is renewed, and a new generation of Leydig cells is formed. During this period, increases in photoperiod will not cause recrudescence of the testes. Marshall (1959) believed, on the basis of the histologic appearance of the testes, that the lack of response was the result of unresponsiveness of the testes. However, earlier experiments (Riley and Witschi, 1938; Miller, 1949) had demonstrated that the gonads can respond to gonadotrophin administration. Lofts and Marshall (1958) confirmed this response with small doses of gonadotrophins and abandoned the idea that the refractoriness to light was caused by unresponsiveness of the testes. In any event, the testes will not respond to light for a time interval after regression which depends on the species

(Marshall, 1959). The light-induced gonadal response can be obtained again only after the end of this so called "refractory period." The refractory period plays an important role in the regulation of the gonadal, migratory, and fat deposition cycles of migratory birds (Wolfson, 1959a, b). Wolfson studied the effect of different photoperiods on the gonadal and fat deposition cycles of *Junco hyemalis* and *Zonotrichia albicollis*. In these birds, in the fall and spring, large amounts of fat are deposited in the subcutaneous and interperitoneal depots. These fat depositions are closely associated with the migratory drive (Zugunruhe), and account largely for the increase in body weight at those seasons.

Kobayashi (1954, 1957) proposed on the basis of light-induced molt and gonadal cycles in male and female canaries that the refractory period reflects an increased secretion of TSH at the expense of gonadotrophin secretion. This hypothesis needs further verification, however, for gonadotrophins have been found in the anterior pituitaries of drakes during the refractory period.

Fall migration will not be discussed because too little is known about the regulation and physiologic conditions associated with it.

Wolfson (1959a, b) investigated the ability of various photoperiods to induce gonadal and fat deposition in birds caught in the fall and spring. These birds were exposed to light schedules of 9 L(ight) + 15 D(ark) hours; 12 L + 12 D; 15.5 L + 8.5 D; 20 L + 4 D; and 24 L and 9 L + 15 D; 12 L + 12 D; 20 L + 4 D and 24 L, respectively. The experiments showed: (1) the rate of the gonadal and fat responses is a reflection of photoperiod, the rate being greater with longer photoperiods; (2) the degree of response is greater with longer photoperiods; (3) even under short photoperiods (9 L), a response can be obtained; (4) the time interval between gonadal stimulation and regression is smaller for the longer photoperiods.

Wolfson (1959a, b) formulated his summation hypothesis on the basis of these results. The hypothesis is that the sum of the photoperiods and not the changes in daylight to which the birds are subjected determines the response.

Subsequent experiments were designed to test the importance of the dark period by interrupting the dark periods by short light periods. These experiments tested the hypothesis of Jenner and Engels (1952) and Kirkpatrick and Leopold (1952) that the dark period has a positive effect. Wolfson compared the effect of 8 L + 7.25 D to 1.5 L + 7.25 D with 8 L + 8 D and found no difference between the treatments. Thus, 8 + 1.5 L in 24 hours was as effective as 16 L per 24 hours, whereas previous experiments had shown that 9.5 L in one dose per 24 hours was relatively ineffective. This evidence made a positive effect of dark periods seem unlikely.

Experiments were then designed to test the effectiveness of different dark periods in breaking up the refractory period. Exposure to darkness had been used for centuries by the Dutch to interrupt the refractory period (Rowan, 1938b; Damste, 1947). The experiments by Wolfson demonstrated that 12 hours of uninterrupted darkness per 24 hours were required to abolish the refractoriness to light. However, 12 hours darkness alone does not seem to be sufficient to abolish refractoriness, because on 16 L + 16 D the refractory period is not broken. This suggests that the photoperiod may also have an effect.

On the basis of these results, the regulation of gonadal and migratory cycles can be tentatively explained for birds of the temperate zone. For the present discussion the gonadal and migratory (fat deposition) cycles will be regarded as one, although there are some quantitative differences with respect to the rate of response. Nonmigratory species and races do not show the fat deposition cycles shown by migratory races of the same species; the discussion here, therefore, is concerned only with the gonadal cycles. In late summer and early fall the birds enter what Wolfson calls a preparatory phase (similar to Marshall's (1959) regeneration phase). Birds need exposure to at least 12 hours of darkness per 24 hours to enter this physiologic state. After exposure to such dark periods for a certain length of time, depending on the species, the birds will go into the progressive phase. During this phase the rate of gonadal response depends on the summation of photoperiods. In the spring the accumulated effects of the photoperiods become effective in stimulating the gonads, and, if ecologic conditions are satisfactory, breeding can start.

For birds migrating to the equatorial zone or remaining in the temperate zone, the same current of events occurs except that a cycle of fat deposition is added to the gonadal cycle. According to Wolfson's hypothesis, the rate of response is determined by the summation of photoperiods so that the response can occur near the equator even though no change in photoperiod occurs. For transequatorial migrants, the exposure to daylight would increase in October and November and decrease after December. Again summation of photoperiod would be the deciding factor, provided that the exposure to enough short days has occurred to break up the refractory period.

Marshall (1959) has criticized Wolfson's hypothesis mainly on the basis of field studies showing that adult rooks, mallards, and starlings show sexual displays in the fall at the same time that in starlings the bills become yellow and 13.6 per cent of the rooks show spermatogenesis. This, according to Marshall, argues against a need for an exposure to short days to obtain a response, because the response is obtained before the shortest day. As Farner (1959) stated, these phenomena can be explained by assuming that the refractory period ends relatively early in the late summer, when the photoperiod is still long enough to cause stimulation. Not all individuals show these cycles because certain other ecologic factors interfere with the response. Evidence that a refractory period may be short or even absent is found in the experiments of Kirkpatrick (1959) with bobwhite quail.

Marshall and Disney (1956) subjected the "summation of photoperiod" hypothesis to an experimental test with the tropical nonmigratory *Quelea quelea* and observed no response when the daily photoperiod was increased 5 minutes over the natural photoperiod, although the summation of the photoperiods was an amount which the birds

under natural conditions would have experienced only after a period of 27 years. The test proves that the summation of photoperiods does not hold true for this species, but it does not eliminate the possibility that it may hold true for temperate zone birds of the Northern hemisphere. In any controversy of this kind it would seem desirable that experiments be undertaken with the same species. Any comparison between *Quelea quelea* and *Zonotrichia albicollis* should take into account the different ecologic factors which may play a role in the determination of gonadal and migratory cycles. For some species living in the temperate zone of the Northern hemisphere, light may be the most important single stimulating factor; for another species, for instance *Melopsittacus undulatus* in a different but temperate zone environment, light may not be a factor (Vaugien, 1951, 1953).

Experiments in which short photoperiods of one to several minutes interrupt long dark periods should be mentioned here. Farner (1959), in a well conducted series of experiments, determined the rate constant of Equation 1 for various lengths of photoperiods with light given in different doses. He established that 6 hours of light in equally spaced 50-minute doses resulted in k value similar to that for 12 hours of light given in one dose. The effectiveness of the short photoperiod was dependent on the intervening dark periods. Farner proposed the following hypothesis to explain this effect: a substance generated during the photoperiod decays gradually during the dark period, but remains able to stimulate the hypophysis for a certain length of time. It has been estimated that it takes about 1 minute to generate the substance in equilibrium amounts, whereas it has been estimated that the decay of the substance once generated, takes at least a few hours (Farner, 1959). This hypothesis does not assign any positive function to the dark period as suggested by Jenner and Engels (1952) and Kirkpatrick and Leopold (1952).

Although light plays a powerful role in inducing spermatogenesis in drakes, cycles of testicular activity can occur in the absence of light. Benoit, Assenmacher and

Brard (1956) kept young Pekin drakes in total darkness and found that testicular size showed definite cycles which were unrelated to temperature or changes in light outside the pens; however, the cycles of the individual birds parallelled each other. Unfortunately, no data are available on spermatogenesis under these conditions.

Recently, Benoit, Assenmacher and Brard (1959) reported that drakes kept under continuous light after the age of 3 weeks showed maximal testicular size later than birds kept under natural daylight. After maximal size was obtained the testes showed regular cycles that were apparently unrelated to outside conditions and again the cycles of the individual males paralleled each other.

Vaugien (1951) showed that ovulation and egg laying occur in budgerigars, *Melopsittacus undulatus*, kept in darkness, and Vaugien (1953) contended that males reached full spermatogenesis sooner in darkness than when kept under light. Marshall and Serventy (1958) criticized this interpretation and stated that spermatogenesis had occurred faster under light. They believed that Vaugien (1953) had misinterpreted the histologic data, which, according to Marshall and Serventy, showed that post nuptial degeneration of the tubules had occurred. Marshall and Disney (1957) confirmed, however, that spermatogenesis would occur in total darkness in Zebra finches, *Peophila castanotus*. These experiments show that gametogenesis does not require light although light may regulate the cycle.

An example of the "breaking through" of the inherent rhythm in spite of photoperiods may be found in Australian silver gulls, *Larus novae-hollandiae*, kept in the Washington Zoo. For two seasons the gulls nested in November, then adapted to the northern spring and summer but later reverted back to nesting during the Australian spring (Davis, 1945). In short-tailed shearwaters, *Puffinus tenuirostris*, the internal rhythm seems to regulate the onset of the breeding season independently of the photoperiod (Marshall and Serventy, 1959). The different examples show that in some species, *e.g.*, ducks, light is the main regulatory factor in the initiation of gametogenesis, although cycles can occur in the absence of light. In other species, *e.g.*, short-tailed shearwaters, the inherent rhythm seems to regulate the onset of gametogenesis, and in species in the tropics, *e.g.*, *Quelea quelea*, light can affect the initiation of gametogenesis (Marshall and Disney, 1956) but in their natural habitat, rainfall and the availability of long green grass initiate gametogenesis and determine breeding success (Marshall and Serventy, 1957).

3. Temperature

Considerable observational data from field studies (Marshall, 1959) indicate that temperature may be an important factor in the regulation of the breeding season. No experimental data seem to be available to demonstrate clearly that temperature is the factor *per se* and is not affecting the breeding season by making the required food available, but investigations have been made to determine the effect of temperature on the light-induced gonadal response. Burger (1949) mentions that the testes of starlings kept at 98 to 100°F. were larger than those kept at 60 to 70°F., but that the number of eggs laid by house wrens was lower when the birds were kept at 77°F. than at 67°F. Farner and Wilson (1957) determined the effect of temperature on the rate constant k in Equation 1 and found that

$$K_b/K_a = 1 + C(T_b - T_a) \qquad 2$$

in which C = constant, K_a = rate constant at temperature A, K_b = rate constant at temperature B, T_a = temperature A, T_b = temperature B.

The results showed that $C = 0.009$ for white crowned sparrows; $C = 0.02$ for juncos (data of Jenner and Engels, 1956); $C = 0.02$ for starlings (Burger's data). The conclusion is that temperature affects the light-induced gonadal response but the effect is rather slight.

Kosin and his co-workers carried out extensive investigations on the effect of temperature on the reproduction of turkeys which, although domesticated, have seasonal breeding cycles. Their work showed that pretreating the toms with a temperature of 65°F. during the period January to March, when outside temperatures may be as low as −20°F., resulted in earlier production of sperm with high fertilizing capacity (Burrows and Kosin, 1953; Kosin, Mitchell and St. Pierre, 1955a). On the other hand, "cooling" the toms to 65°F. in the period May to July, when outside temperatures may range between 60° and 100°F., prevented the drop in spermatogenesis and fertility experienced by toms kept outside (Kosin, Mitchell and St. Pierre, 1955b; Law and Kosin, 1958). Kosin (1958) established that the respiration rate of turkey semen, especially during the second hour of incubation, was affected by the environment in which the donors were kept. The respiration rate was higher for semen from toms kept at 65°F., especially during the summer, suggesting that high temperatures may be more harmful than low temperatures. In view of the fact that body temperatures rose in the toms kept outside during the summer (Kosin, Mitchell and St. Pierre, 1955b), it seems that the higher body temperature may have affected spermatogenesis, as discussed in the beginning of the present chapter. Constant temperature 50° ± 5°F. depressed over-all egg production by turkey hens (Mitchell and Kosin, 1954). Preheated (50° ± 5°F.) hens laid initially at a somewhat higher rate than the hens kept outside, where temperatures were as low as 10°F., but the birds kept in the constant environment had a greater tendency to become broody with an accompanying decrease in the rate of lay (Mitchell and Kosin, 1954; Kosin, Mitchell and St. Pierre, 1955a). Eggs from turkey hens in the constant environment were significantly smaller (84.5 *versus* 96.7 gm.) than those from hens kept outside.

4. Rainfall

Marshall (1959) reviewed the evidence that rainfall may be involved in regulation of the breeding cycles. Serventy and Marshall (1957) observed that unseasonal precipitation in Australia was followed by the appearance of spermatogenesis in a large number of terrestrial as well as aquatic species. Marshall and Disney (1957) analyzed experimentally in what manner the rain or increased humidity had its effect. Rainfall induced adult nonbreeding *Quelea quelea* to molt from one breeding plumage dress

to the other without the normally intervening neutral dress. The urge to build nests was also stimulated by rainfall or humidity, but for the construction to be successful long green grass was required. This grass normally becomes available after the rain. After the nests are built, breeding can proceed; at the same time the seed heads, the staple food of the nestlings, normally appear in the grass. Whether the relationship between the initiation of ovulations and appearance of seed heads is coincidental was not determined. These results suggest that rainfall affects the breeding cycle directly and also indirectly by making suitable nesting material (and food?) available so that reproduction can occur.

5. Food

The availability of food may affect breeding success, but no evidence is available that demonstrates that a specific food supply regulates the breeding cycle of birds (Marshall, 1959).

6. Vocalizations

Vaugien (1951) found that female budgerigars, *Melopsittacus undulatus*, would lay in complete darkness, provided they could hear the vocalizations of courting pairs of budgerigars in the aviary. Ficken, van Tienhoven, Ficken and Sibley (1960) investigated the effects of vocalizations by the birds' own mates on gametogenesis. The gonads of pairs isolated from hearing other pairs remained inactive, whereas pairs which could hear others showed full spermatogenesis and ovulations, whether or not they could see the other pairs. No quantitative investigations were made to determine how many pairs were required to start the chain of events.

7. Nesting Site

Marshall (1952) reported that arctic birds of a variety of species seem to be adversely affected by lack of nesting sites. A rather detailed investigation of nonbreeding, or rather decreased laying, has been made by Barry (1960) for the brant, *Branta bernicla hrota*, and blue and snow geese, *Chen caerulescens*. The data from the two species agree closely enough to be treated here as one group. Barry (1960) found a correlation between snow cover and the date of first egg, whereas the correlation between date of first egg and clutch size was 0.79 to 0.85. From his data it appears that the ovaries are in the beginning stages of development when the birds arrive at their breeding grounds in the arctic and that full ovarian development occurs during the prenesting interval. Ovulation seems to be dependent on the availability of nesting sites, although lack of food was not completely excluded as a factor. A sharp decrease in average clutch size takes place when the interval between arrival on the breeding grounds and laying of the first egg exceeds 7 to 10 days.

Barry (1960) counted the number of atretic and ruptured follicles and compared these with the average clutch sizes. In this manner he could show that each egg not laid because of unfavorable conditions was represented by an atretic follicle.

For the males of these species the situation seems somewhat different. Testicular weights decrease and lipoidal infiltration of the tubules starts, apparently immediately after the males arrive at the breeding grounds. Corroborating evidence for the hypothesis that spermatogenesis may already be past its peak on arrival at the breeding grounds is found in the fact that neither Barry (1960) nor the Eskimos in this area have ever seen brant or snow geese copulate. Also, sperm were found in the oviduct of a brant killed on arrival at the breeding grounds. It was not possible to establish whether the rate of testicular collapse would proceed at different rates in the presence or absence of nesting sites and plentiful food. Marshall and Roberts (1959) studied the fish-eating cormorants, *Phalacrocorax carba* and *P. africanus*, which breed in the northern Lake Victoria region. These species apparently can breed the year around, but within the species different segments of the population are in different phases of the reproductive cycle, so that no pair breeds twice without a pause long enough for another pair to breed at the nest they have just abandoned. It seems from the observations that the availability of nests and nesting sites determines the breeding behavior for each segment of the population.

Vaugien (1948), with very few birds, showed that canaries would not lay when the female was deprived of cotton to line the nest bowl. The condition of the ovary was not mentioned. However, when the nest bowl was warmed by an electric coil, ovipositions occurred in the absence of the cotton lining. Unfortunately, no information concerning the ovaries was published and so few birds were used that any interpretation is very tentative.

8. Psychic Factors

A variety of psychic factors have been shown to affect the breeding of birds. Craig (1913) noticed that a dove which had failed to lay started to do so 9 days after Craig started to stroke her daily. Matthews (1939) later established that an isolated female pigeon could be stimulated to lay a normal clutch by the sight of another pigeon or even the sight of herself in the mirror. Vaugien (1948) noted that the canary needs a partner, male or female, in order to lay. House sparrows, in which the male and female are dimorphic, are apparently more discriminating than pigeons, in which male and female look alike. Female sparrows will not show any oviduct response (as a reflection of estrogen secretion) if caged with other females, but will show enlarged oviducts when caged with males (Polikarpova, 1940, cited by Lehrman, 1959). This response may be partly the result of the nest building which is largely done by the male. It may thus have been the nest built by the male rather than the male *per se* to which the female responded. Burger (1953) observed that caging female starlings with males increased the response of testes to light.

Captivity prevents ovarian development in pintail ducks, *Anas acuta*, captured from migrating flocks while spermatogenesis in the males is unimpaired (Phillips, 1959). The inhibition is mediated by way of the pituitary, which, in the captive birds, contains no detectable amounts of gonadotrophins. Vaugien (1954a) found that wing clipping of house sparrows, so that they could not perch, prevented their testes from being stimulated by light, as measured by spermatogenesis and bill color. The birds did respond to PMS injections, suggesting that the inability to perch prevented the secretion of gonadotrophins. Ficken, van Tienhoven, Ficken and Sibley (1960) found that mirrors in cages of pairs of budgerigars delayed ovulations but did not affect spermatogenesis. In this respect the budgerigars may differ from pigeons in which a mirror was stimulatory when one female was in a cage. We were not able to find evidence about the effect of mirrors in cages with pairs of pigeons.

The observations and experiments reviewed indicate that light may be a very important factor in determining the onset of gametogenesis, of migration, and of fat deposition in certain migratory birds. However, other factors (e.g., rain) may modify the onset of breeding, and in some species these factors rather than light seem to be most important. Such species can then breed at more irregular intervals when conditions are favorable, e.g., after rainfall. Some tropical species such as the sooty terns, *Sterna fuscata*, breed every 9.6 months (Chapin, 1954), apparently stimulated, not by outside factors, but by an inherent rhythm (Marshall, 1959). The multiplicity of factors determining breeding cycles of avian species makes it unlikely that any hypothesis will be useful when it takes into account only one of these factors such as light.

The discussion of the initiation of the breeding cycle should be followed by a discussion of the factors which terminate the cycle, but relatively little is known. In those species in which the male helps in incubation or in building the nest or stays with the female while she is incubating, the release of prolactin in response to visual and emotional stimuli may cause the regression of the testes. Some evidence for this is found in the experiments by Patel (1936) in which the sight of an incubating mate caused crop gland development in the male. Experimentally, crop gland development can be induced by prolactin, and prolactin is known to cause regression of the gonads. In polygamous species the regression of the testes does not seem to occur until rather late in the summer when decreasing daylight may be a causative factor.

For the females a distinction should be made between *determinate* and *indetermi-*

nate layers. The former lay a definite number of eggs per clutch whether or not eggs are removed. Examples are brant, snow geese (Barry, 1960), budgerigars, *Agapornis roseicollis, A. taranta, A. fischeri*. From the rather scanty data available, it seems that two mechanisms are involved in making these birds determinate layers. In brant and snow geese only a limited number of follicles (5 to 6) reach ovulatory size, and these are ovulated when conditions are appropriate (Barry, 1960). Ovulation, or atresia of the largest follicle, permits the next follicle to reach maturity so that it can be ovulated if conditions are right. In *Agapornis* and in budgerigars more follicles mature than are necessary for the clutch, but after the normal number of eggs (5 to 6) are laid, a general atresia of the other follicles occurs. This information on *Agapornis* and budgerigars was kindly given to me by Dr. W. C. Dilger. The factors causing this atresia are unknown.

Indeterminate egg laying has been observed in many species (Lehrman 1959, and his chapter in this book). In brief, the evidence suggests that the female starts to incubate after a certain number of eggs are present in the nest, whether laid by herself or placed in the nest by others. After this incubation starts (and prolactin is released?) degeneration of the follicles takes place and no further ovulations occur. Lehrman (1959) cites Poulsen's work in which laying could be repressed in pigeons if 2 eggs were placed in the empty nest. As pigeons are determinate layers, he could not obtain more than 2 eggs by removal of 1 or 2 eggs as they were laid. This whole field of investigations on the physiologic mechanisms involved in *determinate* and *indeterminate* layers is virtually unexplored, in spite of many field observations which suggest what mechanisms may be involved.

The following may serve to summarize the present concepts of the regulation of the breeding cycle of seasonally reproducing birds.

Various stimuli or combinations of stimuli, such as light, rainfall, availability of food and nesting material, and vocalization by other birds in the flock, may initiate gametogenesis. In many species the males reach the peak of gonadal activity before the females (Benoit, 1956); an exception is the turkey in which the female responds to increased photoperiods before the male does (Margolf, Harper and Callenbach, 1947). The sexual behavior of the male, his singing, and the initiation of nest building, all of which may be dependent on temperature, availability of nest sites, etc., stimulate the females (Benoit, 1956; Lehrman, 1959). Under the influence of this stimulation the female will copulate, and ovulate. She may now lay a more or less predetermined number of eggs (determinate layer) or she may lay eggs until the presence of a sufficient number stimulates incubation behavior and the degeneration of follicles still present in the ovary.

Destruction of the nest may restart a new cycle; or, in some species, a new cycle may be started after the first hatch has fled the nest. At the end of the summer, in temperate zone birds, the gonads regress, and, in migratory species, fat is deposited in intraperitoneal and subcutaneous depots. Migration southward starts under the influence of yet unknown factors. The refractory period, which varies in length for different species, is terminated under the influence of short days. In the spring gonadal activity is reinitiated, fat deposition takes place, and migration north starts again, either because of an "inherent rhythm," or under the influence of photostimulation. For many species we know nothing about the regulatory factors involved in their migrations; therefore, the above generalizations should be taken as tentative even for the best studied species such as those of the genera *Junco* and *Zonotrichia*.

D. REGULATION OF THE REPRODUCTIVE CYCLE OF THE FOWL

For convenience of discussion the reproductive cycle of the fowl will be divided into an annual cycle and the laying cycle which encompasses only part of the annual cycle.

The annual cycle of females resembles the cycle of wild birds, especially in breeds and strains in which broodiness still occurs. The cycle of the male is virtually absent and males produce sperm all year. Seasonal variations in fertility may occur, but these fluctuations may be a reflection of high temperature, and they are probably not a reflection of changes in photoperiodicity. Roosters have been kept for years without molting, although hens normally molt. The hens which show broodiness may become broody several times when not allowed to incubate, and they produce eggs between the broody periods. Legait (1959) studied the annual cycle of Rhode Island Red hens which were allowed to incubate the eggs. Her study encompasses all phases of the annual cycle with special attention to the incubation period. Unfortunately, the results seem to be based on 1 or 2 birds for each phase of the cycle, but, if allowance is made for the small numbers, several conclusions may be deduced from the data.

1. The diameters of the nuclei of the paraventricular cells are about 6.24 μ during the annual rest and during the molt; they are somewhat larger, 6.4 to 6.6 μ, during laying, and considerably larger during incubation, 7 to 12 μ.

2. During molting many granules of NSM are present in the paraventricular cells, and the posterior lobe also contains NSM in abundance. During incubation, the amount of NSM in the paraventricular cells and posterior pituitary lobe is small.

3. During laying the percentage of A_2 cells in the cephalic lobe of the anterior pituitary is at its maximum and β-cells are at a minimum. The β-cells increase during incubation.

4. In the caudal lobe of the anterior pituitary, δ-cells increase during incubation and decrease sharply during the molt.

5. Adrenal weight is low during the molt and annual rest, but is high during incubation. Legait (1959) showed that the diameter of the nuclei of the neurosecretory cells and adrenal weights parallel each other.

6. During incubation and molt, the ovarian weight is quite small (2 to 3 gm.).

The annual cycle seems to be regulated largely by light. Recent investigations all indicate, directly or indirectly, that the daily increment in the photoperiod may be more important than the length of photoperiod (Sykes, 1956; Morris and Fox, 1958). The experiments carried out by Morris and Fox (1958) showed particularly clearly the importance of daily increments in photoperiod. The correlation between the summation of daily light changes and the age of sexual maturity was 0.96, an unusually high correlation in biologic experimentation.

A question which has been raised in connection with the practice of providing artificial light for growing chickens is that of refractoriness. Tomhave (1954) and Shutze, Jensen and Matson (1959) found that artificial light provided during the growing period causes lowered egg production even when the artificial light is supplied only during the period from hatching to 8 weeks of age. Hutt, Goodwin and Urban (1956) suggested that the failure of ovaries to develop in some birds may be the result of artificially long photoperiods during the growing period. Experiments reported for the domestic Pekin drake indicate also that raising young drakes under continuous light delays the onset of maximal testicular size in the first breeding season (Benoit, Assenmacher and Brard, 1959). Further experiments are needed to determine whether the observed effect is essentially the same as the refractoriness in seasonally reproducing birds and whether it can be interrupted by exposure to short days.

After egg laying has started, 13 to 14 hours of light per 24 hours seem to be optimum, provided the photoperiod is given in one dose (Dobie, Carver and Roberts, 1946). With interrupted photoperiods the results are similar to those described for seasonally reproducing birds (Fraps, 1959). When hens are exposed to continuous light, egg production is higher initially than in birds exposed to 13- to 14-hour photoperiods, but egg production decreases sooner (Penquite and Thompson, 1933; Greenwood, 1958). This decrease may be the result of refractoriness of the hypothalamus or of the pituitary to light (Byerly and Moore, 1941). Greenwood (1958) observed that chickens kept in a constant environment (continuous light?) showed no molting, but there was a steadily decreasing rate of egg production and of hatchability of fertile eggs. After the birds were 3.5 years old, 94 per cent died, all of adenocarcinomas. Although carried out with a limited number of birds, the experiment suggests that molting observed in birds under continuous light is precipitated by factors other than light. The high mortality may have been the result of the continuous light, although in Greenwood's experiment other environmental factors cannot be separated from the light effect. However, data obtained by Benoit, Assenmacher and Brard (1959) with ducks suggest that light may be the most important factor. These investigators found poorer survival by Pekin drakes raised and kept under continuous light than by ducks kept either under daylight conditions or in total darkness.

Greenwood's data (1958) also suggest that a constant environment is not very desirable for optimal reproduction, an observation confirmed in the experiments with turkeys, mentioned before. Byerly and Moore (1941) demonstrated that an unnatural photoperiod of 14 L + 12 D resulted in considerably increased egg production and clutch (number of eggs laid on consecutive days) length. They offered the following explanation for this phenomenon.

1. The long dark period prevents the onset of refractoriness to light stimulation.

2. The limiting effect of the onset of darkness is partially removed. As will be discussed later, the onset of darkness may determine the length of the clutch (Warren and Scott, 1936). No further experimental work to test the hypothesis of Byerly and Moore (1941) seems to have been reported. The effects of intensity, wavelength, and interrupted photoperiods have been discussed previously for seasonally reproducing birds. The experimental evidence indicates no fundamental differences between such birds and chickens; thus no further discussion seems to be required. Photoperiod is the main regulator of gonadal activity, but other factors such as nutrition and temperature may modify the response to light; some of these factors are discussed later when consideration is given to the several hypotheses offered to explain the timing of the ovulation cycle.

An understanding of the regulation of the laying cycle requires a short introduction to the events which occur in the formation of the egg after ovulation. Excellent reviews on this subject are available for more details (Romanoff and Romanoff,

1949; Fraps, 1955b). After ovulation, the yolk (secondary oocyte) either falls into the ovarian pocket and is subsequently engulfed by the funnel of the oviduct, or it may immediately fall into the funnel when the latter is partly covering the mature follicle.

The yolk is moved down the oviduct by peristaltic movements, and, during this passage, albumen is deposited around it. The albumen has been accumulated in the glands of the oviduct during the period between successive yolks coming down the oviduct (Conrad and Scott, 1942). On passage of the yolk, the albumen is hydrated and transferred to the lumen of the oviduct (Smith, Hoover, Nordstrom and Winget, 1957). Part of the albumen accumulation in the magnum of the oviduct seems to occur continuously whereas another part is secreted in larger quantities when ovulation is imminent (Smith, Court and Martin, 1959). The egg is transferred from magnum to isthmus where the membranes are formed around the albumen. After this stage is completed, the egg is moved into the shell gland where the thin albumen is added through the egg membranes to give the egg its plumped appearance. This process takes 3 to 5 hours, and during this process shell deposition also starts (Bradfield, 1951). Of the egg-shell calcium, 60 to 75 per cent comes directly from the food (Driggers and Comar, 1949). These workers found that an egg laid within 10 minutes after an oral dose of Ca^{45} contained radioactive calcium, evidence for the very rapid transfer as well as for the continuous deposition of calcium while the egg is in the oviduct. In some breeds of chickens porphyrin is deposited on the shell to give it a brown color. According to recent *in vitro* studies, the porphyrin is synthesized from δ-amino-levulinic acid by the shell gland tissue (Polin, 1957). *In vitro* no difference was found between the amount of porphyrin synthesized by tissue from breeds laying white-shelled eggs and breeds laying brown-shelled eggs. Polin (1957) suggested that white shells are white because of a lack of δ-amino-levulinic acid in the tissues, and not because of a lack of enzyme systems for the synthesis of porphyrin from δ-amino-levulinic acid. During the sojourn in the shell gland, the egg is rotated on its longitudinal axis (Conrad and Phillips, 1938), which causes some of the mucin material in the albumen to form strands. The formation of these twisted strands squeezes out some of the water to form the inner thin albumen (Conrad and Phillips, 1938). Shell formation continues until complete oviposition occurs.

The physiologic mechanisms which initiate oviposition are not well understood. A variety of treatments, including injection of posterior pituitary hormone, vasopressin, and oxytocin can cause premature oviposition. Soft-shelled eggs can be obtained in this manner (Burrows and Byerly, 1942; Burrows and Fraps, 1942). It is known that the posterior pituitary glands of chickens contain vasopressin and oxytocin (de Lawder, Tarr and Geiling, 1934; Heller, 1950); however, posterior pituitary removal does not interfere with either ovulation or oviposition, although it does result in *diabetes insipidus*, thus indicating that the antidiuretic hormone is absent (Shirley and Nalbandov, 1956a). An analogous situation is observed in rats from which the posterior pituitary is removed. Such rats are unable to nurse their young because the milk ejection cannot occur in the absence of the posterior pituitary hormones. After a subsequent pregnancy these rats will deliver the young normally indicating normal release of oxytocin. The dams can nurse their young normally in spite of *diabetes insipidus* (Benson and Cowie, 1956). These data indicate that oxytocin can be released from the regenerated stalk, where the NSM from the hypothalamic nuclei has accumulated. This release occurs in response to a reflex stimulus, but for some reason, the antidiuretic hormone is not released. It is entirely possible, therefore, that the posterior pituitary hormones, or rather the NSM from the hypothalamus, are involved in oviposition, but this is a matter of speculation.

In addition to posterior pituitary hormones, acetylcholine injections cause premature expulsion of the egg, and ephedrine delays oviposition (Weiss and Sturkie, 1952). As mentioned, the ruptured follicle and the largest maturing follicle may secrete a hormone involved in expulsion of the egg, but no evidence is available as to the nature of this hormone. Fraps (1942) showed that premature induction of ovulation with LH also resulted in premature expulsion of the oviducal egg. This means that either LH *per se* caused the expulsion or that the ovulation liberated a hormone which caused expulsion of the egg. "Spontaneous" ovulation is preceded by increased activity of the funnel of the oviduct, as was shown in a film by Warren and Scott. It is possible that such activity also causes contractions in the shell gland that would result in oviposition. That this is not the only mechanism involved in oviposition is evident from the terminal oviposition in a clutch which is not accompanied by ovulation. Before oviposition takes place, the egg is turned 180° on its short axis so that it is laid blunt end first (Bradfield, 1951). The findings by Olsen and Byerly (1932) that about 80 per cent of the eggs are laid small end first, were criticized by Bradfield (1951). He states that normally the bird gets up, turns the egg in the shell gland, settles again, and lays the egg about one hour later. According to Bradfield (1951), Olsen and Byerly (1932) disturbed the hens when they picked them up to determine the orientation of the egg at oviposition and thus prevented the egg from being turned. Bradfield used radiographic examination which did not disturb the hens.

Fraps (1955b) has presented a detailed study of the time relationships between ovulations, between ovipositions, and between ovulations and ovipositions. His terminology will be used here. This discussion will be largely devoted to the relationship between events in the egg laying cycle of chickens kept under 14 hours of light, from 6 a.m. to 8 p.m. The oviposition cycle is the number of consecutive days on which oviposition occurs plus the number of days on which oviposition fails to occur before its resumption.

In the following equation some of the relationships are presented:

$$f = n/(n + z) \qquad\qquad 3$$

in which f = oviposition frequency within a cycle, n = number of days on which oviposition occurs (singly or consecutively),

z = number of days intervening before oviposition is resumed. The discussion will be mainly concerned with those cycles in which $z = 1$, the so-called closed cycles. Using Fraps' terminology, the consecutive ovipositions of a cycle may be called C_1, ... C_n. The difference in time of day when successive ovipositions occur has been called "lag"; total lag is the difference in time of day between first and last oviposition of a clutch; mean lag is total lag divided by $(n - 1)$. Fraps calculated the mean lag from a large number of observations in which birds were exposed to artificial light from 6 a.m. to 8 p.m. From these calculations the following became apparent: (1) the lag of the terminal oviposition is greater than at preceding places in a clutch; (2) this lag decreases as n increases; (3) lag for positions between the initial and terminal ovipositions decreases as n increases and this lag may approach zero for large n.

These facts for the oviposition clutch have a bearing on the ovulatory cycle. Warren and Scott (1935) established that ovulation occurs within 14 to 75 minutes after oviposition of an egg, except in case of the last oviposition of a clutch. Ovulation, however, is not caused by oviposition. When the egg in the oviduct is broken so that it is expelled prematurely ovulation does not occur prematurely (Warren and Scott, 1935). Premature expulsion of an egg caused by injection of posterior pituitary extracts is not followed by premature ovulation. On the other hand, oviposition can be induced prematurely by inducing premature ovulation with LH (Fraps, 1942).

Fraps (1955b) calculated the regression of interval between oviposition and ovulation on mean lag between successive eggs. The regression showed that for each increase in mean lag of 1 hour the mean interval between oviposition and ovulation increased about 10 minutes. By considering these characteristics (Fraps, 1955b for details) for ovulation and oviposition clutches, Fraps observed that the lag between the first and second ovulations of a clutch was of the same order of magnitude as the lag between penultimate and ultimate ovipositions in the clutch. A consideration of lags in the ovulation sequence compared to lag in the oviposition sequence showed that the lag for the second place in the ovulation sequence remained relatively large, whereas in the oviposition sequence it became rapidly smaller as the number of eggs per clutch increased. Thus, the time that the second egg remains in the oviduct decreases more rapidly as clutch length increases. Another important characteristic of the ovulation cycle is the interval between terminal ovulation of one clutch, C_n, and ovulation of the first follicle, C_1', of the next clutch, an interval which is of the order of 44 hours when $n = 2$ and 40 hours when $n = 6$. The difference between this value and the mean interval between ovulations in a clutch gives an approximation of the "period of lapse." This period of lapse approximates the additional time elapsing between C_n and C_1 follicles over what might be expected, had ovulation occurred on the day of the missed ovulation.

In order to explain these conclusions of Fraps, consideration will now be given to the effect of environmental factors on the ovulation sequence. A fundamental study by Warren and Scott (1936) demonstrated: (1) under normal daylight, the onset of darkness seems to determine the termination of the clutch and more than 90 per cent of the eggs are laid during the day; (2) when lighting is continuous and entirely artificial, time of laying is equally distributed over the 24 hours; (3) when light and dark periods were reversed, the hens would lay in the dark for a few days, demonstrating that oviposition can occur in the dark; the hens would shift gradually to laying in the light period; (4) hens laid 90 per cent of the eggs during the day when daylight was supplemented with continuous artificial light; this was attributed to a psychologic factor.

McNally (1947) found that the period of feeding determined the time of oviposition for chickens kept under continuous light, and Fraps, Neher and Rothchild (1947) investigated both the effect of feeding and time of light with respect to time of lay. Birds were first exposed to 14 hours light; they laid during the light period. After the oviposition pattern was established, lights were turned on continuously, and eggs were still laid dur-

ing the daytime. By changing the period at which the birds were fed and tended, the investigators were able to shift the time of lay to the period in which feed was available. An incidental observation was that the time of minimal body temperature coincided with the time of release of gonadotrophin to cause ovulation. We have tried to establish experimentally whether lowering of body temperature would result in premature ovulations. Hens were placed in refrigerators (with good ventilation), with and without lights. This was done during the period of the cycle (day of lay of the last egg of the clutch) when progesterone injections cause premature ovulations. Body temperature dropped 1° to 3°F., but in no case were we able to induce premature ovulation. This suggests that the observation made by Fraps, Neher and Rothchild (1947) may be the result of coincidence.

Bastian and Zarrow (1955) recorded activity of hens during light and dark periods and found that practically all activity occurred during the light hours. As release of the gonadotrophin for ovulation occurs during the dark period of a 14 L + 10 D day, the investigators determined the effect of light and enforced activity on ovulation of the C_1 follicle. Enforced activity on the evening (9:00 p.m.) of oviposition of the terminal egg of a clutch delayed ovulation 26 minutes. A combination of light and enforced activity caused a delay of 2.16 to 4.5 hours. Light plus Nembutal anesthesia (to prevent increased activity) did not affect the time of ovulation. They concluded that the daily fluctuations in light and activity of the hen prevented the release of the hormone for ovulation on the day of lay of the last egg of the clutch.

A brief discussion of the hormonal relationships in the induction of ovulation is required before the hypotheses offered to explain the laying cycle of chickens can be considered.

For the present it will be assumed that LH and the ovulation-inducing hormone are the same, a point not proven but made very acceptable by the observation that as little as 1 μg. LH from chicken pituitaries can induce ovulation in 50 per cent of experimental birds (Fraps, Fevold and Neher,

1947). Ovulation occurs 6 to 7 hours after intravenous LH injection (Fraps, Riley and Olsen, 1942). After intravenous progesterone injection which induces gonadotrophin release from the pituitary, ovulation occurs in 7 to 8 hours (Fraps, 1955b). The question of how long the pituitary would have to remain active in order to secrete enough gonadotrophin for ovulation was investigated by Rothchild and Fraps (1949a). Hypophysectomy was performed at various intervals before "spontaneous" ovulation. The results showed that ovulation would still occur in 60 per cent of the cases when the interval was 5 hours, but only 20 per cent would ovulate when the interval was 7.2 hours. Progesterone-induced ovulation provided, of course, a better estimate how long it takes to secrete sufficient gonadotrophin because the time of stimulation of the pituitary can be timed better. As the intervals between LH or progesterone injection and ovulation agreed rather closely, it was assumed that the stimulation for gonadotrophin secretion after progesterone was immediate. Rothchild and Fraps (1949b) established that the pituitary has to remain *in situ* 2 to 4 hours after the injection of progesterone in order to obtain ovulation. The question as to the duration of stimulation of the pituitary was investigated by "blocking" the stimulus with atropine (van Tienhoven, 1955), and by destroying the hypothalamic centers (Ralph and Fraps, 1959) at various time intervals after progesterone injection. In van Tienhoven's experiments the estimate was that 26 minutes was the minimum and about 2.5 hours the maximum, whereas Ralph and Fraps found that the lesion had to be made within 2 hours after the injection.

In a typical closed cycle which has been discussed so far, the C_1 follicle is ovulated about 6:00 a.m. on day 1 and laid the next day about 8:00 a.m. The C_2 follicle ovulates about 8:30 a.m. of day 2 and is laid about 10:00 a.m. of day 3. The C_n follicle is ovulated about noon and laid in the afternoon of the nth + 1 day of the cycle. On this day no ovulation occurs in spite of: (1) greater sensitivity of the C_1' follicle (first follicle in the second clutch) at this time to LH than any subsequent follicles

of the same clutch (Fraps, 1946; Bastian and Zarrow, 1953); and (2) competence of the pituitary to secrete ovulation-inducing amounts of gonadotrophin when stimulated by progesterone. Neher and Fraps (1950) were, for example, able to add as many as 13 eggs to the clutch by injecting progesterone at times calculated to stimulate ovulation at a time corresponding to the nth + 1 follicle of the clutch. In this manner, the C_1' follicle became the nth + 1 follicle of the first clutch. By injecting progesterone from then on at 26-hour intervals more eggs were added to the clutch. Thus, the situation is, in a typical closed cycle, that ovulation fails to occur in spite of the presence of an ovulable follicle and in spite of the ability of the pituitary to secrete enough gonadotrophin.

Various hypotheses have been proposed to explain this phenomenon. Bastian and Zarrow (1953) and Fraps (1955b) agree that light and activity are the regulatory mechanisms which impose the rhythm of ovulations. Bastian and Zarrow (1953) proposed that two independent rhythms, a 24-hour daily rhythm and rhythmic maturation of follicles, interact to produce an asynchronous ovulation cycle. The inference would be, if this is true, that succeeding follicles in a clutch would be more and more immature as the ovulations of the clutch progressed. Some evidence was obtained to show that this occurred: the yolks of the second and third eggs of 2- and 3-egg clutches were indeed smaller than the yolk of the first egg of the clutch (Bastian and Zarrow, 1953); furthermore, the follicles became less and less sensitive to LH. As stated above, the first follicle of a clutch is more sensitive to LH than the succeeding ones. Thus, the failure of the C_1' follicle to ovulate as the nth + 1 follicle would be due to its low sensitivity to LH. This is not in agreement with Fraps' data (1955b) showing that the sensitivity to gonadotrophins for the follicles of a clutch is about the same at the same time interval after the preceding ovulation. Thus, the follicle is equally sensitive to LH at the same interval *after previous ovulation* as all follicles of the clutch are after that interval. Inasmuch as no ovulation occurs, sensitivity of the C_1 follicle increases, so that at the same

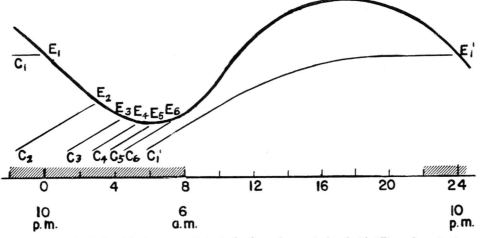

Fig. 18.11. Relationship between diurnal rhythm of neural threshold (E) and excitation hormone concentration (C) 7-day cycle. Shaded areas are times when release of ovulation-inducing hormone occurs according to Fraps (1954). (From R. M. Fraps, Proc. Nat. Acad. Sc., **40**, 348–356, 1954.)

interval *before* expected ovulation the C_1 follicle is more sensitive than the other follicles. Fraps' hypothesis can be explained best by reference to Figure 18.11. According to him, diurnal variations in threshold occur, as represented by the curve E_1, E_2 ... E_6. C_1, C_2 ... C_6, C'_1 indicate the excitation hormone levels. Only when these hormone levels reach the threshold values, do ovulations take place. Follicle C'_1 would not be ovulated as follicle C_7 of the previous clutch because the threshold value of E_7 is too high and cannot be reached. When the threshold values go down, the hormone level reaches its threshold value and C'_1 ovulates. This hypothesis needs experimental testing to demonstrate the fluctuations in the excitation hormone and the diurnal rhythm in thresholds.

Nalbandov (1959b) proposed a mechanism based on a phenomenon discovered by Huston and Nalbandov (1953). When a loop of thread was placed lengthwise in the oviduct of laying hens, ovulation was interrupted and the ovary remained fully functional, but no follicular maturation occurred. Evidence was obtained that this effect was probably neural in nature. Secondly, not more than one ovulation per hen was obtained. However, daily progesterone injections induced ovulations in the same hen at different days. The experiments thus showed: (1) the thread inhibited gonadotrophin release, but enough gonadotrophin was secreted to prevent atresia of the follicles and regression of the comb (Huston and Nalbandov 1953); (2) according to van Tienhoven (1959) and Nalbandov (1959c), the results of this experiment indicate that gonadotrophin is secreted or released as a complex, for when progesterone causes release of hormone for ovulation it also causes maturation of the next largest follicle.

Further investigations showed that a thread placed in the isthmus prevented ovulation for a longer time and in a greater percentage of birds than did a thread placed in the funnel (infundibulum) or in the upper, middle, or lower magnum (van Tienhoven, 1953). Sykes (1953) subsequently showed that a thread in the shell gland caused premature oviposition but no change in ovulations. Nalbandov (1959c) proposed that, after ovulation, the egg in the oviduct inhibits gonadotrophic secretion until the egg passes from isthmus to shell gland. The pituitary then requires time to recover and produce enough gonadotrophin to induce the next ovulation. Clutch length thus would become a function of recovery rate of the pituitary. This recovery rate would be affected by light only insofar as light causes production of gonadotrophins. The hypothesis is attractive because it provides for an internal mechanism for the regulation of ovulation. It fails to account for the shift in ovulation time by 12 hours when the time of feeding is shifted 12 hours. A more serious objection to the hypothesis is that release of gonadotrophin from the pituitary, and subsequent ovulation, can be induced by progesterone injection, during the "recovery" period. In Nalbandov's hypothesis one of the crucial points in the regulation of timing is the slow recovery by the pituitary, but the fact that the release of enough gonadotrophin can be induced to stimulate ovulation indicates that the pituitary is competent, but that a stimulus is lacking or that the threshold is too high for the stimulus to be effective.

In each of the hypotheses, fluctuations in threshold of the ovary to LH (Bastian and Zarrow, 1953), neural threshold (Fraps, 1955b), or pituitary recovery (Nalbandov, 1959c) are an essential part of the hypothesis. Whether these changes actually occur remains to be proven in each case, and, therefore, it seems that judgment as to the correctness of each hypothesis must be withheld. Indirect evidence from other species can often be marshalled, but applying data obtained with one species to another species is fraught with danger, especially in the case of a species which has been as strongly influenced by artificial selection as the chicken.

1. Use of Birds in Bioassays

Birds can be used in a variety of bioassays that will be described briefly in this chapter. In several cases reference will be made to reviews because they contain the essential information on sensitivity and details of procedures.

GONADOTROPHIN ASSAYS. *Total gonadotrophins.* 1. One-day-old cockerels are kept in shipping boxes with food and water. Injections are made subcutaneously at 12-hour intervals and the chicks are killed 12 hours after the last injection. Usually a total of 5 injections is made (Breneman and Mason, 1951). At autopsy the testes are removed and weighed to the nearest 0.1 mg. With this assay a minimal total dosage of 5.0 I.U. PMS, 5.0 μg. FSH, or 50 μg. LH give responses significantly different from water-injected controls. The index of precision for each of the three gonadotrophins in this assay was 0.5734, 0.5766, and 0.4459, respectively (Breneman, Zeller and Beekman, 1959). Each of the gonadotrophins gave a linear log dose-response relationship. No response was obtained with human chorionic gonadotrophin nor was there evidence of a FSH-LH synergism. Ten to fifteen chicks should be used for each point on the regression. In this assay no reduction of error mean square was obtained by adjusting testes weights for differences in body weight of the chicks by the use of a covariance analysis (Phillips, 1959). By measuring P^{32} uptake by chick testes Florsheim, Velcoff and Bodfish (1959) were able to detect 0.1 I.U. of human chorionic gonadotrophin, 0.05 I.U. of PMS, and 0.5 to 1.0 μg. of LH and FSH.

2. Nalbandov and Baum (1948) proposed the use of estrogen-inhibited roosters. According to their data, FSH would cause an increase in testicular size and an increase in tubule diameter, but no increase in comb size, whereas LH would cause an appreciable increase in comb size, but only a small increase in testicular size. By this method an estimate of FSH and LH content could be made in unpurified gonadotrophin extracts. As far as the author is aware, no use has been made of this method to make such estimates.

LH assay (Weaver-Finch test). In this assay male, female, castrate, or noncastrate *Euplectes, Steganura,* or *Quelea* are partially deplumed and given a rest for 5 days. The feather follicles reorganize and the tips of new feathers are formed. The material is injected subcutaneously in 1 or 2 doses. In a positive reaction a colored bar is formed on the new feather. The test is specific for LH and human chorionic gonadotrophin (Witschi, 1955; Segal, 1957). The response is not affected by the presence of FSH, prolactin, ACTH, or TSH in the material to be tested, and as little as 5 μg. LH can be detected (Witschi, 1955; Segal, 1957).

Prolactin assay. Several methods for the assay of prolactin on pigeons have been described in a review by Meites and Turner (1950). In each of the assays the stimulation of the pigeon crop gland is measured. A very sensitive method has recently been described by Grosvenor and Turner (1958). Adult pigeons, *Columba livia*, between 240 and 360 gm. were kept in a room with a temperature between 78 and 80°F., artificial light-supplemented daylight during daylight hours. Two solutions to be tested were injected intradermally on opposite sides of each crop sac. The volume injected was 0.1 ml. Four injections were made at 24-hour intervals in the same area marked with a nontoxic dye. The birds were killed 24 hours after the last injection, and the crop sac dissected and stretched over a light source. The area stimulated was estimated with the aid of plastic discs with diameters ranging from 0.5 to 4.0 cm. With 15 pigeons per dose level and a linear log dose-response relationship was found for a range of 0.00072 to 0.02240 mg. per bird (1 mg. = 20 I.U.). The index of precision was $\lambda = 0.11$.

ACTH. Bates, Lahr and Miller (1940) used 2-day-old chicks for the assay of ACTH. White Leghorn cockerels were injected 3 times per day for 5 days. The adrenals were weighed. Ten mg. of a partially purified ACTH preparation resulted in a 25 per cent increase in adrenal weight. The assay, however, is relatively insensitive.

TSH. In order to compare different methods it was necessary to convert U.S.P. to Junkmann-Schoeller (J.S.) units. In these calculations 1 I.U. = 1 U.S.P. unit = 0.1 J.S. unit (Brown, 1959). The use of chicks for bioassay of TSH has been reviewed by Turner (1950) and by Brown (1959).

1. Gravimetric methods are too insensitive to be of much value.

2. Histometric methods. One-day-old cockerels are injected five times at 12-hour intervals and the chicks killed 12 hours after the last injection. The thyroids are removed, fixed in Bouin's solution, sectioned at 4 to 6 μ, stained with hematoxylin and eosin, or Mason's triple chrome stain. The height of one cell in each of 100 acini is measured, the cells to be measured being selected at random or the height of the highest and lowest cell in each of 50 acini is measured. If the latter method is used the acini are selected at random. In our laboratory the highest and lowest cell in each of 20 acini is measured and with this method 0.003 U.S.P. units can be detected (van Tienhoven, unpublished data). The assay can be made more sensitive by adapting Uotila and Kannas' (1952) technique of projecting the thyroid section on a screen and estimating the percentage of epithelium. Using this method, 0.0001 U.S.P. units can be detected (Saatman and van Tienhoven, unpublished data).

3. Intracellular droplet method. In this method 3-day-old chicks are injected with the preparation to be assayed and the chicks killed 2 hours later. The thyroids are removed and fixed in Carnoy's fluid for 1 hour at room temperature, embedded in paraffin, sectioned at 4 μ, and stained with Heidenhain's azan. The droplets in 25 successive cross sections of follicles are counted. The assay is about 70 times as sensitive as the gravimetric method and 5 times as sensitive as the cell height measurement method.

4. I^{131} depletion method. Bates and Cornfield (1957) used 1-day-old chicks and injected them with 0.2 ml. I^{131} solution (2 to 3 μc.). After 24 hours counts were made *in vivo* with the aid of a scintillation counter. The assay solution was injected and simultaneously 0.2 cc. of a solution containing 8 μg. thyroxine and either 5.0 or 0.5 mg. propylthiouracil (PTU) was injected. The PTU was injected to prevent re-utilization of I^{131}, and the thyroxine was used to inhibit secretion of TSH from the chick's anterior pituitary. This procedure was repeated daily for 2 to 3 days and daily counts were made. A linear relationship between log dose and response was obtained. The index of accuracy was $\lambda = 0.20$.

5. I^{131} accumulation. One-day-old cockerels are kept without food or water and receive 5 injections at 12-hour intervals. Twelve hours after the last injection 0.1 to 10 μc. I^{131} are given and the chicks are killed 5 hours later. Thyroids are removed and radioactivity counted. This test can detect 0.001 and 0.005 U.S.P. units, whereas the histometric methods (cell height) could not detect these levels (Shellabarger, 1954).

OXYTOCIC PRINCIPLE. Adult chickens (1.8 to 2.2 kg.) are anesthetized with sodium phenobarbital and blood pressure is taken with the aid of a mercury manometer with

SUBMAMMALIAN VERTEBRATES

a recording pen. Blood pressure is taken from the ischiatic vein. Injections of the assay material are made in the crural vein. Material can be injected at 3- to 5-minute intervals and materials or doses can be used in any desired sequence. A drop in blood pressure of 20 to 40 mm. Hg (Thorp, 1950) is caused by 0.2 units of oxytocin.

ANDROGEN. Assays for androgen activity can be made with capons and with baby chicks. Dorfman (1950) has given a detailed account of the methods used and their sensitivity. Also part of the problems involved in the bioassay have been discussed previously in this chapter.

A very sensitive method which does not seem to have been used very extensively is the sparrow bill test. Either adult females or adult castrated males can be used. Local applications of as little as 1.0 μg. testosterone in 16 divided doses will evoke a response in 4 of 6 castrated males. The response consists of blackening of the bill.

Acknowledgements. I would like to acknowledge the great help received from Dr. R. E. Phillips. He has discussed many points of avian biology with me and has greatly improved the manuscript by suggesting changes in grammar, as well as by pointing out ambiguities in the original draft. Thanks are also due to Dr. Richard M. Fraps, who in spite of sickness, showed interest in this paper while it was being written and who encouraged me to undertake this assignment. Finally, my thanks to my wife for encouragement and much help in completing a large, but short-time assignment.

IV. References

ADAMS, J. L. 1955. Progesterone-induced unseasonable molt in single comb White Leghorn pullets. Poultry Sc., **34**, 702–707.

ADAMS, J. L. 1956. A comparison of different methods of progesterone administration to the fowl in affecting egg production and molt. Poultry Sc., **35**, 323–326.

ADAMS, J. L., AND HERRICK, R. B. 1955. Interaction of the gonadal hormones in the chicken. Poultry Sc., **34**, 117–121.

ADAMSTONE, F. B., AND CARD, L. E. 1934. The effects of vitamin E deficiency on the testis of the male fowl (*Gallus domesticus*). J. Morphol., **56**, 339–359.

AKPINAR, A. C., AND SHAFFNER, C. S. 1953. Reproductive ability of chickens implanted at nine weeks of age with estrogen pellets. Poultry Sc., **32**, 119–122.

ALTERKIRCH, HOFFMANN, AND SCHAAF. 1955. Doppelpaarungen in der Geflügelzucht. Arch. Geflügelz. Kleintierk., **4**, 185–189.

ARISTOTLE. 1883. *History of Animals*, Book III, paragraph 5, R. Cresswell, Translator. London: George Bell and Sons.

ARON, M., AND BENOIT, J. 1934. Sur le conditionnement hormonique du développement testiculaire chez les oiseaux. Rôle de la thyroïde. Compt. rend. Soc. biol., **116**, 218–220.

ASMUNDSON, V. S., GUNN, C. A., AND KLOSE, A. A. 1937. Some responses of the immature female fowl to injections of mare gonadotropic hormone and oestrin. Poultry Sc., **16**, 194–206.

ASMUNDSON, V. S., AND WOLFE, M. J. 1935. Effect of pregnant mare's serum on the immature fowl. Proc. Soc. Exper. Biol. & Med., **32**, 1107–1109.

ASPLIN, F. D., AND BOYLAND, E. 1947. The effects of pyrimidine sulphonamide derivatives upon the blood-clotting system and testes of chicks and the breeding capacity of adult fowls. Brit. J. Pharmacol. Chemotherap., **2**, 79–92.

ASSENMACHER, I. 1958. La mue des oiseaux et son déterminisme endocrinien. Alauda, **26**, 241–289.

ASSENMACHER, I. 1958. Recherches sur le contrôle hypothalamique de la fonction gonadotrope préhypophysaire chez le canard. Arch. Anat. microscop. Morphol expér., **47**, 447–572.

ASSENMACHER, I., AND BENOIT, J. 1958. Quelques aspects du contrôle hypothalamique de la fonction gonadotrope de la préhypophyse. In *Pathophysologia Diencephalica, Symposium Internationale Milano*, pp. 401–427. Berlin: Springer Verlag.

BAILEY, R. E. 1950. Inhibition with prolactin of light-induced gonad increase in white-crowned sparrows. Condor, **52**, 247–251.

BAILEY, R. E. 1952. The incubation patch of Passerine birds. Condor, **54**, 121–136.

BAKER, R. C., HILL, F. W., VAN TIENHOVEN, A., AND BRUCKNER, J. H. 1957. The effect of nicarbazin on egg production and egg quality. Poultry Sc., **36**, 718–726.

BARRY, T. W. 1960. Breeding biology of the Atlantic Brant (*Branta bernicla hrota*). M.S. Thesis, Cornell University.

BARTHOLOMEW, G. 1949. The effect of light intensity and day length on reproduction in the English sparrow. Bull. Mus. Comp. Zool., **101**, 433–476.

BASTIAN, J. W., AND ZARROW, M. X. 1955. A new hypothesis for the asynchronous ovulatory cycle of the domestic hen (*Gallus domesticus*). Poultry Sc., **34**, 776–788.

BATES, R. W., AND CORNFIELD, J. 1957. An improved assay method for thyrotrophin using depletion of I^{131} from the thyroid of day-old chicks. Endocrinology, **60**, 225–238.

BATES, R. W., LAHR, E. L., AND MILLER, R. A. 1940. Preparation of adrenotropic extracts and their assay on two-day chicks. Endocrinology, **27**, 781–792.

BATES, R. W., LAHR, E. L., AND RIDDLE, O. 1935. The gross action of prolactin and follicle-stimulating hormone on the mature ovary and sex accessories of fowl. Am. J. Physiol., **111**, 361–368.

BATES, R. W., RIDDLE, O., AND LAHR, E. L. 1937. The mechanism of the anti-gonad action of prolactin in adult pigeons. Am. J. Physiol., **119**, 610–614.

BAUM, G. J., AND MEYER, R. K. 1956. Influence of diethylstilbestrol on lipids in intact and hypohpysectomized cockerels. Endocrinology, **58**, 338–346.

BENOIT, J. 1935. Stimulation du développement testiculaire par l'éclairement artificiel. Compt. rend. Soc. biol., **118**, 664–668.

BENOIT, J. 1936. Rôle de la thyroïde dans la gonado-stimulation par la lumière articièlle chez le canard domestique. Compt. rend. Soc. biol., **123**, 243–246.

BENOIT, J. 1937a. Thyroïde et croissance testiculaire chez le canard domestique. Compt. rend. Soc. biol., **125**, 459–460.

BENOIT, J. 1937b. Thyroïde et croissance du pénis chez le canard domestique. Compt. rend. Soc. biol., **125**, 461–463.

BENOIT, J. 1950a. Reproduction charactères sexuels et hormones. Déterminisme du cycle saisonnier. In *Traité de Zoologie*, P. P. Grassé, Ed., Vol. 15, pp. 384–478. Paris: Masson et Cie.

BENOIT, J. 1950b. Les glandes endocrines. In *Traité de Zoologie*, P. P. Grassé, Ed., Vol. 15, pp. 290–334. Paris: Masson et Cie.

BENOIT, J. 1956. États physiologiques et l'instinct de reproduction chez les oiseaux. In *L'Instinct dans le comportement des animaux et de l'homme*, pp. 177–260. Paris: Masson et Cie.

BENOIT, J., AND ARON, M. 1934a. Sur le conditionnement hormonique du développement testiculaire chez les oiseaux. Injections d'extrait préhypophysaire chez le canard. Remarques sur divers éléments d'interprétation des expériences. Influence de l'age. Compt. rend. Soc. biol., **116**, 215–218.

BENOIT, J., AND ARON, M. 1934b. Sur le conditionnement hormonique du développement testiculaire chez les oiseaux. Résultats de la thyroïdectomie chez le coq et le canard. Compt. rend. Soc. biol., **116**, 221–223.

BENOIT, J., AND ASSENMACHER, I. 1955. Le contrôle hypothalamique de l'activité préhypophysaire gonadotrope. J. Physiol., **47**, 427–567.

BENOIT, J., AND ASSENMACHER, I. 1959. The control by visible radiations of the gonadotrophic activity of the duck hypophysis. Recent Progr. Hormone Res., **15**, 143–164.

BENOIT, J., ASSENMACHER, I., AND BRARD, E. 1956. Apparition et maintien de cycles sexuels non saisonniers chez le canard domestique placé pendant plus de trois ans à l'obscurité totale. J. Physiol., 48, 388–391.

BENOIT, J., ASSENMACHER, I., AND BRARD, E. 1956. Apparition et maintien de cycles sexuels non saisonniers chez le canard domestique placé pendant plus de trois ans à l'obscurité totale. J. Physiol., **48**, 388–391.

BENOIT, J., ASSENMACHER, I., AND BRARD, E. 1959. Action d'un éclairement permanent prolongé sur l'évolution testiculaire du canard Pékin. Arch. Anat. microscop. Morphol. Expér., **48** bis, 5–11.

BENOIT, J., AND OTT, L. 1944. External and internal factors in sexual activity. Effect of irradiation with different wave-lengths on the mechanism of photostimulation of the hypophysis and on testicular growth in the immature duck. Yale J. Biol. & Med., **17**, 27–46.

BENSON, G. K., AND COWIE, A. T. 1956. Lactation in the rat after hypophysial posterior lobectomy. J. Endocrinol., **14**, 54–65.

BERNSTORF, E. C. 1957. Differences in response of the capon comb to intraperitoneally and subcutaneously injected testosterone propionate. Endocrinology, **60**, 173–184.

BHADURI, J. L., BISWAS, B., AND DAS, S. K. 1957. The arterial system of the domestic pigeon (*Columbia livia* Gmelin). Anat. Anz., **104**, 1–14.

BIRD, S., PUGSLEY, L. I., AND KLOTZ, M. O. 1947. The quantitative recovery of synthetic estrogens from tissues of birds (*Gallus domesticus*), the response of the birds' testis, comb and epidermis to estrogen and of humans to ingestion of tissues from treated birds. Endocrinology, **41**, 282–294.

BISHOP, M. W. H., AND SALISBURY, G. W. 1955. Effect of sperm concentration on the oxygen uptake of bull semen. Am. J. Physiol., **180**, 107–112.

BISSONNETTE, T. H. 1930. Studies on the sexual cycle in birds. I. Sexual maturity, its modification and possible control in the European starling (*Sturnus vulgaris*). Am. J. Anat., **45**, 289–305.

BISSONNETTE, T. H. 1931. Studies on the sexual cycle in birds. V. Effects of light of different intensities upon the testis activity of the European starling (*Sturnus vulgaris*). Physiol. Zool., **4**, 542–574.

BISSONNETTE, T. H. 1932. Studies on the sexual cycle in birds. VI. Effects of white, green, and red lights of equal luminous intensity on the testis activity of the European starling (*Sturnus vulgaris*). Physiol. Zool., **5**, 92–123.

BISWAL, G. 1954. Additional histological findings in the chicken reproductive tract. Poultry Sc., **33**, 843–851.

BLACKSHAW, A. W., SALISBURY, G. W., AND VAN-DEMARK, N. L. 1957. Factors influencing metabolic activity of bull spermatozoa I. 37, 21 and 5°C. J. Dairy Sc., **40**, 1093–1098.

BLIVAISS, B. B. 1947. Interrelations of thyroid and gonad in the development of plumage and other sex characters in Brown Leghorn roosters. Physiol. Zool. **20**, 67–107.

BOAS, N. F. 1949. Isolation of hyaluronic acid from the cock's comb. J. Biol. Chem., **181**, 573–575.

Boas, N. F. 1958. The effect of desoxycorticosterone acetate on testis size and function in the cockerel. Endocrinology, 63, 323–328.

Boas, N. F., and Ludwig, A. W. 1950. The mechanism of estrogen inhibition of comb growth in the cockerel with histologic observations. Endocrinology, 46, 299–306.

Bolton, W. 1953. Observations on the vitamin metabolism of the common fowl. III. The effects of oestradiol dipropionate, testosterone propionate and progesterone injections on immature pullets on the riboflavin content of the magnum. J. Agric. Sc., 43, 116–119.

Bolton, W. 1955. The effect of injections of oestradiol dipropionate into immature pullets upon the manganese content of the blood plasma and of some tissues. Brit. J. Nutrit., 9, 170–171.

Bonadonna, T. 1954. Observations on the submicroscopic structures of Gallus gallus spermatozoa. Poultry Sc., 33, 1151–1158.

Bradfield, J. R. G. 1951. Radiographic studies on the formation of the hen's egg shell. J. Exper. Biol., 28, 125–140.

Bradley, O. C. 1950. The Structure of the Fowl, 3rd ed., Graham, Ed. Philadelphia: J. B. Lippincott Company.

Brant, J. W. A., and Nalbandov, A. V. 1956. Role of sex hormones in albumen secretion by the oviduct of chickens. Poultry Sc., 35, 692–700.

Breitenbach, R. P., and Meyer, R. K. 1959. Pituitary prolactin levels in laying, incubating and brooding pheasants (Phasianus colchicus). Proc. Soc. Exper. Biol. & Med., 101, 16–19.

Breneman, W. R. 1942. Action of prolactin and estrone on weights of reproductive organs and viscera of the cockerel. Endocrinology, 30, 609–615.

Breneman, W. R. 1950. A study of the pituitary-gonad-comb relationship in normal, unilateral castrated and caponized chicks. J. Exper. Zool., 114, 115–135.

Breneman, W. R. 1953. The effect of gonadal hormones alone and in combination with pregnant mare serum on the pituitary, gonad, and comb of White Leghorn cockerels. Anat. Rec., 117, 533–534.

Breneman, W. R. 1955. Reproduction in birds: the female. In Comparative Physiology of Reproduction, Memoirs of the Society of Endocrinology, Vol 4, pp. 94–110.

Breneman, W. R. 1956. Steroid hormones and the development of the reproductive system in the pullet. Endocrinology, 58, 262–271.

Breneman, W. R., and Mason, R. C. 1951. Androgen influence on pituitary-gonad interrelationship. Endocrinology, 48, 752–762.

Breneman, W. R., Zeller, F. J., and Beekman, B. E. 1959. Gonadotrophin assay in chicks. Poultry Sc., 38, 152–158.

Broadfoot, D. I., Pomeroy, B. S., and Smith, W. M., Jr. 1956. Effects of infectious bronchitis in baby chicks. Poultry Sc., 35, 757–762.

Brown, J. R. 1959. The measurement of thyroid-stimulating hormone (TSH) in body fluids: a critical review. Acta Endocrinol., 32, 289–309.

Brown, L. T., and Knigge, K. M. 1958. Cytology of the pars distalis in the pituitary gland of the chicken. Anat. Rec., 130, 395–396.

Brown, W. O. 1953. The effect of deoxypentose nucleic acid on the impaired oviduct response to oestrogen in the folic acid-deficient chick. Biochim. et Biophys. Acta, 11, 162–163.

Bruckner, J. H., and Hill, F. W. 1959. Observations on restricted feeding of growing pullets. In Proceedings Cornell Nutrition Conference, pp. 104–111.

Buckner, G. D., Insko, W. M., Jr., Henry, A. H., and Wachs, E. F. 1951. Influence of vitamin D on the growth of New Hampshire cockerels, their combs, wattles, gonads and uropygeal glands. Poultry Sc., 30, 267–268.

Bülbring, E. 1937. The standardization of cortical extracts by the use of drakes. J. Physiol., 89, 64–80.

Bülbring, E. 1940. The relation between cortical hormone and the size of the testis in the drake, with observations on the effect of different oils as solvents and on desoxycorticosterone acetate. J. Pharmacol. & Exper. Therap., 69, 52–63.

Burger, J. W. 1943. Some aspects of colored illumination on sexual activation of the male starling. J. Exper. Zool., 94, 161–168.

Burger, J. W. 1949. A review of experimental investigations on seasonal reproduction in birds. Wilson Bull., 61, 211–230.

Burger, J. W. 1953. The effect of photic and psychic stimuli on the reproductive cycle of the male starling, Sturnus vulgaris. J. Exper. Zool., 124, 227–240.

Burmester, B. R., and Card, L. E. 1939. The effect of resecting the so-called "chalaziferous region" of the hen's oviduct on formation of subsequent eggs. Poultry Sc., 18, 138–145.

Burmester, B. R., and Nelson, N. M. 1945. The effect of castration and sex hormones upon the incidence of lymphomatosis in chickens. Poultry Sc., 24, 509–515.

Burrows, W. H., and Byerly, T. C. 1936. Studies of prolactin in the fowl pituitary. I. Broody hens compared with laying hens and males. Proc. Soc. Exper. Biol. & Med., 34, 841–844.

Burrows, W. H., and Byerly, T. C. 1942. Premature expulsion of eggs by hens following injection of whole posterior pituitary preparations. Poultry Sc., 21, 416–421.

Burrows, W. H., and Fraps, R. M. 1942. Action of vasopressin and oxytocin in causing premature oviposition by domestic fowl. Endocrinology, 30, 702–705.

Burrows, W. T., and Kosin, I. L. 1953. The effects of ambient temperature on production and fertilizing capacity of turkey spermatozoa. Physiol. Zool., 26, 131–146.

Buss, I. O., Meyer, R. K., and Kabat, C. 1951. Wisconsin pheasant reproduction studies based on ovulated follicle technique. J. Wildlife Mgmt., **15**, 32–46.

BYERLY, T. C., AND MOORE, O. K. 1941. Clutch length in relation to period of illumination in the domestic fowl. Poultry Sc., **20**, 387–390.

CAMPOS, A. C., AND SHAFFNER, C. S. 1952. The genetic control of chick comb and oviduct response to androgen and estrogen. Poultry Sc., **31**, 567–571.

CARIDROIT, F., AND RÉGNIER, V. 1944. Influence de l'obscurité sur la crête equilibrée de chapons et interprétation. Compt. rend. Soc. biol., **138**, 157–158.

CARSON, J. R., JUNNILA, W. A., AND BACON, B. F. 1958. Sexual maturity and productivity in the chicken as affected by the quality of illumination during the growing period. Poultry Sc., **37**, 102–112.

CHAPIN, J. P. 1954. The calendar of the wide-awake fair. Auk, **71**, 1–15.

CHESTER JONES, I. 1957. *The Adrenal Cortex.* Cambridge: Cambridge University Press.

CHU, J. P. 1940. The effects of oestrone and testosterone and of pituitary extracts on the gonads of hypophysectomized pigeons. J. Endocrinol., **2**, 21–37.

CHU, J. P., AND YOU, S. S. 1946. Gonad stimulation by androgens in hypophysectomized pigeons. J. Endocrinol., **4**, 431–435.

CLAVERT, J. 1948. Contribution à l'étude de la formation des oeufs télolécithiques des oiseaux: mécanismus de la formation de la coquille. Bull. Biol. France et Belgique, **82**, 289–339.

CLAVERT, J. 1958. Contribution à l'étude de la vitellogenèse chez les oiseaux. Phases physiologiques et rôle de la folliculine dans la vitellogenèse. Arch. Anat. microscop. et Morphol. expér., **47**, 654–675.

CLERMONT, Y. 1958. Structure de l'épithélium séminal et mode de renouvellement des spermatogonies chez le canard. Arch. Anat. microscop. et Morphol. expér., **47**, 47–66.

CLERMONT, Y., AND BENOIT, J. 1955. Absence de stimulation de la spermatogenèse du canard Pékin par le propionate de testostérone. Compt. rend. Soc. biol., **149**, 1333–1336.

COMMON, R. H., AND BOLTON, W. 1946. Influence of gonadal hormones on the serum lipochrome and riboflavin of the domestic fowl. Nature, London, **158**, 95–96.

COMMON, R. H., MAW, W. A., AND JOWSEY, J. R. 1953. Observations on the mineral metabolism of pullets. IX. The effects of estrogen and androgen administered separately on the retention of calcium by the sexually immature pullet. Canad. J. Agric. Sc., **33**, 172–177.

CONNER, M. H. 1959. Effects of various hormone preparations and nutritional stresses in chicks. Poultry Sc., **38**, 1340–1343.

CONNER, M. H., AND FRAPS, R. M. 1954. Premature oviposition following subtotal excision of the hen's ruptured follicle. Poultry Sc., **33**, 1051.

CONRAD, R. M., AND PHILLIPS, R. E. 1938. The formation of the chalazae and inner thin white in the hen's egg. Poultry Sc., **17**, 143–146.

CONRAD, R. M., AND SCOTT, H. M. 1942. The accumulation of protein in the oviduct of the fowl. Poultry Sc., **21**, 81–85.

COOMBS, C. J. F., AND MARSHALL, A. J. 1956. The effects of hypophysectomy on the internal testis rhythm in birds and mammals. J. Endocrinol., **13**, 107–111.

COOPER, D. M., AND SKULSKI, G. 1955. The effect of the continuous feeding of furazolidone on the growth of gonads in single comb White Leghorn cockerels. Vet. Rec., **67**, 541.

COOPER, D. M., AND SKULSKI, G. 1957. Effect of feeding 2-amino-5-nitrothiazole and 2-acetyl-amino-5-nitrothiazole on reproduction in the fowl. J. Comp. Path. & Therap., **67**, 186–195.

COWLES, R. B., AND NORDSTROM, A. 1946. A possible avian analogue of the scrotum. Science, **104**, 586–587.

CRAGLE, R. G., SALISBURY, G. W., AND MUNTZ, J. H. 1958. Distribution of bulk and trace minerals in bull reproductive tract fluids and semen. J. Dairy Sc., **41**, 1273–1277.

CRAGLE, R. G., SALISBURY, G. W., AND VANDEMARK, N. L. 1958. Sodium, potassium, calcium, and chloride distribution in bovine semen. J. Dairy Sc., **41**, 1267–1272.

CRAIG, W. 1913. The stimulation and inhibition of ovulation in birds and mammals. J. Anim. Behav., **3**, 215–221.

CRAVENS, W. W. 1949. The nutrition of the breeding flock. In *Fertility and Hatchability of Chicken and Turkey Eggs*, L. W. Taylor, Ed., pp. 1–51. New York: John Wiley and Sons, Inc.

CREW, F. A. E. 1923. Studies in intersexuality. II. Sex reversal in the fowl. Proc. Roy. Soc. London, ser. B, **95**, 265–278.

DAMSTÉ, P. H. 1947. Experimental modification of the sexual cycle of the greenfinch. J. Exper. Biol., **24**, 20–35.

DANTSCHAKOFF, W., AND GUELIN-SCHEDRINA, A. 1933. Keimzelle und Gonade. VI. Asymmetrie der Gonaden beim Huhn. A. Primäre quantitative asymmetrie der Gonadenanlagen. Ztschr. Zelforsch. mikroskop. Anat. **19**, 50–78.

DAS, B. C., AND NALBANDOV, A. V. 1955. Responses of ovaries of immature chickens to avian and mammalian gonadotrophins. Endocrinology, **57**, 705–710.

DAVIS, M. 1945. A change of breeding season by Australian gulls. Auk, **62**, 137.

DELAWDER, A. M., TARR, L., AND GEILING, E. M. K. 1934. The distribution in the chicken hypophysis of the so-called posterior lobe principles. J. Pharmacol. & Exper. Therap., **51**, 142.

DEMEIO, R. H., RAKOFF, A. E., CANTAROW, A., AND PASCHKIS, K. E. 1948. Mechanism of inactivation of α-estradiol by rat liver "*in vitro.*" Endocrinology, **43**, 97–104.

DHARMARAJAN, M. 1950. Effects on the embryo of staleness of the sperm at the time of fertilization in the domestic hen. Nature, London, **165**, 398.

DOBIE, J. B., CARVER, J. S., AND ROBERTS, J. 1946. Poultry lighting for egg production. Bull. Washington State Agric. Exper. Sta., 471, 1946.

DOMM, L. V. 1931. Precocious development of sexual characters in the fowl by homeoplastic hypophyseal implants. II. The female. Proc. Soc. Exper. Biol. & Med., 29, 310–312.

DOMM, L. V. 1937. Observations concerning anterior pituitary-gonadal interrelations in the fowl. Cold Spring Harbor Symposia Quant. Biol., 5, 241–253.

DOMM, L. V. 1939. Modifications in sex and secondary sexual characters in birds. In Sex and Internal Secretions, 2nd ed., E. Allen, C. H. Danforth and E. A. Doisy, Eds., pp. 227–327. Baltimore: Williams & Wilkins Company.

DOMM, L. V., AND VAN DYKE, H. D. 1932. Precocious development of sexual characters in the fowl by daily injections of Hebin. II. The female. Proc. Soc. Exper. Biol. & Med., 30, 351–353.

DORFMAN, R. I. 1950. Androgens. In Hormone Assay, C. W. Emmens, Ed., pp. 291–324. New York: Academic Press, Inc.

DORFMAN, R. I. AND SHIPLEY, R. A. 1956. Androgens. New York: J. Wiley & Sons, Inc.

DRAGER, G. A. 1945. The innervation of the avian hypophysis. Endocrinology, 36, 124–129.

DRIGGERS, J. C., AND COMAR, C. L. 1949. The secretion of radioactive caclium (Ca⁴⁵) in the hen's egg. Poultry Sc., 28, 420–424.

DUCHAINE, S. A., DRIGGERS, J. C., AND WARNICK, A. C. 1957. The effect of progesterone on egg formation in sixteen-week old pullets. Poultry Sc., 36, 940–944.

DULIN, W. E. 1953. The effects of adrenocorticotropin on the White Leghorn cockerel and capon. Endocrinology, 53, 233–235.

DULIN, W. E. 1955. The effect of cortisone on the White Leghorn cockerel and capon. Poultry Sc., 34, 73–77.

EATON, R. D., CARSON, J. R., AND BEALL, G. 1955. The effect of diethylstilbestrol implantation in the immature cockerel on reproductive performance at maturity. Poultry Sc., 34, 861–867.

EL ZAYAT, S. Unpublished results, 1960.

EL ZAYAT, S., AND VAN TIENHOVEN, A. 1959. The effect of storage on the metabolic rates and morphology of cock semen diluted with three different dilluents. Poultry Sc., 38, 1201.

ENGELS, W. L., AND JENNER, C. E. 1956. The effect of temperature on testicular recrudescence in Juncos at different photoperiods. Biol. Bull., 110, 129–137.

ETZOLD, T. 1891. Die Entwicklung der Testikel von Fungilla domestica von der Winterruhe bis zum Eintritt der Brunstzeit. Ztschr. Wiss. Zool., 52, 46–84.

FARNER, D. S. 1959. Photoperiodic control of annual gonadal cycles in birds. In Photoperiodism, R. B. Withrow, Ed., A. A. A. S. Publ., 55, 717–750.

FARNER, D. S., AND WILSON, A. C. 1957. A quantitative examination of testicular growth in the white-crowned sparrow. Biol. Bull., 113, 254–267.

FICKEN, R. W., VAN TIENHOVEN, A., FICKEN, M. S., AND SIBLEY, F. C. 1960. Effect of visual and vocal stimuli in breeding in the Budgerigar (Melopsittacus undulatus). Anim. Behav., 8, 104–106.

FLEISCHMANN, W., AND FRIED, I. A. 1945. Studies on the mechanism of the hypercholesteremia and hypercalcemia induced by estrogen in immature chicks. Endocrinology, 36, 406–415.

FLERKÓ, B. 1957. Le rôle des structures hypothalamiques dans l'action inhibitrice de la folliculine sur la sécrétion de l'hormone folliculostimuline. Arch. Anat. microscop. et Morphol. exper., 46, 159–172.

FLIPSE, R. J. 1956. Metabolism of glycine by bovine spermatozoa. Science, 124, 228.

FLIPSE, R. J., AND ALMQUIST, J. O. 1958. Metabolism of bovine semen. IV. Effects of glycine and glycerol on the glycolytic and respiratory activity of bovine spermatozoa. J. Dairy Sc., 41, 1787–1791.

FLORSHEIM, W. H., VELCOFF, S. M., AND BODFISH, R. E. 1959. Gonadotrophin assay based on augmentation of radiophosphate uptake by the chick testis. Acta Endocrinol., 30, 175–182.

FOOTE, R. H. 1950. The preservation of bovine spermatozoa in synthetic media. Ph.D. Thesis, Cornell University.

FOX, T. W. 1955. Effects of progesterone on growth and sexual development in S. C. White Leghorns. Poultry Sc., 34, 598–602.

FRANCIS, D. W., AND SHAFFNER, C. S. 1956. An investigation of the morphological changes in young chickens and the reproductive performance of adult chickens fed furazolidone or nitrofurazone. Poultry Sc., 35, 1371–1381.

FRANTZ, W. L. 1958. Some factors effecting spermatokinesis in the testes of the house sparrow (Passer domesticus). Endocrinology, 63, 507–516.

FRAPS, R. M. 1942. Synchronized induction of ovulation and premature oviposition in the domestic fowl. Anat. Rec., 84, 521.

FRAPS, R. M. 1946. Differential ovulatory reaction of first and subsequent follicles of the hen's clutch. Anat. Rec., 96, 573–574.

FRAPS, R. M. 1950. Action of progesterone on the immature avian gonad. Med. Landbouw Hogeschool Opzoek Sta. Gent., 15, 767–769.

FRAFS, R. M. 1954. Neural basis of diurnal periodicity in release of ovulation-inducing hormone in fowl. Proc. Nat. Acad. Sc., 40, 348–356.

FRAPS, R. M. 1955a. The varying effects of sex hormones in birds. In Comparative Physiology of Reproduction, Memoirs Society of Endocrinology, 4, 205–218.

FRAPS, R. M. 1955b. Egg production and fertility in poultry. In Progress in the Physiology of Farm Animals, J. Hammond, Ed., Vol. 2, pp. 661–740. London: Butterworth & Company, Ltd.

FRAPS, R. M. 1959. Photoperiodism in the female domestic fowl. In *Photoperiodism*, R. B. Withrow, Ed., A. A. A. S. Publ., **55**, 767–785.

FRAPS, R. M., AND CASE, J. F. 1953. Premature ovulation in the domestic fowl following administration of certain barbiturates. Proc. Soc. Exper. Biol. & Med., **82**, 167–171.

FRAPS, R. M., FEVOLD, H. L., AND NEHER, B. H. 1947. Ovulatory response of the hen to presumptive luteinizing and other fractions from fowl anterior pituitary tissue. Anat. Rec., **99**, 571–572.

FRAPS, R. M., HOOKER, C. W., AND FORBES, T. R. 1948. Progesterone in blood plasma of the ovulating hen. Science, **108**, 86–87.

FRAPS, R. M., HOOKER, C. W., AND FORBES, T. R. 1949. Progesterone in blood plasma of cocks and nonovulating hens. Science, **109**, 493.

FRAPS, R. M., NEHER, B. H., AND ROTHCHILD, I. 1947. The imposition of diurnal ovulatory and temparature rhythms by periodic feeding of hens maintained under continuous light. Endocrinology, **40**, 241–250.

FRAPS, R. M., RILEY, G. M., AND OLSEN, M. W. 1942. Time required for induction of ovulation following intravenous injection of hormone preparations in fowl. Proc. Soc. Exper. Biol. & Med., **50**, 313–317.

FRAPS, R. M., SOHN, H. A., AND OLSEN, M. W. 1956. Some effects of multiple pellet implants of diethylstilbestrol in 9-week-old chickens. Poultry Sc., **35**, 665–668.

GARDINER, V. E., PHILLIPS, W. E., MAW, W. A., AND COMMON, R. H. 1952. Vitamin A ester and Vitamin A alcohol in the serum of the oestrogenized immature pullet. Nature, London, **170**, 80.

GLICK, B. 1957. Experimental modification of the growth of the Bursa of Fabricius. Poultry Sc., **36**, 18–23.

GOODWIN, K., COLE, R. K., HUTT, F. B., AND RASMUSEN, B. A. 1955. Endocrine relationships in males of a relatively infertile strain of White Leghorn fowls. Endocrinology, **57**, 519–526.

GRAUER, R. C., SAIER, E. L., STRICKLER, H. S., AND CUTULY, E. 1958. Influence of varying proportions in combinations of estrone, estradiol and estriol on biological response. Proc. Soc. Exper. Biol. & Med., **98**, 308–312.

GREELEY, F., AND MEYER, R. K. 1953. Seasonal variation in testis stimulating activity of male pheasant pituitary glands. Auk, **70**, 350–358.

GREEN, J. D. 1951. The comparative anatomy of the hypophysis with special reference to its blood supply and innervation. Am. J. Anat., **88**, 225–311.

GREENWOOD, A. 1935. Perforation of the oviduct in the domestic fowl. Tr. Dyn. Aspects Growth, **10**, 81–90.

GREENWOOD, A. W. 1958. Long term effects of a constant environment. Poultry Sc., **37**, 1208–1209.

GREENWOOD, A. W., AND CHU, J. P. 1939. On the relation between thyroid and sex gland functioning in the Brown Leghorn fowl. Quart. J. Exper. Physiol., **29**, 111–119.

GRIGG, G. W. 1957. The structure of stored sperm in the hen and the nature of the release mechanism. Poultry Sc., **36**, 450–451.

GRIGG, G. W., AND HODGE, A. J. 1949. Electron microscopic studies of spermatozoa. 1. The morphology of the spermatozoon of the common domestic fowl (*Gallus domesticus*). Australian J. Sc. Res., ser. B, **2**, 271–286.

GROSVENOR, C. E., AND TURNER, C. W. 1958. Assay of lactogenic hormone. Endocrinology, **63**, 530–534.

HALE, E. B. 1955. Duration of fertility and hatchability following natural matings in turkeys. Poultry Sc., **34**, 228–233.

HALLER, R. W., AND CHERMS, F. L. 1959. A comparison of several treatments on terminating broodiness in Broad Breasted Bronze turkeys. Poultry Sc., **38**, 1211.

HAMMOND, J., JR. 1954. Light regulation of hormone secretion. Vitamins & Hormones, **12**, 157–206.

HAQUE, M. E., LILLIE, R. J., SHAFFNER, C. S., AND BRIGGS, G. M. 1949. Response of vitamin-deficient chicks to the sex hormones. Poultry Sc., **28**, 914–920.

HARRIS, P. C., AND SHAFFNER, C. S. 1956. Effect of season and thyroidal activity on the molt response to progesterone in chickens and pigeons. Poultry Sc., **35**, 1146–1147.

HAYS, F. A. 1945. The primary sex ratio in domestic chickens. Am. Naturalist, **79**, 184–186.

HELLER, H. 1950. The comparative physiology of the neurohypophysis. Experientia, **6**, 368–376.

HENDRICKS, S. B. 1956. Control of growth and reproduction by light and darkness. Am. Scientist, **44**, 229–247.

HERRICK, E. H. 1951. The influence of androgens in a female turkey. Poultry Sc., **30**, 758–759.

HERRICK, E. H., EIDE, I. M., AND SNOW, M. R. 1952. Vitamin E in pituitary gland function of fowls. Proc. Soc. Exper. Biol. & Med., **79**, 441–444.

HERRICK, E. H., AND FINERTY, J. C. 1940. The effect of adrenalectomy on the anterior pituitaries of fowls. Endocrinology, **27**, 279–282.

HERRICK, E. H. AND TORSTVEIT, O. 1938. Some effects of adrenalectomy in fowls. Endocrinology, **22**, 469–473.

HERRICK, R. B., AND ADAMS, J. L. 1956. The effects of progesterone and diethylstilbestrol injected singly or in combination, on sexual libido, and the weight of the testes of single comb White Leghorn cockerels. Poultry Sc., **35**, 1269–1273.

HERTZ, R. 1945. The quantitative relationship between stilbestrol response and dietary "folic acid" in the chick. Endocrinology, **37**, 1–6.

HERTZ, R. 1948a. Interference with estrogen-induced tissue growth in the chick genital tract by a folic acid antagonist. Science, **107**, 300.

HERTZ, R. 1948b. The role of factors of the B-complex in estrogen metabolism. Recent Progr. Hormone Res., **2**, 161–170.

HERTZ, R., DHYSE, F. G., AND TULLNER, W. W. 1949. Elevation of biotin activity in serum of estrogen treated chicks; relationship to hormone-induced avidin formation in the oviduct. Endocrinology, **45**, 451–454.

HERTZ, R., FRAPS, R. M., AND SEBRELL, W. H. 1943. Induction of avidin formation in the avian oviduct by stilbestrol plus progesterone. Proc. Soc. Exper. Biol. & Med., **52**, 142–144.

HERTZ, R., FRAPS, R. M., AND SEBRELL, W. H. 1944. Endocrinological aspects of avidin formation in the avian oviduct. Science, **100**, 35–36.

HERTZ, R., LARSEN, C. D., AND TULLNER, W. W. 1947. Inhibition of estrogen-induced tissue growth with progesterone. J. Nat. Cancer Inst., **8**, 123–126.

HERTZ, R., SCHRICKER, J. A., AND TULLNER, W. W. 1951. Dietary and dosage factors affecting thyroxine inhibition of estrogen-induced lipemia in the chick. Endocrinology, **49**, 168–171.

HERTZ, R., AND SEBRELL, W. H. 1944. Impairment of response to stilbestrol in the oviduct of chicks deficient in *L. casei* factor ("folic acid"). Science, **100**, 293–294.

HEWITT, W. F., JR. 1947. The essential role of the adrenal cortex in the hypertrophy of the ovotestis following ovariectomy in the hen. Anat. Rec., **98**, 159–180.

HILL, F. W., CAREW, L. B., JR., AND VAN TIENHOVEN, A. 1958. Effect of diethylstilbestrol on utilization of energy by the growing chick. Am. J. Physiol., **195**, 654–658.

HILL, R. T., AND PARKES, A. S. 1934. Hypophysectomy of birds. III. Effects on gonads, accessory organs and head furnishings. Proc. Roy. Soc., London, ser. B, **116**, 221–236.

HIMENO, K., AND TANABE, Y. 1957. Mechanism of molting in the hen. Poultry Sc., **36**, 835–842.

HOCHBAUM, A. 1944. *The Canvasback on a Prairie Marsh*. Washington: American Wildlife Institute.

HÖHN, E. O. 1950. Physiology of the thyroid gland in birds: a review. Ibis, **92**, 464–473.

HÖHN, E. O. 1960. Action of certain hormones on the thymus of the domestic hen. J. Endocrinol., **19**, 282–287.

HOLLANDER, W. F. 1949. Bipaternity in pigeons. J. Hered., **40**, 271–277.

HOSODA, T., KANEKO, T., MOGI, K., AND ABE, T. 1954. Effect of thyroxine on vitellin production in the fowl. In *Proceedings World's Poultry Congress Exposition, 10th Congress, Edinburgh*, Part 2, pp. 134–136.

HOSODA, T., KANEKO, T., MOGI, K., AND ABE, T. 1955a. Serological studies on egg production in the fowl. I. On the locus of serum vitellin production. Poultry Sc., **34**, 9–14.

HOSODA, T., KANEKO, T., MOGI, K., AND ABE, T. 1955b. Effect of gonadotrophic hormone on ovarian follicles and serum vitellin of fasting hens. Proc. Soc. Exper. Biol. & Med., **88**, 502–504.

HOSODA, T., KANEKO, T., MOGI, K., AND ABE, T.

1956. Forced ovulation in gonadotrophin-treated fasting hens. Proc. Soc. Exper. Biol. & Med., **92**, 360–362.

HOWES, C. E., AND HUTT, F. B. 1952. Breed resistance to nutritional encephalomalacia in the fowl. Poultry Sc., **31**, 360–365.

HURST, R. O., KUKSIS, A., AND BENDELL, J. F. 1957. The separation of oestrogens from avian droppings. Canad. J. Biochem. Physiol., **35**, 637–640.

HUSTON, T. M., AND NALBANDOV, A. V. 1953. Neurohumoral control of the pituitary in the fowl. Endocrinology, **52**, 149–156.

HUTT, F. B. 1937. Gynandromorphism in the fowl. Poultry Sc., **16**, 354–355.

HUTT, F. B. 1949. *Genetics of the Fowl*. New York: McGraw-Hill Book Company, Inc.

HUTT, F. B., GOODWIN, K., AND URBAN, W. D. 1956. Investigations of nonlaying hens. Cornell Vet., **46**, 257–273.

JAAP, R. G. 1933. Testis enlargement and thyroid administration in ducks. Poultry Sc., **12**, 322.

JAAP, R. G., AND ROBERTSON, H. 1953. The chick comb response to androgen in inbred Brown Leghorns. Endocrinology, **53**, 512–519.

JENNER, C. E., AND ENGELS, W. L. 1952. The significance of the dark period in the photoperiodic response of male juncos and white-throated sparrows. Biol. Bull., **103**, 345–355.

JOWSEY, J. R., OLIVER, W. F., MAW, W. A., AND COMMON, R. H. 1953. Observations on the mineral metabolism of pullets. The effects of gonadal hormones on retention and turnover of calcium by the skeleton. Canad. J. Agric. Sc., **33**, 216–224.

JUHN, M., AND GUSTAVSON, R. G. 1930. The production of female genital subsidiary characters and plumage sex characters by injection of human placental hormone in fowls. J. Exper. Zool., **56**, 31–61.

JUHN, M., AND HARRIS, P. C. 1956. Responses in molt and lay of fowl to progesterone and gonadotrophins. Proc. Soc. Exper. Biol. & Med., **92**, 709–711.

JUHN, M., AND HARRIS, P. C. 1958. Molt of capon feathering with prolactin. Proc. Soc. Exper. Biol. & Med., **98**, 669–672.

KABAT, C., BUSS. I. O., AND MEYER, R. K. 1948. The use of ovulated follicles in determining eggs laid by the ring-necked pheasant. J. Wildlife Mgmt., **12**, 399–416.

KAR, A. B. 1947a. The hormonal influence in the normal functioning of the uropygial gland in the fowl. Anat. Rec., **99**, 75–89.

KAR, A. B. 1947b. Responses of the oviduct of immature female fowl to injection of diethylstilbestrol and the mechanism of perforation of the oviduct in the domestic fowl. Poultry Sc., **26**, 352–363.

KAR, A. B. 1949. Testicular changes in the juvenile pigeon due to progesterone treatment. Endocrinology, **45**, 346–348.

KIRKPATRICK, C. M. 1955. Factors in photoperiodism of Bobwhite quail. Physiol. Zool., **28**, 255–264.

KIRKPATRICK, C. M. 1959. Interrupted dark period: Tests for refractoriness in Bobwhite quail hens. In *Photoperiodism*, R. B. Withrow, Ed., pp. 751–758. A. A. A. S. Publication 55.

KIRKPATRICK, C. M., AND LEOPOLD, A. C. 1952. The role of darkness in sexual activity of the quail. Science, **116**, 280–281.

KLINE, I. T. 1955. Relationship of vitamin B_{12} to stilbestrol stimulation of the chick oviduct. Endocrinology, **57**, 120–128.

KLINE, I. T., AND DORFMAN, R. I. 1951a. Testosterone stimulation of the oviduct in vitamin-deficient chicks. Endocrinology, **48**, 39–43.

KLINE, I. T., AND DORFMAN, R. I. 1951b. Estrogen stimulation of the oviduct in vitamin-deficient chicks. Endocrinology, **48**, 345–357.

KNOCHE, H. 1956. Die Verbindung der Retina mit den vegetativen Zentren des Zwischenhirnes und mit der Hypophyse. Verhandl. anat. Gesellsch., Versamml., 140–148.

KNOCHE, H. 1957. Die retino-hypothalamische Bahn von Mensch, Hund und Kaninchen. Ztschr. mikro-anat. Forsch., **63**, 461–486.

KOBAYASHI, H. 1958. On the induction of molt in birds by 17α-oxyprogesterone 17-capronate. Endocrinology, **63**, 420–430.

KOBAYASHI, H. 1954. Loss of responsiveness of the sex gland to the stimulus of light and its relation to molting in the canary. Ann. Zool. Japan., **27**, 128–137.

KOBAYASHI, H. 1957. Physiological nature of refractoriness of ovary to the stimulation of light in the canary. Ann. Zool. Japan., **30**, 8–18.

KOCH, F. C., AND GALLAGHER, T. F. 1934. The effect of light on the comb response of capons to testicular hormone. J. Biol. Chem., **105**, xlix.

KORNFELD, W. 1958. Endocrine influences upon the growth of the rudimentary gonad of the fowl. Anat. Rec., **130**, 619–638.

KORNFELD, W. 1960. Experimentally induced proliferation of the rudimentary gonad of an (*sic*) intact domestic fowl. Nature, London, **185**, 320.

KORNFELD, W., AND NALBANDOV, A. V. 1954. Endocrine influences on the development of the rudimentary gonad of fowl. Endocrinology, **55**, 751–761.

KOSIN, I. L. 1944. Some aspects of the biological action of X-rays on cock spermatozoa. Physiol. Zool., **17**, 289–319.

KOSIN, I. L. 1958. Metabolism of turkey semen as affected by the environment of donor birds. Poultry Sc., **37**, 376–388.

KOSIN, I. L., AND ISHIZAKI, H. 1959. Incidence of sex chromatin in *Gallus domesticus*. Science, **130**, 43–44.

KOSIN, I. L., MITCHELL, M. S., AND ST. PIERRE, E. 1955a. Ambient temperature as a factor in turkey reproduction. 1. The effect of preheating males and females on their subsequent breeding pen performance. Poultry Sc., **34**, 484–496.

KOSIN, I. L., MITCHELL, M. S., AND ST. PIERRE, E.

1955b. Ambient temperature as a factor in turkey reproduction. 2. The effect of artificially lowered air temperature on the breeding activity of males in late spring and in summer. Poultry Sc., **34**, 499–505.

KUHLENBECK, H. 1937. The ontogenetic development of the diencephalic centers in a bird's brain (chick) and comparison with the reptilian and mammalian diencephalon. J. Comp. Neurol., **66**, 23–75.

KUMARAN, J. D. S., AND TURNER, C. W. 1949a. Endocrine activity of the testis of the White Plymouth Rock. Poultry Sc., **28**, 636–640.

KUMARAN, J. D. S., AND TURNER, C. W. 1949b. The endocrinology of spermatogenesis in birds. I. Effect of estrogen and androgen. Poultry Sc., **28**, 593–602.

KUMARAN, J. D. S., AND TURNER, C. W. 1949c. The endocrinology of spermatogenesis in birds. II. Effect of androgens. Poultry Sc., **28**, 739–746.

KUMARAN, J. D. S., AND TURNER, C. W. 1949d. The endocrinology of spermatogenesis in birds. III. Effect of hypo- and hyper-thyroidism. Poultry Sc., **28**, 653–665.

KUSHNER, K. 1954. Izvetiya Akademii Nauk, SSSR Ser. Biol. No. 1, 32–52, as cited by Rothchild in *Fertilization*.

LAKE, P. E. 1954. The relationship between morphology and function in fowl spermatozoa. In *Proceedings Xth World's Poultry Congress, Edinburgh*, Part 2, pp. 79–85.

LAKE, P. E. 1956. The structure of the germinal epithelium of the fowl testis with special reference to the presence of multinuclear cells. Quart. J. Microscop. Sc., **97**, 487–497.

LAKE, P. E. 1957. The male reproductive tract of the fowl. J. Anat., **91**, 116–129.

LAKE, P. E. 1958. *In vitro* storage of fowl spermatozoa. In *Proceedings XIth World's Poultry Congress, Mexico City*, in Press.

LAKE, P. E., BUTLER, E. J., McCALLUM, J. W., AND MacINTYRE, I. J. 1958. A chemical analysis of the seminal and blood plasma of the cock. Quart. J. Exper. Physiol., **43**, 309–313.

LAKE, P. E., AND McINDOE, W. M. 1959. The glutamic acid and creatine content of cock seminal plasma. Biochem. J., **71**, 303–306.

LAKE, P. E., SCHINDLER, H., AND WILCOX, F. H. 1959. Long distance transportation of fowl semen by air. Vet. Rec., **71**, 52–54.

LAMOREUX, W. F. 1943. Effect of differences in light and temperature upon the size of combs on White Leghorns. Endocrinology, **32**, 497–504.

LAMOREUX, W. F., AND HUTT, F. B. 1939. Breed differences in resistence to a deficiency of Vitamin B_1 in the fowl. J. Agric. Res., **58**, 307–316.

LAMOREUX, W. F., AND HUTT, F. B. 1948. Genetic resistance to deficiency of riboflavin in the chick. Poultry Sc., **27**, 334–341.

LANDAUER, W. 1951. The hatchability of chicken eggs as influenced by environment and heredity. Storrs Agric. Exper. Sta. Bull. 262.

LANDAUER, W. 1954. The effect of estradiol benzoate and corn oil on bone structure of growing cockerels exposed to vitamin D deficiency. Endocrinology, **55**, 686–695.

LANDAUER, W. 1957. Primary sex ratio of fowl. Nature, London, **180**, 1139–1140.

LANDSMEER, J. M. F. 1951. Vessels of the rat's hypophysis. Acta Anat., **12**, 82–109.

LAW, G. R. J., AND KOSIN, I. L. 1958. Seasonal reproductive ability of male domestic turkeys as observed under two ambient temperatures. Poultry Sc., **37**, 1034–1047.

LAYNE, D. S., COMMON, R. H., MAW, W. A., AND FRAPS, R. M. 1957. Presence of progesterone in extracts of ovaries of laying hens. Proc. Soc. Exper. Biol. & Med., **94**, 528–529.

LAYNE, D. S., COMMON, R. H., MAW, W. A., AND FRAPS, R. M. 1958. Presence of oestrone, oestradiol and oestriol in extracts of ovaries of laying hens. Nature, London, **181**, 351–352.

LEACH, R. B., MADDOCK, W. O., TOKUYAMA, I., PAULSEN, C., AND NELSON, W. O. 1956. Clinical studies of testicular hormone production. Recent Progr. Hormone Res., **12**, 377–398.

LEGAIT, H. 1959. Contribution à l'étude morphologique et expérimentale du système hypothalamoneuro-hypophysaire de la poule Rhode-Island. Thèse d'agrégation de l'enseignement supérieur, Louvain.

LEGAIT, H., AND LEGAIT, E. 1955. Nouvelles recherches sur les modifications de structure du lobe distal de l'hypophyse au cours de divers états physiologique expérimentaux chez la poule Rhode Island. Compt. Rend. A. Anat., **42**, 902–907.

LEHRMAN, D. S. 1958. Effect of female sex-hormones on incubation behavior in the ring dove (*Streptopelia risoria*). J. Comp. Physiol. Psychol., **51**, 142–145.

LEHRMAN, D. S. 1959. Hormonal responses to external stimuli in birds. Ibis, **101**, 478–496.

LEHRMAN, D. S., AND BRODY, P. 1957. Oviduct response to estrogen and progesterone in the ring dove (*Streptopelia risoria*). Proc. Soc. Exper. Biol. & Med., **95**, 373–375.

LEONARD, S. L. 1937. Luteinizing hormone in bird hypophyses. Proc. Soc. Exper. Biol. & Med., **37**, 566–568.

LEROY, P. 1952. Réactions testiculaires de l'oiseau soumis à des injections de cortisone. Ann. Endocrinol., **13**, 991–997.

LEROY, P. 1953. Involution testiculaire profonde sous l' action combinée du diéthylstilbestrol et de la cortisone. Ann. Endocrinol., **14**, 662–667.

LEROY, P. 1956. Croissance dysharmonique de la crête du coq domestique maintenu à l'obscurité. Compt. rend. Acad. Sc., **243**, 210–212.

LEROY, P. 1958. Croissance de la crête du coq domestique maintenu à l'obscurité. Ann. Endocrinol., **19**, 55–68.

LEROY, P., AND BENOIT, J. 1956. Surrénalectomie bilatérale chez le canard mâle adulte; action sur le testicule. J. Physiol., Paris, **46**, 422–428.

LIBBY, D. A., SCHAIBLE, P. J., MEITES, J., AND

REINEKE, E. P. 1953. Value of progesterone and estradiol on growth and finish in broilers. Poultry Sc., **32**, 1086–1088.

LINK, R. P., AND NALBANDOV, A. V. 1955. Effect of desoxycorticosterone-acetate on young chicks. Am. J. Vet. Res., **16**, 433–436.

LOFTS, B., AND MARSHALL, A. J. 1956. The effects of prolactin administration on the internal rhythm of reproduction in male birds. J. Endocrinol., **13**, 101–106.

LOFTS, B., AND MARSHALL, A. J. 1958. An investigation of the refractory period of reproduction in male birds by means of exogenous prolactin and follicle stimulating hormone. J. Endocrinol., **17**, 91–98.

LOFTS, B., AND MARSHALL, A. J. 1959. The postnuptial occurrence of progestins in the seminiferous tubules of birds. J. Endocrinol., **19**, 16–21.

LORENZ, F. W. 1939. Relation of blood-lipid level to reproduction in the domestic fowl. In *Proceedings VIIth World's Poultry Congress and Exposition, Cleveland*, pp. 113–115.

LORENZ, F. W. 1954. Effects of estrogens on domestic fowl and applications in the poultry industry. Vitamins & Hormones, **12**, 235–275.

LORENZ, F. W. 1959. Reproduction in the domestic fowl: physiology of the male. In *Reproduction in Domestic Animals*, H. H. Cole and P. T. Cupps, Eds., Vol. 2, pp. 343–398. New York: Academic Press, Inc.

LOWE, J. S., MORTON, R. A., CUNNINGHAM, N. F., AND VERNON, J. 1957. Vitamin A deficiency in the domestic fowl. Biochem. J., **67**, 215–223.

LUTWAK-MANN, C. 1958. The dependence of gonadal function upon vitamins and other nutritional factors. Vitamins & Hormones, **16**, 35–75.

LYMAN, C. P. 1942. Toxic effect of adrenalin on young pigeons. Auk, **59**, 322–325.

LYTLE, I. M., AND LORENZ, F. W. 1958. Progesterone in the blood of the laying hen. Nature, London, **182**, 1681.

MACARTNEY, E. L. 1942. Diurnal rhythm of mitotic activity in the seminiferous tubules of the domestic fowl. Poultry Sc., **21**, 130–135.

MANN, T. 1954. *The Biochemistry of Semen*. New York: John Wiley & Sons, Inc.

MARGOLF, P, H., HARPER, J. A., AND CALLENBACH, E. W. 1947. Response of turkeys to artificial illumination. Pennsylvania Agric. Exper. Sta. Bull. 486.

MARLOW, H. W., AND RICHERT, D. 1940. Estrogens of the fowl. Endocrinology, **26**, 531–534.

MARSHALL, A. J. 1951. The refractory period of testis rhythm in birds and it's possible bearing on breeding and migration. Wilson Bull., **63**, 238–261.

MARSHALL, A. J. 1952. Non-breeding among arctic birds. Ibis, **94**, 310–333.

MARSHALL, A. J. 1955. Reproduction in birds: the male. In *Comparative Physiology of Reproduction*. Memoirs Society of Endocrinology, Vol. 4, pp. 75–89.

MARSHALL, A. J. 1959. Internal and environ-mental control of breeding. Ibis, **101**, 456–478.

MARSHALL, A. J., AND COOMBS, C. J. F. 1957. The interaction of environmental, internal and be-havioural factors in the rook, *Corvus f. frugilegus* Linnaeus. Proc. Zool. Soc., London, **128**, 545–589.

MARSHALL, A. J., AND DISNEY, H. J. DE S. 1956. Photostimulation of an equatorial bird (*Quelea quelea*, Linnaeus). Nature, London, **177**, 143–144.

MARSHALL, A. J., AND DISNEY, H. J. DE S. 1957. Experimental induction of the breeding season in a xerophilous bird. Nature, London, **180**, 647–649.

MARSHALL, A. J., AND ROBERTS, J. D. 1959. The breeding biology of equatorial vertebrates: reproduction of Cormorants (*Phalacrocoracidae*) at latitude 0°20′ N. Proc. Zool. Soc., London, **132**, 617–625.

MARSHALL, A. J., AND SERVENTY, D. L. 1958. The internal rhythm of reproduction in xerophilous birds under conditions of illumination and darkness. J. Exper. Biol., **35**, 666–670.

MARSHALL, A. J., AND SERVENTY, D. L. 1959. Experimental demonstration of an internal rhythm of reproduction of a transequatorial migrant (the short-tailed Shearwater, *Puffinus tenuirostris*). Nature, London, **184**, 1704–1705.

MARTIN, J. E., GRAVES, J. H., AND DOHAN, F. C. Local inhibition by estrone of testosterone-induced growth of the capon's comb. Am. J. Vet. Res., **16**, 141–146.

MARZA, V. D., AND MARZA, E. V. 1935. The forma-tion of the hen's egg. Quart. J. Microscop. Sc., **78**, 133–189.

MASON, K. E. 1939. Relation of the vitamins to the sex glands. In *Sex and Internal Secretions*, 2nd ed., E. Allen, C. H. Danforth and E. A. Doisy, Eds., pp. 1149–1212. Baltimore: Wil-liams & Wilkins Company.

MASON, K. E. 1949. Nutrition and reproduction. Surv. Biol. Progr., **1**, 89–114.

MASON, R. C. 1952. Synergistic and antagonistic effects of progesterone in combination with estrogens on oviduct weight. Endocrinol., **51**, 570–572.

MATSUO, S. 1954. Studies on the acidophilic cells of the anterior pituitary in the fowl. Japan. J. Zool. Sc., **25**, 63–69 (Japanese with English summary).

MATTHEWS, L. H. 1939. Visual stimulation and ovulation in pigeons. Proc. Roy. Soc., London, ser. B, **126**, 557–560.

McCARTNEY, M. G. 1951. The physiology of re-production in turkeys. 2. Degree and dura-tion of fertility and hatchability in broody and non-broody pullets. Poultry Sc., **30**, 663–667.

McNALLY, E. H. Some factors that affect oviposi-tion in the domestic fowl. Poultry Sc., **26**, 396–399.

MAUGER, H. M., JR. 1941. The autonomic in-nervation of the female genitalia in the do-mestic fowl and its correlation with the aortic branchings. Am. J. Vet. Res., **2**, 447–452.

MEITES, J. 1949. Relation of food intake to growth-depressing action of natural and arti-ficial estrogens. Am. J. Physiol., **159**, 281–286.

MEITES, J., AND TURNER, C. W. 1950. Lactogenic hormone. In *Hormone Assay*, C. W. Emmens, ED., pp. 237–260. New York: Academic Press, Inc.

METUZALS, J. 1955. Die Innervation der Drüsen-zellen der Pars distalis der Hypophyse bei der Ente. Ztschr. Zellforsch., **43**, 319–334.

MIKAMI, S. I. 1954. Cytochemical studies on the anterior pituitary of the fowl. Japan. J. Zoot. Sc., **25**, 55–62 (Japanese with English sum-mary).

MIKAMI, S. I. 1954. Cytochemical studies on the anterior pituitary of the fowl. II. Effects of thyroidectomy and castration. Jap. J. Zoot. Sc., **26**, 245–251 (Japanese with English summary).

MILLER, A. H. 1949. Potentiality for testicular recrudescence during the annual refractory pe-riod of the golden-crowned sparrow. Science, **109**, 546.

MILLER, R. A. 1938. Spermatogenesis in a sex-reversed female and in normal males of the domestic fowl, *Gallus domesticus*. Anat. Rec., **70**, 155–189.

MILLER, R. E. 1955. A study of the pineal body in a strain of early maturing White Leghorn cockerels. M.S. Thesis, Cornell University.

MITCHELL, M. S., AND KOSIN, I. L. 1954. The effect of controlled ambient temperature on some factors associated with egg laying in turkeys. Poultry Sc., **33**, 186–191.

MOORE, C. R. 1939. Biology of the testis. In *Sex and Internal Secretions*, 2nd ed., E. Allen, C. H. Danforth, and E. A. Doisy, Eds., pp. 353–451. Baltimore: Williams & Wilkins Company.

MOORE, W. W. 1958. Ovulation following treat-ment with dibenamine and dibenzyline. Fed. Proc., **17**, 113.

MORAVEC, D. F., MUSSEHL, F. E., AND PACE, D. M. 1954. Physiological characteristics of turkey semen. 2. Factors affecting motility and ferti-lizing capacity. Poultry Sc., **33**, 1126–1129.

MORGAN, W., AND KOHLMEYER, W. 1957. Hens with bilateral oviducts. Nature, London, **180**, 98.

MORRIS, D. M. 1951. The influence of thyroid hormone and androgen on comb growth in the White Leghorn cockerel. Endocrinology, **48**, 257–263.

MORRIS, T. R., AND FOX, S. 1958. Light and sexual maturity in the domestic fowl. Nature, Lon-don, **181**, 1453–1454.

MOSZKOWSKA, A. 1958. L'antagonisme épiphyso-hypophysaire. Étude *in vivo* et *in vitro* chez l'embryon de poulet Sussex. Ann. Endocrinol., **19**, 69–79.

MUNRO, S. S. 1938a. Functional changes in fowl sperm during their passage through the excur-rent ducts of the male. J. Exper. Zool., **79**, 71–92.

MUNRO, S. S. 1938b. The effect of testis hormone on the production of sperm life in the vas deferens of the fowl. J. Exper. Biol., 15, 186–196.

NAGRA, C. L., MEYER, R. K., AND BILSTAD, N. Cloacal glands in Japanese quail (*Coturnix coturnix Japonica*): histogenesis and response to sex steroids. Anat. Rec., 133, 415.

NAKAJO, S., AND TANAKA, K. 1956. Prolactin potency of the cephalic and caudal lobe of the anterior pituitary in relation to broodiness in the domestic fowl. Poultry Sc., 35, 990–994.

NALBANDOV, A. V. 1945. A study of the effect of prolactin on broodiness and on cock testes. Endocrinology, 36, 251–258.

NALBANDOV, A. V. 1953. Endocrine control of physiological functions. Poultry Sc., 32, 88–103.

NALBANDOV, A. V. 1956. Effect of progesterone on egg production. Poultry Sc., 35, 1162.

NALBANDOV, A. V. 1958. *Reproductive Physiology*. San Francisco; W. H. Freeman and Company.

NALBANDOV, A. V. 1959a. Role of sex hormones in the secretory function of the avian oviduct. In *Comparative Endocrinology*, A. Gorbman, Ed., pp. 524–532. New York: John Wiley & Sons.

NALBANDOV, A. V. 1959b. Mechanisms controlling ovulation of follicles. Anat. Rec., 134, 614.

NALBANDOV, A. V. 1959c. Neuroendocrine reflex mechanisms: bird ovulation. In *Comparative Endocrinology*, A. Gorbman, Ed., pp. 161–173. New York: John Wiley & Sons.

NALBANDOV, A. V., AND BAUM, G. J. 1948. The use of stilbestrol inhibited males as test animals for gonadotrophic hormones. Endocrinology, 43, 371–379.

NALBANDOV, A. V., AND CARD, L. E. 1943a. Effects of stale sperm on fertility and hatchability of chicken eggs. Poultry Sc., 22, 218–226.

NALBANDOV, A. V., AND CARD, L. E. 1943b. Effects of hypophysectomy of growing chicks. J. Exper. Zool., 94, 387–413.

NALBANDOV, A. V., AND CARD, L. E. 1946. Effect of FSH and LH upon the ovaries of immature chicks and low-producing hens. Endocrinology, 38, 71–78.

NALBANDOV, A. V., AND JAMES, M. F. 1949. The blood vascular system of the chicken ovary. Am. J. Anat., 85, 347–378.

NALBANDOV, A. V., MEYER, R. K., AND McSHAN, W. H. 1946. Effect of purified gonadotropes on the androgen-secreting ability of testes of hypophysectomized cocks. Endocrinology, 39, 91–104.

NALBANDOV, A. V., MEYER, R. K., AND McSHAN, W. H. 1951. The role of a third gonadotrophic hormone in the mechanism of androgen secretion in chicken testes. Anat. Rec., 110, 475–494.

NALBANDOV, O., AND NALBANDOV, A. V. 1949. The effect of follicle stimulating hormone upon oxygen consumption of chick ovary slices. Endocrinology, 45, 195–203.

NEHER, B. H., AND FRAPS, R. M. 1950. The addition of eggs to the hen's clutch by repeated injections of ovulation-inducing hormones. Endocrinology, 46, 482–488.

NEHER, B. H., OLSEN, M. W., AND FRAPS, R. M. 1950. Ovulation of the excised ovum of the hen. Poultry Sc., 29, 554–557.

NELSON, O. E., AND STABLER, R. M. 1940. The effect of testosterone propionate on the early development of the reproductive ducts in the female sparrow hawk (*Falco sparverius sparverius*). J. Morphol., 66, 277–297.

NICHOLAS, J. E., CALLENBACH, E. W., AND MURPHY, R. R. 1944. Light intensity as a factor in the artificial illumination of pullets. Bull. Pennsylvania Agric. Exper. Sta., 462.

NISHIYAMA, H. 1954. Studies on the reproductive physiology of the cock. V. The influence of androgen on the accessory organs of the phallus. In *Proceedings Xth World's Poultry Congress, Edinburgh*, Part 2, pp. 88–91.

NISHIYAMA, H. 1955. Studies on the accessory reproductive organs in the cock. J. Agric. Fac. Kyūshū Univ., 10, 277–305.

NOBLE, G. K., AND WURM, M. 1940. The effect of testosterone propionate on the black-crowned night heron. Endocrinology, 26, 837–850.

NOVAK, J., AND DUSCHAK, F. 1923. Die Veränderungen der Follikel-hüllen beim Haushuhn nach der Follikelsprung. Ztschr. Anat. Entwicklungsmech., 69, 483–492.

OHNO, S., KAPLAN, W. D., AND KINOSITA, R. 1960. On the sex-chromatin of *Gallus domesticus*. Exper. Cell Res., 19, 180–183.

OKSCHE, A., LAWS, D. F., KAMEMOTO, F. I., AND FARNER, D. S. 1959. The hypothalamo-hypophysial neurosecretory system of the white-crowned sparrow, *Zonotrichia leucophrys gambelii*. Ztschr. Zellforsch., 51, 1–42.

OLSEN, M. W. 1942. Maturation, fertilization, and early cleavage in the hen's egg. J. Morphol., 70, 513–533.

OLSEN, M. W. 1956. Fowl pox vaccine associated with parthenogenesis in chicken and turkey eggs. Science, 124, 1078–1079.

OLSEN, M. W., AND BYERLY, T. C. 1932. Orientation of the hen's egg in the uterus and during laying. Poultry Sc., 11, 266–271.

OLSEN, M. W., AND FRAPS, R. M. 1944. Maturation, fertilization, and early cleavage of the egg of the domestic turkey. J. Morphol., 74, 297–309.

OLSEN, M. W., AND FRAPS, R. M. 1950. Maturation changes in the hen's ovum. J. Exper. Zool., 114, 475–489.

OLSEN, M. W., AND MARSDEN, S. J. 1953. Embryonic development in turkey eggs laid 60 to 224 days following removal of males. Proc. Soc. Exper. Biol. & Med., 82, 638–641.

OLSEN, M. W., AND MARSDEN, S. J. 1954. Development of unfertilized turkey eggs. J. Exper. Zool., 126, 337–347.

OLSEN, M. W., AND MARSDEN, S. J. 1956. Parthenogenesis in eggs of Beltsville small white turkeys. Poultry Sc., 35, 674–682.

OLSEN, M. W., AND NEHER, B. H. 1948. The site of fertilization in the domestic fowl. J. Exper. Zool., 109, 355–366.

OPEL, H., AND NALBANDOV, A. V. 1958. A study of

hormonal control of growth and ovulation of follicles in hypophysectomized hens. Poultry Sc., **37**, 1230–1231.

ORTAVANT, R. 1959. Spermatogenesis and morphology of the spermatozoon. In *Reproduction in Domestic Animals*, H. H. Cole and P. T. Cupps, Eds., Vol. 2, pp. 1–50. New York: Academic Press, Inc.

PAREDES, J. R., AND GARCIA, T. P. 1959. Vitamin A as a factor affecting fertility in cockerels. Poultry Sc., **38**, 3–7.

PARKER, J. E. 1956. Rate of comb growth in New Hampshire cockerels as related to their subsequent reproductive performance in flock matings. Poultry Sc., **35**, 1030–1033.

PARKER, J. E., AND McSPADDEN, B. J. 1943. Influence of feed restriction on fertility in male domestic fowls. Poultry Sc., **22**, 170–177.

PARKES, A. S. 1952. Relation between effect and method of administration of androgens and oestrogens to fowl. Ciba Foundation Colloquia Endocrinol., **3**, 248–252.

PARKES, A. S., AND SELYE, H. 1936. Adrenalectomy of birds. J. Physiol., **86**, 35p–37p.

PASVOGEL, M. W. 1952. Correlation between the egg laying ability of pullets and certain hormonally controlled characteristics of the full brothers. Ph.D. thesis, University of Illinois.

PATEL, M. D. 1936. The physiology of the formation of "pigeon's milk". Physiol. Zool., **9**, 129–152.

PAYNE, F. 1940. "Signet-ring" or "castration" cells in the chick. Anat. Rec., **76**, 29–37.

PAYNE, F. 1943. The cytology of the anterior pituitary of broody fowls. Anat. Rec., **86**, 1–13.

PAYNE, F. 1944. Anterior pituitary-thyroid relationship in the fowl. Anat. Rec., **88**, 337–350.

PAYNE, F. 1947. Effects of gonad removal on the anterior pituitary of the fowl from 10 days to 6 years. Anat. Rec., **97**, 507–517.

PAYNE, F. 1955. Acidophilic granules in the gonadotropic secreting basophiles of laying hens. Anat. Rec., **122**, 49–55.

PEARL, R., AND BORING, A. M. 1918. Sex studies. X. The corpus luteum in the ovary of the domestic fowl. Am. J. Anat., **23**, 1–35.

PENQUITE, R., AND THOMPSON, R. B. 1933. Influence of continuous light on Leghorns. Poultry Sc., **12**, 201–205.

PEREK, M., ECKSTEIN, B., AND SOBEL, H. 1957. Histological observations on the anterior lobe of the pituitary gland in moulting and laying hens. Poultry Sc., **36**, 954–958.

PERRY, J. C. 1941. The antagonistic action of adrenalin on the reproductive cycle of the English sparrow, *Passer domesticus* (*Linnaeus*). Anat. Rec., **79**, 57–77.

PFEIFFER, C. A. 1947. Gonadotrophic effect of exogenous sex-hormones on the testes of sparrows. Endocrinology, **41**, 92–104.

PHILLIPS, R. E. 1943. Ovarian response of hens and pullets to injections of ambinon. Poultry Sc., **22**, 368–373.

PHILLIPS, R. E. 1959. Endocrine mechanisms of the failure of Pintails (*Anas acuta*) to reproduce in captivity. Ph.D. thesis, Cornell University.

PINO, J. A., ROSENBLATT, L. S., AND HUDSON, C. B. 1954. Inhibition of pituitary gonadotropin secretion in domestic fowl by Enheptin (2-amino,5-nitrothiazole). Proc. Soc. Exper. Biol. & Med., **87**, 201–207.

POLIN, D. 1957. Formation of porphyrin from delta amino-levulinic acid by uterine and liver tissue from laying hens. Proc. Soc. Exper. Biol. & Med., **94**, 276–279.

POLIN, D., AND STURKIE, P. D. 1957. The influence of the parathyroids on blood calcium levels and shell deposition in laying hens. Endocrinology, **60**, 778–784.

POLIN, D., AND STURKIE, P. D. 1958. Parathyroid and gonad relationship in regulating blood calcium fractions in chickens. Endocrinology, **63**, 177–182.

POLIN, D., STURKIE, P. D., AND HUNSAKER, W. 1957. The blood calcium response of the chicken to parathyroid extracts. Endocrinology, **60**, 1–5.

POOLE, H. K. 1959. The mitotic chromosomes of parthenogenetic and normal turkeys. J. Hered., **50**, 151–154.

POOLE, H. K., AND OLSEN, M. W. 1957. The sex of parthenogenetic turkey embryos. J. Hered., **48**, 217–218.

POOLE, H. K., AND OLSEN, M. W. 1958. Incidence of parthenogenetic development in eggs laid by three strains of dark Cornish chickens. Proc. Soc. Exper. Biol. & Med., **97**, 477–478.

PORTIER, P. 1920. Régénération du testicule chez le pigeon carencé. Compt. rend. Acad. Sc., **170**, 1339–1341.

RAHN, H., AND PAINTER, B. T. 1941. A comparative histology of the bird pituitary. Anat. Rec., **79**, 297–311.

RALPH, C. L. 1959. Some effects of hypothalamic lesions on gonadotrophin release in the hen. Anat. Rec., **134**, 411–431.

RALPH, C. L., AND FRAPS, R. M. 1959. Effect of hypothalamic lesions on progesterone-induced ovulation into the hen. Endocrinology, **65**, 819–824.

RALPH, C. L., AND FRAPS, R. M. 1960. Induction of ovulation in the hen by injection of progesterone in the brain. Endocrinology, **66**, 269–272.

RAMSAY, W. N. M., AND CAMPBELL, E. A. 1956. Some effects of oestradiol benzoate on iron metabolism in the immature pullet. Quart. J. Exper. Physiol., **41**, 271–274.

RANNEY, R. E., AND CHAIKOFF, I. L. 1951. Effect of functional hepatectomy upon estrogen-induced lipemia in the fowl. Am. J. Physiol., **165**, 600–603.

RANNEY, R. E., ENTENMAN, C., AND CHAIKOFF, I. L. 1949. The lecithin, cephalin, and sphingomyelin contents of plasma and liver of the fowl; their metabolic interrelationships as shown by the administration of diethylstilbestrol. J. Biol. Chem., **180**, 307–313.

REDMAN, C. E., AND SMYTH, J. R., JR. 1957. The effect of Furzaolidone (*sic*) on the reproduction ability of the male turkey. Poultry Sc., **36**, 437–443.

RICHARDSON, K. C. 1935. The secretory phenomena in the oviduct of the fowl, including the process of shell formation examined by microincineration technique. Philos. Tr. Roy. Soc. London, ser. B, **225**, 149–195.

RIDDLE, O. 1918. Further observations on the relative size and form of the right and left testes of pigeons in health and disease and as influenced by hybridity. Anat. Rec., **14**, 283–334.

RIDDLE, O., AND BATES, R. W. 1939. The preparation, assay and actions of lactogenic hormone. In *Sex and Internal Secretions*, 2nd ed., E. Allen, C. H. Danforth and E. A. Doisy, Eds., pp. 1088–1117. Baltimore: Williams & Wilkins Company.

RILEY, G. M. 1937. Experimental studies on spermatogenesis in the house sparrow, *Passer domesticus (Linnaeus)*. Anat. Rec., **67**, 327–351.

RILEY, G. M., AND FRAPS, R. M. 1942a. Biological assays of the male chicken pituitary for gonadotropic potency. Endocrinology, **30**, 529–536.

RILEY, G. M., AND FRAPS, R. M. 1942b. Relationship of gonad-stimulating activity of female domestic fowl pituitaries to reproductive condition. Endocrinology, **30**, 537–541.

RILEY, G. M., AND WITSCHI, E. 1938. Comparative effects of light stimulation and administration of gonadotropic hormones on female sparrows. Endocrinology, **23**, 618–624.

RINGOEN, A. 1942. Effects of continuous green and red light illumination on gonadal response in the English sparrow, *Passer domesticus (Linnaeus)*. Am. J. Anat., **71**, 99–116.

RINGOEN, A. R. 1943. Effects of injections of testosterone propionate on the reproductive system of the female English sparrow, *Passer domesticus (Linnaeus)*. J. Morphol., **73**, 423–440.

ROLLO, M., AND DOMM, L. V. 1943. Light requirement of the weaver finch. I. Light period and intensity. Auk, **60**, 357–367.

ROMANOFF, A. L. 1960. *The Avian Embryo*. New York: Macmillan Company.

ROMANOFF, A. L., AND ROMANOFF, A. J. 1956. *The Avian Egg*. New York: John Wiley & Sons.

ROTHSCHILD, LORD. 1956. *Fertilization*. New York: John Wiley & Sons, Inc.

ROTHCHILD, I., AND FRAPS, R. M. 1944a. On the function of the ruptured ovarian follicle of the domestic fowl. Proc. Soc. Exper. Biol. & Med., **56**, 79–82.

ROTHCHILD, I., AND FRAPS, R. M. 1944b. Relation between light-dark rhythms and hour of lay of eggs experimentally retained in the hen. Endocrinology, **35**, 355–362.

ROTHCHILD, I., AND FRAPS, R. M. 1949a. The interval between normal release of ovulating hormone and ovulation in the domestic hen. Endocrinology, **44**, 134–140.

ROTHCHILD, I., AND FRAPS, R. M. 1949b. The induction of ovulating hormone release from the pituitary of the domestic hen by means of progesterone. Endocrinology, **44**, 141–149.

ROWAN, W. 1925. Relation of light to bird migration and developmental changes. Nature, London, **115**, 494–495.

ROWAN, W. 1938a. London starlings and seasonal reproduction in birds. Proc. Zool. Soc., **108**, 51–77.

ROWAN, W. 1938b. Light and seasonal reproduction in animals. Biol. Rev., **13**, 374–402.

SAEKI, Y. 1955. Cytological study of the anterior pituitary of the hen in various stages of broody periods. Bull. Nat. Inst. Agric. Sci., ser. Animal Husbandry, **10**, 53–62. Biol. Abstr., **33**, ref. 33510, 1959.

SAEKI, Y., AND TANABE, Y. 1955. Changes in prolactin content of fowl pituitary during broody periods and some experiments on the induction of broodiness. Poultry Sc., **34**, 909–919.

SAEKI, Y., HIMENO, K., TANABE, Y., AND KATSURAGI, T. 1956. Comparative gonadotrophic potency of anterior pituitaries from cocks, laying hens and non-laying hens in molt. Endocrinol. Japon., **3**, 87–91.

SARKAR, B. C. R., LUECKE, R. W., AND DUNCAN, C. W. 1947. The amino acid composition of bovine semen. J. Biol. Chem., **171**, 463–465.

SCHARRER, E., AND SCHARRER, B. 1954. Hormones produced by neurosecretory cells. Recent Progr. Hormone Res., **10**, 183–232.

SCHILDMACHER, H. 1939. Über die kuenstliche aktivierung der Hoden einiger Vogelarten im Herbst durch Belichtung und Vorderlappenhormone. Biol. Zentralbl., **59**, 653–657.

SCHINDLER, H., WEINSTEIN, S., MOSES, E., AND GABRIEL, I. 1955. The effects of various diluents and storage times on the fertilizing capacity of cock semen. Poultry Sc., **34**, 1113–1117.

SCHÖNBERG, H., AND GHONEIM, A. 1946. Influence of different synthetic oestrogenic compounds on the egg-laying capacity of the growth of poultry. Nature, London, **157**, 77–78.

SCHOOLEY, J. P. 1937. Pituitary cytology in pigeons. Cold Spring Harbor Symposia Quant. Biol., **5**, 165–177.

SCHOOLEY, J. P., AND RIDDLE, O. 1938. The morphological basis of pituitary function in pigeons. Am. J. Anat., **62**, 313–349.

SCHOOLEY, J. P., RIDDLE, O., AND BATES, R. W. 1941. Replacement therapy in hypophysectomized juvenile pigeons. Am. J. Anat., **69**, 123–157.

SCOTT, H. M., AND PAYNE, L. F. 1937. Light in relation to the experimental modification of the breeding season of turkeys. Poultry Sc., **16**, 90–96.

SEGAL, S. J. 1957. Response of Weaver finch to chorionic gonadotrophin and hypophysial luteinizing hormone. Science, **126**, 1242–1243.

SERVENTY, D. L., AND MARSHALL, A. J. 1957. Breeding periodicity in western Australian birds: with an account of unseasonal nestings in 1953 and 1955. Emu, **57**, 99–126.

SHAFFNER, C. S. 1954. Feather papilla stimulation by progesterone. Science, **120**, 345.

SHAFFNER, C. S. 1955. Progesterone induced molt. Poultry Sc., **34**, 840–842.

SHELLABARGER, C. J. 1953. Observations of the pineal in the White Leghorn capon and cockerel. Poultry Sc., **32**, 189–197.

SHELLABARGER, C. J. 1954. Detection of thyroid stimulating hormone by I^{131} uptake in chicks. J. Appl. Physiol., **6**, 721–723.

SHIRLEY, H. V., JR., AND NALBANDOV, A. V. 1956b. Effect of neurohypophysectomy in domestic chickens. Endocrinology, **58**, 477–483.

SHIRLEY, H. V., JR., AND NALBANDOV, A. V. 1956b. Effects of transecting hypophyseal stalks in laying hens. Endocrinology, **58**, 694–700.

SHUTZE, J. V., JENSEN, L. S., AND MATSON, W. E. 1959. Effect of lighting regimes on growth and subsequent egg production of chickens. Poultry Sc., **38**, 1246.

SIMON, D. 1960. Contribution a l'étude de la circulation et du transport des gonocytes primaires dans la blastodermes d'oiseau cultivés *in vitro*. Arch. Anat. microscop. et Morphol. expér., **49**, 93–176.

SINGHER, H. O., KENSLER, C. J., TAYLOR, H. C., JR., RHOADS, C. P., AND UNNA, K. 1944. The effect of vitamin deficiency on estradiol inactivation by liver. J. Biol. Chem., **154**, 79–86.

SMITH, A. H., HOOVER, G. N., NORDSTROM, J. O., AND WINGET, C. M. 1957. Quantitative changes in the hen's oviduct associated with egg formation. Poultry Sc., **36**, 353–357.

SMITH, A. H., COURT, S. A., AND MARTIN, E. W. 1959. Formation of albumen precursors by the hen's oviduct. Am. J. Physiol., **197**, 1041–1044.

STAMMLER, J., KATZ, L. N., PICK, R., AND RODBARD, S. 1955. Dietary and hormonal factors in experimental atherogenesis and blood pressure regulation. Recent Progr. Hormone Res., **11**, 401–447.

STANLEY, A. J., AND WITSCHI, E. 1940. Germ cell migration in relation to asymmetry in the sex glands of hawks. Anat. Rec., **76**, 329–342.

STOKSTAD, E. L. R. 1954. Pteroylglutamic acid. IV. Biochemical systems. In *The Vitamins*, W. H. Sebrell, Jr., and R. S. Harris, Eds., Vol. III, pp. 124–142. New York: Academic Press, Inc.

STURKIE, P. D. 1951. Effects of estrogen and thyroxine upon the plasma proteins and blood volume in the fowl. Endocrinology, **49**, 565–570.

STURKIE, P. D. 1954. *Avian Physiology*. Ithaca: Comstock Publishing Associates.

STURKIE, P. D. 1955a. Effects of gonadal hormones on blood sugar of the chicken. Endocrinology, **56**, 575–578.

STURKIE, P. D. 1955b. Absorption of egg yolk in body cavity of the hen. Poultry Sc., **34**, 736–737.

SURFACE, F. M. 1912. The histology of the oviduct of the domestic hen. Maine Agric. Exper. Sta. Bull., **206**, 395–430.

SYKES, A. H. 1953. Premature oviposition in the hen. Nature, London, **172**, 1098–1099.

SYKES, A. H. 1956. Short day-length and egg production in the fowl. J. Agric. Sc., **47**, 429–434.

TABER, E. 1948. The relation between ovarian growth and sexual characters in brown Leghorn chick treated with gonadotrophins. J. Exper. Zool., **107**, 65–107.

TABER, E. 1951. Androgen secretion in the fowl. Endocrinology, **48**, 6–16.

TABER, E., CLAYTOR, M., KNIGHT, J., FLOWERS, J., GAMBRELL, D., AND AYERS, C. 1958. Some effects of sex hormones and homologous gonadotrophins on the early development of the rudimentary gonad in fowl. Endocrinology, **63**, 435–448.

TABER, E., CLAYTOR, M., KNIGHT, J., GAMBRELL, D., FLOWERS, J., AND AYERS, C. 1958. Ovarian stimulation in the immature fowl by desiccated avian pituitaries. Endocrinology, **62**, 84–89.

TABER, E., AND SALLEY, K. W. 1954. The effects of sex hormones on the development of the right gonad in female fowl. Endocrinology, **54**, 415–424.

TABER, E., SALLEY, K. W., AND KNIGHT, J. S. 1956. The effects of hypoadrenalism and chronic inanition on the development of the rudimentary gonad in sinistrally ovariectomized fowl. Anat. Rec., **126**, 177–194.

TANAKA, T., AND ROSENBERG, M. M. 1955. Effect of testosterone and dienestrol diacetate on hemoglobin levels of cockerels and capons. Poultry Sc., **34**, 1429–1437.

TANNENBERG. 1789. Spice ligieum observationum circa partes genitales masculas avium. Dissertation, Göttingen. Cited by T. Etzold in Ztschr. Wissensch. Zool., **52**, 46–84, 1891.

TAPPER, D. N., AND KARE, M. R. 1956. Distribution of glucose in blood of the chicken. Proc. Soc. Exper. Biol. & Med., **92**, 120–122.

THORP, R. H. 1950. Posterior pituitary lobe, hormones. In *Hormone Assay*, C. W. Emmens, Ed., pp. 108–139. New York: Academic Press, Inc.

TOMHAVE, A. E. 1954. Influence of artificial lights during rearing of the egg production of October hatched New Hampshires. Poultry Sc., **33**, 725–729.

TURNER, C. W. 1950. Thyrotropic hormone. In *Hormone Assay*, C. W. Emmens, Ed., pp. 215–235. New York: Academic Press, Inc.

TURNER, C. W. 1959. Role of thyroid, adrenal and posterior pituitary hormones in reproductive processes. In *Reproduction in Domestic Animals*, H. H. Cole and P. T. Cupps, Eds., Vol. 7, 156–183. New York: Academic Press, Inc.

UOTILA, U., AND KANNAS, O. 1952. Quantitative histological method of determining the proportions of the principal component of thyroid tissue. Acta Endocrinol., **11**, 49–60.

URIST, M. R. 1959. The effects of calcium deprivation upon the blood, adrenal cortex, ovary, and skeleton in domestic fowl. Recent Progr. Hormone Res., **15**, 455–477.

URIST, M. R., SCHJEIDE, O. A., AND McLEAN, F. C. 1958. The partition and binding of calcium in the serum of the laying hen and of the estrogenized rooster. Endocrinology, **63,** 570–585.

van DRIMMELEN, G. C. 1951. Artificial insemination of birds by the intraperitoneal route. Onderstepoort J. Vet. Res., Suppl. I.

van LIMBORGH, J. 1957. De ontwikkeling van de asymmetrie der gonaden by het embryo van de eend. Ph.D. thesis, University of Utrecht.

VANSTONE, W. E., DALE, D. G., OLIVER, W. F., AND COMMON, R. H. 1957. Sites of formation of plasma phospho protein and phospho lipid in the estrogenized cockerel. Canad. J. Biochem. Physiol., **35,** 659–665.

van TIENHOVEN, A. 1953. Further study of the neurogenic blockage of LH release in the hen. Anat. Rec., **115,** 374–375.

van TIENHOVEN, A. 1955. The duration of stimulation of the fowl's anterior pituitary for progesterone-induced LH release. Endocrinology, **56,** 667–674.

van TIENHOVEN, A. 1957. A method of "controlling sex" by dipping of eggs in hormone solutions. Poultry Sc., **36,** 628–632.

van TIENHOVEN, A. 1958. Effect of progesterone on broodiness and egg production of turkeys. Poultry Sc., **37,** 428–433.

van TIENHOVEN, A. 1959. Reproduction in the domestic fowl: physiology of the female. In *Reproduction in Domestic Animals,* H. H. Coles and P. T. Cupps, Eds., Vol. II, pp. 305–342. New York: Academic Press, Inc.

van TIENHOVEN, A. 1960. The metabolism of rooster sperm in different diluents. J. Agric. Sc., **54,** 67–80.

van TIENHOVEN, A., CRAWFORD, R. D., AND DUCHAINE, S. A. 1957. The effect of Nicarbazin on spermatogenesis and semen quality. Poultry Sc., **36,** 760–762.

van TIENHOVEN, A., NALBANDOV, A. V., AND NORTON, H. W. 1954. Effect of dibenamine on progesterone-induced and "spontaneous" ovulation in the hen. Endocrinology, **54,** 605–611.

van TIENHOVEN, A., SALISBURY, G. W., VANDEMARK, N. L., AND HANSEN, R. G. The preferential utilization by bull spermatozoa of glucose as compared to fructose. J. Dairy Sc., **35,** 637–641.

van TIENHOVEN, A., THOMAS, H. C., AND DREESEN, L. J. 1956. The effect of sulfamethazine feeding on the thyroids, and testes of single comb White Leghorn cockerels. Poultry Sc., **35,** 179–191.

VAUGIEN, L. 1948. Recherches biologiques et expérimentales sur le cycle reproducteur et la mue des oiseaux passériformes. Bull. Biol. France et Belgique, **82,** 166–213.

VAUGIEN, L. 1951. Ponte induite chez la Perruche ondulée maintenue à l'obscurité et dans l'ambiance des volières. Compt. Rend. Acad. Sc., **232,** 1706–1708.

VAUGIEN, L. 1953. Sur l'apparition de la maturité sexuelle des jeunes Parruches ondulées males soumises à diverses conditions d'éclairement: Le développement testiculaire est plus rapide dans l'obscurité complète. Bull. Biol. France et Belgique, **87,** 274–286.

VAUGIEN, L. 1954a. Effet de la section des rémiges sur la réponse sexuelle du moineau domestique soumis à l'éclairement artificiel. Bull. Biol. France et Belgique, **88,** 52–67.

VAUGIEN, L. 1954b. Sur les réactions ovariennes du moineau domestique soumis durant le repos sexuel à des injections de gonadotrophine sérique du jument gravide. Bull. Biol. France et Belgique, **89,** 1–15.

VAUGIEN, L. 1956. Ponte du chardonneret induite, en toutes saisons, par l'injections de gonadotrophine équine. Compt. rend. Acad. Sc., **243,** 444–446.

VAUGIEN, L. 1957. La réaction ovarienne provoquée chez le serin des jardins par la gonadotrophine équine est liée à l'état initial de la gonade. Compt. rend. Acad. Sc., **245,** 1268–1271.

von FABER, H. 1954. Über die Beeinflussung der Nebenschilddrüse durch Verabreichung von Stilboestrol allein und kombiniert mit Thyroxin b.z.w. Testosterone propionat an Hähne. Endokrinologie, **32,** 295–302.

von FABER, H. 1958. Geschlechtsunterschiede im Wachstum und in den inner sekretorischen Organen des Sperbers, *Accipiter nisus nisus* L. Acta Endocrinol., **28,** 410–416.

WARREN, D. C., AND SCOTT, H. M. 1935. The time factor in egg formation. Poultry Sc., **14,** 195–207.

WARREN, D. C., AND SCOTT, H. M. 1936. Influence of light on ovulation in the fowl. J. Exper. Zool., **74,** 137–156.

WEISS, H. S., AND STURKIE, P. D. 1952. Time of oviposition as affected by neuromimetic drugs. Poultry Sc., **31,** 227–231.

WHEELER, N. C., SEARCY, G. L., AND ANDREWS, F. N., 1942. The effect of epinephrine upon semen production in the domestic fowl. Endocrinology, **30,** 369–374.

WILCOX, F. H., AND SHORB, M. S. 1958. The effect of antibiotics on bacteria in semen and on motility and fertilizing ability of chicken spermatozoa. Am. J. Vet. Res., **19,** 945–949.

WILLIAMS, D. D. 1958a. A histological study of the effects of subnormal temperatures on the testis of the fowl. Anat. Rec., **130,** 225–241.

WILLIAMS, D. D. 1958b. Effect of heat on transplanted testis material of the fowl. Transplant. Bull., **5,** 32–35.

WINCHESTER, C. F. 1939. Influence of thyroid on egg production. Endocrinology, **24,** 697–701.

WINCHESTER, C. F., COMAR, C. L., AND DAVIS, G. K. 1949. Thyroid destruction by I[131] and replacement therapy. Science, **110,** 302–304.

WINGSTRAND, K. G. 1951. *The Structure and Development of the Avian Pituitary.* Lund, Sweden: C. W. K. Gleerup.

WINTER, H. 1958. Persistent right oviducts in fowls including an account of the histology of the fowl's normal oviduct. Australian Vet. J., **34,** 140–147.

WITSCHI, E. 1935. Seasonal sex characters in birds and their hormonal control. Wilson Bull., **47**, 177–188.

WITSCHI, E. 1937. Effect of gonadotropic and oestrogenic hormones on regenerating feathers of Weaver finches (*Pyromelana franciscana*). Proc. Soc. Exper. Biol. & Med., **35**, 484–489.

WITSCHI, E. 1955. Vertebrate gonadotrophins. In *Comparative Physiology of Reproduction.* Memoirs Soc. Endocrinol., **4**, 149–163.

WITSCHI, E., AND FUGO, N. W. 1940. Response of sex characters of the adult female starling to synthetic hormones. Proc. Soc. Exper. Biol. & Med., **45**, 10–14.

WITSCHI, E., AND RILEY, G. M. 1940. Quantitative studies on the hormones of human pituitaries. Endocrinology, **26**, 565–576.

WITSCHI, E., STANLEY, A. J., AND RILEY, G. M. 1937. Gonadotropic hormones of the hypophysis of the turkey. Proc. Soc. Exper. Biol & Med., **36**, 647–651.

WOLFSON, A. 1945. The role of the pituitary, fat deposition and body weight in bird migration. Condor, **47**, 95–127.

WOLFSON, A. 1954a. Notes on the cloacal protuberance, seminal vesicles, and a possible copulatory organ in small passerine birds. Bull. Chicago Acad. Sc., 1954. **10**, 1–23.

WOLFSON, A. 1954b. Sperm storage at lower-than-body temperature outside the body cavity of some passerine birds. Science, **120**, 68–71.

WOLFSON, A. 1959a. Ecologic and physiologic factors in the regulation of spring migration and reproductive cycles in birds. In *Comparative Endocrinology,* A. Gorbman, Ed., pp. 38–70. New York: John Wiley & Son.

WOLFSON, A. 1959b. The role of light and darkness in the regulation of spring migration and reproductive cycles in birds. In *Photoperiodism,* R. B. Withrow, Ed. A. A. A. S. Publication 55, pp. 679–716.

WOLFSON, A., AND HARRIS, B. K. 1959. Maintenance of gonadal activity with testosterone following inhibition of the pituitary with short days. Anat. Rec., **134**, 656.

WOMACK, E. B., KOCH, F. C., DOMM, L. V., AND JUHN, M. 1931. Some factors affecting the comb growth response in the Brown Leghorn Capons. J. Pharmacol. & Exper. Therap., **41**, 173–178.

WONG, H. Y. C., AND HAWTHORNE, E. W. 1954. Influence of filtered and no sunlight on weight and comb response in androgen treated cockerels. Am. J. Physiol., **179**, 419–420.

WONG, H. Y. C., LAVENDA, N., HAWTHORNE, E. W. 1954. Effect of exercise on comb response of androgen-treated capons. Am. J. Physiol., **178**, 269–270.

YAO, T. S., AND OLSEN, M. W. 1955. Microscopic observations of parthenogenetic embryonic tissues from virgin turkey eggs. J. Hered., **46**, 133–134.

YEATES, N. T. M. 1954. Day light changes. In *Progress in the Physiology of Farm Animals,* J. Hammond, Ed., Vol. I, pp. 363–392. London: Butterworth & Company.

YOUNG, W. C. 1953. Gamete-age at the time of fertilization and the course of gestation in mammals. In *Pregnancy Wastage,* E. T. Engle, Ed., pp. 38–50. Springfield, Ill.: Charles C Thomas.

ZARROW, M. X., AND BASTIAN, J. W. 1953. Blockade of ovulation in the hen with adrenolytic and parasympatholytic drugs. Proc. Soc. Exper. Biol. & Med., **84**, 457–459.

ZARROW, M. X., KORETSKY, I. B., AND ZARROW, I. G. 1951. Failure of folic acid antagonist to interfere with the action of testosterone propionate on the combs and testes of young cockerels. Endocrinology, **48**, 125–132.

ZUCKERMAN, S. 1955. The possible functional significance of the pituitary portal vessels. Ciba Foundation Colloquia Endocrinol., **8**, 551–586.

Hormonal Regulation of Reproductive Behavior

19

The Hormones and Mating Behavior[1]

William C. Young, Ph.D.

PROFESSOR OF ANATOMY, THE UNIVERSITY OF KANSAS, LAWRENCE, KANSAS

I. Introduction

Reproductive behavior is composed of the parts of the total behavior pattern which subserve reproduction more directly and importantly than any other vital activity. Migration, whether it is the long distance seasonal migration of many birds and fishes, the shorter seasonal migration of certain mammals, or the vernal migration to the water of many amphibians, belongs in this category. Aggressive behavior manifested during the establishment of territoriality and in the attainment of dominance within a group is an element in social behavior, but it is also a step toward the achievement

[1] Many of the investigations to which there is reference were made possible by grants from the Committee for Research in Problems of Sex, National Academy of Sciences–National Research Council. Latterly, assistance has been provided by Research Grants M-504 to M-504(C8) from the National Institute of Mental Health, of the National Institutes of Health, Public Health Service.

of reproduction. Courtship with display and vocalization is directed toward this end, as is the behavior culminating in sexual union. Nest building, incubational behavior, and care of the young after hatching or during the suckling period are final steps in the reproduction of many species. Among the components of the total pattern of reproductive behavior in the lower vertebrates and mammals are the prototypes of much of the behavior seen in man—aggressiveness, courtship, mating, and care of the young. It follows therefore that comparative study of the factors regulating and mediating the display of this behavior should be as helpful in the clarification of the many problems in man as has been the comparative approach in the study of other vital activities.

The difficulties encountered in initiating such studies are documented in the *History of the National Research Council Committee for Research in Problems of Sex* (Aberle and Corner, 1953). They are reflected in the circumstance that single chapters were considered sufficient for the subject in the first and second editions of *Sex and Internal Secretions* (Stone, 1932b, 1939b). Since then, however, an accelerated pace has been maintained, so much so that an appraisal of progress can best be achieved by separate treatments of mating behavior, parental behavior, aggressiveness, human sexuality, and the problem of the neural mechanisms mediating such behavior. Mating behavior will be dealt with in this chapter.

The dependence of mating behavior on the gonadal hormones has long been recognized. Their role in the expression of sexual behavior in man is equivocal (see chapter by Money; in addition, Creevy and Rea, 1940; Tauber, 1940; Carmichael, Noonan and Kenyon, 1941; Filler and Drezner, 1944; Carter, Cohen and Shorr, 1947; Kinsey, Pomeroy and Martin, 1948; Kinsey, Pomeroy, Martin and Gebhard, 1953; Perloff, 1949; Waxenberg, Drellich and Sutherland, 1959; and many others), but for most vertebrates for which data exist the full display of mating behavior is given only when the gonadal hormones are present. The relationship may be more direct than any other between endocrine substances and behavior.[2] When the gonads are removed mating behavior becomes greatly reduced in intensity or is no longer displayed; on replacement of the hormone it is again exhibited. If an inadequate amount is given, a partial response may be detected, or, as in a number of rodents and the cow, when an improper balance is administered an atypical pattern may be shown (Boling, Young and Dempsey, 1938; Melampy, Emmerson, Rakes, Hanka and Eness, 1957). However, when the threshold of the proper hormones is reached and, in species requiring estrogen and progesterone, the correct balance is given in the proper sequence, the pattern of behavior identical with that displayed before gonadectomy is restored. In what follows, the observations and experiments supporting this conclusion are reviewed, factors which influence, modify, and limit the action of gonadal hormones are enumerated, and suggestions are made with respect to the character and scope of problems awaiting further study.

The discussion will begin with a description of mating behavior, for the end points investigators have used in obtaining their data have been derived from the elements or measures composing this behavior.[3,4] As the substance of our description becomes apparent, many will feel that a disproportional space has been given to the rat and guinea pig. This is explained by the circumstance that the rat and guinea pig have

[2] From the fact that deviations of behavior are well known in dysfunction of the parathyroid, the thyroid, the pituitary, and the adrenal cortex, and in hyperinsulinism (Hoskins, 1934; Shock, 1944; Sherman, 1945; Medvei, 1949; Young, 1954), it might be concluded that general behavior is dependent on a normal functioning of these glands and therefore that a direct relationship exists. This may be true for cortisone and related steroids secreted by the adrenal cortex (Rome and Braceland, 1950, 1951, 1952; Derbes and Weiss, 1951). For the other endocrine organs, however, there still is no unequivocal proof of a one-to-one relationship between the active principles produced by these glands and the changes in behavior associated with deficiencies or with excessive quantities. An indirect relationship traceable to derangements of metabolism or to physical deformity and handicap seems more likely.

[3] Many articles in which mating behavior is described are cited in the older reviews (Stone, 1932b, 1939b; Young, 1941; Beach, 1942e, 1946, 1947, 1948, 1951, 1952; Bullough, 1945; Hartman, 1945; Collias, 1950). A number of newer studies containing bibliographies or unusually complete descriptive accounts of mating behavior are noted here (Schlosberg, Duncan and Daitch, 1949; Baerends, Brouwer and Waterbolk, 1955; Morris, 1955b; Aronson, 1957; for fishes. Noble and Aronson, 1942; Aronson, 1944; Russell, 1955; for amphibians. Domm and Davis, 1948; Guhl, 1949; Richdale, 1951; Hinde, 1952, 1955a, b; Hale, 1955; Morris, 1954; Wood-Gush, 1954; Moynihan and Hall 1955; for birds. Macirone and Walton, 1938; Stone and Ferguson, 1940; Snell, Fekete, Hummel and Law, 1940; Pearson, 1940; Beach and Holz, 1946; Reed, 1946; Reed and Reed, 1946; Beach and Pauker, 1949; Young and Grunt, 1951; Enders, 1952; Rowley and Mollison, 1955; Scott and Lloyd-Jacob, 1955; Larsson, 1956; Green, Clemente and de Groot, 1957; Rosenblatt and Aronson, 1958a, b; Beach and Rabedeau, 1959; for small mammals including the rabbit, cat and dog. Burger, 1952; for the domestic pig. Hafez, 1952; for the ewe. Carpenter, 1942a, b; Yerkes, 1943; Stellar, 1960; for infrahuman primates).

[4] It is of historic interest that endocrinologists, physiologists, biochemists, and anatomists who have contributed so importantly to our knowledge of the microscopic anatomy and physiology of reproduction, have given little attention to problems centering around the hormonal regulation of reproductive behavior. Much of the work in this field has been done by psychologists and much of the support that has encouraged effort in this direction can be attributed to their foresight, activity, and persistence. Endocrinologists, physiologists, and anatomists have done little with behavior, probably because of the former rather generally held belief, best expressed perhaps by Stockard and Papanicolaou (1919) and Moore and Gallagher (1930), that behavioral end points are so vague as to be of little value in experimental studies. This circumstance in the development of the subject is reflected by the absence of any discussion of the hormones and behavior in most textbooks of endocrinology.

been favored subjects for investigation, that much of the thread of thought which follows was developed during investigations of these species, and that for problems of concern to the endocrinologist this work still is the richest source of information. At the same time, we do not belittle the fact that much has been learned from observations and experiments on other lower mammals, submammalian vertebrates, infrahuman primates, and man. Important concepts not appreciated at the time were developed from early and relatively isolated studies of the ringdove (Craig, 1914, 1918) and chicken (Goodale, 1918). Latterly, careful observations by ethologists and zoologists have provided the substance for a comparative consideration of many problems. Some of the descriptions, notably that of the male guppy (Baerends, Brouwer and Waterbolk, 1955), are more refined than any given of a mammal and all are of value for the breadth they add to what otherwise would have been a laboratory study in the narrower sense.

II. Mating Behavior

A. THE MALE

The behavior varies from species to species, but in many species and particularly in mammals genital examination, if not copulation with ejaculation, is usually immediate when individuals of opposite sexes are placed together (Hamilton, 1914; Stone, 1922; Bingham, 1928; Yerkes and Elder, 1936; Young and Grunt, 1951; Larsson, 1956). In such a situation the interval between the beginning of a test and the first display of interest in the establishment of sexual relations may be taken as a measure of the strength of sexual behavior (Soulairac and Coppin-Monthillaud, 1951). The subsequent behavior is composed of several elements. The number distinguished depends somewhat on the investigator, but also on experience. In general when a species has been used extensively as have the rat and guinea pig the later articles should be consulted (Stone, Tomilin and Barker, 1935; Stone and Ferguson, 1940; Beach, 1944b; Beach and Holz, 1946; Soulairac and Coppin-Monthillaud, 1951; Young and Grunt, 1951; Larsson, 1956).

When a female rat is placed in a cage with a cage-adapted male the latter usually begins to copulate immediately. Often, however, he begins in a few seconds to examine her anogenital region. Another precopulatory act is a nibbling at the head or body. The copulatory act is described as coming with such a definiteness and orderly sequence of elements that it can easily be distinguished from precopulatory behavior (Stone, 1922). The male mounts the female from the rear and clasps his forelegs about her laterolumbar region in what Beach (1944b) calls a *clasp-without-palpation.* While clasping the female, the male palpates her sides with rapid movements of his forelimbs and simultaneously his pelvic region is moved in rapid, piston-like thrusts *(palpation-with-pelvic-thrusts).* He then slips off the female's back rather weakly. In nearly every instance this termination of contact with the female indicates a failure to achieve intromission; behavior of this type is designated an *incomplete copulation* or *attempt.* With what Beach designates *copulation* or *complete copulation,* the palpation-with-pelvic-thrusts occurs, but a new element is added. After a final and unusually forceful thrust, the male lunges backward and often throws himself several inches from the female. This backward lunge nearly always is indicative of intromission. Stone and Ferguson (1940) estimated from a cinematographic study that the duration of these intromissions is $1/3$ to $2/3$ of a second and that during each intromission 2 and 9 pelvic thrusts occur. When intromission is terminated by ejaculation the backward lunge is omitted. Instead the male continues to press against the female, thus prolonging intromission, and then, releasing his clasp, slowly raises his forelegs as the ejaculate is emitted and the penis withdrawn. In most tests ejaculation is not seen during the first intromission, but it has been observed at this time in tests involving observations of sexual behavior over a period of hours (Beach, 1956). Usually, however, from 3 to 44 intromissions precede ejaculation. A spell of recovery, the *refractory period,* is then required, during which the male is uninfluenced by any sexual stimuli (Larsson, 1956). Satiation is not reached until there have been 3 to 10 ejaculations and the activity culminating in these ejaculations may be spread over as much as 3 hours (Stone and Ferguson, 1940; Beach and Jordan, 1956). A quiescent or *recovery period* of 24 hours or more follows (Stone, Ferguson and Wright, 1940), although 5 or 6 days and even longer may be necessary (Beach and Jordan, 1956; Larsson, 1956). Beach and Jordan studied the changes in behavior preceding each successive ejaculation up to and including the sixth. The number of intromissions before ejaculation decreased from an average of 10.6 to 4.1. Ejaculation-latency (interval from the first mount to ejaculation) decreased from an average of 450 to 132 seconds. The refractory period (period of sexual inactivity following all but the terminal ejaculation) increased from an average of 324 to 818 seconds.

Unless otherwise noted, the description of the behavior shown by the male guinea pig is taken from that given by Young and Grunt (1951). When a female in heat is placed with a male he begins to follow her almost immediately, usually sniffing at the anogenital region. This behavior is *nuzzling*. Within a few seconds he may mount her, usually posteriorly but often elsewhere. If the forepaws are placed on the back of the female without other contact, the act is *abortive mounting* (Valenstein, Riss and Young, 1954), but if the back of the female is covered it is *mounting*. Mounting may be accompanied by pelvic thrusts without intromission, but often it is followed by *intromission* with or without pelvic thrusts. The duration of intromission varies, depending partly on the male and partly on the responsiveness of the female. Frequently she withdraws from the male at the instant of intromission, in which case there is no opportunity for pelvic thrusts. More often there is a series of pelvic thrusts lasting 2 to 5 seconds or more. Following intromission of this type, males and females usually clean the genitalia even though there was no ejaculation. Ejaculation is known to have occurred only if the final thrust is conspicuously prolonged and accompanied by a drawing in of the flanks as in a spasm; both animals then fall back on their haunches and clean the genitalia. If the

male is watched, he can be seen to drag his butt along the floor of the cage somewhat as a dog infested with worms will do. During the test a sniffing or nibbling at the hair anywhere on the body of the female may be seen. The element is designated *sniffing and nibbling*.

In the guinea pig, in contrast to the rat, the single ejaculation usually marks the end of any strong interest in the female; in most tests it is accomplished within 10 minutes. If after ejaculation the first estrous female is replaced by a second, there may be a revival of interest (Grunt and Young, 1952c), but this feature of behavior has not entered into the determination of the strength of sexual behavior. Interest is also restimulated in the male monkey by the introduction of a second female (Carpenter, 1942a) and in the bull by a change of teasers (Cembrowicz, 1952; Almquist and Hale, 1956). The presence of a new estrous female does not have such an effect on a satiated male rat (Larsson, 1956).

Ejaculation can be distinguished more easily in the guinea pig than in the rat; indeed it was not until 1934 that ejaculation was identified as a discrete element in the rat (Stone and Barker, 1934). As recently as 1946 Beach and Holz wrote, "ejaculation referred solely to observable mating reactions," apparently without implication as to the discharge of seminal fluid.

These elements of the mating behavior pattern, along with the length of the interval between the beginning of the test and ejaculation in the guinea pig, are the end points that were used in the development of the scoring systems now prevalent in this country. The elements are given different values in an ascending order. In the rat the order is *mounting and clasp-without-palpation, mounting and clasp-with-palpation and pelvic thrusts* (referred to as *attempts* by Stone, Tomilin and Barker, 1935 and as *incomplete copulation* by Beach and Holz, 1946), *copulation* which consists of mounting, palpation and pelvic thrusts followed by the backward lunge signifying that intromission has occurred, and *ejaculation*. In the guinea pig the order is *sniffing and nibbling, nuzzling, abortive mounting* (scored as nuzzling), *mounting, intromission*, and *ejaculation*.

The ascending order is justified by the circumstance that in both species the elements tend to appear in this sequence during sexual maturation (Stone, 1924b; Avery, 1925; Louttit, 1929; Webster and Young, 1951). Except for some cats given maximal sexual experience (Rosenblatt and Aronson, 1958a), the order of disappearance following castration is the reverse of that during development in the rabbit (Stone, 1932a), hamster (Beach and Pauker, 1949), rat (Stone, 1939a; Beach, 1944b), and guinea pig (Grunt and Young, 1953). The sequence in which the elements reappear in the castrated male given androgen is the same as the order of appearance in the maturing animal (Stone, 1939a; Beach, 1944b; Grunt and Young, 1953).

In the laboratory at Kansas and elsewhere there has been concern that the same score can be achieved in more ways than one (Clark and Aronson, 1951; Valenstein, Riss and Young, 1954; Larsson, 1956). In studies of the guppy, the problem is complicated by the fact that excited males copulate with few or no preliminary acts; consequently, the most excited as well as the least excited individuals have low copulatory scores. During work with the male guinea pig it was found that subjects displaying little mounting and having only a few intromissions and possibly an ejaculation late in the test period often attain scores no higher than animals displaying much of only the lower measures of behavior. The possibility that this paradox might seriously lessen the validity of the scoring procedure has been checked. All the sexual behavior displayed during the tests was recorded (Riss, 1955); the average scores were then calculated and compared with the average quantity of each measure of behavior and the latency of ejaculation. Inspection of the table prepared by Riss reveals that both methods yielded rank-orders that were essentially the same; consequently, the general accuracy of the older method is assumed. It is recommended, however, that in careful studies both methods should be used.

Soulairac (1952a), Soulairac and Coppin-Monthillaud (1951), and Larsson (1956) in their work on the rat departed from the methods for estimating the strength of sexual behavior used by Stone, and by Beach during the first 10 to 15 years of his investigational activity. Sixty-minute rather than 10-minute tests were given and especial value was attached to the initial interval when the male displays no activity in the presence of the female, the number of intromissions preceding each ejaculation, the duration of each series of copulations, the intromissions per minute, the length of the refractory period following each ejaculation, and the number of ejaculations in 60 minutes.

Since the early 1950's, important changes in the procedure have been adopted by Beach and his associates (Beach and Jordan, 1956; Beach and Fowler, 1959). More recently similar procedures have been used in studies of the hamster (Beach and Rabedeau, 1959). Briefly, special observation cages and a recording system were devised. The latter consisted of three manually operated microswitches, each of which activates a marker which records on waxed paper pulled by a constant speed kymograph. Equally, if not more important, is the lengthening of the test until a criterion of sexual exhaustion has been met—in this case the lapse of 30 minutes without any mounting of the incentive female. Data contributing to six measures of sexual capacity are recorded: latency to the first intromission, frequency of ejaculation, intromissions per ejaculation, the frequency of mounts without intromission, the intercopulatory interval, and the postejaculatory interval.

Scoring procedures helpful in the selection of chickens and cattle for breeding have been devised by Wood-Gush and Osborne (1956) and Bane (1954), but will not be described here. They would be of value in endocrinological studies of behavior in these species.

Thus far in the discussion of patterns of behavior and scoring methods no reference has been made to the duality of "functions" or "mechanisms" first noted by Craig (1918) and later given prominence by Nissen (1929), Beach (1942e, 1947, 1947–48,

1956, 1958), Soulairac (1952a–c), and Baerends, Brouwer and Waterbolk (1955). Not unrelated is the organic separation of activities associated with courtship and spawning which Clark, Aronson and Gordon (1954) felt may exist in the fishes they studied.

Nissen, obviously influenced by Moll (1897) and Gerhardt (1924), divided sexual "drive" into two behavior sequences, a *contrectation* drive which brings animals into the proximity of the sex object and, in rats, leads to nosing of the genitalia, gentle biting, and other sex play, and a *detumescence* drive which culminates in coitus.

Beach postulated that one of the two mechanisms is "erotic sensitivity" or the "susceptibility to sexual arousal." He thought of the arousal mechanism as being organized and functional in sexually inexperienced animals. It can be "conditioned" to a variety of nonsexual cues. "In male rats, cats, and dogs," he writes, "sexual arousal can be conditioned to new cues, but there is no evidence that females are similarly affected by experience." The sexual responsiveness of male primates is more labile and modifiable than that of male rodents and carnivores, and female primates differ from the females of lower species in that the *arousal mechanism* can be affected.

The other function is that of "potency" or the "capacity for sexual performance" ("mating responses" in Beach, 1947). It includes "the promptness with which mating is initiated, the frequency of copulation, and the rapidity with which ejaculation occurs." The function is mediated by what he calls the "executive" or "consummatory mechanism." It is thrown into action when sexual arousal reaches a threshold level. He continues: "The functional organization of the CM (consummatory mechanisms) is probably complete in inexperienced male and female rats, rabbits, dogs, and cats. The motor pattern of copulation is stereotyped and invariable, and is not materially altered by experience."

Development of the concept seems to have followed observations on the copulatory behavior of partially decorticate rats (Beach, 1940, 1944b, 1956). There was a proportional decrease in the percentage of tests in which copulatory behavior occurred, but the number of copulations during each positive test was not affected, even in the lesion group in which the percentage of postoperative copulators was lowest. As Beach interpreted the results, there had been a decrease in the ease of arousal to the point of the practical abolition of copulatory behavior, but without an effect on the actual copulatory pattern.

Experiments on the guinea pig (Valenstein, Riss and Young, 1955) have also provided evidence for dual functions, *excitability*, corresponding to susceptibility to sexual arousal, and the *capacity for response* corresponding to the capacity for sexual performance and depending on the existence of an organized neural pattern. The suggestion originated from the observation that an occasional male will achieve a complete copulation in only 1 or 2 of 10 tests with an estrous female, whereas in the other tests he will give the appearance of being generally indifferent. The capacity for the sexual response exists, but the level of excitability or arousal is so low that copulation usually does not occur. Under other conditions, excitability is shown, but no organized pattern is present and the male does not know how to copulate. Certain males brought up under conditions of isolation (see Table 19.3, groups II and IV) display excitability, but they lack an organized pattern and copulation is not achieved. In this respect the male guinea pig resembles the ringdove (Craig, 1914) and chimpanzee (Nissen, 1956) rather than the rat (Beach, 1958).

The place of the concept of duality of function in the present context is especially well indicated by Baerends, Brouwer and Waterbolk (1955) in their discussion of the structure of courting behavior of the male guppy, *Lebistes reticulatus*. The terms "appetitive behavior" and the "consummatory act" introduced by Craig (1918) are used. The former is variable in form and leads the animal toward the external situation necessary for evoking the consummatory act which is rigid and stereotyped. Craig reserved the term consummatory act for the final activity of definitive behavioral complexes and emphasized that after its performance appetitive behavior ceases and is succeeded by a state of relative rest. If the behavior of the male rat and guinea pig is placed within this frame of reference, the behavior leading up to ejaculation is appetitive; ejaculation, as the final act, is consummatory.

The concept of a duality of "function" has been described largely for purposes of clarification of terminology; it has not influenced the methods of scoring which are based on the display of the two functions as a sequence. The concept will be encountered again in the discussion of the role of the testis hormone in the display of sexual behavior (p. 1207), and in the presentation of the problem of the mechanism of hormone action (p. 1205).

The term "pseudofemale behavior" was coined by Morris (1954, 1955a) as a designation for feminine responses exhibited by males—presentation, squatting, lordosis, and others, depending on the species. Behavior of this sort is a part of the normal repertoire of many species and is displayed under a variety of conditions: by rhesus monkeys, rats, the lizard, *Anolis carolinensis*, and the ten-spined stickleback in the presence of aggressive males (Hamilton, 1914; Beach, 1939; Noble and Greenberg, 1941a; Carpenter, 1942b; Morris, 1952); by strongly excited male rats during mating tests (Stone, 1924a; Beach, 1945a); by sexually frustrated fish (Morris, 1952, 1955a); by sexually thwarted zebra finches (Morris, 1954); by fishes, pigeons, and hamsters in situations in which the stimulus was not apparent or at least not recorded (Riddle, 1924; Carpenter, 1933a; Beach, 1947; Schlosberg, Duncan and Daitch, 1949); and in newborn male guinea pigs (Boling, Blandau, Wilson and Young, 1939). At intervals of 2, 3, or 4 weeks, during a study of the stability of a conditioned breathing response to light, a formerly dominant male rabbit assumed the female role toward its two male partners (Brown, 1937). The display of feminine behavior has not entered into the scoring of males, but the frequency of its occurrence in the absence of any endocrine pathologic condition is of interest for the discussion of the determinants of

patterns of sexual behavior given elsewhere (p. 1222).

In the domestic rat, but not in the wild Norway rat (Richter and Uhlenhuth, 1954), running is stimulated by testicular secretions, for after castration, decreases of 30 to 95 per cent occur (Hoskins, 1925a; Wang, Richter and Guttmacher, 1925; Heller, 1932; Richter, 1933). During the first 3 to 5 months of life, and possibly longer (Slonaker, 1912), the amount of activity rises; thereafter there is a gradual decline. Stone and Barker (1934) could find no significant relationship between the amount of running activity and the strength of sexual behavior as measured in direct tests or in an obstruction apparatus.

The differences between individuals of a species is a subject of universal comment. In the guinea pig and rat they are manifested by variations in the elements of the pattern and by variations in the scores. Some individuals ejaculate relatively soon after the beginning of a test and, in the guinea pig, without previous intromissions. In other animals ejaculation occurs later and is preceded by a number of intromissions. An occasional male will nuzzle and mount a female in heat, but in repeated 10-minute tests will not achieve ejaculation. Some animals of this type regularly require more time, others are not known ever to have copulated. The amount of running by apparently healthy males of the same age also varies greatly. It may be no more than a few hundred revolutions per day or it may be several thousand. In male cats conspicuous differences between individuals are seen in the pattern of decline in sexual behavior following castration (Rosenblatt and Aronson, 1958a).

The behavior characteristics of individuals tend to persist in rats and guinea pigs (Avery, 1925; Hitchcock, 1925; Stone, 1927; Stone, Tomilin and Barker, 1935; Stone, Ferguson and Wright, 1940; Stone and Ferguson, 1940; Shirley, 1928; Anderson, 1936; Beach, 1940, 1942g, 1944b; Soulairac, 1950; Young and Grunt, 1951; Grunt and Young, 1952b), chickens (Guhl, Collias and Allee, 1945; Wood-Gush and Osborne, 1956), hamsters (Beach and Pauker, 1949), rabbits (Stone, 1932a), cats (Green, Clemente and de Groot, 1957), bulls (Hart, Mead and Regan, 1946), chimpanzees (Yerkes, 1939; Young and Orbison, 1944), and doubtless many other species. Usually they cannot be related to visible differences in the testes or to the quantity and quality of the semen (Lagerlöf, 1954; Burrows and Titus, 1939; Beach, 1940; Young, 1949; Craig, Casida and Chapman, 1954; Wood-Gush and Osborne, 1956; Jakway and Young, 1958), although Rasmussen (1952) reported an inverse relationship between fertility and strength of sex drive in the rats he studied.

Differences in behavior are not necessarily related to the quantity of testicular hormone, provided a certain minimum is present. In an older study, examination of the accessory reproductive organs by techniques employed for hormone detection revealed that the relatively inactive rats in a group were actively secreting male hormone (Heller, 1932). More recently it was found that the behavioral differences in male guinea pigs before castration continued to be displayed when the animals received equivalent amounts of testosterone propionate after castration (Grunt and Young, 1952b). This lack of correlation between patterns and the strength of mating behavior, and levels of gonadal hormones is suggestive with respect to the role of the hormones in the expression of mating behavior and is discussed elsewhere (p. 1199).

The extent to which mating behavior in the male is dependent on testicular secretions cannot easily be deduced from the effects of castration. Their variation from species to species and from individual to individual of the same species is in fact so great that it has done much to nurture the doubt that gonadal hormones are the primary agents on which the sexual response depends (Kinsey, Pomeroy, Martin and Gebhard, 1953, p. 728 and elsewhere). The impact of the book (and the earlier volume on the male) on those not familiar with the experimental studies was such that a fairly detailed analysis of what has been found is given.

Courtship activity of the gobiid fish, *Bathygobius soporator*, was not reduced by castration, but the subjects became nondiscriminatory and courted males and gravid and nongravid females in a like manner (Tavolga, 1955). A castrated salmon parr showed no interest in females (Jones and King, 1952). Male *Hemichromis bimaculatus*, on the other hand, exhibited typical movements of courtship and brooding for 202 days after castration (Noble and Kumpf, 1936). During this time at least one male entered into as many as 13 successive spawnings with a normal female. Other males, castrated before the first spawning, took part in at least 11 successive spawnings in 146 days. At each spawning nuptial colors and genital tubes developed.

Male frogs castrated by Shapiro (1937a) displayed no signs of sexual activation when 70 per cent of the control animals were mating. Steinach (1894, 1910), on the other hand, reported that frogs displayed some degree of sexual behavior months after castration. The same articles contain reports of a diminished but nevertheless conspicuous sexual activity in male rats as much as a year after castration. The point may not be important, but it is recorded for what it is worth: the 1894 article, in which an interest was expressed in clinical observations on the sexual behavior of human castrates, emphasizes the retention of sexual behavior by castrates. The 1910 article, which seems to have been written out of a background of interest in the endocrine regulation of mating behavior, emphasizes the loss of libido following castration.

The postcastrational behavior of several species of birds has been described. Complete castration of the pigeon did not prevent entirely the development of copulatory ability in all cases, but in others primary sexual activity was abolished (Carpenter, 1933a). The frequency of billing was reduced by castration, but it was eliminated in only 3 of 14 cases (Carpenter, 1933b). His results are taken to demonstrate "that the sexual hormones are of fundamental importance in predisposing sexual activity." Two of 16 gonadless pigeons "developed complete and emphatic masculine behavior" (Riddle, 1925) and he adds, " . . . it is clear, that the thing which is usually accomplished with the aid of the testis increction may also be accomplished without it."

An incomplete and weak pattern of sexual behavior was displayed by two turkeys, castrated at 9 weeks of age (Scott and Payne, 1934). Sexual behavior is "wanting" in castrated ducks and roosters (Goodale, 1913, 1916b), but elsewhere (Goodale, 1916a, 1918) it is evident that capons frequently crow and sometimes tread hens, although ordinarily these phases of the behavior of the cock are not manifested. Benoit (1929) stated that the capon normally shows no interest in hens, but one in which no testicular tissue could be found and which possessed a comb and wattles typical of the capon did tread hens. Domm (1927) referred to capons in his pens which crowed and trod hens, but when such individuals were examined small nodules of testicular tissue were found.

When articles dealing with mating behavior in castrated lower mammals are reviewed, the conclusions must be evaluated carefully. The significance of the statement that male guinea pigs castrated at 30 days of age have repeatedly been utilized as testers for estrous females (Moore, 1928; Moore and Gallagher, 1930) is lessened by the statement (Moore and Gallagher, 1930) that "such animals usually do not carry on copulation, but their pursuing instincts are still strong."

Display of the normal strength of copulation by the rat 4 months, 6 months, and 1 year after castration (Steinach, 1894) has not since been reported. To be sure, copulatory activity as long as 8 months after castration was recorded by Stone (1927), but "copulatory" denoted the overt elements of the copulatory response without indication as to insemination or intromission. In a later report (Stone, 1939a) the last ejaculation was seen 30 days after castration and the mean number of copulations at this time was 21.8 in 5 controls and 3.6 in 10 experimental animals.

The normally developed penis in the male guinea pig which retained its sexual ardor 6 months after castration (Guimarais, 1928) suggests there was androgenic stimulation. In a more recent study no such persistence of mating behavior was evident in any of 60 castrated males (Grunt and Young, 1953). Seward's (1940) statement that a prepuberally castrated guinea pig went through the

entire copulatory pattern approximately a month after castration is not believed to constitute evidence for the postcastrational display of a strong sex drive. It is clear from the scale of sexual agressiveness he used and from what we now know about the sexual behavior of this species that intromission was not always distinguished and that ejaculation was not identified.

To the casual reader there is an ambiguity in the use of the word copulation which may have influenced our concepts of the effects of castration on lower mammals. Intromissions preceding ejaculation, and intromissions accompanied by ejaculation are a part of the complete masculine response, but in much of the work on the effects of castration, ejaculation was not the end point. In the articles on the rat before 1934, copulation was used without implication as to insemination (Stone, 1927) or even intromission in the case of castrated males. "Complete copulation" in the contemporary literature on the mating behavior of the rat does not include ejaculation. Mounting was an end point in a study of castration and replacement therapy in which the guinea pig was used (Sollenberger and Hamilton, 1939), but reference was made to copulatory behavior. For the careful reader, this use of copulation is not confusing, but for the hasty reader the effects of castration could easily be minimized, because the lower elements of the mating behavior pattern are influenced less by castration than are intromission and ejaculation (Stone, 1923, 1932a; Beach, 1944b; Beach and Pauker, 1949; Grunt and Young, 1953; Riss, Valenstein, Sinks and Young, 1955).

If allowance is made for the considerations discussed above, the investigations reported during the last 30 years are believed to lead to the conclusion that a gradual and conspicuous decrease in mating behavior follows the castration of such laboratory mammals as the rat, guinea pig, rabbit, hamster, and cat (Stone, 1923, 1927, 1932a, 1939a; Nissen, 1929; Beach, 1942d, 1944b; Beach and Holz, 1946; Beach and Pauker, 1949; Grunt and Young, 1952b, 1953; Green, Clemente and de Groot, 1957; Rosenblatt and Aronson, 1958a). The pattern of behavior still contains some of the mating reactions up to and including various degrees of mounting (Stone, 1927, 1932a; Beach, 1944b; Beach and Holz, 1946; Grunt and Young, 1953), but as the decrease in the score in one experiment indicates, the change is great, from an average of 7.8 in 290 tests before castration to an average of 2.0 in the tests of 29 animals 14 weeks after castration (Grunt and Young, 1952b).

Preliminary observations suggested that male dogs exhibit the full capacity for coitus and orgasm several months after castration (Beach, 1947–48). Subsequently (Beach, 1952), this extreme view was modified in a statement that the average sexual performance declines progressively after removal of the testes. Nevertheless, a real difference exists between the reaction of dogs and rodents to castration. Beach writes: " ... nearly all animals retain some ability to penetrate the receptive bitch even two years after the operation. Furthermore, there are at least a few individuals in which there occurs no detectable loss of sexual responsiveness or ability to copulate. In point of fact some dogs are more vigorous and potent two years after castration than they were preoperatively."

The behavior of the boar is said to be "greatly altered" by castration (Wallace, 1949), but the descriptive account elsewhere in the article suggests that many elements of the mating behavior pattern are retained:

"One week after the operation there was a striking change in the animal's behaviour; from being excitable and one of the most ferocious of the boars, he was now sluggish, rather plaintive and exceedingly unwilling even to approach the dummy sow. After several attempts at the first trial he was forcibly driven and held right up to the dummy, when he mounted and mating reactions followed normally. In the next few weeks he fell again into the routine of collections, and though reluctant would always mount."

Parenthetically we would note that the interval necessary to drop the copulatory drive of the rabbit below the effective minimum for copulation varies directly with the strength of drive at the time of castration (Stone, 1932a), and that castration depresses mating tendencies of the rat and hamster least in the most vigorous copulators and most in the less active individuals (Beach, 1948; Beach and Pauker, 1949). Experience with the guinea pig has been different. The capacity for ejaculation is lost earlier by low score males, but when the average precastrational score was taken as 100 per cent and the subsequent change as the percentage of variation from this level, the scores of the high, medium, and low score animals decreased at the same rate and to approximately the same base-line (Grunt and Young, 1953).

While discussing the effect of castration on the behavior of the rat and guinea pig, we would direct attention to data collected by Beach (1942d) and Grunt (1954). Beach described the intense excitement of prepubertally castrated and presumably sexually inexperienced male rats when confronted with a receptive female:

"They dashed wildly about the testing cage, often running in close circles around the female. Vigorous digging in the sawdust covering the cage floor was common. Some males lay on one side and moved all four legs in rapid running movements. Most of the males pursued the female, crowding her roughly against the cage walls, jumping over her and often landing directly upon her back.... The amount, intensity and duration of the sort of behavior described above appeared to be inversely related to the vigor and frequency of masculine copulatory responses."

Grunt has noted what may be a corresponding behavior during tests of castrated, sexually experienced male guinea pigs. The behavior, *nondirected hyperexcitability,*— not to be confused with the "state of agitation" described by Craig (1918) and Dell (1958)—is characterized by a sudden straightening of the limbs, a jumping into the air, and frequently by a turning of the head. These actions occur suddenly and do not fit into any sequence of behavior usually seen. The excited movements seem to occur without reference to the female or to the other behavior exhibited during the test. The amount of the behavior increased as overt sexual behavior decreased. When such castrates were given 25 μg. or more testosterone propionate per 100 gm. body weight daily the behavior decreased, whereas overt sexual behavior increased.

Relatively few castrated infrahuman primates have been studied. Thorek (1924) castrated six male monkeys and reported that impotence set in gradually. About the end of 4 or 5 months all were sexually impotent and unable to react with an erection in the presence of females. A baboon, *Papio hamadryas*, was castrated by Zuckerman and Parkes (1939) in November, 1934. Until the middle of 1935, they wrote, he seemed aggressively masculine in his general and sexual behavior, but thereafter his attitude became more feminine. Beginning in November 1936, testosterone propionate was given weekly. From then on there was a considerable increase in the animal's vitality, aggressiveness, and sexual interest. The conclusion that "the development of sexual behavior in the prepuberally castrated chimpanzee is similar to that in the normal animal" (Clark, 1945) would be more convincing if data from systematic tests of the castrated male and control individuals had been presented. Even though no data are given, Zuckerman's comments in the discussion of a paper by Beach (1952) are relevant:

"I recall some experiments of my own— I am afraid the details escape me now—on a male drill, and on a few male rhesus monkeys, which suggested that after castration sexual activity declined rather considerably. In the case of the drill I certainly remember that its sexuality became intensified after injection of androgen. The other thing I remember is that the intact adult male chimpanzee may occasionally manifest weak sexuality."

A conspicuous feature of many of the studies reviewed above is that the behavioral changes following castration are not as immediate as the changes in the accessories. Hypotheses have been advanced to account for this fact by Steinach (1894), Nissen (1929), and Beach (1942e, 1944a). The essential similarity of those proposed by Steinach and Beach is a reminder that there is probably no other phase of the problem of the hormones and mating behavior in which our progress in that time has been so negligible.

"Dementsprechend würde sich die Thatsache, dass das Begattungsvermögen beim Menschen und, wie wir sahen, auch bei der Ratte monatelang nach der Castration unverändert erhalten bleibt, durch den Umstand erklären, dass die zur Zeit gesteigerte Erregbarkeit der betreffenden Centralorgane den Ausfall der von den Keimdrüsen zufleissenden Impulse überdauert und erst nach längerem Fortbestehen ganz allmählich abklingt" (Steinach, 1894, p. 338).

"Since testicular hormones are probably dissipated within a few days after castration, the more prolonged survival of sexual responsiveness is best explained on the basis of a relatively enduring change in the nervous system. It may be suggested that once the c.e.m. (central excitatory mechanism) has been sensitized by androgen, this neural mechanism remains in an excitable state for some time after the responsible hormones are withdrawn. In the absence of testicular androgens the essential central nervous elements gradually lose their responsiveness" (Beach, 1944a, p. 130).

Nissen's hypothesis contains inconsistencies,[5] but is mentioned here because of the emphasis subsequent workers (Carter, Cohen and Shorr, 1947; Lehrman, 1956;[5] Rosenblatt and Aronson, 1958a) have placed on the possibility that gonadal hormones exert their action through peripheral rather than central nervous structures. The gradual decrease in sexual behavior in the male, he postulates, is associated with the gradual loss in the capacity of the penis for tumescence, and thus in the capacity for initiating the sensory impulses resulting in sexual behavior.

A hypothesis entirely different from those advanced by Steinach, Nissen, and Beach

[5] The postcastrational changes in the uterine or vaginal epithelium which Nissen postulated may mediate sexual behavior in the female, must have been presumed to be rapid because he was aware that the changes in behavior following ovariectomy are immediate. However, he cited no histologic evidence, and the writer knows of no evidence, that what he calls "interpolated structures" atrophy more rapidly in the spayed female than in the castrated male.

Lehrman's view expressed in 1956 has been modified. See his thoughtfully prepared discussion in his chapter in this book.

followed the discovery that the adrenal cortex is a source of androgenic substances. The suggestion was made that such androgen compensates for the loss of testicular androgen following castration (Sollenberger and Hamilton, 1939; Spiegel, 1939; Hamilton, 1943a). Supporting evidence, however, has not been advanced. On the contrary, castrate men are found in which urinary titers are very low (Hamilton, 1943b). The level of sexual activity attained by pre-puberally castrated male hamsters was not lower in animals that were castrated and adrenalectomized (Warren and Aronson, 1957). In two experimental studies the post-castrational sexual behavior of the adult male dog and hamster was not altered further by adrenalectomy (Schwartz and Beach, 1954; Warren and Aronson, 1956). Neither desoxycorticosterone acetate nor cortisone substituted for testosterone in the restoration of mating behavior in the castrated male cat (Green, Clemente and de Groot, 1957). Also in the male cat, the persistence of sexual behavior after castration could not be attributed to any androgens secreted by the adrenal cortex (Cooper and Aronson, 1958).

As in other fields of endocrinologic study, investigators interested in the hormonal control of mating behavior turned from experiments involving ablation of the organs thought to be involved to replacement therapy. Gonad transplantation, the administration of crude extracts, and treatment with chemically purified and synthetic hormones were attempted. The results following gonad transplantation and the use of crude extracts are largely of historical interest and are summarized in the older reviews. The discussion which follows is limited to the results obtained after administration of the synthetic androgens, for the most part, testosterone propionate.

In general, claims of the effectiveness of testosterone propionate have been advanced with fewer reservations than those with respect to the effects of castration. Infrequent injections into male salmon parr were only partly effective in restoring the pattern of behavior in castrates (Jones and King, 1954). On the other hand, the full pattern of behavior was induced in young male guppies by treatment with pregneninolone or testosterone (Eversole, 1941). Daily injections of testosterone propionate or acetate were effective in castrated cockerels (Roussel, 1936; Davis and Domm, 1943), rats (Shapiro, 1937b; Moore and Price, 1938; Stone, 1939a; Beach, 1944b; Beach and Holz-Tucker, 1949), rabbits (De Fremery and Tausk, 1937), and guinea pigs (Moore and Price, 1938; Grunt and Young, 1952b). When castration was performed several weeks or months before the beginning of replacement therapy, 4.5 to 8.9 mg. restored copulatory ability in the rat, and 150 mg. did so in the rabbit. When rats were castrated and injected daily beginning 48 hours later, 50 to 75 μg. of testosterone propionate were sufficient for the maintenance of most of the measures of sexual behavior at the precastrational level. After the attainment of this level by injected, castrated guinea pigs at the end of the 8 weeks, 25 μg. per 100 gm. body weight per day was more than a maintenance dose.

Results obtained by Grunt and Young (1952b, 1953) suggested new concepts of the role of testicular hormone in the maintenance of male sexual behavior. As we have noted (p. 1179), every colony of animals contains males showing different degrees of sexual performance. The point was made the object of an experiment in which males were divided into high, medium, and low score groups on the basis of their performance in 10 preliminary tests. They were then castrated and, after the regressive changes had reached a base-line, injected daily with 25 μg. hormone per 100 gm. body weight. It was found that individuals characteristically high, medium, or low score before gonadectomy returned to the corresponding level during the period of replacement therapy. Hormone injections of 50, 75, and 100 μg. per 100 gm. body weight daily were no more stimulating to sexual behavior than the smaller quantity. Subsequently, 8 low score males were injected daily for 30 days with 500 μg. testosterone propionate per 100 gm. body weight, but not even this large amount raised the level of the animals' performance above that during the pretreatment period (Riss and Young, 1954).[6]

These data from the male guinea pig, especially when they are considered against the background of information collected from the female (p. 1190), from the experiments on the action of heterosexual hormones in other species (p. 1198), and from studies of the effects of certain drugs on behavior patterns of the rat (Soulairac and Coppin-Monthillaud, 1951), support the hypothesis that a somatic or constitutional factor limits the action of the hormone, and accounts for the differences displayed during the precastrational period. As Grunt and Young (1952b) visualized the situation, animals in their reactivity to testosterone propionate could be likened to an exposed but undeveloped photographic film or plate, the hormone to the developer. The pattern of behavior or "picture" that would be brought out by the hormone would depend on what had been taken; with this the character of

the soma was held to be analogous. The amount of hormone or "developer," provided a certain minimum or threshold (defined in this case as the smallest amount of hormone that will restore sexual behavior to the precastrational level) was present, would be of no consequence.

The hypothesis that the action of testosterone propionate on the tissues mediating sexual behavior[7] is limited by the responsiveness of the tissues and that excessive quantities are without effect has implications for the frequently expressed view that a direct relationship exists between the amount of circulating androgen and the strength of sexual behavior. The former hypothesis was suggested by what was seen following the injection of an androgen into the guinea pig. The latter opinion is supported by reports that supplementary androgen administered to intact rats and rabbits tends to increase the amount of sexual behavior (Stone, 1938; Beach, 1940, 1942e, 1942h, 1947; Cheng and Casida, 1949; Cheng, Ulberg, Christian and Casida, 1950; Kagan and Beach, 1953; Craig, Casida and Chapman, 1954), and that a quantity of testosterone propionate greater than that required to restore the normal level of mating activity in castrates increased the strength of behavior beyond this level (Beach and Holz-Tucker, 1949).

Within the last year there has been some modification of this view. The results from an investigation in which there was a comparison of the pre- and postcastrational sexual activity of male rats receiving the same amount of androgen per animal postoperatively were taken to indicate that some of the individual differences shown by castrated males were due in part to differences in the hormone dosages, but that the rela-

---

[6] Elsewhere (Young, 1954), attention is directed to the striking parallel between the reaction of male guinea pigs to testosterone propionate and the recorded reactions of patients receiving corticotrophin or cortisone. The susceptibility of persons to these substances is subject to much variation and does not seem to bear a direct relation to dosage or the length of time during which the drugs are administered, apart from the fact that there seems to be an ill defined threshold which must be exceeded before mental symptoms can be expected (Trethowan and Cobb, 1952). It is emphasized also that the major psychic alterations which develop under the influence of corticotrophin and cortisone represent, in most instances, intensification of pre-existing disorders of personality (Rome and Braceland, 1950, 1951, 1952), or were determined, at least, by previous personality patterns (Fox and Gifford, 1953; Gifford, 1953). Observations by Cleghorn (1952) and by Goolkes and Schein (1953), on the other hand, suggest that the parallel is coincidental. Until the problem has been resolved, the possibility that basically similar relationships exist in the response to gonadal hormones and cortisone should not be overlooked. Of interest in connection with the reaction to adrenal cortical steroids, is the observation (Moog, 1953) that the experimental maximum of alkaline phosphatase in the duodenal wall of the mouse did not rise after an 18-day maximum was reached, even when the dosage of cortisone was increased 3-fold. The fact is taken to indicate that the rate at which the enzyme-synthesizing mechanism operates and the extent to which it proceeds are controlled by the reacting tissue.

[7] Our use of the term "tissues mediating mating behavior" is frankly ambiguous and requires explanation. When the role of the gonadal hormones is "activational" as it is in the adult, we think of them as acting on the nervous tissues and possibly on the muscular tissues participating in the display of mating behavior. If the role is "organizational," as it may be during the embryonic and fetal periods (p. 1222), the action is presumed to be on the neural centers that later become involved in the display of mating behavior.

tively small differences in androgen level did not account for all the variance between castrates (Beach and Fowler, 1959).

To the extent that they exist, the differences between the rat and guinea pig could be one of species. A point is made of this in a recent study in which a long experience with the response of individual muscles and other tissues and organs of male guinea pigs to testosterone propionate is summarized (Kochakian and Cockrell, 1958). The stronger than normal responses displayed by the rat, mouse, and hamster are not encountered in the guinea pig. The latter species apparently possesses some mechanism or mechanisms to protect it from large amounts of androgen. A corresponding difference in the effect of testosterone propionate on the sexual maturation of the two species has also been noted (Gerall, 1958).

The efforts to restore normal running activity in castrated male rats have yielded results unlike those obtained during efforts to restore mating behavior. In 15 experiments with castrated rats and in 3 with senile rats, testis grafts and the injection of macerated testicular tissue did not bring about any significant improvement in activity (Hoskins, 1925b). Bull testis extract given during a 15-day period was without consistent effect in 9 intact and 4 castrated animals (Heller, 1932). Richter and Wislocki (1928), on the other hand, transplanted testes into the recti muscles and wall of the scrotum and found that, when the grafts became vascularized and "took," an increase in activity occurred, but the increase was much less than that seen by Wang, Richter and Guttmacher (1925) following the transplantation of ovaries into castrated males. The latter result appears to be anomalous, but more recently quantities of testosterone propionate up to 25 mg. did not increase the bodily activity of 9 senile males (Hoskins, Levene and Bevin, 1939), whereas estriol glucuronide and two other estrogens fed to senile male rats 3 to 7 times a week for 3 to 5 weeks were generally effective in augmenting activity (Hoskins and Bevin, 1940). The suggestion which comes from these studies is that running activity in the male is induced by estro-

gens as it is in the female (Richter and Hartman, 1934; Young and Fish, 1945).

B. THE FEMALE

As in the male, an understanding of the relationship between the hormones and mating behavior depends on a knowledge of the behavior. In fishes, and apparently in amphibians (Noble and Aronson, 1942), mating behavior in the female is largely in the nature of a passive response. Indicators of receptivity are noted (Schlosberg, Duncan and Daitch, 1949; Clark and Aronson, 1951; Baerends, Brouwer and Waterbolk, 1955; Morris, 1955b), but sharp end points have not been described. Birds and mammals are different. In the latter especially mating or estrous behavior is well defined. It includes some form of presentation or lordosis, frequently a male-like mounting of other animals with or without copulatory thrusts, and, especially in the rat, a great increase in running activity. Although the point has not been checked by comparable observations of the two sexes, records of the display of masculine sexual behavior by female mammals give the impression that it is displayed more commonly than is feminine behavior by males (Beach, 1947). This is certainly true in the guinea pig and a similar difference between the sexes has been noted in fishes (Morris, 1955a).

Not every species displays the three types of estrous behavior. The rat and domestic pig (Altmann, 1941) do so, but cyclic running activity as such has not been identified in the guinea pig. It is probable, if our knowledge of other species were more complete, that an increase in general activity, if not in running activity, would be found to be associated with the mating period. The restless, irritable, and explorative behavior conspicuous in the estrous rhesus monkey (Carpenter, 1942a) is an example.

In studies of the guinea pig and rat quantitative estimates of the duration of heat have been made by recording the length of time lordosis can be elicited in response to fingering (Young, Dempsey, Hagquist and Boling, 1937, 1939; Blandau, Boling and Young, 1941). The average duration of the single lordosis and the interval from the first lordosis to the longest lordosis are recent additions to the information collected at the time of estrus (Goy and Young, 1957b). When the rat has been used there has been a numerical evaluation of the responses such as lordosis, quivering of the ears, darting, and crouching when the female is approached by the male or fingered (Ball, 1937b), or the calculation of a quotient, the *copulatory quotient,* which is the number of lordosis responses divided by the number of times the female was mounted by the male multiplied by 100 (Beach, 1944c). In a study of the female rabbit the number of successful matings was divided by the attempts made by the male. A proportion was obtained which could be plotted for each day (Klein, 1952). Receptivity of the female cat can be assessed by daily 10-minute mating tests with especially trained males. The end point chosen for quantitative assessment of the behavioral change was the first occurrence of full mating accompanied by the presence of sperm in the vaginal smear (Michael and Scott, 1957).

Mounting, or pseudomale behavior, as Morris (1955a) calls it, is measured in the guinea pig by watching animals known to be about to come into heat and counting the number of times individuals mount other animals (Young and Rundlett, 1939; Goy and Young, 1957b), and in the rat by dividing the sum of points obtained in a test by the duration of the test (Koster, 1943).

Running activity, the first of the elements of female sexual behavior to be studied (Slonaker, 1912), has long been measured by means of activity wheels. That developed by Farris (1941) is probably the most elaborate. The number of revolutions of a turntable is registered by a magnetic counter which is photographed at selected intervals by a time-lapse mechanism. Total activity including restlessness is better measured by stabilimeter cages in which any movement of the animal rocks the cage in a motion which is recorded (Richter, 1927; Wilbur, 1936; Hunt and Schlosberg, 1939; Smith, 1940; Bousfield and Mote, 1943; Eayrs, 1954). Eayrs pointed out that, although both types of apparatus are believed to measure the same thing, the two techniques measure components of activity having different motivational significance.

The temporal relationships between lordosis, male-like mounting, and running activity are generally close because in lower mammals all are displayed near the time of ovulation. The quantitative relationships are not close. Some rats are relatively inactive at the time of estrus (Hitchcock, 1925; Stone and Barker, 1934). Male-like mounting in guinea pigs is variable (Avery, 1925), but the amount is not related to the duration of estrus (Young, Dempsey and Myers, 1935; Young, Dempsey, Hagquist and Boling, 1939). The variability within each type of behavior has the effect of creating differences between individual females that are fully as striking as those between males (Hitchcock, 1925, Young and Fish, 1945, for running activity in the female rat; Young, Dempsey and Myers, 1935, Young, Dempsey, Hagquist and Boling, 1939, for the length of heat and the amount of mounting activity in the guinea pig; Blandau, Boling and Young, 1941, for the length of heat in the rat; Young and Orbison, 1944, for the character of sexual responses in the chimpanzee; de Alba and Asdell, 1946, for the strength of heat in the cow; Michael, 1958, for the behavior patterns in the female cat).

The length of heat in the guinea pig is not related to the number of developing follicles (Young, Myers and Dempsey, 1933) or to the ovarian condition, at least, within the limits of the ovarian pathology encountered by Young, Dempsey, Myers and Hagquist (1938). Nor is the estrone content of the follicular fluid necessarily related to the degree of sexual desire in the mare (Andrews and McKenzie, 1941). In what appears to be the single study in which such data were collected, male-like mounting was generally proportional to the number of developing follicles (Young, Dempsey, Myers and Hagquist, 1938), although numerous exceptions were found. Cystic follicles frequently occur in nymphomanic cattle (Pearl and Surface, 1915; Calder, 1927; Hammond, 1927; Fernandez, 1940; Walton, Edwards and Hammond, 1940), although not all cows with cystic ovaries are nymphomanic (Casida, McShan and Meyer, 1944).

The absence of estrous behavior following ovariectomy provides convincing evidence for the importance of this organ in lower mammals and in the infrahuman primates which have been studied (Ball, 1936; Robson, 1938; Young and Orbison, 1944). The experiments of Allen and Doisy (1923) demonstrated that substances within the Graafian follicle are directly responsible, but a more complete understanding of the nature of the relationship was obtained after purified preparations became available. It was then shown that the display of the copulatory response and male-like mounting by ovariectomized guinea pigs depends on the subcutaneous[8] injection of a relatively small quantity of an estrogen followed after an interval by the injection of a small amount of progesterone (Dempsey, Hertz and Young, 1936; Young and Rundlett, 1939). An atypical response sometimes follows injection of the estrogen, but restoration of the behavior characteristic of the individual before ovariectomy depends on supplementary treatment with progesterone (Boling, Young and Dempsey, 1938). Although in different proportions, the same combination of hormones was later found necessary for the stimulation of estrus in the rat (Boling and Blandau, 1939; Beach, 1942a), mouse (Ring, 1944), hamster (Frank and Fraps, 1945; Kent and Liberman, 1947), and cow (Melampy, Emmerson, Rakes, Hanka and Eness, 1957). Even in the rabbit, a species in which the preovulatory swelling and ovulation depend on the stimulation of copulation, there is a brief period when an injection of progesterone will heighten the degree of estrus in an already moderately

[8] For the estrogens, and possibly for progesterone, the manner of injection is important. Intraperitoneal injections of an estrogen into female guinea pigs in amounts that are generally ineffective when given subcutaneously are ineffective. When a divided dose of an estrogen given subcutaneously was followed by an intravenous injection of water-soluble estrone and subcutaneously administered progesterone, the length of heat was 15.7 hours compared with 9.3 hours in the estrogen-conditioned animals injected only with progesterone (Collins, Boling, Dempsey and Young, 1938). Differences in the manner of injection which are not always clear from the published articles make comparison difficult. This circumstance must be kept in mind in the remarks which follow.

estrous animal (Sawyer and Everett, 1959). In the four small mammals the amount of estradiol benzoate necessary to condition the animals for heat varies from 5 to 33 R.U., the amount of progesterone that will bring such animals into heat is from 0.05 to 0.4 mg. (Table 19.1). In contrast to the male which requires numerous daily injections for the restoration of normal mating behavior, the female is brought into heat by single injections of each hormone given 24 to 38 hours apart.

When the response of the female guinea pig to estrogen and progesterone was being studied it was clearly apparent that the amounts of these substances sufficient to induce a vigorous lordosis and mounting behavior were not stimulating normal estrous vaginal changes and that the females would not accept the males. It was later found that stimulation of the vaginal changes characteristic of heat in intact females required treatment with larger quantities of estrogen given over a period of 72 hours followed by progesterone (Ford and Young, 1951). Depending on the animal, some adjustment of the amounts of hormone and intervals may be necessary, but when such a procedure is employed spayed animals will accept the male. Of especial interest for experimental studies, is the demonstration by Larsson (1957) that the sexual activity of the male rat is not influenced by the way estrus is induced in the female, *i.e.*, whether it is by

TABLE 19.1

Amounts of estrogen and progesterone required for the induction of sexual receptivity

Species	Estradiol Benzoate	Progesterone	References
	R.U.	mg	
Guinea pig..	5	0.1	Dempsey, Hertz and Young (1936); Hertz, Meyer and Spielman (1937); Collins, Boling, Dempsey and Young (1938)
Rat.........	10	0.4	Boling and Blandau (1939)
Mouse......	10	0.05	Ring (1944)
Hamster....	33	0.05	Frank and Fraps (1945)

hormones received endogenously or exogenously.

In connection with the above described findings in the guinea pig, *i.e.*, the apparent relatively higher threshold of vaginal epithelium to estrogenic stimulation, and the dependence of cornification on a small amount of progesterone, three observations on other species should be noted here. In the ewe the hormonal requirements for the vaginal changes characteristic of estrus and the behavior changes are about the same (Robinson, Moore and Binet, 1956). In the cat vaginal cornification does not seem to be dependent on progesterone (Ford, 1954). In the cat, in experiments with amounts of two estrogens below 12 μg. per day, at which dosage the latent period to mating exceeded 7 days, the appearance of a fully cornified vaginal smear invariably preceded the mating response (Michael and Scott, 1957; Harris, Michael and Scott, 1958). At high dose levels the occurrence of mating preceded the vaginal smear change by about 24 hours. A comparison of the vaginal and central nervous system thresholds to estrogenic stimulation must await the results from measurements of the mean rate of release at these sites which these investigators appear to have undertaken.

Estrogen and progesterone participate in the induction of heat in the ewe, but the sequence is different from that in rodents. It is clear from studies of ewes at the beginning of the breeding season (Schinckel, 1954a, b), from studies of anestrous ewes given pregnant mare serum (PMS) and progesterone (Dutt, 1953; Robinson, 1954b), and from experiments on spayed ewes given estrogen and progesterone (Robinson, 1954a, 1955; Robinson, Moore and Binet, 1956) that normal heat behavior is not displayed unless treatment with an estrogen of endogenous or exogenous origin is preceded by progesterone. Progesterone, 12.5 mg., twice daily for 3 days followed 2 days later by 1000 I.U. of PMS was an optimal treatment when anestrous ewes were used (Robinson, 1954b). When the effectiveness of progesterone and estradiol was tested on spayed ewes, 75 mg. of progesterone given in 6 injections over 3 days followed 2 days later by 38 μg. of estradiol induced heat in

90% of the injected animals (Robinson, 1955).

Except that estrogen and progesterone act together in the induction of heat in laboratory rodents, the cow, and the ewe, the processes whereby this end is achieved are not known. The subject is discussed in the section on the mechanism of hormone action (p. 1204) where the important studies of Sawyer and Markee (1959), Sawyer and Everett (1959), and Kawakami and Sawyer (1959a, b) are related to the problem. What might be thought of as a complication is that progesterone terminates estrus in the rabbit (Makepeace, Weinstein and Friedman, 1937; Sawyer and Everett, 1959), ferret (Marshall and Hammond Jr., 1945), sheep and goat (Phillips, Fraps and Frank, 1946), reduces the estrogen-induced sexual activity of the rhesus monkey (Ball, 1941a), antagonizes the effect of estradiol on spayed gilts (Day, Anderson, Hazel and Melampy, 1959), and, in large doses, antagonizes the action of estrogen in ovariectomized cows (Melampy, Emmerson, Rakes, Hanka and Eness, 1957). We cannot reconcile such actions with its role as a priming substance in the ewe beginning with the ovulation preceding heat. Sawyer and Everett (1959), citing the study by Dutt (1953), refer to such an estrus as one "that appears on the 'rebound' from progesterone treatment."

The termination of estrus by progesterone is not inconsistent with its action in helping to stimulate heat. In the guinea pig, rat, mouse, hamster, and cow the small amount of progesterone produced in the developing follicle about the beginning of the preovulatory swelling touches off the estrus-mechanism, but the larger amounts produced about the time of ovulation may be inhibitory. Experimental evidence supporting this view has recently been provided by Sawyer and Everett (1959) and by Kawakami and Sawyer (1959a) in their investigations which are reviewed in more detail elsewhere (p. 1206).

A purified estrogen alone or an estrogenic substance is said to be sufficient for the stimulation of mating reactions in ovariecto mized cats (Bard, 1939; Maes, 1939; Michael and Scott, 1957; Harris, Michael and Scott, 1958), dogs (Kunde, D'Amour, Carlson and

Gustavson, 1930; Robson and Henderson, 1936; Robson, 1938; Leathem, 1938), ferrets (Marshall and Hammond, Jr., 1945), goats (Phillips, Fraps and Frank, 1946), and monkeys (Ball, 1936; Hartman, 1938). This could be taken to indicate that progesterone is not involved in the induction of sexual receptivity in these species.

Theoretically, there is no reason why estrogens alone should not be sufficient, but for several of these species an important point has yet to be checked. Until the character of the behavior induced by the estrogen has been shown to be identical or nearly identical with that displayed before ovariectomy, the possibility of action by a small amount of progesterone should not be excluded. Of the investigators mentioned above, Bard appears to be the only one who compared the behavior following treatment with that before ovariectomy. He states that 2000 Allen-Doisy R.U. of estradiol benzoate were sufficient to throw many cats into full heat and that the estrus induced in this way was in every respect the same as that which occurs spontaneously. He never encountered a cat in which full estrus could not be provoked by giving estradiol benzoate or some other form of estrin.

When the hormonal induction of mating behavior in the male was being described, it was pointed out that individuals which were characteristically high, medium, or low score before castration returned to the corresponding level during the period of replacement therapy, whether the amount of injected testosterone propionate was 25 or 500 μg. per 100 gm. body weight per day. During studies in which the hormonal induction of estrous behavior in ovariectomized females was being investigated, some attention was given to the character of the behavior following repeated injections, although the experiments were not as systematic as those on the male. Nevertheless, the tendency for a particular type of response to recur was revealed when the length of estrus and the character of the lordosis were being recorded (Boling, Young and Dempsey, 1938; Goy and Young, 1957b), when mounting behavior was being studied (Young and Rundlett. 1939), and during an investigation of the hormonal control of running activity (Young and Fish, 1945).

Despite an earlier report to the contrary (Collins, Boling, Dempsey and Young, 1938), and the fact that the length of heat in the female guinea pig is not related to the number of developing follicles (Young, Myers and Dempsey, 1933; Young, Dempsey, Myers and Hagquist, 1938), Goy and Young (1957b) found that the length of heat in spayed injected animals is related to the conditioning quantity of estrogen. However, this lengthening was made by the addition of weak responses without any alteration in the intensity curves; consequently, the increase in the duration of estrus may not represent a prolongation of the period of receptivity to the male. Other data obtained during the same experiment are consistent with this suggestion. Tentatively, therefore, the guinea pig seems to be a species in which large quantities of male and female hormones are not more stimulating to sexual behavior than threshold amounts.

The hormonal basis for male-like mounting is in need of clarification. This behavior coincides closely with estrus in many species and is generally thought to be stimulated by the ovarian hormones present at this time (Hamilton, 1914, Carpenter, 1942b, for the rhesus monkey; Corner, 1921, McKenzie, 1926, Altmann, 1941, for the pig; Williams, 1921, Hammond, 1927, for the cow; Long and Evans, 1922, Hemmingsen, 1933, Beach, 1938, 1942f, Ball, 1940, for the rat; Hammond, 1925, for the rabbit; Loeb, 1914, Avery, 1925, Louttit, 1927; Young, Dempsey and Myers, 1935, for the guinea pig; Yerkes, 1939, for the chimpanzee; Markley and Bassett, 1942, for the marten; Pearson, 1944, for the shrew; Shadle, 1946, for the porcupine; Beach, 1947, for the dog and cat. It is exhibited by some apparently normal chickens (Domm, 1947; Guhl, 1949) and turkeys (Hale, 1955).

Uncertainty with respect to the hormonal basis of mounting behavior is introduced by the fact that such behavior is seen under a variety of conditions. In the guinea pig it is easily induced by injections of estrogen and progesterone (Young and Rundlett, 1939) except in a strain in which it is not displayed spontaneously (Goy and Young, 1957b).

Tablets of stilbestrol dipropionate or estradiol were effective incitants in intact cows and heifers unless a functioning corpus luteum was present (Hammond, Jr., and Day, 1944). Male-like behavior is displayed at other times than at estrus by cows with ovaries containing cystic follicles or that are otherwise diseased (Pearl and Surface, 1915; Calder, 1927; Fernandez, 1940; Casida, McShan and Meyer, 1944; Garm, 1949; Wayman and Asdell, 1952), by apparently healthy cows which are not in heat when they are mounted by estrous cows (Weber, 1911; Hammond, 1927; de Alba and Asdell, 1946; Roark and Herman, 1950), and by an anestrous ewe which had not been brought into heat following treatment with pregnant mare serum and testosterone (Cole, Hart and Miller, 1945). On two occasions an anestrous lioness (female B) performed the gross coital movements of the male after an estrous animal (female A) had forced herself under B's body (Cooper, 1942). Gassner (1952), in contrast to Garm (1949), doubts that nymphomania in cows is a consequence of hyperestrogenism; he suggests that it is caused by certain metabolites of an androgenic nature secreted by the ovary or, more likely, by the adrenal cortex.

The problem is further complicated by results which led Beach and Rasquin (1942) to express doubt that mounting behavior by the female rat is stimulated by ovarian hormones. They presented evidence (1) that masculine copulatory reactions are exhibited by intact females with equal frequency at all stages of the estrous cycle, (2) that ovariectomy prepuberally or during adulthood eliminated receptive behavior, but had no obvious effect on the execution of the male pattern, and (3) that injection of estrogen and progesterone into spayed females revived receptivity without altering masculine behavior. In the same year Beach (1942b) reported that testosterone propionate increased the masculine reactions of females 95 per cent; consequently, as far as this hormone is concerned, an influence on the display of masculine behavior by the female is not questioned.

As matters stand, the necessity for androgens need not be invoked to account for the male-like mounting displayed so commonly by the female guinea pig. The rat is responsive to exogenous androgen but does not require hormones of ovarian origin. The cow requires some hormone of ovarian or adrenal origin, but, in the opinion of Gassner, probably a metabolite of androgenic nature having its origin in the adrenal cortex. Hammond, Jr., and Day (1944) found, however, that estrogenic substances were effective stimulants of masculine behavior by cows. Reconciliation of the diverse observations may not be easy, but it should not be impossible.

Investigations of running activity have been limited to the rat; consequently, what is said with respect to its hormonal control applies with certainty only to this species. In contrast to the experience when the hormonal requirements of the mating response were being studied (Boling and Blandau, 1939; Beach, 1942a), single injections of estradiol benzoate with or without progesterone were ineffective (Young and Fish, 1945). On the other hand, the addition of human pregnancy urine to the drinking water, daily injections of estrone, or the implantation of pellets of estrone restored activity to a level only slightly below that displayed before ovariectomy (Richter and Hartman, 1934; Young and Fish, 1945). For some reason, when pellets of estrone were implanted the activity tended to be cyclic, even though the amount absorbed from day to day must have been nearly uniform. In a recent personal communication, Dr. Ernst Bárány of the Department of Pharmacology, Uppsala, has written that running activity was increased in some spayed female rats when 0.5 μg. of estradiol benzoate was given in a single injection; 5 or 10 μg. seem to have been more effective. Latency was always about 48 hours. Estrone was not more active weight for weight than estradiol. Explanation should be sought for what appear to be contradictory results.

A consideration of the data bearing on the hormonal regulation of mating behavior in the female suggests the following generalization. Display of the three types of estrous behavior, the copulatory response, male-like mounting, and running activity, is induced by the gonadal hormones, and possibly, in the case of running activity in the wild Norway rat (Richter and Uhlenhuth, 1954) and mounting behavior in the cow (Gassner, 1952), by substances of adrenal cortical origin. The lack of a direct quantitative relationship between the components of the total pattern is believed to be accounted for by the existence of different mechanisms, each of which has its own threshold or level of responsiveness to the hormone or combination of hormones for which it is a target organ. Often within individuals this reactivity is remarkably constant, for following ovariectomy and replacement therapy with the appropriate hormones, each type of behavior tends to be displayed in the amount shown before the operation.

The relationship between estrus and the time of follicular growth and ovulation is summarized in the writer's earlier review (Young, 1941). It is sufficient to note here that in spontaneously ovulating mammals below the primates mating behavior usually is restricted to the hours or days preceding or immediately after ovulation. The occasional cow may be an exception. Folley (1952) states: "Provided a cow will stand quietly in stocks, the bull will mount at any time during the oestrous cycle and the cow will allow that." According to Burger (1952), sows not in heat will "ride" proestrous penmates. When ovulation is dependent on the stimulus of copulation as in the rabbit, cat, and ferret, indications are that heat does not occur unless large follicles ready for the preovulatory swelling are present (Robinson, 1918; Pincus and Enzmann, 1937; Dawson and Friedgood, 1940). In infrahuman primates which have been studied females become sexually receptive considerably earlier in the follicular phase than do lower mammals and willingness to accept the male is apparent during more of the cycle. Carpenter (1942b) states that free-ranging rhesus monkeys have a period of receptivity occupying about one-third of the reproductive cycle. The chimpanzee is not greatly different; in adult females the first marked willingness to accept the male coincides with the attainment of genital swelling early in the follicular phase (Yerkes and Elder, 1936; Young and Orbison, 1944). Termination of the period of receptivity is within 1 or 2 days after ovulation and detumescence on approxi-

mately day 18 to 20 of the 35- to 37-day cycle (Yerkes and Elder, 1936; Young and Yerkes, 1943). During the luteal phase there is a general absence of sexual interest (Young and Orbison, 1944). A diagrammatic representation of the relationships in lower mammals and primates including man is reproduced in Figure 19.1.

At this point the statement of a concept which has emerged from experimental studies of the guinea pig is appropriate. It applies to the male as well as to the female and is mentioned because it is a part of a thread of thought which has developed from the work as a whole rather than from any single facet. The concept is based on the distinction between "responsiveness" and "vigor." It had its genesis in the observations suggesting that differences in the character of the response to gonadal hormones are related to the character of the soma (Young, Dempsey, Myers and Hagquist, 1938), but clarification was achieved only after the behavior of female guinea pigs from different genetical strains had been studied (Goy and Young, 1957b).

Responsiveness in the female is a measure of the effectiveness of a hormone in inducing the estrus characteristics of the individual, but regardless of the character of the estrus relative to that displayed by other animals. Vigor refers to the character of the estrus, i.e., the length of time strong lordoses can be elicited, the duration of the maximal lordosis, and the amount of male-like mounting. Responsiveness in the male is the effectiveness of a hormone in maintaining or restoring the pattern of behavior characteristic of the individual, but regardless of the pattern relative to that seen in other animals. Vigor refers to the character of the behavior including such measures as length of the interval between the beginning of a test and ejaculation, the number of intromissions preceding ejaculation, and the length of the recovery period following ejaculation.

It is clear from work with the female (1) that responsiveness and vigor are influenced by the genetical background (p. 1215), and (2) that they are separable in the sense that a responsive animal may be high or low in vigor and vice versa. Examination of Table VI in the review by Young (1957) reveals

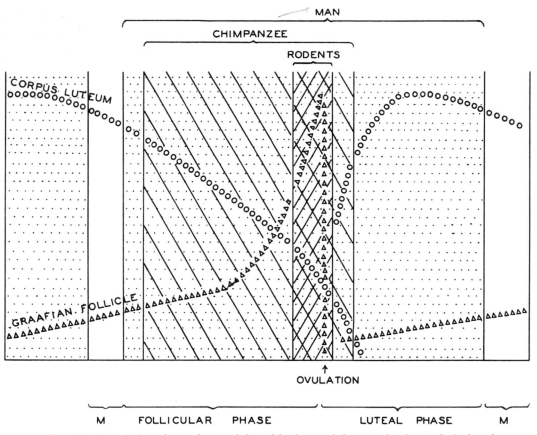

FIG. 19.1. Association of sexual receptivity with phases of the reproductive cycle in female laboratory rodents, the chimpanzee, and man. (From W. C. Young, *Pregnancy Wastage,* Charles C Thomas, 1953. With permission of the publisher.)

that the highly inbred strain 13 females are highest in vigor despite the fact that they are lowest in responsiveness. Strain 2 females are highest in responsiveness but intermediate in vigor. The genetically heterogeneous females are lowest in vigor but intermediate in responsiveness. A comparable analysis of males has not been made.

III. Problems Common to the Male and Female

Thus far in our consideration of the hormones and mating behavior, reference has been made to a number of problems common to both sexes, but for the most part the discussion has dealt with those related rather specifically to one sex or the other. Turning now to problems common to both sexes we find a number that are of importance.

A. SPECIFICITY OF THE RELATIONSHIP BETWEEN THE HORMONES AND RESPONSE

What probably is an oversimplified concept has been presented. It is that androgens stimulate masculine behavior in males and that estrogens, or estrogens and progesterone, stimulate feminine behavior in females. There is evidence, however, for many deviations from this relationship in intact untreated animals, as well as in animals under experimental conditions. The occurrence of these deviations is the basis for much of the doubt that has been expressed with respect to the specificity of sex hormone action.

An early opinion was that ovarian hormones stimulate only female morphologic and behavioral characters and that testicular hormones stimulate only male sex characters (Lipschütz, 1924, 1927; Steinach and Kun, 1928). Moore (1941, 1947) and Beach (1947), calling attention to the many observations and experiments bearing on the subject, were among the first to question this concept. More recently, opinions have been expressed which are even more critical. Eayrs (1952) states " ... there is no truly specific relationship between any one hormone and the pattern of behavior which it facilitates." Kinsey, Pomeroy, Martin and Gebhard (1953, pp. 729, 748) concluded that, even for lower mammals, the designation "sex hormone" is unfortunate; they are simply "among the physiologic agents which step up the general level of metabolic activity in an animal's body, including the level of its nervous function and therefore of its sexual activity."

The approach we have chosen in discussing the problem is through an analysis of the many deviations from the relatively straightforward relationships described thus far. The nature of these deviations is indicated in Table 19.2, which contains a list of 8 possible relationships between behavioral response and gonadal hormone action. Relationships 1, 5, and 7 are commonly encountered and have been discussed; the less common relationships 2, 3, 4, 6, and 8 will now be reviewed.

Relationship 2. A number of instances of the display of masculine behavior by males in response to estrogen action can be cited. Some fishes (Aronson, 1957), castrated male rats (Ball, 1937a, 1939; Beach, 1942d), castrated cats (Green, Clemente and de

TABLE 19.2

Eight possible relationships between behavioral response and gonadal hormone action

Relationship	Sex	Hormonal Stimulus	Induced Behavior
1*	Male	Androgenic	Masculine
2	Male	Estrogenic	Masculine
3	Male	Androgenic	Feminine
4	Male	Estrogenic	Feminine
5*	Female	Estrogenic	Feminine
6	Female	Androgenic	Feminine
7†	Female	Estrogenic	Masculine
8	Female	Androgenic	Masculine

* The typical relationship.
† A common relationship.

Groot, 1957), and capons (Goodale, 1918; Finlay, 1925; Davis and Domm, 1943; Guhl, 1949) receiving implanted ovaries or estrogens displayed varying degrees of masculine behavior. As these reports are read, one generalization seems justified. It is that in several instances the estrogenic substances were not strongly effective in stimulating masculine behavior (Ball, 1937a, 1939; Beach, 1942d). In another study (Mühlbock, 1940), 2 castrated male rats injected daily for a long time with 1 mg. estradiol did not retain the copulatory ability present at the beginning of the injection period. Ball (1937a) stated that estradiol restored the ejaculatory pattern in some castrated male rats, but Beach (1956) in a number of attempts was not able to induce ejaculatory responses in estrogenized, castrated male rats. Because a broad experience with fishes is summarized, Aronson's comment is quoted: "Thus while certain androgens seem to duplicate the endocrine function of the testes the effectiveness of the estrogens is less clear."

Guinea pigs have been used (Antliff and Young, 1956). The reproductive performance of 30 intact male guinea pigs was determined. The animals were then castrated and, beginning either immediately or 10 weeks later, 28 were injected daily with estradiol, estrone, or testosterone propionate. Regardless of when the injections were begun, the results were approximately the same. When they were started immediately after castration and continued for 16 weeks, the average scores in the last five tests were 24.8 per cent below the precastrational level in the males receiving testosterone propionate, 46.1 per cent in the males receiving estrone, and 74.5 per cent in those receiving estradiol. When treatment was started 10 weeks after castration and continued for 16 weeks the average scores based on the last 5 tests were 14.0 per cent below the precastrational level in the males receiving testosterone propionate, 23.9 per cent lower in the males receiving estrone, and 78.1 per cent lower in the males receiving estradiol. The latter level was close to that to which the behavior of the untreated castrates had regressed. No male receiving an estrogen ejaculated and only when estrone was given was intromission achieved by some animals. Clearly estrone was a better substitute for testosterone propionate than estradiol, but not even this substance substituted completely.

Male cats appear to be different. The response to 6000 R.U. of estradiol or to 1 to 5 mg. stilbestrol was normal, provided castration had been performed recently. Otherwise, not even testosterone propionate was effective (Green, Clemente and de Groot, 1957).

Relationship 3. The display of feminine responses by intact untreated male monkeys, rats, lizards, fishes, pigeons, hamsters, and rabbits has been noted (p. 1179). In a rat displaying this behavior spontaneously, histologic examination of the testes and seminal vesicles indicated that spermatogenic and androgenic activity were normal (Beach, 1945a). Castration was followed by an immediate loss of the female response, but after an interval and following the injection of testosterone propionate, the frequency of lordosis and hopping compared favorably with that seen preoperatively. Presumably, therefore, the feminine behavior was shown in response to androgenic stimulation of testicular origin. As Beach stated, cases of this kind are not common. In our opinion they correspond to the much more frequently occurring relationship 7 in which estrogenic substances are responsible for the masculine behavior displayed by females.

Elsewhere it is reported that 7 of 8 intact male rats displayed elements of the female pattern of behavior following injections of 10 to 23 mg. testosterone propionate (Beach, 1941). The responses were observed frequently enough to assure Beach of their presence, but they were described as being difficult to elicit, sluggishly performed, and quickly terminated. Two of 4 male mice showed lordosis during injections of 2 mg. of testosterone proportionate over a 7-day period (Engel, 1942). Male lizards receiving testosterone propionate displayed elements of the female pattern of behavior, provided they were subordinate during fights within the group (Noble and Greenberg, 1941a). In neither of the last two studies were quantitative data given.

Relationship 4. Injections of estrogens into male laughing gulls stimulate them to respond to the sex call of the males and to "food beg" with lowered head, a posture necessary for copulation of the female with the male (Noble and Wurm, 1940b). The male herring gull appears to react less definitely. Injections of stilbestrol into the eggs fairly early in incubation and into the birds for 22 months after hatching had little effect on the behavior of three males. Three weeks after the injections were discontinued their activity approached that of many testosterone-injected male birds (Boss, 1943). Some castrated male rats and guinea pigs receiving implants of ovaries (Steinach, 1912), and some intact and castrated male rats and mice treated with estrogens displayed feminine behavior (Kun, 1934; Ball, 1939; Engel, 1942). In Ball's experiments pellets of estrone were without effect, but 8600 R.U. estradiol benzoate administered within 2 weeks were followed by lordosis in response to vigorous mounting by males. The behavior is described as being "at a very low level" and Dr. Ball pointed out that much more estrogen was required than would have been necessary to produce corresponding reactions in spayed females. An estimation of "how much more" can be made from the work of Boling and Blandau (1939) when they showed that estrous behavior was displayed by 18 of 20 female rats receiving single injections of 100 R.U. estradiol benzoate; 10 R.U. were sufficient when supplementary progesterone was given. The subcutaneous implantation of from 1 to 160 diethylstilbestrol tablets weighing between 50 and 1000 mg. each was without apparent effect on the sexual behavior of the adult boar (Wallace, 1949).

Nothing that is reported by Kawakami and Sawyer (1959a), following the injection of male rabbits with estrogen and progesterone, is inconsistent with what has been found when other male mammals have been given female hormones. The only observable effect on two intact males was an inhibition of sexual aggressiveness. One of the 2 was castrated and 4 months later injected with estrogen and progesterone. At this time he lost interest in mounting females and the electroencephalogram (EEG) arousal threshold had dropped, as it does in females similarly treated, but it is not stated that estrus was induced.

Relationship 6. The display of feminine behavior by females treated with androgens has been reported. The action of small amounts of androgen in the production of breeding behavior in the black-crowned night heron (Noble and Wurm, 1940a) is believed to be normal. Three intact and 3 spayed lizards containing pellets of testosterone propionate displayed estrous behavior and accepted other treated females or males in copulation (Noble and Greenberg, 1941b). In an experiment involving injections of testosterone propionate into a female mammal, 4 of 10 spayed rats exhibited lordosis, 7 showed the hopping response, and 1 displayed quivering of the ears (Beach, 1942b). It was said of the reactions that they did not appear frequently. Treatment with testosterone propionate in various combinations and amounts after PMS was followed by the appearance of estrous responses in anestrous ewes (Cole, Hart and Miller, 1945), but ovulation also occurred in some animals; consequently, the the hormone responsible for estrus cannot be stated with certainty.

Striking effects are described by Klein (1952) in his review of experiments performed by Gaston Mayer and himself. Following the implantation of pellets of testosterone propionate or acetate into the ears of intact female rabbits, estrous behavior was displayed that was comparable with and even stronger than that which followed treatment with estrogens. As in the work on the ewe, identification of the hormonal stimulus is made difficult by the occurrence of ovulation with "generations and generations" of corpora lutea. Intact female cats, on the other hand, were brought into heat with testosterone propionate, and ovulation did not occur. Largely because of the striking display of feminine behavior by rabbits containing pellets of androgen (Klein, 1952), Kawakami and Sawyer (1959a) studied the effects of androgen on the behavior of estrogen-primed ovariectomized female rabbits and on the associated EEG arousal thresholds. With a high dose especially, estrus was maintained, but it

should be noted that in this experiment the testosterone appears to have substituted for progesterone in maintaining estrus rather than to have acted by inducing estrus.

The strongest opinion that androgen stimulates feminine behavior in females is perhaps that held by clinicians. Their many reports that androgens increase sexual desire in the human female (Shorr, Papanicolaou and Stimmel, 1938; Loeser, 1940; Salmon, 1942; Salmon and Geist, 1943; Greenblatt, 1943; Abel, 1945; Carter, Cohen and Shorr, 1947; Foss, 1951; Waxenburg, Drellich and Sutherland, 1959), apparently more effectively than endogenous estrogens, certainly strengthens the likelihood suggested by much of the work with lower mammals that androgen substitutes for estrogen. However, before the possibility of such an action is given complete acceptance, we should be able to exclude the remote possibility that the effective substance is the androgen rather than a metabolite with estrogenic action (Dorfman and Ungar, 1953; Dorfman and Shipley, 1956; West, Damast, Sarro and Pearson, 1956; Davis and Plotz, 1957).

Relationship 8. The frequency with which masculine behavior is displayed by intact females suggests that the neural mechanisms mediating this behavior are well developed. If so, it could follow that the display of masculine behavior by the female in response to androgenic stimulation is more easily achieved than the display of feminine behavior by males in response to estrogenic stimulation (relationship 4). From what follows and from the numerous cases cited by Dorfman and Shipley, (1956, pp. 194–197), this seems to be true, but it will be clear, that even here, there is much evidence for the refractoriness encountered in the other relationships involving the action of heterosexual hormones.

No details are given, but pregneninolone and testosterone induced male mating behavior in immature and mature female guppies after 20 days of treatment (Eversole, 1941), and methyl-dihydrotestosterone injected into intact female mekadas was effective as early as the 3rd day (Okada and Yamashita, 1944). Elements of male sexual behavior appeared in a definite sequence following the implantation of pellets of testosterone propionate into female *Xiphophorus helleri* (Noble and Borne, 1940), a species which has long been known to undergo spontaneous sex reversal from female to male (Essenberg, 1926). The change is less pronounced in adult female platyfish given methyl testosterone; they exhibited the first phase of courtship behavior, but precopulatory and copulatory behavior were not seen (Laskowski, 1953). Female lizards given pellets of testosterone propionate displayed courtship behavior and went through the complete male copulatory pattern (Noble and Greenberg, 1941b). Injections of large amounts of testosterone propionate induced male behavior in adult and immature female black-crowned night herons. Smaller quantities induced female behavior and estrogens appear to have been without effect except on the genital tract (Noble and Wurm, 1940a). Female canaries sang following injections of testosterone propionate (Leonard, 1939) and also exhibited posturing and pairing characteristics of males, but they did not tread receptive females (Shoemaker, 1939). Free-living valley quail containing pellets of testosterone propionate assumed the male role without copulating. Their reactions were described as being slower and weaker than those of males given the hormone (Emlen and Lorenz, 1942). The same hormone did not induce male behavior in female herring gulls (Boss, 1943). The administration of androgen to intact hens (Hamilton and Golden, 1939), ovariectomized poulards (Davis and Domm, 1941), and to ovariectomized pullets (Davis and Domm, 1943) was followed by crowing and some "waltzing," but no copulatory behavior. The latter was observed in 3 of 24 brown leghorn pullets some of which were observed 4 years (Domm and Blivaiss, 1947), and in 1 of 2 white Leghorn hens several months after the implantation of pellets of testosterone propionate (Zitrin, 1942). A regimen of 500 mg. testosterone propionate per day into female chicks stimulated comb and wattle growth, but no crowing, wing-flapping, or other cock-like attitudes occurred during the 55 days they were observed (Hamilton, 1938). In another

expriment crowing, described as a short, feeble, high-pitched squeak which lasted about a second, was observed in 10 of 75 female chicks containing pellets of testosterone or given oil solutions (Hamilton and Golden, 1939). The crowing behavior disappeared frequently after the 1st week and almost completely by the 4th week, although the comb showed a continued response to androgen.

An intersexed mouse whose usual behavior was that of a female displayed the copulatory pattern of the male when injected with large doses of testosterone propionate (Raynaud, 1938). Except for this somewhat ambiguous case, masculinization of a female mammal by the use of purified androgenic substances seems first to have been achieved by Hu and Frazier (1939). Adult female rabbits injected 6 days a week with 1 mg. testosterone propionate for 21 to 32 days displayed vigorous masculine behavior which persisted after the injections until the external genitalia had returned to the female type. The female rabbits into which Klein (1952) implanted pellets of testosterone propionate or acetate displayed "quite a typical" male behavior, provided they were with other females. As we have noted (p. 1196), feminine responses were exhibited when they were in the presence of males. When 100 mg. testosterone propionate were administered to anestrous female sheep 3 days before PMS was given they mounted other females (Cole, Hart and Miller, 1945), but the authors note that such animals were also subject to their own estrogen and progesterone as well as to exogenous androgen. Mounting behavior and aggressiveness were displayed by 3 intact and 3 ovariectomized dairy heifers receiving 25 mg. testosterone propionate daily (Gassner, 1952). In this work the behavior displayed by the ovariectomized animals could not be ascribed to the presence of functioning follicles.

An increase in the amount and strength of masculine behavior followed the injection of testosterone propionate into intact (Ball, 1940) and spayed female rats (Beach, 1942b). Ball injected 2 mg. twice a week following a 3-week period when half this amount had been given. She regarded the reactions as definitive but also as somewhat rudimentary. In Beach's experiments each female received 24 mg. over a period of 2 weeks. This amount of androgen was followed by a shift from a peak at the level of "sexual clasp" (the measure of lowest degree) to a peak at "palpation and thrust," the next higher measure. The complete pattern, *i.e.*, palpation with pelvic thrusts and a backward lunge (copulation), composed 8 per cent of the total responses compared with 1 per cent after ovariectomy, and 60 to 65 per cent in normal males. It is evident from a later publication (Beach and Holz-Tucker, 1949) that 50 to 75 μg. testosterone propionate daily (0.7 to 1.0 mg. over a 2-week period) is sufficient to maintain this level of behavior in the male. We assume that the display of the copulatory response in 8 per cent of the tests when females were injected required about three times the amount of hormone that was necessary for induction of the corresponding response in 60 to 65 per cent of the tests when males were injected.

Some female guinea pigs are responsive to testosterone propionate. Frequent injections or pellet implantation is followed by a random display of mounting. In addition, that displayed by spayed animals containing pellets and injected with estrogen and progesterone exceeds by far that exhibited in response to the same treatment before pellet implantation or after the pellet has been absorbed (Goy and Young, 1958). On the other hand, the androgen given these animals was not effective in strain 2 females which do not show mounting behavior spontaneously.

When explanation is sought for what might seem to be anomalous effects it is clear that more than one problem exists. The estrogenic stimulation of masculine behavior in the male (relationship 2) and the androgenic stimulation of feminine reactions in the female (relationship 6) may well be comparable with the many actions of heterosexual hormones on the genital tracts and accessories described by Burrows (1949) in his review. A mimicking action by heterosexual hormones is common and in studies involving the tissues mediating behavior, as in studies of tissues of the genital tract (Hisaw, 1943), the effective quantity of the heterosexual hormones tends to be large. This fact alone attests to a considerable degree of specificity.

The stimulation of feminine behavior in the male (relationships 3 and 4) and of masculine behavior in the female (relationships 7 and 8) is another problem. It was long ago suggested that each sex contains the mechanism capable of mediating the behavior of the opposite sex (Goodale, 1918; Sand, 1919; Pézard, 1922; Finlay, 1925; Zawadowsky, 1926; Beach, 1938, 1941, 1945a), and that under suitable stimulation the behavior of the opposite sex is displayed. We reaffirm the general truth of this hypothesis, but will point out that often in many lower vertebrates and mammals the hormone of the opposite sex is not a "suitable" stimulus to induce the full behavior of that sex. The point is illustrated by what is seen in the relationships 3, 4, 7, and 8. The tissues mediating masculine behavior in females are very responsive to estrogens (relationship 7). They will respond to androgens (relationship 8), but not infrequently the behavior is obtained only with difficulty and at a low level. Rarely, as in the case described by Beach (1945a), the tissues mediating feminine behavior in males are very responsive to androgens (relationship 3); more often, however, they are refractory. They are also refractory to estrogens (relationship 4) and this fact is reflected by the difficulty in stimulating feminine responses in males when estrogens are administered. We feel that the responses members of the different sexes give to hormonal stimulation are predetermined; in this sense a specific rather than a nonspecific relationship exists. This view was well expressed by Boss (1943) when he wrote: "... genetical factors are strongly involved, not only in determining the specific behavior pattern of the taxonomic unit, but also of the sex. It is a widely if not a generally valid rule that the same amounts of a hormone do not produce identical reactions in the two sexes of a given species." The view is also consistent with the conclusions reached by Burns (1942, 1949) during his studies of the role of fetal gonadal hormones in sexual differentiation.

Before leaving the subject of the specificity of the relationship between hormone and response, we would recall the results from the numerous attempts to substitute adrenal steroids and other compounds for progesterone (Hertz, Meyer and Spielman, 1937; van Heuverswyn, Collins, Williams and Gardner, 1939; Soderwall, 1940; Torstveit and Mellish, 1941; Isaacson, 1949; Melampy, Emmerson, Rakes, Hanka and Eness, 1957). Heat behavior was induced in estrogen-conditioned females by a number of these substances, but their relative effectiveness was much less than that of progesterone. In a study in which the female guinea pig was used the relative effectiveness of a number of adrenal steroids and similar compounds was from ¼ (desoxycorticosterone acetate) to 1/40 (11-ketoprogesterone, 11-hydroxyprogesterone, and corticosterone). Hydrocortisone, cortisone, 17-hydroxy-desoxycorticosterone, 17-hydroxyprogesterone, 21-desoxyhydrocortisone, adrenosterone, 4-androstene-3,17-dione, and the amorphous fraction were ineffective or had only slight activity (Byrnes and Shipley, 1955).

B. THE MANNER OF HORMONE ACTION, *I.E.*, ORGANIZATION OR ACTIVATION

An important problem pertaining to the hormonal regulation of mating behavior has to do with the manner of hormone action. It has long been recognized that these substances might organize patterns of behavior (Steinach, 1912, 1913, 1916; Sand, 1919; Lipschütz, 1924; Nissen, 1929); in the opinion of the writer, this would be in the sense of producing changes in the responses to hormones different from those normally associated with an individual, giving due regard to age, sex, strain, and species. Or, the hormones might simply activate an individual to respond in accordance with the character of a substrate already established (Goodale, 1918; Ball, 1937a, 1939; Young, Dempsey, Myers and Hagquist, 1938; Beach, 1941, 1945a). The possibility that they might do both has received less emphasis; conceivably the action could be organizational before birth or hatching, or before sexual maturation, and activational in the adult.

The behavior of the congenitally anomalous freemartin (Folley and Malpress, 1944; de Alba and Asdell, 1946) and sex-intergrade pigs (Baker, 1925) provides some support for the hypothesis that gonadal hormones organize patterns of behavior. More direct evidence comes from a number of experimental studies.

Dantchakoff (1938a, b, 1947) stated that female guinea pigs born to mothers given intrauterine injections of testosterone propionate contained a normal female genital tract with ovaries and a more or less well developed epididymis, ductuli efferentes, prostate, Cowper's gland, and penis. In their behavior, when they were given male hormone, they performed completely as males. Males receiving testosterone propionate prenatally and after birth possessed only the male genital tract and its accessories, but the development of most parts was precocious as was the display of masculine behavior (Dantchakoff, 1938c). If such transformations can be produced, the fact would suggest strongly that male hormone has an organizing action on the tissues mediating mating behavior, at least when the hormone is present in the early stages of embryonic or fetal development. Unfortunately, many details of Dantchakoff's procedure are not clear from her articles, and no controls were established in the form of animals receiving androgen postnatally only. Partly because of this circumstance, new experiments were undertaken (Phoenix, Goy, Gerall and Young, 1959; Tedford and Young, 1960). From what follows it will be clear that an androgen when given prenatally does have an organizing action on the tissues mediating mating behavior.

Pregnant females were injected intramuscularly with 5 mg. of testosterone propionate on day 10 of the pregnancy and with 1 mg. daily from day 11 to day 68 of the gestation period. At birth the external genitalia of the female offspring were indistinguishable macroscopically from those of the sibling males and examination of the genital tracts by laparotomy was necessary for identification of the sex. Internally there were hypertrophied Wolffian ducts (detectable microscopically), failure of Müllerian duct-urogenital sinus fusion, and, by the time of sexual maturation, abundant evidence of ovarian dysfunction. Tests given after these female hermaphrodites had been gonadectomized and injected with estrogen and progesterone, or with an androgen, revealed that striking modifications of the behavior pattern had been produced.

Much less of the feminine measures of behavior was displayed; there was a decrease in the percentage of tests positive for estrus, in the duration of estrus, and in the duration of maximal lordosis. An effect on the tissues mediating the masculine component of the pattern was revealed by the greater amount of male-like mounting. The hermaphroditic females had become more responsive to the androgen than ovariectomized but otherwise normal females. The effects on the females receiving the androgen prenatally were permanent. During pregnancy there were no detectable effects on the "mothers" into which the hormone was being injected (Diamond, 1960), and there were no lasting effects. Any effects on normal young females treated with testosterone propionate postnatally from day 1 to day 80 were transitory (Phoenix, Goy, Gerall and Young, 1959).

The ovarian dysgenesis, clearly apparent only after sexual maturity, was manifested by disparities in the process of folliculogenesis. They varied from retardation of follicular development, but with eventual ovulation and formation of normal-appearing corpora lutea, to anovulatory follicular development. The dysgenesis is believed to reflect damage, possibly in the nature of a masculinization, to the hypothalamicopituitary gonadal axis and to provide evidence for a central as opposed to an exclusively peripheral action of the androgen (Tedford and Young, 1960).

Some precocity of behavior may have been shown by the male siblings; the possibility is being tested by Dr. A. A. Gerall. However, after sexual maturity the behavior of the male siblings was not significantly different from that of the untreated controls (Phoenix, Goy, Gerall and Young, 1959).

The portion of the embryonic and fetal periods during which the androgen must be administered in order to masculinize the female is being determined. At the time of the present writing it is clear that 40 mg. testosterone propionate given between days 15 and 20 of gestation were without any detectable effect on the behavior displayed after the attainment of adulthood. However, the period 30 to 65 days of gestation is critical in the sense that injections of androgen need not be started before this time in order to suppress lordosis and intensify masculinity (Goy, Bridson and Young, 1961). The results from experiments in progress may reveal that the critical period is even shorter.

The injection of estrogens into most pregnant female mammals that have been studied soon terminates the pregnancy by resorption or abortion, but some work has been done with the chicken. Domm and Davis (1948) observed the behavior of intersexual brown Leghorn fowls resulting from a single injection of each of several estrogens on or before the 4th day of incubation. Some individuals were similar to normal males in their general appearance, but others were nearly indistinguishable from females. The sexual reactions of the intersexual males are described as varying from essentially masculine in the case of those transformed the least to neutral in the case of those whose general appearance was altered the most. Confusion and the ability to perform only certain preliminary phases of masculine behavior are noted, but there was no squatting when they were placed with normal males.

The action of the exogenous hormone in this experiment can be thought of as depending on the interpretation of what happened. If the changes are regarded as having been in the direction of feminization, it could be considered that the estrogen left its imprint on the tissues mediating mating behavior and that a modification of organization occurred. But Domm and Davis seem to have regarded the change as a "displacement reaction," displayed when the normal male pattern was impossible, rather than as feminization. The abnormal behavior was attributed to the low level of hormone concentration.

Use of the Sweltzer technique (Pincus and Hopkins, 1958), which involves dipping the eggs into solutions of steroids (or other substances) before they are incubated, may be advantageous in future studies of the effect of prenatally administered hormones on the behavior displayed as adults. In their frankly preliminary communication Pincus and Hopkins noted that masculinization of the female was not accomplished as easily as feminization of the male. This relationship is the reverse of that encountered in mammals and is not unexpected. If it is seen generally in birds, extensive experiments will be of more than ordinary interest.

Results from a series of experiments on intact albino rats during the prepubertal period are not suggestive of an organizational action; on the contrary, damaging effects are indicated, but in view of what has been found during the work on the guinea pig, the rat should be restudied. Females injected with androgens or estrogens during the first 10 days after birth experienced a permanent impairment of cyclic reproductive function. They are described as displaying no sexual behavior (Wilson, Young and Hamilton, 1940; Wilson, Hamilton and Young, 1941; Wilson, 1943). The effect could not be attributed solely to gonadal failure because in neither group could estrus be induced with estrogen and progesterone, even with 10 or more times the quantity of estrogen required to condition normal animals. Treatment of males with androgen induced serious alterations of structure and function accompanied by impotence, especially when 0.75 to 36.0 mg. of testosterone propionate were given between the day of birth and day 28 (Wilson and Wilson, 1943). Ejaculation was less frequent in the injected animals and the mean number of mountings per test was low.

In other experiments on immature rats no such damaging action followed the administration of testosterone propionate into males or of estradiol benzoate into females; instead, the precocious activation of previously organized neuromuscular mechanisms was reported (Stone, 1940; Beach, 1942c). In comparing these results with those obtained by Wilson, Young and Hamilton (1940), Wilson, Hamilton and Young (1941), Wilson (1943), and Wilson and Wilson (1943) the circumstance should be

considered that administration of the hormones was not begun by Stone and Beach until day 22 to 26 and day 14, respectively. That the age of the animal at the time of treatment could be crucial has been brought out by Barraclough (1955) and by Doeg and Leathem (1958) and traced to an imbalance induced at the hypophyseal level. In mice injected with estradiol or testosterone at 5 days of age there was a premature opening of the vagina followed by conspicuous irregularities in the cycles. Abnormalities of the latter type were much less marked when treatment with the steroids was delayed until the 20th day.

Results different from those reported by Wilson and Wilson (1943) were also obtained when young male guinea pigs, castrated the day of birth, were injected daily with testosterone propionate for 120 days (Riss, Valenstein, Sinks and Young, 1955; Gerall, 1958). The animals appeared normal and the development of behavior was not different from that in intact controls. The difference in this case may be attributable to the greater maturity of the guinea pig at birth.

The suggestion from the work on sexually immature animals that androgens and estrogens do not have an organizing action on patterns of behavior is reinforced by the demonstration that the development of sensitivity to gonadal hormones can occur when the gonads are absent. Female guinea pigs and rats spayed immediately after birth and first injected with estrogen and progesterone 10 months (rat) and 2 years (guinea pig) later were as reactive as animals ovariectomized during adulthood (Wilson and Young, 1941). A female rat in which there was congenital absence of the ovaries, tubes, and uterus displayed typical feminine behavior following injections of estrogen and progesterone (Beach, 1945b). The male is not different, for the capacity to respond to androgen develops in the absence of the testes (Beach and Holz, 1946; Riss, Valenstein, Sinks and Young, 1955).

The problem of the manner of hormone action in adults was brought into sharp focus by Ball (1937a), although Goodale had noted as early as 1918 that the behavior of the capon receiving an implanted ovary was either wholly unmodified or, if modified, it was not in the direction of feminization. Ball demonstrated that female hormones, instead of feminizing the castrated male rat as Kun (1934) had claimed, increased their male activity.

New evidence that hormones activate adults in accordance with previously organized neural mechanisms rather than organizing new patterns has recently been provided (Goy and Young, 1958). Female guinea pigs from a genetically heterogeneous stock (T stock) displaying male-like mounting spontaneously and from a strain (strain 2) in which this behavior is not shown (Goy and Young, 1957b) were spayed and brought into heat with estrogen and progesterone. On completion of the control tests, 15-mg. pellets of testosterone propionate were implanted into each animal. Estrus was again induced 24 days later by repeating the previous treatment, and 4 months later, without additional androgen, a final test was made. The average number of mounts per test in the T stock animals was 2.3, 41.8, and 3.8, respectively. In the strain 2 animals the averages were 0.0, 0.0, and 1.3. Two points are clear: (1) the androgen activated the T stock females to display mounting at the time of the second test, but there was no lasting, organizational effect; (2) the androgen was not effective in stimulating mounting in a strain which does not display this behavior spontaneously, consequently in these animals there was no evidence either for an activating or an organizing action.

C. AGE OF THE ANIMAL AND THE HORMONAL REGULATION OF MATING BEHAVIOR

Most of the attention devoted to the hormonal regulation of mating behavior has been centered on the adult during the period of reproductive activity. No investigator has tested a group of animals from youth to old age in an effort to relate any changes in the strength and pattern of behavior to changes in quantity of hormone or in reactivity of the tissues mediating such behavior. Considerable information exists but it is fragmentary and interpretation is difficult.

Injections of a pituitary gonadotrophic substance (hebin) into 3-day old male chicks were followed 6 days later by crowing and after 10 days by initial treading reactions (Domm and Van Dyke, 1932a). Injections of androgen were followed by crowing on the 4th day of age and by treading on the 15th day (Hamilton, 1938; Breneman, 1939; Noble and Zitrin, 1942). A comparison of the effective quantities in young birds and in somewhat older cockerels (Davis and Domm, 1943) can only be made by inference; 0.5 to 1.0 mg. daily seems to have been sufficient for the younger birds, whereas 2.50 to 3.75 mg. were required for two older birds. Apparently the sensitivity of 30-day chicks was not greater than that of 2-day chicks.

Of the investigations in which mammals were used, that by Steinach and Kun (1928) was one of the first. Control male rats in their colony were not attaining maturity until 60 to 70 days of age, but experimental animals given 9 to 18 injections of a water-soluble extract of anterior pituitary beginning at 4 to 5 weeks of age displayed mature sexual behavior as early as 38 to 45 days of age. More recently, data have been obtained bearing on the response of prepubertal rats and guinea pigs to testosterone propionate. The report by Stone (1940) that the median age of the first copulation (mounting, palpation and pelvic thrusts with intromission) in the intact rat was set ahead about 20 days was confirmed by Beach (1942c). In Stone's experiment 0.62 mg. testosterone propionate was injected daily; in Beach's experiment 1.0 mg. was given. As in the case of the chicken, comparison with the adult is hazardous, but the report (Beach and Holz-Tucker, 1949) that 50 to 75 μg. testosterone daily is necessary for the maintenance of the preoperative level of copulation in adults suggests that the sensitivity of the young rats used by Stone and Beach to testosterone propionate was less than in the adults used by Beach and Holz-Tucker.

Results from two studies of young guinea pigs are presented for comparison with those obtained from the chicken and rat. The development of mating behavior was followed by weekly tests from within a week after birth to 120 days of age (Riss,

Valenstein, Sinks and Young, 1955; Gerall, 1958). Experimental males were castrated within 2 days after birth and injected daily with up to 500 μg. testosterone propionate per 100 gm. body weight. In neither experiment, and contrary to what was found in the rat, was the time of the first ejaculation or the ultimate level of sexual behavior affected; mounting may have been precocious.

Examination of data obtained from young female chickens and prepubertal female rats and guinea pigs injected with gonadotrophic hormone, with estradiol benzoate alone, or with estradiol benzoate in combination with progesterone reveals results that are not clear. Masculine head furnishings and an "astonishing hypertrophy" of the oviducts were seen in brown Leghorn females receiving daily injections of pituitary gonadotrophin for 14 to 36 days beginning at 21 to 47 days of age, but behavior was "apparently unaffected" (Domm and Van Dyke, 1932b). Female white Leghorn chicks injected with 0.17 mg. estradiol benzoate daily beginning the 15th day of age squatted for treading males after 18 to 26 treatments, but chicks in which injections were started the 2nd day and continued for 34 days were never seen to squat for a treading male (Noble and Zitrin, 1942).

Estrous reactions were induced in 4 of 18 spayed female rats given estradiol benzoate and progesterone beginning the 20th day, and in 6 of 20 ovariectomized guinea pigs injected beginning the 15th day. By the 30th day all of 6 injected rats and 14 injected guinea pigs responded, from which it was concluded (1) that mating behavior can be induced precociously, and (2) that the sensitivity to estrogen which is characteristic of the adult does not develop until after the 20th day (Wilson and Young, 1941). The possibility of inducing precocious estrous behavior in the female rat was demonstrated shortly thereafter by Beach (1942c).

The information yielded by these experiments on young male and female animals is not sufficient to justify more than the cautious generalization that early in the prepubertal period the tissues mediating mating behavior acquire the responsiveness to androgenic or estrogenic stimulation which characterizes them as adults. In neither the rat nor the guinea pig does the presence of the gonads seem necessary for the acquisition of this responsiveness.

Scattered data contribute information with respect to changes in sexual behavior associated with advancing adulthood and old age but the lacunae are large. In old rats running activity in the male (Hitchcock, 1925) and female (Slonaker, 1924) is less than in young rats. A number of observations on the male rabbit (Stone, 1932a), rat (Stone, 1939a; Beach and Holz, 1946), and guinea pig (Grunt and Young, 1952a) indicate that copulation frequency is lower in old animals. Some of the most careful observations have been reported by Larsson (1956, 1958a). Ejaculations per hour by male rats increase up to 1 year of age and decrease after 20 months. Intromissions per hour are greatest at puberty and decline slowly but steadily thereafter. The duration of each series of copulations is prolonged as animals age, likewise the length of the refractory periods. Light had a greater inhibitory effect on the number of ejaculations per hour in the older animals than in the younger ones (Larsson, 1958c). The difference was attributed to an enhancement of the inhibitory influence of unconditioned and conditioned stimuli with increasing age.

The relationship between age and the character of copulatory behavior in female laboratory mammals does not seem to have been investigated. The only information we have found was obtained during a relatively short period when the hormonal regulation of estrous behavior in the female guinea pig was first being studied (Young, Dempsey, Hagquist and Boling, 1939). Table 2 in that article contains a record of the length of consecutive heat periods in 30 females during the academic years 1935–36 and 1936–37. The mean length of the first 4 heat periods in 1935–36 was 7.3 hours; the mean length of 4 heat periods 6 to 9 months later was 8.1 hours. It is clear that the detection of any changes as the female guinea pig ages will depend on observations of animals older than 12 to 18 months.

If the figures presented by Hitchcock

(1925), Slonaker (1924), Stone (1932a, 1939a), Grunt and Young (1952a), and Larsson (1956, 1958a) are indicative of changes in the running activity of male and female rats and in the mating behavior of male rats and guinea pigs, these changes could be attributed to a reduction in the quantity of endogenous hormones, or to a decrease in the sensitivity of the tissues to such hormones. Indirect evidence supports the former rather than the latter hypothesis, although until the point has been checked experimentally the possibility that both changes occur may not be excluded.

Hooker (1937) concluded from assays of bull testis extract that after 5 years of age the hormone content gradually decreases. Determination of the male hormone in urine from men of different ages led Kochakian (1937) to conclude that the amount excreted by men 50 to 76 years of age is only about 1/6 that excreted by men 22 to 29 years of age. According to Dingemanse, Borchardt and Laqueur (1937), old men excrete less capon comb-growth-promoting substance than middle-aged men. Schou (1951), after making serial determinations over 10 years, stated that there is a steady decrease in the excretion of androgenic substance between the 39th and 62nd years. With advancing age the production of 11-desoxy-17 ketosteroid precursors is markedly reduced. Some of the decline is attributed to a decrease in androgen precursor from the testes (Pincus, 1956). In women a secretory decline in ovarian estrogen is gradual, with a sharp drop in the 7th to 9th decades.

The results from two experiments involving the injection of gonadal hormones into old rats are consistent with the suggestion that the decrease in the intensity of reproductive behavior in old animals is attributable to a decreased production of hormones, but, unfortunately, they do not eliminate the possibility that the amount of injected hormone simply compensated for a decrease in responsiveness. Hoskins and Bevin (1940) showed that the running activity of old male rats was increased by injections of estriol glucuronide. (It will be recalled that under experimental conditions estrogens seem to be more effective than androgens in the stimulation of running activity in the male rat.) Minnick, Warden and Arieti (1946) injected 8 28-month-old male rats with 1.25 mg. of testosterone propionate for 15 days and 9 with a preparation from pregnant mare serum. In both groups the average copulatory scores increased approximately 10-fold after only 8 days of treatment.

It is obvious from this miscellaneous information that alterations in sexual behavior as animals mature and age may be assumed. How much should be attributed to changes in the quantity of gonadal hormones and how much to changes in the reactivity of the tissues mediating such behavior can only be conjectured.

D. PROBLEM OF THE MECHANISM AND SITE OF ACTION OF GONADAL HORMONES

Little to nothing is known about the mechanism whereby gonadal hormones stimulate mating behavior. At the molecular level the likelihood that such information will be revealed in the near future is not great. Beyond the statement that gonadal hormones bring about their many effects by regulating the activity of tissue enzymes, this basic endocrinologic problem has not been answered (Dempsey, 1948; Pincus, 1952; Zuckerman, 1952; Szego and Roberts, 1953; Kochakian, 1959; chapter by Villee), even by those who have examined the tissues which, by virtue of their accessibility and structure, are best adapted to histochemical and cytochemical procedures. Furthermore, the neural tissues mediating mating behavior have not been identified in the sense that attention can be directed to cells in which change or changes in response to hormonal stimulation could be correlated with the expression of sexual behavior. We suggest, however, that when the mechanism of hormone action has been worked out for the more accessible tissues, such as the uterine epithelium (Rosa and Velardo, 1959) or myometrium (Csapo, 1955, 1959a, b), much of the knowledge will be applicable to the tissues mediating mating behavior. The response is to the same hormones, many of the same problems of reactivity exist, and a number of the same rules apply. With respect to the latter, the synergism between the estrogens and progesterone is encountered in both types of tissue, and there is a consistency of species differences in certain behavioral and tissue responses to androgens (Gerall, 1958). To the writer, one of the most impressive examples of this parallelism is the responses of vaginal epithelium and the neural tissues mediating mating behavior. In the guinea pig, normal-appearing vaginal cornification (Ford and Young, 1951) and normal mating behavior are induced only when the administration of an estrogen is followed by progesterone. In the ewe, on the other hand, there is a reversal of this relationship. Normal vaginal responses are induced only when an estrogen is preceded by progesterone, and normal behavioral responses depend on the same sequence of hormonal action (Robinson, Moore and Binet, 1956; Moore and Robinson, 1957).

At the molar level we may be somewhat better off, because the search for the neural correlates of sexual behavior has been a subject of research in many laboratories (see reviews by Beach, 1942e, j, 1943, 1947, 1948, 1951, 1958; and the recent articles by Harris, Michael and Scott, 1958; Kawakami and Sawyer, 1959a; Sawyer and Kawakami, 1959). In considering what has been accomplished and the problems, it is well to start with the suggestion contained in a number of the articles cited above that in the male and female two different mechanisms are involved. The significance of this fact, if it may be so regarded, is that the emergence of a single explanation, applicable to the two sexes, for the mechanism of action of the gonadal hormones in bringing sexual behavior to expression is unlikely.

The evidence for the suggestion that two mechanisms are involved comes from many sources. It has long been held that the neural mediators of sexual behavior in male mammals are different from those in females (Beach, 1942e, 1943, 1951, 1958). The neocortex is more heavily involved in mating performance in the male than in the female. As we noted earlier, the disappearance or reduction of mating behavior after hormonal withdrawal is gradual rather than abrupt in the male, whereas it is abrupt in the female. When replacement therapy is given, the restoration of mating behavior is slow in the male rather than immediate, as it is in the female. In males a single chemical substance, an androgen, is effective in maintaining sexual behavior, but in females of many species two substances, an estrogen and progesterone are involved. In the female rabbit, EEG arousal thresholds have been correlated with mating behavior, but in males sex drive could not be correlated with arousal thresholds (Kawakami and Sawyer, 1959).

Whether the female or male is being investigated, some knowledge of the time required for the hormones to exert their effects, coupled with information bearing on the temporal and qualitative aspects of gonadal hormone metabolism would be important in any analysis of the mechanisms of hormonal action. When females were being studied it became clear that up to 24 hours elapse after the injection of an estrogen before the animals are conditioned to respond to progesterone. The latter substance, on the other hand, was effective in an average of about 5 hours (Collins, Boling, Dempsey and Young, 1938; Boling and Blandau, 1939; Frank and Fraps, 1945). Inasmuch as both hormones were contained in the same oily vehicle and injection was subcutaneous, more than a matter of transport from the site of injection must be involved. This consideration is emphasized by the results obtained when estrogens were placed directly on the reactive tissue in the case of the vagina, or on what is believed to be the reactive tissue in the case of the brain. After intravaginal administration of estrone, the mitotic activity of the epithelial cells did not begin until after a latent period of 12 hours (Biggers and Claringbold, 1955). Whether the administration of estrogen to female cats was subcutaneous or direct in the posterior hypothalamus, the latent period to mating was at least 3 days (Harris, Michael and Scott, 1958). The slower and more gradual action of androgens might handicap a worker seeking to learn something about the temporal relationships between hormone and response in the male. Nevertheless, in the male as in the female the interval before overt responses can be elicited may well exceed (1) the time required for the transport of effective quantities of the hormones to the tissues on which they act, and (2) the period during which the chemical integrity of the injected hormones is maintained (Fee, Marrian and Parkes, 1929; Kochakian, 1939; Davis and Plotz, 1957). Inquiries into the mechanism of hormonal action should be directed toward the events taking place during this interval.

References to relationships specific for the female have been made by Young (1941) and de Alba and Asdell (1946). The former noted that estrogens stimulate responses approximating those of the true heat, but the responses fall short of those displayed when progesterone is given. At the time, the nature of this "facilitating action" was not known; it was only known that the chain of events initiated by the estrogen requires progesterone for its completion and that the latter hormone acts to terminate heat as well, at least in the rabbit, ferret, sheep, and goat (Makepeace, Weinstein and Friedman, 1937; Marshall and Hammond, Jr., 1945; Phillips, Fraps and Frank, 1946; and more recently, Sawyer and Everett, 1959). De Alba and Asdell postulated the development of a refractory condition and central nervous block after the threshold to estrogen has been reached in the cow, but if such a state develops, the means are not known. Such a block was not observed by Melampy and Rakes (1958).

More precise information with respect to the neural responses of estrogen-primed rabbits to progesterone is contained in the study of Kawakami and Sawyer (1959a). Sawyer and Everett (1959) had previously shown that progesterone at first facilitates and subsequently inhibits the release of pituitary ovulating hormone and that these effects are paralleled by a heightened degree of estrus and later by a depression of heat to the anestrous state. In the investigation by Kawakami and Sawyer, alterations in two types of neural thresholds accompanying these changes were followed: (1) the EEG arousal threshold for direct stimulation of the midbrain reticular formation, and (2) the EEG after-reaction threshold for low frequency stimulation of hypothalamic or rhinencephalic nuclei. Presumptive evidence is presented for believing that the former is more closely linked to sexual behavior and the

latter to pituitary activation. Briefly, a lowering of the arousal threshold soon after the administration of progesterone and its elevation later correlated with the behavioral changes and were taken as evidence for the action of progesterone on central nervous system tissues. Presumably because of the authors' opinion that it was not possible to do so, neither the significance of the lowered threshold for the change in behavior was indicated, nor was any clue given with respect to the nature of the initial preparatory or priming action of the estrogen.

Identification of the neural tissues involved in the display of sexual behavior is a part of the problem of the mechanism of action of the hormones in bringing such behavior to expression. In the case of female lower mammals, this behavior, whether it be appetitive or consummatory, is thought to be associated with subcortical tracts and nuclei rather than with the cortex (Beach, 1958b). This belief is consistent with the opinion that a sexual center or centers might be found and much effort has been directed toward this objective. In their brief review of the early investigations, Harris, Michael and Scott (1958) stated that, largely from negative evidence from ablation experiments the neural area on which the integrity of the mechanism for the full expression of sexual behavior depends lies somewhere in the upper mesencephalon, hypothalamus, or preoptic region. Confirmation of this hypothesis was thought to be given by Kent and Liberman (1949) who placed progesterone directly into the third ventricle of the hamster brain and observed typical mating behavior within an hour. The results obtained following refinements of this procedure on female cats have not only added support to this view, but would seem to have excluded the involvement of the cerebellum, preoptic region, frontal white matter, caudate nucleus, thalamus, and amygdaloid complex, although in 4 of 11 members of the latter group (preoptic region to amygdaloid complex) some components of the sexual response were seen (Harris, Michael and Scott, 1958).

The direction of attention to these effects of steroid hormones when they are placed in contact with the hypothalamus must not divert effort from investigations of other parts of the brain. In this connection, the concluding statements by Kawakami and Sawyer (1959a) are relevant and cautionary. In their words, "the areas in the brain which are affected by steroids are so extensive as to suggest that the whole nervous system is influenced primarily and localized systems of integrated behavior secondarily. Sex steroids affect simultaneously ... the midbrain reticular system, which probably includes a mamillary body mating-behavior 'center' and the rhinencephalic-hypothalamic system, which includes the basal tuberal gonadotropic 'center'."

When the male is considered, very different facets of the problem of the mechanism of hormone action are encountered (Nissen, 1929; Beach, 1942e, 1958; Soulairac, 1952a–e; Soulairac and Coppin-Monthillaud, 1951; Larsson, 1956; Lehrman, 1956; Rosenblatt and Aronson, 1958a, b).

The concept that male sexual behavior has appetitive and consummatory portions has been discussed (p. 1178). Not unrelated in the minds of investigators interested in the mechanism of hormonal action, is the circumstance that these parts of the pattern are thought to be mediated by different parts of the nervous system. Walton (1950) stated, the motor activities in the pattern, associated by the writer with the appetitive portion, are innervated by the voluntary central nervous system and all have a high degree of cortical representation. Erection and ejaculation, regarded as consummatory, are innervated through the sacral autonomic nerves and may be stimulated to function independently of the motor part of the pattern.

Beach who has considered this dichotomy more persistently than any other investigator states in his review published in 1958 that the mechanisms cannot yet be described in precise neurologic terms, but it is possible to indicate something with respect to their composition. According to him, the consummatory mechanism (CM) of male (and female) primates embrances centers and systems extending into the neocortex. The cortex and various subcortical tracts and nuclei are thought to be involved in the CM of male carnivores, but not in female carni-

vores, and not in the male or female rat. In the animals composing these last groups, the highest essential centers of the CM lie in the diencephalon. It is because of this, apparently, that the coital act can be performed without practice. The latter, however, is certainly not true in the guinea pig, another rodent (Valenstein, Riss and Young, 1955; Valenstein and Young, 1955; Goy and Young, 1957a); consequently cortical involvement would be assumed in males and females of this species. The arousal mechanism (AM) is said not to depend on the cortex in female rodents or carnivores. In these groups the AM is diencephalic, but the AM of male rodents and carnivores and of male and female primates includes cortical elements. Influenced by the observation that castrated carnivores and primates can copulate, provided the requisite degree of arousal is attained, Beach concluded that in the males of many species the CM does not depend on androgen. To the reviewer, this conclusion may require modification. For one thing, agreement is not general that castration of carnivores and primates is without effect (p. 1183) and that any apparent effects can be counteracted by a sufficiently high degree of arousal. For another, ejaculation, a consummatory response in the male, is the first element to disappear following castration.

The dependence of the AM on gonadal hormone stimulation is not questioned. A hypothesis that has long had general acceptance was advanced by Beach (1942e, 1944b, and elsewhere). Androgens are assumed to raise the excitability of the central excitatory mechanism (c.e.m.), thus increasing the male's susceptibility to arousal, and to lower the thresholds in the neural circuits mediating the male copulatory pattern. Elevation of the c.e.m. is also related to the excitatory value of the stimulus object; consequently, hormonal and psychologic factors are mutually compensatory in elevating excitability. Like androgen, estrogen when present in the male is said to raise the excitability of the c.e.m. and thus to increase his susceptibility to arousal. In the female it is believed to function by lowering the threshold in the neural circuits mediating the copulatory pattern.

That more is involved may be indicated by scattered observations on the rat and guinea pig. Male rats with inadequate penile development are hyperactive in their display of the lower measures of sexual behavior when they are in the presence of estrous females (Beach and Holz, 1946). Male guinea pigs also display hyperactivity, but in the experiments in which this hyperactivity was recorded the most accurately, it seems to have been an expression of the lack of organization of the motor centers traceable to insufficient contact with other animals (Valenstein, Riss and Young, 1955) rather than to any underdevelopment of genital structures. The writer assumes that hyperactivity of this sort is explained by the inability of the animal to achieve the outlet that is had when ejaculation occurs. A different type of hyperactivity is displayed by castrated male rats and guinea pigs (Beach, 1942d; Grunt, 1954). This nondirected hyperexcitability, as Grunt called it, seems to be a reflection of a frustration and is regarded as an indicator of cortical activity in the absence of androgenic stimulation. While discussing the problem with Dr. John Money, the suggestion was made that the effect of the gonadal hormones on central nervous tissue could be in the nature of a coordinating or integrating action rather than a matter of excitation. Such a hypothesis is consistent with the display of the nondirected hyperexcitability described by Grunt. However, it may not be applicable to the female, the effect of ovarian hormones on the tissues mediating lordosis may be of another order.

Nissen (1929), Lehrman (1956), and Rosenblatt and Aronson (1958a) have contributed to the raw material to be examined in considering the subject. All stress the role of peripheral structures, but see the chapter by Lehrman for a full discussion of the problem. Nissen, in an article containing a point of view which still finds expression, postulated that some organ other than the gonads, but in functional dependence on them, effects a tumescence or tension in itself or in another tissue or organ. This tension initiates afferent impulses which stimulate sex activity. In the male the penis or prostate was thought of as the hormone-dependent organ or "interpolated structure"; in the female, sensory impulses initiating sexual behavior were believed to be initiated in their turn by tension in the uterine or vaginal tissues.

Lehrman in his more recent discussion of the subject emphasizes that any conclusion that behavior patterns are organized and originate in neural centers is based on *a priori* statements and has yet to be demonstrated. Writing out of a background of observations on maternal behavior, he added that patterns of this behavior reflect relationships between the center and the periphery which have not been sufficiently considered. The criticism is directed to the view that hormones act on central nervous mechanisms specific for the behavior pattern concerned (Lashley, 1938; Tinbergen, 1951) to the exclusion of peripheral receptors. Or, it may have been stimulated by the emphasis Beach (1942e) placed on the action of gonadal hormones in increasing the excitability of the c.e.m. and in lowering the threshold of motor circuits without mentioning their possible action on receptors as he has done elsewhere (Beach and Levinson, 1950). As matters stand, judgement with respect to Lehrman's criticism must be withheld. His suggestion is consistent with the clinical opinion that the effect of androgens in increasing libido in women may be ascribed to local changes in the external genitalia (Carter, Cohen and Shorr, 1947). Support would also seem to come from an experimental study containing evidence (1) that there is an increased olfactory sensitivity in women after puberty or following the administration of estrogens, and (2) that in male rats olfactory sensitivity is decreased by castration (Le Magnen, 1952a, b, 1953). Temporarily at least, the case is weakened by the failure of Carr and Pender (personal communication) to find that gonadal secretions have a measurable effect on the absolute olfactory threshold of male rats for urine from estrous females.

Soulairac (1952a–e) has advanced a hypothesis which must also be considered in any discussion of the mechanism of hormonal action. According to him, the number of ejaculations decreased following treatment of the rat with testosterone propionate, thyroxine, or stilbestrol, whereas intromissions and the length of the refractory period were unaffected. Inhibition of the pituitary was assumed to account for this alteration in the pattern and Soulairac concluded that the primary factor for the regulation of ejaculation resides in this gland. The frequency of intromissions and the duration of copulatory activity, on the other hand, were increased by the neuro-excitatory drugs, caffeine and strychnine; these elements therefore were concluded to be dependent on the central nervous system and sensory stimulation. Prostigmine and aneurine prolonged the refractory period without influencing the duration of copulatory activity; the refractory period therefore is concluded to depend on the state of metabolism of the nervous tissue, in particular the enzymatic processes controlling synaptic transmission and other neuronal activity.

The validity of this hypothesis has yet to be established. In a sense it is an extension of the view that patterns of male behavior are composed of appetitive and consummatory portions (Craig, 1918; Nissen, 1929; Beach, 1942e, 1947, 1956, 1958b; Baerends, Brouwer and Waterbolk, 1955). The more recently expressed doubt that the inter-relationship between neural activity and behavior in the male cat is a unitary variable (Rosenblatt and Aronson, 1958a) is a part of the trend. If the different components of sexual behavior are relatively independent, as they have long appeared to be in the female (Young and Rundlett, 1939; Beach, 1943), analysis of the mechanism of hormonal action will be greatly complicated. Miller (1957) stated that help may come from studies involving electrical stimulation of different parts of the brain, and it has (Kawakami and Sawyer, 1959a, b; Sawyer and Kawakami, 1959), but even this optimistic note is tempered by the enumeration of complications in the articles published simultaneously by Green, Clemente and de Groot (1957) and by Herbert and Zuckerman (1957). We have enumerated other considerations which we believe must be taken into account before a synthesis, corresponding to those attempted by Beach (1958) and Dell (1958), of all that is involved in the hormonal stimulation of mating behavior may be claimed. It would be surprising if there are not many additional considerations which are not now apparent.

E. NONGONADAL HORMONES AND MATING BEHAVIOR

Information bearing on the relationship of nongonadal hormones to mating behavior has been obtained from many studies in which attention was directed particularly to the pituitary, adrenal cortex, and thyroid. Because of the chemical similarity between adrenal cortical and gonadal hormones, the likelihood of direct action would seem greatest in the case of the adrenal cortex, but except for one report based on a study of the rat (Richter and Uhlenhuth, 1954), and another based on a clinical study (Waxenberg, Drellich and Sutherland, 1959), little evidence in support of such a possibility can be found.

The results obtained by Soulairac, Teysseyre and Soulairac (1955) following the injection of cortisone into male rats are admittedly difficult to interpret; at the best an indirect rather than a direct action is indicated. Desoxycorticosterone acetate administered to castrated male hamsters did not increase their sexual activity (Warren and Aronson, 1956), nor did adrenalectomy of the mature male appreciably effect reproductive behavior or the ability to impregnate females when the animals were maintained on desoxycorticosterone acetate. As we have noted (p. 1199), desoxycorticosterone acetate (van Heuverswyn, Collins, Williams and Gardner, 1939; Marvin, 1958; Melampy, Emmerson, Rakes, Hanka and Eness, 1957), an aqueous adrenal cortical extract (Torstveit and Mellish, 1941), and a number of other steroids isolated from the adrenal cortex or having adrenal hormone-like activity (Byrnes and Shipley, 1955) substituted for progesterone in the induction of estrus in spayed guinea pigs and ovariectomized cows, but all lacked the potency of progesterone.

Ring (1945) postulated that estrogen injected into the spayed female rat indirectly stimulates the adrenal cortex to release substances having progesterone activity and that estrus might result from the synergistic action of the two hormones. The writer does

not feel that the percentage of spayed adrenalectomized female rats brought into heat
by estradiol benzoate alone was sufficiently
low to give strong support to this hypothesis. Simpson and Williams (1949) also rejected the suggestion as being unlikely.
Noting that the dose of estradiol required
to induce mating in spayed-adrenalectomized and in spayed rats was the same, they
expressed doubt that the adrenal cortex participates in the induction of heat responses
in females. Shortly thereafter a single report
of such activity appeared (Christy, Dickie
and Woolley, 1950) ; spayed female mice
with adrenal cortical hyperplasia or neo-
plasma are said to have exhibited irregular
cycles and to have mated in normal fashion.
However, until cases involving a comparable
action by normal adrenal glands are found,
the weight of the evidence is against the direct participation of cortical hormones in
the stimulation of mating behavior.

A recent suggestion that the adrenal has
the sort of action on behavior generally attributed to the gonadal hormones followed
the observation that gonadectomy does not
greatly reduce the running activity of male
or female wild Norway rats (Richter and
Uhlenhuth, 1954). The authors postulated
that steroids from the adrenals contribute
to the production of running activity. In
support of the hypothesis they pointed out
(1) the adrenals of wild rats are larger than
those of domesticated rats, (2) they contain
more Sudan IV stained lipids, and (3) the
sharp drop in activity after gonadectomy of
domestic rats can be entirely or partially
prevented by therapy with cortisone or
desoxycorticosterone acetate.

Waxenberg, Drellich and Sutherland
(1959) have summarized their clinical notes
on 14 patients with metastatic breast cancer
for whom there was objective evidence of
improvement following adrenalectomy and
who reported sex functioning before the operation. In 12 there was a postoperative decrease in all the variables not previously at
zero levels. After presenting evidence that
oophorectomy has little effect on sexual behavior, it was concluded that any discussion
of the hormonal basis of human sexuality
must concern itself as much with the adrenals as with the ovaries.

The possibility of a direct action by the
pituitary is thought to be excluded by the
numerous reports of mating behavior by hypophysectomized male and female rats (Nelson and Gallagher, 1936; Mühlbock, 1940;
Astwood and Dempsey, 1941; Ball, 1941b),
female rabbits (Robson and Schönberg,
1937), female dogs (Robson and Henderson,
1936), and female cats (Maes, 1940). Indirect effects are of course assumed. The reduction in the running activity of the rat to
a level one-third to one-half that before
hypophysectomy (Levinson, Welsh and
Abramowitz, 1941) may be such an effect.
Dempsey's (1939) failure to induce estrus in
completely hypophysectomized guinea pigs
may also have been a consequence of effects
on metabolism rather than anything more
direct.

The thyroid has received much attention,
but quantitative and well controlled data
are not numerous. Too often it is simply
stated that mating did or did not occur following treatment with thyroid substances,
antithyroid drugs, or after thyroidectomy.
Numerous reports of this type are cited in
some recent reviews (Maqsood, 1952; Young,
Rayner, Peterson and Brown, 1952; Peterson, Webster, Rayner and Young, 1952). In
the same articles efforts are made to account
for the many contradictory statements and
to indicate something of what must be done
if the problem is to be clarified.

Maqsood directs attention to the precocious sexual behavior of young male rabbits
and lambs, to the improved libido of adult
male rabbits and goats (quoted from Turner,
Mixner and Reineke, 1943), and to the prevention of the seasonal decline in libido in
rams resulting from the administration of
thyroxine or other thyroid substances in
"optimal doses." He states that thyroxine
when injected in large doses adversely affected development of the gonads and accessory sex organs in the growing male rabbit,
and emphasizes the importance of considering the normal rate of thyroxine secretion
when thyroid materials are being administered. The inference seems clear that the reduction or loss in sexual interest by guinea
pigs (Döderlein, 1928), white Leghorn hens
(Belawenetz, 1928; Collias, 1946), and cows
(Van Landingham, Hyatt, Weakley, and

Henderson, 1947) should be regarded as an adverse effect of the thyroid substance given these animals. Blaxter's (1952) comment, however, on the claim that cows are more difficult to get to calf following the feeding of iodinated casein should be noted.

"The interpretation of such data is extremely difficult and cannot warrant the conclusion they drew. In other experiments with Jersey cows given iodinated casein throughout the larger part of their lactation the cows reproduced quite normally. Holstein cows, under the same conditions, however, failed or were slow to conceive. Some of these cows were closely related and the small numbers (total 20) again make conclusion difficult. In Crichton's experiments lasting for 4 years, neither the interval between calvings nor the number of services necessary for conception revealed any effect of either iodinated protein or l-thyroxine administration on reproductive performance.

"There is thus no reliable evidence of any gross abnormality in the reproductive performance of the hyperthyroid dairy cow. At the same time there is insufficient evidence available to judge whether a small impairment does not in fact take place."

Numerous reports state that the strength of sexual behavior was reduced if not abolished in hypothyroid males and females (Rickey, 1925, in thyroidectomized male rats; Petersen, Spielman, Pomeroy and Boyd, 1941, in the thyroidectomized bull; Brody and Frankenbach, 1942, Spielman, Petersen, Fitch and Pomeroy, 1945, in thyroidectomized cows; Blivaiss, 1947a, b, in thyroidectomized brown Leghorn hens and roosters; Maqsood, 1952, in thyroidectomized and thiouracil-fed male rabbits; Peterson, Webster, Rayner and Young, 1952, in thyroidectomized, but not in propylthiouracil-fed, female guinea pigs). A restoration of sexual behavior followed the feeding of thyroid substance to the bull and cows. After a rest of 90 days the administration of a single 5-gm. dose of dinitrophenol to the bull restored normal activity and sexual behavior in 12 hours. The elevation in metabolism seems to have been regarded as the common denominator.

Rickey (1925) noted that thyroidectomized female rats mated, and Lee (1925)

reported that thyroidectomized female rats showed the same heat reactions when placed with males that were displayed by normal females. Folley (1938) stated that 3 weeks after weaning no difficulty was encountered in mating 8 of 10 rats thyroidectomized during lactation. Treatment with antithyroid drugs did not prevent female (Krohn and White, 1950; Leathem, 1951) or male (Jones, Delfs and Foote, 1946) rats from mating. Chu (1945) states that 14 thyroidectomized female rabbits became pregnant 17 to 108 days after the operation and Krohn (1951) writes that, although thyroidectomized rabbits were occasionally reluctant to mate, in general they did so and brought their litters to term. There was said to be no evidence of infertility when thyroidectomized hens and roosters were mated (Greenwood and Blyth, 1929). As we have noted, thyroidectomy of the female guinea pig was followed by a reduction in the percentage found in heat, but it did not prevent all from coming into heat and mating (Petersen, Webster, Rayner and Young, 1952). Daily injections of thyroxine for several weeks increased general excitability as reflected in heightened startle reflexes, but did not raise sexual excitability in the male rat (cited as unpublished, Beach, 1942e).

From these results it is apparent that reproductive processes, including the display of mating behavior in the male and female, often require a functioning thyroid gland, that a level of thyroid activity exists which is optimal for reproduction, and that deviations in either direction may be followed by changes in if not the elimination of mating behavior. But a considerable deviation can occur without preventing reproduction and therefore mating. Something of the range within which mating can occur is indicated by data presented in three studies. Following thyroidectomy of 32 female rabbits the basal metabolic rate fell 25 to 30 per cent below normal, but in tests of their reproductive performance the animals were mated 63 times (Sax and Leibson, 1937). In a later experiment involving thyroidectomy and treatment with a thyroid preparation the range of basal metabolic rate within which mating occurred was 1.56 to 3.32 cal. per kg. per hour (Sachs, 1939). Not all the female rabbits thyroidectomized by Krichesky (1939) mated, but the oxygen consumption of those that did varied from 14 to 38 per cent below average.

Results from the only experiments in which the measurement of sexual behavior was attempted are consistent with the hypothesis that marked deviations from the normal level of thyroid activity are not incompatible with the capacity for mating. In a study in which the male guinea pig was used (Young, Rayner, Peterson and Brown, 1952; Young and Peterson, 1952) it was found that, within the limits of an extreme hyperthyroidism and an extreme hypothyroidism, as estimated from measurements of oxygen consumption, heart rate, and the concentration of serum protein-bound iodine, the change in sexual behavior was not greater than in the controls. It was also shown that thyroid activity in groups of untreated high score and low score males was not different, thus eliminating the possibility that a deficiency of thyroid function could have accounted for the differences. In thyroid-parathyroidectomized male rats mating performance within 30 days after the operation was not significantly different from that in the preoperative tests (Heidenreich, Alexander and Beach, 1953). Transitory decreases in sexual behavior followed the administration of thyroxine and benzylthiouracil to male rats (Soulairac, Desclaux and Coppin, 1950), but by the 6th day the activity of the animals receiving thyroxine was again normal and by the 14th day normal or nearly normal activity was being displayed by those receiving the goitrogen. The circumstance that the changes following the establishment of opposite states were so nearly parallel made interpretation difficult.

A study of the female guinea pig in which measurements of sexual behavior were made revealed that the percentage of surgically thyroidectomized animals showing heat responses was 57.8 compared with 84.6 in the controls, 89.7 in females fed propylthiouracil in the drinking water, and 94.7 in animals injected with thyroxine (Peterson, Webster, Rayner and Young, 1952). The sensitivity of propylthiouracil-fed ovariectomized individuals to estrogen and progesterone was not different from that of the controls, but later tests of females thyroid-ectomized and given I^{131}, ovariectomized, and injected with estradiol and progesterone revealed that fewer animals came into heat and that heat was shorter than in the controls (Hoar, Goy and Young, 1957). The reduced number of corpora lutea was suggestive of a hypo-ovarian condition; probably therefore the effect was general rather than confined to the neural tissues mediating mating behavior, but a lowered responsiveness of the experimental females to estradiol was also shown.

These data from the male and female guinea pig and from the male rat do not necessarily contradict the claims based on studies of other species such as the bull (Peterson, Spielman, Pomeroy and Boyd, 1941) that sexual behavior is inhibited in hypothyroid individuals. It is thought rather that the relationship between the thyroid and reproduction varies from species to species and from individual to individual (Young and Peterson, 1952):

"There may be species or individuals in which the range of thyroid activity compatible with reproduction extends from a relatively high degree of hyperthyroidism to a relatively low degree of hypothyroidism. The male guinea pig would seem to fall in this category. There may be other species in which the limits compatible with reproduction are narrower and they may lie in the middle of what we refer to as the spectrum of the thyroid activity, or they may lie toward either end. Reproduction in a species or individual dependent on a high level of thyroid activity might be adversely affected by a change toward hypothyroidism, whereas the converse might be true for a species or individual normally functioning at a relatively low level."

The nature of any stimulating or supporting action of the thyroid on mating behavior is unknown. When the male guinea pig was being studied the rate of oxygen consumption was increased from 52.4 to 80.1 cc. per 100 gm. body weight per hour by the injection of thyroxine without increasing the average strength of sexual behavior (Young, Rayner, Peterson and Brown, 1952), and depressed to 37.3 cc. by thyroidectomy and injections of I^{131} without decreasing the average score significantly (Young and Peterson, 1952). In another experiment

(Peterson and Young, 1955) the mean rate of oxygen consumption of male guinea pigs exposed to cold was 77.3 cc. per 100 gm. body weight per hour whereas that of males kept at room temperature was 52.0, but the difference in mating behavior scores was not significant. Clearly in these experiments a considerable change in oxygen consumption was not accompanied by changes in sexual behavior.

Under other conditions, a relationship was found between the rate of oxygen consumption and the amount of sexual behavior. When males were given daily tests of sexual vigor the oxygen consumption of animals in 3 of 4 strains correlated significantly with sexual behavior (Riss, 1955). On the other hand, when the oxygen consumption of the fourth strain was elevated to a point approximating that of the strain having the highest rate, sexual behavior did not increase proportionately. In a subsequent experiment the rate of energy output was elevated by a change from isolation to unisexual group-living and the intensity of the sexual response increased correspondingly (Riss and Goy, 1957). As before, the extent of the effect was limited by the nature of the animal. No assumptions were made concerning the physiologic meaning of the relationship between the rate of oxygen consumption and the strength of sexual behavior. The increased energy output may have permitted the change in activity, but there is no evidence that it was primary to the change.

F. THE SOMATIC FACTOR AND MATING BEHAVIOR

When the data bearing on the hormonal regulation of mating behavior in the male and female were being reviewed attention was directed to evidence for the conclusion that the character of the behavior induced by gonadal hormones is determined in a large part by the nature of the soma or substrate[9] on which the hormones act. Ad-

[9] In this review and in other discussions of the subject by the author and his associates soma or substrate is used in the sense of all the tissues mediating sexual behavior. The capacity for response to hormonal stimulation is assumed to be a function of the character of those tissues, however it is determined.

ditional evidence is provided by the many studies revealing the difficulty of inducing the behavior of the opposite sex by the administration of heterosexual hormones (p. 1198).

The principle seems first to have been stated by Goodale (1918), who was impressed by the failure of ovaries implanted into capons to feminize their behavior and he wrote, "the character of the sexual reactions seems to depend upon the substratum, while the gonad merely determines that it shall be given expression." Statement of the principle was also made or at least implied following the discovery that there is no constant relationship between the concentration of gonadal hormone and the amount of running activity in male rats (Heller, 1932), after investigations of the effects of heterosexual hormones on behavior (Ball, 1937a; Beach, 1941, 1942d), following efforts to correlate the ovarian condition and follicular development with mating behavior (Young, Dempsey, Myers and Hagquist, 1938), following the demonstration that individual differences in behavior before gonadectomy persisted throughout an experimental period when all the animals received the same hormonal treatment (Boling, Young and Dempsey, 1938; Boling, Blandau, Rundlett and Young, 1941; Young and Fish, 1945; Beach and Holz-Tucker, 1949; Grunt and Young, 1952b), and after observations that varied behavioral patterns were displayed by male rats in which there was no evidence of differences in the secretion of testicular androgens (Soulairac, 1950). Extension of the principle to tissues other than those mediating behavior is indicated by the substance of many articles reviewed by Hamilton (1948).

We dwell on the relationship between the character of the substrate and the pattern of behavior because the former as a determinant of the latter has much to do with the consistency with which the differences between individuals are displayed and with the circumstance that the same hormone given to different animals in the same amounts brings out such different patterns of behavior. It follows that identification of factors modifying the substrate or soma would help us in our analysis of the basis for the differences between individuals.

The possibility that differences in re-activity of the soma are associated with age, inherent rhythms in the tissues, seasonal changes, and the nutritional level is dis-cussed by Young (1941). More recently, new information bearing on the influence of age (Hooker, 1942; Price and Ortiz, 1944; Price, 1947; Thung, Boot and Mühlbock, 1956), season (Bates and Riddle, 1941; Quin and Van Der Wath, 1943; Bradbury, 1944; Mc-Cormack and Elden, 1945; Phillips, Fraps and Frank, 1946; Lyman and Dempsey, 1951; Denniston, 1957; Michael and Scott, 1957; Harris, Michael and Scott, 1958; Kaw-akami and Sawyer, 1959a), and inherent rhythms (Emmens, 1939; del Castillo and di Paola, 1942; Jones and Astwood, 1942; Clark, 1947; Gillman and Gilbert, 1948) has been presented, but as we noted in 1941, when animals are homogeneous with respect to these factors, all can be eliminated.

An effect of abnormal thyroid activity in the male guinea pig can be discounted by the demonstration that the strength of sexual behavior can be so different in in-dividuals in which the level of thyroid ac-tivity is so nearly the same. Some limiting action was demonstrated by Riss (1955) and by Riss and Goy (1957), but not even in the rigorous tests they gave was evidence found that oxygen consumption fixes the strength of sexual behavior. In the female, on the other hand, the level of thyroid ac-tivity seems to be important for the main-tenance of normal responsiveness (Innes, Young and Webster, 1947; Peterson, Web-ster, Rayner and Young, 1947; Peterson and Young, 1955; Hoar, Goy and Young, 1957), but as with age, seasonal changes, and the nutritional level, deviations from the mean can easily be detected and controlled. This leaves us with little to fall back on except the genetical factor and experience, possi-bilities that must be considered separately.

The assumption that genetical factors are influential in determining the character of the soma is based on many observations. An impaired sexual behavior was encoun-tered in inbred rats in which demonstrable defects in folliculogenesis and germ cells did not exist (Evans, 1928; Craig, Casida

and Chapman, 1954). Evidence that differ-ences in the running activity of rats are in-herited is presented by Rundquist (1933) and Brody (1942). Rasmussen (1952) esti-mated the strength of sex drive of male and female rats tested in a modified Columbia obstruction apparatus and conducted se-lective breeding for five generations. In the first generation of selection the differences in the number of crossings were not great, but in the F_5 generation male and female offspring of parents with high sex drive crossed about six times as frequently as the offspring of parents with low sex drive. Symptoms of heat vary in breeds of cattle (Lagerlöf, 1951). The Simmenthaler cows in Switzerland, the Telemark cows in Nor-way, and the Swedish Highland breed have as a rule intense and pronounced heat symp-toms. In the Swedish red cattle the heat is often so weak that in winter it is detected with difficulty. Three triplet Shorthorn bulls raised in the same environment were alike in their lack of interest in serving (Olson and Petersen, 1951). The mating behavior of six pairs of twin bulls was followed from 1½ to 7 years. During this time the indi-vidual pairs were extraordinarily alike, but the differences between the pairs were very great (Bane, 1954). Differences in libido in the brown Leghorn cock are under genetical control (Wood-Gush and Osborne, 1956). In a breeding experiment it was revealed that the females had made a significant con-tribution to the genetical variance (Wood-Gush, 1958a).

The highly inbred guinea pigs (strains 2 and 13) in the colony at Kansas exhibit significant differences in their patterns of behavior. Males in strain 2 nibble and nuz-zle more actively, whereas the frequency of mounting, intromission, and ejaculation is greater in strain 13 (Valenstein, Riss and Young, 1954). Their rates of sexual matura-tion are slower than that of males from the genetically heterogeneous stock. The differ-ences were not overcome by injecting ani-mals castrated soon after birth with large amounts of androgen (Riss, Valenstein, Sinks and Young, 1955). The possibility that quantitative or qualitative nutritional factors in the mother's milk or some feature of the care might account for the differences was excluded in an experiment in which in-bred and genetically heterogeneous young were interchanged the day of birth. As before, the sexual behavior of the inbreds was significantly lower than that of the heterogeneous males (Valenstein and Young, 1953).

Genetical factors are important deter-minants of the character of the soma in the female. Ovariectomized guinea pigs from the inbred strains and genetically hetero-geneous stock at Kansas have been studied following their injection with controlled quantities of estradiol benzoate and proges-terone (Goy and Young, 1957b). As in the male, differences were seen in every measure of behavior studied: responsiveness to treat-ment as determined by the percentage of females brought into heat, duration of the induced heat, length of the interval between injection of progesterone and the beginning of heat, duration of maximal lordosis, in-terval between the beginning of heat and maximal lordosis, and amount of male-like mounting. The rank order of these measures varies greatly and, with respect to the be-havior of males from the same strains, unpredictably (Young, 1957).

Attempts have been made to study the mode of inheritance of the elements com-posing the patterns of behavior in males and females. The display of courtship and copulatory behavior in crosses of the two fishes, *Xiphophorus* (*Platypoecilus*) *macu-latus* and *X. helleri*, was recorded in an in-herently difficult study (Clark, Aronson and Gordon, 1954). Some influence of heredity was revealed, but the genetical data were not such that a precise analysis in Men-delian terms could be made. No special cor-relations were possible between known genes and behavioral elements of the parental species, between diagnostic morphologic features and behavior, or between court-ship and copulatory behavior. Intraspecies crosses have been studied in the guinea pig and their behavior reported briefly (Jak-way, 1959; Goy and Jackway, 1959). This species, and doubtless other mammals, pre-sents some advantages not possessed by fishes, notably the numerous well defined measures displayed by the female. On the other hand, as in the work on fishes, analysis

has been of average rather than of indi-vidual performance. In their inheritance, elements of the patterns behave independ-ently. Within the male, dominance of the lathargic strain 13 type of behavior is limited to the lower measures (circling, nuzzling, mounting). A dominance of the strain 2 type of behavior is suggested for the higher measures (rate of intromission and number of ejaculations). Within the female three independent genetical factors appear to determine the character of estrus. Latency and duration of heat, and percent-age of response show phenotypic dominance of the strain 2 type. Duration of the maxi-mal lordosis is determined by a single ge-netical factor without dominance. Inherit-ance of male-like mounting is also of an intermediate type, but more than one ge-netical factor is indicated and the possi-bility of modifiers exists. Beyond observa-tions of this type, little progress has been made, but the possibility of further analy-sis is clearly evident.

The suggestion that the character of the soma is influenced by experience or perhaps better, until the type of experience can be defined, by contact with other animals, is based on studies of cattle, chickens, ring-doves, turkeys, cats, rats, dogs, guinea pigs, and chimpanzees. The problem is dis-cussed by Beach (1942e, 1942i, 1947, 1947–48, 1958a), Ford and Beach (1951), Kagan and Beach (1953), Valenstein, Riss and Young (1955), Valenstein and Young (1955), Valenstein and Goy (1957), Goy and Young (1957a), Young (1957), Rosen-blatt and Aronson (1958a, b), Zimbardo (1958), Wortis and Rosenblatt (1959), Wood-Gush (1958b), Schein and Hale (1959). What seems to be the first demon-stration of the importance of contact with other animals for the organization of the mature pattern of behavior was given by Craig (1914) following his study of ring-doves reared in isolation. For many years little was done with the factors to which he directed attention, but since 1940 the im-portance of psychologic factors for the or-ganization and modification of patterns of mating behavior has been the subject of many articles and discussions.

Conditioned reflexes leading to copulation

and ejaculation in bulls are inhibited by strange surroundings, by delays in admitting the bull to the cow in estrus, by pain at the time of service, and by too frequent services under the same conditions (Milovanov and Smirnov-Ugrjumov, 1944). White Leghorn cocks tend to be consistent in the frequency of matings when they are not inhibited by the presence of other males. When, however, 4 cocks raised together without contact with hens for about 3 months were placed in a pen containing 7 hens, a suppression developed which tended to persist after the dominant cock was removed (Guhl, Collias and Allee, 1945). No clearcut difference was found between brown Leghorn males reared in isolation until the age of 6½ months and males which had been reared with other birds (Wood-Gush, 1958b). In an experiment with turkeys, birds raised in groups displayed less apparent sexual behavior than the isolated birds (Schein and Hale, 1959). This result will be recalled when that obtained by Beach (1942i) on rats is described (second paragraph below).

From what was observed during a study of the male dog (Beach, 1947–48), satisfactory sexual relations were placed high on the list of experiences augmenting sexual interest in later tests. Attack or aggression by a female, however, is an experience which can have a depressing effect. Rosenblatt and Aronson (1958a) reported that castration of the male cat was followed by the eventual loss of sexual behavior with copulatory responses dropping out first, followed some time later by the loss of mounting behavior. On the other hand, sexual experience before castration retarded the loss of sexual behavior for periods up to 2½ years.

Following a study of the rat, Beach (1942i) reported (1) that the proportion of copulators was highest among males raised in isolation, and (2) that during tests in which no copulation occurred, males raised in isolation tended to be more responsive to the female than males raised with females. The high incidence of copulations among the isolated animals was attributed to two factors: greater excitability resulting from the novelty of contact with a second animal, and greater weight. The relative sexual inactivity of males raised in segrega-tion was attributed partially to an increase in homosexual tendencies.

In a later study (Kagan and Beach, 1953) male rats were placed in individual cages from the 36th day of age until the end of the experiment. From day 37 to day 100 the animals were given different kinds of experience. Males in group A were exposed once a week to a receptive female, group B males were exposed at weekly intervals to a male, group C males were placed once a week in an empty cage, and group D males received no conditioning. Beginning day 99 the rats were tested with a receptive female. No group differed significantly with respect to the number of males displaying some copulatory behavior, but the complete pattern including ejaculation was displayed more than twice as frequently by the males lacking previous contact with other rats than it was by the animals which had been exposed to either males or females. The data are taken to indicate that patterns of social behavior formed before complete mating is physically possible tend to persist and partially to inhibit the normal sexual responses.

The results from a recent study of rats reared in isolation (Zimbardo, 1958) are at variance with those reported by Beach and Kagan. Except for the frequency of mounts, according to Zimbardo, the differences in sexual performance between males reared in isolation and those reared in part-time cohabitation are large and, in general, statistically reliable. The latter mounted faster than those reared in isolation, copulated sooner and with greater frequency, and had a larger percentage of the total group ejaculating. Zimbardo concluded that the sexual performance of male rats reared in isolation is inferior to that of rats reared in cohabitation and that in this respect the rat is similar to, rather than different from, the guinea pig.

The development of sexual behavior in chimpanzees was studied by Nissen (1954). Males and females, after having been raised in a nursery for 2 to 3 years, were transferred to large cages where they lived in sex-mixed groups. Before puberty the sexes were separated and placed in adjacent cages so that they could still have visual and auditory contact with each other. Starting well after puberty the animals were paired under observation in male-female combinations, and in such a way that the younger inexperienced animal was with an older experienced animal of the opposite sex. In many hundreds of sessions the complete pattern did not occur, although almost all the component or unit acts composing the pattern did appear. In Nissen's words, except for minor modifications, the component acts are either innate or learned in early life without the act of learning being observed. The complete sequential pattern of mating behavior, on the other hand, is not innately determined, or at best, the innate factor is only a readiness or predisposition to learn.

The establishment of the biologically effective pattern of mating behavior, in which there is a precise temporal organization of the components and in which the response of each animal is adjusted to that of the other, seems to be a matter of trial-and-error learning, which can be viewed in terms of the statistical probability that certain concatenations of behavior on the part of the two animals will occur. Several factors can be identified as increasing or decreasing such a probability. First and foremost is the activity level, the more and the more varied the activity, the more likely is the occurrence of the critical pattern. Closely related with this first factor is that of age. As the chimpanzee matures, he slows up in the amount of activity in which he engages. As he slows up, the probabilities of there being the concatenation mentioned above are reduced.

The guinea pig probably has been studied more completely than any other species. Preliminary experiments yielded data bearing on the performance of segregated *versus* isolated males, the influence of frequent copulatory experience, the strength of sexual behavior of dominant and submissive males, and the effect of confinement of adult males with females.

When relatively young and sexually inexperienced males were tested (Young, Grunt and Valenstein, 1951), experience gained during 10 tests did not reveal any difference between the performance of 37 males raised with other males and that of 32 isolated males which could not be accounted for by adaptation to the presence of another animal at the time of the tests.

In an experiment in which frequent sexual experience was given (Riss, unpublished data), 4 males having average scores of 11.2, 8.4, 6.6, and 5.5 in 10 perliminary tests were tested daily for 51 days. Improvement was shown by the male whose score was 6.6. He became the most active copulator in the group with an average score of 9.2 for the last 20 of the 51 daily tests, but he was the only male whose behavior changed.

A comparison of these results obtained on the guinea pig with those obtained by Larsson (1959) on the rat would be of interest, but different data were recorded so a comparison cannot be made. Larsson found, however, that learning intervened only in determining the lengths of the postejaculatory latencies; the other changes appearing in the pattern of behavior with increasing age were consequences of maturing processes.

In a study of dominance and submissiveness (Riss, unpublished data) the behavior of 16 male guinea pigs that had received 10 preliminary tests deviated markedly in a competitive situation, according to the dominance or submissiveness of the animal, but when they were replaced in isolation the behavior returned to a level not greatly different from that shown during the preliminary tests. Clearly this experience had little or no lasting influence on the pattern of behavior characterizing the individuals.

Sexual performance was affected significantly in these experiments only after a number of low score males had been confined with adult females for 60 days (Riss and Young, 1953). Before their confinement with the females the average score achieved by 7 males in 10 tests was 3.8 whereas after confinement and return to isolation the average score in 10 tests was 4.9. The difference is significant at the 5 per cent level. A group of 7 males never removed from isolation had average scores of 4.5 and 4.7.

If any impression came out of these preliminary experiments, it was one of fixation or stability of the individual pattern of sexual behavior. Not until experiments were performed in which very young animals were used, was there any clear indication of the extent to which contact with other animals affects patterns of behavior in the male guinea pig (Valenstein, Riss and Young,

TABLE 19.3

Comparison of sexual behavior of male guinea pigs raised in isolation with that of males raised with females

Data obtained from 7 tests, day 77 to 120, after all males were isolated.

(From E. S. Valenstein, W. Riss and W. C. Young, J. Comp. & Physiol. Psychol., **48**, 397, 1955.)

Animals (Group)	No.	Lower Measures		Mountings		Intromissions		Ejaculations		Average Score
		Average per animal	Per cent dis-playing	Average per animal	Per cent dis-playing	Average per animal	Per cent dis-playing	Average per animal	Per cent dis-playing	
Heterogeneous males (I)										
Isolated day 25..............	7	70.2	100	17.4	71	12.6	71	4.4	71	7.5
Social situation..............	7	36.4	100	19.6	100	20.6	100	6.7	100	9.9
Strain 2 males (II)										
Isolated day 25..............	17	149.0	100	1.2	35	0.5	6	0.06	6	3.9
Social situation..............	19	97.3	100	18.0	100	18.0	90	3.7	84	6.8
Strain 13 males (III)										
Isolated day 25..............	7	129.4	100	2.0	71	0.0	0	0.0	0	3.6
Social situation..............	7	96.4	100	6.4	86	7.6	57	0.6	57	3.0
Heterogeneous males (IV)										
Isolated day 10..............	10	120.8	100	10.6	30	6.5	30	1.5	30	4.9
Social situation..............	10	52.9	100	14.3	100	19.6	100	5.3	100	8.1

1955). The subjects were from the genetically heterogeneous stock and the inbred strains 2 and 13. Experimental males (the isolated males) were placed alone with their mothers from the day of birth until day 25 and isolated thereafter. Control males (the socially reared males) were raised with animals of the same age from the day of birth until day 73 when they were isolated; the mothers were removed on day 25. Both groups of males were given the first of 7 weekly tests on day 77.

The data (Table 19.3, group I) revealed that the performance of the genetically heterogeneous males raised in the social situation was somewhat better than that of the males brought up in isolation, although the difference is not statistically significant. The clearest picture came from the results obtained from strain 2 males in which the development of the measures of behavior above mounting seemed almost completely dependent on the contact they had had with other young animals (Table 19.3, group II). The strain 13 males showed some development of the complete sexual pattern following their experience in the social situation (Table 19.3, group III), but the level reached, although significantly higher than that attained by the isolated males, was considerably below that of the strain 2 and heterogeneous males.

As the work progressed, male cage-mates

were found to provide sufficient experience for the organization of sexual behavior in other males. Males raised with spayed females, on the other hand, performed more poorly than males of the same strain raised with intact females or males (Valenstein and Goy, 1957). Apropos of this, it has been observed repeatedly in the Kansas laboratory that even a sluggish male mounted by an estrous female is stimulated to mount in return. Untreated spayed females, however, have never been observed to initiate mounting. It is possible, therefore, that the poorer performance of the males raised with spayed females is explained by a lack of provocation to attempt mounting and thereby to gain experience.

A number of conclusions became apparent. (1) The importance of contact with other animals for the development of normal patterns of sexual behavior in the male guinea pig has been demonstrated. (2) The influence exerted by contact with other animals operates within the limits of a certain genetical background. (3) The influence of contact with other animals can be exerted very early in the life of an individual.

Just how early in the life of a male contact with other animals can be effective was shown by Valenstein in an experiment designed to test the hypothesis that the very slight differences in the heterogeneous animals weaned on day 25 and brought up in the two social situations might be explained by the earlier maturation of animals in this stock. He suggested that if males were weaned and isolated at 10 days of age instead of on day 25, a greater difference might be shown between the isolated animals and those brought up in the social situation. In the first test a completely convincing confirmation of the hypothesis was given (Table 19.3, group IV). The failure to obtain a greater difference in the earlier experiment with the heterogeneous males (group I) was obviously attributable to the circumstance that the contact these animals had with other animals during the first 25 days was sufficient to insure the development of essentially normal patterns of sexual behavior.

The possibility that an adult male without previous opportunity for organization of the higher measures of sexual behavior could improve his sexual performance by contact with other animals at an older age has been investigated (Valenstein and Goy, 1957). Each of several genetically heterogeneous males which had not exhibited any of the more mature behavior in tests given during the period of isolation was placed with 2 females for 23 days when they were 320 to 430 days of age. In subsequent tests all these males demonstrated the ability to mount, to have intromissions, and to ejaculate. Strain 2 males at older ages did not acquire the copulatory pattern so readily; 2 of 5 achieved intromission and ejaculation after being placed with females, but none of the remaining 3 displayed any of the higher measures of sexual behavior. The result is consistent with the earlier finding (Valenstein, Riss and Young, 1955) that young males from this strain require a longer time to organize this pattern of behavior. The data as a whole indicate that the emergence of sexual behavior patterns in the male guinea pig is not restricted to an early critical period comparable with that described in the literature dealing with imprinting (Lorenz, 1937). On the other hand, an analysis of the data presented by Valenstein and Goy (1957) reveals that contact with other animals is not as effective in organizing tissues for mating in older males as it is in young males.

What was regarded as a crucial test of the effect of the experiential factor on the character of the soma was a comparison of the response of isolated and socially reared strain 2 males to androgenic stimulation (Valenstein and Young, 1955). Following 7 tests which revealed the difference in their performance, the males brought up under the two social conditions were castrated, allowed to go without treatment until the regression in sexual behavior had reached the base-line of change, and then injected daily with testosterone propionate until the precastrational level of behavior was reached. The return of each group to the level characterizing it before castration is evidence for the conclusion that the responsiveness of the tissues mediating mating behavior to androgenic stimulation had been altered by a psychologic factor.

The results from the studies on the male guinea pig are felt to have provided a sound basis for a hypothesis that would account for the establishment of patterns of sexual behavior in this species. They suggest that the nervous organization on which response to sexual stimulation depends is influenced at a very early age by contact with other animals. On the other hand, genetical as well as experiential factors are important and the pattern displayed in response to androgenic stimulation is a resultant of the co-action of the two factors. But indirectly the testicular hormone may also be involved in the establishment of these patterns of behavior. To be sure, their organization, as estimated by mounting proficiency, can occur in the absence of the testes (Beach and Holz, 1946; Riss, Valenstein, Sinks and Young, 1955). On the other hand, if the organization of these patterns depends on experience gained through mounting, the testis hormone, by increasing this activity, may exert an indirect influence on the neural tissues in which the organization of patterns occurs.

Before leaving the male, we would call attention to the hypothesis that in the rat and guinea pig the copulatory response is innate rather than acquired (Stone, 1922; Louttit, 1929; Beach, 1942g, 1942i, 1951; Kagan and Beach, 1953). The data reviewed for the guinea pig prompted us to question the validity of the hypothesis for this species. The report that palpation with pelvic thrusts occurs in the rat as early as day

21 (Beach, 1942c) suggested that such contact with siblings might be sufficient to organize the adult pattern of sexual behavior in this species (Valenstein, Riss, and Young, 1955). Beach (1958a) believes, however, from the results of a more recent experiment, that this possibility can be excluded.

Males were isolated at 14 days just when the eyes are opening and before they could possibly have had experience mounting their cage-mates. At age 90 to 100 days 13 experimental animals and 12 siblings which had been reared together were tested. In the first 10-minute test, 4 of the experimental and 5 of the control males mated. The copulatory performance of the experimental animals was perfect. Without exception the first mount resulted in intromission. The latencies (seconds from the time the female is placed in the cage to the first intromission) were 195, 180, 60, and 8 seconds. In the controls the latencies were 110, 105, 75, 40, and 25 seconds. The average number of intromissions before ejaculation was 8.2 for the experimental males and 7.0 for the controls. Zimbardo (1958) was frankly critical of this latter experiment and, as we have noted, states that his results are in agreement with those obtained from the guinea pig. If he is correct, the rat is not a species in which development of the copulatory response by the male is innate; on the contrary, it should be placed with the guinea pig, cat, and chimpanzee in which some influence of contact with other animals contributes to the patterning of sexual behavior.

Regardless of the status of the rat,[10] for

[10] The reader who has reached this point will be keenly aware of the extent to which data from the rat and guinea pig have contributed to the thinking of investigators interested in the hormones and mating behavior. He will also recall that there are many references to similarities and differences between these species. For his convenience, they are listed here.

Differences between the species would appear to be more numerous than similarities. The hormones which elicit male and female behavior are the same (Dempsey, Hertz and Young, 1936; Boling and Blandau, 1939; Beach, 1942a; Stone, 1939a; Beach and Holz-Tucker, 1949) and in both species it is clear that differences between individuals have a somatic rather than a hormonal basis (Young,

no investigator has denied that there is some influence of contact with other animals, the conclusion is clear that in all species studied the character of sexual behavior is influenced by an experiential factor. Of importance for one who would generalize, is the fact that most studies were of male; only in Nissen's work on the chimpanzee were data obtained from the female. As a means of narrowing this gap, a study of the female guinea pig was undertaken (Goy and Young, 1957a). The results, although leaving much to be explained, are striking. In the strains which display mounting behavior the amount displayed by females reared in isolation was consistently less than that displayed by females raised with other animals. In all strains the duration of heat was shorter in the isolated females, as was the duration of lordosis. The effect on mounting behavior was not unexpected, especially if this measure of estrous behavior is a homologue of the behavior displayed by the male (Beach, 1943). At the moment, however, we cannot account for the shorter duration of heat and maximal lordosis in the isolated females. These measures are generally thought to be reflex in nature and therefore independent of any influence from other animals.

A final suggestion with respect to ex-

Dempsey, Myers and Hagquist, 1938; Beach and Holz-Tucker, 1949; Grunt and Young, 1952b; Valenstein and Young, 1955; Goy and Young, 1957b). The basic pattern of behavior in females of the two species is similar (Ball, 1937b; Young, Dempsey and Myers, 1935; Blandau, Boling and Young, 1941), but the patterns of behavior characteristic of the males are different (Stone, 1922, 1924b; Stone, Tomilin and Barker, 1935; Stone and Ferguson, 1940; Beach, 1944b; Beach and Holz, 1946; Young and Grunt, 1951). In the male rat the strength of sexual behavior is considered proportional to the amount of exogenous testicular hormone (Beach and Holz-Tucker, 1949; Beach, 1956); data from the male and female guinea pig do not support such a conclusion (Grunt and Young, 1952b; Riss and Young, 1954; Goy and Young, 1957b). Male-like mounting by the female rat does not coincide closely with estrus and appears to be displayed independently of the ovarian hormones (Beach and Rasquin, 1942); in the female guinea pig mounting is displayed only during the proestrum and estrus, or in spayed animals only following treatment with estrogen and progesterone (Young, Dempsey, Hagquist and Boling, 1939; Young and Rundlett, 1939; Goy and Young, 1957a, b).

perience and the determination of the nature of the response to gonadal hormones has a genesis that is entirely different from anything presented in the earlier part of our discussion. Green, Clemente and de Groot (1957) reported that prepubertal male cats displayed masculine behavior when testosterone was administered, and feminine behavior when stilbestrol tablets were given intramuscularly. They characterized the effect as "reversible." When adult males were treated, masculine behavior was displayed, not only in response to testosterone propionate, but also in response to the female hormones, estradiol and stilbestrol; this effect was "irreversible."

The authors' explanation for the different action of the steroids before and after puberty was frankly speculative. It seemed "unlikely that education in any ordinary sense is involved after the first coitus," and they suggest that "the type of first sexual experience may determine the subsequent behavioral reaction to hormones that have the same effect on the secondary sex characteristics and reproductive tract both before and after puberty."

Elsewhere they continue, "Perhaps the simplest explanation is that before sexual experience, the steroids set the stage for later education and determine the animal's receptivity to another kind of experience; that is, they determine the mood of the prepuberal animal. Without full experience then, the mood is reversible; but once experience has been acquired, the pattern of behavior is set and is not changed by the administration of the steroids of the opposite sex. The steroids in the adult would thus be assumed to increase drive in a nonspecific way." Clearly, in this latter investigation, there are difficulties, especially if an extension of the hypothesis to the female is to be inferred. At this stage, a considered evaluation of what is proposed cannot be given.

For all who are investigating the patterning of mating behavior through contact with other animals, the circumstance that some of the results have varied when the development of such behavior in different species was being studied need not concern us, except as it stimulates further and better designed experiments and reveals any evolutionary trend. A common denominator is that at many levels the experiential factor has been demonstrated to be related to the character of the behavior brought to expression by the gonadal hormones. Against this background, a number of problems are of obvious interest: identification of the effective element or elements in the contact with other animals, the locus of action—whether it is on the arousal mechanism or the consummatory mechanism, or both, any relationship between the age of the animal and the influence of these experiential factors on the character of behavior, any effect of the presence of gonadal hormones on the learning process, and, no doubt, others. Fortunately, most of these problems are already receiving attention.

IV. Concluding Remarks

The frequency with which reference is made to the many articles that have appeared since sexual behavior was discussed in the second edition of *Sex and Internal Secretions* attests to the activity during that interval. The years were characterized by a gratifying accumulation of data, by important advances in methodology, and by a challenging speculation with respect to factors regulating the display of sexual behavior during adulthood and influencing its development in young animals. These have been seen to be genetical, psychologic or experiential, and hormonal. The part played by each can be visualized by recalling two generalizations which emerged from the numerous data reviewed in the preceding sections. The first is that the pattern of mating behavior is mediated by tissues in which a certain organization has developed or, perhaps better, by tissues on which a certain character has been conferred. The second is that mating behavior is always displayed with a certain strength or vigor, regardless of the pattern. We will risk a temporary confusion by adding that, whereas the strength or vigor of behavior can be thought of and dealt with as a separate concept, in the animal it is also a part of the pattern of behavior (Young, 1957). No species is an exception to these generalizations and they are applicable to both sexes.

In the adult, and possibly in the neonatal and sexually immature animal as well, there is no evidence that the hormones have any effect on the organization of the tissues mediating mating behavior. Genetical factors are of obvious importance and account for the differences between species, for the differences between sexes, and, in subhuman species if not in man as well, for many of the differences between individuals. Psychologic or experiential factors are also important, and, as with genetical factors, the extent depends on the species and the sex. But, in contrast to the genetical factors, the influence of psychologic factors is greater in the higher than in the lower mammals. These factors probably have achieved a dominant role in man in whom there is a clear dependence on his culture (Ford and Beach, 1951; Mead, chapter 24), his experience (Heller and Maddock, 1947; Kinsey, Pomeroy, Martin and Gebhard, 1953; and many others), and his sex of assignment and rearing (Finesinger, Meigs and Sulkowitch, 1942; Ellis, 1945; Money, 1955; Money, Hampson and Hampson, 1955, 1957; Hampson, Hampson and Money, 1955; Hampson, Money and Hampson, 1956). In two lower mammals, the guinea pig and cat, psychologic factors are clearly operative (Valenstein, Riss and Young, 1955; Rosenblatt and Aronson, 1958a, b); more in the male, we believe, than in the female (Young, 1957). The conclusion that, in even the neonatal and young animal, the development of the pattern of behavior may be independent of gonadal hormone action is based on results from a number of experiments. When the gonads have been removed within a day or two after birth or have been congenitally absent, normal patterns of behavior were later displayed, provided of course the appropriate hormones were administered, and in the male, provided there had been contact with other animals (Wilson and Young, 1941; Beach, 1945b; Beach and Holz, 1946; Riss, Valenstein, Sinks and Young, 1955).

During the prenatal period the situation is quite different. The operation of genetical factors is assumed, but more dramatic is the demonstrated action of hormonal factors, especially on the female (Phoenix, Goy, Gerall and Young, 1959). During this period they seem to be organizational, very much as they are organizational in the differentiation of the genital tracts (Burns, 1942, 1949, and his chapter in this book; Jost, 1947, 1953, 1957; Wells, Cavanaugh and Maxwell, 1954; Price, 1957). Preliminary evidence indicates that when a male hormone is present, the capacity for the eventual display of masculine behavior develops and the capacity for the display of feminine behavior is suppressed in males and in females. Without more information, the comparison may not be extended to the role of a fetal female gonadal hormone. Development of the capacity for displaying the copulatory response (lordosis) may require the presence of such a hormone or it may be genetically determined, but experiments comparable with those performed especially by Jost and by Wells, Cavanaugh and Maxwell have yet to be performed by investigators interested in the development of the capacity for displaying mating behavior.

Returning now to the concept that mating behavior is always displayed with a certain strength or vigor, we find ourselves limited to the postpubertal period when the complete pattern is displayed. As we have noted, the potential strength or vigor with which mating behavior is displayed is a part of the pattern and as such is genetically and, in man, possibly psychologically determined. But in all subhuman mammals and almost certainly in the human male (see chapter by Money), the strength or vigor of male behavior is related to the gonadal hormones. The evidence is not clear for the human female. The retention of sexual responsiveness after the natural or a surgical menopause (Filler and Drezner, 1944) suggests an emancipation from hormonal control. On the other hand, the enhanced sexual desire following the administration of testosterone propionate (Shorr, Papanicolaou and Stimmel, 1938; Salmon, 1942; Greenblatt, 1943; Carter, Cohen and Shorr, 1947) suggests that, as in the male, emancipation is not complete.

The view we have attempted to express

with respect to the role of gonadal hormones in the development and expression of mating behavior was long ago stated by Zuckerman and Parkes (1939) in another context: "Androgen stimulation induces the two main types of change. The first leads to assumption of permanent characters, the second to the assumption of characters which disappear when androgen stimulation ceases."

Their thought was of secondary sexual characters, of genital tract structure, and, we would guess, only incidentally of behavior. Twenty years later we may go further than the data available to them permitted and extend the hypothesis to the tissues mediating mating behavior. We would direct attention to the possibility that in these tissues the same rules apply, but, in addition to hormonal (and genetical) factors, psychologic factors have appeared, and, as animals have evolved, a picture has been created in which there is a mingling and in some way an interaction of all these factors. Elucidation of the manner in which this occurs and its extent will depend on the continued effort of investigators from many disciplines.

A final remark has to do with an aspect of the subject that has not had treatment in the present review. The discussion up to this point has dealt principally with mating behavior, that restricted part of the total behavior which subserves reproduction more directly than it does any other vital activity. However, as investigations have proceeded, it has become apparent that the action of the gonadal hormones is much broader than we realized years ago when attention was first being focused on the relationship of these substances to mating behavior. The fact will be apparent from what has been written about the role of these substances in parental behavior (chapter by Lehrman) and in social behavior (chapter by Guhl). Recent work suggests that this concept may be extended even further. Not all the behavior associated with the male or the female is reproductive. Many differences between the behavior of males and females have been described, and many more are a part of the cultural lore. The subject is too vast for review here, but two examples will be mentioned. The male chimpanzee is said to be a fighter and a bluffer, the female is treacherous and more difficult than the male to bluff consistently (Yerkes, 1943; Hebb, 1946). Differences between the sexes are seen in the play configuration of preadolescent children (Erikson, 1951). In their chapter in this book, Hampson and Hampson have discussed this "psychologic sex" and suggested that it "does not have an innate, preformed instinctive basis as some have maintained," but rather is "undifferentiated at birth ... a sexual neutrality in the place of the Freudian bisexuality ... and that the individual becomes differentiated as masculine or feminine, psychologically, in the course of the many experiences of growing up."

As evidence has accumulated (Burns, 1942, 1949, and his chapter in this book; Jost, 1947, 1953, 1957; Wells, Cavanaugh and Maxwell, 1954) that the fetal gonad (probably the testis rather than the ovary) is the source of a hormone with androgenic properties, investigators have asked if the action of this substance may not extend beyond the genital tract and tissues mediating mating behavior, to the "behavior beyond that which is purely sexual" (Phoenix, Goy, Gerall and Young, 1959). Undoubtedly this hypothesis will soon be tested. If it is found to be true, an unsuspected action of the gonadal hormones will have been revealed, an action, we predict, that will be a bond between the work of the experimental embryologists who have concerned themselves so completely with all that is involved in the development and differentiation of the genital tracts, and the work of the psychologists and psychiatrists for whom the development and differentiation of neural tissues presents problems of equal interest and importance. In addition, a big circle will have been completed. Analysis of sexual differentiation during the embryonic and fetal periods began with the work of the experimental embryologists, much of which is reviewed in Editions 1 and 2 of *Sex and Internal Secretions*. A segment of the work reviewed in this chapter was started in that atmosphere, and attention is directed to the fact that, once the basis was established, much of the conceptualization outlined here developed from the investigations and thought of that group of older colleagues.

V. References

ABEL, S. 1945. Androgenic therapy in malignant disease of the female genitalia; preliminary report. Am. J. Obst. & Gynec., 49, 327–342.

ABERLE, S. D., AND CORNER, G. W. 1953. *Twenty-five Years of Sex Research. History of the National Research Council Committee for Research in Problems of Sex 1922–1947.* Philadelphia: W. B. Saunders Company.

ALLEN, E., AND DOISY, E. A. 1923. An ovarian hormone: preliminary report on its localization, extraction and partial purification, and action in test animals. J. A. M. A., 81, 819–821.

ALMQUIST, J. O., AND HALE, E. B. 1956. An approach to the measurement of sexual behaviour and semen production of dairy bulls. In *Proceedings III International Congress on Animal Reproduction,* pp. 50–59. London: Brown, Knight and Truscott, Ltd.

ALTMANN, M. 1941. Interrelations of the sex cycle and the behavior of the sow. J. Comp. Psychol., 31, 481–498.

ANDERSON, E. E. 1936. Consistency of tests of copulatory frequency in the male albino rat. J. Comp. Psychol., 21, 447–459.

ANDREWS, F. N., AND MCKENZIE, F. F. 1941. Estrus, ovulation and related phenomena in the mare. Univ. Missouri Coll. Agric. Res. Bull., No. 329.

ANTLIFF, H. R., AND YOUNG, W. C. 1956. Behavioral and tissue responses of male guinea pigs to estrogens and the problem of hormone specificity. Endocrinology, 59, 74–82.

ARONSON, L. R. 1944. The sexual behavior of Anura. 6. The mating pattern of *Bufo americanus, Bufo fowleri, and Bufo terrestris.* American Museum Novitates, No. 1250.

ARONSON, L. R. 1957. Reproductive and parental behavior. In *The Physiology of Fishes,* Margaret E. Brown, Ed., pp. 272–304. New York: Academic Press, Inc.

ASTWOOD, E. B., AND DEMPSEY, E. W. 1941. The induction of estrous behavior in hypophysectomized rats. Abstract, Proc. Am. Physiol. Soc., Am. J. Physiol., 133, P198.

AVERY, G. T. 1925. Notes on reproduction in guinea pigs. J. Comp. Psychol., 5, 373–396.

BAERENDS, G. P., BROUWER, R., AND WATERBOLK, H. TJ. 1955. Ethological studies on *Lebistes reticulatus* (Peters). I. An analysis of the male courtship pattern. Behaviour, 8, 249–334.

BAKER, J. R. 1925. On sex-intergrade pigs: their anatomy, genetics, and developmental physiology. Brit. J. Exper. Biol., 2, 247–263.

BALL, J. 1936. Sexual responsiveness in female monkeys after castration and subsequent estrin administration. Psychol. Bull., 33, 811.

BALL, J. 1937a. Sex activity of castrated male rats increased by estrin administration. J. Comp. Psychol., 24, 135–144.

BALL, J. 1937b. A test for measuring sexual excitability in the female rat. Comp. Psychol. Monogr., 14, No. 1.

BALL, J. 1939. Male and female mating behavior in prepubertally castrated male rats receiving estrogens. J. Comp. Psychol., 28, 273–283.

BALL, J. 1940. The effect of testosterone on the sex behavior of female rats. J. Comp. Psychol., 29, 151–165.

BALL, J. 1941a. Effect of progesterone upon sexual excitability in the female monkey. Psychol. Bull., 38, 533.

BALL, J. 1941b. Mating behavior induced in hypophysectomized female rats by injected estrogen. Proc. Soc. Exper. Biol. & Med., 46, 669.

BANE, A. 1954. Studies on monozygous cattle twins. XV. Sexual functions of bulls in relation to heredity, rearing conditions and somatic conditions. Acta agric. scandinav., 4, 95–208.

BARD, P. 1939. Central nervous mechanisms for emotional behavior patterns in animals. A. Res. Nerv. & Ment. Dis., Proc., 19, 190–218.

BARRACLOUGH, C. A. 1955. Influence of age on the response of preweaning female mice to testosterone propionate. Am. J. Anat., 97, 493–522.

BATES, R. W., AND RIDDLE, O. 1941. Annual variation in the response of crop-sacs and viscera of pigeons to prolactin. Endocrinology, 29, 702–709.

BEACH, F. A., JR. 1938. Sex reversals in the mating pattern of the rat. J. Genet. Psychol., 53, 329–334.

BEACH, F. A., JR. 1939. The neural basis of innate behavior. III. Comparison of learning ability and instinctive behavior in the rat. J. Comp. Psychol., 28, 225–262.

BEACH, F. A. 1940. Effects of cortical lesions upon the copulatory behavior of male rats. J. Comp. Psychol., 29, 193–245.

BEACH, F. A. 1941. Female mating behavior shown by male rats after administration of testosterone propionate. Endocrinology, 29, 409–412.

BEACH, F. A. 1942a. Importance of progesterone to induction of sexual receptivity in spayed female rats. Proc. Soc. Exper. Biol. & Med., 51, 369–371.

BEACH, F. A. 1942b. Male and female mating behavior in prepuberally castrated female rats treated with androgens. Endocrinology, 31, 673–678.

BEACH, F. A. 1942c. Sexual behavior of prepuberal male and female rats treated with gonadal hormones. J. Comp. Psychol., 34, 285–292.

BEACH, F. A. 1942d. Copulatory behavior in prepuberally castrated male rats and its modification by estrogen administration. Endocrinology, 31, 679–683.

BEACH, F. A. 1942e. Analysis of factors involved in the arousal, maintenance and manifestation of sexual excitement in male animals. Psychosom. Med., **4**, 173–198.

BEACH, F. A. 1942f. Execution of the complete masculine copulatory pattern by sexually receptive female rats. J. Genet. Psychol., **60**, 137–142.

BEACH, F. A. 1942g. Analysis of the stimuli adequate to elicit mating behavior in the sexually inexperienced male rat. J. Comp. Psychol., **33**, 163–207.

BEACH, F. A. 1942h. Effects of testosterone propionate upon the copulatory behavior of sexually inexperienced male rats. J. Comp. Psychol., **33**, 227–247.

BEACH, F. A. 1942i. Comparison of copulatory behavior of male rats raised in isolation, cohabitation, and segregation. J. Genet. Psychol., **60**, 121–136.

BEACH, F. A. 1942j. Central nervous mechanisms involved in the reproductive behavior of vertebrates. Psychol. Bull., **39**, 200–226.

BEACH, F. A. 1943. Effects of injury to the cerebral cortex upon the display of masculine and feminine mating behavior by female rats. J. Comp. Psychol., **36**, 169–199.

BEACH, F. A. 1944a. Experimental studies of sexual behavior in male mammals. J. Clin. Endocrinol., **4**, 126–199.

BEACH, F. A. 1944b. Relative effects of androgen upon the mating behavior of male rats subjected to forebrain injury or castration. J. Exper. Zool., **97**, 249–295.

BEACH, F. A. 1944c. Effects of injury to the cerebral cortex upon sexually-receptive behavior in the female rat. Psychosom. Med., **6**, 40–55.

BEACH, F. A. 1945a. Bisexual mating behavior in the male rat: effects of castration and hormone administration. Physiol. Zool., **18**, 390–402.

BEACH, F. A. 1945b. Hormonal induction of mating responses in a rat with congenital absence of gonadal tissue. Anat. Rec., **92**, 289–292.

BEACH, F. A. 1946. Hormones and mating behavior in vertebrates. Recent Progr. Hormone Res., **1**, 27–63.

BEACH, F. A. 1947. A review of physiological and psychological studies of the sexual behavior in mammals. Physiol. Rev., **27**, 240–306.

BEACH, F. A. 1947–48. Sexual behavior in animals and men. Harvey Lectures, Series 43, pp. 254–280.

BEACH, F. A. 1948. *Hormones and Behavior.* New York: Paul B. Hoeber, Inc.

BEACH, F. A. 1951. Instinctive behavior: reproductive activities. In *Handbook of Experimental Psychology,* S. S. Stevens, Ed., pp. 387–434. New York: John Wiley & Sons.

BEACH, F. A. 1952. Sex and species differences in the behavioural effects of gonadal hormones. Ciba Foundation Colloquia Endocrinol., **3**, 3–17.

BEACH, F. A. 1956. Personal communication.

BEACH. F. A. 1958a. Normal sexual behavior in male rats isolated at fourteen days of age. J. Comp. & Physiol. Psychol., **51**, 37–38.

BEACH, F. A. 1958b. Neural and chemical regulation of behavior. In *Biological and Biochemical Bases of Behavior,* H. F. Harlow and C. N. Woolsey, Eds., pp. 263–284. Madison: University of Wisconsin Press.

BEACH, F. A., AND FOWLER, H. 1959. Individual differences in the response of male rats to androgen. J. Comp. & Physiol. Psychol., **52**, 50–52.

BEACH, F. A., AND HOLZ, A. M. 1946. Mating behavior in male rats castrated at various ages and injected with androgen. J. Exper. Zool., **101**, 91–142.

BEACH, F. A., AND HOLZ-TUCKER, A. M. 1949. Effects of different concentrations of androgen upon sexual behavior in castrated male rats. J. Comp. & Physiol. Psychol., **42**, 433–453.

BEACH, F. A., AND JORDAN, L. 1956. Sexual exhaustion and recovery in the male rat. Quart. J. Exper. Psychol., **8**, 121–133.

BEACH, F. A., AND LEVINSON, G. 1950. Effects of androgen on the glans penis and mating behavior of castrated male rats. J. Exper. Zool., **114**, 159–171.

BEACH, F. A., AND PAUKER, R. S. 1949. Effects of castration and subsequent androgen administration upon mating behavior in the male hamster (*Cricetus auratus*). Endocrinology, **45**, 211–221.

BEACH, F. A., AND RABEDEAU, R. G. 1959. Sexual exhaustion and recovery in the male hamster. J. Comp. & Physiol. Psychol., **52**, 56–61.

BEACH, F. A., AND RASQUIN, P. 1942. Masculine copulatory behavior in intact and castrated female rats. Endocrinology, **31**, 393–409.

BELAWENETZ, S. 1928. Über die Wirkung der Thyreokrinfütterung auf die Hoden der weissen Ratten. Anat. Anz., **65**, 155–161.

BENOIT, J. 1929. Le déterminisme des caractères sexuels secondaires du coq domestique. Arch. Zool. Exper. et Genet., **69**, 217–499.

BIGGERS, J. D., AND CLARINGBOLD, P. J. 1955. Mitotic activity in the vaginal epithelium of the mouse following local oestrogenic stimulation. J. Anat., **89**, 124–131.

BINGHAM, H. C. 1928. Sex development in apes. Comp. Psychol. Monogr., **5**, No. 1.

BLANDAU, R. J., BOLING, J. L., AND YOUNG, W. C. 1941. The length of heat in the albino rat as determined by the copulatory response. Anat. Rec., **79**, 453–463.

BLAXTER, K. L. 1952. Some effects of thyroxine and iodinated casein on dairy cows, and their practical significance. Vitamins & Hormones, **10**, 217–250.

BLIVAISS, B. B. 1947a. Interrelations of thyroid and gonad in the development of plumage and other sex characters in brown Leghorn roosters. Physiol. Zool., **20**, 67–107.

BLIVAISS, B. B. 1947b. Development of secondary sexual characters in thyroidectomized brown Leghorn hens. J. Exper. Zool., **104,** 267–310.

BOLING, J. L., AND BLANDAU, R. J. 1939. The estrogen-progesterone induction of mating responses in the spayed female rat. Endocrinology, **25,** 359–364.

BOLING, J. L., BLANDAU, R. J., RUNDLETT, B., AND YOUNG, W. C. 1941. Factors underlying the failure of cyclic mating behavior in the albino rat. Anat. Rec., **80,** 155–171.

BOLING, J. L., BLANDAU, R. J., WILSON, J. G., AND YOUNG, W. C. 1939. Post-parturitional heat responses of newborn and adult guinea pigs. Data on parturition. Proc. Soc. Exper. Biol. & Med., **42,** 128–132.

BOLING, J. L., YOUNG, W. C., AND DEMPSEY, E. W. 1938. Miscellaneous experiments on the estrogen-progesterone induction of heat in the spayed guinea pig. Endocrinology, **23,** 182–187.

BOSS, W. R. 1943. Hormonal determination of adult characters and sex behavior in herring gulls (*Larus argentatus*). J. Exper. Zool., **94,** 181–209.

BOUSFIELD, W. A., AND MOTE, F. A., JR. 1943. The construction of a tilting activity cage. J. Exper. Psychol., **32,** 450–451.

BRADBURY, J. T. 1944. The estrous rabbit as a quantitative assay animal. Endocrinology, **35,** 317–324.

BRENEMAN, W. R. 1939. Variations in the reaction of chicks to different methods of administering androgens. Endocrinology, **24,** 55–62.

BRODY, E. G. 1942. Genetic basis of spontaneous activity in the albino rat. Comp. Psychol. Monogr., **17,** No. 5.

BRODY, S., AND FRANKENBACH, R. F. 1942. Growth and development. LIV. Age changes in size, energy metabolism and cardiorespiratory activities of thyroidectomized cattle. Univ. Missouri Coll. Agric. Res. Bull., No. 349.

BROWN, R. H. 1937. Stability of conditioning and sexual dominance in the rabbit. Science, **86,** 520.

BULLOUGH, W. S. 1945. Endocrinological aspects of bird behavior. Biol. Rev., **20,** 89–99.

BURGER, J. F. 1952. Sex physiology of pigs. Ondespoort J. Vet. Res., Suppl. No. 2.

BURNS, R. K., JR. 1942. Hormones and experimental modification of sex in the opossum. Biol. Symposia, **9,** 125–146.

BURNS, R. K. 1949. Hormones and the differentiation of sex. Survey Biol. Progr. **1,** 233–266.

BURROWS, H. 1949. *Biological Actions of Sex Hormones,* 2nd ed. Cambridge: Cambridge University Press.

BURROWS, W. H., AND TITUS, H. W. 1939. Some observations on the semen production of the male domestic fowl. Poultry Sc., **18,** 8–10.

BYRNES, W. W., AND SHIPLEY, E. G. 1955. Guinea pig copulatory reflex in response to adrenal steroids and similar compounds. Endocrinology, **57,** 5–9.

CALDER, A. 1927. A case of partial sex-trans-

formation in cattle. Proc. Roy. Soc., Edinburgh, **47,** 222–229.

CARMICHAEL, H. T., NOONAN, W. J., AND KENYON, A. T. 1941. The effects of testosterone propionate in impotence. Am. J. Psychiat., **97,** 919–943.

CARPENTER, C. R. 1933a. Psychobiological studies of social behavior in Aves. I. The effect of complete and incomplete gonadectomy on the primary sexual activity of the male pigeon. J. Comp. Psychol., **16,** 25–57.

CARPENTER, C. R. 1933b. Psychobiological studies of social behavior in Aves. II. The effect of complete and incomplete gonadectomy on secondary sexual activity with histological studies. J. Comp. Psychol., **16,** 59–97.

CARPENTER, C. R. 1942a. Sexual behavior of free ranging Rhesus monkeys (*Macaca mulatta*). I. Specimens, procedures and behavioral characteristics of estrus. J. Comp. Psychol., **33,** 113–142.

CARPENTER, C. R. 1942b. Sexual behavior of free ranging Rhesus monkeys (*Macaca mulatta*). II. Periodicity of estrus, homosexual, antoerotic and non-conformist behavior. J. Comp. Psychol., **33,** 143–162.

CARR, W. J., AND PENDER, B. 1958. Personal communication.

CARTER, A. C., COHEN, E. J., AND SHORR, E. 1947. The use of androgens in women. Vitamins & Hormones, **5,** 317–391.

CASIDA, L. E., MCSHAN, W. H., AND MEYER, R. K. 1944. Effects of an unfractionated pituitary extract upon cystic ovaries and nymphomania in cows. J. Anim. Sc., **3,** 273–282.

CEMBROWICZ, H. J. 1952. Fertility levels of bulls kept at an artificial insemination centre. J. Agric. Sc., **42,** 323–334.

CHENG, P., AND CASIDA, L. E. 1949. Effects of testosterone propionate upon sexual libido and the production of semen and sperm in the rabbit. Endocrinology, **44,** 38–48.

CHENG, P., Ulberg, L. C., Christian, R. E., AND CASIDA, L. E. 1950. Different intensities of sexual activity in relation to the effect of testosterone propionate in the male rabbit. Endocrinology, **46,** 447–452.

CHRISTY, N. P., DICKIE, M. M., AND WOOLLEY, G. W. 1950. Estrus and mating in gonadectomized female mice with adrenal cortical abnormalities. Endocrinology, **47,** 129–130.

CHU, J. P. 1945. The influence of the thyroid on pregnancy and parturition in the rabbit. J. Endocinol., **4,** 109–114.

CLARK, E. AND ARONSON, L. R. 1951. Sexual behavior in the guppy, *Lebistes reticulatus* (Peters). Zoologica, **36,** 49–66.

CLARK, E., ARONSON, L. R., AND GORDON, M. 1954. Mating behavior patterns in two sympatric species of xiphophorin fishes: their inheritance and significance in sexual isolation. Bull. Am. Museum Nat. History, **103,** 135–225.

CLARK, G. 1945. Prepubertal castration in the

male chimpanzee, with some effects of replacement therapy. Growth, **9**, 327–339.

CLARK, G. 1947. Threshold bleeding and the sex skin in the castrate female chimpanzee. Endocrinology, **41**, 327–329.

CLEGHORN, R. A. 1952. Alterations in psychological states by therapeutic increase in adrenal cortical hormones. Ciba Foundation Colloquia Endocrinol., **3**, 187–196.

COLE, H. H., HART, G. H., AND MILLER, R. F. 1945. Studies on the hormonal control of estrous phenomena in the anestrous ewe. Endocrinology, **36**, 370–380.

COLLIAS, N. 1946. Effect of thyroxin on mating frequency of domestic hens. Abstract, Proc. Am. Soc. Zool., Anat. Rec., **94**, 362.

COLLIAS, N. E. 1950. Hormones and behavior with special reference to birds and the mechanisms of hormone action. In *Steroid Hormones*, E. S. Gordon, Ed., pp. 277–329. Madison: University of Wisconsin Press.

COLLINS, V. J., BOLING, J. L., DEMPSEY, E. W., AND YOUNG, W. C. 1938. Quantitative studies of experimentally induced sexual receptivity in the spayed guinea-pig. Endocrinology, **23**, 188–196.

COOPER, J. B. 1942. An exploratory study on African lions. Comp. Psychol. Monogr., **17**, No. 7.

COOPER, M., AND ARONSON, L. 1958. The effect of adrenalectomy on the sexual behavior of castrated male cats. Abstract, Proc. Am. Soc. Zool., Anat. Rec., **131**, 544.

CORNER, G. W. 1921. Cyclic changes in the ovaries and uterus of the sow, and their relation to the mechanism of implantation. Contr. Embryol., Carnegie Inst. Washington, **13**, 117–146.

CRAIG, J. V., CASIDA, L. E., AND CHAPMAN, A. B. 1954. Male infertility associated with lack of libido in the rat. Am. Naturalist, **88**, 365–372.

CRAIG, W. 1914. Male doves reared in isolation. J. Anim. Behav., **4**, 121–133.

CRAIG, W. 1918. Appetites and aversions as constituents of instincts. Biol. Bull., **34**, 91–107.

CREEVY, C. D., AND REA, E. 1940. The treatment of impotence by male sex hormone. Endocrinology, **27**, 393–394.

CSAPO, A. 1955. The mechanism of myometrial function and its disorders. In *Modern Trends in Obstetrics and Gynecology*, 2nd series, pp. 20–49. London: Butterworth & Company.

CSAPO, A. 1959a. Function and regulation of the myometrium. Ann. New York Acad. Sc., **75**, 790–808.

CSAPO, A. 1959b. Regulation of the myometrium. In *Cell, Organism, and Milieu*, D. Rudnick, Ed., pp. 107–120. New York: Ronald Press.

DANTCHAKOFF, V. 1938a. Rôle des hormones dans la manifestation des instincts sexuels. Compt. rend. Acad. Sc., **206**, 945–947.

DANTCHAKOFF, V. 1938b. Sur les effects de l'hormone male dans une jeune cobaye femelle

traité depuis un stade embryonnaire (inversions sexuelles). Compt. rend. Soc. biol., **127**, 1255–1258.

DANTCHAKOFF, V. 1938c. Sur les effets de l'hormone male dans un jeune cobaye male traité depuis un stade embryonnaire (production d'hypermales). Compt. rend. Soc. biol., **127**, 1259–1262.

DANTCHAKOFF, V. 1947. Actions de la testostérone sur les énergies globales de l'organisme. Compt. rend. Soc. biol., **141**, 114–116.

DAVIS, D. E., AND DOMM, L. V. 1941. The sexual behavior of hormonally treated domestic fowl. Proc. Soc. Exper. Biol. & Med., **48**, 667–669.

DAVIS, D. E., AND DOMM, L. V. 1943. The influence of hormones on the sexual behavior of domestic fowl. In *Essays in Biology*, pp. 171–181. Berkeley: University of California Press.

DAVIS, M. E., AND PLOTZ, E. J. 1957. Progesterone, the pregnancy hormone. Fertil. & Steril., **8**, 603–618.

DAWSON, A. B., AND FRIEDGOOD, H. B. 1940. The time and sequence of preovulatory changes in the cat ovary after mating or mechanical stimulation of the cervix uteri. Anat. Rec., **76**, 411–429.

DAY, B. N., ANDERSON, L. L., HAZEL, L. N., AND MELAMPY, R. M. 1959. Synchronization of estrus and ovulation in swine. J. Anim. Sc., **18**, 909–917.

DE ALBA, J., AND ASDELL, S. A. 1946. Estrous behavior and hormones in the cow. J. Comp. Psychol., **39**, 119–124.

DE FREMERY, P., AND TAUSK, M. 1937. Geschlechtliche Aktivität kastrierter männlicher Kaninchen nach Behandlung mit Testosteronpropionat. Acta brev. neerl. Physiol., **7**, 164–165.

DEL CASTILLO, E. B., AND DI PAOLA, G. 1942. Cyclical vaginal response to the daily administration of estradiol in castrated rats. Endocrinology, **30**, 48–53.

DELL, P. C. 1958. Some basic mechanisms of the translation of bodily needs into behaviour. In *Ciba Foundation Symposium on the Neurological Basis of Behaviour*, pp. 187–203. Boston: Little, Brown & Company.

DEMPSEY, E. W. 1939. The relationship between the central nervous system and the reproductive cycle in the female guinea pig. Am. J. Physiol., **126**, 758–765.

DEMPSEY, E. W. 1948. The chemical cytology of endocrine glands. Recent Progr. Hormone Res., **3**, 127–157.

DEMPSEY, E. W., HERTZ, R., AND YOUNG, W. C. 1936. The experimental induction of oestrus (sexual receptivity) in the normal and ovariectomized guinea pig. Am. J. Physiol., **116**, 201–209.

DENNISTON, R. H. 1957. Sexual behavior and physiology cycle in an annual breeding wild rodent. Abstract, Proc. Am. Soc. Zool., Anat. Rec., **128**, 539.

DERBES, V. D. AND WEISS, T. E. 1951. *Untoward*

Reactions of Cortisone and ACTH. Springfield, Ill.: Charles C Thomas.

DIAMOND, M. 1960. Comparative behavior and structural effects of androgen injected into pregnant and nonpregnant guinea pigs. Abstract, Proc. Am. Soc. Zool., Anat. Rec., **137**, 349.

DINGEMANSE, E., BORCHARDT, H. AND LAQUEUR, E. 1937. LXIX. Capon comb growth-promoting substances ("male hormones") in human urine of males and females of varying ages. Biochem. J., **31**, 500–507.

DÖDERLEIN, G. 1928. Experimenteller Hyperthyreoidismus und seine Wirkung auf Fortpflanzung und Nachkommenschaft. Arch. Gynäk., **133**, 680-719.

DOEG, L. H., AND LEATHEM, J. H. 1958. Estrous cycles in mice following prepuberal steroid administration. Proc. Pennsylvania Acad. Sc., **32**, 202–210.

DOMM, L. V. 1927. New experiments on ovariotomy and the problem of sex inversion in the fowl. J. Exper. Zool., **48**, 31–173.

DOMM, L. V. 1947. Spontaneous male copulatory behavior in the brown Leghorn hen. Abstract, Proc. Am. Soc. Zool., Anat. Rec., **99**, 554.

DOMM, L. V., AND VAN DYKE, H. B. 1932a. Precocious development of sexual characters in the fowl by daily injections of hebin. I. The male. Proc. Soc. Exper. Biol. & Med., **30**, 349–350.

DOMM, L. V., AND VAN DYKE, H. B. 1932b. Precocious development of sexual characters in the fowl by daily injections of hebin. II. The female. Proc. Soc. Exper. Biol. & Med., **30**, 351–353.

DOMM, L. V., AND BLIVAISS, B. B. 1947. Induction of male copulatory behavior in the brown Leghorn hen. Proc. Soc. Exper. Biol. & Med., **66**, 418–419.

DOMM, L. V., AND DAVIS, D. E. 1948. The sexual behavior of intersexual domestic fowl. Physiol. Zool., **21**, 14–31.

DORFMAN, R. I., AND SHIPLEY, R. A. 1956. *Androgens. Biochemistry, Physiology, and Clinical Significance.* New York: John Wiley & Sons.

DORFMAN, R. I., AND UNGAR, F. 1953. *Metabolism of Steroid Hormones.* Minneapolis: Burgess Publishing Company.

DUTT, R. H. 1953. Induction of estrus and ovulation in anestrual ewes by use of progesterone and pregnant mare serum. J. Anim. Sc., **12**, 515–523.

EAYRS, J. T. 1952. Sex differences in the maturation and function of the nervous system in the rat. Ciba Foundation Colloquia Endocrinol., **3**, 18–33.

EAYRS, J. T. 1954. Spontaneous activity in the rat. Brit. J. Anim. Behav., **2**, 25–30.

ELLIS, A. 1945. The sexual psychology of human hermaphrodites. Psychosom. Med., **7**, 108–125.

EMLEN, J. T., JR., AND LORENZ, F. W. 1942. Pairing responses of free-living valley quail to sex hormone pellet implants. Auk, **59**, 369–378.

EMMENS, C. W. 1939. Time-to-time variation in the response of ovariectomized mice to oestrone. Nature, London, **143**, 476–477.

ENDERS, R. K. 1952. Reproduction in the mink (*Mustela vison*). Proc. Am. Phil. Soc., **96**, 691–755.

ENGEL, P. 1942. Female mating behavior shown by male mice after treatment with different substances. Endocrinology, **30**, 623.

ERIKSON, E. 1951. Sex differences in the play configuration of preadolescents. Am. J. Orthopsychiat., **21**, 667–692.

ESSENBERG, J. M. 1926. Complete sex-reversal in the viviparous teleost *Xiphophorus helleri*. Biol. Bull., **51**, 98–111.

EVANS, H. M. 1928. Sterility in inbred rats. Am. J. Physiol., **85**, 154–157.

EVERSOLE, W. J. 1941. The effects of pregneninolone and related steroids on sexual development in fish (*Lebistes reticulatus*). Endocrinology, **28**, 603–610.

FARRIS, E. J. 1941. Apparatus for recording cyclical activity in the rat. Anat. Rec., **81**, 357–362.

FEE, A. R., MARRIAN, G. F., AND PARKES, A. S. 1929. The significance of the occurrence of oestrin in male urine. J. Physiol., **67**, 377–382.

FERNANDEZ, N. P. 1940. Nymphomania with sex reversal in a pedigreed Sahiwal heifer treated back to fertility. Indian J. Vet. Sc. & Anim. Husbandry, **10**, 98–102.

FILLER, W., AND DREZNER, N. 1944. The results of surgical castration in women under forty. Am. J. Obst. & Gynec., **47**, 122–124.

FINESINGER, J. E., MEIGS, J. V., AND SULKOWITCH, H. W. 1942. Clinical, psychiatric and psychoanalytic study of a case of male pseudohermaphroditism. Am. J. Obst. & Gynec., **44**, 310–317.

FINLAY, G. F. 1925. Studies on sex differentiation in fowls. Brit. J. Exper. Biol., **2**, 439–468.

FOLLEY, S. J. 1938. Experiments on the relation between the thyroid gland and lactation in the rat. J. Physiol., **93**, 401–412.

FOLLEY, S. J. 1952. In Discussion of paper by M. Klein. Ciba Foundation Colloquia Endocrinol., **3**, 323–337.

FOLLEY, S. J., AND MALPRESS, F. H. 1944. The artificial induction of lactation in the bovine by the subcutaneous implantation of synthetic oestrogen tablets. J. Endocrinol., **4**, 1–18.

FORD, C. S., AND BEACH, F. A. 1951. *Patterns of Sexual Behavior.* New York: Harper & Brothers.

FORD, D. H. 1954. The role of progesterone in the production of vaginal changes in ovariectomized female rats. Endocrinology, **55**, 230–231.

FORD, D. H., AND YOUNG, W. C. 1951. The role of progesterone in the production of cyclic vaginal changes in the female guinea pig. Endocrinology, **49**, 795–804.

Foss, G. L. 1951. The influence of androgens on sexuality in women. Lancet, 1, 667–669.

Fox, H. M., and Gifford, S. 1953. Physiological responses to ACTH and cortisone. A preliminary theoretical formulation. Psychosom. Med., 15, 614–631.

Frank, A. H., and Fraps, R. M. 1945. Induction of estrus in the ovariectomized golden hamster. Endocrinology, 37, 357–361.

Garm, O. 1949. A study on bovine nymphomania. Acta Endocrinol., Suppl. 3, 2, 1–144.

Gassner, F. X. 1952. Some physiological and medical aspects of the gonadal cycle of domestic animals. Recent Progr. Hormone Res., 7, 165–208.

Gerall, A. A. 1958. An attempt to induce precocious sexual behavior in male guinea pigs by injections of testosterone propionate. Endocrinology, 63, 280–284.

Gerhardt, U. 1924. Versuch einer vergleichenden Analyse des männlichen Geschlechtstriber der Tiere. Ztschr. ges. Anat., Abt. III, 25, 661–695.

Gillman, J., and Gilbert, C. 1948. Differential reactions in the reproductive tract of baboons having different physiological backgrounds evoked by prolonged oestrogen stimulation. South African J. M. Sc., 13, 121–143.

Glaser, G. H. 1953. Psychotic reactions induced by corticotropin (ACTH) and cortisone. Psychosom. Med., 15, 280–291.

Goodale, H. D. 1913. Castration in relation to the secondary sexual characters of brown Leghorns. Am. Naturalist, 47, 159–169.

Goodale, H. D. 1916a. A feminized cockerel. J. Exper. Zool., 20, 421–428.

Goodale, H. D. 1916b. Gonadectomy in relation to the secondary sexual characters of some domestic birds. Carnegie Inst. Washington, Pub. No. 243.

Goodale, H. D. 1918. Feminized male birds. Genetics, 3, 276–299.

Goolkes, P., and Schein, J. 1953. Psychic effects of ACTH and cortisone. Psychosom. Med., 15, 589–613.

Goy, R. W., Bridson, W. E., and Young, W. C. 1961. The maximally effective period for the behavioral modification of female guinea pigs treated prenatally with testosterone propionate. Abstract, Proc. Am. A. Anat., Anat. Rec., in press.

Goy, R. W., and Jakway, J. S. 1959. The inheritance of patterns of sexual behaviour in female guinea pigs. Anim. Behav. 7, 142–149.

Goy, R. W., and Young, W. C. 1957a. Somatic basis of sexual behavior patterns in guinea pigs: factors involved in the determination of the character of the soma in the female. Psychosom. Med., 19, 144–151.

Goy, R. W., and Young, W. C. 1957b. Strain differences in the behavioral responses of female guinea pigs to α-estradiol benzoate and progesterone. Behaviour, 10, 340–354.

Goy, R. W., and Young, W. C. 1958. Responses of androgen-treated spayed female guinea pigs to estrogen and progesterone. Abstract, Proc. Am. Soc. Zool., Anat. Rec., 131, 560.

Green, J. D., Clemente, C. D., and de Groot, J. 1957. Rhinencephalic lesions and behavior in cats. An analysis of the Klüver-Bucy syndrome with particular reference to normal and abnormal sexual behavior. J. Comp. Neurol., 108, 505–545.

Greenblatt, R. B. 1943. Testosterone propionate pellet implantation in gynecic disorders. J. A. M. A., 121, 17–24.

Greenwood, A. W., and Blyth, J. S. S. 1929. An experimental analysis of the plumage of the brown Leghorn fowl. Proc. Roy. Soc., Edinburgh, 49, 313–355.

Grunt, J. A. 1954. Exogenous androgen and non-directed hyperexcitability in castrated male guinea pig. Proc. Soc. Exper. Biol. & Med., 85, 540–542.

Grunt, J. A., and Young, W. C. 1952a. Changes in strength of sex drive in the male guinea pig from age 22 to 439 days. Abstract, Proc. Am. Soc. Zool., Anat. Rec., 113, 596.

Grunt, J. A., and Young, W. C. 1952b. Differential reactivity of individuals and the response of the male guinea pig to testosterone propionate. Endocrinology, 51, 237–248.

Grunt, J. A., and Young, W. C. 1952c. Psychological modification of fatigue following orgasm (ejaculation) in the male guinea pig. J. Comp. & Physiol. Psychol., 45, 508–510.

Grunt, J. A., and Young, W. C. 1953. Consistency of sexual behavior patterns in individual male guinea pigs following castration and androgen therapy. J. Comp. & Physiol. Psychol., 46, 138–144.

Guhl, A. M. 1949. Heterosexual dominance and mating behavior in chickens. Behaviour, 2, 106–120.

Guhl, A. M., Collias, N. E., and Allee, W. C. 1945. Mating behavior and the social hierarchy in small flocks of white Leghorns. Physiol. Zool., 18, 365–390.

Guimarais, A. 1928. Effets de la castration sur les cornes peniennes et les denticules du cul-de-sac du penis chez le cobaye. Compt. rend. Soc. biol., 98, 551–552.

Hafez, E. S. E. 1952. Studies on the breeding season and reproduction of the ewe. J. Agric. Sc., 42, 189–265.

Hale, E. B. 1955. Defects in sexual behavior as factors affecting fertility in turkeys. Poultry Sc., 34, 1059–1067.

Hamilton, G. V. 1914. A study of sexual tendencies in monkeys and baboons. J. Anim. Behav., 4, 295–318.

Hamilton, J. B. 1938. Precocious masculine behavior following administration of synthetic male hormone substance. Endocrinology, 23, 53–57.

Hamilton, J. B. 1943a. Evidences of marked stimulation by sex hormones in certain eunuchs, phenomena interpreted tentatively to result from changed function of the adrenal glands following castration. Abstract, Proc. Am. A. Anat., Anat. Rec., **85**, 314.

HAMILTON, J. B. 1943b. Demonstrated ability of penile erection in castrate men with markedly low titers of urinary androgens. Proc. Soc. Exper. Biol. & Med., **54**, 309–312.

HAMILTON, J. B. 1948. The role of testicular secretions as indicated by the effects of castration in man and by studies of pathological conditions and the short lifespan associated with maleness. Recent Progr. Hormone Res. **3**, 257–322.

HAMILTON, J. B., AND GOLDEN, W. R. C. 1939. Responses of the female to male hormone substances. With notes on the behavior of hens and newly-hatched female chicks. Endocrinology, **25**, 737–748.

HAMMOND, J. 1925. *Reproduction in the Rabbit*. London: Oliver and Boyd, Ltd.

HAMMOND, J. 1927. *The Physiology of Reproduction in the Cow*. Cambridge: Cambridge University Press.

HAMMOND, J., JR., 1945. Induced ovulation and heat in anoestrous sheep. J. Endocrinol., **4**, 169–180.

HAMMOND, J., JR., AND DAY, F. T. 1944. Oestrogen treatment of cattle: induced lactation and other effects. J. Endocrinol., **4**, 53–82.

HAMPSON, J. L., HAMPSON, J. G., AND MONEY, J. 1955. The syndrome of gonadal agenesis (ovarian agenesis) and male chromosomal pattern in girls and women: psychologic studies. Bull. Johns Hopkins Hosp., **97**, 207–226.

HAMPSON, J. G., MONEY, J., AND HAMPSON, J. L. 1956. Hermaphroditism: recommendations concerning case management. J. Clin. Endocrinol., **16**, 547–556.

HARRIS, G. W., AND MICHAEL, R. P. 1958. Hypothalamic mechanisms and the control of sexual behaviour in the female cat. Proc. Physiol. Soc., J. Physiol., **142**, 26P.

HARRIS, G. W., MICHAEL, R. P., AND SCOTT, P. P. 1958. Neurological site of action of stilboestrol in eliciting sexual behaviour. In *Ciba Foundation Symposium on the Neurological Basis of Behaviour*, pp. 236–254. Boston: Little, Brown & Company.

HART, G. H., MEAD, S. W., AND REGAN, W. M. 1946. Stimulating the sex drive of bovine males in artificial insemination. Endocrinology, **39**, 221–223.

HARTMAN, C. G. 1938. Some observations on the bonnet macaque. J. Mammal., **19**, 468–474.

HARTMAN, C. G. 1945. The mating of mammals. Ann. New York Acad. Sc., **46**, 23–44.

HEBB, D. O. 1946. Behavioral differences between male and female chimpanzees. Bull. Canad. Psychol. A., **6**, 56–58.

HEIDENREICH, W. F., III, ALEXANDER, C. E., AND BEACH, F. A. 1953. Survival of mating behavior in male rats after thyroid-parathyroidectomy. Endocrinology, **52**, 719.

HELLER, C. G., AND MADDOCK, W. O. 1947. The clinical uses of testosterone in the male. Vitamins & Hormones, **5**, 393–432.

HELLER, R. E. 1932. Spontaneous activity in male rats in relation to testis hormone. Endocrinology, **16**, 626–632.

HEMMINGSEN, A. M. 1933. Studies on the oestrus-producing hormone (oestrin). Skandinav. Arch. Physiol., **65**, 97–250.

HERBERT, J., AND ZUCKERMAN, S. 1957. Effect of cerebral lesions upon oestrus in ferrets. Nature, London, **180**, 547–548.

HERTZ, R., MEYER, R. K., AND SPIELMAN, M. A. 1937. The specificity of progesterone in inducing sexual receptivity in the ovariectomized guinea pig. Endocrinology, **21**, 533–535.

HINDE, R. A. 1952. The behaviour of the great tit (*Parus major*) and some other related species. Behaviour, suppl. II, 1–201.

HINDE, R. A. 1955a. A comparative study of the courtship of certain finches (*Fringillidae*). Ibis, **97**, 706–745; and **98**, 1–23.

HINDE, R. A. 1955b. The courtship and copulation of the greenfinch (*Chloris chloris*). Behaviour, **7**, 203–233.

HISAW, F. L. 1943. Androgens and experimental menstruation in the monkey (*Macaca mulatta*). Endocrinology, **33**, 39–47.

HITCHCOCK, F. A. 1925. Studies in vigor. V. The comparative activity of male and female albino rats. Am. J. Physiol., **75**, 205–210.

HOAR, R. M., GOY, R. W., AND YOUNG, W. C. 1957. Loci of action of thyroid hormone on reproduction in the female guinea pig. Endocrinology, **60**, 337–346.

HOOKER, C. W. 1937. Testis hormone in relation to age. Endocrinology, **21**, 655–658.

HOOKER, C. W. 1942. Pubertal increase in responsiveness to androgen in the male rat. Endocrinology, **30**, 77–84.

HOSKINS, R. G. 1925a. Studies on vigor. II. The effect of castration on voluntary activity. Am. J. Physiol., **72**, 324–330.

HOSKINS, R. G. 1925b. Studies on vigor. IV. The effect of testicle grafts on spontaneous activity. Endocrinology, **9**, 277–296.

HOSKINS, R. G. 1934. Endocrinology. In *The Problem of Mental Disorder*, M. Bentley and E. V. Cowdry, Eds., pp. 234–238. New York: McGraw-Hill Book Company.

HOSKINS, R. G., AND BEVIN, S. 1940. The effect of estriol glucuronide on the spontaneous activity of senile male rats. Endocrinology, **26**, 829–832.

HOSKINS, R. G., LEVENE, H. M., AND BEVIN, S. 1939. The relationship of male sex hormone to the level of bodily vigor in senility. Endocrinology, **25**, 143–144.

HU, C. K., AND FRAZIER, C. N. 1939. Masculinization of adult female rabbit following injection of testosterone propionate. Proc. Soc. Exper. Biol. & Med., **42**, 820–823.

HUNT, J. McV., AND SCHLOSBERG, H. 1939. General activity in the male white rat. J. Comp. Psychol., **28**, 23–38.

INNES, W. A., YOUNG, W. C., AND WEBSTER, R. C. 1947. The suppressing effect of thiouracil-induced hypothyroidism on the conditioning action of estradiol benzoate as measured by the mating response in female guinea pigs. Abstract, Proc. Am. Soc. Zool., Anat. Rec., **99**, 593.

ISAACSON, J. E., JR. 1949. Induction of psychic estrus in the hamster with desoxycorticosterone acetate and its effects on the epithelium of the lower reproductive tract. Endocrinology, **45**, 558–563.

JAKWAY, J. S. 1959. Inheritance of patterns of mating behaviour in the male guinea pig. Anim. Behav. **7**, 150–162.

JAKWAY, J. S., AND YOUNG, W. C. 1958. An inherited spermatogenic hypoplasia in the guinea pig. Fertil. & Steril., **9**, 533–544.

JONES, G. E. S., AND ASTWOOD, E. B. 1942. The physiological significance of the estrogen:progesterone ratio on vaginal cornification in the rat. Endocrinology, **30**, 295–300.

JONES, G. E. S., DELFS, E., AND FOOTE, E. C. 1946. The effect of thiouracil hypothyroidism on reproduction in the rat. Endocrinology, **38**, 337–344.

JONES, J. W., AND KING, G. M. 1952. The spawning of the male salmon parr (*Salmo salar* Linn. juv.). Proc. Zool. Soc., London, **122**, 615–619.

JOST, A. 1947. Recherches sur la différenciation sexuelle de l'embryo de lapin. I. Introduction et embryologie génital normal. II. Action des androgènes de synthèse sur l'histogenèse genital. III. Rôle des gonades foetales dans la différenciation sexuelle somatique. Arch Anat. microscop. et Morphol. exper., **36**, 151–200; 242–270; 271–315.

JOST, A. 1953. Problems of fetal endocrinology: the gonadal and hypophyseal hormones. Recent Progr. Hormone Res. **8**, 379–418.

JOST, A. 1957. The secretory activities of fetal endocrine glands and their effect upon target organs. Macy Foundation Conferences on Gestation, **3**, 129–171.

KAGAN, J., AND BEACH, F. A. 1953. Effects of early experience on mating behavior in male rats. J. Comp. & Physiol. Psychol., **46**, 204–208.

KAWAKAMI, M., AND SAWYER, C. H. 1959a. Neuroendocrine correlates of changes in brain activity thresholds by sex steroids and pituitary hormones. Endocrinology, **65**, 652–668.

KAWAKAMI, M., AND SAWYER, C. H. 1959b. Induction of behavioral and electroencephalographic changes in the rabbit by hormone administration or brain stimulation. Endocrinology, **65**, 631–643.

KENT, G. C., JR., AND LIBERMAN, M. J. 1947. Vaginal smears and mating responses in ovariectomized hamsters following estrone and progesterone injections with special reference to the vaginal smear in induced mating. J. Exper. Zool., **106**, 267–280.

KENT, G. C., JR., AND LIBERMAN, M. J. 1949. Induction of psychic estrus in the hamster with progesterone administered via the lateral brain ventricle. Endocrinology, **45**, 29–32.

KINSEY, A. C., POMEROY, W. B., AND MARTIN, C. E.

1948. *Sexual Behavior in the Human Male.* Philadelphia: W. B. Saunders Company.

KINSEY, A. C., POMEROY, W. B., MARTIN, C. E., AND GEBHARD, P. H. 1953. *Sexual Behavior in the Human Female.* Philadelphia: W. B. Saunders Company.

KLEIN, M. 1952. Administration of sex hormones and sexual behavior. Ciba Foundation Colloquia Endocrinol., **3**, 323–337.

KOCHAKIAN, C. D. 1937. Excretion of male hormones. I. Endocrinology, **21**, 60–66.

KOCHAKIAN, C. D. 1939. The excretion and fate of androgens. The excretion of injected testosterone and its various derivatives. Endocrinology, **24**, 331–334.

KOCHAKIAN, C. D. 1959. Mechanisms of androgen actions. Lab. Invest., **8**, 538–556.

KOCHAKIAN, C. D., AND COCKRELL, D. 1958. Response of individual muscles of the guinea pig to "large" doses of testosterone propionate. Proc. Soc. Exper. Biol. & Med., **97**, 148–149.

KOSTER, R. 1943. Hormone factors in male behavior of the female rat. Endocrinology, **33**, 337–348.

KRICHESKY, B. 1939. The influence of thyroidectomy on the period of gestation in the rabbit. Am. J. Physiol., **126**, 234–236.

KROHN, P. L. 1951. The effect of thyroidectomy on reproduction in the female rabbit. J. Endocrinol., **7**, 307–309.

KROHN, P. L., AND WHITE, H. C. 1950. The effect of hypothyroidism on reproduction in the female albino rat. J. Endocrinol., **6**, 375–385.

KUN, H. 1934. Psychische Feminierung und Hermaphrodisierung von Männchen durch weibliches Sexualhormon. Endokrinologie, **13**, 311–323.

KUNDE, M. M., D'AMOUR, F. E., CARLSON, A. J., AND GUSTAVSON, R. G. 1930. Studies on metabolism. VIII. The effect of estrin injections on the basal metabolism, uterine endometrium, lactation, mating and maternal instincts in the adult dog. Am. J. Physiol., **95**, 630–640.

LAGERLÖF, N. 1951. Hereditary forms of sterility in Swedish cattle breeds. Fertil. & Steril., **2**, 230–242.

LAGERLÖF, N. 1954. Infertility factors in Swedish cattle breeds. Acta endocrinol., **17**, 239–249.

LARSSON, K. 1956. Conditioning and sexual behavior in the male albino rat. In *Acta Psychologica Gothoburgensia,* Vol. 1, Stockholm: Almquist and Wiksell.

LARSSON, K. 1957. The effects of spontaneous and oestrogen-induced oestrus in the female rat determined by the copulatory response of the male. Acta endocrinol., **26**, 366–370.

LARSSON, K. 1958a. Sexual activity in senile male rats. J. Gerontol., **13**, 136–139.

LARSSON, K. 1958b. Aftereffects of copulatory activity of the male rat. I. J. Comp. & Physiol. Psychol., **51**, 325–327.

LARSSON, K. 1958c. Age differences in the diurnal periodicity of male sexual behavior. Gerontologia, **2**, 64–72.

LARSSON, K. 1959. Experience and maturation in the development of sexual behaviour in male puberty rat. Behaviour, **14**, 101–107.

LASHLEY, K. S. 1938. Experimental analysis of instinctive behavior. Psychol. Rev., **45**, 445–471.

LASKOWKSI, W. 1953. Reaktionen der primären und sekundären Geschlechtsmerkmale von Platypoecilus variatus (♂ Heterogamet) und Platypoecilus maculatus (♂ Homogamet) auf Sexualhormone. Roux' Arch. Entwicklungsmech. Organ., **146**, 137–182.

LEATHEM, J. H. 1938. Experimental induction of estrus in the dog. Endocrinology, **22**, 559–567.

LEATHEM, J. H. 1951. Influence of thiouracil on reproduction in the rat and on organ histology of offspring. Abstract, Proc. Am. A. Anat., Anat. Rec., **109**, 318.

LEE, M. O. 1925. Studies on the oestrous cycle in the rat. I. The effect of thyroidectomy. Endocrinology, **9**, 410–420.

LEHRMAN, D. S. 1956. On the organization of maternal behavior and the problem of instinct. In Fondation Singer-Polignac, *L'Instinct dans la Comportement de Animaux et de l'Homme*, pp. 475–520. Paris: Masson et Cie.

LE MAGNEN, J. 1952a. Les phenomènes olfactosexuels. Arch. Sc. physiol., **6**, 125–160.

LE MAGNEN, J. 1952b. Les phenomènes olfactosexuals chez le rat blanc. Arch. Sc. physiol., **6**, 295–331.

LE MAGNEN, J. 1953. L'olfaction: le fonctionnement olfactif et son intervention dans les régulations psycho-physiologiques. J. Physiol., Paris, **45**, 285–326.

LEONARD, S. L. 1939. Induction of singing in female canaries by injections of male hormone. Proc. Soc. Exper. Biol. & Med., **41**, 229–230.

LEVINSON, L., WELSH, J. H., AND ABRAMOWITZ, A. A. 1941. Effect of hypophysectomy on diurnal rhythm of spontaneous activity in the rat. Endocrinology, **29**, 41–46.

LIPSCHÜTZ, A. 1924. *The Internal Secretions of the Sex Glands*. Baltimore: The Williams & Wilkins Company.

LIPSCHÜTZ, A. 1927. On some fundamental laws of ovarian dynamics. Biol. Rev., **2**, 263–280.

LOEB, L. 1914. The correlation between the cyclic changes in the uterus and the ovaries in the guinea-pig. Biol. Bull., **27**, 1–44.

LOESER, A. A. 1940. Subcutaneous implantation of female and male hormone in tablet form in women. Brit. M. J., **1**, 479–482.

LONG, J. A., AND EVANS, H. M. 1922. The oestrous cycle in the rat and its associated phenomena. Mem. Univ. California, **6**, 1–148.

LORENZ, K. S. 1937. The companion in the bird's world. Auk, **54**, 245–273.

LOUTTIT, C. M. 1927. Reproductive behavior of the guinea pig. I. The normal mating behavior. J. Comp. Psychol., **7**, 247–265.

LOUTTIT, C. M. 1929. Reproductive behavior of the guinea pig. II. The ontogenesis of the reproductive behavior pattern. J. Comp. Psychol., **9**, 293–304.

LYMAN, C. P., AND DEMPSEY, E. W. 1951. The effect of testosterone on the seminal vesicles of castrated, hibernating hamsters. Endocrinology, **49**, 647–651.

MACIRONE, C., AND WALTON, A. 1938. Fecundity of male rabbits as determined by "dummy matings." J. Agric. Sc., **28**, 122–134.

MAES, J. P. 1939. Neural mechanism of sexual behavior in the female cat. Nature, London, **144**, 598–599.

MAES, J. 1940. Hypophysectomie et comportement sexuel de la chatte. Compt. rend. Soc. biol., **133**, 92–94.

MAKEPEACE, A. W., WEINSTEIN, G. L., AND FRIEDMAN, M. W. 1937. The effect of progestin and progesterone on ovulation in the rabbit. Am J. Physiol., **119**, 512–516.

MAQSOOD, M. 1952. Thyroid functions in relation to reproduction of mammals and birds. Biol. Rev., **27**, 281–319.

MARKLEY, M. H., AND BASSETT, C. F. 1942. Habits of a captive marten. Am. Midland Naturalist, **28**, 604–616.

MARSHALL, F. H. A., AND HAMMOND, J., JR. 1945. Experimental control by hormone action of the oestrous cycle in the ferret. J. Endocrinol., **4**, 159–168.

MARVIN, H. N. 1958. Copulatory reflex by progesterone and desoxycorticosterone acetate. Proc. Soc. Exper. Biol. & Med., **97**, 197–198.

McCORMACK, G., AND ELDEN, C. A. 1945. Seasonal variation of rabbits to pituitary extract. Endocrinology, **37**, 297–299.

McKENZIE, F. F. 1926. The normal oestrous cycle in the sow. Univ. Missouri Coll. Agric. Res. Bull., No. 86.

MEDVEI, V. C. 1949. Endocrine disorders and the mind. Practitioner, **162**, 139–147.

MELAMPY, R. M., EMMERSON, M. A., RAKES, J. M., HANKA, L. J., AND ENESS, P. G. 1957. The effect of progesterone on the estrous response of estrogen-conditioned ovariectomized cows. J. Anim. Sc., **16**, 967–975.

MELAMPY, R. M., AND RAKES, J. M. 1958. Induced estrus in ovariectomized cows. Iowa State Coll. J. Sc., **33**, 85–90.

MICHAEL, R. P. 1958. Sexual behavior and the vaginal cycle in the cat. Nature, London, **181**, 567–568.

MICHAEL, R. P., AND SCOTT, P. P. 1957. Quantitative studies on mating behaviour of spayed female cats stimulated by treatment with oestrogens. Proc. Physiol. Soc., J. Physiol., **138**, 46–47P.

MILLER, N. E. 1957. Experiments on motivation. Studies combining psychological, physiological, and pharmacological techniques. Science, **126**, 1271–1278.

MILOVANOV, V. K., AND SMIRNOV-UGRJUMOV, D. V. 1944. *Artificial Insemination of Farm Animals*. Moscow.

MINNICK, R. S., WARDEN, C. J., AND ARIETI, S. 1946. The effects of sex hormones on the copulatory behavior of senile white rats. Science, **103**, 749–750.

MOLL, A. 1897. Untersuchungen über die Libido sexualis. Berlin: Fischer.

MONEY, J. 1955. Hermaphroditism, gender and precocity in hyperadrenocorticism: psychologic findings. Bull. Johns Hopkins Hosp., **96**, 253–264.

MONEY, J., HAMPSON, J. G., AND HAMPSON, J. L. 1955. An examination of some basic sexual concepts: the evidence of human hermaphroditism. Bull. Johns Hopkins Hosp., **97**, 301–319.

MONEY, J., HAMPSON, J. G., AND HAMPSON, J. L. 1957. Imprinting and the establishment of gender role. A. M. A. Arch. Neurol. & Phychiat., **77**, 333–336.

MOOG, F. 1953. The functional differentiation of the small intestine. III. The influence of the pituitary-adrenal system on the differentiation of phosphatase in the duodenum of the suckling mouse. J. Exper. Zool., **124**, 329–346.

MOORE, C. R. 1928. On the properties of the gonads as controllers of somatic and psychical characteristics. XI. Hormone production in the normal testes, cryptorchid testes and non-living testis grafts as indicated by the spermatozöon motility test. Biol. Bull., **55**, 339–357.

MOORE, C. R. 1941. On the role of sex hormones in sex differentiation in the opossum (*Didelphys virginiana*). Physiol. Zool., **14**, 1–47.

MOORE, C. R. 1947. *Embryonic Sex Hormones and Sexual Differentiation*. Springfield, Ill.: Charles C Thomas.

MOORE, C. R., AND GALLAGHER, T. F. 1930. Seminal-vesicle and prostate function as a testis-hormone indicator; the electric ejaculation test. Am. J. Anat., **45**, 39–69.

MOORE, C. R., AND PRICE, D. 1938. Some effects of testosterone and testosterone-propionate in the rat. Anat. Rec., **71**, 59–78.

MOORE, N. W., AND ROBINSON, T. J. 1957. The behavioral and vaginal response of the spayed ewe to estrogen injected at various times relative to the injection of progesterone. J. Endocrinol., **15**, 360–365.

MORRIS, D. 1952. Homosexuality in the tenspined stickleback (*Pygosteus pungitius* L.). Behaviour, **4**, 233–261.

MORRIS, D. 1954. The reproductive behaviour of the zebra finch, (*Poephila guttata*), with special reference to pseudofemale behaviour and displacement activities. Behaviour, **6**, 271–322.

MORRIS, D. 1955a. The causation of pseudofemale and pseudomale behaviour; a further comment. Behaviour, **8**, 46–56.

MORRIS, D. 1955b. The reproductive behaviour of the river bullhead (*Cottus gobio* L.), with special reference to the fanning activity. Behaviour, **7**, 1–33.

MOYNIHAN, M., AND HALL, M. F. 1955. Hostile, sexual, and other social behaviour patterns of the spice finch (*Lonchura punctulata*) in captivity. Behaviour, **7**, 33–76.

MÜHLBOCK, O. 1940. Keine antagonistische Wirkung des Oestradiolbenzoates auf die Kopulationsfähigkeit männlicher mit Testosteronpropionat behandelter Ratten. Acta. brev. neerl. Physiol., **10**, 69–74.

NELSON, W. O., AND GALLAGHER, T. F. 1936. Some effects of androgenic substances in the rat. Science, **84**, 230–232.

NISSEN, H. W. 1929. The effects of gonadectomy, vasotomy and injections of placental and orchic extracts on the sex behavior of the white rat. Genet. Psychol. Monogr., **5**, 451–547.

NISSEN, H. W. 1954. Personal communication.[11]

NOBLE, G. K., AND KUMPF, K. F. 1936. The sexual behavior and secondary sex characters of gonadectomized fish. Abstract, Proc. Am. Soc. Zool., Anat. Rec., **67**, Suppl. 1, 113.

NOBLE, G. K., AND WURM, M. 1940a. The effect of testosterone propionate on the black-crowned night heron. Endocrinology, **26**, 837–850.

NOBLE, G. K., AND WURM, M. 1940b. The effect of hormones on the breeding of the laughing gull. Abstract, Proc. Am. Soc. Zool., Anat. Rec., **78** (Suppl. 1), 50.

NOBLE, G. K., AND BORNE, R. 1940. The effect of sex hormones on the social hierarchy of *Xiphophorus helleri*. Abstract, Proc. Am. Soc. Zool., Anat. Rec., **78**(Suppl. 1), 147.

NOBLE, G. K., AND GREENBERG, B. 1941a. Induction of female behavior in male *Anolis carolinensis* with testosterone propionate. Proc. Soc. Exper. Biol. & Med., **47**, 32–37.

NOBLE, G. K., AND GREENBERG, B. 1941b. Effects of seasons, castration and crystalline sex hormones upon the urogenital system and sexual behavior of the lizard (*Anolis carolinensis*). I. The adult female. J. Exper. Zool., **88**, 451–479.

NOBLE, G. K., AND ARONSON, L. R. 1942. The sexual behavior of Anura. I. The normal mating pattern of *Rana pipiens*. Bull. Am. Museum Nat. Hist., **80**, 127–142.

NOBLE, G. K., AND ZITRIN, A. 1942. Induction of mating behavior in male and female chicks following injection of sex hormones. Endocrinology, **30**, 327–334.

OKADA, Y. K., AND YAMASHITA, H. 1944. Experimental investigation of the manifestation of secondary sexual characters in fish, using the Mekada, *Oryzias latipes* (Temminck & Schlegel) as material. J. Fac. Sc. Imp. Univ. Tokyo., Sect. IV, **6**, 383–437.

---

[11] The material cited in this chapter was selected from the substance of a talk given by Dr. Nissen and entitled, "Development of Sexual Behavior in Chimpanzees." The complete paper is contained in an unpublished symposium, "Genetic, Psychological, and Hormonal Factors in the Establishment and Maintenance of Patterns of Sexual Behavior in Mammals." A copy of the symposium is on file in the University of Kansas Library, F 591.16 Sy68 1954.

OLSON, H. H., AND PETERSEN, W. E. 1951. Uniformity of semen production and behavior in monozygous triplet bulls. Abstract, Forty-sixth annual meeting of the American Dairy Science Association. J. Dairy Sc., 34, 489.

PEARL, R., AND SURFACE, F. M. 1915. Sex Studies. VII. On the assumption of male secondary sex characters by a cow with cystic degeneration of the ovaries. Maine Agric. Exper. Sta. Bull., No. 237, 65–80.

PEARSON, O. P. 1944. Reproduction in the shrew (Blarina brevicauda Say). Am. J. Anat., 75, 39–93.

PERLOFF, W. H. 1949. Role of the hormones in human sexuality. Psychosom. Med., 11, 133–139.

PETERSEN, W. E., SPIELMAN, A., POMEROY, B. S., AND BOYD, W. L. 1941. Effect of thyroidectomy upon sexual behavior of the male bovine. Proc. Soc. Exper. Biol. & Med., 46, 16–17.

PETERSON, R. R., WEBSTER, R. C., RAYNER, B., AND YOUNG, W. C. 1952. The thyroid and reproductive performance in the adult female guinea pig. Endocrinology, 51, 504–518.

PETERSON, R. R., AND YOUNG, W. C. 1955. Prolonged cold, sex drive and metabolic responses in the male guinea pig. Am. J. Physiol., 180, 535–538.

PÉZARD, A. 1922. Modifications périodiques ou définitives des caractères sexuels secondaires chez les Gallinacés. Ann. Sc. Nat. (Bot. et Zool.), 83–104.

PHILLIPS, R. W., FRAPS, R. M., AND FRANK, A. H. 1946. Ovulation and estrus in sheep and goats. In The Problem of Fertility, E. T. Engle, Ed., pp. 11–48. Princeton: Princeton University Press.

PHOENIX, C. H., GOY, R. W., GERALL, A. A., AND YOUNG, W. C. 1959. Organizing action of prenatally administered testosterone propionate on the tissues mediating mating behavior in the female guinea pig. Endocrinology, 65, 369–382.

PINCUS, G. 1952. Some basic hormone problems. J. Clin. Endocrinol., 12, 1187–1196.

PINCUS, G. 1956. Aging and urinary steroid excretion. In Hormones and the Aging Process, E. T. Engle, and G. Pincus, Eds., pp. 1–20, New York: Academic Press, Inc.

PINCUS, G., AND ENZMANN, E. V. 1937. The growth, maturation and atresia of ovarian eggs in the rabbit. J. Morphol., 61, 351–383.

PINCUS, G., AND HOPKINS, T. F. 1958. The effects of various estrogens and steroid substances on sex differentiation in the fowl. Endocrinology, 62, 112–118.

PRICE, D. 1947. An analysis of the factors influencing growth and development of the mammalian reproductive tract. Physiol. Zool., 20, 213–247.

PRICE, D. 1957. Influence of hormones on sex differentiation in explanted fetal reproductive tracts. Macy Foundation Conferences on Gestation, 3, 173–186.

PRICE, D., AND ORTIZ, E. 1944. The relation of

age to reactivity in the reproductive system of the rat. Endocrinology, 34, 215–239.

QUIN, J. I., AND VAN DER WATH, J. G. 1943. The effects of diethylstilboestrol and pregnant mare serum on the oestrous cycle of Merino ewes. Onderstepoort J. Vet. Sc. & Anim. Ind., 18, 139–147.

RASMUSSEN, E. W. 1952. The relation between strength of sexual drive and fertility as evident from experimental investigations. In The Second International Congress of Physiology and Pathology of Animal Reproduction and of Artificial Insemination, Vol. I, pp. 188–191. Copenhagen.

RAYNAUD, A. 1938. Comportement sexuel des souris femelles intersexueés. Compt. rend. Soc. biol., 127, 993–995.

REED, C. A. 1946. The copulatory behavior of small mammals. J. Comp. Psychol., 39, 185–206.

REED, C. A., AND REED, R. 1946. The copulatory behavior of the golden hamster. J. Comp. Psychol., 39, 7–12.

RICHDALE, L. E. 1951. Sexual Behavior in Penguins. Lawrence: University of Kansas Press.

RICHTER, C. P. 1927. Animal behavior and internal drives. Quart. Rev. Biol., 2, 307–343.

RICHTER, C. P. 1933. The effect of early gonadectomy on the gross body activity of rats. Endocrinology, 17, 445–450.

RICHTER, C. P., AND WISLOCKI, G. B. 1928. Activity studies on castrated male and female rats with testicular grafts, in correlation with histological study of the grafts, Am. J. physiol., 86, 651–660.

RICHTER, C. P., AND HARTMAN, C. G. 1934. The effect of injection of amniotin on the spontaneous activity of gonadectomized rats. Am. J. Physiol., 108, 136–143.

RICHTER, C. P., AND UHLENHUTH, E. H. 1954. Comparison of the effects of gonadectomy on spontaneous activity of wild and domesticated Norway rats. Endocrinology, 54, 311–322.

RICKEY, E. 1925. The thyroid influence on the behavior of the white rat. Comp. Psychol. Monogr., 2, No. 12.

RIDDLE, O. 1924. A case of complete sex-reversal in the adult pigeon. Am. Nat., 58, 167–181.

RIDDLE, O. 1925. Birds without gonads: their origin, behaviour, and bearing on the theory of the internal secretion of the testis. Brit. J. Exper. Biol., 2, 211–246.

RING, J. R. 1944. The estrogen-progesterone induction of sexual receptivity in the spayed female mouse. Endocrinology, 34, 269–275.

RING, J. R. 1945. The hormonal induction of mating responses in the spayed-adrenalectomized female rat. Endocrinology, 37, 237–244.

RISS, W. 1955. Sex drive, oxygen consumption and heart rate in genetically different strains of male guinea pigs. Am. J. Physiol., 180, 530–534.

RISS, W., AND YOUNG, W. C. 1953. Somatic, psychological, and androgenic determinants in the development of sexual behavior in the male guinea pig. Abstract, Proc. Am. Psychol. A., Am. Psychol., **8**, 421.

RISS, W., AND YOUNG, W. C. 1954. The failure of large quantities of testosterone propionate to activate low drive male guinea pigs. Endocrinology, **54**, 232–235.

RISS, W., VALENSTEIN, E. S., SINKS, J., AND YOUNG, W. C. 1955. Development of sexual behavior in male guinea pigs from genetically different stocks under controlled conditions of androgen treatment and caging. Endocrinology, **57**, 139–146.

RISS, W., AND GOY, R. W. 1957. Modification of sex drive and O₂ consumption by isolating and grouping male guinea pigs. J. Comp. & Physiol. Psychol., **50**, 150–154.

ROARK, D. B., AND HERMAN, H. A. 1950. Physiological and histological phenomena of the bovine estrual cycle with special reference to vaginal-cervical secretions. Univ. Missouri Coll. Agric. Res. Bull., No. 455.

ROBINSON, A. 1918. The formation, rupture, and closure of ovarian follicles in ferrets and ferretpolecat hybrids, and some associated phenomena. Tr. Roy. Soc., Edinburgh, **52**, 303–362.

ROBINSON, T. J. 1954a. The necessity for progesterone with estrogen for the induction of recurrent estrus in the ovariectomized ewe. Endocrinology, **55**, 403–408.

ROBINSON, T. J. 1954b. The production of coincident oestrus and ovulation in the anoestrus ewe with progesterone and pregnant mare serum. J. Endocrinol., **10**, 117–124.

ROBINSON, T. J. 1955. Quantitative studies on the hormonal induction of oestrus in spayed ewes. J. Endocrinol., **12**, 163–173.

ROBINSON, T. J., MOORE, N. W., AND BINET, F. E. 1956. The effect of the duration of progesterone pretreatment on the response of the spayed ewe to oestrogen. J. Endocrinol., **14**, 1–7.

ROBSON, J. M. 1938. Induction of oestrous changes in the monkey and bitch by triphenyl ethylene. Proc. Soc. Exper. Biol. & Med., **38**, 153–157.

ROBSON, J. M., AND HENDERSON, W. R. 1936. The action of oestrin on the bitch. Proc. Roy. Soc., London, ser. B. **120**, 1–14.

ROBSON, J. M., AND SCHÖNBERG, A. 1937. Oestrous reactions, including mating, produced by triphenyl ethylene. Nature, London, **140**, 196.

ROME, H. P., AND BRACELAND, F. J. 1950. Use of cortisone and ACTH in certain diseases: psychiatric aspects. Proc. Staff Meet. Mayo Clin., **25**, 495–498.

ROME, H. P., AND BRACELAND, F. J. 1951. The effect of ACTH, cortisone, hydrocortisone and related steroids on mood. J. Clin. & Exper. Psychopath., **12**, 184–191.

ROME, H. P., AND BRACELAND, F. J. 1952. Psychological response to corticotropin, cortisone and related steroid substances (psychotic reaction types). J. A. M. A., **148**, 27–30.

ROSA, C. G. 1959. Histochemical observations of oxidative enzyme systems in the uterus and vagina of the rat. Ann. New York Acad. Sc., **75**, 491–503.

ROSA, C. G., AND VELARDO, J. T. 1959. Histochemical observations of oxidative enzyme systems in the uterus and vagina of the rat. Ann. New York Acad. Sc., **75**, 491–503.

ROSENBLATT, J. S., AND ARONSON, L. R. 1958a. The decline of sexual behavior in male cats after castration with special reference to the role of prior sexual experience. Behaviour, **12**, 285–338.

ROSENBLATT, J. S., AND ARONSON, L. R. 1958b. The influence of experience on the behavioural effects of androgen in prepubertally castrated male cats. Anim. Behav., **6**, 171–182.

ROUSSEL, G. 1936. L'acétate de testostérone, hormone testiculaire synthétique. Bull. Acad. Méd., **115**, 458–461.

ROWLEY, I., AND MOLLISON, B. C. 1955. Copulation in the wild rabbit, *Oryctolagus cuniculus*. Behaviour, **8**, 81–84.

RUNDQUIST, E. A. 1933. Inheritance of spontaneous activity in rats. J. Comp. Psychol., **16**, 415–438.

RUSSELL, W. M. S. 1955. Experimental studies of the reproductive behaviour of *Xenopus laevis*. I. The control mechanisms for clasping and unclasping, and the specificity of hormone action. Behaviour, **7**, 113–188.

SACHS, M. G. 1939. On the causes of sterility in experimental athyreosis. Bull. Biol. et Méd. exper., URSS, **7**, 521–523.

SALMON, U. J. 1942. Rationale for androgen therapy in gynecology. J. Clin. Endocrinol., **1**, 162–179.

SALMON, U. J., AND GEIST, S. H. 1943. Effect of androgens upon libido in women. J. Clin. Endocrinol., **3**, 235–238.

SAND, K. 1919. Experiments on the internal secretion of the sexual glands, especially on experimental hermaphroditism. J. Physiol., **53**, 257–263.

SAWYER, C. H., AND EVERETT, J. W. 1959. Stimulatory and inhibitory effects of progesterone on the release of pituitary ovulating hormone in the rabbit. Endocrinology, **65**, 644–651.

SAWYER, C. H., AND KAWAKAMI, M. 1959. Characteristics of behavioral and electroencephalographic after-reactions to copulation and vaginal stimulation in the female rabbit. Endocrinology, **65**, 622–630.

SAWYER, C. H., AND MARKEE, J. E. 1959. Estrogen facilitation of release of pituitary ovulating hormone in the rabbit in response to vaginal stimulation. Endocrinology, **65**, 614–621.

SAX, M. G., AND LEIBSON, R. G. 1937. The significance of the active substances of the thyroid for intra-uterine development of mammals. Bull. Biol. et Méd. exper., URSS, **4**, 496–498.

SCHINKEL, P. G. 1954a. The effect of the presence of the ram on the ovarian activity of the ewe. Australian J. Agric. Res., **5**, 465–469.

SCHINKEL, P. G. 1954b. The effect of the ram on

the incidence and occurrence of oestrus in ewes. Australian Vet. J., **30**, 189–195.

SCHLOSBERG, H., DUNCAN, M. C., AND DAITCH, B. H. 1949. Mating behavior of two live-bearing fish, *Xiphophorus helleri* and *Platypoecilus maculatus*. Physiol. Zool., **22**, 148–161.

SCHEIN, M. W., AND HALE, E. B. 1959. The effect of early social experience on male sexual behaviour of androgen injected turkeys. Anim. Behav., **7**, 189–200.

SCHOU, H. I. 1951. The excretion of gonadotrophin and androgenic substances by normal men between 39 and 63 years of age: serial determinations over ten years. Acta Endocrinol., **8**, 149–154.

SCHWARTZ, M., AND BEACH, F. A. 1954. Effects of adrenalectomy upon mating behavior in castrated male dogs. Abstract, Proc. Am. Psychol. A., Am. Psychol., **9**, 467.

SCOTT, H. M., AND PAYNE, L. F. 1934. The effect of gonadectomy on the secondary sexual characters of the bronze turkey (*M. gallopavo*). J. Exper. Zool., **69**, 123–136.

SCOTT, P. P., AND LLOYD-JACOB, M. A. 1955. Some interesting features in the reproductive cycle of the cat. In *Studies on Fertility*, R. G. Harrison, Ed., vol. 7, pp. 123–129. Oxford: Blackwell Scientific Publications.

SEWARD, J. P. 1940. Studies on the reproductive activities of the guinea pig. III. The effect of androgenic hormone on sex drive in males and females. J. Comp. Psychol., **30**, 435–449.

SHADLE, A. R. 1946. Copulation in the porcupine. J. Wildlife Mgmt., **10**, 159–162.

SHAPIRO, H. A. 1937a. The biological basis of sexual behaviour in amphibia. IV. J. Exper. Biol., **14**, 38–47.

SHAPIRO, H. A. 1937b. Effect of testosterone propionate on mating. Nature, London, **139**, 588–589.

SHERMAN, M. 1945. *Intelligence and Its Deviations*. New York: Ronald Press.

SHIRLEY, M. 1928. Studies of activity. I. Consistency of the revolving drum method of measuring the activity of the rat. J. Comp. Psychol., **8**, 23–38.

SHOCK, N. W. 1944. Physiological factors in behavior. In *Personality and the Behavior Disorders*, J. McV. Hunt, Ed., pp. 582–618. New York: Ronald Press.

SHOEMAKER, H. H. 1939. Effect of testosterone propionate on behavior of the female canary. Proc. Soc. Exper. Biol. & Med., **41**, 299–302.

SHORR, E., PAPANICOLAOU, G. N., AND STIMMEL, B. F. 1938. Neutralization of ovarian follicular hormone in women by simultaneous administration of male sex hormone. Proc. Soc. Exper. Biol. & Med., **38**, 759–762.

SIMPSON, S. A., AND WILLIAMS, P. C. 1949. Mating of spayed-adrenalectomized rats given oestrogen. J. Endocrinol., **6**, 169–170.

SLONAKER, J. R. 1912. The normal activity of the albino rat from birth to natural death, its rate of growth and the duration of life. J. Anim. Behav., **2**, 20–42.

SLONAKER, J. R. 1924. The effect of pubescence, oestruation and menopause on the voluntary activity in the albino rat. Am. J. Physiol., **68**, 294–315.

SMITH, K. U. 1940. An improved stabilimeter method for recording activity in laboratory animals. J. Exper. Psychol., **27**, 89–93.

SNELL, G. D., FEKETE, E., HUMMEL, K. P., AND LAW, L. W. 1940. The relation of mating, ovulation, and the estrous smear in the house mouse to time of day. Anat Rec., **76**, 39–54.

SODERWALL, A. L. 1940. Induction of sexual receptivity in estrogen-conditioned spayed female guinea pigs by orally administered progesterone and pregneninolone. Endocrinology, **27**, 840–841.

SOLLENBERGER, R. T., AND HAMILTON, J. B. 1939. The effect of testosterone propionate upon the sexual behavior of castrated male guinea pigs. J .Comp. Psychol., **28**, 81–92.

SOULAIRAC, A. 1950. L'effet de groupe dans le comportement sexuel de rat mâle. Coll. Internat. C. N. R. S. Paris, **34**, 91–97.

SOULAIRAC, A. 1952a. Action du propionate de testostérone sur le comportement sexuel du rat mâle adulte normal. Compt. rend. Soc. biol., **146**, 55–58.

SOULAIRAC, A. 1952b. Action de la thyroxine et du diéthylstilboestrol sur le comportement sexuel du rat mâle normal. Compt. rend. Soc. biol., **146**, 199–201.

SOULAIRAC, A. 1952c. Analyse expérimentale des actions hormonales sur le comportement sexuel du rat mâle normal. J. Physiol., Paris, **44**, 327–330.

SOULAIRAC, A. 1952d. Étude expérimentale du comportement sexuel male. Indépendance relative des diverse éléments moteurs chez de rat male normal. Ann. Endocrinol., **13**, 775–780.

SOULAIRAC, A. 1952e. La signification physiologique de la période réfractaire dans le comportement sexuel du rat male. J. Physiol., Paris, **44**, 99–113.

SOULAIRAC, A., AND COPPIN-MONTHILLAUD, M. 1951. Données expérimentales sur les relations hormono-nerveuses dans le comportement sexuel du rat mâle. J. Physiol., Paris, **43**, 869–872.

SOULAIRAC, A., DESCLAUX, P., AND COPPIN, M. 1950. Action de la thyroïd sur le comportement sexuel du rat mâle. J. Physiol., Paris, **42**, 729–730.

SOULAIRAC, A., TEYSSEYRE, J., AND SOULAIRAC, M.-L. 1955. Action de l'administration chronique de cortisone sur le comportement sexuel du rat male. Effets concomitants sur le système nerveux et sur différentes glandes endocrines. Ann. Endocrinol., **16**, 694–701.

SPIEGEL, A. 1939. Auftreten von Adenomen der Nebennierenrinde mit vermännlichender Wirkung bei Frühkastrierten Meerschweinchenmännchen. Klin. Wchnschr., **18**, 1068–1069.

SPIELMAN, A. S., PETERSEN, W. E., FITCH, J. B., AND POMEROY, B. S. 1945. General appearance, growth and reproduction of thyroidectomized bovine. J. Dairy Sc., **28,** 329–337.

STEINACH, E. 1894. Untersuchungen zur vergleichenden Physiologie der männlichen Geschlechtsorgane insbesondere der accessorischen Geschlechtsdrüsen. Arch. ges. Physiol., **56,** 304–338.

STEINACH, E. 1910. Geschlechtstrieb und echt sekundäre Geschlechtsmerkmale als Folge der innersekretorischen Funktion der Keimdrüsen. Zentralbl. Physiol., **24,** 551–566.

STEINACH, E. 1912. Willkürliche Umwandlung von Säugetier-männchen in Tiere mit ausgeprägt weiblichen Geschlechtescharackteren und weiblicher Psyche. Arch. ges. Physiol., **144,** 71–108.

STEINACH, E. 1913. Feminierung von Männchen und Maskulierung von Weibchen. Zentralbl. Physiol., **27,** 717–723.

STEINACH, E. 1916. Puberstätsdrüsen und Zwitterbildung. Roux' Arch. Entwicklungsmech. Organ., **42,** 307–332.

STEINACH, E., AND KUN, H. 1928. Die entwicklungsmechanische Bedeutung der Hypophysis als Aktivator der Keimdrüseninkretion. Versuche an infantilen, eunuchoiden und senilen Männchen. Med. Klin., **24,** 524–528.

STELLAR, E. 1960. The marmoset as a laboratory animal: maintenance, general observations of behavior, and simple learning. J. Comp. & Physiol. Psychol., **53,** 1–10.

STOCKARD, C. R., AND PAPANICOLAOU, G. N. 1919. Vaginal closure membrane, copulation, and the vaginal plug in the guinea-pig, with further considerations of the oestrous rhythm. Biol. Bull., **37,** 222–245.

STONE, C. P. 1922. The congenital sexual behavior of the young male albino rat. J. Comp. Psychol., **2,** 95–153.

STONE, C. P. 1923. Experimental studies of two important factors underlying masculine sexual behavior. The nervous system and the internal secretion of the testis. J. Exper. Psychol., **6,** 85–106.

STONE, C. P. 1924a. A note on "feminine" behavior in adult male rats. Am. J. Physiol., **68,** 39–41.

STONE, C. P. 1924b. The awakening of copulatory ability in the male albino rat. Am. J. Physiol., **68,** 39–41.

STONE, C. P. 1926. The initial copulatory response of female rats reared in isolation from the age of twenty days to the age of puberty. J. Comp. Psychol., **6,** 73–83.

STONE, C. P. 1927. The retention of copulatory ability in male rats following castration. J. Comp. Psychol., **7,** 369–387.

STONE, C. P. 1932a. The retention of copulatory ability in male rabbits following castration. J. Genet. Psychol., **40,** 296–305.

STONE, C. P. 1932b. Sexual drive. In *Sex and Internal Secretions,* 1st ed., E. Allen, Ed., pp.

828–879. Baltimore: The Williams & Wilkins Company.

STONE, C. P. 1938. Activation of impotent male rats by injections of testosterone propionate. J. Comp. Psychol., **25,** 445–450.

STONE, C. P. 1939a. Copulatory activity in adult male rats following castration and injections of testosterone propionate. Endocrinology, **24,** 165–174.

STONE, C. P. 1939b. Sex Drive. In *Sex and Internal Secretions,* 2nd ed., E. Allen, C. H. Danforth and E. A. Doisy, Eds., pp. 1213–1262. Baltimore: The Williams & Wilkins Company.

STONE, C. P. 1940. Precocious copulatory activity induced in male rats by subcutaneous injections of testosterone propionate. Endocrinology, **26,** 511–515.

STONE, C. P., AND BARKER, R. G. 1934. Spontaneous activity, direct and indirect measures of sexual drive in adult male rats. Proc. Soc. Exper. Biol. & Med., **32,** 195–199.

STONE, C. P., TOMILIN, M. I., AND BARKER, R. G. 1935. A comparative study of sexual drive in adult male rats as measured by direct copulatory tests and by the Columbia obstruction apparatus. J. Comp. Psychol., **19,** 215–241.

STONE, C. P., AND FERGUSON, L. W. 1940. Temporal relationships in the copulatory acts of adult male rats. J. Comp. Psychol., **30,** 419–433.

STONE, C. P., FERGUSON, L. W., AND WRIGHT, C. 1940. Consistency in lengths of post-ejaculatory quiescent periods in adult male rats. Proc. Soc. Exper. Biol. & Med., **45,** 120–121.

SZEGO, C. M., AND ROBERTS, S. 1953. Steroid action and interaction in uterine metabolism. Recent Progr. Hormone Res., **8,** 419–469.

TAUBER, E. S. 1940. Effects of castration upon the sexuality of the adult male. A review of relevant literature. Psychosom. Med., **2,** 74–87.

TAVOLGA, W. N. 1955. Effects of gonadectomy and hypophysectomy on prespawning behavior in males of the gobiid fish, *Bathygobius soporator.* Physiol. Zool., **28,** 218–233.

TEDFORD, M. D., AND YOUNG, W. C. 1960. Ovarian structure in guinea pigs made hermaphroditic by the administration of androgen prenatally. Abstr., Proc. Am. A. Anat., Anat. Rec., **136,** 325.

THOREK, M. 1924. Experimental investigation of the role of the Leydig, seminiferous and Sertoli cells and effects of testicular transplantation. Endocrinology, **8,** 61–90.

THUNG, P. J., BOOT, L. M., AND MÜHLBOCK, O. 1956. Senile changes in the oestrous cycle and in ovarian structure in some inbred strains of mice. Acta endocrinol., **23,** 8–32.

TINBERGEN, N. 1951. *The Study of Instinct.* Oxford: Clarendon Press.

TORSTVEIT, O., AND MELLISH, C. H. 1941. Guinea pig copulatory reflex in response to aqueous extracts of adrenal cortex. Proc. Soc. Exper. Biol. & Med., **46,** 239–240.

TRETHOWAN, W. H., AND COBB, S. 1952. Neuropsychiatric aspects of Cushing's syndrome. Arch. Neurol. & Psychiat., **67,** 283–309.

TURNER, C. D. 1939. The modification of sexual differentiation in genetic female mice by the prenatal administration of testosterone propionate. J. Morphol., **65,** 353–381.

TURNER, C. W., MIXNER, J. P., AND REINEKE, E. P. 1943. Thyroprotein for sterile goats. Dairy Goat J., **21,** 1 and 21.

VALENSTEIN, E. S., AND YOUNG, W. C. 1953. Resistance of strain differences in male sex drive and growth to maternal influence prior to weaning in the guinea pig. Abstract, Proc. Am. Soc. Zool., Anat. Rec., **117,** 604.

VALENSTEIN, E. S., RISS, W., AND YOUNG, W. C. 1954. Sex drive in genetically heterogeneous and highly inbred strains of male guinea pigs. J. Comp. & Physiol. Psychol., **47,** 162–165.

VALENSTEIN, E. S., RISS, W., AND YOUNG, W. C. 1955. Experiential and genetic factors in the organization of sexual behavior in male guinea pigs. J. Comp. & Physiol. Psychol., **48,** 397–403.

VALENSTEIN, E. S., AND YOUNG, W. C. 1955. An experiential factor influencing the effectiveness of testosterone propionate in eliciting sexual behavior in male guinea pigs. Endocrinology, **56,** 173–177.

VALENSTEIN, E. S., AND GOY, R. W. 1957. Further studies of the organization and display of sexual behavior in male guinea pigs. J. Comp. & Physiol. Psychol., **50,** 115–119.

VAN HEUVERSWYN, J., COLLINS, V. J., WILLIAMS, W. L., AND GARDNER, W. U. 1939. The progesterone-like activity of desoxycorticosterone. Proc. Soc. Exper. Biol. & Med., **41,** 552–554.

VAN LANDINGHAM, A. H., HYATT, G., WEAKLEY, C. A,. AND HENDERSON, H. O. 1947. Further observations on the effects of feeding thyroprotein to dairy cows. J. Dairy Sc., **30,** 576–577.

WALLACE, C. 1949. The effects of castration and stilboestrol treatment on the semen production of the boar. J. Endocrinol., **6,** 205–217.

WALTON, A. 1950. Patterns of male sex behaviour. Society for the Study of Fertility (Great Britain). Proc. Edinburgh Conference, **1,** 40–44.

WALTON, A., EDWARDS, J., AND HAMMOND, J. 1940. Fertility in farm animals. J. Roy. Agric. Soc. England, **100,** 1–12.

WANG, G. H., RICHTER, C. P., AND GUTTMACHER, A. F. 1925. Activity studies on male castrated rats with ovarian transplants, and correlation of the activity with the histology of the grafts. Am. J. Physiol., **73,** 581–599.

WARREN, R. P., AND ARONSON, L. R. 1956. Sexual behavior in castrated-adrenalectomized hamsters maintained on DCA. Endocrinology, **58,** 293–304.

WARREN, R. P., AND ARONSON, L. R. 1957. Sexual behavior in adult male hamsters castrated-

adrenalectomized prior to puberty. J. Comp. & Physiol. Phychol., **50,** 475–480.

WAXENBERG, S. E., DRELLICH, M. G., AND SUTHERLAND, A. M. 1959. The role of hormones in human behavior. I. Changes in female sexuality after adrenalectomy. J. Clin. Endocrinol., **19,** 193–202.

WAYMAN. O., AND ASDELL, S. A. 1952. Studies in the physiology of bovine nymphomania. Cornell Vet., **42,** 296–303.

WEBER, E. 1911. Untersuchungen über die Brunst des Rindes. Arch. Wissensch. prakt. Tierheilk., **37,** 382–406, 442–454.

WEBSTER, R. C., AND YOUNG, W. C. 1951. Adolescent sterility in the male guinea pig. Fertil. & Steril., **2,** 175–181.

WELLS, L. J., CAVANAUGH, M. W., AND MAXWELL, E. L. 1954. Genital abnormalities in castrated fetal rats and their prevention by means of testosterone propionate. Anat. Rec., **118,** 1ʋ9–133.

WEST, C. D., DAMAST, B. L., SARRO, S. D., AND PEARSON, O. H. 1956. Conversion of testosterone to estrogens in castrated, adrenalectomized human females. J. Biol. Chem., **218,** 409–418.

WILBUR, K. M. 1936. A method for the measurement of activity of small animals. Science, **84,** 274.

WILLIAMS, W. L. 1921. *The Diseases of the Genital Organs of Domestic Animals.* Ithaca: The author.

WILSON, J. G. 1943. Reproductive capacity of adult female rats treated prepuberally with estrogenic hormone. Anat. Rec., **86,** 341–363.

WILSON, J. G., YOUNG, W. C., AND HAMILTON, J. B. 1940. A technic suppressing development of reproductive function and sensitivity to estrogen in the female rat. Yale. J. Biol. & Med., **13,** 189–202.

WILSON, J. G., HAMILTON, J. B., AND YOUNG, W. C. 1941. Influence of age and presence of the ovaries on reproductive function in rats injected with androgens. Endocrinology, **29,** 784–789.

WILSON, J. G., AND YOUNG, W. C. 1941. Sensitivity to estrogen studied by means of experimentally induced mating responses in the female guinea pig and rat. Endocrinology, **29,** 779–783.

WILSON, J. G., AND WILSON, H. C. 1943. Reproductive capacity in adult male rats treated prepuberally with androgenic hormone. Endocrinology, **33,** 353–360.

WOOD-GUSH, D. G. M. 1954. The courtship of the brown Leghorn cock. Brit. J. Anim. Behav., **2,** 95–102.

WOOD-GUSH, D. G. M. 1958a. Genetic and experience on the mating behaviour of the doerels. Proc. Roy. Phys. Soc. Edinburgh, **27,** 6–8.

WOOD-GUSH, D. G. M. 1958b. The effect of experience on the mating behavior of the domestic cock. Anim. Behav., **6,** 68–71.

WOOD-GUSH, D. G. M., AND OSBORNE, R. 1956.

A study of differences in the sex drive of cockerels. Brit. J. Anim. Behav., **4**, 102–110.

WORTIS. J., AND ROSENBLATT, J. S. 1959. Sexual deviation and plasticity of the sex pattern. In *Biological Psychiatry*, pp. 82–89. New York: Grune & Stratton.

YERKES, R. M. 1939. Social dominance and sexual status in the chimpanzee. Quart. Rev. Biol., **14**, 115–136.

YERKES, R. M. 1940. Social behavior of chimpanzees: dominance between mates, in relation to sexual status. J. Comp. Psychol., **30**, 147–186.

YERKES, R. M. 1943. *Chimpanzees. A Laboratory Colony*. New Haven: Yale University Press.

YERKES, R. M. AND ELDER, J. H. 1936. Oestrus, receptivity, and mating in chimpanzee. Comp. Psychol. Monogr., **13**, No. 5.

YOUNG, W. C. 1941. Observations and experiments on mating behavior in female mammals. Quart. Rev. Biol., **16**, 135–156; 311–335.

YOUNG, W. C. 1949. Strength of sex drive and fertility in the male guinea pig. Abstract, Proc. Am. A. Anat., Anat. Rec., **103**, 525.

YOUNG, W. C. 1953. Gamete-age at the time of fertilization and the course of gestation in mammals. In *Pregnancy Wastage*, E. T. Engle, Ed., pp. 38–50. Springfield, Ill.: Charles C Thomas.

YOUNG, W. C. 1954. Behavior and intelligence. In *Glandular Physiology and Therapy*, ed. 5, Council on Pharmacy and Chemistry of the American Medical Association, pp. 515–534. Philadelphia: J. B. Lippincott Company.

YOUNG, W. C. 1957. Genetic and psychological determinants of sexual behavior patterns. In *Hormones, Brain Function, and Behavior*, Hudson Hoagland, Ed., pp. 75–98. New York: Academic Press, Inc.

YOUNG, W. C., MYERS, H. I., AND DEMPSEY, E. W. 1933. Some data from a correlated anatomical, physiological and behavioristic study of the reproductive cycle in the female guinea pig. Am. J. Physiol., **105**, 393–398.

YOUNG, W. C., DEMPSEY, E. W., AND MYERS, H. I. 1935. Cyclic reproductive behavior in the female guinea pig. J. Comp. Psychol., **19**, 313–335.

YOUNG, W. C., DEMPSEY, E. W., HAGQUIST, C. W., AND BOLING, J. L. 1937. The determination of heat in the guinea pig. J. Lab. & Clin. Med., **23**, 300–302.

YOUNG, W. C., DEMPSEY, E. W., MYERS, H. I., AND HAGQUIST, C. W. 1938. The ovarian condition and sexual behavior in the female guinea pig. Am. J. Anat., **63**, 457–487.

YOUNG, W. C., DEMPSEY, E. W. HAGQUIST, C. W., AND BOLING, J. L. 1939. Sexual behavior and sexual receptivity in the female guinea pig. J. Comp. Psychol., **27**, 49–68.

YOUNG, W. C., AND RUNDLETT, B. 1939. The hormonal induction of homosexual behavior in the spayed female guinea pig. Psychosom. Med., **1**, 449–460.

YOUNG, W. C., AND YERKES, R. M. 1943. Factors influencing the reproductive cycle in the chimpanzee; the period of adolescent sterility and related problems. Endocrinology, **33**, 121–154.

YOUNG, W. C., AND ORBISON, W. D. 1944. Changes in selected features of behavior in pairs of oppositely sexed chimpanzees during the sexual cycle and after ovariectomy. J. Comp. Psychol., **37**, 107–143.

YOUNG, W. C., AND FISH, W. R. 1945. The ovarian hormones and spontaneous running activity in the female rat. Endocrinology, **36**, 181–189.

YOUNG, W. C., AND GRUNT, J. A. 1951. The pattern and measurement of sexual behavior in in the male guinea pig. J. Comp. & Physiol. Psychol., **44**, 492–500.

YOUNG, W. C., GRUNT, J. A., AND VALENSTEIN, E. S. 1951. Strength of sex drive during repeated tests of behavior in the male guinea pig. Abstract, Proc. Am. Soc. Zool., Anat. Rec., **111**, 487.

YOUNG, W. C., AND PETERSON, R. R. 1952. Reproductive performance in extremely hypothyroid male guinea pigs. Endocrinology, **51**, 344–345.

YOUNG, W. C., RAYNER, B., PETERSON, R. R., AND BROWN, M. MACN. 1952. The thyroid and reproductive performance in the adult male guinea pig. Endocrinology, **51**, 12–20.

ZAWADOWSKY, M. 1926. Bisexual nature of the hen and experimental hermaphroditism in in hens. Tr. Lab. Exper. Biol., Zoopark. Moscow, **2**, 164–179.

ZIMBARDO, P. G. 1958. The effects of early avoidance training and rearing conditions upon the sexual behavior of the male rat. J. Comp. & Physiol. Psychol., **51**, 764–769.

ZITRIN, A. 1942. Induction of male copulatory behavior in a hen following administration of male hormone. Endocrinology, **31**, 690.

ZUCKERMAN, S. 1952. Chairman's closing remarks. Ciba Foundation Colloquia Endocrinol., **3**, 239–246.

ZUCKERMAN, S., AND PARKES, A. S. 1939. Observations on secondary sexual characters in monkeys. J. Endocrinol., **1**, 430–439.

20

GONADAL HORMONES AND SOCIAL BEHAVIOR IN INFRAHUMAN VERTEBRATES

A. M. Guhl, Ph.D.

PROFESSOR OF ZOOLOGY, KANSAS STATE UNIVERSITY,

MANHATTAN, KANSAS

I. Introduction

Most investigations of the influence of gonadal hormones on behavior have been focused on reproductive behavior, probably because the various patterns are readily observable and follow a sequence or reaction chain which facilitates analysis. Social behavior patterns, on the other hand, are often less obvious; indeed, it was not until 1939 that their manifestation was related to gonadal hormones (Allee, Collias and Lu-

therman, 1939; Noble, 1939a, Yerkes, 1939). Since then, this latter relationship has been abundantly demonstrated. It has been found also that social relationships sometimes facilitate and sometimes inhibit the display of sexual behavior. It is the object of this chapter to discuss the influence of gonadal hormones on certain social behavior patterns and, reciprocally, the influence that some social factors have on the display of sexual behavior.

II. Social Organization

The term social is used here in a broad sense, which is generally acceptable to zoologists working in the field of sociobiology. Social behavior is any behavior caused by or affecting another animal, usually of the same species. Although sexual and parental behavior are also social, this chapter is concerned essentially with agonistic behavior, which includes aggressive and defensive actions and escape and submissive behavior. Agonistic behavior is especially important during the etstablishment of any degree of intraspecific organization. Because it is so conspicuous at such times, there is a tendency to report the behavior of animals which are organized on the basis of such behavior. However, there are groups which might be integrated as a social unit through other behavior patterns; e.g., reciprocal interactions such as grooming, play, parent-young relations (Carpenter, 1942, 1952;

1240

Scott, 1945), or what Schneirla (1946) includes under trophallactic relationships.

Social organizations can be classified into two general categories: social hierarchies and territories. Some species show either one or the other seasonally or throughout the year, whereas others may have elements of both concurrently. Still others have territories during the reproductive phase and hierarchy during the rest of the year. Once established, or even during the incipient stages, a pattern of social organization is typical for a given species. The variation is considerable from species to species, although comparable types of organization are found throughout the vertebrates.

Allee (1952) recognized two major kinds of hierarchies: one based on unidirectional (despotic) domination and the other based on relative despotism in which pecking between any two individuals is bidirectional. The former is often referred to as a "peck-right" system, in which the individuals are ranked in an order according to the number of individuals each can dominate without any attack or threat in return. Such a dominance order is usually quite stable, and species so organized are suitable for experimentation insofar as controlled situations can be maintained. A hierarchy based on bidirectional pecking is more fluid because there is an exchange of aggressive acts, and the individual delivering the most "pecks" is considered the dominant member of the pair. In species so organized there is an overlap with territoriality, inasmuch as each individual becomes more dominant as it approaches the center of its territory.

Credit for the development of the concept of territoriality is usually given to Howard (1920), although Lack (1953) and Carpenter (1958) cite even older reports in which some aspects of this behavior were recognized. Evidences of territoriality are often reported in studies on reproductive behavior and have been found in various classes of vertebrates.

Territorial organization has many forms, depending on how it functions for a particular species. It is often defined as "a defended area." However, there is no evidence that it is the area *per se* that is defended. According to Emlen (1957), "the term territory is generally applied to an area or space in which a particular animal is aggressive and largely if not supremely dominant with respect to certain categories of intruders." The biologic significance of territory for birds has been discussed by Hinde (1956a), and for all vertebrates by Carpenter (1958). The latter concluded that territoriality apparently, when once established, reduces stress, pugnacity, and nonadaptive energy expenditure.

Aggressive behavior has the tendency to disperse the individuals, as manifested in territorialism. Such behavior is mediated by hormones. Some behavior patterns operate in the opposite direction and result in aggregations by members of the species (Allee, 1931). No gonadal hormones have been discovered which influence gregariousness (other than sexual and parental bonds). Emlen (1952) discussed the social forces which cause the centripetal and centrifugal actions in flocks of birds, and concluded that flocking responses have their physiologic basis in stereotyped neural patterns and are influenced by hormonal factors only so far as these incite disruptive responses associated with sexual or parental activity.

Tendencies to aggregate or to disperse may be seasonal or diurnal (Emlen, 1952), and physical factors such as temperature and light may exert an action (Allee, Emerson, Park, Park and Schmidt, 1949, p. 393). Species of vertebrates vary in the relative distance at which one individual will tolerate the presence of another. Hediger (1950, p. 111) calls this "individual distance" and distinguishes between "distance animals" and "contact animals." The relative proximity at which chaffinches tolerate each other varies with dominance rank and with sex (Marler, 1956). Dominant females allowed subordinate females to come closer than other females, and males permitted females to come closer than males. Submissive behavior promotes toleration. The forces of mutual attraction may develop early in life (Collias, 1952, 1956) by mechanisms that suggest imprinting (Lorenz, 1935).

In many instances changes in agonistic behavior appear to precede sexual behavior and thereby to prepare the proper social environment for sexual and parental behavior. Moynihan (1958) described the behavior of several species of North American gulls in the process of pair formation. The hostility which precedes pairing is associated with the establishment of their territories. Pair-formation activities seem to be followed by a reduction of intersexual hostility and the gradual emergence of sexual behavior. According to Tinbergen (1953), the pre-nuptial behavior of the female appeases the male, suppresses her escape behavior and, together with the courting by the male, facilitates the synchronization of sexual behavior patterns.

The selective value of aggressiveness has been discussed by Collias (1944) and Carpenter (1958). Selection may operate on the level of the individual, with the more aggressive ones usually having precedence to food, mates, and cover. On the group level the more socially stable units conserve energy and may leave more progeny.

III. Historical Background

The discovery of a social organization based on agonistic behavior was made by Schjelderup-Ebbe (1913) during a study of calls or sounds made by chickens. Later he summarized observations of the domestic fowl and other birds (Schjelderup-Ebbe, 1935). Many of these were repeated by Sanctuary (1932) and Masure and Allee (1934a), working with chickens. Masure and Allee (1934b) also observed common pigeons and shell parakeets and discovered, contrary to Schjelderup-Ebbe, that some birds do not show absolute dominance, but rather bidirectional pecking (called peck-dominance in the earlier reports). Allee (1936) summarized these initial observations and suggested a plan for analytical studies, which included alteration of the physiologic state by hormonal treatment. Noble and his associates (Noble, 1939a, b; Noble and Curtis, 1939; Noble and Borne, 1940; Noble and Wurm, 1940; Noble and Greenberg, 1941) made extensive studies of behavior which stimulated a general interest in the relationship between the endocrines and social behavior in fishes, amphibians, reptiles, and birds. The social organization in baboons was described by Zuckerman (1932), and in monkeys by Maslow (1934). Carpenter (1934) reported

the virtual absence of a dominance order in the howler monkey. Yerkes (1939) observed dominance relations between unisexual and heterosexual pairs of chimpanzees and related changes in dominance-submission to the sexual status of the female.

Since this early period, many investigations have been directed at a clarification of the relationship between the gonadal hormones and social, but particularly agonistic, behavior. Something of the progress that has been made will be apparent from what follows. However, many reviews already exist[1] and in this place a particular effort will be made to present a contemporary cross-sectional view of the subject that will contain an indication of the many problems that are in need of study.

IV. Methods

Many experimental techniques have been used in studies of agonistic behavior. As would be expected, they vary greatly, depending on the species, the question it is hoped the experiments will answer, and the connotation of aggressiveness that is accepted. Potter and Allee (1953), Kislack and Beach (1955), Scott and Fredericson (1951), and Scott (1958b) considered aggressiveness as a tendency to start fights. According to this view, the levels of aggressiveness would be measured by latency, *i.e.*, the time between the meeting of two individuals in a test situation and the first overt display of agonistic behavior. However, the term as it is used in this chapter refers to the ability to be self-assertive or to display independence of action (Collias, 1944). Aggressiveness in this sense is a tendency whereas aggression is an activity. Factors

[1] Comprehensive reviews of aggressive behavior among vertebrates, including a discussion of hormonal factors, have been prepared by Collias (1944, 1950). Social organization and related phenomena in vertebrates were considered by Allee, Emerson, Park, Park and Schmidt (1949), Allee (1952), Tinbergen (1953) and Scott (1956, 1958a). General information bearing on the territorial behavior of vertebrates has been brought together by Bourliere (1952) and Carpenter (1958). Other reviews deal with the social behavior of fishes (Aronson, 1957; Baerends, 1957), birds (Hinde, 1956a), ungulates (Darling, 1952), other lower mammals (Hediger, 1952), and subhuman primates (Carpenter, 1952)

which evoke aggression seem to vary among species and may include such as close proximity, training, sex hormone, and pain resulting from attack. The pattern of response may depend on the stimulus situation, the strength of the stimulation received, and the physiologic state or level of response threshold.

In general, in studies of aggressiveness, conditions are best controlled when the animals are observed in pairs or in small groups and this has long been done by many investigators. Paired encounters were used by Maslow (1936) to determine dominance relationships among subhuman primates. If the pairings were made between unacquainted individuals, they were called initial encounters or initial contacts. These were used by Collias (1943) to determine the factors which make for success in establishing dominance in chickens, and by Braddock and Braddock (1955) in their work on the fish, *Betta splendens*. Pairings of mice were used to analyze the effects of thiamine deficiency on fighting success (Beeman and Allee, 1945) and to condition individuals to win or to lose encounters (Ginsburg and Allee, 1942). Pairings of chimpanzees were made in order to ascertain the effects of the female sexual cycle in female pairs (Crawford, 1940) and between mates (Yerkes, 1940; Young and Orbison, 1944). Corresponding techniques served to test the effects of gonadal hormones in chickens (Allee, Collias and Lutherman, 1939; Allee and Collias, 1940) and of androgen in mice (Beeman, 1947).

Support for the opinion that staged initial pair contests in neural areas, or cages, give better estimates of levels of aggressiveness than rank in a social order or the frequency and intensity of aggression comes from a recounting of what has been found during work with chickens. In a flock of chickens the frequency of pecks delivered by an individual on others is not a measure of the individual's native aggressiveness. In the determination of a peck-order the tabulation of pecks delivered by each bird usually shows no apparent correlation with rank in the social order. Those in the top rank have more individuals to peck and therefore the highest rate of pecking may be expected.

However, the highest rates of pecking by one bird on another may occur between birds at any level above the lowest ranks. These interindividual interactions have been called "antipathies." Unexpected toleration, *i.e.*, low rates of pecking, also may be found at any level. Antipathies may develop when the flock is assembled as a result of a hard fight, or later when a revolt is unsuccessful. Toleration may follow a passive submission in the initial meeting of unacquainted birds. Furthermore, the rate at which one bird pecks another may vary from week to week according to incidents which arise. The peck-order is learned and the laws of reinforcement and extinction apply.

Rank in the hierarchy, or the number of individuals dominated, may be used as a measure of aggressiveness, and may agree with the results of paired encounters (Guhl, 1953). However, the reliability of estimates based on rank in the hierarchy or the number of individuals dominated may depend on the conditions under which the flock was first assembled. At the first meeting the birds engage in initial encounters by pairs which meet at random. Fatigue may set in early for those engaged in lengthy fights, and such individuals may refrain from fighting, or lose subsequent encounters. If new individuals are added after the peck-order is formed, they usually assume low rank. A significant correlation was found by Guhl and Allee (1944) between seniority and social position. These results lead to the conclusion that stimulus situations and other factors (Allee, Collias and Lutherman, 1939) which make for winning encounters need to be controlled and that this can best be done in initial paired encounters.

When groups of animals were employed in the study of aggressive behavior the desirability of certain practices became apparent. Sanctuary (1932) found, when strange hens were added to organized flocks, that the fewer the newcomers in relation to the residents, the greater was the disadvantage to the introduced hens. Flocks of equal size could be combined with the least disparity. In another study social organization was kept in a state of flux by regularly shifting hens from isolation to a flock or between flocks (Guhl and Allee, 1944). The degree of domination or subordination of a hen may be measured by the number of individuals it pecks or avoids. The top-ranking hen habitually pecks all and submits to none, whereas the one lowest in rank has a strong habit for avoidance and does no pecking. Those in intermediate ranks show varying degrees of both habits commensurate with social status. Therefore, the frequency with which individuals display dominance or submissiveness may be altered by subflocking without disrupting the dominance relations among the birds in the smaller groups (Guhl, 1950).

Of extreme importance in the methodology for studying aggressive behavior is the control of what we will refer to as the elements composing the substrate. The problem can be explained, but it will be at some length.

V. Elements Comprising Substrate

The study of animal behavior is beset with problems of multifactorial relationships. This produces either a perplexing situation or an intriguing one, depending on the viewpoint. It is virtually impossible to control all of the known factors in a single experiment, and some apparently minor ones may gain in their influence when others are controlled. There is a continual interaction between the environment and the organism. The experimenter is one of the factors. The importance of this fact, which is also recognized clinically (Matarozzo, Saslow, Matarozzo and Phillips, 1958), has not always been appreciated. The presence of the investigator, his mannerisms, and the methods of handling the animals may alter behavior. It must be recognized, too, that behavior is the expression of an effort to adapt or to adjust, and different conditions may lead to different results. Animals are often maintained in one location and moved to another for experimentation. Many animals can adapt readily to such techniques, but the time required for adjustments should be considered. In general, domestic species adjust to laboratory conditions with less difficulty than do wild animals; Hediger (1950) suggests that the confined environment of wild animals requires certain features of their natural environment. Other parts of the substrate are the genic background, meteorologic conditions, and the interaction of drives. All these factors will be considered in the discussion of the influence of the endocrines on social behavior which follows.

A. HEREDITY AND LEVELS OF AGGRESSIVE BEHAVIOR

The wealth of information from comparative studies provides abundant evidence that the genic background influences the character of an animal's behavior. We will mention only a few: phylogenetic studies of social behavior patterns have been made for orders of insects (Michener, 1953), termites (Emerson, 1938; Schmidt, 1955), bees (Michener and Michener, 1951; Michener, 1953), fishes (Winn, 1958), and birds, e.g., anis (Davis, 1942) and tits (Hinde, 1952). The importance of the genic factor is also apparent from observations of and experiments with hybrids (e.g., finches, Hinde, 1956b), from the existence of species differences (e.g., fishes, Schlosberg, Duncan and Daitch, 1949; Clark, Aronson and Gordon, 1954) and breed differences (e.g., dogs, Scott and Charles, 1953, 1954; chickens, Potter, 1949; Hale, 1954; Allee and Foreman, 1955). Scott (1954) discussed the effects of selection and domestication on various behavior patterns in the dog. In genetically different stocks of male guinea pigs, factors peculiar to the strains affected the behavioral responses to testosterone propionate (Riss, Valenstein, Sinks and Young, 1955). Strain differences were also found in the response of female guinea pigs to estradiol and progesterone (Goy and Young, 1957). Most of the studies cited above were not concerned with agonistic behavior per se, but it must be presumed that strain differences would be as important for the display of agonistic behavior as for all other social behavior including reproductive behavior.

Some breeds of domestic animals have been developed by selection for particular behavior patterns. Terriers among dogs, gamecocks among chickens, and Siamese fighting fish have a long, and largely unknown, history of selection for fighting ability. Scott (1942) found that inbred strains of C57/10 black, C3H agouti, and C (Bagg) mice differed in aggressiveness, activity, and other traits. When C57/10 and C progeny were cross-fostered the behavior characteristic of the strains remained true to heredity (Fredericson, 1952).

A selective breeding program for levels of aggressiveness in Leghorn chickens was conducted by Guhl, Craig and Mueller (1960). The males and females of the parent generation were of different strains merely because these were available, and there was no information on the relative aggressiveness of either strain. Selection in each generation was based on the percentage of initial encounters won, as supported by rankings in the peck-order. Individuals ranking highest and lowest were used for breeding. This technique limited the number of individuals which could be tested. Some of the results are indicated in Figure 20.1 for four generations of selection. Reciprocal crosses were made with the

breeders of the F_3 generation, and their offspring tended to be intermediate in aggressiveness. These results are indicated by four points in the F_4. However, due to uncontrollable circumstances, only a few of these chicks lived to sexual maturity and testing. The upper points are means of 7 males and 8 females from "high" dams, and the lower two points are the means of 3 males and 1 female from "low" dams. The number of individuals selected for breeding and their tested progeny is given beneath the figure for all generations except the crosses. A χ^2 analysis based on the mean percentage of encounters won by individuals from the "high" and "low" lines showed statistically significant differences between the two lines of selection from the F_2 through the F_4 in both sexes.

Calhoun (1956) made an interesting attempt to determine the extent to which heredity might modify social behavior. He used physiologically unstable DBA/2 and physiologically stable C57BL/10 inbred mice. Among other differing traits, the

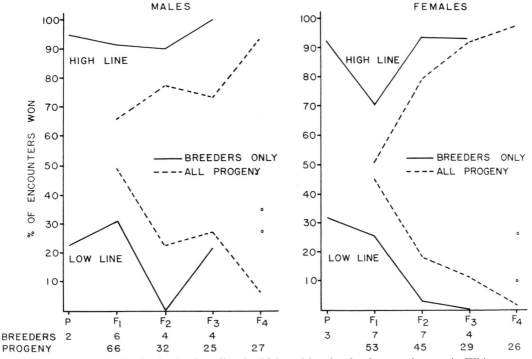

FIG. 20.1. Results of selective breeding for high and low levels of aggressiveness in White Leghorn chickens. Figures show the percentage of initial encounters won by sires, dams, and their progeny. All encounters were between individuals of high and low lines.

DBA/2 mice have a high incidence of mammary tumors and marked susceptibility to lethal audiogenic seizures, whereas the C57BL/10 strain has a low incidence of mammary tumors and susceptibility to audiogenic seizures. Both lines had been through extensive artificial selection and always reared in small cages with a restricted social environment. He wished to ascertain whether exposure to a more complex physical and social milieu than previously experienced in many generations of rearing would provide a marked taxing of the physiologic homeostatic mechanisms available to the mice. Four colonies, two of each strain, were established in standardized pens with 17.5 M.^{2} of floor space. The arrangement of nests, food, and water encouraged social interactions. The DBA's fought more frequently and intensely than did the C57's, and the latter developed more toleration and made more passive social adjustments. The C57 mice were more successful in reproduction and died off at a lower rate than did the more aggressive DBA mice.

B. METEOROLOGIC FACTORS

Some of the more immediate effects of meteorologic factors on reproductive and parental behavior can be readily observed. Modification of other forms of social behavior, such as shifts between group living and territoriality, have been reported in some vertebrates to be associated with marked changes in the weather. Petersen (1955) noted that the activity of migratory bank swallows on arrival in the spring was influenced by weather conditions. Days of fair weather with temperatures near or above normal appeared to be necessary for taking up territories. Collias and Taber (1951) found that ring-necked pheasants roosted closer together and in larger groups when the weather was very cold. According to Stoddard (1931), the male of the bobwhite quail (*Colinus virginianus*) tolerates other males until the first warm days of February. Actions preliminary to pairing may be noted, although the coveys do not break up normally until late April, and even then may reassemble to a certain extent when the weather is cold and raw.

Apparently, adverse weather conditions exert some suppressive effect on aggressiveness, and with increased toleration the territorialism reverts to flocking. Scott and Fredericson (1951) concluded that heat and probably cold tend to reduce the amount of fighting behavior in mice and rats. Combats between mice were more sluggish and shorter at temperatures over 28°C.; inexperienced mice did not fight at 27 to 28°C.

C. PSYCHOLOGIC FACTORS

In a social organization based on domination, each individual forms special habits toward each member of the group. As these habits of domination or subordination become well established, the agonistic behavior patterns are reduced in intensity and become symbolic. This mutual interindividual adaptation promotes toleration and has been called social inertia. Such adjustments have been demonstrated in small flocks of chickens (Guhl and Allee, 1944; Guhl, 1958). Evidence that the principles of complex learning apply to agonistic behavior would seem to have been provided following the training of chickens (Radlow, Hale and Smith, 1958), mice, rats (Ginsburg and Allee, 1942; Scott and Fredericson, 1951), and rhesus monkeys (Miller, Murphy and Mirsky, 1955; Murphy, Miller and Mirsky, 1955) to be either dominant or subordinate. In connection with all this, it is appropriate to ask what effect the psychologic state associated with social inertia has on the behavioral response to hormonal treatment, be it reproductive or social.

Taking the former first, Baerends and Baerends-Van Roon (1950) found in the cichlid fish, *Hemichromis*, that males that were unsuccessful in establishing territories lacked color markings, but when the dominant and territorial male was removed one of these showed reproductive markings and set up territory. When the new dominant was removed a third male reacted similarly. They concluded that "although many of the members of the school are physiologically able to assume reproductive markings and to perform reproductive activities, in a number of them the reproductive motivation was suppressed by the activities of the territorial fish." In chickens.

males ranking lowest in the peck-order among the cocks may show varying degrees of suppression of sexual behavior to the point of psychologic castration (Guhl, Collias and Allee, 1945; Guhl and Warren, 1946). One male failed to mate with the hens of the flock even when his social superiors were temporarily removed, but he did mate with strange hens from another flock. Similar situations have been reported by Darling (1952) among wild white cattle of Northumberland, England, and water buffalo of southeast Asia. It is pertinent to the point being discussed that the dominant bull water buffalo must have two other bulls to dominate before he is potent.

The habits associated with the independence of action at top levels in a peck-order may suppress receptivity in females of some species. Hens at upper ranks in the flock tended to be least receptive and those at the lowest levels the most receptive. The females at the top of the hierarchy were in the habit of dominating, whereas those at the bottom submitted readily. The submissive attitude is a component of receptivity. When the degree of domination or submissiveness was altered by subflocking, the differences in the rates of displaying the submissive sexual crouch were reversed (Guhl, 1950). With fewer birds to dominate there was less reinforcement of the aggressive habit and the sexual crouch was evoked. Similar tests with other species of vertebrates should be made to determine the extent to which this psychologic effect is applicable. Relationships between physiologic and psychologic aspects of display behavior in birds have been discussed by Armstrong (1947, Ch. 22). He states that the interconnection of internal and environmental factors has the broad effect of bringing the birds into breeding condition, and the fine adjustments which achieve the final sexual synchronization are given by psychologic factors.

D. SOCIAL INERTIA AND THE DEVELOPMENT OF SOCIAL BEHAVIOR

To answer the second part of the question, social inertia is also important for the development of social behavior. Chicks reared in groups established certain behavior patterns in relation to each other (Guhl, 1958), the social inertia mentioned above, and required 8 to 13 weeks to develop a new peck-order. Similar chicks reared in partial isolation and assembled at 8 to 10 weeks of age were devoid of such habits. They engaged in fighting and pecking, and formed peck-orders in a matter of hours. Chicks treated with an androgen while reared together established peck-orders somewhat earlier than normal group-reared chicks.

Another experiment was devised to compare the effects of androgen with those of social inertia. The specific question was whether chicks treated with androgen during partial isolation from hatching would form a peck-order earlier than treated chicks reared as a group. There were 5 groups of chicks (Fig. 20.2). Two groups of 11 each were pen-reared controls; the individuals of one group received 0.5 mg. testosterone propionate daily, those in the other group were normal controls. Three groups composed of 10 chicks each were reared in partial isolation and treated with the androgen. One was assembled when 31 days old, another at 41 days, and the third when 51 days old. The establishment of dominance relationships (peck-rights) was observed for 56 days in the pen-reared groups and for 7 days after assembly in the case of the 3 isolation-reared groups.

The results are shown in Figure 20.2. The ratios at each curve indicate the number of peck-rights established at that point in relation to the possible number of unidirectional dominance relations in the flock. The group assembled on day 31 nearly completed a peck-order in 1 week, and exceeded the treated males reared as a group. The treated chicks assembled on day 41 failed to establish any dominance relations on the first day and formed only 20 out of a possible 45 pecking relationships by the end of a week. This performance was inferior to the normal pen-reared controls. The results with the group assembled on day 31 indicate that in the absence of social inertia, androgen treatment resulted in some precociousness of agonistic behavior.

The results obtained from the males assembled on day 41 are difficult to explain. In nature behavior patterns tend to appear

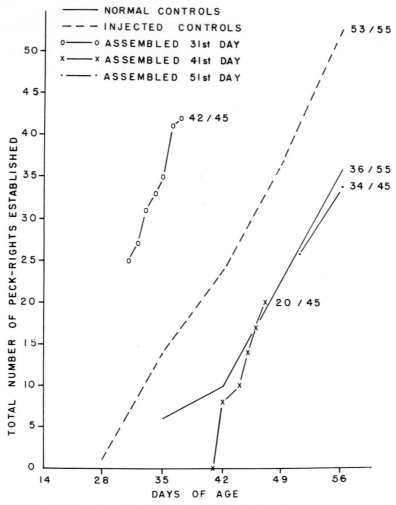

Fig. 20.2. The total number of peck-rights established at various ages among males reared as a group and others reared in partial isolation and assembled at different ages. The isolated chicks and one group, reared together, were injected with an androgen (Guhl, 1958).

in a certain sequence; sexual behavior usually follows agonistic behavior. However, the typical behavior of this group was sexual. Attempts to mount were frequent and the birds showed strong avoiding reactions. The indications were that at this age there was a conflict between aggressive behavior and the newly developed sexual behavior, which had not yet been subjected to any adjustment The group assembled on day 51 showed both aggressive and sexual behavior, but with somewhat better adjustment to the conflicting drives. Untreated females (not shown in Fig. 20.2) assembled from isolation did not show this complication, because sexual behavior patterns appear much later in the female. The significant point is that hormonal treatment may shorten the time between the appearance of sequential behavior patterns to the point where psychologic adjustments cannot be made and an imbalance of drives occurs. Endogenous hormones rise more slowly in concentration and allow more time for experience, or learning the adaptive process. In large groups the variability of individuals in development is also a complicating factor.

In the same series of experiments an attempt was made to demonstrate the influence of social inertia on the development of social behavior by normal male chicks.

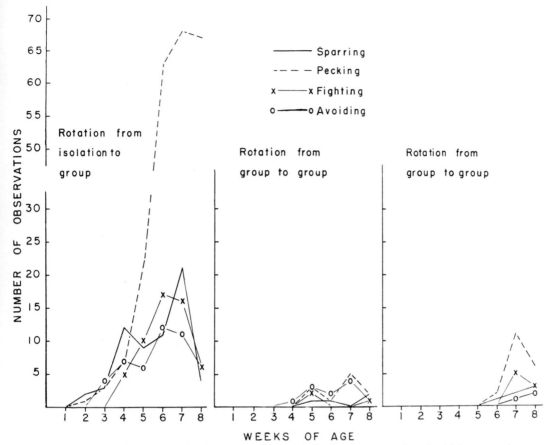

Fig. 20.3. Differences in the frequency of some behavior patterns of male chicks rotated between isolation and a group, and of others rotated from group to group. The results of group-to-group rotation for each of these two groups are shown separately, and these show social inertia (Guhl, 1958).

Four groups of 10 chicks each were used. The cages were similar except that one was partitioned for partial isolation. Two types of rotating group memberships were devised. Every other day, from the 3rd day of age, 1 chick was taken from isolation and placed with one group and a group member was placed in isolation. Chicks were also shifted between the other two groups which were maintained as flocks. Rotation followed a schedule and a chick was in isolation (or in one of the three group cages) for 20 days. Those returned to isolation had nearly 3 weeks during which any social habits or individual recognition might be extinguished, whereas those rotated between flocks continued to have social contacts but with different individuals. The results are given in Figure 20.3 and show that the group into which isolates were rotated had the highest frequency of agonistic behavior. In addition to the reduced social inertia, the newcomers from isolation acted as a greater stimulus for aggression than did newcomers from the cages containing flocks of chicks.

E. INTERACTION OF DRIVES

The tendencies toward aggressiveness and submissiveness may be viewed as drives in the sense that they are forces prompting an animal to activity directed toward certain ends. In a flock of goats (Scott, 1948), delayed feeding increased the amount of fighting in dominant animals, and recent feeding decreased the amount of aggression in dominant animals. In subordinate individuals, delayed feeding caused them to take more punishment but almost never caused aggression. It was concluded that dominance strongly modified the effect of frustration in causing aggression, and that frustration caused aggression in situations in which animals were in the habit of being aggressive. In goats there was no fighting and no dominance when they were given plenty of food scattered about to prevent crowding while feeding.

In mice hunger and thirst did not affect the tendency to fight (Ginsburg and Allee, 1942), nor did vitamin B_1 deficiency cause a loss of social status in high ranking individuals until they were in an advanced stage of avitaminosis (Beeman and Allee, 1945). Aggressive behavior was not affected until the individual was physically weakened, and staged pair contacts were strongly influenced by psychologic factors. In the chaffinch (Marler, 1955) starvation, however, reduced the tendency of subordinates to avoid dominant individuals. Inasmuch as females are less aggressive than males, and avoidance reactions are less intense, the toleration which developed toward low ranking individuals was more pronounced in female flocks. In rats Hall (1936) found that nonhungry individuals display greater emotionality than do hungry rats. He concluded that "needs, other than the need to escape, inhibit the display of emotional behavior by distracting the animal from the fear-provoking aspects of the situation."

Among birds there are a number of situations in which two or more drives are in conflict. The conflict may be between aggressive and sexual activities, or between attacks and escape behavior. What makes the conflict apparent is that sometimes the resultant pattern of behavior is atypical of the drives in conflict. These patterns are called displacement activities and have been variously named and defined. According to Bastock, Morris and Moynihan (1953) "displacement activities apparently can occur in two situations. (1) Displacement activities may be performed by an animal in which two or more incompatible drives are strongly activated; each drive prevents the expression of the other(s). (2) Displacement activities may also be performed by an animal in which one drive is, at the

same time, both activated and thwarted." A number of such conflicting situations is mentioned by Armstrong (1947, pp. 99–101).

An interesting study of the conflict between the tendencies of attacking, fleeing, and courting in the male chaffinch was made by Hinde (1953). The male is dominant over the female in winter, and in the spring the dominance is reversed. The male's display occurs in those situations in which his tendencies to approach (court) and to flee from the female are in approximate balance. A similar analysis can be applied to the female. Attempts to copulate may be unsuccessful if the sex drives of both individuals are not sufficient to inhibit aggressive behavior.

The presentation of the material which follows is given with the assumption that the many factors enumerated above have been controlled.

VI. Gonadal Hormones and Social Behavior

A. SOCIAL BEHAVIOR AND THE REPRODUCTIVE CYCLE

The stimulating action of gonadal hormones on social behavior might long ago have been postulated from the close relationship between reproductive state and behavior, in wild species in which reproduction is generally seasonal, and in many laboratory and domesticated species in which cyclic activity is continuous without intervening periods of anestrum. Relationships of this sort are well known in birds (Armstrong, 1947) and many mammals: the red deer, *Cervus elaphus* (Darling, 1937), the wapiti, *Cervus canadensis*, the moose, *Alces americana shirasi*, the chamois, *Rupicapra rupicapra*, the wild boar, *Sus scrofa europ.* (Altmann, 1952, 1956), and others. Territorialism may develop during the breeding cycle among frogs (Martof, 1953; Test, 1954) and reptiles (Greenberg and Noble, 1944). In fish, seasonal modification in breeding aggregations has been described by Aronson (1957). It is common knowledge that the males of many species show combative behavior during the breeding season. Rowan (1931) observed that the male bobolink attacks other males in the spring, although peaceful unisexual flocks are formed when the breeding season wanes. Fighting during the reproductive phase was reported in the gentoo penguin, *Pygoscelis papua* (Roberts, 1940) and in the herring gull, *Larus argentatus* (Boss, 1943).

Studies have been made which show a cyclic relationship between changes in the size of the gonads and the sequence of social and reproductive behavior patterns occurring before and during the breeding season. Such a relationship is presumed to be universal in seasonal breeders—the exception would be the *cause célèbre*. Changes in the grouping and dominance relations among free ranging ring-necked pheasants (*Phasianus colchicus*) are related to sea-

sonal increase in the weight of the testes (Collias and Taber, 1951). During the gonadal quiescence of winter the birds remain in marshes as small groups with shifting memberships. Evidence of peck-orders among cocks and hens was found. The males pecked the females during competition for food. As the breeding season advanced there was a gradual increase in antagonism between members of the same sex and in attraction between individuals of opposite sexes (Fig. 20.4). With an increase in testis weight the male groups broke up, territories were established, and harems were formed. Cocks that ranked high in the winter dominance order established territories, whereas those of low social status failed to do so. Genelly (1955) reported on

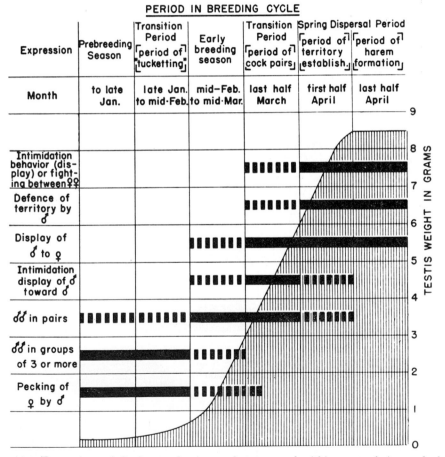

Fig. 20.4. Expressions of display or dominance between and within sexes of ring-necked pheasants, from January through April. Broken lines represent infrequent occurrence; solid line, frequent occurrence. The sequence of behavior changes is superimposed upon the increase in testis size (Collias and Taber, 1951).

a study of the annual cycle of the California quail (*Lophortyx californica*). Of
particular interest is the shift from a peck-
order type of organization during sexual
quiescence to territoriality during the breeding season. The establishment of breeding
territories by the Anna hummingbird (*Ca-
lypte anna*) has been correlated with testis

volume and histologic changes (Williamson,
1956).

An extensive study in which behavior was
related to the seasonal cycle was made by
Petersen (1955) with the migratory bank
swallow (*Riparia riparia*). These birds arrived in the spring in flocks which congre-
gated at breeding sites on warm days.

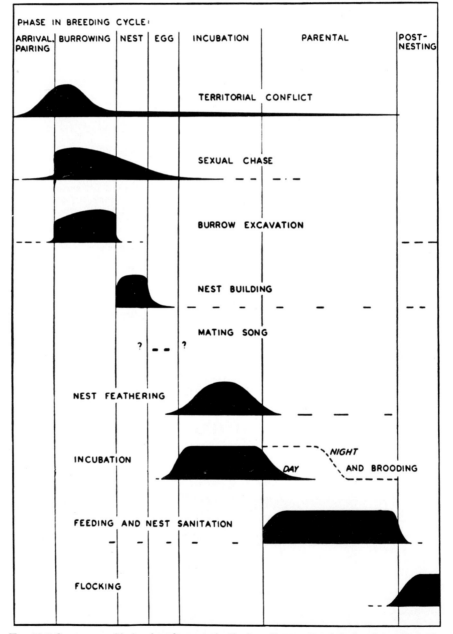

FIG. 20.5. Summary of behavior elements in the breeding cycle of the bank swallow (Petersen, 1955).

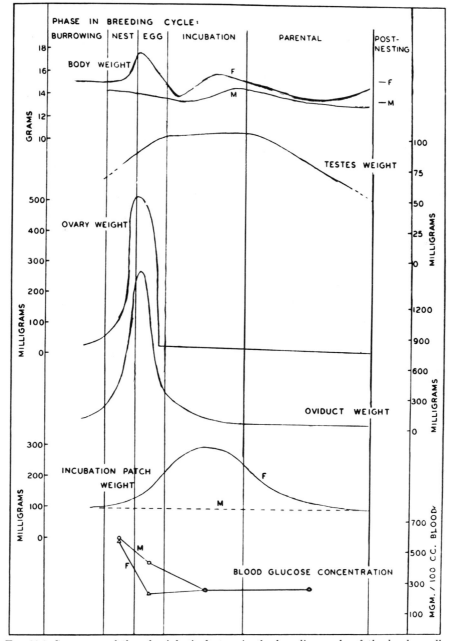

FIG. 20.6. Summary of the physiologic factors in the breeding cycle of the bank swallow (Petersen, 1955).

Unpaired birds, probably males, selected burrowing sites and set up limited territory. Pairing resulted from the persistent returning by the female to an area in the face of aggressive attack. After the pair-bond was formed, both mates shared in the attack on trespassers. After the reproductive cycle was completed, and after the end of nest-ing, toleration of other individuals was restored and flocking ensued. Peterson related the sequence of social, sexual, and parental behavior patterns (Fig. 20.5) to physiologic and morphologic changes (Fig. 20.6).

Modifications in agonistic behavior occur in continuous breeders and under the nonseasonal conditions of the laboratory. The nonspawning cichlid fish, *Aeguidens latifrens*, fights the male more often than does the gravid female (Breder, 1934). Female guinea pigs become submissive to, or tolerant of, the male during estrus (Young, Dempsey and Myers, 1935). According to Pearson (1944) the female short-tailed shrew, *Blarina brevicauda*, fights the male when nonreceptive, but during estrus is quite docile, as is the golden hamster (Kislack and Beach, 1955). Female chimpanzees become dominant (in the sense of attaining a response priority during food-getting tests) over other females during the period of maximal genital swelling (Crawford, 1940).

Not to be overlooked is the probable significance of the fact that such changes in behavior are seen in females, in which ovarian activity is cyclic, rather than in males in which testicular activity is continuous.

B. ANDROGENS AND AGGRESSIVENESS

In most subhuman vertebrates which have been observed in sociobiologic studies the males are more aggressive than the females and aggressiveness increases during the sexual development of maturing animals as well as during the breeding season. That early castration of domestic male animals reduces pugnacity has long been known (Rice, 1942). Goodale (1913) noted the lack of combativeness in the capon, and Scott and Payne (1934) found that castration eliminates fighting in the tom of the bronze turkey, *Meleagris gallopavo*. According to Uhrich (1938), male mice castrated as adults continue to fight, whereas those gonadectomized prepubertally rarely fight. Evans (1936) observed that castrated males of the lizard, *Anolis carolinensis*, continue to fight, and that females rarely fight unless they are ovariectomized. From this, he concluded that ovarian hormones inhibit fighting. However, Greenberg and Noble (1944) expressed the opinion that both sexes are innately aggressive and that the seasonal increase in testicular hormone in the male transforms mere antagonism into territoriality. Castration of the male gobiid fish, *Bathygobius soporator*, results in the disappearance of combative behavior, but courtship is not impaired. Nonspawning males show normal combat, and hypophysectomy

is followed by a cessation of both combat and courtship (Tavolga, 1955). A continued display of pugnacity was observed in castrated starlings, *Sturnus vulgaris* (Davis, 1957a), and in castrated male pigeons (Carpenter, 1958). Geldings ranked among mares in a common dominance order (Montgomery, 1957). These observations point to androgen concentration in the blood as influencing the level of combativeness. Apparently, however, the extent to which castration affects the level of aggressiveness varies among species, and according to the age at which the animal is gonadectomized. The experimenter's connotation of aggressive behavior and the method of its measurement may result in variations in the interpretation of the effects of castration.

The administration of androgen often produces an increase in aggressiveness in normal adults and in castrates, and precocity in immature individuals of either sex. Treatment of fishes has been followed mostly by observations of sexual behavior (Aronson, 1957, p. 286), but Noble and Borne (1940) reported advancement in rank by spayed and intact female swordtails, *Xiphophorus helleri*, after implanting pellets of testosterone. Juvenile and young adult urodeles, *Triturus viridescens*, treated with whole pituitary and luteinizing hormone (LH) fraction pre-empted first place in their hierarchies (Evans, 1956). Male *Anolis* treated with testosterone propionate fought more than the controls (Noble and Greenberg, 1941). Subordinate males of *Sceloporus grammicus* received an androgen (Perandren) and rose in their respective hierarchies (Evans, 1946). Among birds, androgen treatment caused an increase in aggressiveness in the ringdove, *Streptopelia risoria* (Bennett, 1940), the herring gull, *Larus argentatus* (Boss, 1943), and in poulards (Davis and Domm, 1943). Female rats injected with androgen became irritable and pugnacious (Ball, 1940; Huffman, 1941; Beach, 1942). Tollman and King (1956) injected an androgen into young gonadectomized male and female C57BL/10 mice and found that the males responded more aggressively toward each other than did the females. They concluded that either the nervous systems of both sexes responded differentially to the hormone or that females do not provide as adequate a stimulus for aggressive responses as do males.

Increase in the social status of androgen-treated individuals has been recorded for chickens (Allee, Collias and Lutherman, 1939; Douglis, 1948), mice (Beeman, 1947), and chimpanzees (Clark and Birch, 1945; Birch and Clark, 1946). However, three males of free-living valley quail which received pellets of testosterone propionate became pugnacious toward other males but failed to alter their positions in the peck-order of the covey (Emlen and Lorenz, 1942). Hens receiving androgen also failed to rise in the social order (Williams and McGibbon, 1956). In both of these instances the group remained intact, and presumably the social habits withstood the influence of lowered thresholds for aggressive action produced by the androgen. These results differ from those obtained by Allee, Collias and Lutherman (1939), as did the procedure, because in the latter experiment pair contests were conducted between individuals of different flocks containing the treated birds. It is possible that a treated hen, if promptly returned to her flock from an initial encounter (which she usually won), was still highly stimulated, and if she engaged in fighting with a threatening superior penmate, a reversal of dominance would occur.

An experiment which is the converse of those described above has recently been performed, but not previously reported, by Robert Buchholz of Kansas State University. He attempted to determine whether a low ranking bird could be made the dominant individual in the flock by varying the psychologic state rather than by treatment with androgen. The chickens used were males which had been reared together. The lowest ranking bird, which had never been observed to peck a penmate, was selected for experimentation. When 11 weeks old, 7 birds were isolated for 33 days to extinguish the memory of past associations. When approximately 16 weeks old, the lowest ranking male was placed into a pen for 1 week to give him the advantage associated with prior residence. When a female was added he dominated her without any difficulty. After 2 days she was removed and a former

penmate, which was immediately above him in rank previously, was introduced. The formerly subordinate male gained dominance over him and all of his other former penmates which were introduced during the course of 1 day in the reverse of the former peck-order. By this method the original lowest ranking male became the top ranked bird. It is apparent that the chicken as well as the mouse (Ginsburg and Allee, 1942) is a species in which psychologic factors can be instrumental in the attainment of a state that formerly would have been thought of as solely the consequence of hormonal action.

Changes in agonistic behavior after the cessation of hormonal treatment have been investigated. Birch and Clark (1946) noted a reversal of dominance to the pretreatment status in adult ovariectomized chimpanzees, whether they were given methyl testosterone or estradiol. In ringdoves Bennett (1940) also found a tendency of previously treated birds to return to their former social rank. However, Allee, Collias and Lutherman (1939) reported that the social position which treated hens won persisted as long as these flocks were under observation. These contrasting results on the two species of birds may perhaps be explained on the basis of qualitative differences in the social inertia of these species. In the peck-right system found in chickens, repeated pecking reinforces the unidirectional pecking and maintains dominance relations, whereas the bidirectional pecking characteristic of doves results in a more fluid social order. Thus, the relative permanence of social gains or losses induced by exogenous hormone may be influenced, among other factors, by the type of social behavior patterns peculiar to the species.

C. ESTROGENS AND SUBMISSIVENESS

The reports that have been made following observations and experiments on the relationship between estrogens and the social order have resulted in a confused picture. There are species such as the red-necked phalarope, *Phalaropus lobatus*, in which the female in the reproductive phase is the more colorful, sings, fights, and entices the male (Tinbergen, 1935). But in the case of many of the lower mammals that have been studied, the female is submissive when follicular development is at its height, and resistant to the male or even strongly aggressive at other times. This was long ago noted in the female guinea pig (Young, Dempsey and Myers, 1935) and has more recently been recorded for other species. The female opossum has been observed after a heat period to attack and kill a male double her weight (Hartman, 1945). Pearson (1944) states that the nonreceptive female short-tailed shrew faces the male whenever he is near and repulses his advances with lunges, loud squeaks, and sometimes a long, shrill chatter. Evans' (1937) observation that ovariectomy of the lizard, Anolis carolinensis, increased the territorial response, may not be unrelated. The change in behavior at estrus, such as that described for the guinea pig, opossum, and shrew, was made the subject of an investigation by Kislack and Beach (1955). Intact, estrous and diestrous females, and estrogen-treated spayed animals were tested in pairs with males. Spayed hamsters were continually aggressive, although somewhat less so than intact diestrous females. The administration of estrogen alone was followed by a slight increase in aggressiveness, but progesterone injected after estrogen eliminated fighting and reduced other forms of aggression. Progesterone alone had no influence on the behavior of spayed hamsters. It was concluded that there is a negative relationship between sexual receptivity and aggressiveness, which depends in large measure on ovarian secretions. In the words of the authors, the ovarian hormones that render the female receptive also inhibit her tendency to attack the male.

In other experiments the results of treatment with estrogens were ambivalent or negative. Allee and Collias (1940) injected estradiol into intact hens and discovered only a slight tendency toward reduced aggressiveness and lowered status in the peck-order, even when large amounts were given. Both male and female chicks of the domestic fowl injected with an estrogen formed a hierarchy which was determined largely by avoidance reactions (Guhl, 1958). Individuals of both sexes gave the submissive sexual crouch when a hand was held over them. Pecking was rare and the social order was called an avoidance-order rather than a peck-order. Emlen and Lorenz (1942), on the other hand, did not observe a behavioral response in valley quail given estrogen. Shoemaker (1939) and Noble and Wurm (1940) also obtained negative results with canaries and night herons, respectively.

Young rhesus monkeys were tested with an androgen and an estrogen (Mirsky, 1955). Unisexual social groups of 5 were organized on a hierarchial system. Those in ranks 5 and 2 received implanted pellets of the androgen or the estrogen in two different periods separated by an interval without treatment. Two pairs of males and two pairs of females of known dominance relations were tested. The subordinate member of each pair was given either androgen or estrogen. In no case was hormone administration accompanied by a significant decrease in either dominance or subordinate behavior scores.

Except for the report that a prepubertally castrated male showed enhanced dominance status under androgen therapy, and subordinate status as a result of estradiol administration (Clark and Birch, 1945), investigations on the chimpanzee have yielded results that are not clear. According to Yerkes (1939), the importance of the sexual condition was established. The dominant female of a pair, when in estrus, ordinarily grants privilege to her subordinate companion, whereas the subordinate female, when in estrus, may achieve privilege and act as if temporarily in control. The statement is not made that the subordinate member of a pair becomes dominant when she is in estrus. Crawford (1940) provided additional evidence that a response priority in a food competition situation is related to the sexual status of the females. In 9 of 13 pairs in which changes in response priority occurred, the subordinate member obtained food more often when in the follicular phase of the cycle. Again, the behavior was described as a yielding of priority by the dominant subject with only the weak suggestion of an increase in aggressiveness on the part of the subordinate animal. However, Birch and Clark (1946, 1950) and Clark and

Birch (1945) state that estrogens increase the aggressiveness and dominance tendency of female chimpanzees and that the granting-of-privilege concept is superfluous.

Certain circumstances should be noted in any consideration of these latter studies. Only three females were used and Yerkes and Crawford had observed much variability in their experiments. Further, the subjects had been ovariectomized postpubertally and had been together intermittently for several years. The dominance order was Lia, Nira, May. Nira was paired with Lia in a food competition situation before, during, and after treatment, and May was tested similarly in pairings with both of her social superiors. Nira obtained higher competition scores during treatment, whereas May failed to show any changes. Before ovariectomy, May mated readily with the males when she was in the swelling phase, whereas Nira during 5 years as a mature female had been known to copulate only once despite frequent attempts to breed her. Two questions arise: Did Nira's failure to breed before ovariectomy indicate abnormality? Did agonistic experiences before ovariectomy augment or suppress any probable effects of estrogenic treatment?

D. ARE AGGRESSIVENESS AND SUBMISSIVENESS SEPARATE BEHAVIOR PATTERNS?

Before leaving the subjects of estrogens and submissiveness, and androgens and aggressiveness, the alternative possibilities must be considered that these antithetical behaviors are (1) independent tendencies or (2) extremes on the same scale of social interactions. As a starting point for the discussion, the reader will be reminded that, except for the claim by Birch and Clark that estrogens increase the aggressiveness of the female chimpanzee, opinion is general that dominance is lowered (or submissiveness is increased) by these hormones (Collias, 1944; Beach, 1948). To the holder of this view who also accepts the conclusion that androgens enhance aggressiveness, it is only a step to the hypothesis that aggressiveness and submissiveness are independent traits, that aggressiveness is essentially but by no means exclusively masculine and submissiveness essentially but by no means ex-

clusively feminine. But the alternative concept that aggressiveness and submissiveness are merely opposites on the same scale of social interactions must be considered. Support for such an opinion might come from the fact that both types of reaction are shown by the same individual in appropriate situations. However, this is also true of sexual behavior, but in the case of sexual behavior, a rather convincing body of evidence has accumulated that two mechanisms are involved (for a review of the subject see the chapter by Young, and for new data obtained during an investigation of the patterns of inheritance of masculine and feminine behavior in female guinea pigs see Goy and Jakway, 1959). A solution of the problem may come from further work with gamecocks which have been selected for persistence in fighting and may fight to the death without showing avoidance behavior. It was a strain of guinea pigs (strain 2), in which the females normally display little or no masculine behavior, that provided the genetical evidence for the independence of masculine and feminine components of sexual behavior (Goy and Jakway, *loc. cit.*).

E. GONADAL HORMONES AND THE DEVELOPMENT OF SOCIAL BEHAVIOR

A discussion of the development of social behavior should be related to the heredity-environment or instinct-learning controversy, which, however, is beyond the scope of this chapter. Should there be a need for references to recent views on this subject, several publications are available (Tinbergen, 1951; Lehrman, 1953; and Emlen, 1955). Some observational studies on the socialization of young animals have been reported for birds (Collias, 1952), mice (Williams and Scott, 1953), sheep (Scott, 1945), sheep and goats (Collias, 1956), and dogs (Scott and Marston, 1950). Most of the experimental studies have been focused on the precocious display of sexual behavior and are discussed in the chapter by Young.

Collias (1950) began treatment of male and female domestic chicks with testosterone and estradiol when they were 2 days old. Dosages of 0.1, 0.3, 0.5, and 0.7 mg. of either hormone were given daily to different chicks for 30 days. The number of aggressive pecks observed was proportional to the dosage of androgen given to male chicks. With the lower dosage, pecking was more frequent than attempted matings. Testosterone was more effective than estradiol in inducing aggressive behavior. Males were much more responsive to the androgen than females. Submissive behavior was not reported. The conditions under which these chicks were reared were not given, nor were the dominance relations mentioned.

Experiments to determine the approximate age at which chicks develop agonistic behavior and establish a social order, and the effects of gonadal hormones and social inertia on the precocity of such behavior were reported by Guhl (1958). In small groups of chicks the males developed aggressive behavior earlier than the females; in mixed flocks there were heterosexual peck-orders, with males pecking more frequently than females. There was a gradual trend toward unisexual pecking. Some chicks were reared in partial isolation from the second day after hatching and assembled into groups when their respective control flocks of the same sex established a peck-order (8 to 9 weeks for males, 10 weeks for females). These birds formed a peck-order in a matter of hours, indicating that it did not require 8 to 10 weeks of learning to form a dominance order. This difference between group-reared and assembled isolation-reared birds may have been related to either the maturation of the endocrine and nervous systems, or it may be that social inertia in the group-reared chicks suppressed the influences of developmental processes thereby producing a time lag in the evocation of agonistic behavior.

As a part of the same investigation, individuals in small unisexual groups were injected with either testosterone or diethylstilbestrol. Each treated group was matched with a control group from the same hatch. In all but one group the injections were begun the 2nd or 3rd day after hatching. Dominance or subordination was established somewhat earlier in the treated groups, depending on the hormone used. The androgen-treated chicks, irrespective of sex,

showed increased aggressiveness, whereas the estrogen-treated chicks, again irrespective of sex, were more submissive and the social order was determined by the consistent avoidance by each chick of specific penmates. However, the differences between the means of experimentals and controls are small and do not suggest any marked precocity in agonistic behavior as a result of treatment with gonadal hormones.

In the same study (Guhl, 1958) capons were used to determine the age at which dominance-subordination relations (peck-rights) may be established in the absence of androgen (Table 20.1). For comparison there was one group of normal males and one group of capons receiving large dosages of testosterone propionate daily (0.5 mg. beginning the 10th day which was increased by 0.5 mg. weekly for 4 weeks). Caponization was on the 9th day of age, and therefore the untreated capons had little or no endogenous androgen (Breneman and Mason, 1951). The mean age at which the untreated capons established peck-rights was 13.7 weeks, whereas the mean for the normal males was 9.9 weeks, and for the treated capons 7.8 weeks. It is of interest that a social order developed by the 17th week in the apparent absence of androgen, and that the high level of treatment enhanced the formation of a peck-order over the controls by only 1 week, the 12th week compared with the 13th week for the normal males.

VII. Releasers and Other Mechanisms in Social Behavior

Secondary sex characters such as adornment and color, postures, odors, and certain sounds, have a place in the mediation of social behavior and are thought to function as releasers of specific behavior patterns. Such stimuli may be simple or very complex configurations (Tinbergen, 1951).

In an excellent review of the behavior of cichlid fishes, Baerends and Baerends-Van Roon (1950) related chromatophores to behavior patterns. Six types of chromatophores were discussed showing various methods of development and control. In *Tilapia natalensis* the black reproductive markings developed under the physiologic conditions typical of the reproductive pe-

TABLE 20.1

The effect of androgenic treatment on the development of peck-rights in caponized chicks as compared with normal cockerels and capons of the same age

Arrows indicate deviations from a straight-line peck-order.

Number Pecked	Peck-order	Weeks of Age												
		5	6	7	8	9	10	11	12	13	14	15	16	17
Normal males														
8	GV				1	3	3	1						
7	GY		1		3	2		1						
6	VY			2	1			1	1	1				
5	V							2	2	1				
3	R						1			2				
3	VV					1		1		1				
3	RY			1	1					1				
1	YY				1									
0	BB													
36	Total		1	3	7	6	4	6	3	6				
Androgen-treated capons, 10th day to 63rd day														
9	GB	3	2	1	2			1						
8	GV	5		1	1		1							
7	B		2	1	2		2							
5	R	2		1	1	1								
5	VB		1		2		1		1					
4	Y			1	1	1	1							
4	BB					1		2	1					
2	V						1	1						
1	GR						1							
0	VY													
45	Total	10	5	5	9	3	7	4	2					
Capons														
8	R									2	1	4	1	
7	GV			1	1		1	2		2				
6	GY				1			1	1	2				1
4	GR							1	1	1				1
4	B								1				1	2
4	VY											1		3
2	GB											1		1
1	GG													1
0	G													
36	Total			1	2	0	1	4	3	7	1	6	2	9

riod, but contraction and expansion were controlled by the nervous system. The bright red markings of *Hemichromis* were also shown only when the fish engaged in courtship. The reproductive colors function in fighting displays and in territoriality during the breeding season. Nonterritorial fish were pale, and individuals crossing territorial boundaries were not molested if their chromatophores were contracted. It was suggested that the development of these chromatophores probably is under the control of the pituitary.

Noble and Curtis (1939) found that ripe females of *Hemichromis bimaculatus* selected bright red males when given a choice among females and males in different stages of maturity. Tests by Tinbergen (1951, p.

27) showed that the red undersides of the three-spined stickleback, *Gasterosteus aculeatur*, elicited aggression irrespective of the size or shape of the models. Apart from color, a head-downward posturing was also effective. The hormonal relation to color or posturing was not established. In *Gambusia hurtadoi* the intensity of yellow markings on the dorsal fin, at the base of the caudal fin, and on the ventral portion of the caudal peduncle were correlated with rank in the social hierarchy (McAlister, 1958).

Evans (1955) discussed various types of releasers found among reptiles, which included postures, colors, and sounds. Many of these occur only in sexually mature individuals. Nocturnal species tend to use auditory cues whereas diurnal species do much posturing, often with pigmented areas drawing attention to these movements. The close relationship between hostile and sexual behavior patterns was shown by Greenberg and Noble (1944) in *Anolis carolinensis*, because reaction patterns may shift readily from one form to the other in either direction. The crest in this species was stimulated by testosterone propionate.

Color in birds was one of the first of the secondary sex characters to receive attention in its relation to agonistic behavior (Huxley, 1934). The songs of birds are generally accepted as indicators of the reproductive phase and often are related to territoriality (Armstrong, 1947, p. 293).

Lorenz (1950, p. 242), in his discussion of the subject, defined a social releaser as a "device—either a property of color and/or shape, or a special sequence of movements, or, for that matter, of sounds, or a scent—specifically differentiated to the function of eliciting a response in a fellow member of the species. To every releaser, as an organ for sending out sign stimuli, there corresponds a perceptual correlate, an 'organ' to receive sign stimuli and to activate the answering reaction." The latter he called a releasing mechanism. The point of interest is whether any of the releasers, or the so-called releasing mechanisms, are influenced by gonadal hormones.

With respect to the former, when they are clearly defined secondary sex characters, the answer has been given in countless in-

vestigations and reviews (see particularly Lipschütz, 1924, chapter 2; Allen, Danforth and Doisy, 1939, p. 185, 251, 340, 499, 545; Beach, 1948, chapter 10; and the chapters by Forbes and van Tienhoven in this book). Whether the functioning of releasing mechanisms, that is, visual, auditory, olfactory, and tactile receptors, and central neural tissues, is influenced by gonadal hormones is less certain. The subject is discussed at length by Lehrman and Young in the parts of their chapters dealing with the mechanism of the hormone actions which stimulate parental and mating behavior. Briefly, the opinion has been expressed that gonadal hormones act on peripheral receptors (Carter, Cohen and Shorr, 1947; Beach and Levinson, 1950) and olfactory sensitivity (LeMagnen, 1952a, b, 1953). Tavolga (1955) castrated males of the gobiid fish, *Bathygobius soporator*, and noted that they act as though they do not "perceive" the difference between males, gravid females, and nongravid females. He concluded that testicular hormones affect the threshold of visual, chemical, and possibly auditory sense organs.

Particularly pertinent to the subject is the discussion presented by Birch and Clark (1950) following their investigation of the mechanism of estrogen-induced dominance in chimpanzees. As they wrote, the problem centers around the differential effectiveness of estrogen in producing changes in the dominance status of males and females. Testosterone, whether given to males or females, was assumed to facilitate aggressive behavior by an action on the central nervous tissues. Estradiol reduced aggressive tendency in the two sexes and the effect was assumed to be central. But there is a second effect on the female which is peripheral and results in the swelling and increased irritation of the sex skin. The facts that dominance-status paralleled the engorgement of the sex skin, and that prevention of the latter by the simultaneous administration of progesterone reduced the dominance-status, were the basis for concluding that the peripheral effectiveness of estrogens accounts for their effects on dominance. The case is weakened, unfortunately, by the authors' failure to eliminate the possibility that the progesterone given to inhibit sex-skin tumescence may also have antagonized other actions of the estrogen (for a discussion of this action of progesterone see the chapters by Hisaw, Villee and Young on the ovary). If progesterone had this effect in these animals, the reduction in dominance which followed its administration was not necessarily related in any direct way to the prevention of swelling.

VIII. Social Stress and the Endocrine System

Heretofore, discussion has been limited to the gonadal hormones and aggressiveness. There remains another axis, i.e., the effect of aggressiveness on reproduction. The nature of the relationship does not appear to be that of a feed-back, as our statement of the problem suggests. Females as well as males are affected, and much of what has been done indicates that the pituitary-adrenal axis is involved. Mammals with cyclic populations seem most susceptible.

Christian (1950) reviewed the symptoms and conditions associated with the die-offs in mammals having population cycles. These were related to the general-adaptation syndrome of Selye (1947). A working hypothesis was developed for the population crash which terminates the cycle. "Exhaustion of the adrenopituitary system resulting from increased stresses inherent in a high population, especially in winter, plus the late winter demands of the reproductive system, due to increased light and other factors, precipitate population-wide death with the symptoms of adrenal insufficiency and hypoglycemic convulsions." Elements of this hypothesis are supported by rather impressive evidence.

Southwick, (1955a, b), in a carefully controlled experiment with house mice (Mus musculus), found that the amount of aggressive activity increased as the density of the population increased. Crowcraft and Rowe (1957) in a similar experiment, but with some modifications, found that reduced fecundity of the females was the most important single factor limiting population growth. They concluded that some factor other than fighting or food shortage appears to inhibit ovarian activity. Christian (1955) showed that mice mantained in groups have

heavier adrenal glands than mice kept in isolation, and that the adrenals and reproductive organs of wild house mice are more responsive to stress than those of laboratory albino mice. In a subsequent study of populations of different sizes and of isolated controls, and with food and water in excess, Christian (1956) analyzed the endocrine responses. The results were indicative of an amount of stress proportional to population density. The secretion of adrenocorticotrophin increased in response to stress and gonadotrophin decreased. Increased adrenal size and low eosinophil counts were taken as evidence for an increase in adrenocortical activity in a dense population of the meadow vole, Microtus pennsylvanicus (Louch, 1958). The results from one study of the chicken (Siegel, 1959) suggests that the response of this species may perhaps be similar to that of the mouse and meadow vole. The adrenals were heavier in birds under crowded conditions than in those with more floor space per bird. With progressive decrease in the density of the flocks, adrenal weights declined.

Three urban populations of Norway rats (Rattus norvegicus) with histories of stable high population densities were reduced by trapping to an average of 32 per cent below the maximal density. There was a mean decline of 28.3 per cent in the adrenal weights immediately following population reduction, and 7 months later the adrenal weights were 22.4 per cent below the original values (Christian and Davis, 1955). Richter (1954) found that the cortexes of adrenal glands were much smaller in the domesticated laboratory rat than in the wild Norway rat. Population cycles of the vole (Microtus arvalis Pallus) in Germany were investigated by Frank (1957). He concluded that intraspecific social behavior was of great importance for the events of population dynamics. Crowding favored competition and caused a state of psychologic excitement which was transformed by the pituitary-adrenocortical system into physical stress. This, acutely combined with the stress of food shortage, produces a "readiness" for a crash in the vole population. The ultimate trigger was an additional stress of meteorologic events. Davis (1957b) stated that competition and fighting increase as the population increases and this results in a number of responses including the hypertrophy of the adrenal cortex. A number of ensuing responses reduces the reproductive rate and increases mortality. Thus reproduction is reduced or, if the behavior patterns and physiologic responses are not precisely adjusted, a population decline may occur. In this manner, behavior acts as a homeostatic mechanism for populations.

Conceivably, this important generalization is premature, at least in this form. The extensive data on the Iowa muskrat, *Ondatra zibethicus* (Errington, 1957), do not indicate that social stress is a major factor in the population cycle of this species. There may be other exceptions. In addition, the application of newer tests of adrenal function would be desirable.

IX. Concluding Remarks

Much work has been done in an effort to ascertain whether a relationship exists between gonadal hormones and the social behavior which is displayed so conspicuously at the time of reproduction. There will be disappointment that more exact information has not been obtained. This can be explained in part by the circumstance that endocrinologic, neurologic, and psychologic processes of the most complex types are involved. Such being the case, any analysis of the many problems requires the utilization of endocrinologic, neuroanatomic, neurophysiologic, and psychologic techniques. Unfortunately, however, application of the rigorous tests which are a part of these techniques has not been possible. The end points thus far available to the investigator of social behavior are not as sharp as those on which the endocrinologist would insist; neural centers which might be inactivated or stimulated electrically or chemically are not known to exist, and the psychologist is handicapped by the variables inherent in any study of a behavior involving interaction with other animals. On the other hand, it may be expected that as more work is done, the handicaps imposed by these restrictions will be overcome and a more gratifying progress may be anticipated.

X. References

ALLEE, W. C. 1931. *Animal Aggregations: A Study in General Sociology.* Chicago: University of Chicago Press.

ALLEE, W. C. 1936. Analytical studies of group behavior in birds. Wilson Bull., **48**, 145–151.

ALLEE, W. C. 1952. Dominance and hierarchy in societies of vertebrates. In *Structure et Physiologie des Sociétés Animales.* Colloques Internationaux 34, P. P. Grassé, Ed., pp. 157–181. Paris: Centre National de la Recherche Scientifique.

ALLEE, W. C., AND COLLIAS, N. E. 1940. The influence of estradiol on the social organization of flocks of hens. Endocrinology, **27**, 87–94.

ALLEE, W. C., COLLIAS, N. E., AND LUTHERMAN, C. Z. 1939. Modification of the social order in flocks of hens by the injection of testosterone propionate. Physiol. Zool., **12**, 412–440.

ALLEE, W. C., EMERSON, A. E., PARK, O., PARK, T., AND SCHMIDT, K. P. 1949. *Principles of Animal Ecology.* Philadelphia: W. B. Saunders Company.

ALLEE, W. C., AND FOREMAN, D. 1955. Effects of an androgen on dominance and subordinance in six common breeds of *Gallus gallus.* Physiol. Zool., **28**, 89–115.

ALLEN, E., DANFORTH, C. H., AND DOISY, E. A. 1939. *Sex and Internal Secretions*, 2nd ed. Baltimore: The Williams & Wilkins Company.

ALTMANN, M. 1952. Social behavior of elk, *Cervus canadensis* Nelsoni, in the Jackson Hole area of Wyoming. Behaviour, **4**, 116–143.

ALTMANN, M. 1956. Patterns of social behavior in big game. In *Transactions 21st North American Wildlife Conference*, pp. 528–545. Washington, D. C.: Wildlife Management Institute.

ARMSTRONG, E. A. 1947. *Bird Display and Behaviour.* London: Lindsay Drummond.

ARONSON, L. R. 1957. Reproductive and parental behavior. In *The Physiology of Fishes*, Vol. 2., M. E. Brown, Ed., pp. 271–304. New York: Academic Press, Inc.

BALL, J. 1940. The effect of testosterone on the sex behavior of female rats. J. Comp. Psychol., **29**, 151–165.

BAERENDS, G. P. 1957. Behavior: the ethological analysis of fish behavior. In *The Physiology of Fishes*, Vol. 2, M. E. Brown, Ed., pp. 229–269. New York: Academic Press, Inc.

BAERENDS, G. P., AND BAERENDS-VAN ROON, J. M. 1950. An introduction to the study of the ethology of cichlid fishes. Behaviour, suppl. I. Leiden: E. J. Brill.

BASTOCK, M., MORRIS, D., AND MOYNIHAN, M. 1953. Some comments on conflict and thwarting in animals. Behaviour, **6**, 66–84.

BEACH, F. A. 1942. Male and female mating behavior in pre-puberally castrated female rats treated with androgens. Endocrinology, **31**, 673–678.

BEACH, F. A. 1948. *Hormones and Behavior.* New York: Paul B. Hoeber, Inc.

BEACH, F. A., AND LEVINSON, G. 1950. Effects of androgen on the glans penis and mating behavior of castrated male rats. J. Exper. Zool., **114**, 159–171.

BEEMAN, E. 1947. The effect of male hormone on aggressive behavior in mice. Physiol. Zool., **20**, 373–405.

BEEMAN, E., AND ALLEE, W. C. 1945. Some effects of thiamine on the winning of social contacts in mice. Physiol. Zool., **18**, 195–221.

BENNETT, M. A. 1940. The social hierarchy in ringdoves. II. The effect of treatment with testosterone propionate. Ecology, **21**, 148–165.

BIRCH, H. G., AND CLARK, G. 1946. Hormonal modification of social behavior. II. The effects of sex-hormone administration on the social dominance status of the female-castrate chimpanzee. Psychosom. Med., **8**, 320–331.

BIRCH, H. G., AND CLARK, G. 1950. Hormonal modification of social behavior. IV. The mechanism of estrogen-induced dominance in chimpanzees. J. Comp. & Physiol. Psychol., **43**, 181–193.

BOSS, W. R. 1943. Hormonal determination of adult characters and sex behavior in herring gulls (*Larus argentatus*). J. Exper. Zool., **94**, 181–203.

BOURLIERE, F. 1952. Le territorialisme dans l'organisation sociales des vertébrés. In *Structure et Physiologie des Sociétés Animales*. Colloque Internationaux 34, P. P. Grassé, Ed., pp. 199–206. Paris: Centre National de la Recherche Scientifique.

BRADDOCK, J. C., AND BRADDOCK, Z. I. 1955. Aggressive behavior among females of the Siamese fighting fish, *Betta splendens*. Physiol. Zool., **28**, 152–172.

BREDER, C. M., JR. 1934. An experimental study of the reproductive habits and life history of the cichlid fish, *Aequidens latifrens* (Steindachner). Zoologica, **18**, 1–42.

BRENEMAN, W. R., AND MASON, R. C. 1951. Androgen influence on pituitary-gonad interrelationship. Endocrinology, **48**, 752–762.

CALHOUN, J. B. 1956. A comparative study of the social behavior of two inbred strains of house mice. Ecol. Monogr., **26**, 81–103.

CARPENTER, C. R. 1934. A field study of the behavior and social relation of howling monkeys. Comp. Psychol. Monogr., **10**, 1–168.

CARPENTER, C. R. 1942. Societies of monkeys and apes. Biol. Symp., **8**, 177–204.

CARPENTER, C. R. 1952. Social behavior in nonhuman primates. In *Structure et Physiologie des Sociétés Animales,* Colloques Internationaux 34, P. P. Grassé, Ed., pp. 227–245. Paris: Centre National de la Recherche Scientifique.

CARPENTER, C. R. 1958. Territoriality: a review of concepts and problems. In *Behavior and Evolution*, A. Roe and G. G. Simpson, Eds., pp. 224–250. New Haven: Yale University Press.

CARTER, A. C., COHEN, E. J., AND SHORR, E. 1947. The use of androgens in women. Vitamins & Hormones, **5**, 317–391.

CHRISTIAN, J. J. 1950. The adrenopituitary system and population cycles in mammals. J. Mammal., **31**, 247–259.

CHRISTIAN, J. J. 1955. Effect of population size on the adrenal glands and reproductive organs of male mice in populations of fixed size. Am. J. Physiol., **182**, 292–300.

CHRISTIAN, J. J. 1956. Adrenal and reproductive responses to population size in mice from freely growing populations. Ecology, **37**, 258–273.

CHRISTIAN, J. J., AND DAVIS, D. E. 1955. Reduction of adrenal weight in rodents by reducing population size. In *Transactions 20th North American Wildlife Conference*, pp. 177–198. Washington, D. C.: Wildlife Management Institute.

CLARK, E., ARONSON, L. R., AND GORDON, M. 1954. Mating behavior patterns in two sympatric species of xiphophorin fishes: their inheritance and significance in sexual isolation. Bull. Am. Museum Nat. Hist., **103**, 141–225.

CLARK, G., AND BIRCH, H. G. 1945. Hormonal modification of social behavior. I. The effect of sex-hormone administration on the social status of a male-castrate chimpanzee. Psychosom. Med., **7**, 321–329.

COLLIAS, N. E. 1943. Statistical analysis of factors which make for success in initial encounters between hens. Am. Naturalist, **77**, 519–538.

COLLIAS, N. E. 1944. Aggressive behavior among vertebrate animals. Physiol. Zool., **17**, 83–123.

COLLIAS, N. E. 1950. Hormones and behavior with special reference to birds and the mechanisms of hormone action. In *A Symposium on Steroid Hormones*, E. S. Gordon, Ed., pp. 277–329. Madison: University of Wisconsin Press.

COLLIAS, N. E. 1952. The development of social behavior in birds. Auk, **69**, 127–159.

COLLIAS, N. E. 1956. The analysis of socialization in sheep and goats. Ecology, **37**, 228–239.

COLLIAS, N. E., AND TABER, R. D. 1951. A field study of some grouping and dominance relations in ring-necked pheasants. Condor, **53**, 265–275.

CRAWFORD, M. P. 1940. The relation between social dominance and the menstrual cycle in female chimpanzees. J. Comp. Psychol., **30**, 483–513.

CROWCRAFT, P., AND ROWE, F. P. 1957. The growth of confined colonies of the wild housemouse (*Mus musculus* L.). Proc. Zool. Soc. London, **129**, 359–370.

DARLING, F. F. 1937. *A Herd of Red Deer*. London: Oxford University Press.

DARLING, F. F. 1952. Social life in ungulates. In *Structure et Physiologie des Sociétés Animales*. Colloques Internationaux 34, P. P. Grassé, Ed., pp. 221–226. Paris: Centre National de la Recherche Scientifique.

DAVIS, D. E. 1942. The phylogeny of social nesting in the Crotophaginae. Quart. Rev. Biol., **17**, 115–134.

DAVIS, D. E. 1957a. Aggressive behavior in castrated starlings. Science, **126**, 253.

DAVIS, D. E. 1957b. Role of behavior in population forces. Anat. Rec., **128**, 537.

DAVIS, D. E., AND DOMM, L. V. 1943. The influence of hormones on the sexual behavior of domestic fowl. In *Essays in Biology,* pp. 171–181. Berkeley: University of California Press.

DOUGLIS, M. 1948. Social factors influencing the hierarchies of small flocks of the domestic hen: Interactions between resident and part-time members of organized flocks. Physiol. Zool., **21**, 147–182.

EMERSON, A. E. 1938. Termite nests—a study of the phylogeny of behavior. Ecol. Monogr., **8**, 247–284.

EMLEN, J. T., JR. 1952. Flocking behavior in birds. Auk, **69**, 160–170.

EMLEN, J. T., JR. 1955. The study of behavior in birds. In *Recent Studies in Avian Biology*, A. Wolfson, Ed., Ch. 5. Urbana: University of Illinois Press.

EMLEN, J. T., JR. 1957. Defended area? A critique of the territory concept and of conventional thinking. Ibis, **99**, 352.

EMLEN, J. T., JR., AND LORENZ, F. W. 1942. Pairing responses of free-living valley quail to sex-hormone pellet implants. Auk, **59**, 369–378.

ERRINGTON, P. L. 1957. Of population cycles and unknowns. Cold Spring Harbor Symposia Quant. Biol., **22**, 287–300.

EVANS, L. T. 1936. Behavior of castrated lizards. J. Genet. Psychol., **48**, 217–221.

EVANS, L. T. 1937. Differential effects of the ovarian hormones on the territorial reaction time of female *Anolis carolinensis*. Physiol. Zool., **10**, 456–463.

EVANS, L. T. 1946. Behavior of *Sceloporus grammicus microleptidotus* as modified by certain endocrines. Anat. Rec., **94**, 63.

EVANS, L. T. 1955. Group processes in lower vertebrates. Macy Foundation Conferences on Group Processes, **1**, 268–269.

EVANS, L. T. 1956. Endocrine effects upon urodele hierarchies. Anat. Rec., **124**, 400.

FRANK, F. 1957. The causality of microtine cycles in Germany. J. Wildlife Mgmt., **21**, 113–121.

FREDERICSON, E. 1952. Reciprocal fostering of two inbred mouse strains and its effect on the modification of inherited aggressive behavior. Am. Psychol., **7**, 241–242.

GENELLY, R. E. 1955. Annual cycle in a population of California quail. Condor, **57**, 263–285.

GINSBURG, B., AND ALLEE, W. C. 1942. Some effects on conditioning on social dominance and subordination in inbred strains of mice. Physiol. Zool., **15**, 485–506.

GOODALE, H. D. 1913. Castration in relation to the secondary sexual characters in Brown Leghorns. Am. Naturalist, **47**, 159–169.

GOY, R. W., AND JAKWAY, J. S. 1959. The inheritance of patterns of sexual behavior in female guinea pigs. Anim. Behav., **7**, 142–149.

GOY, R. W., AND YOUNG, W. C. 1957. Strain difference in the behavioral responses of female guinea pigs to α-estradiol benzoate and progesterone. Behaviour, **10**, 340–354.

GREENBERG, B., AND NOBLE, G. K. 1944. Social behavior of the American chameleon (*Anolis carolinensis*, Voigt). Physiol. Zool., **17**, 392–439.

GUHL, A. M. 1950. Social dominance and receptivity in the domestic fowl. Physiol. Zool., **23**, 361–366.

GUHL, A. M. 1953. Social behavior of the domestic fowl. Tech. Bull. 73., Agric. Exper. Sta. Manhattan: Kansas State University.

GUHL, A. M. 1958. The development of social organization in the domestic chick. Anim. Behav., **6**, 92–111.

GUHL, A. M., AND ALLEE, W. C. 1944. Some measurable effects of social organization in flocks of hens. Physiol. Zool., **17**, 320–347.

GUHL, A. M., COLLIAS, N. E., AND ALLEE, W. C. 1945. Mating behavior and the social hierarchy in small flocks of White Leghorns. Physiol. Zool., **18**, 365–390.

GUHL, A. M., CRAIG, J. V., AND MUELLER, C. D. 1960. Selective breeding for aggressiveness in chickens. Poultry Sc., **39**, 970–980.

GUHL, A. M., AND WARREN, D. C. 1946. Number of offspring sired by cockerels related to social dominance in chicken. Poultry Sc., **25**, 460–472.

HALE, E. B. 1954. Androgen levels and breed differences in the fighting behavior of cocks. Bull. Ecol. Soc. Am., **35**, 71.

HALL, C. S. 1936. Emotional behavior in the rat. II. The relationship between need and emotionality. J. Comp. Psychol., **22**, 61–68.

HARTMAN, C. G. 1945. The mating of mammals. Ann. New York Acad. Sc., **46**, 23–44.

HEDIGER, H. 1950. *Wild Animals in Captivity*. London: Butterworth and Company, Ltd.

HEDIGER, H. 1952. Beiträge zur Säugetier-Soziologie. In *Structure et Physiologie des Sociétés Animales*. Colloques Internationaux 34, P. P. Grassé, Ed., pp. 297–321. Paris: Centre National de la Recherche Scientifique.

HINDE, R. A. 1952. The behavior of the great tit (*Parus major*) and some other related species. Behaviour, Suppl. II.

HINDE, R. A. 1953. The conflict between drive in the courtship and copulation of the chaffinch. Behaviour, **5**, 1–31.

HINDE, R. A. 1956a. The biologic significance of the territories of birds. Ibis, **98**, 340–369.

HINDE, R. A. 1956b. The behavior of certain cardueline F_1 interspecies hybrids. Behaviour, **9**, 202–213.

HOWARD, H. E. 1920. *Territory in Bird Life*. London: Murray.

HUXLEY, J. S. 1934. Threat and warning coloration in birds. In *Proceedings 8th International Ornithology Congress,* pp. 430–455. Oxford: Oxford University Press.

HUFFMAN, J. W. 1941. Effect of testosterone propionate upon reproduction in the female. Endocrinology, **29**, 77–79.

KISLACK, J. W., AND BEACH, F. A. 1955. Inhibition of aggressiveness by ovarian hormones. Endocrinology, **56**, 684–692.

LACK, D. 1953. *The Life of the Robin.* London: Penguin Books.

LEHRMAN, D. S. 1953. A critique of Konrad Lorenz's theory of instinctive behavior. Quart. Rev. Biol., **28**, 337–363.

LE MAGNEN, J. 1952a. Les phenomènes olfacto-sexuels. Arch. Sc. physiol., **6**, 125–160.

LE MAGNEN, J. 1952b. Les phenomènes olfacto-sexuels chez le rat blanc. Arch. Sc. physiol., **6**, 295–331.

LE MAGNEN, J. 1953. L'olfaction: le fonctionnement olfactif et son intervention dans les régulations psycho-physiologiques. J. Physiol., Paris, **45**, 285–326.

LIPSCHÜTZ, A. 1924. *The Internal Secretions of the Sex Glands.* Baltimore: The Williams & Wilkins Company.

LORENZ, K. 1935. Der Kumpan in der Umweldt des Vogels. J. Ornithol., Leipzig, **83**, 137–213; 289–413.

LORENZ, K. 1950. The comparative method of studying innate behavior patterns. In *Physiological Mechanisms in Animal Behavior*, Symposia of the Society for Experimental Biology, No. 4, J. F. Danielli and R. Brown, Eds., pp. 221–268. New York: Academic Press, Inc.

LOUCH, C. D. 1958. Adrenocortical activity in two meadow vole populations. J. Mammal., **39**, 109–116.

MARLER, P. 1955. Studies of fighting in chaffinches. I. Behavior in relation to social hierarchy. Brit. J. Anim. Behav., **3**, 111–117.

MARLER, P. 1956. Studies of fighting in chaffinches. III. Proximity as a cause of aggression. Brit. J. Anim. Behav., **4**, 23–30.

MARTOF, B. S. 1953. Territoriality in the green frog, *Rana clamitans.* Ecology, **34**, 165–174.

MASLOW, A. H. 1934. Dominance and social behavior in monkeys. Psychol. Bull., **31**, 688.

MASLOW, A. H. 1936. The role of dominance in the social and sexual behavior of infrahuman primates. IV. The determination of hierarchy in pairs and in a group. J. Genet. Psychol., **49**, 161–198.

MASURE, R., AND ALLEE, W. C. 1934a. The social order in flocks of the common chicken and the pigeon. Auk, **51**, 306–327.

MASURE, R., AND ALLEE, W. C. 1934b. Flock organization of the shell parakeet *Melopsittacus undulatus* Shaw. Ecology, **15**, 388–398.

MATAROZZO, J. D., SASLOW, G., MATAROZZO, R. G., AND PHILLIPS, J. S. 1958. Stability and modifiability of personality patterns manifested during a standardized interview. In *Psychopathology of Communication*, P. H. Hoch and J. Zubin, Eds., pp. 98–125. New York: Grune & Stratton, Inc.

MCALISTER, W. H. 1958. The correlation of coloration with social rank in *Gambusia hurtadoi.* Ecology, **39**, 477–482.

MICHENER, C. D. 1953. Problems in the development of social behavior and communication among insects. Tr. Kansas Acad. Sc., **56**, 1–15.

MICHENER, C. D., AND MICHENER, M. H. 1951. *American Social Insects.* New York: D. Van Nostrand Company.

MILLER, R. E., MURPHY, J. V., AND MIRSKY, I. A. 1955. The modification of social dominance in a group of monkeys by interanimal conditioning. J. Comp. & Physiol. Psychol., **48**, 392–396.

MIRSKY, A. F. 1955. The influence of sex hormones on social behavior of monkeys. J. Comp. & Physiol. Psychol., **48**, 327–335.

MONTGOMERY, G. G. 1957. Some aspects of the sociality of the domestic horse. Tr. Kansas Acad. Sc., **60**, 419–424.

MOYNIHAN, M. 1958. Notes on the behavior of some North American gulls. III. Pairing behavior. Behaviour, **13**, 112–130.

MURPHY, J. V., MILLER, R. E., AND MIRSKY, I. A. 1955. Interanimal conditioning in the monkey. J. Comp. & Physiol. Psychol., **48**, 211–214.

NOBLE, G. K. 1939a. The experimental animal from the naturalist's point of view. Am. Naturalist, **73**, 113–126.

NOBLE, G. K. 1939b. Neural basis of social behavior in vertebrates. Collecting Net, **14**, 121–124.

NOBLE, G. K., AND BORNE, R. 1940. The effect of sex hormones on the social hierarchy of *Xiphophorus helleri.* Anat. Rec., **78**, 147.

NOBLE, G. K., AND CURTIS, B. 1939. The social behavior of the jewel fish, *Hemichromis bimaculatus,* Gill. Bull. Am. Museum Nat. Hist., **76**, 1–46.

NOBLE, G. K., AND GREENBERG, B. 1941. Induction of female behavior in male *Anolis carolinensis* with testosterone propionate. Proc. Soc. Exper. Biol. & Med., **47**, 32–37.

NOBLE, G. K., AND WURM, M. 1940. The effect of testosterone propionate on the black-crowned night heron. Endocrinology, **26**, 837–850.

PEARSON, O. P. 1944. Reproduction in the shrew (*Blarina brevicauda*, Say). Am. J. Anat., **75**, 39–93.

PETERSEN, A. J. 1955. The breeding cycle of the bank swallow. Wilson Bull., **67**, 235–286.

POTTER, J. H. 1949. Dominance relations between different breeds of domestic hens. Physiol. Zool., **22**, 261–280.

POTTER, J. H., AND ALLEE, W. C. 1953. Some effects of experience with breeds of *Gallus gallus* L. on behavior of hens toward strange individuals. Physiol. Zool., **26**, 147–161.

RADLOW, R., HALE, E. B., AND SMITH, W. I. 1958. Note on the role of conditioning in the modification of social dominance. Psychol. Rept., **4**, 579–581.

RICE, V. A. 1942. *Breeding and Improvement of Farm Animals*, 3rd ed. New York: McGraw-Hill Book Company, Inc.

RICHTER, C. P. 1954. The effect of domestication and selection on the behavior of the Norway rat. J. Nat. Cancer Inst., **15**, 727–738.

RISS, W., VALENSTEIN, E. S., SINKS, J., AND YOUNG, W. C. 1955. Development of sexual behavior in male guinea pigs from genetically different stocks under controlled conditions of androgen treatment and caging. Endocrinology, **57**, 139–146.

ROBERTS, B. 1940. The breeding of penguins. Brit. Graham Land Expedition, 1934–37, Sc. Rept., **1**, 195–254.

ROWAN, W. 1931. *The Riddle of Migration*. Baltimore: The Williams & Wilkins Company.

SANCTUARY, W. 1932. A study in avian behavior to determine the nature and persistency of the order of dominance in the domestic fowl and to relate these to certain physiologic reactions. Master's thesis, Massachusetts State College, Amherst.

SCHJELDERUP-EBBE, T. 1913. Hønsenes stemme. Bidrag til Hønsenes psykologi. Naturen, **37**, 262–276.

SCHJELDERUP-EBBE, T. 1935. Social behavior in birds. In *A Handbook of Social Psychology*, C. Murchison, Ed., Ch. 20. Worcester: Clark University Press.

SCHLOSBERG, H., DUNCAN, M. C., AND DAITCH, B. H. 1949. Mating behavior of two live-bearing fish, *Xiphophorus helleri* and *Platypoecilus maculatus*. Physiol. Zool., **22**, 148–161.

SCHMIDT, R. S. 1955. The evolution of nest-building behavior in *Apicotermes* (Isoptera). Evolution, **9**, 157–181.

SCHNEIRLA, T. C. 1946. Problems in biopsychology of social organization. J. Abnormal & Social Psychol., **41**, 385–402.

SCOTT, H. M., AND PAYNE, L. F. 1934. The effect of gonadectomy on the secondary characters of the bronze turkey (*M. gallopavo*). J. Exper. Zool., **69**, 123–136.

SCOTT, J. P. 1942. Genetic difference in the social behavior of inbred strains of mice. J. Hered., **33**, 11–15.

SCOTT, J. P. 1945. Social behavior, organization, and leadership in a small flock of domestic sheep. Comp. Psychol. Monogr., **18**, 1–29.

SCOTT, J. P. 1948. Dominance and the frustration-aggression hypothesis. Physiol. Zool., **21**, 31–39.

SCOTT, J. P. 1954. The effects of selection and domestication upon the behavior of the dog. J. Nat. Cancer Inst., **15**, 739–758.

SCOTT, J. P. 1956. The analysis of social organization in animals. Ecology, **37**, 213–221.

SCOTT, J. P. 1958a. *Animal Behavior*. Chicago: University of Chicago Press.

SCOTT, J. P. 1958b. *Aggression*. Chicago: University of Chicago Press.

SCOTT, J. P., AND CHARLES, M. S. 1953. Some problems of heredity and social behavior. J. Gen. Psychol., **48**, 209–230.

SCOTT, J. P., AND CHARLES, M. S. 1954. Genetic differences in the behavior of dogs: a case of magnification by thresholds and by habit formation. J. Genet. Psychol., **84**, 175–188.

SCOTT, J. P., AND FREDERICSON, E. 1951. The causes of fighting in mice and rats. Physiol. Zool., **24**, 273–309.

SCOTT, J. P., AND MARSTON, M. 1950. Critical periods affecting the development of normal and maladjustive social behavior in puppies. J. Genet. Psychol., **77**, 25–60.

SELYE, H. 1947. The general-adaptive-syndrome and the diseases of adaption. In *Textbook of Endocrinology*, pp. 837–866. Montreal: Montreal University.

SHOEMAKER, H. H. 1939. Effects of testosterone propionate on behavior of the female canary. Proc. Soc. Exper. Biol. & Med., **41**, 299–302.

SIEGEL, H. S. 1959. The relation of density to weight of adrenal glands in chickens. Ecology, **40**, 495–498.

SOUTHWICK, C. H. 1955a. The population dynamics of confined house mice supplied with unlimited food. Ecology, **36**, 212–225.

SOUTHWICK, C. H. 1955b. Regulatory mechanisms of house mouse populations: social behavior affecting litter survival. Ecology, **36**, 627–634.

STODDARD, H. L. 1931. *The Bobwhite Quail*. New York: Charles Scribner's Sons.

TAVOLGA, W. N. 1955. Effects of gonadectomy and hypophysectomy on prespawning behavior in males of the gobiid fish, *Bathygobius soporator*. Physiol. Zool., **28**, 218–233.

TEST, F. H. 1954. Territoriality in amphibians. Bull. Ecol. Soc. Am., **35**, 64.

TINBERGEN, N. 1935. Field observations of East Greenland birds. I. The behavior of the red-necked phalarope (*Phalaropus lobatus* L.) in spring. Ardea, **24**, 1–42.

TINBERGEN, N. 1951. *The Study of Instinct*. Oxford: Clarendon Press.

TINBERGEN, N. 1953. *Social Behavior in Animals*. London: Methuen & Company, Ltd.

TOLLMAN, J., AND KING, J. A. 1956. The effects of testosterone propionate on aggression in male and female C57BL/10 mice. Brit. J. Anim. Behav., **4**, 147–149.

URICH, J. 1938. The social hierarchy in albino mice. J. Comp. Psychol., **25**, 373–413.

WILLIAMS, C., AND MCGIBBON, W. H. 1956. An analysis of the peck-order of the female domestic fowl (*Gallus domesticus*). Poultry Sc., **35**, 969–976.

WILLIAMS, E., AND SCOTT, J. P. 1953. The development of social behavior patterns in the mouse, in relation to natural periods. Behaviour, **6**, 35–65.

WILLIAMSON, F. S. L. 1956. The molt and testis cycle of the anna hummingbird. Condor, **58**, 342–366.

WINN, H. E. 1958. Comparative behavior and ecology of fourteen species of darters (*Pisces, Percidae*). Ecol. Monogr., **28**, 155–191.

YERKES, R. M. 1939. Social dominance and sexual status in the chimpanzee. Quart. Rev. Biol., **14**, 115–136.

YERKES, R. M. 1940. Social behavior of chimpanzees: dominance between mates, in relation to sexual status. J. Comp. Psychol., **30,** 147–186.

YOUNG, W. C., DEMPSEY, E. W., AND MYERS, H. I. 1935. Cyclic reproductive behavior in the female guinea pig. J. Comp. Psychol., **19,** 313–335.

YOUNG, W. C., AND ORBISON, W. D. 1944. Changes in selected features of behavior in pairs of oppositely sexed chimpanzees during the sexual cycle and after ovariectmy. J. Comp. Psychol., **37,** 107–143.

ZUCKERMAN, S. 1932. *The Social Behavior of Monkeys and Apes.* New York: Harcourt, Brace & Company.

21

HORMONAL REGULATION OF PARENTAL BEHAVIOR IN BIRDS AND INFRAHUMAN MAMMALS

Daniel S. Lehrman, Ph.D.

PROFESSOR OF PSYCHOLOGY AND DIRECTOR, INSTITUTE OF ANIMAL
BEHAVIOR, RUTGERS, THE STATE UNIVERSITY,
NEWARK, NEW JERSEY

I. Introduction

Almost all species of birds and mammals exhibit special behavior patterns the function of which is to warm, feed, protect, or otherwise foster the development of their eggs and/or young. Although these behavior patterns vary widely in form, physiologic organization, ontogenetic origin, and degree of psychologic complexity, it is nevertheless sometimes convenient to group them together under the rubric of "parental behavior." Such behavior is of course appropriate to, and ordinarily occurs only at, the stage of the reproductive cycle when there are eggs or young present or impending. Its regulation is, therefore, in part, a function of the reproductive cycle, and it is the purpose of this chapter to discuss the relationships between the (endocrine) reproductive cycle and the occurrence and organization of parental behavior.

Decisions about what should be included in such a discussion are not easy to make, because what we call "parental behavior" is not always as clearly differentiated within the animal's repertoire of behavior patterns as it is in our own conceptions. For example, mice of almost any age, either sex, and any physiologic condition may do a certain amount of nest-building, which is, to the observer, only quantitatively different from the more intense nest-building of the pre-parturient animal. Should a detailed discussion of such behavior necessarily be included in a chapter on "parental behavior"? The nest-building of most species of birds is associated with the period of maximal sexual activity, and in some cases is incorporated into the courtship pattern. How do we, for purposes of a book like this, draw a sharp line between "sexual behavior" and "parental behavior"? It is obvious that such decisions must sometimes be more or less arbitrary.

For the purpose of this discussion, "parental behavior" will include nest-building and behavior toward eggs and young, ending with the time at which the young are able to obtain food independently of their parents.

It is perhaps inevitable that detailed physiologic experimentation should be for the most part limited to a few species of animals which are cheap and easy to breed in the laboratory, like rats, mice, and guinea pigs; or economically important, like domestic chickens; or similar to human beings, like monkeys and chimpanzees. This concentration of analytic work on a relatively few species has the effect of partially concealing from view the enormous diversity of behavioral and physiologic patterns that characterize the adaptation of animals to their environment. The diversity of behavior in different species, and of the physiologic mechanisms underlying the behavior, may be just as great as is their diversity of form. This is not the appropriate place for an exhaustive survey of the varieties of parental behavior found in nature, but it may help to put the available work on hormonal regulation of such behavior into perspective if we from time to time briefly indicate the types which can be found, and point out that they are by no means limited to those characteristic of domestic and laboratory animals.

II. Hormones and Parental Behavior in Birds

A. NEST-BUILDING

1. Varieties of Nest-building

Structure and location. Each species of bird has its characteristic method of providing a place for the deposition and incubation of the eggs, and the variability of nest construction within species is quite small. Between species, however, there are very wide variations. Some species build only above the ground (American robin, Herrick, 1911) or over water (tricolored red-winged blackbird, Emlen, 1941), some build only on the ground (herring gull,

Tinbergen, 1953), in burrows that they make in the ground (bank swallow, Petersen, 1955), or in natural cavities (purple martin, Allen and Nice, 1952). The pied-billed grebe builds a semifloating nest on the water (Glover, 1953). The Baltimore oriole builds an elaborate covered woven nest of grasses (Herrick, 1911), the Florida jay a woven open cup (Amadon, 1944b), the storm petrel a simple scrape with a few scraps of material laid in it (Davis, 1957), the black guillemot no nest at all, merely holding the egg on top of the webs of its feet (Storer, 1952). Swifts use their own saliva as cementing material, or in some species as almost the sole building material (Lack, 1956a). Various species of megapodes, instead of building nests, build large mounds of vegetable material which creates the incubation temperature when it rots (Fleay, 1937; Frith, 1956b). Most birds build individual nests, but some species build communal nests in which several birds lay (smooth-billed ani, Davis, 1940a), or massive woven communal structures within which each pair has a separate chamber (sociable weaverbird, Friedmann, 1930).

Share of the sexes in building. Male and female may share in nest-building, either approximately equally, as in house sparrows (Daanje, 1941), Florida jays (Amadon, 1944b), and great crested grebes (Simmons, 1955a), or in a variety of special ways. In a number of species, the male is more active in nest-building at first, with the female doing more of it later on (*e.g.*, red-backed shrike, Kramer, 1950; herring gull, Paludan, 1951; cliff swallows, Emlen, 1954; black-headed gull, Ytreberg, 1956). A frequently occurring special case is one in which the male builds the nest, and the female merely adds the lining (house wren, Kendeigh, 1941; graceful warbler, Simmons, 1954; coot, Kornowski, 1957). In the green heron, the male at first selects the nest site, and does all of the gathering, carrying, and weaving of twigs into the nest. He does not permit the female to enter the nest until some time after he has taken up his territory. Once he has allowed her to enter the nest, however, he does most of the gathering and carrying of twigs, and the female does most of the building (Meyerriecks, 1960).

The male may build the nest with little or no help from the female, as in the redshank (Grosskopf, 1958), the rook (Marshall and Coombs, 1957), and many species of weaver finches (Friedmann, 1949). In the zebra finch (Morris, 1954), and the bronze mannikin (both of them weaver finches) (Morris, 1957), the male builds the covered nest, and the female shapes the inside by sitting in it and making appropriate turning movements. In most species of megapodes, it is the males alone that construct the large mounds in which the eggs are to be laid (Coles, 1937, Frith, 1956b).

An interesting variation of male nest-building is one in which the male builds several nests and the female selects one of them as the repository of the eggs. This occurs in several species of wrens, in which the nests are built by the male before the arrival of the female in the spring, and in which the female may line the nest she selects (long-billed marsh wren, Weller, 1935; house wren, Kendeigh, 1941; European wren, Armstrong, 1955). The male Carolina wren builds several such nests, but when the female arrives, both may build a new nest for the eggs (Kendeigh, 1941; Nice and Thomas, 1948). A similar pattern is found in many waders, in which the male makes several nests (mere scrapes in the sand) in the presence of the female, during courtship, and the female lays eggs in one of them (ringed plover, Laven, 1940a; lapwing, Laven, 1941).

Building by the unassisted female is far more common than building by the male alone. When the nest is built entirely by the female, the role of the male may vary greatly. In some species, the male and female associate only for the purposes of courtship and copulation, and nest-building and rearing of the young are done elsewhere entirely by the female (Gould's manakin, Chapman, 1935; boat-tailed grackle, McIlhenny, 1937; bower birds, Marshall, 1954; blackcock and ruff, Selous, quoted by Armstrong, 1947). When the male and female associate on a territory during the breeding season, the role of the male may vary from complete indifference to the nest-building activities of the female (ovenbird, Hann, 1937), through merely accompanying her on her trips when she collects material (great tit, Hinde, 1952; bullfinch, Nicolai, 1956) to collecting material, but not building (pied-billed grebe, Glover, 1953; Clark nutcracker, Mewaldt, 1956). Observers of some species have noted that the males show all the elements of the nest-building behavior in their courtship or other behavior, without ever integrating them into effective building (great reed warbler, Kluyver, 1955). Schantz (1937) observed a nest built by a male song sparrow, a species in which the nest is ordinarily built entirely by the female (Nice, 1943).

In some species of birds, the male may play an important part in the selection of the site, even when he does not participate in nest-building (Hinde, 1952; Haartman, 1957).

2. Correlations between Nest-building and Other Behavior

As a first step in gaining some insight into the relationship between nest-building behavior and the reproductive cycle, let us consider how the occurrence of nest-building is related to other behavioral aspects of the cycle.

Copulation and nest-building. In a number of species, it has been reported that nest-building begins at about the time when the female becomes sexually receptive. The female snow bunting, after being vigorously courted by the male over a 2 to 3 week period, permits copulation for the first time on the same day on which she first picks up and carries nesting material (Tinbergen, 1939b). The female ruffed grouse, too, becomes sexually receptive the day she begins to build a nest (Allen, 1934). In both species, the nest is built entirely by the female. Nest-building and copulation may also begin at the same time in species in which both sexes build (house sparrow, Daanje, 1941; cedar waxwing, Putnam, 1949; gulls, Paludan, 1951; Brewer's blackbird, Williams, 1952).

Many observers have noted that, in various species of birds, copulation is limited to the nest-building period, which comes to an end before the eggs are laid (tricolored red-winged blackbird, Emlen, 1941; purple martin, Allen and Nice, 1952). This implies that the eggs, some of which may be ovu-

lated 8 or 10 days after the last copulation, must be fertilized by spermatozoa held in the oviduct for at least that time. Elder and Weller (1954) found that domestic mallard ducks could lay fertile eggs up to 17 days after being isolated from drakes, and Riddle and Behre (1921) report female ring doves laying fertile eggs after up to 8 days of isolation. Domestic hens may lay fertile eggs after 20 or more days of isolation (Hartman, 1939).

It will be recalled that the male house wren builds several nests before the arrival of the female in spring, and that the female finishes one of them some time after her arrival. In this species, copulation is limited to the period of *female* nest-building (Kendeigh, 1941). In the cliff swallow, another species in which the male does a substantial amount of nest-building before the pair is established in spring, copulation between members of the pair is not seen until the nest is well under way (the mechanics of copulation in this species are such that it cannot be performed at the nest-site unless there is a partially built nest there). However, promiscuous copulations not involving the members of the forming pair may be seen earlier, at the places where mud is being gathered for the nests (Emlen, 1954).

Female white-crowned sparrows seem to start building a few days before the first copulations are observed (Blanchard, 1941). In domestic canaries, the peak of copulatory activity is normally slightly later than that of nest-building activity. However, if the partially built nest is removed each day, so that no nest accumulates in the nest-bowl, the peaks of copulation and of nest-building activity occur at the same time. This indicates that the peak of copulation usually occurs later than that of nest-building behavior only because the presence of the nest inhibits nest-building activity (Hinde, 1958).

Various elements of the nest-building behavior, such as the billing or carrying of nesting material, are sometimes observed as part of courtship activity early in the season (Noble, Wurm and Schmidt, 1938; Armstrong, 1947).

Most of the correlations discussed in the foregoing paragraphs are derived from field observations, which vary widely with respect to the continuity of observation, number of birds observed, distribution of observations during the day and during the cycle, etc. There is nevertheless a strong impression that, in many species of birds, the physiologic conditions encouraging copulation (*i.e.*, sexual receptivity of the female) are the same as those inducing nest-building.

Nest-building not correlated with copulation. There are some significant exceptions to this general impression. The female rook usually does not permit copulation until after the nest has been built by the male (Marshall and Coombs, 1957). In the European coot, another species in which the nest is built by the male, copulation is also delayed until after the main shell of the nest is built (Kornowski, 1957). In these cases it may be suggested that the nest-building activity of the male may play some role in stimulating those physiologic changes in the female which induce sexual receptivity (see below, p. 1275.

Nest-building during incubation. Cases in which nest-building continues into the incubation period are for the most part of two general types. (a) There are some species in which the main part of the nest is completed before any eggs are laid, and in which the *lining* of the nest (with a material different from that used for the main construction) may continue during incubation (Cape weaver, Skead, 1947; graceful warbler, Simmons, 1954; bank swallow, Petersen, 1955). This suggests that, in such species, the selection of the different materials may have different hormonal bases, a suggestion for which there is some experimental evidence (see below, p. 1274). (b) Many species of gulls, terns, and shorebirds continue to build up the nest during the incubation period by virtue of a tendency to pick up nesting materials and drop or incorporate them in the nest whenever the birds' need to sit on the eggs is frustrated, or in conflict with some other behavioral tendency. Such nest-building has been called "displacement nest-building" (Tinbergen, 1952). It may occur, for example, when the bird is sitting on eggs abnormal in shape, size, or number (Moynihan, 1955; Baggerman, Baerends, Heikens

and Mook, 1956), or when the members of the pair relieve each other at the nest (*e.g.*, Cuthbert, 1954; Ytreberg, 1956). Baerends (1959) found that such displacement nest-building by a sitting bird also occurs when the temperature of the eggs departs too much from an optimal level.

3. Nest-building and Gonadal Cycles

So far, we have established a probable temporal relationship between nest-building and copulation, at least in those species in which the female participates in nest-building. As a further step in the analysis of the cyclic basis of nest-building behavior, we may now look into the relationship between the timing of nest-building activity and of the maximal activity of the ovarian follicle. In the absence of very much direct evidence on this point, let us adopt the somewhat roundabout procedure of considering, first, the timing of follicle growth, and then the timing of nest-building activity, in the cycle.

Relation of follicle growth to time of egg-laying (see chapter by van Tienhoven). The ovary of a bird at the egg-laying stage looks like a cluster of ova of varying size, the largest being the one that is nearest to being ovulated. If these ova are measured at the autopsy of a laying bird, the measurements form a graded series, which can be arranged in order, from most mature to least mature. If the interval between successive eggs is known for the species, and if the time of last ovulation is known for the individual, it is a simple matter to calculate the age (in days before ovulation) of each of the larger ova. The size of the ova can then be plotted as a function of pre-ovulatory age. In addition, the growth rate at each day before ovulation can be calculated by comparing the sizes of successive ova, the growth rate between day a and day b being a function of the increase in size of the ovum between day a and day b, in relation to the absolute size on day a (Romanoff, 1943).

In a wide variety of species of birds which have been studied, there is a sharp increase in follicle growth rate starting from 4 to 11 days pre-ovulation, depending on the species (Romanoff and Romanoff, 1949). Romanoff (1943) has shown that the actual growth rates, and the changes in growth rates, are identical in a number of species.

Riddle (1916) found that the rate of growth of the ovum of the domestic hen increased quite suddenly by a factor of about 25, some 5 to 8 days before ovulation (cf. Stieve, 1919; Warren and Conrad, 1939; Marza and Marza, 1935). In seasonal breeding birds (including most wild birds) the picture is basically the same. The ovary remains in a regressed state during the off-season; ova increase in size slowly during the early part of the breeding season, then very rapidly during the few days before ovulation. Bissonnette and Zujko (1936) found that the size of the largest ovum of the female starling increases very slowly for about 108 days (from December to March), and then very rapidly for about 26 days. During the 108-day period of slow growth, the growth rate remains stable at about 0.009 mm. per day; it then increases quite suddenly to 0.285 mm. per day, an increase of about 31.6 times.

The 26-day period of rapid growth found by Bissonnette and Zujko is based on the average sizes of ova from many different birds, which may have been at slightly different stages of the cycle, although collected on the same days. When the sizes of the various ova in individual ovaries are plotted as a function of serial position, in birds that are already ovulating, it becomes apparent that the period of final rapid growth in any one ovum is about 10 to 11 days.

Riddle (1911) and Bartelmez (1912) reported that the growth rate of ova in the domestic pigeon increases sharply (by 8 to 20 times) starting 5 to 8 days before ovulation (cf. Cuthbert, 1945). Stieve (1919) found that the volume of the largest ovum of the female jackdaw, after having remained quite constant during the months before the breeding season, increases from 24 cu. mm. to 1600 cu. mm. during the last 5 days before ovulation.

Paludan (1951) observed that the ova of two species of gull, observed in the wild, grew most rapidly during the last 9 to 10 days before ovulation.

It is clear that the characteristic pattern of growth of the avian follicle is that of a long period of slow, steady growth followed by the sudden onset of a short period of extremely rapid growth which ends only when the ovum is ovulated. This final period of rapid growth lasts from about 4 to about 11 days, depending on the species.

Relation of nest-building behavior to time of egg-laying. In most species of wild birds, nest-building appears to be sharply limited to a few days during the cycle. Female ruffed grouse begin to build about 6 days before the first egg (Allen, 1934). Tricolored red-winged blackbirds (Emlen, 1941) and song sparrows (Nice, 1937) start about 4 to 5 days before the first egg. Similar patterns are found in other species of passerine birds (*e.g.*, Clark nutcracker, Mewaldt, 1956; snow bunting, Tinbergen, 1939b).

The usual description of this type of relationship in the literature of field ornithology merely states that nest-building takes place during the few days before the first egg. When more exact quantitative observations are made, however, the situation seems somewhat more complex. Hinde (1958) weighed the amount of nesting material built into the nest on each day of the cycle in a number of female domestic canaries. He found that the intensity of nest-building activity reached a peak some time before the laying of the first egg, and then waned. The timing of the peak was subject to considerable variation, ranging in different individuals from 7 to 0 days before the first egg. Field observations on the cedar waxwing by Putnam (1949) show a similar pattern. In this species nest-building activity reached a peak 2 or 3 days before the laying of the first egg.

In some species the first egg appears, not immediately on the completion of the nest, but after an interval of several days following the last nest-building activity (purple martin, Allen and Nice, 1952; white-crowned sparrow, Blanchard, 1941; ovenbird, Hann, 1937; shrike, Miller, 1931). No information is available concerning possible differences in pre-ovulation changes in the ovary between species having the two different patterns.

Data on nest-building behavior and gonadal condition. The data so far presented clearly suggest that nest-building behavior is often associated with the period of maximal follicle growth. In a few cases, observations of follicle growth and of nest-building behavior have been made on the same species, and have usually led to the conclusion that this association does in fact exist. Emlen (1941, tricolored red-winged blackbird), Paludan (1951, herring gull), Petersen (1955, bank swallow), and Marshall and Coombs (1957, rook) have all noted that the period of nest-building coincides with that of maximal follicle growth. Mr. S. Glucksberg, in an unpublished study, destroyed the nests of several pairs of ring doves at the end of each day, and made daily counts of the number of pieces of nesting material built into the nest. He found that the amount of nest-building activity increased with increasing follicle size, reaching a peak at the time of ovulation. Similar observations have been made by Clausen (1959) on the homing pigeon.

Unfortunately, there are not yet any data on nest-building and male gonadal cycles to compare with those available for the relationship of this behavior to the female cycle. It is clear that the nest-building activity of seasonal breeding birds in which the male participates in building usually occurs during the part of the year when testicular secretory activity is at its height (Marshall and Coombs, 1957), but no observations have been made on detailed changes in testicular activity, correlated with detailed observations on behavior.

4. Physiologic Induction of Nest-building Behavior

The foregoing discussion makes it plain that, in the large number of species in which the female does most or all of the nest-building, nest-building behavior is associated with the final period of maximal follicle activity. We may now examine evidence bearing more or less directly on the problem of the hormonal induction of nest-building behavior. This evidence may be divided into two general categories: the induction of nest-building behavior by direct injection of hormones; and the elicitation of nest-building behavior by external stimuli.

Hormonal induction of nest-building behavior. The coincidence of nest-building behavior and the period of rapid follicle growth just preceding egg laying strongly suggests that nest-building behavior is induced by ovarian hormones. We have gone into such detail about these and other coincidences because very little direct experimental evidence is available, but what evidence there is confirms the impression that ovarian hormones often provide the physiologic background for nest-building behavior.

Lehrman (1958b) reported that the injection of 0.4 mg. diethylstilbestrol daily over a 7-day period induces nest-building behavior in ring doves. Hinde and Warren (1959) indicate that the injection of estrogenic hormone into female canaries also induces nest-building behavior, but only in near-lethal doses. Hinde's observations on the nest-building behavior of canaries (1958) indicate that these birds change over from the use of grass to the use of feathers (which is the nest lining) shortly before egg-laying is due. This change-over occurs to some extent even though the stimulus situation in the cage remains the same (the nest is removed daily so that the birds cannot be stimulated by a completed nest). This suggests that the change from the use of grass to the use of feathers is controlled in part by a change in hormonal condition, although such a change has not yet been induced by means of hormone administration. The suggestion is particularly interesting in view of the facts that, in some species of birds, the building of the main part of the nest stops abruptly with the beginning of egg-laying, but the addition of a lining of different material may continue thereafter, and that in still other species, the male may build the main part of the nest, whereas the female merely adds the lining (see above, page 1270.

Cole and Hutt (1953) studying a number of nonlaying hens, found on autopsy that some of them had ovulated, failing to lay because of interrupted oviducts, impacted oviducts, etc. Others had not ovulated. The ovulators among the nonlayers were seen to enter nests on about 47 per cent of the observed days (about the same percentage as in the case of normal laying hens). Nonovulators entered the nests in only 5 per cent of the cases. This indicates that the behavior toward the nest is influenced by hormones associated with ovulation, even in those birds in which the egg could not be produced because of abnormalities in the oviduct.

Progesterone has not yet been shown to induce nest-building behavior in birds. Warren and Hinde (1959) found that this hormone had no effect upon nest-building in the domestic canary, either alone or in combination with estrogen.

In view of the correlation between nest-building behavior, on the one hand, and, on the other hand, follicle growth, oviduct growth (Petersen, 1955), and the readiness of the female to copulate, it is interesting to note that estrogenic hormone induces oviduct development in various birds (Brant and Nalbandov, 1956; Lehrman and Brody, 1957; see chapter by van Tienhoven), and female sex behavior in the domestic chicken (Adams and Herrick, 1955).

Although it is reasonably certain that estrogenic hormone is the principle physiologic initiator of nest-building in those typical species in which the female does most or all of the nest-building, the situation is most unclear in those cases in which the male participates. Although we have noted in our laboratory that nest-building can be induced in ring doves by estrogen injection, and not by testosterone (see above), we do not yet have adequate observational evidence concerning the specific effects of estrogen injections on the male and on the female. This evidence, when it is available, will be important and interesting, because in these birds the male typically brings the nesting material to the nest, and the female builds it into the nest (Goodwin, 1955). In the brush turkey, the male builds a large mound by scraping leaves, mold, soil, etc., backwards with his feet. The female later lays the eggs in holes burrowed into this mound, and they are incubated by heat generated by decaying leaves and mold. The male's head and neck are almost featherless, and covered with a red skin. This skin becomes brilliant red in each breeding season, a few days before the beginning of mound-building. This suggests, of course, that in this case male sex hormone is involved in nest-building activity. However, during the period of most intense mound-building activity, the male does not allow the female near the area, which suggests further problems about the relationship between male sex behavior, mound-building, and the hormonal bases thereof (Fleay, 1937). In the black-crowned night heron both the male and the female normally participate in nest-building, incubation, and the rearing of the young. Noble and Wurm (1940) found that testosterone propionate would induce nest-building behavior in both males and females, whereas estrogenic hormones had no effect on the nest-building behavior of either sex. Further, they found that the change in color of the bills (yellowish to black) and legs (yellowish to rich pink), which normally occurs in both sexes at the beginning of the breeding season in the spring, can be induced in the off-season by injection of testosterone propionate, but not by estrogenic hormones. The hormonal background of nest-building behavior in this case is different from that of the species in which the female alone builds the nest, but it is also different from the situation in the ring dove, in which both sexes take part in building.

These cases indicate the complexity of patterns and mechanisms involved, and are only a sample of the considerable variety of unsolved problems posed by the nest-building behavior of many species of wild birds, problems which are only hinted at in the work so far done on domesticated birds.

Induction of nest-building by external stimuli. In species in which the female builds the nest unassisted (and this includes most of the species for which useful information is available), it seems that stimuli provided from the environment, including stimuli coming from the behavior of the male, may induce the hormonal changes which lead to the onset of nest-building. Howard (1920) described the typical breeding pattern of many species of songbirds, in which the male arrives first on the spring migration, and has his territory established by the time the female arrives some time later. The male appears to be ready to court and eager to copulate as soon as the female arrives, but the female at first does not permit copulation. There is a period of some days or weeks during which the courtship attempts of the male end in "sexual flights" during which the male chases the female through the territory in a characteristically zig-zag flight path, at the end of which contact is abruptly broken off. Only after a period of such flights is the female ready to copulate. Tinbergen (1939b) reported that the female snow bunting begins to build a nest (and to copulate) after about three weeks of this type of courtship stimulation by the male. Captive female chaffinches build nests and lay eggs more readily when they are stimulated by males (Marler, 1956). Vaugien (1948), working with serins, and Polikarpova (1940), working with house sparrows, found that females placed in cages without males would build no nests, whereas the presence of a male bird in a cage stimulated the females to build. Male and female herring gulls both build, but the female seems to become stimulated to take a greater part in nest-building by the activities of the male, who is more active at the beginning (Paludan, 1951).

Lehrman (1958a) reported that, when a pair of ring doves which have had previous breeding experience are placed together in a breeding cage with an empty nest bowl and a supply of nesting material, nest-building occurs after a 1- to 3-day period of courtship. If a male and female are kept for several days in a cage containing no nest bowl and no nesting material, they will be ready to start building a nest immediately after the subsequent introduction of nesting material into the cage. If both birds have been pretreated with estrogen before being introduced into the cage (see above), the nest-building starts immediately, rather than after a preliminary period of courtship (Lehrman, 1958b). This suggests that participation in courtship may have brought the birds into nest-building condition *because* it stimulates the secretion of estrogen. This is confirmed by Lehrman, Brody and Wortis (1961), who found that the oviduct of the female ringdove increases in weight about 5-fold, solely as the result of association with a male for 7 days. Significant increases in oviduct weight can be seen after less than 48 hours of stimulation by the courting male.

Warren and Hinde (1960) found that the presence of the male domestic canary speeds up the development of nest-building behavior in the female in spring, when nest-building is presumably induced by endogenous estrogen. On the other hand, the presence of males has no effect upon nest-building behavior induced by estrogen injection in the winter. This undoubtedly means that the stimulation of nest-building behavior by the presence of the male is, at least in part, by way of the stimulation of estrogen secretion.

Lack (1956b) noted that the male and female members of a pair of swifts (which keep the same mates year after year) may arrive at the nesting place on different days, but that nest-building does not start until the second member of the pair arrives from the south, even though the two members of the pair collect and use the material independently of each other. Many field observers have noted that the songs and postures of male birds may stimulate nest-building behavior on the part of the female, but it is not always certain in these cases whether what is at issue is the stimulation of a hormonal change by the behavior of the male, or the stimulation of a behavioral response of which the female is capable as a result of hormonal changes which have already taken place. There is no doubt that both of these effects occur (Blanchard, 1941; Armstrong, 1955).

Other external factors, such as the occurrence of rainy seasons for tropical birds (Bullough 1951), the presence of suitable nesting sites (Lack, 1933; Marler, 1956), etc., seem to stimulate the onset of nest-building behavior.

B. EGG-LAYING

1. Egg-laying Behavior in Birds

The typical egg-laying pattern of the domestic hen, in which eggs are laid on several consecutive days, there is a gap of one or more days, and egg-laying is then resumed, and in which such clutches occur repeatedly during much of the year, is by no means typical of the egg-laying behavior of most species of birds. In fact, there occurs among wild birds just as great a variety of egg-laying patterns, and therefore of relevant endocrine situations, as we noted in the case of nest-building.

Size of clutch. Birds typically lay a clutch consisting of a definite number of eggs, and then incubate the eggs until they hatch. Some species of birds produce only one such clutch per year; others may breed twice, or even three times a year, but with the breeding always restricted to a definite part of the year. In the temperate zones breeding is always in the spring and summer; in the tropics some species may breed during the wet season, others during the dry season, and in a few cases breeding may be all year round.

The number of eggs constituting a clutch varies from species to species within wide limits. Some birds, such as the large penguins, most auks and murres, petrels, and some others lay only 1 egg. Some birds, such as most species of pigeons and doves, characteristically lay 2 eggs. Most gulls lay and incubate 3-egg clutches. Most songbirds lay from 4 to 7 eggs. Large clutches, rather variable in size, are laid by ducks and geese, and gallinaceous birds such as partridges, pheasants, etc., may lay up to 20 eggs in a clutch. The domestic chicken is, of course, derived by selection from ancestral birds of the latter type (Mayaud, 1950).

Laying pattern. In those species in which the clutch consists of more than one egg, the interval between eggs is subject to wide interspecific variation (Mayaud, 1950). Data on the exact time of egg-laying are not as generally available for wild birds, of course, as they are for domestic birds, but certain wild birds, such as some species of ducks, appear to have a pattern like that of the domestic hen—they lay eggs at intervals of 20 to 24 hours. Most pigeons lay their 2 eggs about 40 hours apart (Whitman, 1919). Although the most common pattern appears to be for the birds to lay their eggs on successive days, there are species in which the interval is much longer such as the black-headed gull, in which the interval is about 42 hours (Weidmann, 1956), some boobies, in which the interval may be 6 or 7 days (Mayaud, 1950), and many others.

Brood parasitism. An unusually interest-ing phenomenon which poses several un-usual endocrinologic problems is the occurrence of brood parasitism in several families of birds. Parasitic birds do not build nests of their own, nor do they incubate their eggs. Instead, the female lays her eggs in the nests of other ("host") species, and the hosts incubate the eggs and rear the young. This type of breeding habit appears to have evolved independently in several different families of birds. Of the 200 species of the order Cuculiformes, some 80 are to some degree parasitic (Makatsch, 1937), including all 40 of the species of cuckoos living in the old world (Southern, 1954). Parasitism has also evolved among the cowbirds, a subfamily of blackbirds living in the new world (Friedmann, 1929), and in the honey guides of Africa (Friedmann, 1955). In addition, individuals of many other species of several families, especially ducks, quail, and pheasants, may breed parasitically more or less frequently (Weller, 1959).

2. Hormonal Relations in Ovulation and Egg-laying

This is not the place for a detailed discussion of the hormonal basis of ovulation and egg-laying, since these matters are extensively discussed in the chapter by van Tienhoven. However, a brief summary will serve as an introduction to certain problems concerning the regulation of egg-laying behavior.

The ovarian follicle grows under the influence of a gonadotrophic hormone from the pituitary gland, which is presumably similar to mammalian follicle-stimulating hormone (FSH). The growing follicle secretes estrogenic hormone, which in turn stimulates growth of the oviduct. When the follicle has reached ovulatory size, an ovulation-inducing hormone, presumably similar to luteinizing hormone (LH), induces the release of the egg. Fraps (1955) suggests that progesterone (or a progestin) from the ovary induces the secretion of the ovulation-inducing hormone by the pituitary gland (Rothchild and Fraps, 1949). Progesterone has been found in the blood plasma of laying hens (Fraps, Hooker and Forbes, 1948; Layne, Common, Maw and Fraps, 1957; Lytle and Lorenz, 1958), nonlaying hens, and cocks (Fraps, Hooker and Forbes, 1949), but not in that of capons. In addition, progesterone induces the formation of secretion products by the albumen-secreting glands in the oviduct, the growth of which has been accomplished under the previous influence of estrogen (Brant and Nalbandov, 1956). It thus seems probable that there is a short episode of progestin secretion by the ovary, just preceding ovulation, and that this follows a period of estrogen secretion. (See chapter by van Tienhoven.)

The actual laying of the egg appears to involve some posterior pituitary activity. Injection of posterior pituitary preparation induces the laying, within 2 to 25 minutes, of eggs already ovulated, but which would not normally have been laid for up to 20 hours (Burrows and Byerly, 1940, 1942). When the neurohypophysis is removed no oviposition takes place until after there has been time for the regeneration of the nerve connection between the hypothalamus and the pituitary gland (Shirley and Nalbandov, 1956a, b). Rothchild and Fraps (1944) removed the ruptured follicles and all the rapidly growing preovulatory follicles in hens, so that an ovulated egg was in the oviduct, but no more eggs could be ovulated. They then placed some of these hens in normally lighted rooms, others in rooms on reversed light cycles. The majority of eggs in both groups were laid during the daylight hours. They therefore concluded that a light-sensitive, nonovarian process was involved in the laying process, in addition to those factors controlling ovulation itself. (See chapter by van Tienhoven.)

3. Stimulation of Ovulation

Our interest in the nature of the conditions stimulating ovulation derives from the fact already pointed out, that nest-building activity is in part based on physiologic conditions induced by hormones coming from the developing egg follicle; and from the further fact that the physiologic events associated with ovulation somehow set the stage for the occurrence of incubation behavior, which normally follows egg-laying.

Neural stimulation of ovulation. It has become abundantly clear in recent years that the activity of the pituitary gland is controlled and influenced in considerable detail by the hypothalamus (Harris, 1955; see chapters by Greep, Everett, and van Tienhoven). The physiologic and anatomic details of the relationship between the hypothalamus and the pituitary gland are adequately discussed in these other chapters, and do not concern us here. We may, however, describe a striking example of the evidence for neural control of pituitary activity. Huston and Nalbandov (1953) sewed a loop of thread into the magnum of the oviducts of a group of domestic hens, and tied it into place, so that it provided a constant mechanical stimulation of the oviduct wall. Domestic hens normally ovulate 30 to 60 minutes after the laying of the previous egg. During the 25 days following the operation, however, 58 to 75 per cent of the operated birds laid no eggs. Among the operated birds which did lay eggs, the mean number of eggs laid was 1.5 per bird; in sham-operated birds with no loop sewed into the oviducts, the number of eggs laid was 5.5 per bird. LH or progesterone injection could induce ovulation at any time in those birds which were not laying because of the presence of the thread. The ova of the experimental birds did not degenerate, and their oviducts and combs remained normal. These data suggest that the mechanical stimulation of the oviduct wall inhibits LH secretion by the pituitary gland, without substantially interfering with the secretion of FSH. Huston and Nalbandov suggest that the presence of an egg in the oviduct acts in this way to prevent the ovulation of the succeeding egg until after the previous egg has been laid.

External stimuli and ovulation. Since the secretion of gonadotrophic hormones can be influenced and controlled by the hypothalamus, and by stimuli arising in the body outside of the central nervous system, it is reasonable to expect that external stimuli representing various environmental situations and events may have an influence, through this neurohypophyseal link, on the activity of the ovary.

(a) Light has long been known to influence gonadal activity. In seasonally reproducing birds, the increasing length of the day is the most important factor which ensures that the reproductive system will be active in the spring. In addition, experimental work with domesticated birds indicates that the timing of ovulation and oviposition during the day are influenced by the day-night light cycle (Farner, 1955; see chapter by van Tienhoven). In addition, there is considerable evidence that other environmental variables, such as those related to temperature, food supply, and so on, play a significant role as regulators of the breeding season (Thomson, 1950; Marshall, 1959).

(b) Stimuli provided by the courting male apparently influence the secretion of gonadotrophic hormones by female birds. It will be recalled that, in our discussion of the hormonal basis of nest-building behavior, we pointed out that nest-building behavior is sometimes induced in the female as a result of stimulation by the courting male, and that there is reason to believe that the basis for this effect is that the courtship of the male stimulates the secretion of estrogenic hormones in the female. We may now examine some further evidence of the effect of stimuli provided by the mate upon the growth and ovulation of the egg. Bartelmez (1912) noted that the ovary of an unmated female domestic pigeon contains follicles which do not exceed 5.5 mm. in diameter. When such a pigeon is placed with a male, she lays an egg after about 8 days (Harper, 1904). The growth of the ovum to the ovulation size of about 20 mm. is clearly caused by stimuli provided by the male. Craig (1911, 1913) kept several pairs of doves so that the males and females could see each other from adjoining cages. The males were allowed in the cages of the females daily, but were prevented from copulating by the experimenter, who separated them with a wand at appropriate times. All of these females laid eggs within 9 days of the beginning of contact with the male, although, when these birds were kept in isolation for a year preceding the beginning of the experiment, 5 out of the 6 females had laid no eggs at all. Matthews (1939) showed that the short period of tactual contact between male and female which Craig had allowed was not necessary for the

stimulation of ovulation. He showed that a female domestic pigeon would lay eggs as a result of seeing a male court her through a glass plate. We have found the same result in my laboratory, using ring doves. Both Matthews and Harper noted that, when two females are placed in a cage together, both may be stimulated to lay eggs. However, Collias (1950) found that ring doves in heterosexual groups laid more eggs than those in unisexual groups of the same size, indicating that the behavior of male doves is more stimulating to the secretion of gonadotrophins in females than is the pseudo-male behavior which some of the female doves will adopt when no males are in the group.

Polikarpova (1940) placed 50 female house sparrows in cages in which they received additional illumination daily, starting in the late fall. Twenty-five of them had males in the cages, the other 25 were alone. After about 50 days, none of the isolated females had started to build a nest, and of 17 such birds killed for autopsy, only 3 showed enlarged oviducts. On the other hand, all the females with males in their cages had nests, and 5 out of 8 birds examined had fully developed oviducts. Burger (1942, 1949) kept female starlings in groups of various sizes, with or without males. He found that, when he provided additional illumination to such females either isolated or in groups, their ova were stimulated to grow to about 3 mm. When groups of males and females were caged together, the ova grew rather larger (5 mm.). When a single male and a single female were caged together, the ova of the female grew to about 10 mm. This indicates that the stimulus for the growth of the ovum is not merely the presence of a male, but probably also the presence of conditions which facilitate the formation of a pairing relationship normal for the species. When Lack (1940, 1941) caged two pairs of robins or chaffinches in one aviary, the dominant pair bred normally, the subordinate pair did not. In such birds, the full expression of normal male courtship behavior toward the female requires that the male be the territory holder, which in turn means that he must be the dominant bird, or the only male, in a considerable space. Vaugien (1948) found that single female serins in individual cages would not lay eggs, but that eggs would be laid within a few days if a male was placed in a cage with the female. In the case of the shell parakeet, Vaugien (1951) showed that the *sounds* made by other birds influenced the growth of the oviduct. When female parakeets were kept isolated in small dark boxes of various sizes, they laid no eggs. When the box was placed inside an aviary containing a breeding pair (so that the experimental bird could hear, but not see the breeding birds) about half of the experimental birds laid eggs within 12 days. When the remaining birds were sacrificed for autopsy some 3 weeks later, they had enlarged oviducts, with the largest ova averaging 9 mm. in diameter. Controls kept out of hearing of breeding birds laid no eggs and, on autopsy, were found to have ova no larger than 1.5 mm. in diameter. Ficken, van Tienhoven, Ficken and Sibley (1959) verified this effect on ovarian activity of sounds made by other individuals in parakeet flocks, and also reported that testis development was stimulated. Marshall (1952, 1954) described the mating behavior of bower birds, in which the male has a special display ground, where he builds a bower and displays to the female. This display stimulates the female to go off and build her nest and rear her young alone.

It is clear from the above data that stimuli provided by the courting male induce the secretion of gonadotrophic hormones by the female, and that this is possibly a source of the synchronization of the sexual cycles of male and female birds during the breeding season.

(c) The presence of an appropriate nesting site and the availability of nesting material seem to be important factors in the conditions stimulating normal gonadotrophin secretion during the breeding season in birds. Lack (1933) observed three colonies of arctic terns at three different locations near a lake. The first location was permanently dry; the second was water-logged for a short period in the spring, because of melting snows; the third was water-logged for a longer period, until a marshy area dried up. Although birds were present from the beginning of the season in all three of these locations, the birds in the first colony laid their eggs earliest, those in the third colony latest. Similar observations were made by Linsdale (1938), who found that the yellow-headed blackbird, which builds its nest *only* over water, will abandon the nest in midbuilding if the water dries up while the nest is being built, and will then build a new nest elsewhere, this involving a delay in ovulation. However, if the eggs are laid first, so that incubation is in progress when the water dries up, the birds stay on. It can thus be stated that the presence of appropriate nesting conditions facilitates ovulation, and thus presumably the secretion of gonadotrophic hormones by the pituitary gland.

The induction of ovulation by the availability of nesting material has been shown experimentally in several species of birds. Like some other tropical species (Roberts, 1937; Bullough, 1951), the red-billed weaver finch of central Africa breeds at irregular times, always following rainfall. Marshall and Disney (1957) showed that the stimulating factor following the rainfall is actually the availability of nesting material. During the dry season, when no reproduction was taking place in free-living birds of the species, Marshall and Disney kept groups of male and female red-billed weavers in four outdoor cages variously provided with combinations of the following: insect food, artificial "rain" from a sprinkler, dry grass of the type normally used by the birds as nesting material, and green grass of the same type. Birds having green nesting grass available built nests, regardless of whether "rain" was falling, and regardless of whether insect food was available. Furthermore, the only females to lay eggs during the experimental period were those in the cages in which the males were building nests. Clearly, manipulation of nesting material by the males induced in the females hormonal changes leading to ovulation. Marshall and Disney also noted that the bills of the females kept with such males assumed breeding color earlier than did other females. This change in color is, of course, under hormonal control (Witschi, 1938).

Whitman (1919) found that various species of doves and pigeons would not ovulate unless nesting material and nesting locations were provided. Lehrman, Brody and Wortis (1961) found that the presence of nesting material plays a significant role in the stimulation of ovulation. Female ring doves kept with males in cages *not* supplied with a nest bowl or nesting material will not ovulate as soon or in as high a percentage of the cases as will such females kept in cages with males and an adequate supply of nesting material (the incidence of ovulations after 6 days in the cage is 55 per cent without nesting material, 95 per cent with nesting material). Differences in oviduct weight (and in frequency of ovulation) between the groups of birds with and without nesting material in the cage do not become apparent until some 5 or 6 days after the birds are placed in the cages, although, as reported above, increases in oviduct weight as a result of association or nonassociation with a *male* are to be seen within less than 48 hours. Since male doves collect most of the nesting material, while the females build most of it into the nest, and since no oviduct development is stimulated by nesting material in the absence of the male, it seems likely that the courtship behavior of the male ring dove which is not yet interested in nesting material causes estrogen secretion (*i.e.*, FSH secretion by the pituitary gland of the female), whereas nesting material (or the behavior of the male which has nesting material available) *later* facilitates the secretion of progesterone (*i.e.*, LH secretion by the female's pituitary gland). We may recall that progesterone induces both the final ovulatory pulse of LH from the hypophysis, and the histologic changes in the oviduct which occur after the albumen-secreting glands have been formed under the influence of estrogen.

From the above data, it is clear that in some species in which the male participates in nest-building, the presence of nesting material and/or the change in behavior of the male which is made possible by the presence of nesting material, helps to stimulate ovulation in the female. There is some evidence that, in those cases in which the female does most or all of the building, ovulation may

also depend to some extent on stimuli provided by the nesting material and/or by participation in nest-building. Polikarpova (1940) starting on January 1st kept 11 female house sparrows in cages supplied with a nest box and nesting material, while 10 females were kept in cages with neither nest box nor nesting material. On April 28th, when birds caught in the wild had fully developed oviducts and eggs ready to ovulate, 10 of the 11 birds with nesting material had enlarged oviducts with a fully formed shell gland, whereas none of the 10 birds without nesting material had advanced beyond the first stage of oviduct enlargement. Vaugien (1948) removed the nest from the cage of female serins while it was being built or just after it was built, and reported that this prevented the birds from laying eggs. When he later replaced nests in the cage, eggs were laid within a few days. Berry (1943, 1944) found that geese of several different species could be induced to lay eggs by the provision of artificial nests, although some of these birds had been in the park for years without laying. Hinde and Warren (1959) found that the absence of nesting material and a nest bowl delay ovulation in domesticated canaries.

The presence of a nest and/or nesting material clearly facilitates ovulation, at least in some species of birds. Further, the effect of the presence of nesting material is, at least in some cases, quantitatively or qualitatively different from the effects of stimuli provided by the courtship of the male.

(d) A special, and most interesting problem is posed by the egg-laying of brood parasites such as the cuckoos and cowbirds. How is the egg-laying behavior of such birds synchronized with the availability of host nests? Although there are some exceptions (Kabat, Buss and Meyer, 1948; Davis, 1958), most birds do not normally lay eggs unless they have first built a nest. Although, as we shall see later, the laying of eggs involves hormonal changes which facilitate the subsequent occurrence of incubation behavior, the brood parasites lay eggs without having built a nest, and without incubating the eggs afterwards.

Hann (1937, 1941) states that the female cowbird first finds the nest by seeing the host building it. She watches intently and for long periods during the nest-building. She visits the nest regularly in the absence of the owners before laying. Hann suggests that the development of the eggs, and their ovulation, in the cowbird are stimulated by the sight of the potential host building a nest, and that this accounts for the synchronization of the laying of the cowbird's and of the host's eggs (note that the parasite's eggs must be laid at a time when a host is prepared to incubate them). According to Hann's observations, the cowbird's egg is laid some 4 to 5 days after she first begins watching, so that his hypothesis about stimulation of ovulation is plausible. However, observation of the behavior of cowbirds (Nice 1949), as well as histologic studies of their ovaries (Davis, 1942a), indicate that the cowbird's eggs are laid in clutches of 3 to 5 eggs, with a rest period of some 5 to 8 days between clutches. This suggests a possibility that the cowbird, when such a clutch is growing, *must* find a nest, and that it finds a series of host nests because it is about to lay the eggs, rather than laying the eggs because it has found the host nests. However, a series of studies by Chance (1940) on the European cuckoo indicates very strongly that a brood parasite may actually be stimulated to lay eggs by the availability of host nests. Chance induced cuckoos to lay abnormally long series of eggs (on the order of 20 to 25) by removing eggs from the nests of foster species (*i.e.*, potential hosts) so that they built new nests and relaid. He thus managed the situation so that potential host nests were available to the cuckoo over a much longer period of time than that during which the cuckoo normally lays eggs, and during which it normally has hosts available. By this method, he induced cuckoos which normally lay 5 to 7 eggs to lay 20 to 25.

The anis are a New World subfamily of cuckoo-like birds, closely related to the parasitic cuckoos. Although not themselves, for the most part, brood parasitic, their breeding habits are peculiar in that some of the species nest in communal nests, several females laying in one nest. In some species only a few of the females will incubate, even though many more have laid the eggs. Davis

(1940, 1942b) reported that these birds may lay their eggs on the ground, even quite far from the nest. Such eggs, of course, are not incubated. He also found that ovulation may be stimulated by the presence or activity of other birds. In several flocks, he noted that no egg-laying might take place for a long time, and that a sudden burst of egg-laying activity would occur after a new female joined the flock. Davis suggested that the breakdown of the normally rigid relationships between nest-building, egg-laying, and incubation, and the ability of these birds to lay eggs in response to visual and/or auditory stimulation by other birds, regardless of whether they have built a nest and regardless of whether they will incubate, may be features of their reproductive cycle which encourage the development of brood parasitism.

Effect of eggs in the nest on ovulation. In nature each species of bird lays a characteristic number of eggs in a clutch, the variation within species sometimes being extremely narrow. In some cases the number of eggs laid is independent of the presence of other eggs in the nest. In other cases the number of eggs laid may be considerably extended by removing eggs as they are laid, the bird continuing to lay until the number of eggs present in the nest is approximately the normal clutch size. The term "determinate layer" is commonly used for those species in which the number of eggs laid is rather rigidly determined by physiologic relationships internal to the bird, whereas the term "indeterminate layer" is used for those species in which the size of the clutch may vary according to the situation in the nest (Cole, 1917; Laven, 1940b; Lack, 1947; Davis, 1955). Among the domestic birds, the pigeon is a familiar example of a determinate layer, whereas the domestic hen is, of course, an indeterminate layer. Among wild birds, too, there are variations from species to species. For example, the lapwing (Klomp, 1951), and some songbirds (Davis, 1955) seem to be determinate layers, attempts to increase the size of the clutch by removing eggs as laid having been unsuccessful. On the other hand, female house sparrows have been reported to lay up to 50 eggs in regular succession when the eggs

were removed daily (Pearl, 1912; Witschi, 1935), and a flicker from whose nest an egg was removed daily, starting with the 2nd egg, laid 72 eggs in 73 days (Phillips, 1887). The wryneck has similarly been reported to lay up to 48 eggs under the same conditions (quoted by Pearl, 1912). Goodwin (1948) reported that the golden pheasant may lay clutches of up to 40 eggs if eggs are removed as laid.

The best experimental work on indeterminate egg-laying has been done with gulls, which normally lay 3 eggs, at intervals of about 2 days (Goethe, 1937; Tinbergen, 1953). In the case of the black-headed gull, the average time between the laying of the 1st and the 3rd eggs is about 84 hours (3½ days) (Weidmann, 1956). The experiments of Weidmann on the black-headed gull may be summarized as follows (see also Ytreberg. 1956):

If the 1st egg is removed just after it is laid, the birds will lay a 4th egg, so that they end up with a 3-egg clutch. In these cases the 4th egg is laid at a normal interval after the 3rd. If successive eggs are removed as they are laid, most birds will lay more than 4 eggs, Weidmann having found birds laying up to 7 eggs. If the 1st egg is left in the nest, and subsequent eggs are removed as they are laid, no birds lay more than 3 eggs. If both eggs are removed after the 2nd egg is laid, some of the birds will lay a 4th egg, others will stop at the 3rd egg and incubate it, although it is now the only egg in the nest. If the birds are allowed to lay 3 eggs, and the whole clutch is removed immediately after the laying of the 3rd egg, all birds desert, none laying a 4th egg.

In seeking to account for these results, it is important to note that gulls begin incubating with the laying of the 1st egg (Tinbergen, 1953; Weidmann, 1956). Weidmann suggested that no additional eggs are laid if the birds *incubate*, even though they are incubating an incomplete clutch. Since many birds will lay a 4th egg if the eggs are removed after the laying of the 2nd egg (when the birds have been incubating for about 2 days), but will lay no 4th egg if the eggs are removed after the laying of the 3rd egg (when the birds have been incubating for about 4 days), Weidmann's suggestion

is that, in these birds, about 4 days of brooding will suppress the production of further eggs. Paludan's (1951) results on the herring gull are in general similar to those of Weidmann. When birds were killed for autopsy after the laying of the 1st egg, a 4th, and sometimes a 5th follicle were found maturing in the ovary; but when the bird was not killed until after it had been incubating for 2 or 3 days these follicles were found degenerating.

If Weidmann is correct in suggesting that participation in incubation provides stimulation which suppresses the production of further eggs, we might expect to find that the addition of eggs to the nest before laying has started would suppress the laying of some or all of the clutch, and that this effect would be found only when the birds start to incubate them before they lay. There is some evidence that these assumptions are indeed true, although they have not yet been thoroughly explored. Poulsen (1953b) found that, although he could not induce domestic pigeons to increase the size of the clutch beyond the normal 2 eggs by removing the 1st egg immediately after it was laid, he could suppress egg-laying altogether in about 50 per cent of the birds by placing 2 eggs in the finished, empty nest, whereupon all the birds immediately began to incubate. We have obtained similar results with the ring dove. Although barn swallows, American magpies (Davis, 1955), and tricolored redwinged blackbirds (Emlen, 1941) do not lay more eggs as a result of having the eggs removed as they are laid, there is some evidence that the addition of eggs near the beginning of egg-laying may inhibit the production of eggs. It may be pointed out that these birds normally do not incubate until after the entire clutch is laid.

It is apparent that stimuli provided by the egg, in all probability through the act of incubation, have, in many species, the ability to change the pattern of pituitary secretion in such a manner that the inhibition or suppression of the full maturation of some of the follicles is brought about. We shall reserve discussion of the nature of the stimulus and of the effect for our analysis of the physiologic basis of incubation behavior (see below, page 1295).

C. INCUBATION

The eggs of birds are fertilized internally, and then laid within a few hours after fertilization. The development of the embryos within the eggs requires temperatures higher than normal environmental temperatures, and this temperature is, in almost all birds, provided by the body of the parent or parents. The parents provide warmth for the eggs by sitting on them in such a way that the eggs are brought into contact with a featherless area or areas on the ventral side of the body. The behavior of the bird in sitting on its eggs is called "incubation" or "incubation behavior," and it is the purpose of this section to discuss the physiologic bases, and the physiologic consequences, of incubation behavior.

1. Incubation Patterns

As in the case of the other types of behavior with which we are dealing, there is an extraordinary interspecific diversity in the patterns of incubation behavior to be found in nature. The roles of the parents, the pattern of attentiveness to the egg, the duration of incubation, etc., show the widest variation. The types of incubation behavior found in nature have been summarized by Kendeigh (1952), and by Skutch (1957), and the following abbreviated summary is adapted from their accounts.

In many species of birds, including most song birds, the female alone does all of the incubation. In most such cases, the incubating bird leaves the nest several or many times each day in order to feed, although there are birds, like some pheasants (Goodwin, 1948; Delacour, 1951), which sit on the eggs for the entire incubation period, without taking any food. Female hornbills also sit on the eggs continuously, but they are fed by the male while doing so. There are some species in which the male does all of the incubation. In phalaropes, unlike most sexually dimorphic birds, the female is more brightly colored than the male, and the role of the sexes in sexual and parental behavior is reversed from the usual pattern: the female defends the territory and the male does all of the incubation, brooding, and caring for the young (Tinbergen, 1935). The male

emperor penguin sits on the eggs continuously for as long as two months, without taking any food (Stonehouse, 1953; Rivolier, 1956).

There are many groups of birds in which both parents share in the incubation activities. These include birds like gulls (Tinbergen, 1953) in which the male and female change places several times during the day, and birds like the Adélie penguin (Sladen, 1953) in which the males and females change places at intervals of several days. The male and female short-tailed shearwater change places on the eggs every 11 to 14 days (Marshall and Serventy, 1956). In pigeons and doves (Whitman, 1919) the female sits on the eggs from late afternoon through the night to midmorning, while the male sits for one long session (about 6 hours) during the day.

2. Hormonal Regulation of Incubation

It is obvious that the diversity of patterns of incubation behavior found among the various species of birds must depend on a considerable diversity of physiologic mechanisms. As usual, however, our information about these mechanisms is limited to relatively few species.

RELATION OF ONSET OF INCUBATION TO TIME OF EGG-LAYING. Since the pattern of endocrine secretion changes so rapidly during the period of egg-laying, we may, as a first step in the analysis of the hormonal basis of incubation behavior, examine the relationship between egg-laying and the onset of incubation behavior in seasonal-breeding birds. This temporal relationship should suggest the identity of the hormone or hormones which underlie the onset of incubation behavior.

The ornithological literature reveals wide variation from species to species with respect to the time when incubation starts. Some birds, such as the snow bunting (Tinbergen, 1939b) and the cedar waxwing (Lea, 1942) do not begin sitting on the eggs until after the last egg is laid. A much more common pattern is for incubation to start just before the laying of the last egg (black-capped chickadee, Odum, 1941; shrikes, Miller, 1931; white-crowned sparrow, Blanchard, 1941; bullfinch, Nicolai, 1956; and many others). In other cases, incubation may start earlier, when only half the clutch has been laid (northern phalarope, Tinbergen, 1935; blackbird, Messmer and Messmer, 1956; yellow-headed blackbird, Fautin, 1941; etc.). Still other species are reported to begin incubating from the laying of the first egg. This is usually reported for water-birds in which both sexes share in incubation, such as gulls (Tinbergen, 1953; Barth, 1955; Ytreberg, 1956), terns (Hardy, 1957), herons (Verwey, 1930; Allen and Mangels, 1940), plovers (Rittinghaus, 1956), etc. There are, however, also occasional reports of songbirds in which incubation begins with the laying of the 1st egg (e.g., Amadon, 1944b; Simmons, 1954).

Field observers report that birds sometimes sit on the nest as if incubating, even before any eggs have been laid (Roberts, 1940; Simmons, 1955b; von Pfeffer-Hülsemann, 1955). This cannot be regarded as reliable evidence of incubation behavior before egg-laying, because the behavior of such birds may lack several important components on true incubation behavior (Simmons, 1955b). The great crested grebe, for example, when sitting on an empty nest-platform before the eggs appear, does not fluff out the feathers on the ventral side of the body as does a sitting bird, nor does it show the characteristic settling-down movement (Simmons, 1955b). The male European jay often sits in the nest during nest-building, although in this species only the female sits on the eggs (Goodwin, 1951). There are, however, reliable experimental demonstrations of incubation behavior before egg-laying in gulls and pigeons. Tinbergen (1953) and Ytreberg (1956) have found that herring gulls and black-headed gulls will sit on eggs placed in the nest shortly before the laying of the bird's own eggs. Poulsen (1953) placed 2 eggs in the finished nest of each of 10 pairs of pigeons which had not yet started to lay. All the birds immediately began to incubate. Lehrman (1958a) found that, when pairs of ring doves were placed in cages containing a nest bowl and nesting material, and tested 7 days later, all of the birds were ready to sit on eggs, although most of them had not yet laid eggs of their own.

The foregoing paragraphs undoubtedly give the impression that there are sharp, well defined, easily observed interspecific differences in the time of onset of incubation behavior, and that it is quite easy to tell when incubation behavior starts. Unfortunately, such is far from being the case. There are extraordinary difficulties in the way of determining when incubation behavior actually starts, and these difficulties have the effect of merging and blurring the distinctions which sometimes seem so easy on the basis of casual field observation (Heinroth, 1922; Nice, 1954). The onset of incubation behavior is often not abrupt, but quite gradual. For example Gurr (1954) reports that the blackbird begins to incubate with the 1st egg, but the proportion of time during which the bird is on the egg increases from about 7 per cent to about 90 per cent during the egg-laying period, with an increment on each day. Kendeigh (1952) studied the incubation behavior of the house wren by means of a device which recorded temperature changes of the eggs, so that he had records of the time actually spent warming the eggs. He showed that the number of periods during which the bird sits on the eggs increases gradually and progressively from about 10 on the first day of egg-laying to about 35 on the last day of the laying of the 5- or 6-egg clutch.

Even when the bird is reported to be sitting from the 1st egg, and where observation seems to indicate that the bird is in fact attending to the egg, analysis of the actual incubation period of the egg frequently reveals that the so-called "incubation" occurring during the early stages of egg-laying is actually not providing much heat for the eggs. Barth (1955) found that, although the 2nd egg of the common gull is laid, on the average, 46 hours after the first, and the 3rd egg 47 hours after the second, the 2nd egg hatches only 4 hours after the first, and the 3rd egg only 21 hours later, indicating that, although the birds are seen to be incubating from the 1st egg, incubation is probably not very effective until the last egg is laid. Similarly, Paludan (1951) found that the 3rd eggs of clutches of herring gulls contained embryos larger than 2nd eggs of the same age, and that embryos in 1st eggs (again of the same age) were even smaller. This indicates that the 3rd egg laid has been incubated more effectively, presumably because *effective* incubation of the last egg of the clutch begins immediately, whereas the earlier eggs are not incubated with complete effectiveness until some days after they are laid. Holstein (quoted by Swanberg, 1950) found that the eggs of a European goshawk which he observed to begin incubating with the 1st egg, all hatched within 48 hours, although 9 days had elapsed between the laying of the 1st and last egg of the clutch.

The problem arises whether the relative ineffectiveness of observed incubation early in egg-laying is based on inadequate behavioral response of the birds to the eggs, or on inadequate temperature exchange between egg and adequately responding bird. I have already indicated that incubation behavior occurring early in egg-laying may be quantitatively very slight compared with that during the incubation period. There is, however, some evidence that, even when birds do sit on the eggs early during the egg-laying period, they may not actually transmit heat to them (Ryves, 1943a, b). Swanberg (1950) reported that, in several species, birds sitting on the eggs early during the egg-laying period do not actually warm the eggs, even though they may be sitting so tightly that it is rather difficult to frighten them away. Arnold (quoted by Swanberg, 1950) observed that blue jays sitting on the eggs early during the egg-laying period had the feathers of the ventral body surface between the body and the eggs, rather than being erected as in a normally incubating bird, so that the naked ventral skin could be applied to the eggs. It is apparent that the important problem of the basis for the ineffectiveness of incubation during the egg-laying period is far from solved, but that the observational data at hand provide an adequate background for defining the problem for experimental attack.

We may summarize by saying that incubation behavior develops gradually during the egg-laying period, appearing at different rates and at different times in different species of birds. In spite of the interspecific differences, there is clearly some relationship between the hormonal changes associated with egg-laying, and the onset of incubation behavior.

ONSET OF INCUBATION BEHAVIOR IN THE MALE. It is not unexpected that the onset of incubation behavior in female birds is related to the production of eggs, and presumably is regulated, in part, by the hormonal changes associated with ovulation and egg-laying. But what of those cases in which the *male* takes part in incubation? Is the onset of readiness to incubate in his case related to the time of production of eggs by the female? The situation is somewhat variable from species to species: in some cases the male begins to sit with the 1st egg (night heron, Noble, Wurm, and Schmidt, 1938; turnstone, Bergman, 1946; Kentish plover, Rittinghaus, 1956; etc.); in other cases the female begins to sit during the egg-laying period, with the male not incubating until some time later (common tern, Palmer, 1941; lapwing, Laven, 1941). In species in which the male does all of the incubating, it is variously reported that the male begins to incubate from the first egg (jacana, Hoffmann, 1949), or that he may not begin to incubate until some of the eggs have already been laid (northern phalarope, Tinbergen, 1935). These field observations are subject to the reservations which we noted above: "incubation" is poorly defined, and quantitative data about the development of the behavior are usually lacking.

Noble, Wurm and Schmidt (1938) reported that male night herons will sit on eggs that are placed in the nest before the female has laid, and that the male does all of the incubating during the first few days. Poulsen (1953) found that both male and female pigeons would sit on eggs offered to them after the nest had been built, but before any eggs had been laid, and we have verified this in the ring dove. Lehrman, Brody and Wortis (1961) found that when a pair of ring doves is placed in a breeding cage with a nest bowl and nesting material, readiness to incubate develops gradually during the 6 to 9 day period *before* eggs are laid, and that this readiness develops earlier in males than in females.

It is obvious that available data on the development of incubation behavior in male birds are quite inadequate. However, they justify the impression that readiness to incubate by the male (in those species in which the male participates in incubation) is more or less synchronized with the laying of eggs by the female, although, understandably, not as closely synchronized as is the case with the incubation behavior of the female.

THE INCUBATION PATCH. (1) *Structure and function.* When a bird sits on its eggs, it erects the contour feathers on the lower ventral body surface, exposing an unfeathered area of skin which in the nonsitting bird is normally covered by the contour feathers lying flat along the body surface (Simmons, 1955b; Barth, 1955). This naked area, called the *incubation patch*, is applied to the surface of the eggs, and is the source of the heat which is exchanged between the body of the parent and the egg. Bailey (1952) has provided a detailed description of the incubation patch, which is not merely a nonfeathered area, but one in which there is a characteristic increase in dermal and subdermal vascularity, accompanied by edema and by a thickening of the smooth muscle layer of the dermal blood vessels (Petersen, 1955). The vascularity and edema are readily apparent to the naked eye: the skin of the incubation patch appears distinctly reddish, thickened, and is sometimes thrown into loose folds.

The area covered by the incubation patch corresponds to the ventral apterium. (The contour feathers of birds grow in definite tracts called *pterylae*; between these pterylae are areas called *apteria*, in which grow only down feathers, or in some cases no feathers at all.) The distribution and shape of the incubation patches in the various orders of birds correspond with the distribution and shape of their respective ventral apteria. Thus songbirds typically have a single ventral patch. Gulls and shorebirds have paired patches lateral to the midline of the body, sometimes accompanied by a small median patch. No incubation patches are found in the pelican-like birds, or in the ducks and their relatives.

The behavior of incubating birds suggests that contact between the ventral apterium and the eggs plays an important role. When starting to sit the bird makes side-to-

side settling movements which suggest to the observer that it is adjusting the contact between the eggs and ventral body surface. The contour feathers remain erected until these settling movements subside, when the feathers are relaxed around the sides of the eggs. When Weller (1958) removed one of the eggs of a nighthawk, the bird, on returning to its eggs, poked with its bill at the incubation patch where the egg should have been, and failed to settle for a considerable time. Gulls have three incubation patches, and the eggs are moved in the nest by the settling motions of the bird and by poking with its bill until each egg is in contact with one of the incubation patches. By observing the under-surface of incubating black-headed gulls from a trench dug under the nest, Beer (1961) found that the settling movements continue until each egg is firmly in contact with one of the patches.

(2) *Incidence.* In almost all cases, the occurrence of incubation patches in the male or in the female of a given species corresponds to the occurrence of incubation behavior. In most species of songbirds only the female incubates, and in almost all cases the incubation patch is found only in the female (Miller, 1931; Price, 1936; Davis, 1941; Dixon, 1949; Putnam, 1949; Brackbill, 1958; and others). In species in which only the male incubates, such as the tinamous (Pearson and Pearson 1955), phalaropes, and jacanas (Bailey, 1952) an incubation patch is seen only in the male. In many groups of birds, both the male and the female participate in incubation, and in these cases, both sexes have an incubation patch. This includes woodpeckers (Howell, 1952), petrels (Fisher, 1952), gulls (Johnston, 1956), and a number of other families (Bailey, 1952).

The coincidence between the occurrence of the incubation patch and of incubation behavior can be followed out in considerable detail. According to Holstein (quoted by Wingstrand, 1943), the male European goshawk has a poorly developed incubation patch, and takes part to only a slight extent in incubation. In the Clark nutcracker, in which the male and female both incubate the eggs (Mewaldt, 1956), unlike most members of its family in which only the female incubates (Amadon, 1944a), both male and female have incubation patches, again unlike most members of the family (Bailey, 1952). Johnston (1956) collected a number of California gulls in the field in May and June when the breeding birds had eggs. All the adult birds that he collected had incubation patches. Of 13 subadult (3-year-old) males, which can be recognized by their plumage, 8 had incubation patches. This is about the same proportion as the proportion of subadult males that breed. Among subadult *females*, which do not breed, no incubation patches were found.

Skutch (1957) points out that there are exceptions to the general trend, in that males of some species have been found to sit on the eggs, although they have no incubation patch. In most of these cases, data are lacking with respect to the details both of the behavior of the male bird and of the temperature of the eggs, so that it is not possible to say whether such birds are actually incubating. A partial exception is the bank swallow, in which Petersen (1955), by measuring the temperature with the bulb of the thermometer placed among the eggs, showed that the egg temperature in one nest rose substantially when the male entered the nest-burrow in the absence of the female. The male in this species has no incubation patch. Since these birds nest in deep burrows in the ground, no details are available about the behavior of the male bird. This observation of a single individual should, of course, be regarded with some caution. Kendeigh (1952) using a thermocouple in nests of the barn swallow and the purple martin, two species closely related to the bank swallow observed by Petersen, found that, although the male often came and stood over the eggs in the nest, the temperature was elevated only when the female was sitting.

In spite of the occasional exceptions, the pattern is generally consistent, and indicates that the physiological conditions giving rise to the formation of the incubation patch may illuminate the background of incubation behavior itself.

(3) *Development.* In several species of song birds the development of the incubation patch may be divided into the following four stages (Bailey, 1952): (a) Defeatherization: the down feathers of the incubation patch area are molted several days before the first egg is laid. (b) Vascularization: the blood vessels of the area begin to increase in size and in number immediately after defeatherization. The vascularization is complete by the time the last egg is laid and incubation begins. (c) Edema: during incubation, the incubation patch continues to become more vascular and edematous. This edematous stage continues throughout incubation and during the period when the newly hatched young are brooded by the parent. (d) Recovery: the vascularity and edema in the dermis begin to subside gradually, starting when the young are about 4 or 5 days old.

Petersen (1955) weighed the skin of the ventral apterium in a number of bank swallows collected during the breeding season. Before egg-laying began, the average weight of the ventral apterium in both males and females was about 93 mg. This weight stayed the same in the males throughout the breeding season. In the females the weight began to increase just before egg-laying, reaching a maximal average weight of about 280 mg. during incubation. We may recall that this is the species in which egg temperatures were found to increase when a male was in the nest.

Some observers have stated that the incubation patch develops a week or so before the laying of the first egg (Nice, 1937; Brackbill, 1958), or that it persists through the summer until the fall molt (Odum, 1941). However, except for those by Bailey and Petersen, the observations on the incubation patch have lacked histologic verification. It is quite probable that observers reporting different time-relationships between the development of the incubation patch and of the ovary are merely referring to the loss of feathers, rather than to the development of vascularity and edema.

(4) *Hormonal basis.* Bailey (1952) studied the hormonal induction of the incubation patch in several species of sparrows and finches. He found that testosterone propionate, administered as pellets, had no effect on the development of the incubation patch. Hypophysectomized birds treated

with estradiol pellets developed full vascularity within 6 to 11 days, although none of them showed either edema or defeatherization. Prolactin (luteotrophic hormone, LTH) injected daily into intact or into hypophysectomized birds had no effect on the ventral apterium. However, when hypophysectomized birds whose ventral apteria had become vascular as a result of treatment with estradiol were treated with prolactin, the apteria became defeathered and edematous within 3 to 4 days. When intact birds were treated with estradiol pellets, a normal brood patch, vascular and edematous, developed within 9 or 10 days. These data indicate not only that the brood patch is formed under the successive influence of estrogen (during egg-laying) and prolactin (during incubation), but that, in these species at least, estrogenic hormone is capable of stimulating release of prolactin from the pituitary gland. An important point is that the effects of the hormones on the ventral apterium were the same in males and in females, although in these species an incubation patch is normally developed only by the female.

PITUITARY HORMONES AND INCUBATION BEHAVIOR. (1) The incidence of endogenous prolactin during the reproductive cycle seems to be closely associated with the occurrence of incubation behavior. Lienhart (1927) found that serum from incubating domestic hens, injected into nonincubating birds, could induce them to sit on eggs. Serum from nonincubating females was not capable of inducing incubation in other birds. This was, I think, the earliest demonstration that the blood of incubating birds contains a factor capable of inducing incubation, and that this factor is not present in the blood of nonincubating birds.

The prolactin content of any tissue or preparation is usually assayed in terms of its effect upon the crop wall of pigeons or doves. The inactive crop wall of these birds is a thin, almost transparent sheet, consisting largely of a thin sheet of muscle with an inner epithelium. During incubation, the wall of the crop thickens and becomes vascular and opaque, largely because of the greatly increased rate of cell division in the epithelium, which becomes many layers

thick, with growth of blood vessels into the subjacent connective tissue. Toward the end of the incubation period, the superficial layers of the lining epithelium desquamate into the lumen, and the resulting cheesy mass of degenerating epithelial cells forms the food substance which is eventually regurgitated to the young (Beams and Meyer, 1931). This proliferation of the crop-sac epithelium is induced solely by prolactin, acting locally (Riddle, 1937; Riddle and Bates, 1939). The standard (Riddle's) method of assaying prolactin, which is used in defining the international unit, depends on the increase in the crop-weight of birds of a standard strain, when the material to be assayed is injected over a period of days (weight method). Other methods depend on the fact that, when a small amount of prolactin is injected intradermally over the crop, a small area of vascularization develops, which can be seen with the naked eye (local response methods) (Reece and Turner, 1936; Lyons, 1937; Riddle and Bates, 1939).

Burrows and Byerly (1936) removed the pituitary glands from domestic fowl and assayed them for prolactin content by Lyons' (local response) method. Considering the amount of prolactin in the pituitary glands of roosters as a unit-standard (1.00), they found that the pituitaries of laying hens contained on the average 1.46 units, and those of incubating hens 4.05 units. Saeki and Tanabe (1955) found that the pituitary glands of laying hens contained, on the average, 0.071 I.U. of prolactin, whereas those of incubating hens contained 0.196 I.U. (Saeki and Tanabe, 1954). Nakajo and Tanaka (1956) found that the prolactin content of the caudal lobe of the anterior pituitary gland was 0.8 Reece-Turner units in nonincubating domestic hens, and that it rose in incubating birds to 1.7 to 2.4 Reece-Turner units. They also found that when incubation was interrupted by continuous lighting of the cages, the level of prolactin in the pituitary gland fell. Breitenbach and Meyer (1959) obtained similar results in the ring-necked pheasant: the prolactin content of the pituitary gland rose sharply while the birds incubated eggs. Byerly and Burrows (1936) measured the prolactin content of the pituitary gland of laying hens in their second laying year, which had been judged genetically broody or nonbroody on the basis of whether they became broody during their first laying year. They found twice as much prolactin in the pituitary glands of the broody type as in those of the nonbroody type.

The growth of the crop of pigeons and doves during the incubation period is, of course, a priori evidence of increased prolactin production. Schooley and Riddle (1938) assayed the prolactin content of the pituitary glands of pigeons, their unit being the increase in crop weight of the host pigeon per milligram of implanted pituitary tissue. They found sexually active adult birds to have 0.14 units of prolactin per pituitary gland, whereas birds in midincubation had 2.50 units. Lahr and Riddle (1938) found a much higher rate of mitosis in the crop epithelium of incubating and of prolactin-injected pigeons than in that of nonincubating pigeons. The pituitary glands of female pigeons contain more prolactin than those of male pigeons (Hurst, Meites and Turner, 1943; Meites and Turner, 1947). Male and female doves both incubate, but the female spends three times as much time on the eggs as the male (Whitman, 1919).

Bailey (1952) assayed the prolactin content of the pituitary glands of California gulls by implanting them over the crops of domestic pigeons. He found that gulls which had brood patches when they were collected (both males and females) had more prolactin in their pituitary glands than those with no incubation patches.

A further indication of the occurrence of prolactin during incubation in birds other than domestic pigeons and chickens is provided by the fact that molting stops during incubation in canaries (as in other birds), and that prolactin inhibits molting when injected during other times of the reproductive cycle (Kobayashi, 1953b).

(2) Injection of prolactin induces incubation behavior in laying domestic hens of broody strains. Riddle, Bates and Lahr (1935) injected prolactin daily into 20 laying hens of broody races. Although clucking

followed by incubation behavior normally occurs only at or near the end of the egg-laying period, all 20 began clucking within 2 to 4 days after the beginning of the injection, except for one bird which clucked on the 1st day, and 1 which did not begin until the 7th day. Sixteen of the 20 birds began sitting on eggs within less than 3 days after the beginning of clucking. When 10 laying hens of a nonbroody race (white Leghorn) were treated in the same way, 7 of the birds began clucking after 3 to 5 days, but only 1 of the 7 incubated on the following day. (Note that up to 15 per cent of broody hens are found in populations of "nonbroody" races.) When prolactin was injected into nonlaying hens, most began clucking after a few days, but none was induced to incubate. The efficacy of prolactin in inducing incubation behavior in the domestic hen has been verified by other investigators (Eigemann, 1937; Riddle, 1937; Nalbandov and Card, 1945; Saeki and Tanabe, 1955).

Mr. Philip Brody and I have tested ring doves (in which both sexes normally incubate) for incubation behavior after injection of various amounts of prolactin. If each bird is injected over a 7-day period with a total of approximately 400 I.U. of prolactin, and the birds are then tested for their response to eggs in individual pairs, each in a single test cage, incubation behavior is seen in approximately 40 per cent of the pairs. In these birds, maximal crop-growth has occurred in response to the prolactin injections (increase in crop weight from ca. 900 mg. to ca. 3000 mg.). When the total amount of prolactin is reduced to 50 I.U., the number of birds in which incubation behavior is induced drops to about 20 per cent. Even with this dosage, however, the lowest we have yet tried, there is a 60 per cent increase in crop weight. Since, in a normal cycle, the birds begin to sit on the eggs some days before there has been any detectable increase in crop weight, these data do not indicate that prolactin plays a role in the onset of incubation behavior in this species. Dr. R. A. Hinde of Cambridge University informs me that, in experiments carried out with Dr. R. P. Warren, he failed to induce canaries of either sex to sit on eggs as a result of prolactin injection. These experiments with ring doves and with canaries were carried out with nonlaying birds and are being continued.

Attempts to induce incubation behavior by prolactin injection in male birds of species in which the male does not normally sit have not been successful. When roosters or capons are injected with prolactin, and then offered eggs, they do not sit, although, in most cases, they utter the clucking sounds characteristic of a hen in the process of becoming broody (Riddle, Bates, and Lahr, 1935; Eigemann, 1937; Nalbandov, 1945; Nalbandov and Card, 1945; Saeki and Tanabe, 1955).

The fact that male domestic chickens do not incubate in response to prolactin injection, in distinction to laying hens, does not necessarily indicate that males and females differ in their capability of incubating, given the proper hormonal situation. We will recall that nonlaying hens do not incubate when injected with prolactin. Presumably the effect of prolactin in inducing incubation in laying hens depends on priming by ovarian hormones, or on recent attachment to the egg-laying place, or on some combination of these. It may well be that when these factors have been analyzed, they will be found to apply to males as well as to nonlaying females.

(3) Other pituitary hormones do not seem to induce incubation behavior. This includes follicle-stimulating hormone (FSH), luteinizing hormone (LH), and thyrotrophic hormone (TSH) (Riddle, Bates and Lahr, 1935; Riddle, 1937).

(4) The antigonad effect of prolactin may be considered relevant to its efficacy in inducing incubation behavior, because the suppression of the secretion of gonadal hormones implies a reduction in gonad-stimulated sexual behavior, which might interfere with the onset of parental behavior (Lehrman, 1955). Bates, Lahr and Riddle (1935) found that injections of prolactin were followed by sharp decreases in the weight of the ovaries and oviducts, which did not occur when FSH was injected with the prolactin (Bates, Riddle and Lahr, 1937). This implies that the antigonad action of prolactin is by way of the suppres-

sion of the secretion of gonad-stimulating hormones by the pituitary glands. Similar effects were found in male domestic chickens (Nalbandov, 1945; Yamashina, 1952). In wild birds prolactin injections can prevent the normal increase in gonad weight caused by increasing light (Bailey, 1950). Prolactin injected during the breeding season is followed by the collapse of the testes and by the lipid metamorphosis (steatogenesis) of the tubules, which normally occur at the end of the breeding season (Coombs and Marshall, 1956; Lofts and Marshall, 1956).

GONADAL HORMONES AND INCUBATION BEHAVIOR. *(1) Testosterone.* The occurrence of endogenous prolactin during incubation, the antigonad effect of prolactin, the effectiveness of prolactin in inducing incubation behavior, and the lack of sexual behavior during periods of incubation all suggest that the gonadal hormones responsible for sexual behavior and nest-building may be incompatible with the performance of incubation behavior, and experimental data in general support this impression.

Champy and Colle (1919) reported that the development of the crop-sac in incubating pigeons was accompanied in the male by a 90 per cent decrease in testis volume, and in the female by atresia of the ovarian follicles. In the domestic hen broody clucking occurs at a time when no eggs are being laid, comb size is minimal, and no copulations are taking place (Collias, 1950). In the wild bank swallow the beginning of incubation is accompanied by a sharp drop in the weight of the ovary (from about 300 mg. to about 53 mg.) and of the oviduct (from about 1500 mg. to about 200 mg.) (Petersen, 1955). Testis weights, which have increased during nest-building and egg-laying, remain high during incubation. Note that in this species the male develops no brood patch and does almost no incubation, unlike the situation in pigeons and doves in which the male participates in the care of the eggs. Marshall and Serventy (1956) found that the testis of the male short-tailed shearwater collapses very quickly after mating, coincident with the onset of his incubation duties (male and female shearwaters take turns in incubating the eggs), whereas in the male satin bower-bird, which does not incubate or feed the young, this change in the testis is delayed several weeks, until the end of the breeding season.

Collias (1940) found that the injection of 1 to 5 mg. per day of testosterone propionate into incubating hens caused the birds to desert their eggs within 3 to 13 days after the first injection. Kosin (1948) administered 10-mg. doses of testosterone propionate by injection into laying turkey hens at 2-week intervals, and found that this treatment prevented the onset of broodiness. On the other hand, male pigeons which normally take part in incubation are not prevented from incubating by testosterone propionate administration, nor do male pigeons discontinue established incubation when injected with as much as 2 mg. testosterone propionate daily (Collias, 1940, 1950, 1952). In the case of the black-crowned night heron, another species in which the male and female appear externally identical, and in which the male and female share the duties of incubation, Noble and Wurm (1940) found that testosterone propionate *induced* incubation behavior when injected into females or males. Riddle and Lahr (1944) similarly report that testosterone propionate, implanted into female ring doves, induced incubation in about 50 per cent of the birds. In unpublished experiments, I have failed to verify this observation. A consideration of the conditions of our experiments and of those of Riddle and Lahr and of Noble and Wurm may reveal a possible cause for the difference in results. The ring doves tested by Riddle and Lahr, and the black-crowned night herons tested by Noble and Wurm, were kept in pairs in the cage during the period of hormone administration. In the case of Riddle and Lahr's ring doves, the tests were performed with unisexual pairs of females. Our experiments, on the other hand, were done by injecting the hormone into the experimental birds during a 1-week period when each bird was alone in an isolation cage. At the end of the treatment period, the birds were placed in pairs in cages containing a nest and eggs. Under these conditions, birds treated with testosterone propionate failed to sit on the eggs, although other hormone treatments did induce incubation behavior (see below). I suggest the possibility that the testosterone propionate treatments, in Riddle and Lahr's experiment, actually induced male courtship behavior, which in those pairs in which the level of response was very different as between one bird and the other, would result in a faster formation of the pair than with untreated pairs of females, and that this courtship behavior, leading to pair formation, stimulated the secretion of endogenous hormones which in turn were responsible for the incubation behavior. When the birds were kept in isolation during the treatment period, the behavioral effects of the male hormone injection could have no stimulating effect on the other bird (see below).

(2) *Estrogens.* Estrogens injected into laying or nonlaying hens failed to induce incubation behavior (Riddle, 1937; Nalbandov, 1945), and FSH also was ineffective (Riddle, Bates and Lahr, 1935). The results from a number of studies have shown that estrogens administered to incubating domestic hens will cause them to discontinue sitting on the eggs. The most systematic of these was that by Godfrey and Jaap (1950) who injected each of 37 sitting hens with 15 mg. diethylstilbestrol. Twenty-eight of the 37 had left the nest by the 4th or 5th day after the treatment. The birds had been sitting from 3 to 7 days at the time of the treatment. Although no untreated controls were used, it is clear that the treatment with diethylstilbestrol interrupted the incubation behavior, which normally lasts much longer than the 12-day maximum found in the responding birds. When the dosage was increased to 30 mg., 100 of 102 treated birds discontinued sitting. Among the 11 birds in the 15-mg. group in which incubation was not interrupted by diethylstilbestrol treatment, 5 left the nest during the 2nd day after injection and returned the following day. In 10 of the 11 incubation was discontinued as a result of a 2nd injection. This effect of exogenous estrogen has been verified for the domestic hen (Collias, 1940; Carson, Eaton and Bacon, 1956) and turkey (Blakely, Anderson and MacGregor, 1951). On the other hand, van Tienhoven (1958) reported that di-

ethylstilbestrol injection failed to interrupt established broodiness in domestic turkeys. The conditions of his experiment were somewhat different from those of Godfrey and Jaap, since his birds were in broody coops with no nests or eggs.

Lehrman (1958b) found that untreated ring doves, with previous breeding experience, placed in pairs in cages containing nests and eggs, would begin to incubate the eggs after 4 to 7 days, during which they went through successive stages of courtship and nest-building. If the birds were injected with diethylstilbestrol (0.4 mg. per day) for 7 days while they were in individual isolation cages, and then immediately placed in the test cages, incubation took place in most of the birds within 1 to 3 days. The estrogen-treated birds immediately engaged in intensive nest-building behavior, in contrast to the untreated birds. It seems probable that the injected estrogen reduced the latency of the incubation response to the eggs, not by any ability to induce incubation behavior directly, but rather because it advanced the cycle from the courtship to the nest-building phase, so that events could occur which lead to the onset of incubation behavior within 2 or 3 days, and which normally do not occur until after the birds have been together for several days. The nature of these events will be discussed later. The fact that estrogen administered under these conditions reduced the latency of (or sped up the development of) the onset of incubation behavior does not necessarily mean that estrogen injected during incubation would not interrupt it in this species.

(3) *Progesterone.* Progesterone (or a gestagen) is of particular interest in connection with the onset of incubation behavior, because its involvement in ovulation (Rothchild and Fraps, 1949; Fraps, 1955) and in the final stages of oviduct development (Mason, 1952; Brant and Nalbandov, 1956; Lehrman and Brody, 1957) indicates that it is present in the blood just before or at about the time when incubation normally starts.

Progesterone or corpus luteum preparations have been reported to be ineffective in inducing broodiness in domestic hens (Riddle, 1937; Eigemann, 1937; Nalbandov, 1945) and canaries (Kobayashi, 1952), and actually to interrupt established broodiness in domestic turkeys (van Tienhoven, 1958), although in all these cases the criterion was the existence of clucking and other broody behavior in birds that were not given an opportunity to sit on eggs.

Riddle and Lahr (1944) implanted pellets of progesterone into adult ring doves kept in unisexual pairs of males or of females in cages provided with a nest or eggs. All 18 doves tested in this way sat on the eggs, most of them within 3 to 7 days after the implantation of the pellets. None of the untreated control birds sat on the eggs during the 3-week test period. Riddle and Lahr allowed some of the progesterone-treated birds to continue sitting on the eggs for the normal incubation period of 14 days, and then at autopsy found that the crop-sac had increased in weight, as normally occurs during incubation. Since it had previously been demonstrated that prolactin induces incubation in laying hens, and that it is the hormone responsible for the growth of the crop, Riddle and Lahr concluded that progesterone induced incubation in their experiments because it had induced prolactin secretion by the birds' pituitary glands. However, Meites and Turner (1947) found that progesterone (and other sex hormones) when injected into pigeons, fail to increase either the crop weight or the prolactin content of the pituitary glands. Furthermore, Lehrman (1958), who also found incubation behavior induced by progesterone in ring doves, kept the birds in isolation during a 7-day period of progesterone treatment, and then placed them in pairs in test cages with nests and eggs. These birds all quickly sat on the eggs, most of them within 20 minutes, and were killed for autopsy immediately after they were found sitting. These birds had crops no heavier than those of untreated control birds which did not incubate. It should be further noted that the crop does not normally begin to increase in weight until some days after incubation has already started. Since Patel (1936) showed that participation in incubation can itself stimulate the secretion of prolactin by the pituitary gland, it appears likely that progesterone induces incubation behavior by a means other than the stimulation of pituitary prolactin, and that the prolactin is secreted as a *result* of participation in incubation (see below). We will recall Marshall and Serventy's (1956) observation that in several species of seasonal-breeding wild birds, the lipid metamorphosis of the testis tubules coincides with the onset of incubation duties in a species in which the male takes part in incubation, and does not take place until some weeks later in a species in which the male does not take part in incubation. Paper chromatographic analysis by Lofts and Marshall (1957) indicates that the lipid contents of these metamorphosed tubules contain progesterone. Lofts and Marshall suggested that the postnuptial avian testis tubule may possess an endocrine function similar to that of the mammalian corpus luteum. At any rate, the association of progesterone with incubation behavior independently of prolactin, at least in some types of birds, needs to be taken seriously.

3. Interaction between Internal and External Environments in the Regulation of Incubation Behavior

Induction of incubation behavior by external stimuli. Male and female ring doves are brought into readiness to incubate by stimuli provided to each other, and by stimulation coming from the presence of the nesting material and/or nest bowl, even in the absence of eggs (Lehrman, 1958a, 1959b). Although doves kept singly in cages containing a nest with 2 eggs will show no interest in the eggs during a 6-week test period, *pairs* of birds kept in a cage with a nest bowl and nesting material will immediately sit upon eggs introduced into the cage by the experimenter after 7 days. If a pair of birds is kept together in a cage, but without a nest bowl or nesting material, they will, for the most part, not subsequently be ready to sit on eggs until after a short period of nest-building activity. Lehrman, Brody and Wortis (1961) tested doves for their response to eggs after varying periods in the cage with a mate or with a mate and nesting material. These birds were killed for autopsy immediately after the test. The data indicate that stimuli from

the male induce growth of the ovary and oviduct in the female and that this growth is additionally fostered by the presence of nesting material. Further, differences between the rates of oviduct growth in birds kept in the cage with and without nesting material closely parallel differences with respect to the rate of onset of incubation behavior. In addition, the onset of incubation behavior is closely related to the occurrence of ovulation, which conforms with and strengthens our earlier suggestion that progesterone is involved in the beginning of incubation behavior in this species (Lehrman, 1959a, b).

Stimulation provided by the egg seems to play a considerable role in the maintenance of incubation behavior in many species of birds. In an often quoted but rather casual experiment Taibell (1928) forced 2 male turkeys to stay on a nest with eggs by holding them down by a cloth bag. These birds developed complete incubation behavior, including delicate treading on the nest, settling on the eggs, etc., in 1 to 4 days. On the other hand, Collias (1950) reported that confinement with eggs is relatively ineffective in stimulating incubation behavior in hens.

The importance of the egg in maintaining and stimulating incubation behavior can be seen from the fact that, when the eggs fail to hatch at the end of the normal incubation period, the bird will often continue sitting for a considerable time. Domestic hens will sit on sterile eggs up to 44 days, which is more than twice the normal incubation period (Saeki and Tanabe, 1954). Other observers (quoted by Katz, 1937) have found incubating hens sitting on artificial eggs for up to 4 months. Night herons breeding in captivity sit on sterile eggs for 40 to 51 days, as compared with the normal incubation period of 22 to 24 days (Noble and Wurm, 1942). Herring gulls, which normally incubate 26 to 27 days, will incubate 56 to 75 days on infertile eggs (Paludan, 1951). The sitting period of domestic pigeons can similarly be extended from 18 to 25 days (Kobayashi, 1953a). These data are especially interesting in view of the fact that, in a normal reproductive cycle, there is a rather striking change in the behavior of incubating birds when the eggs hatch (see below, page 1300.

Adjustment of incubation behavior to the immediate stimulus situation. The hormonally induced modification of the ventral apterium (defeatherization, vascularization, edema) into the incubation patch, which, as we have noted, develops in most types of birds during the egg-laying period, is adapted for the production of localized higher skin temperatures and the transfer of heat between the bird and the eggs. There is much evidence that temperature regulation does in fact play a role in the regulation of the birds' behavior toward the eggs. Many field observations of wild birds indicate that the time spent sitting on the eggs is greater at lower ambient temperatures than at higher (Nice, 1937; Weston, 1947; Nice and Thomas, 1948; Skutch, 1957). Simmons (1954) found that the eggs of the graceful warbler are covered only 9 per cent of the time at an ambient temperature of 90°F., but 57 per cent of the time when the ambient temperature is 60 to 70°F. In the European wren the correlation between air temperature and the time spent on the eggs is −0.74 (P < 0.01) (Whitehouse and Armstrong, 1953; Armstrong, 1955). On very hot days, some birds may stand over the eggs without being in actual contact with them (Brackbill, 1958; Weller, 1958). Weller measured the temperature under an incubating nighthawk sitting on its eggs on the bare roof of a building (this species does not build a nest) and found that, during a very hot day, the temperature under the bird was *lower* than the temperature on the bare roof, indicating that the bird actually cooled the eggs by standing over them. At night, when the bird sat closely on the eggs, the egg temperatures were warmer than the temperatures on the bare roof. Irving and Krog (1956) found that the average temperatures of eggs and young of various species of birds in the Arctic, measured in the nest, were about the same as those found in milder climates, indicating that the varying behavior of the parent in different climates tends to produce regulation of nest temperatures to about the same optimum.

Baerends (1959) experimentally altered the temperatures of artificial eggs being incubated by herring gulls in the wild, by running water of various temperatures through tubes imbedded in the eggs. He found that temperature changes in the eggs (while ambient temperatures remain constant) induce temperature-regulating behavior of the bird (*e.g.*, shivering, panting, increase or decrease of body surface by erection or sleeking of feathers, etc.), as well as restlessness expressed by increased preening and "displacement nest-building," the latter resulting in improvement of the nest structure. In addition, abnormal egg temperatures induce movements which increase the isolation of the eggs from the surrounding air and improve the contact between the eggs and the incubation patches. For example, the bird wobbles from side to side on the eggs, resettles itself on the eggs, shifts the eggs with its bill, etc. Similar behavior is sometimes seen to increase on very hot days (Deusing, 1939).

Behavior which regulates the temperature of the eggs is not restricted to those birds having an incubation patch. The megapodes or mound-builders build large mounds of plant material, sometimes up to 35 feet in diameter and 15 feet high, and lay their eggs in holes dug in these mounds, which are then filled in. Incubation is accomplished by the heat produced by the rotting and fermentation of the materials of which the mound is built (Frith, 1956b). In one genus (*Alectura*), the male works continuously to regulate the temperature, by digging holes in the mound, ramming his head into the hole (apparently to test the temperature), and then adding material (which raises the temperature) or digging off material from the top (which cools the mound), depending upon the temperature in the mound. The skin of the head and upper neck in this species is naked, and, in the male, turns brilliant red at the beginning of the breeding season (Frith, 1956a). It seems not unreasonable to suggest that this change is induced by changes in endocrine secretion, and that these changes in vascularity (and probably other characteristics) of this skin area make it more capable of serving as a temperature-sensing mechanism.

Physiologic effects of stimuli arising from

incubation. We have pointed out that incubation behavior may be maintained long past its normal period by the presence of the eggs. What is the physiologic basis of this effect?

Saeki and Tanabe (1954, 1955) measured the prolactin content of the pituitary glands of domestic hens during different stages of the reproductive cycle under various experimental treatments. They found that the prolactin content of the gland, which is normally much higher during incubation than during laying (see above, page 1289), goes down sharply immediately after the hatching of the eggs. When birds were induced to sit for abnormally long times by substituting sterile eggs for their own eggs, the prolactin content of the pituitary gland remained high as long as the birds continued incubating. Further, they induced a number of laying hens to sit upon eggs by means of prolactin injection; some of these birds stopped sitting when the prolactin injection was discontinued, others continued to sit on the eggs. Autopsy data revealed that the pituitary glands of the birds which continued incubation after the end of the prolactin administration contained a high level of prolactin, whereas the pituitary glands of the birds which stopped incubating after the end of the prolactin injection had little prolactin. It is reasonably clear from these data that the eggs are capable of stimulating prolactin secretion by the pituitary gland of the sitting bird, and that this is probably part of the explanation for the control of incubation behavior by the presence or absence of the eggs.

In the domestic pigeon Patel (1936) showed that the crops of incubating birds increase in weight as long as the birds are sitting, but regress to the resting condition when the birds are removed from the eggs. The crops of ring doves induced to sit upon eggs by progesterone treatment will grow only if the birds are allowed to continue sitting upon the eggs (Riddle and Lahr, 1944; unpublished observations by D. S. Lehrman). In these birds, as in domestic hens, participation in incubation clearly stimulates the secretion of prolactin by the pituitary gland.

In the case of pigeons and doves, prolactin is secreted under the influence of stimuli associated with incubation, even though the bird is not actually sitting on the egg. Patel (1936; Kuroda, 1956) found that the crop of a male pigeon removed from the breeding cage early in incubation, and placed in an adjacent cage from which he could see his mate, would develop as though he were sitting upon the egg himself. If a partition was placed between the two adjacent cages so that the male could not see the female sitting on the eggs, his crop would regress to the resting state. When the females were removed to the adjacent cages, the results were similar, except that some of the males left in the breeding cages abandoned the eggs. In those cases, the crops of the females failed to develop.

Effect of removal of eggs in midincubation. In many species of birds, even in those species which normally produce only one clutch of eggs per year, removal of the eggs during incubation is followed by the building of a new nest and the laying of a new set of eggs (Salomonsen, 1939; Blanchard, 1941; Simmons, 1954; Brackbill, 1958; Grosskopf, 1958; and many others). This clearly suggests that the removal of the eggs permits the secretion of gonadotrophic hormones which had been held under inhibition by stimuli coming from the eggs. Although the mechanism of this probable inhibition is not known, we may recall here the antigonad action of prolactin. The behavior of the male may be a factor in this renewal of gonadotrophic activity. Miller (1931) reports that the male, which is very quiet during the period when the female is sitting on eggs, shows a burst of renewed singing and courting activity when the nest and eggs are destroyed, possibly as a response to the renewed activity of the female released from the nest. Thus, in addition to the removal of any inhibiting effect of the eggs on the secretion of gonadotrophins by the pituitary gland of the female, there is a resurgence of the singing and courting activity of the male, which was partially responsible for the original secretion of gonadotrophin (see above, page 1279).

The time taken for laying new eggs after the destruction or removal of the old clutch varies. Most observers assert that the interval before laying of the new clutch bears no relationship to the age of the old clutch (Amantea, 1928; Nice, 1937, 1949; 'Kobayashi, 1953a; Gurr, 1954). For example, Paludan (1951) notes that, when 35 herring gull nests were destroyed by a storm, the laying of the first eggs of the new clutches was closely spaced between 11 and 14 days later, although the original clutches had varied in age from 1 to 21 days. However, quantitative data from studies of waterfowl (Sowls, 1949) and pheasants (Seubert, 1952) in wildlife preserves indicate that the interval before relaying is somewhat longer, the older the original clutch at the time of its destruction.

4. Some Remarks on the Onset of Incubation

In the light of all the facts just presented, what may we say about the nature of the endocrine changes underlying the onset of incubation behavior during the normal breeding cycle?

The first point to be dealt with is the problem of the exact time when prolactin appears during the cycle. Saeki and Tanabe (1954, 1955) found that the prolactin content of the pituitary gland rises immediately after domestic hens begin to show incubation behavior. However, the spacing of their tests was such that it is not clear whether the prolactin content rises just before or just after the beginning of incubation. Similarly, Bailey's (1952) description of the development of the incubation patch in song birds permits the conclusion that prolactin is secreted during early incubation, but does not reveal whether the secretion of this hormone first reaches significant levels just before or just after the beginning of incubation behavior. Lahr and Riddle (1938) estimated the presence of prolactin in the blood of pigeons by arresting mitoses in the cropsac epithelium by means of colchicine injection, a method which gives a very sensitive indication of the effect of prolactin on the rate of growth in the epithelium (Leblond and Allen, 1937). They found that the average number of mitoses per high power microscopic field rose from about 4 just before the 1st egg to about 32 after the laying of the 2nd egg. They also found that the

injection of 60 I.U. of prolactin would increase the average number of mitoses per field from about 7 to about 25 *within a half hour* after the injection. Since pigeons (at least in captivity) begin to incubate sometime between the laying of the 1st and of the 2nd egg, these data again are not sufficiently exact to indicate whether the prolactin secretion began just before or just after the beginning of incubation behavior.

Inasmuch as the presence of eggs stimulates prolactin secretion, and placing eggs in the newly built nests of black-headed gulls suppresses the laying of subsequent eggs, provided the birds incubate (Weidmann, 1956), Eisner (1958) suggested that prolactin secretion starts as a *result* of the onset of incubation, which in turn is caused by other hormones such as progesterone (Cole, 1930; Riddle and Lahr, 1944; Lehrman, 1958b). This is a plausible suggestion, and should be considered in future research on this problem, despite some difficulties such as the fact that progesterone does not induce incubation behavior in domestic hens (see above, page 1293).

A second problem is the manner of hormone action in inducing incubation behavior. (This is, of course, a problem with respect to *all* hormone-induced behavior.) Some species of birds incubate eggs in spite of the absence of incubation patches (Bailey, 1952). Nevertheless, a number of coincidences suggest that the incubation patch should be investigated as a possible source of stimulation for incubation, or as a source of tension which is reduced by incubation behavior. First is the fact that the occurrence of incubation patches in male and in female birds generally corresponds to that of incubation behavior in the two sexes. Second, the incubation patch normally develops just at the time when incubation behavior is beginning. Third, the characteristics of the incubation patch suggest that it is sensitive to temperature changes and adapted for heat exchange with the egg, and the effects of temperature changes on the incubation behavior of the bird suggest that the temperature-sensitivity of the incubation patch may be an important factor. Finally, prolactin induces incubation behavior in hens only if they are laying at the time of incubation, and prolactin causes change in the ventral apterium only after pretreatment with estrogen.

D. CARE OF THE YOUNG

1. Types of Young and Methods of Feeding Them

Birds vary widely with respect to the degree of development at hatching. Although all sorts of intermediates occur, two types of young are generally recognized among birds.

Precocial young, which emerge from the eggs after a relatively long incubation period, are hatched covered with body feathers, capable of locomotion within a few hours, and capable of picking up food, or in some cases even finding food without the assistance of the parents. Precocial young usually occur among families of water birds or of birds living and feeding on the ground, such as pheasants, cranes, sandpipers, ducks, grebes, etc. (Mayaud, 1950). Methods of feeding and caring for precocial young vary widely. For example, in some species of the mound-building megapodes, the young are completely independent, the parents playing no role in rearing them (Frith, 1956b). In other cases, such as the pheasants and ducks (and domestic chickens), the young follow the parents, thus being led to food, and may be excited to feed by the behavior of the parents in the presence of food (Bent, 1923, 1925; Beebe, 1936). In still other families having precocial young, the young birds, although covered with down and capable of walking, may be fed for some time after hatching by food brought by the parents (terns, Hardy, 1957), or by partially digested food regurgitated by the parents (e.g., penguins, Bagshawe, 1938; gulls, Tinbergen, 1953). Stonehouse (1953) reported that the emperor penguin feeds the young in part by regurgitating "strips of epithelium or similar tissue invested with fat globules" presumably from the crop wall.

Altricial young are hatched naked of feathers, usually blind until the eyes open some days later, and incapable of locomotion or of finding or selecting food, so that they must be fed by the parents for a considerable number of days or weeks (May-aud, 1950; Kendeigh, 1952). Altricial young are fed by a variety of methods. Many insect-eating birds carry food to the young in their bills (Bent, 1942). Other species may regurgitate food which they have carried in the throat (pelicans, Bent, 1922) or regurgitate from the crop or stomach food that has been partly digested (night heron, Allen and Mangels, 1940). In still other species, the regurgitated food may include substances secreted or produced in the digestive tract of the parents. Food regurgitated by the mother hummingbird contains digestive secretions mixed with ingested food (Mayaud, 1950); the young fulmar is fed partly on an oil secreted by the proventriculus of the parents (Fisher, 1952); food regurgitated to young pigeons just after hatching consists of epithelial cells desquamated into the lumen of the crop (Beams and Meyer, 1931).

Young birds are brooded by their parents, who sit on the nests containing the young and allow the young to huddle under them. The parents may cover them for some days after hatching, in a manner somewhat similar to the way in which they sit on eggs, although differences can usually be observed (Tinbergen, 1953). Parents of altricial young may continue to brood them for a number of days or weeks (e.g., Fisher, 1952), whereas precocial young may be brooded for only a short time after hatching or not at all (Kendeigh, 1952).

It is apparent that the types of behavior included in the expression "parental care" vary widely among different groups of birds, and therefore that analysis of the physiologic basis of this type of behavior in a few domesticated species will do no more than suggest the variety of mechanisms which are possible.

Roles of the parents. The roles of the parents in caring for the young need not necessarily be, in all respects, the same as their respective roles in incubating the eggs, a fact of considerable importance for its bearing on the problem of the role of hormones in the induction of behavior toward the young.

In the species in which the male and female both take part in incubation of the eggs, brooding and feeding of the young are similarly carried out by both sexes. This is true in birds of a number of different families, such as cormorants (Mendell, 1936; Kortlandt, 1940), rails (Meise, 1934), gulls and terns (Tinbergen, 1953; Cuthbert, 1954; Hardy, 1957), doves (Whitman, 1919), swifts (Lack, 1956a), petrels (Fisher, 1952; Davis, 1957), storks (Schüz, 1943), herons (Allen and Mangels, 1940), woodpeckers (Bent, 1939), and others. There are a few apparent exceptions, such as the white-tailed kite, in which it is reported that the male sits on the eggs (for much less of the time than does the female), but does not brood the young (Hawbecker, 1942).

In some birds, such as most of the hummingbirds (Pitelka, 1942) and most of the ducks (Delacour and Mayr, 1945), the male takes no part in either incubation or any aspect of the care of the young. There are also a few birds, such as the phalaropes (Tinbergen, 1935), in which the male does all of the caring for the young.

There are many species in which the male, although he takes no part in incubation, regularly feeds the young (Ryves, 1934; Tinbergen, 1939b; Emlen, 1941; Skutch, 1953a; Armstrong, 1955; and many others). It is reported for a number of species that the males take no part in brooding the young, although they do the major share of feeding them (Nice, 1937; Rand, 1940; Odum, 1941; Lea, 1942; Hinde, 1952; Whitehouse and Armstrong, 1953).

In many species of the order Galliformes, which includes the domestic chicken, the male neither broods nor feeds the (precocial) young, but accompanies the family, in effect taking part in leading them to food and in guarding them, although without the behavioral signs of "broodiness" (e.g., clucking, characteristic body position over the young, etc.) which are seen in the female (Kendeigh, 1952; see Kendeigh for survey of parental behavior in birds).

In general we may say that brooding the young, i.e., behavior which is associated with the provision of heat by the parents to young while they are still poikilothermic, is done only by the sex or sexes which, in that species, take part in incubation. Other aspects of parental behavior, such as feeding the young, leading them to food, guarding

them, etc., may be shown (although not necessarily so) by the other sex as well, even though it does not participate in incubation.

2. Hormonal Induction of Parental Behavior toward Young

Prolactin and brooding in female birds. Nalbandov and Card (1945) reported that domestic hens injected with prolactin show a broody response to chicks (which consists of brooding them under body and wings, leading them to feed, calling them, and leading them away from danger by warning signals, etc.). Similar results have been obtained with pheasants (Crispens, 1956), and wild turkeys (Crispens, 1957). Crispens treated hen pheasants with 6 mg. prolactin (presumably about 120 I.U.) per day for 3 days or more, and found that most of them (64 to 91 per cent in different groups) accepted and brooded 2-week-old Leghorn chicks. Two female wild turkeys similarly treated, except that the doses were larger, accepted either young turkeys or young Leghorn chicks.

None of these papers includes information about the status (laying or nonlaying) of the experimental birds beyond the fact that they were mature females.

Prolactin and brooding in male birds. Domestic cocks take no part in the care of the young, and sometimes even kill chicks that are confined with them. We have already noted that such cocks cannot be induced to sit on eggs by prolactin administration. However, a number of workers have reported that prolactin induces cocks to cluck, to lead, and to protect chicks under their body and wings (Nalbandov, 1945; Nalbandov and Card, 1945; Yamashina, 1952). According to Nalbandov and Card, prolactin injection causes cocks to become broody gradually over a 5-day period. On the other hand, *hens* injected with prolactin become broody quite suddenly, just as they normally do at the end of their egg-laying period.

Prolactin and parental feeding in doves. I have found that untreated male or female ring doves, placed singly in cages with 7-day-old young, would make no attempt to feed them (Lehrman, 1955). When similar birds were injected with 400 to 450 I.U. prolactin, and then placed in the cages with the squabs, 10 out of 12 fed the squabs by regurgitating the crop-milk which had been formed under the influence of the exogenous prolactin (Beams and Meyer, 1931; Riddle and Bates, 1939). When birds were similarly injected with prolactin but their crops were anesthetized by the injection of a long-acting local anesthetic into the crop wall or into the skin over the crop, a significant number of birds failed to feed the squabs, compared with control birds in which the anesthetic was injected elsewhere than in the crop. I concluded that the ability of prolactin to elicit the regurgitation-feeding behavior of these birds toward the young depended on stimulation arising in the crop as a result of its engorgement by the action of prolactin (and on the antigonad action of prolactin, which prevented sexual or aggressive behavior from interfering with parental behavior toward the squabs). Although I believe that this was probably correct, there are situations in which doves regurgitate when the crop is *not* engorged, and when there may be little or no prolactin present. The amount of crop-milk produced by parent pigeons decreases starting 2 or 3 days after the hatching of the young; after the young are 7 or 8 days old, the regurgitated crop contents consist entirely of grain, indicating that no crop-milk is being produced (Patel, 1936). Schooley and Riddle (1938) found that the amount of prolactin in the pituitary glands of pigeons with 7 to 15 day old young was considerably lower (1.05 of their units) than in the pituitaries of incubating birds (2.50 units), although it was not as low as in the pituitaries of sexually active birds (0.14 units). There are no data available to indicate whether this low level of prolactin (too low to cause the formation of crop-milk), may nevertheless stimulate regurgitation - feeding of ingested grain. When male pigeons are castrated they may still be able to induce the laying of eggs by females with which they were already mated, and they will sit on eggs and show crop development and crop-milk production during the first incubation period after castration (Kaufman and Dobrowska, 1931; Kaufman, 1932; Patel, 1936). During subsequent incubation periods, however, there

will be no crop development, although the birds may incubate. Since castration does not affect the sensitivity of the crop to prolactin (Riddle and Dykshorn, 1932), the effect of castration in preventing crop development during subsequent incubation periods is presumably due to a failure of prolactin secretion by the pituitary. It may be noted that the acidophilic cells which are associated with the periods when prolactin is being secreted (Schooley, 1937; Payne, 1943; Yasuda, 1953), gradually disappear from the pituitary glands of pigeons during the 2 or 3 months following castration (Schooley, 1937). Kaufman (1932) reported that one such castrated male, after having taken part in incubation, fed the young with grain, although no crop development took place. The role of the condition of the crop in the occurrence of this regurgitation-feeding behavior obviously needs further investigation.

Gonadal hormones and the brooding of young. It is well known that androgenic hormones inhibit the brooding of the young. As long ago as 1916, Goodale observed that capons become broody when kept with chicks, and care for them in normal hen-fashion (Goodale, 1916, 1918). Saeki and Tanabe (1955) have confirmed this observation. Collias (1940) injected 4 mg. testosterone propionate per day into a hen with chicks, and found that she stopped clucking and caring for the chicks after 5 days. Nalbandov (1945) found that the injection of FSH or of 0.1 mg. methyltestosterone per day along with prolactin prevented broodiness from developing in response to the prolactin. Estradiol benzoate has an effect similar to that of testosterone in interrupting broody care of the young (Collias, 1940).

3. Induction of Parental Behavior toward Young by External Stimuli

Changes in behavior of the parents at hatching. We have already pointed out that incubation behavior, and the associated prolactin secretion, can be maintained for abnormally long periods of time by stimuli coming from the eggs. This implies of course that changes in the behavioral and/or physiologic condition of the parent are stimulated by the change from the presence of eggs to the presence of young. Striking changes in behavior can be observed at the time of hatching. For example, a female duck sitting on eggs is very silent. As soon as the eggs are chipped, indicating the onset of hatching, frequent calls can be heard from the mother (Collias and Collias, 1956). It is often reported that in species in which the male takes no part in incubation, but does participate in the feeding of the young, abrupt changes in behavior take place at the time of hatching. The male suddenly begins to spend much more time near the nest and to bring food to the young (Blanchard, 1941; Davis, 1941). Skutch (1953b) pointed out that the males of many species bring food to the female during the incubation period, or carry nesting material toward the nest, etc. thus maintaining a contact with the nest which provides the background for parental feeding by the male. In those species in which the male brings no food or other objects to the nest during the incubation period, he does not begin to bring food to the nest until he has seen the new nestlings, the sight of which stimulates the change in his activity. In the case of the tricolored red-winged blackbird the male leaves the colony area at the beginning of incubation, which is carried out entirely by the female, and then reappears after the eggs have hatched to participate in feeding the young (Emlen, 1941).

Observations of wild birds reveal that newly hatched young often interfere with the incubation of eggs not yet hatched. When the eggs of gulls hatch, for example, the parents appear at first to continue to treat the young just as they did the eggs, but the intensity of this incubation behavior is quickly reduced by the behavior of the young, which crawl about in spite of the parent's effort to push them under its body (Paludan, 1951; Tinbergen 1953; Ytreberg, 1956). If there is a substantial interval between the hatching of the first and the third (last) egg, the incubation of the last egg may be interrupted, and it may die during the hatching process (James-Veitch and Booth, 1954; Ytreberg, 1956). The American coot, an aquatic bird which builds a number of nest-platforms in its marshy

territory, often broods the (precocial) young in a "brood nest" built when the eggs hatch and which is separate from the "egg nest." These birds often desert some of the eggs in the egg nest when enough of them have hatched to stimulate the beginning of brooding at the separate brood nest. The calls of the young appear to stimulate the adults to brood them instead of incubating the eggs (Gullion, 1954).

Stimulation of broodiness by the chicks. Broody behavior toward the chicks is induced in domestic hens by keeping them closely confined with the chicks (Burrows and Byerly, 1938; Collias, 1946; Ramsay, 1953). Broodiness induced by this method develops rather gradually, the bird first showing an incipient brooding posture, then clucking, then showing full broodiness including clucking and hovering over the young, and finally leading them to food, etc. (Ramsay, 1953). Confinement with the young also induces broody behavior in capons (Goodale, 1916) and immature hens, although in the latter the broody behavior develops more slowly than in adult birds (Saeki and Tanabe, 1955). Stanford (1952) induced adult bobwhite quail to become broody toward chicks by confining them in small cardboard boxes. In his experiment more of the males (46.7 per cent) than of the females (23.1 per cent) accepted the young.

In domestic chickens, the development of broodiness appears to be facilitated by keeping the birds in warm (80 to 90°F.), dark coops (Burrows and Byerly, 1938; Yamashina, 1952; Saeki and Tanabe, 1955).

Collias (1946) kept domestic hens brooding for months by repeatedly substituting young chicks for the growing chicks of the previous brood. (Older chicks are less effective in inducing broodiness than are newly hatched birds.) Emlen (1941) extended the parental feeding behavior of tricolored red-winged blackbirds from the normal 11 days to about 17 days by replacing the nestlings with younger birds. On the other hand, attempts to extend the period of crop-milk formation in pigeons by giving newly hatched squabs to the parents to replace the older birds which they were feeding have been unsuccessful (Patel, 1936).

Hormonal correlates of broodiness induced by the young. It will be recalled that a high level of pituitary prolactin is associated with the normal occurrence of incubation behavior, and that when the presence of eggs causes the extension of incubation behavior past the normal period, the prolactin level remains high. The situation is strikingly different with respect to both normally occurring broodiness toward the young and broodiness experimentally induced by the presence of young. The prolactin content of the pituitary gland of hens goes down sharply after hatching, and remains down while the chicks are being brooded (Saeki and Tanabe, 1954). Further, when hens are made broody by being kept with young, the prolactin content of their pituitary glands is not elevated (Burrows and Byerly, 1938; Saeki and Tanabe, 1955). The same is true of immature hens and capons. Both can be induced to become broody by being kept with young, without their pituitary glands showing increased prolactin content (Saeki and Tanabe, 1955).

Although the evidence discussed above indicates that the presence of young does not stimulate any detectable increase in prolactin in the pituitary gland, there is some evidence that the presence of young inhibits or delays the onset of the next cycle of nest-building and egg-laying, and therefore presumably inhibits the secretion of gonad-stimulating hormones by the parent's pituitary gland. In various species of wild birds, a recrudescence of sexual behavior can be noted after removal of the young (Howard, 1940; Blanchard, 1941; Armstrong, 1947). Kobayashi (1953a) found that removing the young of domestic pigeons would cause the laying of new eggs about 6 or 7 days later, although the feeding period is normally about 35 days long. The European wren under normal conditions often produces a second brood during a single breeding season. If the nest is destroyed, the 1st egg of the new clutch will be laid some 5 to 8 days later. However, if the eggs are allowed to hatch normally, the 1st egg of the new brood will not be laid until some 10 to 14 days later. Therefore, the fact that the birds are caring for the nestlings delays the beginning of the new cycle (Armstrong, 1955).

4. Physiologic Nonidentity of Incubation Behavior and Broody Care of the Young

In much of the literature, including particularly the agricultural research literature, the term "broodiness" is used indiscriminately to refer to incubation behavior, brooding of the young, and caring for the young in other ways. I have been rather careful to use the term "incubation" or "incubation behavior" when referring to behavior toward the egg, and to restrict the term "broody" or "broodiness" to behavior toward the young. I believe this distinction is justified, and even necessitated, by a number of lines of evidence.

Distribution of incubation behavior and of parental care of the young. Perhaps the most striking evidence to be found in the natural history of birds for the distinctiveness of incubation behavior and of parental care of the young lies in the fact that in many species of birds the female does all of the incubating, whereas the male plays a major role in feeding the young. Skutch (1953b) points out that in many species of songbirds the male discovers the nestlings when the eggs hatch, in part as a result of his behavior during the incubation period. Males which do not incubate may stand guard at the nest, they may bring food to the female, they may visit the nest occasionally, they may escort the female to and from the nest when she leaves it to feed, etc. In some species it seems fairly clear that the behavior of feeding the nestlings has much in common with that of feeding the female while she is on the nest, as in the Florida jay, in which the male brings food to the female during the incubation period and, after the eggs hatch, brings food to the nest and may either give it to the young, or to the female, who then gives it to the young (Amadon, 1944b).

At least in birds with altricial young a distinction must be made between the parental behavior of feeding the young and that of brooding them (*i.e.*, sitting on them so as to provide heat during their early poikilothermic days). The usual situation in songbird species in which the female incubates and the male feeds the young is that the female also does all of the brooding of the young (Lack, 1946; Putnam, 1949;

Allen and Nice, 1952; Whitehouse and Armstrong, 1953). However, the assumption that the physiologic bases of incubation and of brooding are somewhat different is supported by the fact that, in some species in which both sexes share in incubation and in brooding, the relative share of the sexes in these two behaviors is quite different. For example, although male and female pied-billed grebes both incubate the eggs, the female does most of the brooding of the newly hatched young (Deusing, 1939). In the bank swallow, in which the female does most of the incubating, the male and the female may share more nearly equally in the brooding of the young, although there are no data which indicate whether the male actually provides heat to the young (Petersen, 1955).

Experimental induction of incubation behavior and of broody behavior. The most striking evidence for the distinctness of incubation behavior and of broody care of the young comes from the work of Nalbandov (Nalbandov, 1945; Nalbandov and Card, 1945) who found that prolactin would not induce domestic cocks to sit on eggs, regardless of dosage, but that this hormone induces cocks to adopt chicks, to protect them under their body and wing, to lead them to feed and water, to cluck to them, to protect them against intruders, etc. Further, confining cocks with eggs did not induce them to incubate, although confining them with chicks effectively caused them to become broody and to care for the chicks. Schjelderup-Ebbe (1924) noted great individual differences among domestic hens with respect to the efficiency and intensity of their broody care of chicks. Some hens which incubated eggs very devotedly until hatching showed no interest whatever in the chicks after hatching. Lashley (1915) found that sooty terns who were sitting on eggs less than 2 weeks old would not adopt young chicks. A colony of emperor penguins always includes some nonincubating birds. When the eggs hatch, these birds suddenly become very aggressive and try to get the young. The actual parents sometimes give up the young to such other birds, which then feed the chicks by regurgitation. Further, birds which have played no role in incubating the eggs, and which have been feeding at sea for some weeks or months during the incubation period, may feed the young birds by regurgitation immediately after their arrival in the colony at the end of the incubation period, indicating that the ability to feed the young by regurgitation is not continuous with or conditioned by incubation (Prévost, 1953; Stonehouse, 1953). There are other cases, however, in which behavior toward the eggs and the young may be more or less interchangeable. Allen and Mangels (1940) exchanged eggs and young (age not reported) between different pairs of black-crowned night herons and found that the new contents of the nest were accepted and brooded by both groups of parents, although the sudden appearance of *young* caused considerable disturbance to the parents. Emlen (1941) similarly found that young tricolored redwinged blackbirds introduced into nests in which the incubation of eggs had just begun would readily be accepted and fed.

Hormonal concomitants of incubation and of broodiness. Another indication that the physiologic bases of incubation and broodiness are different may be found in the fact that normally occurring incubation behavior is associated with a high level of prolactin in the pituitary gland, whereas broody care of the young is not (see above). Further, when broody behavior is induced by keeping hens, capons, or cocks with young birds, no increase in prolactin content of the pituitary gland accompanies the onset of this broodiness (Saeki and Tanabe, 1955) in contrast to the situation when incubation is extended by the presence of eggs. Finally, Ramsay (1953) reports that broodiness induced by confinement with young is not associated with the formation of the incubation patch which occurs along with normal broodiness.

Conclusion. Although many more data are obviously needed on the whole range of problems connected with the hormonal basis of incubation and broodiness, it is reasonably clear that incubation behavior, on the one hand, and parental care of the young, on the other, are not identical tendencies. They are differently distributed in the natural history of birds, they are not induced in the same way by external stimuli or by hormone treatment, and they are not accompanied by the same hormonal changes. It is probable that brooding of the young (providing heat) has more in common with incubation behavior than do other aspects of parental care (feeding the young, leading them, protecting them, allowing them to huddle under the wing, etc.), but information which might clarify this point is still inadequate.

Nalbandov (1945) suggested that prolactin induces "broodiness" largely or solely through its antigonad (or, more properly, antigonadotrophic) effect. It should be pointed out, however, that hypophysectomy interrupts incubation behavior of sitting hens within 23 hours (Prohaszka, quoted by Saeki and Tanabe, 1955) thus indicating that the maintenance of incubation behavior does not depend *merely* on the removal of pituitary gonadotrophins. On the other hand, castration alone makes male domestic chickens capable of being rendered broody by confinement with chicks, and this effect is not accompanied by increased prolactin secretion. Note also that prolactin induces incubation behavior in hens only if they were laying at the time of treatment, and that it does not induce incubation behavior at all in males, whereas care of the young is induced by prolactin alone. These data suggest that incubation behavior may be induced by some positive action of prolactin on a tissue previously primed by ovarian hormones, whereas broody care of the young may be facilitated merely by the antigonad action of prolactin.

In any event it now seems desirable to distinguish sharply between behavior toward the eggs (incubation behavior) and behavior toward the young (brooding and parental care). Our knowledge of these matters has now reached the point where the use of the general term "broodiness" to cover all aspects of parental behavior toward the eggs and young may be misleading.[1]

[1] A number of additional references to work on hormonal regulation of behavior in birds may be found in the review by Eisner (1960), which appeared too late to be considered in the preparation of this chapter.

III. Hormones and Parental Behavior in Infrahuman Mammals

The reader will soon become aware of a rather unfortunate difference between our material relating to birds and that relating to mammals. Several rich sources of information with respect to parental behavior and its physiologic bases, on which we have drawn in our discussion of birds, simply do not exist for mammals, or, if so, only to a very restricted degree. The relationship between egg production and broodiness in domestic hens has stimulated a good deal of research on these problems in an agricultural setting, of which we have taken advantage. Farm mammals do not seem to have stimulated interest in the same type of problem except for the case of the control of lactation. Another striking difference between the available information on birds and that on mammals stems from the existence of a large and enthusiastic supply of amateur, semiprofessional, and professional bird-watchers whose contributions range from systematic descriptive accounts of the behavior of various species of birds through a variety of more or less casual experiments which, although usually rather anecdotal, are often extremely suggestive, to excellent experimental studies carried out in the field on relatively undisturbed free-living birds. The natural history of mammals simply has not excited nearly so widespread or so intense an interest in such a variety of people (including the present author). In addition, the places in which most mammals rear their young are very much less accessible than is usually the case with birds, so that opportunities for observation are much more sharply restricted. There are, of course, notable exceptions, such as Darling's (1956) classic field study of the Scottish red deer, Hediger's (1950) interesting and fruitful studies of the behavior of mammals in zoos, Eibl-Eibesfeldt's (1958) remarkably detailed studies of the behavior of a variety of mammals under simulated natural conditions in a research institute, and a number of others.

Another difference between our treatment of birds and of mammals depends on the fact that the relationship between ovulation and other events in the reproductive cycle is typically somewhat different in the two groups. The obvious functional relationships between nest-building and incubation behavior led us to include a treatment of nest-building behavior, even though a strict (and artificial) attempt at definition might result in the conclusion that nest-building was a part of sexual, rather than parental behavior. In birds, ovulation occurs between the building of the nest and the incubation of the eggs, and since the physiologic events associated with ovulation are very much involved both in nest-building behavior and in the onset of incubation behavior, various aspects of ovulation in birds necessarily attracted our attention. In mammals, on the other hand, ovulation and fertilization occur long before the emergence of the fetus from the mother. Since nest-building tends to occur late in pregnancy (see below), the physiology of ovulation does not play the role in establishing parental behavior in mammals that it typically does in birds, and we will therefore need no discussion of ovulation in this part of the chapter.

A. NEST-BUILDING

1. Nest-building Patterns in Mammals

Many mammals build shelters or "nests" of various types, the building and occupation of which is not necessarily closely associated with any particular time in the breeding cycle, as it is in birds. Although laboratory data and some scattered field observations indicate that, in some cases at least, changes in the pattern of building behavior do occur in association with reproduction, most of the data from field observations are not sufficiently detailed to permit any differentiation between the building of shelters and reproductive nesting behavior.

Some types of mammals live the year round without constructing any type of nest or shelter. This mode is characteristic of aquatic mammals in general (Fisher, 1940; Bourliere, 1954) and most ungulates (e.g., Murie, 1951). Other mammals make temporary shelters, which they may change from day to day, or at somewhat longer in-

tervals. The European hare digs small trenches in the ground or in grass, in which it spends most of its time during the day (Eibl-Eibesfeldt, 1958). Many tropical bats take shelter during the day in abandoned bird nests or mammal burrows, or cut the blades of large leaves with their teeth so that part of the leaf falls around the clinging animal (Allen, 1939; Bourliere, 1954). Many of the higher primates build sleeping shelters of light branches, twigs, leaves, etc., in which they take shelter during the night; in most cases a new one is built each day at a different location. The orang-utang and chimpanzee build such nests in trees (Reichenow, 1921; Aschemeier, 1922; Nissen, 1931), whereas the gorilla may build either in trees or on the ground (Yerkes and Child, 1927).

The most common type of shelter among mammals is the burrow (Wunder, 1937; Bourliere, 1954; Krumbiegel, 1955) which is used by mammals of many different orders. These burrows range from the simple holes used by many carnivores (Hamilton, 1939) to the elaborate underground networks of tunnels and galleries dug by many rodents (Eisentraut, 1928; Grassé and Dekeyser, 1955; Eibl-Eibesfeldt, 1958).

Some mammals, mostly rodents, build nests of grass, twigs, and leaves in trees (American red squirrel, Hatt, 1929), on the ground about the bases of trees (dusky-footed wood-rat, Linsdale and Tevis, 1951), on the surface of the water (European water vole, Wunder, 1937), or partly submerged in the water (American beaver, Warren, 1927).

Thorough descriptions of the building, burrowing, and nesting behavior of many species of mammals may be found in the monographs and textbooks by Wunder (1937), Hamilton (1939), Bourliere (1954), Grassé (1955), and Krumbiegel (1955).

2. Hormonal Basis of Nest-building

Timing of nest-building during the reproductive cycle. We have already noted that the building of shelters, burrows, and "nests" usually seems not to be particularly related to pregnancy or to the care of the young. There are some indications, however, even in the observations on the behavior of free-living wild mammals, that behavior with respect to shelters and nests does change about the time of parturition. For example, many female ungulates, which normally live in herds on open range, leave the herd and seek isolation and shelter at the time of parturition (*e.g.*, American elk, Murie, 1951). The wood-mouse lives in a hollow, globular nest of leaves and grass. A male and female may both frequent the same nest, but the female will usually force the male to leave when the litter arrives (Nicholson, 1941). Female domestic mice observed in the laboratory can similarly sometimes be seen, just after parturition, to keep other animals out of a previously common nest (Leblond, 1940).

As the following data secured from laboratory animals suggest, it may well be that our failure more often to relate the nest-building activity of wild mammals to the reproductive cycle is partly a function of the lack of quantitative data.

The female domestic rabbit builds a nest by piling up grasses, hay or straw, burrowing into it, and hollowing it out. She then plucks hair from the ventral surface of her body and lines the nest with it. Sawin and Crary (1953) reported that this nest-building activity takes place about the time of parturition, just before or just after the appearance of the litter, depending on the strain. The plucking of hair is associated with a marked loosening of the hair on the belly, dewlap, and thighs (Sawin and Crary, 1953; Klein, 1956). By weighing the amount of hair obtained on different days by a standard combing technique, it can be shown that the loosening of the hair reaches a peak during the 5 days before parturition (Sawin, Denenberg, Ross, Hafter and Zarrow, 1960). The pregnant African lioness also pulls hair from her belly and around her nipples just before parturition. In this species, gestation lasts about 109 days, and this type of hair-pulling is seen from about 100 days onward (Cooper, 1942). Loosening of the hair in late pregnancy has also been found in the Asiatic squirrel (Landry, 1959).

Similarly, nest-building behavior in the domesticated rat is clearly related to the endocrine condition of the animal. Kinder (1927) measured the amount of nest-building in laboratory rats by counting the number of strips of crepe paper used by them for constructing the nest. She found that males and nonpregnant females, on the average, perform the same amount of nest-building activity per day. However, the amount in the *female* is subject to a 5-day cyclic variation, being minimum at estrus, and maximum midway between the two estrous periods.

In pregnant females there is a sudden rise in nest-building activity about 5 days prepartum, the nest-building continuing at a high level during lactation. Preparturient and lactating females spend almost all their time in nest-building, except when suckling young or eating. Similar observations were made by Sturman-Hulbe and Stone (1929), and by Beach (1937). Obias (1957) compared the nest-building behavior of rats just before and just after parturition, and reported that the amount of nest-building increases at the time of parturition.

Koller (1952, 1956) kept individual domestic mice in cages 40 cm. square. Mice kept under such conditions, and provided with hay as building material, will build a nest each night, which can be removed and weighed the next morning. Koller observed that immature mice (beginning 1 to 2 weeks before maturity), adult males, and nonpregnant females all built small nests which he called "sleeping nests" (*Schlafnester*), the amount of nesting material used per night ranging from about 7 to about 11 gm. Pregnant females, on the other hand, build much larger nests, averaging 45 to 50 gm. per night, starting quite abruptly on the 4th to the 5th day of pregnancy, and therefore about the time when the corpus luteum of pregnancy becomes histologically demonstrable. As in the rats studied by Kinder, the building of these larger nests, which Koller called "brood nests (*Brutnester*), continued during lactation.

Pearson (1944) states that pregnant shrews in captivity build nests no different from those built by nonpregnant animals. However, no quantitative data are given, nor do we have sufficient information about the breeding of these animals to judge the adequacy of the laboratory conditions as a setting for the natural behavior pattern.

Hypophyseal hormones and nest-building behavior. Richter and Eckert (1936) found that hypophysectomy greatly increases the amount of nest-building activity in rats. The 12 animals used in their principal experiment performed about 178 per cent more nest-building behavior (measured by the amount of paper used) after removal of the pituitary gland than before. After more extensive later experiments, Richter (1937) reported that many rats did five times as much nest-building after hypophysectomy as before. These experiments were done with nonpregnant animals, and the amount of nest-building behavior reported after hypophysectomy is comparable with the maximal amount normally seen in pregnant animals. Similar results were obtained by Stone and his co-workers (Stone and King, 1954; Stone and Mason, 1955) who rated the nests built by intact 60-day-old male albino rats, and compared them with the nests built by rats of the same age which had been hypophysectomized at 35 days of age. These ratings were based, not only on the amount of nesting material used, but also on the type of construction, higher ratings being given to nests which, from the point of view of compactness, cover, etc., appeared to be better insulating or heat-conserving devices. When rated in this way hypophysectomized animals were judged to have built "better" nests. In their original paper, Richter and Eckert had noted that normal nonpregnant rats built loose and shapeless nests, whereas hypophysectomized animals constructed woven balls with single small openings to an inner chamber.

An apparent contradiction to the general agreement that hypophysectomy increases both the quantity and the quality of nest-building in domestic rats appears in the study of Obias (1957), who hypophysectomized pregnant rats on the 13th day of gestation. Of his 11 experimental animals, 5 died at parturition. Obias rated the nests built by the hypophysectomized animals and by intact controls during the 10 days before parturition, and the nests built by the surviving hypophysectomites and by the controls during the 10 days after parturition, and found no differences between the intact and the hypophysectomized animals. The failure of hypophysectomy to affect the nature of the nest in pregnant rats, in contrast to the striking effect of this op-

eration in non-pregnant animals, is presumably due to the fact that placental hormones can have the same effect as the relevant pituitary hormones.

Information about the effect of exogenous pituitary or pituitary-like hormones on nest-building activity is scanty. Tietz (1933) injected pregnancy urine into 14 nonpregnant female rabbits, and found that 50 per cent of them built nests, using in part hair which had become loosened as a result of the treatment and which the rabbits pulled out from their bodies. Inspection of the ovaries of these animals through exploratory laparotomies showed that some of the treated rabbits developed corpora lutea, and that the fur became loosened only in those animals in which the corpora lutea developed.

Prolactin did not induce nest-building behavior in either male or female domestic mice (Koller, 1952).

Oddly enough, investigators interested in this subject do not seem to have injected pituitary extracts into hypophysectomized rats, in order to see which pituitary fractions would prevent the increase in nest-building activity after hypophysectomy. However, as will be seen from the next section, data on the effects of nonpituitary hormones on nest-building permit a reasonably good guess as to the nature of the effects of hypophysectomy.

Gonadal and thyroid hormones and nest-building behavior. Removal of the thyroid glands in rats induces a rise in the quantity of nest-building behavior of the same order as that induced by hypophysectomy (Richter and Eckert, 1936; Richter, 1937, 1941). Further, thyroid extract administered to intact rats is capable of inhibiting their nest-building behavior (Richter, 1943). Richter suggests that the enhanced nest-building activity resulting from hypophysectomy is due to the loss of thyroid function, a point which we shall discuss in more detail elsewhere (p. 1346).

The effect of thyroidectomy in the rabbit appears to be different from that in the rat, although data in exactly comparable situations are not available. Chu (1945) removed the thyroid glands from female rabbits which were then allowed to become pregnant from 17 to 108 days later. These animals eventually delivered young normally, but did not build nests or pluck any of their fur.

Richter (1937; Richter and Eckert, 1936) reported that gonadectomy and adrenalectomy both produced very small increases in nest-building behavior in rats. On the other hand, Koller (1956) reported that removal of the gonads of male and nonpregnant female mice caused no change in their nest-building behavior: the low-level nest-building behavior ("sleeping nests") characteristic of such animals before treatment continued unchanged.

In contrast to the failure of gonadectomy to affect the level of nest-building behavior in nonpregnant mice, the striking *increase* in nest-building behavior during pregnancy ("brood-nests") is definitely under gonadal control (Koller, 1952, 1956). Injection of progesterone into intact or gonadectomized female mice very quickly (after 2 or three daily injections of 1.5 I.U. each) induced a marked increase in the amount of nesting material used per night, on the same order as the increase which occurs naturally during pregnancy (from about 10 to 15 gm. to about 50 to 60 gm.). Note that this effect of progesterone did not require previous priming with an estrogen. Large doses of estrone (200 I.U. per animal per day) caused no increase in nest-building activity in spayed female mice; on the contrary, Koller's graphs suggest a slight but consistent *depression* of nest-building activity. If the same treatment is given to *intact* adult female mice, the same slight depression of nest-building activity occurs, but when the injections are discontinued after a 10-day treatment period, a marked increase in nest-building activity is seen (from about 8 gm. to about 20 gm.). It seems likely that this increase in nest-building activity is a result of the secretion of endogenous progesterone stimulated by the estrone injections.

An important finding in Koller's work is that *male* mice, whether intact or castrated, cannot be made to build "brood nests" (*i.e.*, increase the amount of nest-building activity) by treatment with progesterone or with an estrogen. This sex difference is in contrast to the effects of hypophysectomy or thyroidectomy in rats, which are the same in males as in females.

A relationship also exists in the domestic rabbit between progesterone and nest-building behavior, but it seems to be quite different from that which Koller demonstrated in the mouse. Klein (1952, 1956) found that *removal* of the corpus luteum during pregnancy would induce rabbits to show immediate nest-building behavior, including plucking of fur. Removal of the gravid uterus was followed by involution of the corpus luteum, with subsequent nest-building behavior (Zarrow, Sawin, Ross and Denenberg, 1962). Hammond (in Klein, 1952) found that pseudopregnant rabbits often build a nest during the involution of the corpus luteum (after about 16 days of pseudopregnancy). If the uterus and cervix of such a rabbit are removed, the corpus luteum undergoes involution, and the nest is built, after 24 to 29 days instead of after 16 days. These data seem to indicate that nest-building behavior in the female rabbit occurs as a result of, or in association with, the cessation of progesterone secretion, rather than being stimulated by progesterone, as in the mouse. We may note here that, in a normal breeding cycle, the characteristic nest-building behavior of the pregnant mouse starts suddenly about the 4th or 5th day of pregnancy (Koller, 1956), whereas in the rabbit nest-building occurs just before or just after parturition (Sawin and Crary, 1953).

Fisher (1956) has induced nest-building behavior (and other aspects of maternal behavior) in rats by local injection of minute amounts of a testosterone salt (sodium testosterone sulfate) directly into the hypothalamus. At the time of this writing, only a preliminary report of Fisher's work is available, in which he reports the occurrence of nest-building behavior in 19 of 130 *male* rats tested in this manner. Fisher's description leaves no doubt that strongly motivated behavior of various types, normally maternal, was induced by these injections, but since this hormone does not normally cause such behavior on *systemic* injection, it is not yet possible to state what contribution these observations make to an understanding of the normal relationships between

endogenous hormones and nest-building behavior.

3. Induction of Nest-building Behavior by External Stimuli

Temperature changes and nest-building behavior. Kinder (1927) kept rats at various temperatures, and found that the amount of nest-building activity was inversely proportional to the environmental temperature. For example, at room temperatures around 90°F. rats used, on the average, 6 to 11 strips of paper per 6-hour period; when the room temperature fell to 40 to 60°F. the consumption of nesting material rose to 38 to 50 strips during a like period. Nests built at temperatures of 90°F. were small, scattered, and loose, in contrast to the large compact nests built by rats kept in the lower temperatures. Koller (1956) observed similar effects in mice. He found that nest-building did not occur at temperatures above 85°F., and that the amount of nest-building increased with decreasing temperature down to about 50°F.

This effect of temperature on nest-building activity, plus the fact that thyroidectomy increases, and exogenous thyroid extract inhibits, such activity, has suggested to all workers on this problem that nest-building activity serves in part a thermoregulatory function, and that the cyclic variations in nest-building behavior in rats and mice can be partly explained as temperature-regulating devices (Kinder, 1927; Richter, 1937; Koller, 1956). We shall return to this point later, in our discussion of the mechanisms of hormonal effects on behavior (see below, p. 1346).

The effect of the young. Koller (1952, 1956) reported that the introduction of young mice (less than 15 days old) into the cage with an adult female causes an abrupt increase in the amount of nest-building behavior on the following night and on subsequent nights. Females that had been using an average of about 7 gm. of nesting material per night increased their consumption to about 25 gm. This increase in nest-building activity appears to be a consequence of the "adoption" of the young by the female. If the young animals are placed in the cage under a wire cover, so that the female can-

not retrieve them or touch them, they do *not* cause any increase in nest-building activity. Further, about 25 per cent of Koller's subjects killed or ate the young, and in those cases there was no increase in nest-building activity on the night following the introduction of the young. Nest-building activity is normally maintained at a high level after parturition, during the period when the young are being cared for by the mother. Koller found that when the young were removed immediately after parturition the level of nest-building activity (which is very high during the last half of pregnancy) abruptly dropped back to the nonbreeding level.

Leblond (1940) similarly reported that introduction of young mice into the cage induced nest-building behavior in the adults, but beyond this statement his data are ambiguous on this point because his quantitative scores were arrived at by lumping nest-building behavior together with other aspects of "maternal behavior."

Koller reported that male mice kill and eat young animals left in the cage with them, and therefore that no increase in nest-building behavior was induced by this treatment. On the other hand, Leblond and Nelson (1937a; Leblond, 1940) found that "maternal behavior" (which included an undefined amount of nest-building behavior) was induced in male mice by keeping young in their cages. It is not apparent whether this difference between the results of Leblond and Nelson and those of Koller is due to a difference in the strain of mice used or in the conditions of their experiments.

One is tempted to suggest that the ability of young mice to stimulate increased nest-building behavior in adults is due to a hormonal change induced by stimuli coming from the young, but this does not seem very likely. To begin with, the presence of young mice maintains a high level of nest-building behavior in their mothers after parturition, when the level of progesterone (which can induce the nest-building behavior) has fallen abruptly. The presence of the young is known to stimulate and maintain the secretion of prolactin (see below, p. 1325), but prolactin administered to adult females does not induce nest-building behavior. Further, Leblond and Nelson (1937a, b) found that nest-building behavior was induced in hypophysectomized adults when they were caged with young mice, which rather effectively disposes of the possibility of induced hormone secretions. It appears rather that stimuli from the young and the effect of progesterone are complementary mechanisms for maintaining nest-building behavior at a high level during the whole period when such behavior is adaptive.

B. BEHAVIOR DURING PARTURITION

1. Patterns of Parturitive Behavior

Behavior before parturition. In addition to the nest-building behavior already discussed, other changes in behavior take place during late pregnancy. Unfortunately, not much attention has been paid to these aspects of behavior, but it is clear that the special physiologic conditions of pregnancy foster behavioral changes which contribute to the preparation for behavior towards the neonate. According to Schneirla (1950) a pregnant cat reacts differently to her own body from a nonpregnant female. More attention is paid to the licking and grooming of the body, the abdominal and pelvic regions in particular being licked significantly more than in nonpregnant cats. Schneirla suggests that this licking, occurring well before parturition, helps to focus the behavior of the animal toward that part of its body. Later, during parturition, its licking responses to stimuli from the pelvic region will make a significant contribution to the parturition itself.

The preparturient female American elk, which at other times lives gregariously in closely integrated herds, goes into isolation, avoiding other animals, with the result (among others) that the newborn elk at first associates only with its own mother (Altmann, 1952). Similar observations have been made on the European red deer (Darling, 1956) and other ungulates (Bourliere, 1954).

During pregnancy, chimpanzees become increasingly quiet, gentle, and friendly, and less aggressive, both toward human keepers and toward other chimpanzees (Yerkes and Tomilin, 1935; Yerkes and Elder, 1937).

This uncharacteristic gentle behavior persists during lactation, except that if the infant is removed shortly after birth, the mother quickly returns to the usual type of behavior (Nissen and Yerkes, 1943). On the other hand, Wimsatt (1960) stated that pregnant bats become restless and irritable some time before parturition.

It is probable that closer study of the behavior of preparturient animals will yield significant clues to the nature of the physiologic preparation for postparturitive behavior.

Behavior at parturition. Although observations of behavior during parturition have been made on only very few species, it is clear that different types of mammals give birth in different positions, and that the position taken by the mother during parturition is a relatively constant characteristic of the species. A number of ungulates, and the elephant, give birth in a standing position (Hediger, 1952). Other ungulates, such as the American elk (Altmann, 1952), and the guanaco (Hediger, 1952), may give birth in a reclining position. Rodents characteristically give birth sitting or crouching on the hind legs (Eibl-Eibesfeldt, 1958; Dieterlen, 1959), whereas domestic cats crouch and recline in different stages of the process (Cooper, 1944). Some kangaroos and other marsupials lie on the back during parturition (Hediger, 1958). In some species, such as the American buffalo, considerable individual differences are seen; some individuals give birth while standing, others while lying down (McHugh, 1958).

As will be seen, the positions taken by animals of different species are related to the manner in which they establish care of the young, and may be of considerable importance for the analysis of the development of maternal care. Rowell (1960a) observed that when the golden hamster pup begins to emerge, the mother licks it with the rest of her genital area, and that, at this stage, the young appears to be treated as an extension of this area of the mother's body. The parturient American elk lies down and licks her flanks, vulva, and the adjoining area before the calf has begun to emerge. Then, when the calf emerges, the cow licks it (Altmann, 1952). Likewise in domestic goats, the mother licks the kid as the kid is leaving her body, the licking appearing to be continuous with that which occurred before the emergence of the kid began (Blauvelt, 1955). Tinklepaugh and Hartman (1930, 1932) provided a detailed description of the behavior of the rhesus monkey during parturition. The mother monkey gets fetal fluids on her hands by touching her vulva at the beginning of delivery, then vigorously licks the fluid off her hands. The cleaning of the newborn monkey seems to be a continuation of this process. After delivery the mother alternately cleans her own hands and licks the baby's body.

Self-licking and licking of the emerging fetal membranes and young are often associated with maternal assistance to the emerging fetus. The domestic rabbit during parturition stands in a bowed, somewhat crouching position with the back strongly arched, the hind limbs flexed ventrally, and the head bent down between the front legs. In this posture the birth canal is so oriented that a fetus during birth is propelled forwards and downwards between the rabbit's hind-limbs and comes to rest not far from her mouth. When maternal assistance in freeing the newborn young from the fetal membranes is necessary, the mother's mouth is thus automatically in the correct position (Franklin and Winstone, 1954). Tinklepaugh and Hartman (1930) observed that rhesus monkeys actually help pull the young out of the birth canal and then may pull on the cord with the hands, sometimes thus pulling out the placenta. The California sea lion has been observed to turn her head to her vulva and pull with her teeth at the hind flippers which were the only part of the fetus that has emerged. The mother elephant seal may assist during birth by pulling at the emerging young with her hind flippers (Slijper, 1956).

Not all mammals lick the fetal membranes or newborn young, or assist the young during birth. Hartman (1920) reported that the young opossum receives no assistance from its mother, in fact moving from the uterus to the mother's pouch without assistance. In the red kangaroo considerable interindividual variability may be seen (Hediger, 1958), but several observers have seen individuals of this species which gave no direct assistance to the emerging young (the mother lies on her back during parturition), but which, starting with licking in the neighborhood of the vulva when the placental membranes ruptured, continued to lick the underside of the body in a craniad direction, making a narrow track of fur saturated with saliva, which the young followed, thus reaching the pouch (Dathe, 1934; Grassé, Bourliere, and Viret, 1955).

Not all mammals lick the emerging fetus and assist it to emerge. The camelids (camels, llamas, etc.) neither lick the young nor appear to be attracted to the fetal membranes or fluids (Pilters, 1954). Aquatic mammals such as the pinnipeds (seals, etc.), although they sometimes assist in birth, do not lick the young. On the other hand, the hippopotamus, which also gives birth in the water, normally does not assist in birth or pull on or bite the umbilical cord, but it may lick the young (Slijper, 1956).

The fact that in some mammals suckling relationships between mothers and young are adequately established in the absence of any tendency to lick the fetal membranes or the neonate, whereas in other species the licking activity of the mother clearly plays a role in establishing the relationship between mother and young (see below, p. 1312), suggests that (a) the processes of establishment of mother-young relationships vary widely from species to species, and (b) in those species in which licking *does* play a role, the possibility of the existence of other factors making a substantial contribution should not be minimized.

Interaction between mother and young at birth. In many species of mammals, the mother begins to react to the emerging young during parturition, and the mother's behavior toward the young at this stage is, in part, a continuation of her reactions to her own body at the end of pregnancy and the beginning of parturition. The behavior of the young is, of course, also characteristic of the species, both because of differences between the young themselves and because of differences in the situation in which they are placed by the varying behavior of the mother. This leads to different kinds of interaction between young and mothers in different species at the earliest stages of parturition and prenatal care.

Behavior during and just after parturition is thus a mutual affair, involving the structure and behavior both of the mother and of the neonate. Young mammals vary widely with respect to the level of development at birth, some being born very small, blind, and helpless, others larger, well furred, and ready to take solid food within a day or two after birth (Hamilton, 1939). The young of some species are not capable of standing or walking for some time after birth, and thus can suckle only while lying under the mother (Wiesner and Sheard, 1933; Schneirla, 1956). The young of other species can stand almost immediately after birth and characteristically suckle in a standing position (Altmann, 1952; Hediger, 1952). Clearly the behavior of the immediately postparturitive mother and that of the neonate must be adapted to each other. It will be recalled that the mother goat licks the newborn kid as the kid is leaving her body. After parturition, the (standing) mother continues to lick the kid, which is also standing, licking along the kid's back to its anus which is especially vigorously licked. When the mother is licking in the neighborhood of the kid's anus, the head of the kid is in the neighborhood of the mother's teats, and according to Blauvelt (1955), this arrangement of the licking behavior contributes to the first establishment of suckling. Somewhat similar observations are recorded by Altmann (1952) in the American elk. As Schneirla (1956) describes the behavior of the domestic cat during parturition, intervals of intense activity which facilitate the expulsion of the fetuses are interspersed with intervals of exhaustion and rest, which facilitate the initiation of a suckling relationship between the mother and the neonate. The neonate is brought into contact with the abdomen of the mother partly through the behavior of the mother (licking, lying down, etc.), and partly by its own crude orienting responses to tactual and thermal stimuli from the mother (Rosenblatt, quoted by Schneirla, 1956). Rowell (1960a) has made similar observations on the golden hamster.

Although information on behavior during parturition, and on the very earliest stages of mother-young relationship, are available for only very few species of mammals, it is apparent that a wide variety of patterns of such behavior can be found in nature, and that a great deal yet remains to be learned about them.

2. Physiologic Aspects of Parturitive Behavior

In many species of mammals the mother, after licking herself and the emerging young, may tear the fetal membranes, bite through the umbilical cord, and eat the placenta. Placentophagy is widespread, occurring in many different families and orders. Thus the habit of eating the placenta is found among such widely differing mammals as bats (Allen, 1939; Wimsatt, 1945; Ramakrishna, 1950), ungulates (Hediger, 1942, 1955), rodents (Eibl-Eibesfeldt, 1958; Dieterlen, 1959), carnivores (Tembrock, 1957), monkeys (Tinklepaugh and Hartman, 1930; Carpenter, 1934), chimpanzees (Yerkes, 1935; Nissen and Yerkes, 1943), and others.

Placentophagy is, however, by no means universal. In species in which it does occur, it may not occur in every case. For example, Nissen and Yerkes (1943) report that of 29 chimpanzee births observed by the authors, the whole placenta was eaten in 13 cases, bits of the placenta in 4 cases, and there was no eating of the placenta in 10 cases. In all 29 cases, however, the fluids associated with the placenta and amnion were licked up from the floor and from the infants. The camels and their relatives neither lick the young nor eat the placenta (Pilters, 1954; Koford, 1957). In a number of aquatic animals, such as seals (Slijper, 1956), dolphins (McBride and Hebb, 1948; Tavolga and Essapian, 1957), the hippopotamus (Slijper, 1956), etc., the mother pays no attention to the placenta, neither licking it, eating it, or touching it, although she may in some of these animals bite through the cord.

It will not have escaped the attention of the reader that some of these animals which eat the placenta are, at all other times of their life, strictly herbivorous. Hediger (1955) describes how various ungulates, immediately after having given birth, "fall on the amniotic sac and devour it." He adds, "in this situation, the most decided herbivore turns carnivore all of a sudden. I saw bison and antelope cows swallow such large mouthfuls that I was afraid they would choke." The domestic rabbit is also a voracious placentophage (Sawin and Crary, 1953).

It is remarkable that practically no attention has been paid to the problem of how a herbivorous animal is induced to become carnivorous at the time of parturition. A beginning is found in unpublished observations by Dr. Thales Martins, made at the American Museum of Natural History (quoted by Riess, 1950), who offered various diets to groups of guinea pigs, and found that pregnant females showed a significant preference for meat compared with other groups of these animals. Wiesner and Sheard (1933) offered fetuses obtained by cesarian section, with their membranes and with the placenta attached, to some female rats which had given birth about 12 hours previously. The majority of these animals did not respond to the fetus or placenta, although they had, on the day before, delivered and cleaned their own young. They further report that nulliparous females never cleaned or ate fetuses in membranes offered to them, although they accepted pieces of raw meat.

Allan and Wiles (1932) hypophysectomized 12 pregnant cats. Eleven of these animals ignored the kittens at birth, doing no licking, tearing of the membranes, or eating of the placenta. The 12th animal abandoned its kittens when they were 2 days old. Similar results were obtained by Smith (1954) who hypophysectomized 10 pregnant rhesus monkeys, and found that pregnancy and parturition were carried through normally except for unusually difficult labor (see Cross, 1959). Nine of the animals failed to eat the afterbirth, although a few licked it. These data certainly suggest that licking of the fetus and eating of the afterbirth depend on the hormonal condition of the parturient mother. It is to be noted that nutritional requirements of pregnant rats differ in some respects from those of nonpregnant animals, for example, in increased need for salt (Richter and Barelare, 1938), and future research may show some relationship between these changes in nutritional needs and the tendency to lick and eat the placenta. It should be noted that most animals seem to be able to select varying diets in

accordance with varying nutritional needs (Young, 1949, 1959). When the sympathetic ganglia of pregnant cats were removed, the animals did not lick or clean the kittens after parturition (Simeone and Ross, 1938). We might speculate on whether this is due to an effect of maternal sympathectomy on the characteristics of the kitten, on those characteristics of the mother's body which lead to self-licking, or on characteristics of her central nervous system.

Mothers may occasionally eat their neonate young. This happens not infrequently in the domestic rat (Wiesner and Sheard, 1933) and in the domestic mouse (Brown, 1953), and is also seen in the domestic rabbit (Sawin and Crary, 1953). It is not clear what factors contribute to this form of cannibalism, although usually the eating of the infant follows the eating of the placenta and umbilical cord (Wiesner and Sheard, 1933). Indeed, in an animal which is, at the moment, so voraciously carnivorous, the question of why the mothers do *not* usually eat their young may be just as reasonable a question as that of why the mothers sometimes *do* eat them. Eibl-Eibesfeldt (1958), on the basis of his (nonexperimental) observations of parturitions in the domestic rat, believes that the eating of the young is inhibited by a vocalization emitted by the young, which is in part stimulated by the mother's eating of the umbilicus.

It is clear that the behavior of the mother toward the newly born young and toward the placenta, particularly in herbivorous animals, presents a number of problems the investigation of which is now at its earliest stage.[2]

C. RETRIEVING OF THE YOUNG

1. *Retrieving Behavior*

The retrieving to the nest of young which have strayed or become scattered is characteristic of many species of mammals (Causey and Waters, 1936; Wunder, 1937). Different species normally have different ways of managing to retrieve the young. Everyone is familiar with the way domestic cats

[2] Much additional information on parturition may be found in the monograph by Slijper (1960), which appeared too late to be considered in the preparation of this chapter.

pick up their kittens by the nape of the neck (Leyhausen, 1956). Various species of rodents characteristically pick up the young with the mouth, seizing them in the middle of the back, by the skin of the belly, or on the flank (Curio, 1955; Eibl-Eibesfeldt, 1958). At least in the domestic rat, considerable individual differences can be seen, these animals having been seen to pick up young by about 20 different parts of their bodies (Wiesner and Sheard, 1933; Causey and Waters, 1936). Retrieving of the young may be done very vigorously and persistently. One European yellow-necked mouse has been seen to retrieve, in quick succession, 148 young which had been placed in different parts of the living space by the experimenters (Zippelius and Schleidt, 1956).

Some mammals use methods of retrieving the young other than carrying them in the mouth. Some opossums carry their young on the back (Wunder, 1937). Blair (1941) observed that young northern pigmy mice become attached to the nipples of the mother and are dragged about wherever she goes. Similar methods are seen in some bats, in which the young either cling to the underside of the mother's body or attach themselves to the nipple, and are carried by the mothers on their hunting trips (Wunder, 1937; Hamilton, 1939). Beach (1939b) reported that young Central American opossums remain continuously attached to the mother's nipples. When one of the young becomes detached, the mother noses it back under her belly, upon which the young animal rolls over on his back, grasps the mother's ventral hair, and moves over her ventral surface until it finds a nipple and becomes attached.

Young bicolored white-toothed shrews sometimes follow the mother in a "caravan," in which the first young grasps the mother's tail near its base, and the successive young each similarly grabs in its mouth the tail of the young in front of it (Wahlström, 1929; Zippelius, 1957).

In some aquatic mammals, the mother may retrieve the young by swimming after them and guiding them back into place when they get too far away. When the young bottle-nosed dolphin strays from its mother's side she swims after it and pushes

it gently, guiding its direction until it is close to her side again (Tavolga and Essapian, 1957). Mother dolphins support the young to the surface after parturition (McBride and Hebb, 1948; McBride and Kritzler, 1951), and mother dolphins have been seen thus supporting dead young or the remains of dead young (Hubbs, 1953; Moore, 1955).

The domestic rabbit does not seem to retrieve its young (Ross, Denenberg, Frommer and Sawin, 1959), unlike rats which do retrieve, although both nest in burrows.

Retrieving by the male. In most mammals the mother alone attends to the rearing of the young, the father paying little or no attention to them (Bourliere, 1954; Hediger, 1955). In some species, however, retrieving of young by the male has been noted. Horner (1947) reported that male deer mice in captivity often retrieve the young, and Frank (1952) observed the same thing in the common vole of Europe, as did Leblond (1940) in the domestic mouse. On the other hand, the male laboratory rat, at least under the conditions in which such animals are normally kept in the laboratory, does not appear to retrieve the young (Seitz, 1958). Male Galapagos sea lions take part in the care of the young, shepherding them back to shore when they swim far off (Eibl-Eibesfeldt, 1955c), in contrast to most seals, in which the male pays no attention to the young (Bartholomew, 1952, 1953).

2. Physiologic Regulation of Retrieving Behavior

CORRELATION OF RETRIEVING BEHAVIOR AND PHYSIOLOGIC CONDITION. There is considerable evidence that the tendency to retrieve young is linked to, or somehow dependent on, the physiologic conditions associated with the end of pregnancy and the period of lactation. Rabaud (1921a, b) found that pregnant domestic mice began to retrieve young mice offered by the experimenter at about the middle of pregnancy (9 or 10 days). He noted further that retrieving becomes more intense just after parturition, and that, when a pregnant female and a recently postparturitive female were both in a cage, the pregnant one always gave way when both animals attempted to retrieve young. Wiesner and Sheard (1933) found that 19 of 21 primiparous rats tested just after parturition showed the retrieving response to the young, whereas of 21 pregnant nulliparous rats tested 1 to 7 days before parturition, only 4 retrieved young. In another test, they found that only 6 of 34 pregnant nulliparous females tested 1 to 9 days before parturition showed any retrieving behavior. Rowell (1960b) found that pregnant and nonpregnant female golden hamsters accepted and retrieved only 3 out of 33 pups, in contrast to postparturitive animals, which usually accepted and retrieved young pups. In a somewhat similar series of observations Labriola (1953) offered young rats to 10 nonpregnant nulliparous females and to 10 females which had given birth 24 hours previously. None of the nonpregnant animals retrieved any young; all of the postparturitive animals did.

Herter and Herter (1955) found that a pseudopregnant polecat retrieved domestic kittens. Retrieving by pseudopregnant animals has also been noted in the domestic rat (Herold, 1954) and in the dog (Lang, 1931).

Retrieving, of course, continues during the lactation period (Wiesner and Sheard, 1933). The data presented so far might suggest that retrieving behavior is limited to the period at the end of pregnancy and the lactation period following parturition. Unfortunately, the situation is not quite that simple. About 20 per cent of domestic rats retrieve regardless of sex or reproductive condition (Wiesner and Sheard, 1933; Riddle, Hollander, Miller, Lahr, Smith and Marvin, 1942; Riddle, Lahr and Bates, 1942). Frank (1952) found that males and nonpregnant females of the common vole often retrieve young, although not as often as postparturitive females. Leblond (1938, 1940) presented young rats to 12 female rats that were some 6 to 24 weeks past their last parturition, and in which lactation had ceased. Ten of the 12 animals retrieved, retrieving occurring in 90 per cent of the tests.

Rowell (1960b) found that young golden hamsters begin to retrieve younger pups as soon as they are strong enough, and that this retrieving behavior disappears with the onset of aggressive behavior, which appears at different ages in animals reared under different conditions.

The incidence of retrieving behavior suggests a parallel with that of nest-building behavior. Both types of behavior are observed to occur in the mouse starting at 9 or 10 days of pregnancy, whereas in the rat the onset is later, closer to the time of parturition. Both types of behavior are also seen in males and in nonpregnant females, to a lesser degree, and to varying extents by different observers, probably under different conditions. Unfortunately, there does not exist a good study of the correlation between these two types of behavior during a normal reproductive cycle. The best studies of nest-building behavior, such as those of Koller (1952, 1956), were done under conditions in which retrieving was not readily observed, and the best studies of retrieving, such as those of Wiesner and Sheard (1933) and of Beach and Jaynes (1956a, b, c), were done on animals in which nest-building behavior was not being studied. In a number of other studies, nest-building and retrieving were lumped together in order to construct a "maternal behavior" score, which was then used without further differentiation of its components (Leblond, 1940). Closer study of the details of variation between individuals, between species, and during the breeding cycle should be rewarding.

HORMONAL INDUCTION OF RETRIEVING BEHAVIOR. (a) Hypophyseal hormones. Collip, Selye and Thomson (1933) hypophysectomized female rats shortly after parturition, or later during lactation. Lactation ceased and the mammary glands regressed, but retrieving and other aspects of maternal care continued. Other observers have noted that hypophysectomy does not interfere with retrieving behavior (Leblond and Nelson, 1937a; Obias, 1957), even though lactation is suppressed (Leblond, 1940).

Using a more quantitative approach than the earlier investigators, Riddle, Lahr and Bates (1942) found that hypophysectomy actually *increased* retrieving behavior. In both male and female rats, hypophysectomized animals retrieved on 68 to 75 per cent of the tests, compared with only 21 to 23 per cent for intact animals.

The apparently contradictory results of

Allan and Wiles (1932) must be mentioned at this point. They found that cats hypophysectomized during pregnancy deserted their kittens immediately after parturition. Since hypophysectomized rats retrieve apparently normally, even when the hypophysectomy was accomplished during pregnancy (Obias, 1957), the different results obtained by Allan and Wiles presumably represent a difference between cats and rats with respect to the method of control of the mother's behavior toward the young.

Erhardt (1929) induced a nonpregnant female rhesus monkey to adopt a neonatal guinea pig by injecting her with an anterior pituitary extract. Since that time, considerable additional evidence has accumulated implicating hypophyseal hormones in the regulation of retrieving behavior. Riddle, Lahr and Bates (1942) found that prolactin caused substantial increases in retrieving behavior in both male and female rats, whether intact or gonadectomized (Riddle, Lahr and Bates, 1935a, b; Riddle, Hollander, Miller, Lahr, Smith and Marvin, 1942). Luteinizing hormone was similarly able to increase retrieving behavior. The fact that the luteinizing hormone increased retrieving even in gonadectomized animals suggests that there was present in this preparation some material capable of acting directly on nongonadal parts of the soma, and Riddle and Bates (1939) note that Riddle's luteinizing hormone preparations contained "some" prolactin. Prolactin, of course, exerts a luteotrophic action on the ovary (Meites and Shelesnyak, 1957), but since it is effective in inducing retrieving behavior in gonadectomized animals, its luteotrophic effect cannot be the only source of its action in this situation.

FSH seems to have no effect on retrieving behavior (Riddle, Lahr and Bates, 1935a). Animals injected with this substance retrieved young in about the same percentage of cases as did untreated animals (Riddle, Lahr and Bates, 1935b).

(b) *Thyroid*. McQueen-Williams (1935a, b) found that removal of the thyroid glands in male rats induced retrieving and other aspects of parental care of the young, a finding confirmed by Riddle, Lahr and Bates (1936). Thyroidectomy increased the incidence of retrieving in tests of male rats

from about 21 per cent to about 45 per cent (Riddle, Lahr and Bates, 1942).

Dispensa and Hornbeck (1941) injected desiccated thyroid into rats during pregnancy and found no effect on retrieving or other aspects of maternal care. Chu (1945) found that rabbits that became pregnant after thyroidectomy *failed* to care for the young. It should be noted, however, that the behavior of the rabbit differs from that of the rat in that retrieving does not normally occur in this species (Ross, Denenberg, Frommer and Sawin, 1959).

(c) *Gonads*. Castrated male mice show retrieving behavior after some association with the young (Leblond, 1940), but no data are available to indicate whether this behavior is more frequent or more intense than that normally shown by intact males in the same laboratory. Riddle, Lahr and Bates (1942) noted that castration does not itself appreciably increase retrieving behavior in either male or female rats. However, almost all of the substances which, in their study, were found to increase retrieving behavior (*e.g.*, prolactin, "luteinizing hormone" etc.) were more effective in gonadectomized (whether male or female) than in intact animals.

Testosterone injections cause some increase in retrieving behavior in castrated males, intact females, and ovariectomized females, but not in intact males (Riddle, Lahr and Bates, 1942). Fisher's (1956) local injections of sodium testosterone sulfate into the hypothalamus induced retrieving behavior in some cases. As I noted in connection with the induction of nest-building in Fisher's experiment, no data yet exist for comparison of the effects of this androgen with those of other hormones applied in the same manner.

Riddle, Lahr and Bates (1936) found that progesterone was as effective in increasing retrieving behavior as was prolactin.

Retrieving behavior seems to be suppressed by the administration of estrogenic substances. Riddle, Lahr and Bates (1942) treated virgin female rats with estrone for 20 to 26 days. Under this treatment, the mammary glands developed to a degree similar to that found late in pregnancy, but none of the experimental animals would retrieve 3-day-old young rats during the period of estrone treatment. Retrieving, and other aspects of maternal behavior, were shown by these animals *after* withdrawal of the estrone treatment. Weichert and Kerrigan (1942) found that mother rats injected with estrogen during the lactation period allowed the young to become scattered over the cage without retrieving them, and that the young were often found cold outside the nest. Similarly Riddle, Hollander, Miller, Lahr, Smith and Marvin (1942) found that estrone tends to terminate established maternal behavior. They report, however, that this does not happen in hypophysectomized rats.

Apparently contradictory results have been reported by Leblond (1938) who found that male domestic mice showed retrieving behavior after estrin treatments or the implantation of ovarian grafts. Moore (1919) implanted ovaries in gonadectomized male rats, and reported that they subsequently showed maternal behavior, including retrieving. *Intact* male rats similarly implanted with ovaries did not exhibit such behavior. Similar treatment failed to induce maternal behavior in the guinea pig (Moore, 1921).

(d) *Summary remarks.* These data on the hormonal induction of retrieving are rather confused, chaotic, and in many cases contradictory. There has not yet been a study of this problem with a design in which the experience gained during the early experiments was utilized, or in which the importance of statistical analysis was anticipated, or in which a broad range of causal factors was comprehended.

In spite of these inadequacies, a number of points may tentatively be made. The fact that hypophysectomy and prolactin administration both increase the incidence of retrieving behavior suggests that prolactin acts by means of its antigonadotrophic effect. However, prolactin increases retrieving behavior both in hypophysectomized and in gonadectomized animals, which renders it unlikely that prolactin affects retrieving through either antigonadotrophic or luteotrophic effects. The alternative possibility is that hypophysectomy and prolactin, although they both cause increases in retrieving behavior, do so in different ways, or through different kinds of effects on the animal. Closer qualitative analysis of the fine details of the behavior of animals treated in the various ways reported here will undoubtedly reveal many differences that have been obscured in the relatively crude treatments undertaken so far.

Certain similarities between the physiologic bases of nest-building behavior and of retrieving should be noted. Hypophysectomy and thyroidectomy enhance both types of behavior. Progesterone induces both retrieving in rats and nest-building in mice. Even more suggestive, estrogen treatment seems to have the same effect on both types of behavior. It inhibits it during treatment, but causes it to rise above the pretreatment level after withdrawal of the hormone treatment. However, the fact that prolactin induces retrieving behavior (at least in rats), whereas it does not have any effect upon nest-building behavior in the mouse, suggests that the physiologic bases of the two types of behavior are not entirely identical. Coordinated study of both types of behavior in both species would obviously be useful.

INDUCTION OF RETRIEVING BEHAVIOR BY EXTERNAL STIMULI. As Beach (1951) pointed out, the stimulation of retrieving behavior by stimuli provided by the young really presents two quite different problems. First, it is possible that stimuli provided by the young can induce a physiologic state which underlies the capacity to display retrieving behavior. Secondly, there is the problem of what stimuli induce an animal that is physiologically capable of retrieving to do so, and to retrieve some objects rather than others. We shall discuss these problems separately.

(a) *Induction of readiness to retrieve by stimuli from the young.* Wiesner and Sheard (1933), who found that only about 20 per cent of nulliparous, nonpregnant female rats would retrieve young offered to them by the experimenter, succeeded in arousing readiness to retrieve in many of the "nonretrievers" by confining them in cages with young rats for several days, the young being replaced every 2 days by fresh ones. By this procedure, which Wiesner and Sheard called "concaveation," retrieving behavior was induced in 25 out of the 74 nonreactors so tested. Retrieving behavior began from 1 to 4 days after the young were introduced into the cage. Leblond (1938) made similar observations in domestic mice. When he tested 14 virgin female mice, none retrieved young. After concaveation for 2 to 4 days with young mice, 12 of the 14 began to retrieve. This procedure also induced retrieving behavior in previously nonretrieving hypophysectomized mice (Leblond and Nelson, 1936, 1937a), and male mice (Leblond, 1940).

The question arises whether the concaveation procedure really induced a change in underlying physiologic condition, conducive to the onset of retrieving behavior, or whether it merely represents the sampling effects of testing on a number of different days, thus increasing the probability of finding retrieving behavior in animals whose readiness to retrieve varies from day to day. As Wiesner and Sheard (1933) point out, the evidence clearly favors the assumption that exposure to the young does in fact change the condition of the adult being tested. Animals which are found to retrieve without concaveation usually continue to retrieve throughout the period of observation. In addition, removal of the young after retrieving behavior has been established through concaveation results in the disappearance of the retrieving response, as determined by tests some days later.

The nature of the physiologic change induced by concaveation is not clear. Since concaveation induces retrieving behavior in hypophysectomized mice (Leblond, 1937, 1940), we cannot assume that its effect is through the stimulation of hormone secretion. As we have noted in connection with other aspects of retrieving behavior, there are certain similarities between effects of the young on retrieving behavior and on the nest-building behavior observed by Koller (1952, 1956). Both can be induced by confining young with the animals being tested, and both can be induced in hypophysectomized animals. However, Wiesner and Sheard (1933) found that individual rats in which retrieving was induced by concaveation would not necessarily show any onset of nest-building behavior associated with this retrieving. We must thus reiterate that, whereas the physiologic bases of nest-building and of retrieving (at least in domestic rats and mice) undoubtedly have much in common, they are probably not identical.

(b) *Stimuli eliciting retrieving responses.* The stimuli by means of which young animals induce retrieving behavior on the part of the parents may vary considerably from species to species, although information on this problem is fragmentary and incomplete, even for most of the widely used experimental animals. Scott (1945) reported that domestic sheep respond to the sounds of their bleating lambs, and Beach (1951) observed that the squeals uttered by young laboratory rats in response to painful stimulation elicit greatly increased activity in the lactating female. Similar observations have been made on wild meadow mice (Bailey, 1924) and rice rats (Svihal, 1931). According to Zippelius and Schleidt (1956), young of the common vole, domestic mouse, and European yellow-necked mouse induce retrieving behavior on the part of their parents, in part, by uttering supersonic cries with frequencies in the neighborhood of 70 to 80 kc. Domestic cats retrieve their young in response to the cry given by a kitten separated from its mother (Leyhausen, 1956).

Auditory and visual stimuli are also effective. Anesthetized young European yellow-necked mice may be found and retrieved by their mothers, although only if the mother passes close to them, in contrast to active young, which attract the mothers from a considerable distance by their supersonic calls (Zippelius and Schleidt, 1956). Dieterlen (1959) and Eibl-Eibesfeldt (1958) have made observations which suggest that olfactory stimuli are effective in inducing retrieving behavior in the golden hamster and laboratory rat.

Beach and Jaynes (1956a, c) have shown that several different sensory modalities contribute to the stimulation of maternal retrieving behavior in the laboratory rat. The importance of olfaction is demonstrated by the following facts: peripherally blinded females spent more time investigating a small cage made of fine copper-wire mesh containing a young rat than they did a similar cage containing no young rat, whereas anosmic females failed to distinguish between the two cages: young rats sprayed with oil of lavender, and subsequently dried, were retrieved by most females less efficiently and less rapidly than untreated young. Visual stimulation is also significant: when female rats were placed in cages each containing a pair of glass bottles sealed to the floor of the cage, only one of which contained a young rat, 17 of the 25 females which investigated the bottles spent more time at the bottle containing a live young rat than at the empty bottle; on retrieving tests in which intact females were offered normal young and motionless young, there was a tendency for the active young to be retrieved more rapidly. Although freshly killed young were retrieved almost as quickly as normal young, young refrigerated for a short time after being killed were retrieved significantly more slowly. It is not possible to say whether this difference in reaction is based upon olfactory, temperature, or tactual cues. Although a number of stimulus modalities are clearly important, the rats could retrieve in the absence of any one of the modalities tested (i.e., vision, olfaction, cutaneous sensitivity around the mouth). Animals deprived of any 2 of these sensory capacities retrieved less efficiently than animals deprived of only 1, and animals rendered blind, anaptic, and anosmic were the poorest retrievers of all. It is clear from this and other work (e.g., McHugh, 1958) that a variety of different stimuli in different sensory modalities may contribute to the stimulation of retrieving behavior.

Younger mice apparently stimulate more retrieving and other aspects of maternal care than older animals (Wiesner and Sheard, 1933). Leblond (1940) found that 0- to 1-day-old mice were retrieved by lactating females 83 to 85 per cent of the time, whereas 15-day-old young were retrieved only 11 to 15 per cent of the time, the decrease being a steady and gradual one, as revealed by tests using young of intermediate ages. Younger animals provide stronger stimuli for retrieving than older ones even for lactating mothers whose own young are older. Indeed, Wiesner and Sheard (1933) report that, at the end of lactation, the grown-up litter no longer represents an adequate stimulus for retrieving, although the

mother may vigorously retrieve newborn young presented to her. Menzel and Menzel (1953) replaced older puppies with very young ones, and found an increase in maternal care by the mother dog. Presented with newborn puppies, she acts just like an immediately postpartum female. This replacement of older by younger puppies can be effected twice in one lactation period, with the same results.

The most exact and quantitative study of this problem is the very recent one by Rowell (1960c), who studied the retrieving responses of lactating female golden hamsters at various ages postpartum, in response to young of various ages. She found that variations in the amount of maternal retrieving are influenced by three types of variables: (a) the time since the birth of her own litter; (b) similarity between the age of her own young and that of the test young; and (c) variations in the stimuli coming from the test young, which elicit retrieving responses when they are 7 to 10 days old more efficiently than they do at any other age, regardless of the kind of female being tested. Rowell further found that the amount of time spent licking the young, after having retrieved them, decreased steadily and reliably during lactation. Using a litter-replacement technique, she kept various groups of mothers with young of different ages, so that, e.g., some mothers constantly had 2- to 6-day-old litters, some 10- to 14-day-old litters, etc. Under these conditions, the decrease in licking time, characteristic for normal litters, did not occur. Further, these females licked their pups for approximately the same amount of time as was characteristic, in a normal litter, for young of the same age as the test pups. Thus the change in licking time, which always occurs postpartum, is a function of growth changes in the ability of the young to stimulate licking behavior, rather than of physiologic changes in the mother.

The stimuli inducing retrieving behavior are not necessarily specific to the species, as there are many instances recorded of small mammals retrieving young of other species. The laboratory rat readily retrieves young mice (Wiesner and Sheard, 1933; Shadle, 1945; Herold, 1954; Beach and Jaynes, 1956b). When mother laboratory rats are simultaneously given young mice and rats to retrieve, they show some preference for the rats (Wiesner and Sheard, 1933). The common vole retrieves young red-backed voles or field voles offered by the experimenter (Frank, 1952). Cotton rats adopt young laboratory rats (Meyer and Meyer, 1944). Dogs readily adopt puppies of other strains (Menzel and Menzel, 1953), and a polecat has adopted domestic kittens (Herter and Herter, 1955). Kahmann and von Frisch (1952) and Eibl-Eibesfeldt (1958) have summarized observations from many different sources which indicate that many small mammals may adopt young belonging to different species, genera, and even families.

Rats will, however, not retrieve young of *all* other species. Wiesner and Sheard (1933) offered pairs of 1- to 6-day-old rabbits and rats simultaneously to each of 49 lactating female rats, and found that 28 retrieved both the young rat and the young rabbit whereas in 21 cases only the rat was retrieved. In no case did the mother rat retrieve a rabbit while leaving the young rat. Beach and Jaynes (1956b) report that rats will not retrieve young guinea pigs, which, of course, are much larger and more active than 1- to 6-day-old rabbits or rats.

In spite of the fact that they may retrieve young of other species, lactating females of at least some species of mammals discriminate between their own young and other young of the same species, and tend to prefer their own young. When Beach and Jaynes (1956c) tested 16 lactating female rats in several situations in which the retrieving of their own young could be compared with retrieving of other young rats the same age as their own, all but one of the mother rats tended to prefer their own young. When "own" and "alien" young were presented separately, there was a tendency for the own young to be retrieved faster; when the own and the alien young were presented to the mother rat together, there was a tendency for the own young to be retrieved first. Wiesner and Sheard (1933) had found no evidence of preference for retrieving of their own young, but as Beach and Jaynes point out, the earlier tests were considerably less sensitive than the tests used by them. Domestic mice, although they

may retrieve alien young of their own species, will often subsequently eat them (Eibl-Eibesfeldt, 1950). When golden hamsters are offered strange young they often eat them (Lauterbach, quoted by Eibl-Eibesfeldt, 1958). Leblond (1937) points out that domestic mice at first accept alien young as readily as they do their own, and that attachment to their own young develops later.

The stimuli on the basis of which mothers recognize their own young may vary among different types of mammals. In the Galapagos sea lion, maternal care is restricted to the mother's own young. Eibl-Eibesfeldt (1955c) observed that mothers respond only to the calls of their own young, and that they apparently also recognize their young by sniffing at them. In the case of the American elk, on the other hand, Altmann (1952) found that mothers reject strange young on the basis of olfactory and probably also visual cues, whereas the calls of any young are reacted to by many females. Observations by McHugh (1958) indicate that olfactory, visual, and auditory cues are all used by female American bisons in identifying their young.

Beach (1951) noted that considerable individual variability may be seen in the laboratory rat with respect to recognition of the young. Although some females consistently retrieve their own young in preference to others, other individuals seem to make no such distinctions. Similarly, Menzel and Menzel (1953) find that some female dogs only accept their own young, whereas others will readily accept strange puppies. It is not known whether such individual differences exist among nondomesticated species.

Although it may at first seem somewhat contradictory to state that animals which readily adopt young of other species are capable of discriminating their own young from other young of the same species and age, the contradiction is more apparent than real. Most of the experiments on "adoption" of young of other species have involved the presentation of the strange young under conditions in which there was no possibility of choosing between the alien species and the mother's own species. Where such choices are possible, the tendency to prefer young of the mother's own species is readily seen.

In discussing the behavioral and physiologic aspects of mother-young relationships centering around feeding, I shall use the terminology suggested by Cowie, Folley, Cross, Harris, Jacobsohn and Richardson (1951). "Nursing" means behavior on the part of the mother which fosters access to the nipples by the young. "Suckling" is the activity of the young animal sucking the nipple. "Suckling stimulus" is the sum of the stimuli applied by suckling.

1. Behavior of the Nursing Mother

The duration of the period of lactation, which starts about the time of parturition, varies considerably in different species. The young of some species of rodents may feed independently of the mother by the time they are 10 to 14 days old. In other species the nursing period is much longer. Herd-living animals usually nurse the young for several months, whereas some aquatic mammals, such as the sea lions, may continue nursing for up to a year. These differences in duration of the nursing period are, in part, correlated with the conditions of the animal's life. The young of mammals which live in burrows are usually able to get food without the help of the mother by the time they are old enough to leave the burrow; grazing herd-living types tend to remain with their mothers in the herd for a much longer time. The differences in kind and duration of the mother-young relations in these two types of mammals are undoubtedly relevant to the differences in gregariousness which characterize them as adults (Krumbiegel, 1955). This rather general statement is about as far as we can go, because detailed studies of mother-young relationships, suitable for comparative analysis, exist for only a few mammalian species.

I have already pointed out (see above, p. 1312) that the establishment of a nursing-suckling relationship between mother and young is a mutual affair, depending on the behavioral characteristics of both participants. Changes in both the mother and young also contribute to the changing relationships during the later stages of lactation. The best and most detailed analysis of such a relationship is to be found in still unpublished studies on the domestic cat carried out by Rosenblatt, Wodinsky, Turkewitz and Schneirla, at the American Museum of Natural History, and partially summarized by Schneirla (1956, 1959). These workers found that the kittens begin to discriminate among the mother's nipples very shortly after birth. Significant and persistent preferences of individual kittens for specific nipples can be detected before they are 2 days old (Ewer, 1959). In the early days of the kittens' life, nursing episodes tend to be initiated by the behavior of the mother, whereas later nursing episodes are initiated by approaches of the kittens to the mother. The transition is not entirely gradual, but occurs fairly abruptly between the 18th and 27th days after birth.

The mother domestic cat, like many other animals, spends most of her time with the young during the first few days after parturition. Depending on the species, other patterns are also found. The domestic rabbit and European hare, for example, visit the nest only to nurse the young, leaving it at the end of the nursing episode (Cross and Harris, 1952; Krumbiegel, 1955). Bartholomew and Hoel (1953) found that mother Alaska fur seals stay ashore with their young for 1 to 3 days, then leave and stay at sea for 3 to 10 days (Bartholomew, 1959).

The decline of lactation is associated with changes in nursing behavior. The time spent on the nest by domestic mouse mothers decreases from parturition to about 15 days postpartum, and this decrease is paralleled by a decrease in the average length of the nursing episode (Bateman, 1957). Similar observations have been made on dogs which, as lactation declines, assume the nursing posture less and less frequently (Martins, 1949). Hafez (1959), in a brief report, states that day-to-day variations in nursing intervals in the domestic pig are small compared with the individual differences between animals.

2. Milk Ejection

The physiology of milk ejection and of lactation are fully discussed in the chapter by Cowie and Folley, and we need not consider them exhaustively here. However, it will be useful to consider certain aspects of the physiology of milk production which directly influence, or are influenced by, the behavioral interaction between mother and young.

The milk-ejection reflex. When a young mammal suckles, and thus withdraws milk from the mammary gland of its mother, only a small portion of the milk present in the mammary gland at the beginning of the nursing episode is available near the nipple so that it can be withdrawn by the young without active participation on the part of the mother. Most of the milk cannot be extracted without some active participation by the mammary gland, which normally occurs in response to the suckling stimulus (Folley, 1956; Harris, 1958). This active participation of the mammary gland in the ejection of milk, in response to a suckling stimulus, is called "the milk-ejection reflex" (Cowie, Folley, Cross, Harris, Jacobsohn and Richardson, 1951).

The phenomenon of milk ejection has long been known among dairy workers, by whom it has been called "milk let-down" (Ely and Petersen, 1941), a term referring to the sudden flow of milk which occurs 30 to 90 seconds after the beginning of suckling (Harris, 1958). This is commonly observed in the milking of dairy cows, and has been described as occurring in the domestic rabbit (Cross, 1952), in which the suckling young are very active for 30 to 90 seconds after the beginning of suckling, then suddenly become motionless, simultaneously with the beginning of a characteristic gulping sound which indicates that substantial milk flow has begun. By removing the puppies from the nipples of a lactating dog once every minute during a nursing episode, replacing them with other puppies, and then weighing the puppies which had just been allowed to suckle, Gaines (1915) was able to estimate the amount of milk produced by the lactating bitch during each minute of the suckling episode. He found that the flow of milk was very slow during the first minute or so, but then quickly increased. These observations make it clear that the flow of milk during nursing is in part an active response of the mammary gland to

the suckling stimulus, with a latency of 30 to 90 seconds.

Gaines (1915) allowed puppies to suckle an anesthetized lactating bitch, and found that they could not withdraw milk from the mammary gland. Similarly, Cross and Harris (1952) anesthetized a lactating female rabbit, and found that suckling young could obtain no milk from her even after 6 minutes of vigorous suckling, although in normal nursing most of the milk is withdrawn within the first 5 to 6 minutes (Cross, 1952). The milking of amputed cow udders yields considerably less than half the amount which can be got from the same udders, containing the same amount of milk, in the intact cow (Hammond, quoted by Harris, 1958). It is clear that not much milk can be withdrawn, even by normal suckling behavior, from an inactive, nonparticipating mammary gland.

Tgetgel (1926) measured the pressure of milk in the cistern of the mammary gland of a cow (see chapter by Cowie and Folley), and showed that it rose gradually between one milking episode and the next. This is, of course, a consequence of the gradual increase in the amount of milk present in the gland as milk is produced in the alveoli (milk-secreting tubules) to replace that withdrawn at the last milking episode. However, in addition to this gradual rise in pressure between milking episodes, Tgetgel noted an *abrupt* increase in intramammary pressure as a response to the application of the milking stimulus, even when it was applied shortly after milking when the overall pressure in the gland was low. Gaines (1915) had earlier made similar observations on the goat. This rise in milk pressure tends to squeeze the milk out through the nipple. Normally, the nipple's sphincter offers resistence to this pressure, which must be overcome by the mouth of the suckling. However, if a cannula is inserted through the nipple opening, the milk can actually be seen to spurt out of the nipple (Usuelli and Piana, quoted by Folley, 1956).

This increase in intramammary pressure no doubt constitutes the milk-ejection reflex.

Mechanism of milk ejection. What stimulates the mammary gland to eject milk.

and how is this stimulation conveyed to the gland?

The now generally accepted interpretation of the physiologic basis of the milk-ejection reflex was first suggested by Ely and Petersen (1941). They found that motor denervation of one half of the udder of a lactating cow had no effect on either lactation or milk ejection. Further, injection of oxytocin, which is normally produced by the posterior lobe of the pituitary gland, caused milk ejection in cows that were not being milked or suckled. They therefore suggested that the sensory side of the milk ejection reflex consists of stimulation of the nipple by the suckling stimulus, whereas the motor side consists of the release of oxytocin by the posterior lobe of the pituitary gland, which, when it reaches the mammary gland in the circulating blood, directly causes an increase in intramammary pressure and the subsequent ejection of milk.

Andersson (1951a, b) demonstrated that milk ejection in sheep and goats can be induced by direct stimulation of the anterior hypothalamus by implanted electrodes. Cross and Harris (1951, 1952) obtained similar results in the rabbit. They showed that milk ejection occurred in response to electrical stimulation of the supra-optico-hypophyseal tract, and that electrolytic lesions in this region interfered with its occurrence. Lesions in the dorsal and posterior hypothalamus did not have this effect (see also Shimizu, Ban and Kurotsu, 1956). Cross and Harris (1951) also found milk ejection following electrical stimulation of the pituitary stalk. Benson and Cowie (1956) found that removal of the posterior lobe of the pituitary gland abolished the milk ejection response, and that later, after hypertrophy and reorganization of the cut end of the neural stalk, the response was restored. These observations provide confirmation of Ely and Petersen's (1941) hypothesis that the ejection of milk is stimulated in the mammary gland by a hormone secreted by the posterior pituitary. Further evidence is found in the fact that direct stimulation of the hypothalamus increases milk ejection in denervated udders as well as in udders whose neural connection to the central nervous system is intact (Andersson, 1951a). Even more dramatic is the fact that an isolated perfused mammary gland ejects milk when perfused with blood from a cow that has just been suckled, and does not do so when perfused with blood from a cow that was not ejecting milk at the time the blood was withdrawn (Petersen and Ludwick, 1942).

Cross (1950, 1951) found that suckling in rabbits caused an inhibition of urine flow similar to that caused by the injection of posterior pituitary extracts. Andersson and McCann (1955) observed that milk ejection elicited by hypothalamic stimulation in the goat is accompanied by this antidiuretic effect. Hawker and Roberts (quoted by Harris, 1958) assayed the blood in the jugular veins of goats and cows before, during, and after milking. They found the amount of oxytocic hormone in the blood of goats to be higher during milking than before or after. In cows the level of oxytocic hormone activity rises some minutes before the beginning of milking, presumably in response to stimuli associated with the preparations for milking.

It is abundantly clear that milk ejection is stimulated by posterior pituitary substances secreted into the blood in response to suckling stimulation. It is beyond the scope of this chapter to consider in detail which of the substances secreted by this gland is the milk ejection hormone, but overwhelming evidence suggests that it is oxytocin (see chapter by Cowie and Folley; Folley, 1956; Harris, 1958). We may ask *how* this hormone induces milk ejection.

The walls of the milk-secreting alveoli in the mammary gland of the goat contain a network of contractile myo-epithelial fibers, and Richardson (1949) demonstrated that these contract in response to local electrical stimulation, resulting in contraction of the alveoli. Cross (1954) found that a mechanical tap on the mammary gland of a rabbit in the neighborhood of a milk-distended lobule causes a sharp rise in the intralobular pressure. The latency of this rise in pressure is very short, on the order of 1 second compared with 30 to 90 seconds for the milk-ejection reflex. Gaines (1915) had found that the butting of the mammary gland by the kid contributed to the efficiency of milk ejection in the goat, and it may be that the local response of the myo-epithelial cells plays some role here. Linzell (1955) found that oxytocin applied locally in very small amounts induced local contraction of the alveoli. Acetylcholine also produced local contraction. Although the mammary glands of sheep and goats are extensively innervated by sympathetic nerve fibers (but seem to receive no para-sympathetic innervation) (Linzell, 1959), these fibers are vasomotor in their effect; no secretomotor fibers to the mammary gland are known (Harris, 1958) and contraction of the myo-epithelial cells is not induced by stimulating the existing nerves. It there-fore seems very likely that the effector end of the milk-ejection reflex consists of the direct action of oxytocin in the alveoli, where it causes contraction by way of its effect on the myo-epithelial cells of the al-veolar walls. Further light may be cast on this mechanism by a consideration of the effects of emotional disturbance on the milk ejection reflex.

Emotional inhibition of milk ejection. Ely and Petersen (1941) reported that stimuli which seemed to frighten lactating cows inhibited the milk-ejection reflex. Whittlestone (1951, quoted by Whittle-stone, 1954) found that electric shocks ad-ministered to a nursing sow interfered with milk ejection, and that the degree of in-terference was roughly proportional to the intensity of the shock. According to Cross (1952, 1953), emotional disturbance in-duced in lactating rabbits by electric shock, unfamiliar handling procedures and sur-roundings, forcible restraint during nursing, etc., greatly reduced the amount of milk got by the suckling pups.

Braude and Mitchell (1952) found that adrenaline, injected before oxytocin, inhibits the occurrence of the milk-ejection response which normally follows oxytocin injection. Adrenaline also inhibits milk ejection in the cow and in the rabbit (Ely and Petersen, 1941; Cross, 1953). This influence of adrenaline is, of course, consistent with the effects of emotional disturbance.

How does emotional disturbance inhibit milk ejection? There are three general pos-sibilities. (a) Emotional excitation might block or inhibit the secretion of oxytocin by influencing the central neural mechanisms for its release. (b) Adrenaline might, by

causing constriction of the blood vessels in the mammary gland, prevent oxytocin cir-culating in the blood from reaching the myoepithelial cells of the milk-secreting tubules. (c) Adrenaline might inhibit milk ejection by a direct effect on the myo-epi-thelial cells.

The last possibility (direct inhibition of the myoepithelial cells by adrenaline) seems unlikely. Linzell (1955) found that oxy-tocin caused local contraction when applied in extremely small amounts to a mouse mammary gland exposed by dissection. Acetylcholine and other parasympathomi-metic drugs were also effective in producing contraction on local application. On the other hand, adrenaline, when applied locally, caused local vasoconstriction in the capil-laries and arterioles, but no constriction of alveoli or myo-epithelial cells. Adrenaline did *not* prevent the contraction of the al-veoli when oxytocin was applied locally at the same locus to which adrenaline had just been applied, and at which vasoconstriction was at a maximum. Further, Cross (1955a) and Yokoyama (1956) found that mechani-cal taps on a lobule of the mammary gland of a rabbit produced a rise in intralobular milk pressure, even though adrenaline had just been injected, and when as a conse-quence of the adrenaline injection, milk ejection could not be elicited by a suckling stimulus. It therefore seems that the reac-tivity of the contractile elements them-selves is not suppressed by adrenaline.

It is likely, however, that adrenaline *can* interfere with the effect of injected oxytocin on the milk-ejection reflex. Prior systemic injection of adrenaline inhibits the milk-ejection response to subsequent injections of oxytocin in the rabbit (Cross, 1953) and sow (Whittlestone, 1954). In this connec-tion it should be noted again that no se-cretomotor fibers are known in the inner-vation of the mammary gland (Harris, 1958), that there is no parasympathetic in-nervation to the gland tissue, and that the sympathetic innervation seems to consist largely of vasomotor fibers (Linzell, 1959). These observations, together with the fail-ure of local application of adrenaline to in-hibit contraction of the myo-epithelial cells, suggest that the peripheral effect of adrena-line on milk ejection is largely through its vasoconstrictor action, which interferes with the access of oxytocin-carrying blood to the alveoli.

It should, however, not be concluded that there is *no* central inhibition of oxytocin secretion as a consequence of emotional arousal. Cross (1955b) found that when rabbits were suckled while forcibly restrained, the amount of milk removed (estimated from the weights of the pups) was substantially reduced (by 20 to 100 per cent in different animals). This reduction, however, could be restored in about 80 per cent of the 35 subjects by the injection of oxytocin. This suggests that part of the effect of emotional inhibition is the reduction of oxytocin secretion. Cross suggested that the experiments involving exogenous adrenaline probably involved much more adrenaline than is usually present in the blood as a result of emotional disturbance, and that the vasoconstrictor effect of adrenaline in those experiments may thus have been greater than that which normally occurs.

In any event it seems probable that both peripheral effects of adrenaline on the mammary glands and central inhibition of oxytocin secretion are involved in the mechanism of emotional inhibition of milk ejection.

3. Mother-young Relationships and the Regulation of Lactation

SUCKLING AND THE DURATION OF LACTATION. Hammond and Marshall (1925) observed that the mammary glands of rabbits became inactive when the young were removed, whereas lactation was prolonged when the young were kept with the mother. Selye (1934) removed young rats from their mothers at 3 days of age, and found that milk secretion disappeared within 3 to 5 days, and that the alveoli began to disappear after 6 to 8 days. When young were left with the parents, lactation continued for the normal period of approximately 3 weeks (Nicoll and Meites, 1959). Similar results were obtained in the guinea pig (Hesselberg and Loeb, 1937a). Selye and McKeown (1934a) repeatedly replaced young mice by younger litters, so that the mothers were provided with young of suckling age for a much longer period than normal. Under these conditions, lactation was considerably prolonged, although the mammary glands could not be maintained indefinitely solely by continuously offering new young: signs of degeneration of the alveoli were to be noted by about 28 days postpartum. Nicoll and Meites (1959) repeated this experiment with rats, and found that they could maintain active mammary glands during a 70-day lactation period (compared with the normal 20-day period) by repeatedly replacing the litters.

It is apparent that the normal duration of lactation is in part regulated by stimuli provided to the lactating mother by the suckling young. This implies, of course, that the suckling stimulus must be capable of stimulating not only the posterior pituitary substances responsible for the milk ejection reflex, but also, directly or indirectly, must play a role in stimulating the secretion of the anterior pituitary hormones responsible for lactation (see chapter by Cowie and Folley).

SUCKLING AND THE ONSET OF LACTATION. Although it is thus clear that suckling stimuli stimulate the *maintenance* of lactation, it seems that the *onset* of lactation at the time of parturition does not require suckling stimuli (Meites and Turner, 1942b). Klein and Mayer (quoted by Mayer and Canivenc, 1951) tied off the uterine horns of pregnant rats, so that no parturition occurred. Lactation was nevertheless initiated at the normal time for parturition, without any stimulation of the nipples. Meites and Turner (1942c) noted that lactation begins at the time of parturition in nonsuckled rabbits, although it is not maintained unless the animals are suckled. Similarly, Williams (1945) observed milk secretion in the mammary glands of immediately postparturitive, unsuckled mice. The glands are empty of milk within 48 hours, and the alveoli have completely disappeared by the 6th day postpartum. Further, lactation is not initiated by presenting foster young during pregnancy (Masson, 1948; Mayer and Canivenc, 1951), even when the condition of the nipple indicates that active suckling has taken place.

The prolactin content of the pituitary gland normally rises just after parturition, in association with the onset of lactation (Reece and Turner, 1937a). In the rabbit, this initial rise in pituitary prolactin, from about 12 pigeon units per gland to about 23 pigeon units, occurs between the 28th day of pregnancy and the 2nd day postpartum. The rise is the same in suckled and nonsuckled rabbits. However, after the 2nd day postpartum, suckled rabbits have more prolactin in their pituitary glands, and produce more milk from the mammary gland, than nonsuckled animals (Meites and Turner, 1942c; Meites, 1954). Similar data have been obtained from the rat (Meites and Turner, 1948).

In the dairy cow, which is of course highly selected for milk production, lactation can sometimes be started in nonpregnant or even virgin cows by regular manipulation of the teat. In general, however, it is clear that suckling stimuli are not effective in inducing lactation, and that the *initiation* of lactation, as distinct from its *maintenance*, must be explained on the basis of the hormonal changes occurring at the time of parturition.

THE NATURE OF THE SUCKLING STIMULUS. Selye, Collip and Thomson (1934) removed the nipples of the mammary glands on one side of a group of rats and tied off the main milk ducts on the other side. When lactating animals so treated were kept with their young, no involution of the milk-secreting tissue occurred on either side, indicating that the effect of the suckling stimulus on the mammary glands was through a systemic relationship, rather than being local to the tissues in the neighborhood of the stimulation. Ingelbrecht (1935) later demonstrated the same point in an ingenious group of experiments. He sectioned the spinal cord of 10 rats 2 days postpartum between the last thoracic and first abdominal segments, thus ensuring that the 6 posterior nipples were anesthetized, whereas the 6 anterior nipples retained their sensitivity to stimulation. If the anterior (unanesthetized) nipples were covered, so that the young could only suckle from the posterior nipples, all the young died within 48 hours, with empty stomachs. Replacement litters suffered the same fate. If only 4 of the unanesthetized nipples were covered, leaving 2 unanesthetized nipples free for

access by the suckling young, then *all* parts of the mammary glands continued to secrete milk. After two or three groups of young died while attempting to suckle on the posterior nipples, the anterior nipples were uncovered, and a new litter presented to the experimental mothers. They survived, and lactation was maintained throughout the mammary gland tissue. Eayrs and Baddeley (1956) repeated, in essence, the experiment of Ingelbrecht, except that they anesthetized some of the nipples by cutting the dorsal roots of their spinal nerves, rather than by sectioning the spinal cord, and then removed the unanesthetized nipples, whereupon lactation stopped altogether, although the remaining (anesthetized) nipples were vigorously suckled. Lactation was re-established in later broods, the re-establishment of the ability of stimulation of the nipples to induce lactation corresponding with the regeneration of tactual sensitivity in the nipple area. Ernst (1929) showed that denervation of the mammary glands of a dog resulted in regression of the milk-secreting tissue.

Hooker and Williams (1940) and Mixner and Turner (1941) stimulated the nipples of lactating mice, whose young had been removed, by applying turpentine on the nipple surface. Both groups of experimenters found that this treatment retarded the involution of the mammary gland which normally follows the removal of the young. Mixner and Turner suggested that the turpentine acted by inducing hyperemia locally, but Hooker and Williams' observation that, when turpentine was applied only to *some* of the nipples, involution was prevented in *all* the mammae indicates that the action of turpentine is not local, but is through the central effect of the sensory irritation of the nipples.

These experiments clearly demonstrate that the suckling stimulus consists primarily of mechanical and tactual stimuli applied to the nipple, and that its effect is not local on the mammary glands, but through the central effect of the afferent inflow from the nipples.

THE EFFECTS OF THE SUCKLING STIMULUS. (a) *On the pituitary gland.* A number of investigators have studied the effect of suckling stimulation on the prolactin content of the pituitary gland. Meites and Turner (1942a) divided parturitive rats into two groups. The mothers composing the control group were allowed to suckle their young normally, whereas the young of the experimental group were taken away at parturition. At 7 days postpartum, the pituitary glands of all the animals were removed and assayed for prolactin content by a pigeon-crop method. The average amount of prolactin per pituitary gland in the control (suckled) group was 10.75 Reece-Turner units, whereas in the experimental (nonsuckled) group, it was 5.10. In a more recent study, the same authors (Meites and Turner, 1948) repeated this experiment, and extended it to rabbits, with similar results. In the latter species, the prolactin content of the pituitary gland rose to a peak about 5 days postpartum in nonsuckled as well as in suckled animals, but the peak was much higher (87 per cent more prolactin per pituitary gland) in the suckled animals and the prolactin content fell to the prepartum level much more rapidly in the nonsuckled animals (Meites and Turner, 1942c, 1948; Meites, 1954). Rabbits nursing larger numbers of young (5 to 11) had no more prolactin in their pituitary glands than did those nursing only two young (Meites, Bergman and Turner, 1941).

As might be inferred from the observations on lactation described earlier, suckling stimulation, although necessary for the maintenance of prolactin secretion during lactation, does not seem to be necessary for the induction of the immediate postpartum rise in pituitary prolactin content. Reece and Turner (1937b) found that the postpartum increase in pituitary prolactin content, measured 51 hours after parturition, was the same in animals that had been normally suckled and in animals whose young had dropped through a wide wire-mesh screen as they were born.

Although suckling stimulation thus undoubtedly contributes to the maintenance of a high level of prolactin in the pituitary during the lactation period, the *immediate* effect of a single suckling episode is to deplete the prolactin content of the gland. Reece and Turner (1936, 1937a, b) re-moved young rats from their mothers at 36 hours postpartum. At 48 hours postpartum, the young of some of the mothers were permitted to remain with their mothers for 3 hours, during which they suckled. The pituitary glands of these mothers assayed at 5.20 Reece-Turner units of prolactin, compared with 9.20 units in mothers treated exactly the same way, except that they were not allowed the 3-hour suckling period with their young. Clearly, the suckling stimulus causes the release of prolactin from the pituitary gland, and the depletion of its prolactin content. Grosvenor and Turner (1957) found similar results in animals tested 14 days postpartum. These mother rats were isolated from their young for 10 hours. At the end of this isolation period, the control animals were killed for autopsy, whereas the experimental animals were suckled for exactly 30 minutes. The results indicate that the prolactin content of the pituitary gland was reduced about $\frac{1}{3}$ by this suckling stimulation.

Suckling stimulation seems to affect the cytologic appearance of the pituitary gland. Gonadectomy in the female rat induces an increase in the number of basophilic cells in the pituitary gland, in many of which large nucleoli form (see chapter by Purves). Desclin (1936, 1947) removed the ovaries of female rats at parturition. Half of his animals were allowed to keep and nurse their young, whereas the young were removed from the other half. The suckled animals did not develop castration signs in their pituitary glands. Dawson (1946) found that cytologic changes in the pituitary gland of the cat which normally occur during lactation, do not occur after parturition unless the mother cat is allowed to suckle her young (see chapter by Purves).

(b) *On the mammary gland.* Most of the studies to which we have referred seem to contain the implication that the principal effect of suckling stimulation with respect to the stimulation of lactation is the stimulation of prolactin secretion by the pituitary gland. It is, of course, quite clear that prolactin has a substantial influence on milk secretion. The involution of the mammary glands which follows forced weaning in mice can be delayed by prolactin injection (Hooker and Williams, 1941), and local milk formation can be induced in single ducts of the proprely prepared rabbit mammary gland by small local injections of prolactin (Bradley and Clarke, 1956). However, it is now clear that other hormones normally play a role in the maintenance of lactation. Prolactin alone cannot maintain complete milk production in rats hypophysectomized on the fourth day of lactation, whereas adrenocorticotrophic hormone (ACTH) and probably growth hormone have synergistic effects with prolactin on milk production (Cowie, 1957; Williams, 1945).

The recent reviews and experiments by Folley (1956), and by Lyons, Li and Johnson (1958) make it plain that a considerable number of hormones secreted by the pituitary gland and by the ovary participate in the onset and maintenance of milk secretion. There is some evidence that at least one of these hormones, in addition to prolactin, is released in response to suckling stimulation. Gregoire (1947a, b) found that the involution of the thymus which occurs during pregnancy can be maintained after parturition by suckling, whereas the thymus regenerates if suckling is prevented. Injected prolactin does not maintain the involution of the thymus in the absence of suckling. This suggests that the effect of suckling on the condition of the thymus is through the stimulation of the secretion of some other hormone, probably ACTH (Folley, 1956).

Further details of the effects of various hormones on the mammary gland are contained in the chapter by Cowie and Folley. It is sufficient for our purposes to point out that the effects of suckling stimulation are probably somewhat more complex than the stimulation of the secretion of a single hormone by the pituitary.

Loeb and his co-workers found that, when the mammary gland of a lactating guinea pig was ligated on one side, so that suckling took place only on the other side, the gland on the ligated side regressed, whereas only the one on the suckled side was maintained in a secretory condition (Kuramitsu and Loeb, 1921; Hesselberg and Loeb, 1937a, b). They concluded that the stimulation of secretory activity in the mammary gland by suckling is a local effect, probably dependent on milk removal. Somewhat similar observations were made on the rat by Weichert (1942) who noted that, when a lactating rat has a small litter, the pups tend to use the anterior nipples only. In the third week of lactation, the mammary tissue in the neighborhood of the suckled nipples is engorged whereas that in the neighborhood of the nonsuckled nipples is regressed. This regression is not prevented by prolactin injection.

Such data seem to contradict numerous observations (already referred to above) indicating that maintenance of the mammary gland through suckling stimulation is a systemic effect, and that nonsuckled as well as suckled glands in the same animal are maintained by the suckling stimulus (Selye, 1934; Selye, Collip and Thomson, 1934; Turner and Reineke, 1936). This contradiction can readily be resolved by a consideration of the effect of mammary engorgement on the access of circulating hormones to the mammary tissue. Williams (1941) ligated at their midpoints the main ducts of some of the mammary glands in lactating mice, thus preventing milk drainage beyond the ligation, while permitting it up to the ligation. He found that the obstructed portion of the gland became inflamed and necrotic, and that the maintenance of the milk-secreting parenchyma in response to suckling stimulation was considerably reduced. Selye, Collip and Thomson (1934) tied off the milk duct of the mammary gland on one side of lactating rats and removed the nipples on the other side. They found that secretion was continued in both glands, indicating that stimulation on one side maintained secretion on the other side, and also that secretion could be maintained in the engorged gland. However, after about 3 weeks, the milk pressure in the gland seemed to damage the secretory epithelium, resulting in its involution. Cross and Silver (1956) and Cross (1957) ligated the teat duct in rats, resulting in a maximal engorgement of the duct after 24 hours. At this stage, if the ligatures were loosened, milk ejection could be elicited by intravenously injected oxytocin. After 40 hours of such ligation, no response to intravenous oxytocin was observed, and the mammary gland became whitish (instead of pinkish).

Histologic examination showed that the capillary bed was collapsed and almost without blood cells. However, oxytocin directly applied to the alveoli still caused local contraction. Therefore, the engorgement had resulted in a failure of blood circulation of the mammary glands. It seems likely that obstruction of circulation in the mammary gland caused by engorgement by nonwithdrawn milk is adequate to explain the failure of suckling stimulation in some animals so treated to maintain milk secretion. It should be noted that the guinea pig produces relatively little milk, and does not have large cisterns for the storage of milk. Therefore, it might be expected that local engorgement would have more serious effects in such a species than in some others.

THE MECHANISM OF SUCKLING-INDUCED LACTATION. The material just presented, plus the fact that suckling stimulation induces pseudopregnancy (Selye and McKeown, 1934b) and prolongs gestation (Weichert, 1939), clearly indicates that suckling stimulation induces the secretion of prolactin. We may now inquire into the mechanism of this effect.

Herold (1939) reported that section of the pituitary stalk in lactating rats was followed by the gradual cessation of milk secretion and involution of the mammary gland, although the young continued attemps at suckling. Jacobsohn and Westman (1945) and Jacobsohn (1949) sectioned the pituitary stalk in rats and in rabbits, and, like Herold, found that all the young died. However, the involution of the mammary gland was only partial, some of the alveoli in each animal remaining secretory. This is in contrast to the result of forcible weaning of the young or of hypophysectomy, both of which treatments result in cessation of milk secretion and complete involution of the mammary gland. These experiments seem to imply the continuation, after stalk section, of some secretion of lactation-stimulating hormone(s) by the pituitary gland. Desclin (1940) found that the young of 13 out of 22 lactating rats whose pituitary stalks were transected 5 to 6 days postpartum survived, although their weight was abnormally low. Everett (1954, 1956) found that pituitary glands transplanted to the renal capsule continued to secrete prolactin,

and he suggested that neural connections are unnecessary for the maintenance of the secretion of this hormone, and that possibly the neural effect is *inhibition* under appropriate stimulation (Nikitovitch-Winer and Everett, 1958). This is consistent with the results of Jacobsohn's observations, except that the amount of prolactin apparently secreted when the stalk is transected in lactating rats is small compared to the amount produced under suckling stimulation. Rothchild (1960a) showed that rat pituitaries autotransplanted to the renal capsule can secrete enough prolactin to maintain lactation, again at a lower level than in intact lactating animals. He also showed that suckling stimuli cause a reduction of gonadotrophin secretion, and that this effect is probably independent of the effect of such stimuli on prolactin secretion.[3]

Although the experiments cited thus far make it clear that both milk ejection and lactation occur as a response to suckling stimulation, it is not so clear whether both phenomena are primary effects of suckling stimulation (Folley, 1947). Petersen (1948) suggested that suckling might stimulate lactation by inducing the secretion of a *posterior* pituitary hormone which in turn might stimulate the secretion of the lactogenic hormone(s). Benson and Folley (1956, 1957) have provided evidence that oxytocin, the secretion of which is undoubtedly stimulated by suckling (see above), itself stimulates the secretion of prolactin. They removed rat litters at 4 days postpartum, when the treatment of the mothers began. Oxytocin was injected, at various dosage levels, for 9 days, at the end of which time the oxytocin-treated animals had more secretory tissue in their mammary glands (40 to 46 per cent of the area of histologic sections) than did the controls (about 16 per cent). The diameter of the alveoli was also greater in the oxytocin-treated animals (about 50 μ) than in the controls (about 15 μ). Injected prolactin maintained ap-

[3] These experiments were described in a series of important papers on the corpus luteum-pituitary relationship, which appeared too late to be fully considered in the preparation of this chapter Rothchild, 1960b; Rothchild and Dickey, 1960; Rothchild and Quilligan, 1960; Quilligan and Rothchild, 1960).

proximately the same level of secretory tissue (48 per cent of section area) as did oxytocin injection. Oxytocin injected into hypophysectomized females had no effect on the mammary secretory tissue. It should be pointed out that prolactin has a local lactogenic effect when introduced directly into the milk-secreting ducts, whereas oxytocin, as well as other anterior and posterior principles, has no such effect. McCann, Mack and Gale (1959) found that hypothalamic lesions in the supra-opticohypophyseal tracts of lactating rats prevented milk ejection and milk secretion. The loss of milk secretion was noted even when the anterior hypophysis and its portal vessels, as well as the median eminence, all appeared histologically normal. Oxytocin injected into such animals delayed the involution of the mammary glands. Similarly, Donovan and van der Werff ten Bosch (1957) found that destruction of the pituitary portal blood vessels did not result in loss of lactation when oxytocin was administered regularly after the operation, and Desclin (1956a, b) found that oxytocin injected into virgin rats made possible the development of deciduomas in response to irritation of the uterine wall.

It must be concluded that oxytocin is capable of acting as a neurohumor stimulating the secretion of a lactogenic hormone by the pituitary gland.

Tverskoy (1953) milked a goat by injecting oxytocin, then draining the cisterns directly with catheters. The milk yield continued normal, indicating that external stimuli to the nipples were not necessary. When he arranged the catheters for continuous drainage (without oxytocin injection), the milk secretion declined. When the catheters were arranged for continuous drainage, but oxytocin was nevertheless administered twice a day, the milk secretion increased. Tverskoy interpreted this as indicating that the rise in alveolar pressure, caused by the oxytocin injection, was a source of afferent sensory inflow which was the stimulus for the reflex secretion of prolactin. This is an ingenious interpretation, but the simpler conclusion by Benson and Folley from their experiment, namely that oxytocin acts directly as a neurohumor to induce the secretion of prolactin, could apply to this experiment as well.

Cross (1960) points out that other effects of suckling stimulation than the specifically endocrine ones may be related to the maintenance of milk secretion. Suckling induces increased eating and weight gains in mother rats, even when milk withdrawal is prevented by cutting the milk ducts (Cotes and Cross, 1954), and this effect cannot be duplicated by prolactin injection. Nursing mother rats consume more food than nonnursing rats (Slonaker, 1925) (although Bateman (1957) reports that lactating mice spend no more time feeding than do nonlactating ones).

Such effects might contribute to the amount of milk secretion without reference to the stimulation of pituitary hormone secretion. Nevertheless, it is clear that the stimulation provided by suckling causes the release of lactogenic hormones from the pituitary gland, and it now seems likely that this effect is not an effect separate from the stimulation of oxytocin secretion, but rather that the oxytocin secreted by the posterior pituitary as a result of suckling is, at least to some degree, involved in the stimulation of prolactin secretion by the anterior pituitary.[4]

4. Nursing Behavior and the Condition of the Mammary Gland.

Cross (1952) found that rabbits, which normally nurse the young once a day, could not be induced to nurse more often unless loss of milk was prevented by sealing the teats with collodion. He concluded that mammary distension was a factor in the motivation of nursing. Such a conclusion seems reasonable, and there is considerable evidence in its favor. Many observers have noted that the frequency with which young are nursed is in part a function of the stage of lactation, and thus of the amount of milk being produced, although it is not clear

[4] Rothchild and Quilligan (1960) have failed to verify either the induction of pseudopregnancy or the formation of deciduomas by oxytocin injection in the rat. They therefore independently suggested the same explanation as had Tverskoy for the type of results found by Benson and Folley.

whether the milk pressure is responsible for the amount of nursing or *vice versa*, or whether there is a reciprocal relation between the two. Bartholomew and Hoel (1953), for example, found that mother Alaska fur seals stay at sea for 3 to 10 days, then ashore with their pups for 1 to 3 days. As the season progresses (after the birth of the young), the females spend about the same time ashore at each visit, but the time spent at sea between visits increases. Bartholomew and Hoel suggested that the mothers may return when the mammary glands are full, and the diminution of the rate of secretion, or the increase in the pup's demands, could cause the female to stay at sea longer as the season progresses. Similar observations have been made on many mammals (Krumbiegel, 1955).

In many cases a correspondence is observed between the occurrence of lactation and of nursing behavior in response to physiologic stimulation. Allan and Wiles (1932) found that cats hypophysectomized during pregnancy (which, of course, produced no milk) paid no attention to the young, and made no attempt to nurse them. Cannon and his co-workers found that sympathectomized dogs and cats, if they were made pregnant very soon after sympathectomy, might lactate normally after parturition, and in such cases would nurse their young. On the other hand, if parturition did not occur until some time after sympathectomy (*e.g.*, 6 months postoperatively) the mammary glands failed to develop, lactation was not established, and no attempts were made by the mothers to nurse their young. In the case of a cat which had 3 kittens 20 months after sympathectomy, the animal withdrew from the kittens as soon as possible, even after the kittens were forcibly put to her nipples to suckle (Cannon, Newton and Bright, 1929; Cannon, 1930; Cannon and Bright, 1931). Labate (1940) sympathectomized rabbits, then allowed them to mate and delivered the young by cesarian section. In these animals, lactation was normal, as was nursing behavior.

In other cases, however, it is clear that nursing behavior does not necessarily depend on a distended condition of the mammary gland, or on the presence of milk secretion. Hain (1935) found that estrone injected into lactating rats caused the cessation of suckling behavior, although the involution of the mammary glands did not occur until *after* the suckling behavior had stopped. Weichert and Kerrigan (1942) similarly found that estrone injected into rats caused parental care to become sporadic, the pups occasionally being scattered over the cage and inadequately warmed. Intervals between nursing episodes became less and less frequent as the estrone injections continued. These authors also had the impression that the decrease of lactation was a secondary effect of the behavioral disturbance in the mother. Obias (1957) found that rats hypophysectomized during gestation delivered young at the normal time. All nursed their young, although all the young died because no milk was produced. Collip, Selye and Thomson (1933) hypophysectomized lactating rats and found that, although the mammary glands regressed, maternal behavior, including nursing, was not impaired and the young continued to attempt to suckle until they died. Eayrs and Baddeley (1956), who anesthetized the nipples by cutting the dorsal roots of their spinal nerves, found that lactation stopped altogether, although the rats continued to attempt to nurse their young, and the anesthetized nipples were vigorously suckled.

Nelson and Smelser (1933) induced lactation in male guinea pigs by injecting estrone, followed by pituitary extracts. Animals lactating as a result of such treatment refused to nurse young, even though the young animals vigorously tried to suckle.

Although there are many suggestive observations indicating a relationship between mammary engorgement and the motivation to nurse the young, it is apparent that this cannot be the only factor, and, in some species, may not even be an important factor. The exact contribution, if any, which mammary engorgement makes to the regulation of nursing behavior, and the manner in which it may interact with other physiologic factors and with previous experience, remain to be investigated.

IV. General Discussion: the Psychobiology of Parental Behavior and the Role of Hormones

A. LEARNING AND HORMONE-INDUCED PARENTAL BEHAVIOR

1. General: Formulation of the Problems

We have presented a great deal of evidence that the patterns of parental behavior vary in characteristic ways from species to species, and are relatively constant within species. Obviously, then, genetic differences between the species must play a considerable role in the establishment of these differences. Discussions of the role of learning in the development of such behavior patterns are often the occasion for vigorous controversy because various investigators differ with respect to the relative heuristic value which they assign to the formal identification of characters as being "innate" (or "inherited") or "learned" (or "acquired"), and with respect to their method of approach to the study of ontogeny, to the terminology they use to identify the effects of environment and the effects of genetic differences, to the type of behavior which interests them, etc. We cannot go into details of this "nature-nurture" problem here, except for the purpose of bringing into perspective our discussion of the role of learning in the development of parental behavior patterns (for discussion of these problems see Lorenz, 1937; Tinbergen, 1951; Lehrman, 1953, 1956b; Hebb, 1953; Kennedy, 1954; Koehler, 1954; Schneirla, 1956; Eibl-Eibesfeldt and Kramer, 1958).

A first stage in the study of the effect of experience on any behavior pattern is to determine whether and in what ways the pattern can develop when the environment is restricted in various ways, so that particular kinds of experience are not available to the animal. Such experiments may illuminate the contribution of various kinds of environmental experience to the development of the behavior. Furthermore, when we find that particular kinds of experience do *not* contribute to the development of the behavior pattern, we have also learned something significant about the behavior (Tinbergen, 1955). However, since the central problem is that of the *development* of the behavior, experiments of this type do not give a final answer to the question of what *has* contributed to the formation of the behavior (Schneirla, 1956). We do not by any means know all the possible varieties of learning processes (Maier and Schneirla, 1942), and this limits our ability to perceive the most significant relationships during development. Furthermore, we are just beginning to appreciate the variety and subtlety of the ways in which very early experience contributes to the development of adult behavioral capacities in various kinds of animals (Hebb, 1949, 1953; Beach and Jaynes, 1954).

This means that the question of whether any particular kind of learning has or has not contributed to the development of a behavior pattern is only one step in the analysis of its ontogeny. Unfortunately, for the great majority of behavior patterns, this is the only step that has yet been taken.

In dealing with the problem of the contribution of learning to the development of patterns of parental behavior, therefore, we are simply analyzing, to the extent that the available data permit, one of the influences on the ontogeny of the behavior. It should not be thought that we are seeking answers to, or even formulating, "final" questions about the nature of environmental influences. Later parts of this discussion will indicate some of the ways in which experiential influences may be related to various kinds of organic factors during development.

2. Learning and Parental Behavior

BEHAVIOR OF INEXPERIENCED AND OF EXPERIENCED MOTHERS. (*a*) *Comparison of primipara and multipara.* Chimpanzee mothers who have previously borne young appear to be much more efficient and skillful in caring for their infants than are primiparous animals (Yerkes, 1935; Yerkes and Tomilin, 1935; Yerkes and Elder, 1937; Nissen and Yerkes, 1943). Primiparous chimpanzees, when first confronted with their own young, usually appear indifferent to or fearful of the newborn, and handle them clumsily, or not at all. Such an animal is likely to act "surprised, puzzled, baffled, and at a loss as to what to do," and may do such things as holding the infant head down, biting its feet, appearing annoyed when it clings to the mother's body, etc. In contrast, an experienced chimpanzee mother shows a high degree of assurance, directness, and skill in accepting, placing, grooming, cuddling, and in general caring for the young. As Yerkes and Tomilin (1935) say, "the contrast is that of bewilderment and relative uncertainty *versus* familiarity." Similar differences between primiparous and multiparous mothers can be seen in the rhesus monkey (Tinklepaugh and Hartman, 1930), in which primiparous animals seem frightened, excited, and disorganized in the presence of the neonate, compared with multiparous mothers. However, Yerkes (1915) noted that a primiparous rhesus monkey which bore a still birth kept the dead young animal and carried it about the cage for a long period.

Observations in zoos (Hediger, 1955) indicate a similar improvement in maternal care in experienced as compared with inexperienced mothers, in many other animals. Hediger says, "a considerable difference ... may often be seen between the behavior of experienced mothers and those with their first-born young. This distinction is often indeed, so sharp that the first birth might be considered as something like a dress rehearsal, not counting for the propagation of the species, but a preparation for subsequent births."

Ross, Denenberg, Sawin and Meyer (1956) rated the quality of nest-construction of 84 rabbits of various strains, each of which reared four litters of young. They found that the quality of the nest, as rated by various observers, improved linearly up to the third litter. (Deutsch, 1957, felt justified in objecting to this conclusion on the basis of his own observations of two female rabbits which were primiparous at the beginning of his observations, and a third which had had an unstated number of previous litters, and which were able to construct "fairly uniform nests perfectly, even without any previous experience of digging.") On the other hand, a "maternal protection" score, based on ratings of the intensity of the mothers' resistance to the observer's attempts to manipulate the young, did not change from litter to litter

(Denenberg, Sawin, Frommer and Ross, 1958).

Data on the differences between experienced and inexperienced laboratory rats, mice, and guinea pigs are rather contradictory. Primaparous animals seem to care for and retrieve the young perfectly adequately, with a full range of appropriate behavior patterns (Avery, 1925; Wiesner and Sheard, 1933; Lashley, 1938; Beach and Jaynes, 1956a). Some investigators nevertheless report differences between primiparous and multiparous animals. Leblond (1940) tested lactating mice by presenting them with young of various ages. In both mice and rats, younger pups are much stronger stimuli for the retrieving response than are older pups (Wiesner and Sheard, 1933). Leblond found that the average age of the young which his lactating mice would retrieve was greater in multiparous than in primiparous animals. He interpreted this as meaning that the multiparous animals could retrieve in response to somewhat weaker stimulation than that required by the primiparous subjects. Frank (1952) reported that primiparous common voles retrieved less readily and intensely than did multipara.

Beniest-Noirot (1958), studying domestic mice, found no difference in retrieving (or other aspects of maternal behavior) among groups of primiparous females, virgin females, pregnant females, and males, but her data are based on the presence or absence of the behavior in various individuals, and do not include any measure of frequency or intensity. Similarly, Rowell (1960c) found no differences in the proportions of various kinds of responses given to young by primiparous and by multiparous female golden hamsters. Beach and Jaynes (1956a) made a very careful and quantitative comparison of maternal behavior in primiparous and multiparous rats. They graded the rats on the number of pups poorly cleaned, number of pups found outside the nest, quality of the nest, etc. They also tested them for retrieving behavior by a method which yielded data on both the latency and the frequency of retrieving during a test period. They found no difference with respect to any of these measures between primiparous and multiparous animals. The multiparous rats of Beach and Jaynes' experiment had bred in small cages, and had not been tested for retrieving during their first breeding experience; therefore, they had had practically no experience in retrieving. Beach and Jaynes found that retrieving efficiency increased during the first 7 days postpartum, for both primiparas and multiparas. This improvement was a function of practice, because it did not occur unless repeated testing provided practice. Animals tested 1 day postpartum during their first and their second lactation periods showed no improvement.

On the basis of these data, it is not possible to say whether the difference between Beach and Jaynes' conclusions and those of Leblond are due to differences in the amount of retrieving practice obtained by the animals during the first lactation period, to differences in testing methods, or to differences between rats and mice.

Nice (1937) observed that inexperienced song sparrows building their first nests seemed to build just as well as did experienced birds. Marais (quoted by Armstrong, 1947) reared four generations of weaver finches, a bird which normally builds a very elaborate nest, without giving them the opportunity to see any nesting material. Their descendents plaited their elaborate nests in a normal manner. Hinde (quoted by Thorpe, 1956) found that canaries that had never had an opportunity to manipulate nesting materials would, when given grass for the first time, pick it up and carry it to the nest-pan within a minute or so. Observations such as these indicate that, in many birds, nest-building behavior is rather rigidly determined by organic influences. However, Lorenz (quoted by Thorpe, 1956) noted that ravens and jackdaws that are building nests for the first time are uncertain what material to use, and must learn to pick material that can be woven into the nest. Hinde (1958) found that a chaffinch kept in a cage without nesting material developed the habit of plucking its own feathers to use as nesting material (as do many canaries). In the following year, when it was kept in an aviary with plenty of nesting material, it plucked its own feathers nevertheless. Lehrman (1955) reported that ring doves breeding for the second time tended to feed their squabs sooner after

hatching of the eggs than they had at their first breeding.

(b) *Learning or physiologic change?* It is reasonably clear that, in many animals, there is some improvement in the efficiency of parental behavior between the first and subsequent breeding experiences. However, the method used for collecting most of these data is unsatisfactory in several respects. First, the fact that animals engaged in parental behavior are in a constantly changing physiologic condition means that changes in behavior occurring, for example, late in lactation, which might be influenced by experiences earlier in lactation, cannot be expected to be transferred intact to the *beginning* of the next lactation period (when the animal is in a different physiologic condition). Thus, it would be very difficult, by this method alone, to demonstrate the possible importance of concurrent experiences as a factor in the changing pattern of behavior which is so characteristic of the parent-young relationship.

Secondly, many of the conclusions about improved efficiency of maternal behavior in second and later parturitions are based on observations in which there is no adequate control for the age of the animal at the time of the observation, and for the purely physiologic effects of the animal's having gone through the endocrine changes associated with the first breeding experience. Dieterlen (1959) reports that female golden hamsters which give birth for the first time before they are 80 days old often build abnormally small nests, and fail to care for the young properly because they are easily frightened. However, females that do not give birth until they are more than 3 months old are almost always more careful and quieter, even during their first lactation period. Seitz (1954, 1958) found that scores indicating the efficiency and intensity of maternal behavior were higher in rats breeding for the second time than in those breeding for the first time. This difference is associated with a tendency toward increased litter size and greater frequency of litters as the mother matures. Seitz states that as the mother rat grows still older, litter size and maternal behavior tend to *decrease*. This raises the question as to whether the *increase* observed between the first and second litters may not be due to physiologic changes associated with maturity, which are in turn to some extent reversed or over-ridden by approaching senility. Hauschka (1952) states that female mice of a strain in which there is a certain amount of can-nibalism toward the young showed a higher frequency of eating the young with increas-ing age. Hauschka defines age in terms of the litter number, from the first litter through the eighth. In this study, as in some of the other experiments we have men-tioned, age is confounded with experience, so that it is not possible to say whether the changing pattern of behavior is due to the animals' experience or to growth changes, or to some interaction between the two. Controls for age and for previous pregnancy and parturition without opportunity to re-late to the young would be relatively simple to arrange, but this has not been done.

Similar problems are found in the few reports of such work with birds. Verlaine (1934) reported that domestic canaries which built successive nests tended to build better nests later in the season. He implied that this is the result of practice, but it is by no means certain that this is so, because there is no control for the effects of seasonal changes in hormone secretion.

Saeki and Tanabe (1955) found that pro-lactin injected into adult hens with previ-ous brooding experience induced incubation behavior, whereas the same treatment ad-ministered to immature pullets did not have this effect. Here again, the relative effects of previous experience, of age, and of endo-crine condition (the experienced hens were laying eggs before being injected) are not clear.

Craig (1913, 1918) reported that a female ring dove which was never bred, nor had a nest or nesting material, may lay an egg on the floor, but an experienced dove will withhold the egg until a nest is available. Mr. Philip Brody and I, in the course of an experiment on a different problem, have verified this; in our observations, the ex-perienced and inexperienced birds were of the same age.

It is apparent that, although there are many suggestive indications that the first breeding experience may have an influence on the nature and efficiency of subsequent breeding behavior, the problem of behav-ioral changes between first and later breed-ing episodes deserves much closer and better controlled study than has yet been given to it. Attention should also be paid to the probability that phyletic differences in the role of such experience may be very impor-tant (Beach, 1947a, b; Aronson, 1959).

NATURE OF CHANGES IN BEHAVIOR DURING THE BREEDING EPISODE. Beach and Jaynes' (1956a) observations indicate that some im-provement in retrieving behavior occurs as a result of practice during the lactation pe-riod (see also Seitz, 1958). A number of other observations and experiments suggest that, at least in many mammals, the experi-ence of the mother during each stage of the period of maternal care, from parturition on, contributes to the development of be-havior during successive stages.

Blauvelt (1955) reported that the asso-ciation between newborn domestic goats and their mothers during the period im-mediately after birth seems to be a very important part of the process leading to the establishment of the mother-young rela-tionship. A parturitive mother of this spe-cies licks the kid as the kid leaves her body. The kid, lying on the ground, bleats, and the mother stands with her head pointing at the kid until it can stand and walk to her. If the mother's head is held so that she can-not lick the kid during parturition, and she is taken away for a short time, she does not lick the kid again when she has returned, and contact with the kid takes a long and variable time to establish. If a 1-hour-old kid is separated from its mother for just a few minutes, the mother is very disturbed when the kid is reintroduced. If the kid is fed by the mother before the two are separated, then the re-establishment of their relation-ship occurs much more quickly after the kid is returned than if the two are separated before the kid is fed. In 6 cases in which the kids were separated from their mothers for 20 or 30 minutes starting at birth, none was able to establish a successful relationship without help from the experimenter. Her-sher, Moore and Richmond (1958) removed 24 newborn kids from their domestic goat mothers for periods ranging from ½ to 1 hour, starting 5 to 10 minutes immediately following birth. When the kids were returned to the mothers, they were helped to suckle from their own mothers. A control group of 21 mothers was allowed to rear their kids normally. The flock was not further interfered with until 2 or 3 months later when the animals were tested by placing a mother in an experimental room with three kids, including her own. In this situation, the mothers which had been separated from their kids during the hour following birth nursed their own kids less than those mothers which had not been so separated, and nursed other kids more.

Collias (1956) found that sheep are attracted to newborn young by their odor. A ewe could be attracted by a rag rubbed in fresh birth membranes. Collias, like Blauvelt, found that separation of newborn goats and sheep from their mothers for a short period of time resulted in rejection of the infants when they were returned to the mothers, although he found it necessary to keep mother and young separated for somewhat longer times (2 to 4 hours) than had Blauvelt.

Unpublished observations by Tobach, Failla, Cohen and Schneirla at the American Museum of Natural History show that the maternal licking of the neonate kitten appears to be in some respects an extension of her self-licking immediately before parturition. The relationship between mother and young, established in part through such processes, forms the basis for the development of detailed perceptual responses of the animals to each other, as the mother and young become mutually conditioned (Schneirla, 1950, 1959).

The results from an experiment by Labriola (1953) warn us that the type of process described in the preceding paragraphs is by no means the only one contributing to the development of the mother-young relationship, or at any rate that it is not of the same relative importance in all animals. Labriola compared the maternal behavior of primiparous female rats who were allowed to deliver their young normally with the behavior of females whose young were delivered by cesarean section. A further comparison was made with nulliparous nonpregnant animals. The animals were tested for retrieving 24 hours postpartum, after having remained with the young since par-

turition; the test was repeated at 24, 48, and 72 hours postpartum. All the normal controls retrieved young on the first test. Five of 7 cesarean-operated animals retrieved on the first test, 1 on the second, and the last on the third. It is clear that, at least in the rat, the events associated with parturition and the cleaning of the young are not essential for the establishment of retrieving behavior in a majority of the animals. Labriola's subjects were kept with their pups from the time of parturition until the first test, and no observations are available to show what happened during this time. The cesarean-operated females did not lactate, but no observations are available from which we could decide whether this was due to the effects of the operative interference on the animals' endocrine condition, or to the possible nonestablishment of suckling stimulation immediately after delivery.

We may also remind ourselves that camels, llamas and their relatives establish suckling relationships with their young in the complete absence of any tendencies to lick the young, eat the placenta, tear the membranes, or bite the imbilical cord (Pilters, 1954).

RECOGNITION OF YOUNG. The development of recognition of their own young by mother animals is another indication of the occurrence of learning based on originally partially hormone-induced parental behavior patterns. Earlier, in connection with our discussion of the stimulation of retrieving by external stimuli, we discussed a number of cases in which such individual recognition of the young had been demonstrated. It became clear from those cases that many animals are able to recognize their own young (Beach and Jaynes, 1956c), even in species which, under other circumstances, readily adopt young of other species (Frisch and Kahmann, 1952). Some mother chimpanzees have been found to react to their own young differently from any other infants after one year of separation, starting at about one year after birth (Spence, 1937).

Ramsay (1951) found that various domesticated and semidomesticated species of ducks will readily adopt birds of other species hatching from eggs incubated by the experimental birds. In such cases, the parent birds often chase and peck at young which were unlike the ones they had adopted, even though the "strange" young are of their own species. Tinbergen (1939a) found that parent herring gulls react to all young gulls indiscriminately until their young are about 5 days old, after which they recognize their own and attack others.

It is thus apparent that individual recognition of, and response to, particular young animals frequently develops on the basis of originally relatively undifferentiated responses, based in part on the physiologic condition of the parent.

POSSIBLE EFFECTS OF EARLIER EXPERIENCE. Experience gained earlier in life, before parturition, may of course have an effect on the development of parental behavior, and several attempts have been made to demonstrate this. Riess (1950, 1954) reared female rats without access to anything manipulatable; their food was finely pulverized, no nesting material or bedding was permitted in the cages, and the floor was constructed of wide-mesh wire, so that the feces would fall through the floor and be unavailable for carrying. The animals were isolated from other rats. Riess found that animals so reared, when made pregnant and given nesting material, showed no nest-building behavior and decreased retrieving behavior; there was an infant mortality of 75 per cent due to the absence of nursing behavior. The experimental animals did tear the strips of paper (provided as nesting material) from their holders, but carried them about and left them at random on the floor of the testing chamber. The pups were likewise carried about the cage without being gathered into one area. In a less drastic limitation of the animals' environment during development, Kinder (1927) had found that rats reared in cages without paper did as much nest building, when later tested, as those reared in cages with paper, but that the amount of nest-building on the first day of testing was less for the animals reared with restricted experience.

In a previous discussion of this problem (Lehrman, 1953, 1956b) I implied that Riess showed that the animals must learn to carry nesting material, and that practice in carrying food pellets is, for this purpose, equiva-

lent to practice in carrying nesting material. Eibl-Eibesfeldt (1955a, 1956) has shown that this conclusion is incorrect, and has thrown further light on the nature and limitations of the learning process involved. He reared female rats in a manner similar to that devised by Riess, and tested them at the age of 10 to 12 weeks by placing nesting material in their living cages, instead of by moving the animals to a test cage, as had Riess. He thus avoided any interference of exploratory behavior with maternal behavior. Of 29 animals so tested, 8 began building immediately, whereas 3 additional animals began within the first hour. Eleven acted like Riess' rats, carrying nesting material to and fro in the cage, eventually dropping it at random. These animals, however, began to restrict themselves to a single location in the cage after a few hours of such activity, and had built nests by the following morning. Five animals carried nesting material to a single corner of the cage, and there gnawed and played with it, but did not build a nest until the following day. Two of the 29 animals did no building at all. Observations carried out before the introduction of the nesting material showed that 9 of the 29 had established sleeping places in the cage, although the remaining animals had no fixed sleeping locations. The 8 animals which began to build immediately belonged to the group which had fixed sleeping locations. For a further group of experimental animals, Eibl-Eibesfeldt placed a small vertical partition in a corner of the cage so as to make a cubicle open to the rest of the cage. Of the 19 animals tested with this partition, 18 built in this corner immediately after nesting material was introduced for the first time.

It appears from Eibl-Eibesfeldt's data that the failure of nest-building by some of the animals in his and Riess' experiments was due not to a lack of development of the basic responses of picking up and carrying nesting material, but to the failure of the animals to develop an attachment to a particular place in the cage. Further, the more differentiated the living space, and therefore the more stimulation it can offer to attract the animal into one part of the cage, compared to other areas, the less necessity there is for an extended period of development of an attachment to a particular sleeping location.

Birch (1956) raised female rats with wide rubber collars around their necks, which prevented them from licking any part of the body behind the neck. In particular, these collars prevented access to the genital area, which is intensively licked during pregnancy and during the events associated with parturition. The collars were removed 1 to 2 hours before parturition. Birch states that "because of the inadequacy of maternal behavior no offspring survived the nursing period. The latent periods for the initial licking of the young were abnormally long." Birch's hypothesis is that "the self-licking of pregnancy is the experiential basis for the self-licking ... and the pup-licking of parturition, and the pup-licking of the nursing period." Birch's data have never been reported in full; the report here quoted lacks any statement about how many animals were used, the duration of latent periods, details of the survival of the young, quantitative details of the behavior of the mothers, etc. Coomans, in an unpublished study cited by Eibl-Eibesfeldt (1958) repeated Birch's study, using hooded rats (Birch used white rats), and obtained quite different results. He states that no disturbance of maternal behavior was found if the collar was removed before parturition, and that the disturbances that were found when the collars were left on could be attributed solely to mechanical interference with the normal behavior pattern. Since neither the Birch nor the Coomans study has been reported in sufficient detail to permit a replication, it is to be hoped that further work on this problem will provide data that will allow a more confident interpretation. I have gone into detail here only because so many authors have referred to this experiment (Lehrman, 1953, 1956b; Hebb, 1953; Schneirla, 1956).

Beach (1937) found that removal of various amounts of cerebral cortex in female rats caused a degree of disorganization of maternal behavior which was roughly proportional to the amount of cortex removed. This conclusion is based on measures of the amount and the efficiency of nest-building behavior, the time when nest-building behavior starts, efficiency of retrieving young, measures of the amount of licking and cleaning of the young, survival of the young, etc. The disturbance of maternal behavior caused by these lesions is due to more than a *specifically* sensory deficit, since, *e.g.*, animals with lesions of the visual cortex show more disturbance of maternal behavior than do peripherally blinded animals. Beach (1938) further found that animals operated on in infancy were superior in performance to animals undergoing the same operation as adults, although both were deficient when compared with intact animals. The larger the lesions, the greater was the degree of superiority of animals operated on at infancy over those in which the lesion of the same size was made after they became adults.

These findings of Beach on the relative effects of cortical lesions on maternal behavior when the lesions are made early in life or later (greater effect of lesion in adults than in infants, greater disparity between the two groups with larger lesions than with small lesions, effect of lesion a function of size rather than of location, etc.) are strikingly similar to those found by Lashley (1929, 1933) who studied the effects of cortical lesions of various sizes on the learning of complex maze problems in rats; the lesions were made in some animals after the problem was learned and in others before the problem was learned. Damage to the cerebral cortex interferes much more with the retention of a previously learned problem than does a lesion of the same size with the subsequent learning of the same problem. Further, the disparity is greater, the larger the lesion. Benjamin and Thompson (1959) found that the ability of cats to discriminate different degrees of roughness of sandpaper was more seriously impaired by lesions in the somatic sensory cortex when the lesions were made at maturity than when they were made at birth. Beach (1939a) found that the performance of female rats in a maze-learning situation was correlated with the efficiency of their maternal behavior. For example, of 40 rats tested, the 5 which made the fewest errors on the maze retrieved their first pups after an average latency of 3.2 minutes; the 5 poorest maze learners took on the average 360.4 minutes to start retrieving their young.

These experiments of Beach hint that

some generalized learning about the environment which occurs during early life may participate in the organization of maternal behavior.

Stamm (1955) found that lesions in the median cerebral cortex caused more disturbance in the maternal behavior of rats than did lesions of similar size elsewhere on the cortical surface. Rats so treated licked their young and severed the umbilical cords, but did not retrieve the litters together into a nest after parturition and did not permit the young to suckle. However, introduction of foster pups with previous suckling experience markedly changed the behavior of the operated mothers. The foster pups, by hanging onto the nipples of the mother rats, induced lactation, and the operated animals subsequently hovered over the litters, permitting the young to nurse; they then collected and retrieved the pups, which survived. These observations may indicate that the cortical lesion did not interfere with the ability to carry out the maternal behavior, but perhaps reduced the impact of the stimulation which normally elicits this behavior.

INTERACTION OF HORMONAL AND EXPERIENTIAL INFLUENCES. From the foregoing discussion, it is apparent that some behavior patterns are simultaneously influenced by various endocrine conditions and by previous experience. This fact raises some interesting problems concerned with the interrelations of such influences.

Uyldert (1946) allowed 35 primiparous rats to deliver their young on a floor made of wide-mesh wire screen, through which the newborn pups fell, so that the mother had no contact with them. Animals of a control group were allowed to retain their young and to nurse them normally. After the young of the control group were weaned, both groups were allowed to rest for several weeks, following which each animal was injected with 200 μg. of estrone per day for 20 days, which induced mammary development. One day after the cessation of this treatment, rats of both groups were provided with newborn young. Eight of the 9 control animals (animals with previous normal nursing experience) reared from 5 to 8 young each; only 12 of the 35 experimental animals (animals with no previous

experience of nursing young) succeeded in rearing young, and these reared only from 1 to 3 young each. Of the control animals 56 per cent kept all their young alive, compared with 11 per cent of the experimental animals. Clearly, the previous experience of nursing and rearing the young had an effect on the animals' response to the combination of estrone treatment and stimuli from the young. Observations are lacking, however, that would indicate whether the difference between the experimental and control groups resided in the animals' responsiveness to suckling stimulation, or in their behavior toward the young, which might determine whether suckling could take place or not.

Riddle, Lahr and Bates (1935a, b, c, 1942), reported that some virgin rats show retrieving behavior in response to prolactin injection. They stated that the care of the young shown by such animals is not equivalent to that usually seen in multiparous rats, but they did not make a comparison of the effects of the hormone injection on the behavior of virgin and of experienced rats. Loisel (1906) found that a bitch which began to lactate after a pseudopregnancy accepted three young rabbits which were placed with her, licked them, and facilitated their approach to her nipples (they could not suckle). This animal had never seen young before. Fisher (1956) found that a testosterone salt injected locally into the hypothalamus induced intense nest-building and retrieving behavior in some male rats. These animals were presumably quite inexperienced.

In connection with studies of mammalian parental behavior, it is unfortunate that no use has been made of the technique of comparing behavior elicited by hormone treatment in animals without previous experience with that elicited from animals with various amounts and kinds of previous experience. Such a technique has been extremely valuable in studies of sexual behavior. As I have pointed out, comparison of parental behavior at first and at later breeding episodes may not reveal the role of experiential factors in the changing pattern of behavior during each episode. This is sometimes because the experience of the animals during an early phase of the cycle may set the stage for its behavior at a later stage, so that the behavior at the later stage may appear quite normal, even though it is the animal's first experience, and even though learning *did* play a role in the development of the animal's capability for performing this behavior. If, by hormone treatment, we can put the animal directly into the physiologic condition characteristic of a later stage in the cycle, and then confront it with the situation characteristic of that stage, when it has *not* had any experience of the earlier stage, it is sometimes possible to throw into startling relief the role of experience in the progression of stages which normally occurs effectively even in the first breeding episode.

Rosenblatt and Aronson (1958a, b) have shown that previous sexual experience is an important variable affecting the induction of sexual behavior by androgen administration in male cats, and Valenstein, Riss and Young (1955) and Valenstein and Young (1955) found somewhat similar results in the guinea pig. The importance of considering species differences in such matters is seen in the fact that such previous experience appears to be unimportant in rats, compared to the other animals mentioned (Kagan and Beach, 1953; Beach, 1958b). These studies are reported more fully in the chapter by Young.

Lehrman (1955) found that ring doves with previous breeding experience could be induced to feed young doves (by regurgitation) by the injection of approximately 450 I.U. prolactin over 7 days. Similar treatment of birds of the same age, but without previous breeding experience, failed to induce parental feeding behavior. Inexperienced birds so treated showed a striking suppression of sexual behavior, compared with untreated birds, and gave several behavioral signs of tension that are normally seen in animals before they regurgitate. However, they failed to make the approaches to the young which were reliably induced in experienced birds. The experienced birds did a great deal of gentle pecking at the head and body of the stimulus squabs, mostly concentrated on the head (the squabs normally respond to gentle pecking on the head by making the "beg-

ging" movements which elicit regurgitation feeding). The inexperienced birds, on the other hand, did very little pecking of the young (no more than they did at other objects in the cage), and what pecking they did was not in any way directed at or concentrated on the head of the squabs. It was apparent that the prolactin injection had induced in both these groups of birds a condition of tension, probably associated with the engorgement of the crop by the cropmilk produced in response to prolactin treatment, but that the inexperienced birds could not respond differentially to that part of the environment (the squabs) which could potentially provide stimulation which would reduce this tension.

Lehrman and Wortis (1960) used the same method in dealing with incubation behavior induced by progesterone injection. It will be recalled that experienced ring-doves can reliably be induced by progesterone administration to sit on eggs. We have compared the reaction of ring doves with and without previous experience to eggs presented by the experimenter, after the birds were injected with 100 μg. per day of progesterone for 7 days before being tested. Striking differences were found between the behavior of the experienced and of the inexperienced birds. The experienced birds are all recorded as standing near the nest in less than one minute after being introduced into the test cage, whereas the median latency for this behavior in the inexperienced birds was 35 minutes. All of the experienced birds settled on the eggs for the first time within 26 minutes, whereas no inexperienced bird sat on the eggs in less than 56 minutes, and half of them did not sit at all. Birds *not* injected with progesterone pay no attention to the eggs on the first day after being placed in the test cage, regardless of whether they are experienced or not.

It is clear that the animal's previous experience can alter the ways in which its behavior is influenced by hormone treatment, and that the interaction between the effects of previous experience and of hormone treatment is capable of providing a fruitful approach to the analysis of the development of the behavior patterns and of their physiologic bases.

At various points in our discussion, it has become apparent that external stimuli of various kinds, including some produced by other members of the species, may be influential in eliciting the secretion of various hormones. It may be helpful if we briefly discuss the physiologic basis of such responses.

1. Neural Control of Hormone Secretion

Both the anterior lobe and the posterior lobe of the pituitary gland are connected to the hypothalamus, although in quite different ways.

It will be recalled that electrical stimulation of the anterior hypothalamus (Andersson, 1951b), or of the pituitary stalk (Cross and Harris, 1950), induces milk ejection due to the secretion of oxytocin by the posterior pituitary. The principal functional connection between the brain and the posterior lobe is by way of the hypothalamohypophyseal nerve tracts in the pituitary stalk (Green, 1951a). (The secretory cells of the neurohypophysis are themselves neural in embryonic origin.) Harris (1947b) implanted electrodes with their tips in various locations in the hypothalamus, pituitary stalk, and neurohypophysis; the electrodes were connected to a coil imbedded in the skull, so that they could be activated by holding a second coil near the animal's head without actually touching the animal. Harris was able to produce an antidiuretic effect in water-loaded animals by stimulating the neurohypophysis, the supra-opticohypophyseal tract of the hypothalamus, or any part of the intervening nerve pathway. The effects of such electrical stimulation could be duplicated by the injection of posterior pituitary extracts. This and other evidence (Harris, 1955) indicates that the secretory activity of the posterior lobe of the pituitary gland is under neural control, and that the nerve connection between the hypothalamus and the neurohypophysis plays an essential role in the regulation of neurohypophyseal activity.

In contrast to the situation in the posterior hypophysis, the anterior lobe is very sparsely innervated, both in mammals (Rasmussen, 1938; Green, 1951b) and in birds (Wingstrand, 1951). On the basis of a thorough survey of the evidence, Harris (1955) concludes that there is no evidence of a secretomotor innervation of the secretory cells of the anterior hypophysis.

The principal connection between the hypothalamus and the anterior hypophysis appears to be by a portal blood system. In mammals, small branches of the internal carotid arteries form a plexus at the base of the pituitary stalk, from which capillary loops arise and penetrate into the tissue of the median eminence, where they come into intimate relationship with the nerve fibers of various hypothalamic tracts (Harris, 1955). The vessels of this plexus merge to form portal vessels which lie on the surface of the pituitary stalk. Lower down on the stalk, these trunks divide again to distribute their blood to the cells of the anterior hypophysis. The arrangement in birds is similar, except that the capillary network lies on the surface of the median eminence, and its relationship with the nerve fibers of the hypothalamus is accomplished by the looping of nerve fibers from deeper-lying cells to the surface and back (Benoit and Assenmacher, 1955).

Electrical stimulation applied directly to the anterior hypophysis of the female rabbit is ineffective in inducing ovulation (equivalent to stimulation of LH secretion), whereas stimulation of the hypothalamus does induce this response (Markee, Sawyer, and Hollinshead, 1946; Harris, 1948). Since direct stimulation of the pituitary stalk is also ineffective, it seems that the effect of electrically stimulating the hypothalamus is to cause the transmission to the anterior pituitary gland of an excitatory effect by way of structures which are not themselves sensitive to electrical stimulation. (This, it will be seen, is in contrast to the neural excitation of the posterior pituitary.) Harris (1947a) and Green and Harris (1947) suggested that hypothalamic control of anterior pituitary secretion is accomplished through neurosecretory products of hypothalamic cells, which are carried by the portal system from the hypothalamus down to the secretory cells of the pituitary gland. There is now abundant additional evidence of the correctness of Harris' concept of the neurohumoral relationship between the hypothalamus and the anterior pituitary gland (Harris, 1955).

In summary, there is ample anatomic and physiologic basis for concluding that the nervous system exercises detailed control over the activity of both the anterior and the posterior lobe of the pituitary gland.

2. Hormone Secretion as a Reflex

The preceding remarks imply that it should be possible for endocrine secretion to occur as a reflex response to stimulation of afferent neural structures and, therefore, hormone secretion may, in some situations, occur as a reflex response to external stimuli of the kind which we ordinarily know to give rise to behavioral responses. There is considerable direct evidence that this is indeed so.

In his classic papers on sexual cycles, F. H. A. Marshall (1936, 1942, 1956) pointed out the role which external stimuli might play in the regulation of breeding periods. The importance of such factors is becoming increasingly clear, not only in determining the timing of breeding periods during the year, but also in organizing the succession of changes within the breeding season itself (Maschkowzew, 1940; Aschoff, 1955).

Most animals breed only during a particular season of the year, and it has long been known that, in many species of birds and mammals, changes in light stimulation due to the changing length of the day constitute one of the principal regulators of the timing of the breeding season (Rowan, 1926, 1931; Bissonnette, 1937; Farner, 1955). Other factors, such as temperature, also play a role (Pitt, 1929; Marshall and Coombs, 1952; Engels and Jenner, 1956; Marshall and Disney, 1956).

Some tropical and Australian birds breed irregularly, whenever heavy rains occur (Baker, 1938; Marshall, 1951). In such species, the gonads of birds collected in the same locality just before a rainy period are inactive, whereas one or two months after a rainy period, birds of the same species have active gonads, but only in the locality in which the rain has occurred (Keast and Marshall, 1954; Benoit, 1956). We have already discussed (see above, p. 1280) the experimental demonstration by Marshall and Disney (1957) of the nature of this effect.

Stimuli provided by the mate are of importance in the development of gonadal activity in many animals. Although the increasing length of the day in spring initiates gonad development in many birds, it is commonly found that they do not come into full breeding condition unless further stimulated by the presence of the mate (Riley and Witschi, 1938; Bissonnette, 1939; Burger, 1953; for review see Lehrman, 1959a). In colonial birds, mutual stimulation among the members of the colony appears to have the effect of synchronizing their reproductive cycles (Darling, 1938), so that larger colonies have shorter over-all breeding seasons than smaller ones; in very large colonies, groups of birds in any one part of the colony may have their breeding times more closely synchronized than those of the colony as a whole (Neff, 1937; Lack and Emlen, 1939; Disney and Marshall, 1956).

Female rabbits and domestic cats ovulate as a result of the stimulus provided by participation in copulation (Heape, 1905), which causes the release of gonadotrophic hormone from the animal's hypophysis. This effect can be duplicated by artificial mechanical stimulation of the vagina in cats, although less readily in rabbits (Greulich, 1934; Sawyer, 1949; Sawyer and Markee, 1959). Whitten (1956a) has shown that the timing of the estrous cycle of the female mouse can be modified by stimuli provided by male mice. This stimulation is probably olfactory, inasmuch as the length of the estrous period can be changed by placing a male in a small basket within the female's cage for several days, or by placing the females in cages recently vacated by males. Further, removal of the olfactory bulbs causes regression of the ovaries although it seems to have no such effect on the male gonads (Whitten, 1956b; Lamond, 1958, 1959). Conversely, forcing the association of female mice in large groups appears to suppress gonadotrophic activity (Whitten, 1959).

3. Hormone Secretion as a Conditioned Response

It is possible for the secretion of a hormone to occur as a response to a *conditioned* stimulus.

Grachev (1952) inserted a catheter into one mammary gland of a goat, and found that when he milked the other mammary gland, milk was ejected through the catheter. He then arranged to have a bell ring starting 15 seconds before the beginning of milking, and continuing through the milking session. After 18 such pairings of the bell and of the milking stimulus, the sound of the bell, without any accompanying milking stimulus, elicited an ejection of milk from the catheterized gland similar to that usually caused by the milking of the other gland. It is well known to dairy workers that milk ejection can occur in response to stimuli normally associated with the preparations for milking, such as the rattling of buckets, the washing of the udders, etc. (Ely and Petersen, 1941). Clinical reports indicate that lactating human mothers may eject milk in response to stimuli such as the sound of the baby's crying (Newton and Newton, 1948), the sound of the nurse opening the door to bring the baby into the mother's room (Waller, 1938), and other stimuli associated with the anticipation of putting the baby to the breast (Newton and Newton, 1950; Campbell and Petersen, 1953).

The conditioning of anterior pituitary secretions is more difficult to demonstrate, and would not be expected to occur in the same form as the conditioning of posterior pituitary secretion, since the nature of the neurohumoral link between the hypothalamus and the anterior pituitary is such that the interval between external stimulus and hormonal response might be on the order of hours or fractions of an hour, rather than, as in the elicitation of oxytocin secretion from the posterior pituitary, on the order of minutes or fractions of a minute. Nevertheless, Freud and Uyldert (1948a) suggest that the superiority of the maternal care given to adopted young rats, and the higher survival rate of the young, when the foster mothers had had suckling experience, compared with those which had

borne young without being allowed to suckle them (Uyldert, 1943, 1946), is evidence of a conditioned elicitation of lactation. As I indicated earlier (see above p. *000*), the data as presented do not demand such an interpretation, but the possibility is one which should be investigated. Craig (1913) and Whitman (1919) reported that doves reared solely by human keepers, or by foster parents of other species, might, when mature, lay eggs in response to stimulation by a human hand, or by a courting male of the foster species. In this case, we are undoubtedly dealing with some form of conditioning of the secretion of gonadotrophic hormones to external stimuli, but the nature of this conditioning and the course of its development are entirely obscure.

4. Parental Behavior ana Reflexly Induced Hormone Secretion

It is clear from the preceding discussion that there exists a well established anatomic and physiologic basis for the control of endocrine secretion by the nervous system, that this control in fact exists, and that it is therefore possible for an extensive variety of external stimuli, including stimuli provided by other members of the animal's species, to elicit different types of hormone secretion. Many of these stimulus-response relationships, involving the stimulation of hormone secretion, are important features of the physiologic basis of parental behavior and of the establishment of parent-young relationships.

We have pointed out that external stimuli provided by the male may induce endocrine changes in many female birds, which in turn induce nest-building behavior. In some cases, stimuli provided by the nest contribute, in turn, to the stimulation of egg-laying. Stimuli coming from the egg may then elicit the secretion of the pituitary hormone(s) which maintain the bird in a state of readiness to incubate. After the eggs hatch, the presence of the young contributes to the maintenance of the physiologic condition appropriate for parental care of the young, and to the suppression of the secretion of those pituitary hormones

which could induce a new cycle of courtship and nest-building. Thus, the succession
of changes in behavior patterns which characterizes the breeding cycle depends partly
on changes in hormone secretion which are
in turn partially stimulated by the changing
conditions of the environment (Lehrman,
1959a, b).

In mammals, the ability of stimuli provided by the young to induce the maintenance of lactation, and to suppress the
recurrence of estrus, further indicates that
the changing pattern of the behavior of the
mother is kept appropriate to the external
situation partly through the fact that the
endocrine changes which influence her behavior are themselves capable of being influenced by the external situation.

The readiness with which milk ejection
can be conditioned poses a number of problems of special interest in connection with
the development of mother-young relationships in mammals. If the sensations of tension arising from mammary engorgement
play a role, as has been suggested, in the
motivation of maternal nursing behavior, it
must be borne in mind that the milk-ejection response is itself an increase in tension
in the mammary glands. Since young animals characteristically become active just
before and during the time when they are
fed, it seems likely that changes in intramammary tension will occur as conditioned
responses to the sights and sounds characteristic of the young. The occurrence of
such conditioned responses, their manner
of formation, and the contribution they
make to the maintenance of mother-young
relationships are all problems which should
be most rewarding to the investigator who
attacks them.

Both in birds and in mammals, the establishment and maintenance of relations between the parent and the young (or eggs)
is a process, or series of processes, of great
complexity, involving a reciprocal interaction between, on the one hand, hormonal
effects on behavior, and on the other, the
effects of external stimuli (including those
arising from the behavior of the animal and
of its species-mates) on the patterns of hormone secretion.

C. MECHANISMS OF HORMONAL ACTION ON BEHAVIOR

1. Formulation of the Problem

The interpretation of the manner in which
hormones influence behavior patterns is
an extremely complex problem. As Beach
(1948) has pointed out, and as must be
apparent from much of the data presented
in earlier sections of this chapter, a behavioral response does not typically depend
on one and only one hormone, nor is any
hormone known which produces one and
only one effect on the organism. However,
when we know that a hormone has an influence on the development or occurrence
of a behavior pattern, we may usefully ask
which of the various organic effects the hormone is known to have are relevant to its
effect on the behavior pattern, and whether
additional organic effects must be assumed
in order to explain the fact that the hormone has the observed effect on the behavior.

Hormones may influence behavior patterns through either peripheral or central
effects. By "peripheral" effects, I mean that
the hormone may change the animal's behavior by causing changes in structures or
processes external to the central nervous
system, which changes in turn result in
alterations in the pattern of afferent inflow.
Such changes may consist of growth changes
in structures used in the behavior (Lehrman, 1955), of changes in vascularity which
influence the conditions of tension in the
tissues concerned (Clark and Birch, 1946;
Birch and Clark, 1946, 1950), of changes in
sensitivity of a sensory surface (Freud
and Uyldert, 1948b; Schneider, Costiloe,
Howard and Wolf, 1958), of the development of sensitive structures (Beach and
Levinson, 1950), etc.

By "central" effects, I mean that a hormone may influence the animal's behavior
by a direct effect on structures of the central nervous system which are in some way
involved in the organization and production
of the behavior. Such effects may be relatively unspecific excitatory effects influencing "arousal" systems such as the reticular
activating system (Magoun, 1952a, b; Dell,

1958b), or they may be more specific effects on brain structures involved in the organization of specific behavior patterns (Fisher, 1956; Harris, Michael and Scott, 1958).

Morgan (1943, 1957, 1959) proposed the concept of "central motive state," by which he means a state of arousal of a center in the central nervous system which, once aroused, persists without outside support from sensory or other input, which predisposes the organism to react in certain ways to particular stimuli and not to react to others, and which "emits" specific patterns of behavior. This theory is, in many respects, remarkably similar to that of Lorenz (1950) (Beach, 1942; Tinbergen, 1951).

The relevance of Morgan's theory for our problem arises from the fact that he regards as an important corollary of the theory the statement that chemical and hormonal conditions of the blood directly activate the central nervous system and induce central motive states, and that this is the major way in which hormonal effects are exerted upon behavior. In an earlier discussion (Lehrman, 1956b), I heavily emphasized the role of peripheral effects of hormones as the means by which they influence behavior, and implied that direct central effects are of little or no importance. This was in the context of a critical discussion of a theory of behavior which depended, at that time, on the assumption of almost exclusively central forms of organization for most major behavior activities. In this context, I believe I unduly underemphasized the importance of central influences of hormones, and subsequent research confirms this view. On the other hand, Morgan's central theory is in part a reaction against the very influential earlier theory of Cannon (1929, 1934), who believed that most states of motivation depend solely or primarily on the perception of the condition of peripheral structures. In this context, I believe that Morgan somewhat underemphasized the importance of peripheral factors in the development of motive states. At this point, it does not seem to me to be very profitable to attempt to determine which is *in general* "more important," central or peripheral influences, since central and peripheral contributions are undoubtedly both involved in many cases, and are of varying importance in others. I shall attempt to illustrate the ways in which hormones may influence behavior patterns by selecting several patterns of behavior, including some discussed earlier in this chapter, for a further discussion of the mechanisms involved.

2. Examples of Peripheral Contributions to Hormonal Effects on Behavior

Parental feeding behavior in ring doves. Injection of prolactin into ring doves with previous breeding experience causes them to feed young doves provided by the experimenter (Lehrman, 1955). Prolactin has many other effects on doves, some of which may be relevant to this behavioral effect. Prolactin causes the crop to become engorged with the substance which the birds regurgitate to their young (Riddle and Braucher, 1931); it causes a substantial temporary overgrowth of the liver and intestine (Bates, Riddle, Lahr and Schooley, 1937); it inhibits the secretion of FSH by the pituitary gland (Bates, Riddle and Lahr, 1937), resulting in the suppression of gonadal activity (Bates, Lahr and Riddle, 1935).

Riddle (1935) assumed that, if this hormone influences a behavior pattern, it must be because of some interaction between the hormone and nerve tissue itself. In the case of the behavior we are considering, this is not necessarily so, since some of the effects already enumerated might be adequate to account for the arousal of parental feeding behavior. Lehrman (1955) injected prolactin into a group of doves with previous breeding experience and then, before testing them for regurgitation-feeding behavior toward squabs, anesthetized their crops by injecting a long-acting local anesthetic directly into the crop wall. These birds showed a sharply reduced incidence of regurgitation-feeding behavior, and a corresponding reduction in apparent "parental" interest in the squabs, as compared with a control group in which the same amount of the anesthetic was injected into the skin of the back. Lehrman concluded that the prolactin injections had induced regurgitation-feeding behavior through two main effects: it had induced the crop to become engorged by an accumulation of the degenerating epithelial cells which the birds regurgitate to their young (Beams and Meyer, 1931); and, by suppressing gonadal activity (Riddle and Bates, 1933; Nalbandov, 1953) it had eliminated sexual and aggressive behavior which would interfere with the parental behavior (Carpenter, 1933a, b). The fact that emetic responses in the pigeon are easily conditioned to external stimuli (Riddle and Burns, 1931) may be related to the fact that doves with previous breeding experience direct their behavior toward the head of the stimulus squab in such a way as to stimulate it to perform the movements which cause the parents to regurgitate food to it, whereas inexperienced birds show no such behavior.

Now, this experiment does *not* demonstrate conclusively that prolactin does not have any direct effects on the central nervous system which might be relevant to the elicitation of parental feeding behavior. It does show, however, that some of its peripheral effects play an important role. Prolactin has metabolic relations with some other tissues, which are not shared by nerve tissue. Sgouris and Meites (1952) found that prolactin is inactivated (rendered incapable of inducing the development of the pigeon crop) by being incubated *in vitro* with slices of mammary gland, pigeon crop, ovary, or liver, all of which are known to be affected by prolactin *in vivo*. Slices of muscle (which is not known to be changed by prolactin) did not inactivate prolactin solutions. Further, brain slices had no effect.

It should be noted that the distinction between "central" and "peripheral" effects is not a rigid one, and that the behavioral effect of the hormone is not conceivable except in terms of a network of interrelationships between central and peripheral influences. For example, it is not known whether the antigonadotrophic effect of prolactin is exerted directly on the pituitary gland, or on the hypothalamus. Further, is the disappearance of sexual behavior because of the suppression of gonad secretion caused by changes in peripheral structures, or in central ones? Finally, even in cases where peripheral effects are the most important ones, they can only act by altering the activities of central structures.

Nest-building behavior in rats. Hypophysectomy or thyroidectomy causes striking increases in the amount of nest-building activity in rats (Richter, 1937, 1941), in spite of the fact that these operations cause *decreased* "general activity," as measured in an activity wheel (Richter and Wislocki, 1930). What is the basis of this effect?

It will be recalled that Kinder (1927) found that rats tended to do more nest-building at lower temperatures than at higher, and that similar results were obtained in mice by Koller (1956). This, plus the fact that thyroidectomy, which reduces body temperature (Richter, 1941), also causes increased nest-building, led Richter and others to suggest that nest-building behavior is in part a thermoregulatory mechanism, and that its regulation is closely related to factors affecting body temperature. There is a great deal of evidence in support of this view.

Richter (1941) found that thyroidectomized or hypophysectomized rats would die if the ambient temperature was kept only a few degrees below normal room temperatures, *unless* the rats had nesting material available, and could build nests. Stone and Mason (1955) tested hypophysectomized and intact rats in an apparatus in which the rats could rest in either of two chambers, which were kept at different temperatures. Temperatures varied from about 45°F. to about 95°F. The hypophysectomized rats selected the warm box significantly more often than did the controls.

Koller (1956) shaved the hair from the bodies of mice whose nest-building behavior had been measured. In all cases, the amount of nest-building on the next night after the shaving was higher than on the preceding night. Here, too, the amount of nest-building is apparently related to the body's need for heat regulation. In this connection, it may be noted that temperature preferences have been related to hair density in a quite different experimental situation. Herter (1936, 1952) tested the temperature preferences of a number of small mammals in a gradient in which they could come to rest at any temperature in a considerable range. He found that mice and rats of different strains and species have characteristically different temperature preferences, and that these preferences are correlated with the thickness of the skin (Herter, 1941) and with the density of the hair, expressed in terms of number of hairs per unit of area (Herter and Sgonina, 1939). When strains with different temperature preferences are hybridized, variations in the temperature preferences of the offspring are correlated with variations in the density of their body-hair (Herter and Sgonina, 1939; Wolburg, 1952). Hair growth is in part under hormonal control (Mohn, 1958; Rennels and Callahan, 1959), although different skin areas are characterized by specific intrinsic growth properties of the hair and different areas of the body may thus respond differently to the same hormonal conditions (Whiteley, 1958). Hair growth in the domestic mouse is inhibited in late pregnancy (Danneel and Kahlo, 1947; Nay and Fraser, 1955). Progesterone inhibits hair growth in male mice (Danneel and Kahlo, 1947), although it does not seem to do so in rats (Yazaki, 1956; Mohn, 1958). We may recall that nest-building behavior in mice occurs earlier in pregnancy (Koller, 1952) than it does in rats (Wiesner and Sheard, 1933), and that progesterone induces nest-building behavior in mice (Koller, 1952).

It is clear that at least some of the effects of pituitary hormones on nest-building behavior in mammals may be due to alterations in thermoregulatory mechanisms. This, of course, refers only to the regulating effect on the amount of nest-building behavior, and does not necessarily imply anything about the neural organization of the behavior patterns themselves, which is not illuminated by this type of work. Further, we are not justified in assuming that hormonal effects on thermoregulatory processes do not include effects by way of the central nervous system; we can merely say that any such effects are probably not specific to nest-building behavior.

Some further problems. We have already remarked that the presence of incubation patches is, in many species of birds, correlated with the occurrence of incubation behavior (Tucker, 1943; Davis, 1945; Mewaldt, 1952; Parkes, 1953). Since the incubation patch is an area the increased vascularity of which is undoubtedly related to the transmission of heat to the egg, and since variations in ambient temperature (Nice and Thomas, 1948) and in egg temperature (Baerends, 1959) affect the intensity with which the birds sit on the eggs, it may be suggested that a change in skin temperature coinciding with the development of the incubation patch, and the cooling effect on it of sitting on the eggs, may be factors in the motivation of incubation behavior. Prolactin, which contributes to the maintenance of incubation behavior, raises the body temperature of roosters from 2 to 4°F. (Nalbandov, 1953). The rectal temperatures of incubating domestic fowl are not higher than those of nonincubating birds (Simpson, 1911), but Nalbandov (1953) suggests that this is probably the result of the lack of activity of incubating birds. It is unlikely that afferent inflow from the incubation patch is the most important source of motivation to incubate, because some species of birds incubate without possessing such patches. The contribution of such factors to the regulation of incubation behavior should nevertheless be further investigated.

There are other examples of peripheral effects of hormones on behavior, not related to parental behavior, which I have discussed elsewhere (Lehrman, 1956b). We may briefly cite one of them. Adult female dogs squat to urinate; adult males raise one leg (Berg, 1944). Males castrated in infancy do not raise their legs to urinate, but will do so if injected with male hormone. Female puppies and spayed female dogs also show the male micturition pattern if injected with male hormone (Martins and Valle, 1948). Freud and Uyldert (1948b) showed that local anesthesia of the olfactory epithelium caused the disappearance of the male micturition pattern and its replacement by the female pattern. When the anesthesia wore off, the male pattern reappeared.

They suggest that the hormone acts, not by activating or sensitizing a motor structure in the central nervous system, but by changing the pattern of afferent control. Changes in olfactory acuity and in the nasal mucosa characterize different stages of the human menstrual cycle (Elsberg, Brewer and Levy, 1935; Henderson, 1956), and olfactory acuity is affected by sex hormone administration to hypogonadal women (Schneider, Costiloe, Howard and Wolf, 1958; for review see Le Magnen, 1953).

As Morgan (1959) has pointed out, it is not at all necessary that a hormonal effect on behavior be through either exclusively peripheral or exclusively central influences. Both types of effect of the same hormone may contribute. We earlier presented evidence that the condition of mammary engorgement makes some contribution to the regulation of maternal nursing behavior. When Seward and Seward (1940) tested lactating guinea pigs in a device in which they had to cross a barrier to get to their young, and used the strength of the tendency to cross the barrier as an estimate of the intensity of motivation to nurse, they found that animals tested just after being milked consistently showed less of this "drive" than those tested when their mammary glands were full of milk. However, abdominal sympathectomy, which renders the mammary glands incapable of responding to hormone stimulation (Bacq, 1932a, b; Coujard, 1943; Champy, Coujard and Demay, 1950), often fails to prevent the appearance of maternal attempts to nurse the young, although, in most of these reports, it is not clear whether differences between animals with and without previous nursing experience may be important. It is nevertheless clear that, although the state of mammary engorgement, induced by hormones, probably contributes to the regulation of maternal nursing behavior, other factors, possibly including central effects, are also present.

3. Central Hormonal Effects on Behavior

In recent years, a good deal of evidence has been accumulating to show that many of the effects of hormones on behavior patterns are by way of direct chemical effects of the hormones on the central nervous system.

The development of neural mechanisms. Kollros (1942, 1943) found that the implantation of small pellets of thyroxine-saturated agar into the brain of the frog tadpole could cause the lid-closure reflex, the appearance of which is associated with metamorphosis, to develop earlier on the side of the animal on which the pellet was implanted than on the other side, where a control pellet without thyroxine was implanted. Kaltenbach (1953a, b) showed that a variety of structures could be made to metamorphose earlier than normal by local application of thyroxine. Weiss and Rossetti (1951) found that local application of thyroxine in immature tadpoles caused the premature atrophy of Mauthner's cells, accompanied by accelerated growth of neighboring nerve cells, both phenomena associated with normal metamorphosis.

Additional evidence that humoral influences associated with the actions of hormones play a role in the differentiation of neural structures mediating various behavior patterns may be found in a recent important study by Phoenix, Goy, Gerall and Young (1959). These workers administered testosterone propionate to mother guinea pigs during pregnancy, and then studied the sexual behavior of their offspring after they reached adulthood. No effects were observed on male offspring. Genetically female offspring showed greatly reduced capacity for female sexual behavior, and increased tendencies to perform male sexual behavior. The androgen treatment similarly resulted in morphologic hermaphrodites, genetic females in which the external genitalia were, at birth, not distinguishable from those of untreated males. Since the amount of male hormone required to cause suppression of female sexual behavior was less than that required to cause morphologic abnormalities, it is not likely that the effects on sex behavior were mediated by changes in the sex organs. Various abnormalities of the ovarian cycle were also noted (Tedford and Young, 1960), which together with the disturbances of sexual behavior suggest that the effect of the androgen treatment was, or included, an action on the hypothalamus. The involvement of the hypothalamus (or at least of extra-ovarian factors) is suggested by the fact that the ovaries appeared histologically normal until puberty, when the abnormal estrous cycles began (Turner, 1939; Tedford and Young, 1960). At this point it may be remarked that the differences in secretory activity and in responsiveness to gonadal hormones between male and female pituitary glands (Pfeiffer, 1936, 1937) are apparently due, not to sexual differentiation of the hypophysis during development, but to differentiation of the hypothalamus (Harris and Jacobsohn, 1952; Martinez and Bittner, 1956). There is evidence, summarized by Harris (1955), that the hypothalamus is differentiated into male and female types of activity (with respect to its relationship with the pituitary gland), very early in life.

Stimulation and regulation of behavior by central effects. In addition to these effects upon the ontogeny of central mechanisms, evidence has recently accumulated that some of the effects of hormones in arousing and regulating behavior in adult animals are exerted through direct effects on central nervous structures.

Fisher (1956) injected sodium testosterone sulfate into various hypothalamic loci by a cannula introduced through an implanted electrode. In a number of male rats tested by this method, he found various combinations of "maternal" and "sexual" behavior, sometimes occurring simultaneously. Among the responding animals, Fisher noted that the overt responses were characterized by exaggerated speed, compulsiveness, and frequency, as compared with the normal sexual and maternal behavior of untreated animals. In some animals, the behavior continued without decrement for 90 minutes after the chemical stimulus was supplied.

Harris, Michael and Scott (1958) implanted into the brains of ovariectomized female cats a fine platinum wire which had been dipped into a molten fatty acid ester of stilbesterol, so that the tip of the needle was coated with a thin film of the estrogenic substance. Of 17 animals so treated, in which the tip of the implanted wire was

in the posterior hypothalamus, 13 developed estrous behavior, including complete mating responses to male cats. In a control group in which the same implant was made into regions of the brain other than the hypothalamus, only one of the 19 animals showed any estrous response. Although on *systemic* administration of estrogens, mating behavior is stimulated only after a fully cornified vaginal smear has developed (Harris, 1959), 9 of the 13 animals which showed mating behavior in response to the hypothalamic implant had reproductive tracts completely indistinguishable from those of untreated control animals, as shown by vaginal smears, weight of the genital tract, and endometrial development. This experiment makes it seem likely that, although estrous behavior normally occurs at a time when the reproductive tract is in an estrous condition, the behavior itself is aroused not by afferent effects of the condition of the reproductive tract, but by the direct effects of gonadal hormones on the brain.

A number of other experiments show that humoral conditions which are known to affect behavior have direct and, to some extent, local effects on central nervous structures. Flerko and Szentagothai (1957) implanted small fragments of ovarian tissue into various regions of the hypothalamus and hypophysis of female rats. Estrogenic hormone produced by the ovary is capable of inhibiting the secretion of FSH by the pituitary gland (see chapter by Greep). Flerko and Szentagothai found that ovarian fragments implanted into the anterior lobe of the hypophysis had no effect on FSH secretion. Implants in the mammillary region of the hypothalamus failed to induce a significant change in FSH secretion (as indicated by uterine weights), whereas implants into the neighborhood of the paraventricular nuclei caused a significant decrease in uterine weights. From this experiment, it seems probable that the effect of the ovarian hormone on pituitary secretion is mediated by its effect on hypothalamic activity.

Andersson (1953) found that the injection of very small amounts of hypertonic saline solution into the third ventricle of the brain of goats would cause them to drink. Miller, Richter, Bailey and Southwick (Miller, 1957b) repeated this observation in cats, and found that the injection of no more than 0.15 cc. of slightly hypertonic (2 per cent) NaCl solution caused an increase in the volume of water drunk by the animals, whereas injection of the same amount of distilled water decreased consumption. Cross and Green (1959) observed the activity of single neurones in the hypothalamus of rabbits, and found that the rate of firing of neurones in the supra-optic nuclei was increased by small injections of hypertonic NaCl into the carotid arteries, whereas the rate of firing of neurones in the paraventricular nuclei was reduced. These authors were primarily interested in the effects of blood tonicity on posterior pituitary secretion, but their results, taken in conjunction with those of Andersson and of Miller, further indicate the existence of local effects on hypothalamic activity, exerted by humoral conditions known to be relevant to the elicitation of various behavior patterns.

With the exception of the brief report by Fisher (1956), none of the material on direct central behavioral effects of hormones has been related directly to the elicitation of parental behavior. However, the general background of evidence clearly indicates that central influences of the relevant hormones will be an important factor in future research on this, as on other types of behavior.

The problem of the specificity of central neuro-endocrine mechanisms. Some of the evidence cited above has been noted by Morgan (1959) as supporting the concept of "centers" for motivation and for behavior, as places in which "drive" or motivation is aroused, and also from which behavior is "emitted" (Stellar, 1954). As Hinde (1959) points out, the evidence at hand does not permit the firm conclusion that all the important aspects of either the motivation or the organization of the types of behavior patterns we are discussing are gathered together into single loci.

Copulation, or artificial stimulation of the vagina, are followed by changes in electrical activity which can be detected by electroencephalographic techniques, in both the female domestic cat (Porter, Cavanaugh, Critchlow and Sawyer, 1957) and rabbit (Sawyer and Kawakami, 1959). These aftercoital effects can be induced by treatment with some pituitary hormones, such as gonadotrophins and posterior pituitary hormones, which are known to be released as a result of stimuli associated with copulation (Kawakami and Sawyer, 1959a). Sawyer (1959) and his co-workers therefore conclude that these changes in central nervous activity are induced by the effects of the hormones on the nervous system, in effect a feed-back system. Kawakami and Sawyer (1959b) found that various hormones affect the threshold for the arousal of these electroencephalographic changes by electrical stimulation of the brain.

Now, Sawyer (1959) points out that the effects of ovarian hormones on the thresholds for brain stimulation are very widespread and generalized. Effects of hormones on the brain-stem reticular formation (Dell, 1958a, b; Sawyer, 1958) or in other parts of the brain may result in quite specific changes in the activity of, say, a hypothalamic nucleus, although the effects of the injected or endogenous hormone might not themselves be specific to that "center."

The work on the injection of minute quantities of hormones into specific loci, such as that of Harris, Michael, and Scott (1958), and Flerko and Szentogothai (1957), does not yet demonstrate that *specific* "centers" are selectively sensitive to the particular hormones which normally arouse behavior mediated by those centers. The fact that ovarian fragments cause suppression of pituitary activity when implanted into one hypothalamic area, and not in another, may mean *either* that the two areas are differentially sensitive to estrogen, *or* that the nuclei of that region of the brain are all sensitive to estrogen, but only some of them are so related to the pituitary gland that their activity can cause changes in pituitary secretion. Similarly, the demonstration that small amounts of estrogen released into certain hypothalamic nuclei induce female sex behavior should undoubtedly be followed by attempts to determine whether other kinds of chemical stimulation at the same locus will induce the same kind of behavior, and whether stimulation by the same substances at different loci will induce different kinds of behavior. A suggestive indication is found in the paper by Fisher (1956) who found that injection of the same testosterone salt into different hypothalamic loci would result, in some cases, in maternal behavior, in other cases in sexual behavior. Obviously, we must be cautious about interpreting the available data on central effects of hormones as if they demonstrated the existence of different "centers," each specific for a particular behavior pattern, and each selectively sensitive to a particular kind of humoral influence.

Evidence from the effects of brain lesions on various types of motivated behavior, and on the effects of various drugs (reviewed by Miller, 1957a, b; Hinde, 1959) indicate that some treatments appear to have different effects upon a "motive state," depending on how the state is measured. For example, some lesions in the hypothalamus increase the amount of food consumed, whereas they decrease other measures of "hunger," such as the rate at which the animal will press a bar in order to get food. As Hinde (1959) has pointed out, this suggests the need for caution in interpreting evidence that behavior is both motivated and organized in centers specific for the behavior patterns.

An additional reason for reserve in interpreting the effects of hormones upon "centers" lies in the fact that the sensitivity and activity of peripheral sense organs may often be affected by centrifugal influences from the central nervous system (Granit, 1955), and thus that humoral factors influencing the activity of central structures may nevertheless be influencing the character of the behavior by a process which includes peripheral contributions (Lehrman, 1956a; Prechtl, 1956). Although this does not mean that the hormones are not themselves acting on a central state, it does mean that the behavior resulting from the change in the central state is not necessarily organized within, or "emitted" from, the "center."

4. The Importance of Behavioral Analysis

Proper definition of the behavior variables which are influenced by hormones requires a careful analysis of the organization of the over-all behavior pattern of the animal as a prerequisite to studying the behavioral effects of various hormone treatments. For example, in some birds, such as the black-headed gull (Moynihan, 1953) and herring gull (Baerends, 1959) a good deal of nest-building often occurs as a "displacement activity," when the birds are disturbed on the nest by extreme egg temperatures, eggs abnormal in size, shape, or number, and other disturbances at the nest. Since, as I have pointed out, the endocrine condition during the pre-ovulation nest-building period and that during the incubation period are quite different, nest-building during the incubation period may have a very different physiologic basis from that during the normal period of nest-building. If analysis of the behavior had not itself revealed differences in the way in which building takes place at these two periods, the undifferentiated statement that "nest-building" takes place at both of these periods would lead to confusion in the analysis of the hormonal basis of the behavior.

Courting male canaries sometimes dangle a piece of string or cotton before the female. Behavior of this type is sometimes referred to as "incipient nest-building" in the ornithological literature. Shoemaker (1939) found that female canaries injected with testosterone propionate postured like courting males, and also engaged in this string-carrying behavior, reminiscent of the carrying of nesting material. Such birds did not, however, build nests. In this case the nest-building-like behavior of courtship, and real nest-building, are quite differently affected by hormones.

These examples show that a clear understanding of the organization of the behavior, based on an analysis of the over-all behavior pattern, is an important prerequisite for analysis of hormonal effects upon behavior. Simple counts of "carrying nest material," or "nest-building behavior," and studies of the effects upon such counts of hormone injections, could lead to misleading results in the hands of observers who did not have an accurate conception of the organization of the animal's behavior patterns.

1. Taxonomic Differences in Parental Behavior and in the Mechanisms Underlying It

Taxonomic variation in parental behavior patterns. Throughout our discussions of parental behavior, it has been clear that each component of the over-all pattern of parental behavior can occur in a wide variety of forms, and that these forms of behavior are characteristic of the species of animals in which they occur. Generally speaking, patterns of behavior, including parental behavior, may be characteristic not only of species, but also of the higher taxonomic categories, such as genera, families, orders, and even classes. Indeed, in spite of the fact that scattered exceptions may be found, the statements that mammals nurse their young, and that birds incubate their eggs, may be used to characterize membership in these two classes with almost as much precision as any single statement about structure.

Characteristic differences can be found between different orders of mammals with respect to their parental behavior and the structure of parent-young relationships. For example, the herd-living ungulates are usually characterized by a high degree of individual recognition of the young, by a long period of association between mother and young, and by the continuation of occasional nursing behavior long after the young have become capable of grazing for themselves (Altmann, 1952). In most rodents, on the other hand, relations between mother and young are not so long-lasting, "adoption" of young by strange mothers, even of other species, occurs very easily, and the transition between suckling and the eating of solid food is fairly abrupt (Eibl-Eibesfeldt, 1958). Relations between the male and the young, too, are different in different families of mammals. For example, among bears, the male is likely to attack and even

to eat its own young when association between them is forced, as in a zoo cage, although in the various species of wolves, the males often take an active role in the care of the young. Different groups of mammals also have characteristic ways of carrying their young when retrieving them, some carrying the young by the scruff of the neck, some by the belly, and some holding the young in the hands (Curio, 1955; Hediger, 1959).

The type of nest built by birds, the methods and patterns of incubating, and the pattern of parental care of the young may all be characteristic of particular families or genera. For example, Mayr and Bond (1943) noted that different genera of swallows reliably use different methods of nest-building, some laying eggs in natural hollows, some excavating burrows in sand- or mud-banks, others constructing nests of mud. All swifts use their saliva for sticking nesting materials together (Lack, 1956a), and their salivary glands develop and regress seasonally (Johnston, 1958). It is possible to trace, within one family, evolutionary changes in the patterns of parental behavior, as in the case we have already discussed (see above, p. 1277), of the New World cuckoos in which some species are parasitic, others communal nesters, and still others nest in colonies of individual nests (Davis, 1942b).

Although patterns of parental behavior may characterize entire families, we can also find many ways in which closely related animals have differing patterns. For example, the male Galapagos sea lion takes part in the care of the young, unlike other species of seal (Eibl-Eibesfeldt, 1955c). Höhn (1957) reports that female Pacific eiders always fly from the nest when an observer approaches within a few feet, whereas incubating king eiders sit so tight on the eggs that some allow themselves to be picked off the eggs by the observer. Watson (1908) observed that male and female noddy terns change places on the eggs about every two hours, although the closely related sooty terns change places only once a day. Van Oordt (1934) found that common terns began incubating after the laying of the first egg, whereas arctic terns did not begin incubating until the full clutch had been laid. The kittiwake, a species of gull, differs from other gulls with respect to many behavior patterns, most of them adaptations to the kittiwake's peculiar (for a gull) habit of nesting on cliffs (Cullen, 1957). For example, in most gulls, the parent regurgitates food for the young, which picks it up from the ground; the young kittiwake takes the food directly from the bill of its parents.

Differences in hormonal mechanisms in different animals. Beach (1958a) points out that identical hormone treatment may, in many cases, cause quite different forms of behavior in different kinds of animals, and that the evolutionary changes in behavior between different species have therefore affected, not the nature of the endocrine mechanisms inducing the behavior, but rather the nature of the neural and other structures which respond to the hormones. For example, injection of testosterone propionate induces male sex behavior in valley quail (Emlen and Lorenz, 1942) and in ring doves (Bennett, 1940); but the form of the behavior which is induced is quite different in the two species.

However, in spite of the fact that the nature of the endocrine secretions does not appear to change very much during evolution (at least in warm-blood animals), there are many cases in which the patterning of these secretions and the nature of the somatic responses are very different in different animals. We may thus find cases in which the nature of the endocrine mechanisms underlying various behavior patterns itself changes, or is different in different types of animals.

Eckstein (1949) points out that different species of mammals show very different relationships between environmental cycles and the reproductive system. Thus, some breed in spring, some in the autumn, and some breed aperiodically. Some ovulate spontaneously, some only on stimulation (Asdell, 1946). In addition to species differences in the way in which endocrine patterns themselves occur, there are striking differences in the ways in which the hormones influence behavior in different species. For example, Moore (1920) trans-planted ovaries into castrated young rats and guinea pigs. When adult, the rats showed female-like maternal behavior toward young animals, although no such behavioral changes were induced in the guinea pigs. Pregnant mice build substantial nests starting about the middle of pregnancy, whereas the corresponding behavior in rats does not occur until just before parturition (Koller, 1952; Wiesner and Sheard, 1933). This suggests that the hormonal basis of nest-building is different in the two species. Progesterone induces nest-building in mice (Koller, 1956), although it does not appear to have this effect in rabbits (Zarrow, Sawin, Ross and Denenberg, unpublished). Indeed, the fact that experimental *removal* of the corpus luteum during pregnancy induces nest-building behavior in the rabbit (Klein, 1956) suggests that progesterone might have quite opposite effects in the rabbit and in the mouse.

In birds, too, there are many examples of different hormonal responses to similar situations, and of different effects of hormones on patterns of behavior, in different species. Kept under similar conditions of light and temperature, ring doves breed all year, and the related mourning dove breeds only in the spring and summer (Cole, 1933). When sitting on infertile eggs, mourning doves abandon the nest after about 17 days, whereas domestic pigeons continue to sit for about 22 days (Cole and Kirkpatrick, 1915). Progesterone, which induces incubation behavior in ring doves (Riddle and Lahr, 1944; Lehrman, 1958b), has no effect on incubation behavior in chickens (Riddle, 1937) or canaries (Kobayashi, 1952; Kobayashi and Okubo, 1954). Testosterone propionate interrupts established broodiness in hens, but seems to have no effect on established incubation behavior in pigeons (Collias, 1940, 1950). Treatment with estrogen and prolactin, which induces the formation of the incubation patch in finches (Bailey, 1952), fails to induce it in the cowbird, which normally does not incubate eggs (Selander, 1960). Since the pituitary glands of cowbirds have been found to contain prolactin (Höhn, 1959), the failure of brood-patch formation in these parasitic birds is apparently due to the fact that the ventral skin is not sensitive to the hormones which induce it in other species.

It is apparent that, both in birds and in mammals, a variety of hormonal mechanisms, and of types of tissue responsiveness to hormones, may be found in different species, and that, as a consequence, similar behavior patterns in different animals may sometimes be underlain by rather different physiologic mechanisms.

2. Strain Differences and Genetic Factors

Although the study of behavior genetics has been growing very rapidly in recent years (Fuller, 1960; Fuller and Thompson, 1960), little information is available about genetic factors influencing parental behavior. It is to be hoped that this deficiency will soon be remedied.

Different strains of domestic hens differ sharply with respect to the number of birds which become "broody," thus interrupting their egg production (Pearl, 1914). For example, Goodale (1916) noted that only 2 to 3 per cent of White Leghorn hens ever become broody, compared with 93 per cent of Rhode Island Red hens. Riddle, Bates and Lahr (1935) found that prolactin injected into laying hens induced incubation behavior in 16 out of 20 birds of a broody race, but in only 1 out of 10 birds of a nonbroody race. Similarly, Nalbandov and Card (1945) found that the amount of prolactin required to induce roosters to care for chicks was much greater when the birds came from a nonbroody race than when they were of a broody race. For example, White Leghorn roosters required 500 to 700 I.U. of prolactin, whereas Cornish roosters required only 300. (Note that 50 I.U. is sufficient to induce broodiness in a laying *hen*.) Bates, Riddle, and Lahr (1939) found that different races and strains of pigeons differ markedly in their response to prolactin. Some strains required as much as 5 to 8 times as much prolactin as did others, for the same effect on the crop-sac. Byerly and Burrows (1936) found that the pituitary glands of genetically broody hens contained more prolactin than did those of nonbroody birds. This suggests that the broody and nonbroody races may differ not only in their responsiveness to prolactin, but also in their production of this hormone.

Carson, Bacon, Beall and Ryan (1960) found that broodiness interferes with egg production in some strains of fowl, but not in others.

Goodale, Sanborn and White (1920) showed that a nonbroody strain could be quickly developed from a broody one by selective breeding. Yamashina (1956a, b) selected nonbroody females from among a flock of Plymouth Rocks, and mated them with males which could not be made broody by prolactin injection. By this method, he reduced the percentage of broodiness in the flock from 84.5 per cent to 3.8 per cent. Various investigators have shown that broodiness depends on several pairs of genes, some sex-linked, some autosomal (Punnett and Bailey, 1920; Roberts and Card, 1934; Hays, 1940; Kaufman, 1948).

Leopold (1944) compared the behavior of wild turkeys with that of domesticated and hybrid strains. Wild mother birds with young tended to crouch quietly at the approach of a human, whereas the domestic and hybrid mothers noisily led their young away. Leopold related the differences in wildness between the two strains of turkeys in part to differences in adrenal physiology, the ratio of adrenal weight to body weight being more than twice as great in the wild birds as in the domestic strain.

Sawin and Curran (1952) found that various strains of rabbits, developed in their laboratory, differed with respect to the time of nest-building, the average quality of the nest, the choice of location of the nest, and the extent to which young were scattered, or in some cases eaten. The strains which they studied had been produced by selection for studies of growth and differentiation, *not* for breeding characteristics. As we might expect, they found no evidence of a single factor for "maternal behavior," since various of the characters with respect to which they found race differences were correlated with each other in some races, and not in others. In a later study, Sawin and Crary (1953) suggested at least two or three genetic factors, one influencing the time of building and lining the nest, others determining the nature of the nest, the quantity of the lining, etc. Hauschka (1952), studying strains of mice developed for cancer research, found strain differences with respect to the frequency of "cannibalism"—eating of the young.

King (1958) found that females of two closely related subspecies of deer mouse differed with respect to the intensity with which they would protect the young against an intruder. The difference between these two subspecies may be a difference in aggressiveness, which is known to be capable of alteration by selective breeding (Scott, 1958), and which might here be seen to be influencing the expression of parental behavior. A number of other behavioral and physiologic characters which may be related to the expression of parental behavior have been shown to be susceptible of alteration by selective breeding: prolactin content of the pituitary gland (Grosvenor and Turner, 1957); temperature preferences (Wolburg, 1952); exploratory behavior (Carr and Williams, 1957; McClearn, 1959); efficiency of lactation (Falconer, 1953); hoarding (Stamm, 1954, 1956); various aspects of "emotionality" (Broadhurst, 1958), etc. (Fuller, 1960). It may be suggested that systematic study of the genetics of parental behavior may soon be as rewarding as has been the study of various genetic aspects of sexual behavior (Young, 1957).

E. THE ROLE OF PARENTAL BEHAVIOR IN THE DEVELOPMENT OF THE YOUNG

The biologic function of parental behavior is, of course, to provide conditions which foster the development of the eggs and young. The requirements of the eggs and young thus form part of the complex of environmental conditions, in adaptation to which parental behavior has evolved. The characteristics of the parent are, of course, also a source of selection pressure guiding the evolution of the characteristics of the young. This is not the place for a full discussion of this problem, but we may briefly indicate some of the ways in which parental behavior is adapted to the requirements of the development of the young. It is apparent that experience gained from contact with other animals including the parents is prerequisite for the normal display of much of hormonally induced behavior.

1. In Birds

Incubation behavior is clearly related to the fact that most bird embryos require for their development temperatures higher than the usual environmental temperatures. Egg temperatures are consistently maintained at a high level by the transfer of heat between the ventral surface of the incubating parent's body and the surface of the egg (Kossack, 1947). We have already pointed out that the average temperature of eggs during incubation is approximately the same in birds of the same species breeding in different climates, probably indicating that the varying incubation behavior of the parents produces an approximately constant temperature of the eggs (Irving and Krog, 1956). Farner (1958) measured the temperature at the egg-body surface in the nests of incubating yellow-eyed penguins, and compared them with cloacal temperatures. He found that, although the body temperature of the bird did not change during the incubation period, the incubation temperature (temperature at the egg-body interface) gradually increased from about 20 to 25°C. to about 38°C. during the incubation period. This gradual increase in temperature is presumably due to some combination of increasing efficiency of incubation behavior and increasing vascularity of the incubation patch. Metabolic activity of the developing embryo does not seem to be involved, because the curve of temperature change was the same for nests with eggs which failed to develop as for nests with live eggs.

There is great interspecific variation in the speed of development of avian embryos, and in the incubation behavior of the parents (Stresemann, 1934). Some indication of the significance of the details of parental incubation behavior in fostering the development of the eggs may be seen in the fact that great difficulties are encountered in attempting to incubate eggs of wild birds in artificial incubators. Daniel (1957) found that the eggs of red-winged blackbirds developed well in artificial incubators up to the 7th day, and that eggs collected after the 7th day could be brought to hatching in such an incubator, but that it was extremely difficult to keep the embryo alive over the 7th day. It is not known exactly how the behavior of the parent during this period makes it so superior to the best efforts of a human being using an artificial incubator. In the domestic hen, there are several critical periods, during which most deaths of embryos occur in artificial incubators (Romanoff, 1949). New (1957) found that eggs required regular turning between the 4th and 7th day of incubation in order to hatch. Eggs turned only on those 4 days had the same degree of hatchability as eggs turned throughout incubation (21 of 35 eggs so treated hatched, compared with 24 out of 35 eggs turned throughout incubation). If the eggs are turned only between the 8th and 11th day of incubation, the number of eggs which hatch (6 of 35) is the same as in the case of eggs which are not turned at all during incubation. Clearly the behavior of the parents in regularly turning the eggs is an essential prerequisite for the successful development of the embryos (Westerskov, 1956).

Newly hatched altricial birds, such as the house wren (Kendeigh and Baldwin, 1928; Baldwin and Kendeigh, 1932) are poikilothermic at hatching, with the capacity for temperature regulation developing gradually, starting at 3 days post-hatching, and continuing up to about 9 to 12 days of age. The field sparrow becomes homoiothermic at about 7 to 10 days of age (Dawson and Evans, 1957). Precocial birds, such as the western gull (Bartholomew and Dawson, 1952) are in part homoiothermic at hatching; there are some indications that these birds may begin to develop the ability for temperature regulation before hatching. The parents of altricial birds characteristically brood the young much more attentively, and for a longer period, than do the parents of precocial birds (Kendeigh, 1952). Bartholomew and Dawson (1954) studied the development of temperature regulation in young brown pelicans and great blue herons, both altricial species, and in western gulls, a precocial species, all nesting on the same hot, dry island in the Gulf of California. When they deprived the birds of the care of their parents, they found that the young gulls had a consistently greater ca-

pacity for temperature regulation than did either the pelicans or the herons. In the words of these authors, "the successful nesting of these three species in the same area at the same time despite their differences in capacities for temperature regulation, emphasizes the importance of behavior as a supplement for physiological mechanisms in birds."

The feeding behavior of parent birds of different species is differentiated in ways which correspond to the different ways in which their young take food. For example, young passerine birds, such as the European blackbird, at first "beg" for food by lifting the head vertically and opening the gape wide, simultaneously uttering a characteristic sound; the parents of such species feed the young by dropping food into the open mouth (Tinbergen and Kuenen, 1939). Parent gulls, on the other hand, regurgitate fish which they hold in the bill in front of the young, which peck at the bill, stimulated by various aspects of its color and shape (Tinbergen and Perdeck, 1950; Collias and Collias, 1957). Chicks of some such species cannot pick up the food if it is dropped on the ground, but must get it from the bill of the parent (Hardy, 1957). We could compile, from the ornithological literature, a considerable list of the varying details of the manner in which parent birds feed their young, and the correspondences with the forms of behavior of the young.

The development of feeding behavior in young birds seems, in some species at least, to be partly influenced by the behavior of the parents toward the begging young. Rand (1942) reared four loggerhead shrikes by hand to the age of 21 days, when the first signs of pecking at food (instead of simply receiving it from the "parent") appeared. Two of the birds were subsequently kept in a cage with food always present, and hand-feeding was stopped as soon as possible. The remaining two birds had no food in their cage, and were fed exclusively by hand. The first group of two birds never begged after 45 days of age, whereas the second pair of birds (fed by hand) was still begging from their keeper at the age of 7½ months, although they could pick up food from the floor. Rand (1941) found similar results with young curve-billed thrashers: the greater the amount of care devoted to the birds, the longer the period of begging. Craig (1908) stated that the first learning of young pigeons to differentiate individuals comes about because the mother becomes unwilling to feed the young long before the father does so. Petersen (1955) observed that the first flights of nestling bank swallows were induced in part by the increasing reluctance of the parents to feed them.

Of course, these may be largely effects on the *rate* of development of the change from begging to independent feeding, which change may nevertheless occur without being stimulated by any change in the parent's behavior. Miller (1921) found that young house finches being reared by hand abruptly changed from begging to self-feeding without any change in the treatment which they were getting.

Young birds of many species apparently become conditioned to follow parents having particular characteristics by means of a very rapid learning process occurring during a particularly sensitive period shortly after hatching. This is the phenomenon of "imprinting" (Lorenz, 1935; Hinde, Thorpe and Vince, 1956; Hess, 1959).

The experiences of young birds with their parents sometimes also contribute to the nature of their mating preferences in later life, although it has not yet been demonstrated that this effect depends upon as sharp a critical period of learning as does the development of the following response of the young birds themselves. Craig (1914) noted that male ring doves reared by human keepers directed their courtship displays toward men, and particularly toward the human hand. When later allowed to associate with doves, they gave up their attachment to humans very slowly and incompletely, and not in all cases. Nicolai (1956) found that bullfinches reared in isolation accept a human keeper as the "mate." This attachment can be reversed during the bird's first autumn and winter if it meets other bullfinches, but becomes irreversible during the first mating season. The importance of such learned attachments to individuals of the species, based upon early experience with the parent, has been pointed out by a number of authors (Cushing, 1941; Cushing and Ramsay, 1949; Beach and Jaynes, 1954).

In some species of birds, such as the chaffinch, young birds appear to learn several aspects of the species' song through parental example (Thorpe, 1954, 1958), even though the actual expression of the song may not appear until much later, under the influence of androgenic hormone (Poulsen, 1953a). Frisch (1959) found that young redshanks reared from the egg by lapwing foster-parents learned to respond appropriately to the calls of the foster species.

Naturally, the actual physical survival of the young depends on the display of appropriate parental behavior by the parents. Leopold (1944) found a much higher survival ratio among young wild turkeys, whose mothers squat and crouch at the approach of man, than among liberated domestic turkeys in which the mothers scold and noisily herd their young away at the approach of humans. Nalbandov and Card (1945) found that, when young domestic chicks were being cared for by males which had been made "broody" by prolactin injection, the young tended to die of neglect or of attack after the cessation of the injections. This point is so obvious that it requires no further discussion.

2. In Mammals

Although many young mammals at first attempt to suck whatever object they come in contact with after birth (Collias, 1956), the establishment of a suckling relationship with a particular mother, or even a particular nipple, is accomplished very rapidly (Ewer, 1959). Collias (1956) points out that the repeated making and breaking of contact with the nipple during the first hours of the young goat's life seems to facilitate the learning of both the mother and the kid. Frank (1952) noted that young common voles resist being retrieved by other than their own mothers, apparently basing the discrimination on olfactory stimuli. King (quoted by Scott, 1953) found that guinea pigs removed from their mothers immediately after birth, and then replaced after 3 days can no longer develop suckling behavior. Beagle puppies, on the other hand, can be replaced with the mothers as late as 2 to 4 weeks of age, and develop normal suckling. Note that the guinea pig is normally much more precocious in its development than the puppy. Nevertheless, Levy (1934) found that dogs removed from their mothers at birth and returned to them at about 13 days of age had considerable difficulty in establishing suckling.

The licking of newborn young by the mother is, in many species of mammals, an essential condition for the establishment of urination and defecation. Reyniers (1953) found that baby rats isolated at birth die within a few days because they do not urinate, but that the survival of the animals can be assured by stroking the genitals, which reflexly elicits urination; after a few such experiences, urination occurs normally without stimulation by the keeper. Similarly, newborn polecats (Eibl-Eibesfeldt, 1955b) and wood rats (Richardson, 1943) are stimulated to urinate and defecate for the first time by the mother's licking.

In herd-living animals, the experience of the young animal with its mother during very early life apparently plays a vitally important role in enabling it to become integrated with the herd. Scott (1945) took two lambs from their mothers at birth and bottle-fed them for 8 or 9 days, then returned them to the flock. These animals showed little tendency to play with other lambs, and little tendency to stay with the flock while grazing. Similar observations have been made on a foal by Grzimek (1945). Murie (1944) observed that a Dall sheep reared by human beings from a few hours of age later showed no interest in joining nearby sheep. Altmann (1952, 1958) observed that the nursing interactions between baby elks and moose and their mothers form strong conditioned attachments between mother and calf which persists even after weaning. In this connection, Denniston (1956) found that moose calves which lose their mothers at the age of 7 or 8 months have a lower survival rate than do calves which continue to live with their mothers, even though weaning occurs at about 2 months of age. He suggests that protection by the mother is an important factor in ensuring the calf's access to foraging places.

It is well known that the early experiences of animals, including experiences with the parents, have substantial effects on their behavior in later life. Beach and Jaynes (1954) have reviewed most of the literature on this subject, and we need make only a few comments here. Mice reared in isolation are, when adults, more aggressive toward other mice than are those reared by their mothers (Kahn, 1954). It has now been demonstrated many times that handling of rats during infancy causes them to develop into adults showing less signs of "emotionality," and less organic damage under severe stress, than animals reared without such handling (Weininger, 1956; see also Levine, 1959, 1960). Seitz (1954) found that rats reared in small litters and those reared in large litters differed in many significant respects in adulthood. Animals from small litters tended to eat more and to go after food more quickly when hungry than those raised in large litters. The animals raised in large litters hoarded more food in adulthood than those from small litters. Those reared in small litters reacted to new experiences with less "anxiety" and more exploratory behavior in adulthood than those from larger litters. A number of other differences were observed, undoubtedly stemming from the differences in relationships between mother and young, and among the young, which are characteristic of the different litter sizes. In a later paper, Seitz (1959) described the effect on the behavior of cats, when adults, of separating them from their mothers at various ages. Kittens separated from their mothers at 2 weeks of age developed into adults which were more active, more disturbed by novel situations, more aggressive, and slower to learn simple routines, than were kittens which remained with their mothers for 6 or 12 weeks.

Harlow and his students (Harlow and Zimmermann, 1958, 1959; Harlow, 1959) have succeeded in rearing young rhesus monkeys from birth with artificial mothers from which the young could suckle. However, in later (unpublished) observations at the University of Wisconsin, Dr. Harlow has found that monkeys so reared failed to develop sexual behavior at the normal time, that they do not become capable of playing with other young monkeys, and that they remain attached to the "mother" for a very much longer time than do normally reared monkeys. Apparently some aspects of the behavior of the real mother toward the infant, which play a crucial role in the development of various aspects of the behavior of the young, are lacking in the artificial "mothers."

From this small sampling of a very large body of research, it is apparent that the behavior of parents toward the young, both in birds and in mammals, plays an important role in permitting and, to various extents in different kinds of animals, in guiding the development of the behavior of the young in their response to hormonal stimulation and in their integration into relationships with other members of the species.

V. Scientific Names of Animals Mentioned in Text

A. BIRDS

Adélie penguin	*Pygoscelis adeliae*
American coot	*Fulica americana*
American magpie	*Pica pica*
American robin	*Turdus migratorius*
Anis	*Crotophaginae*
Arctic tern	*Sterna paradisaea*
Auks	*Alcidae*
Baltimore oriole	*Icterus galbula*
Bank swallow	*Riparia riparia*
Barn swallow	*Hirundo rustica*
Blackbird	*Turdus merula*
Blackbirds	*Icteridae*
Black-capped chickadee	*Parus atricapillus*
Blackcock	*Lyruris tetrix*
Black-crowned night heron	*Nycticorax nycticorax*
Black guillemot	*Cepphus grylle*
Black-headed gull	*Larus ridibundus*
Blue jay	*Cyanocitta cristata*
Boat-tailed grackle	*Cassidix mexicanus*
Bobwhite	*Colinus virginianus*
Boobies	*Sulidae*
Bower birds	*Ptilonorhynchidae*
Brewer's blackbird	*Euphagus cyanocephalus*
Bronze mannikin	*Lonchura cucullata*
Brown pelican	*Pelicanus occidentalis*
Brush turkey	*Alectura lathami*
Bullfinch	*Pyrrhula pyrrhula*
California gull	*Larus californicus*
Cape weaver	*Hyphantornis capensis*
Carolina wren	*Thryothorus ludovicianus*
Cedar waxwing	*Bombycilla cedrorum*
Chaffinch	*Fringilla coelebs*
Clark nutcracker	*Nucifraga columbiana*
Cliff swallow	*Petrocholidon pyrrhonota*
Common gull	*Larus canus*
Common tern	*Sterna hirundo*
Coot	*Fulica atra*
Cormorants	*Phalacrocoracidae*
Cowbird	*Molothrus ater*
Cranes	*Gruidae*
Cuckoo	*Cuculus canorus*
Cuckoos	*Cuculidae*
Curve-billed thrasher	*Toxostoma curvirostre*
Doves	*Columbidae*
Ducks	*Anatidae*
Emperor penguin	*Aptenodytes forsteri*
European cuckoo	*Cuculus canorus*
European coot	*Fulica atra*
European goshawk	*Accipiter gentilis*
European jay	*Garrulus glandarius*
European robin	*Erithacus rubecula*
European wren	*Troglodytes troglodytes*
Field sparrow	*Spizella pusilla*
Flicker	*Colaptes auratus*
Florida jay	*Aphelocoma coerulescens*
Fulmar	*Fulmaris glacialis*
Geese	*Anserinae*
Golden pheasant	*Chrysolophus pictus*
Gould's manakin	*Manacus vitellinus*
Graceful warbler	*Prinia gracilis*
Great blue heron	*Ardea herodius*
Great crested grebe	*Podiceps cristatus*
Great reed warbler	*Acrocephalus arundinaceus*
Great tit	*Parus major*
Grebes	*Podicipedidae*
Green heron	*Butorides virescens*
Gulls	*Larinae*
Herons	*Ardeidae*
Herring gull	*Larus argentatus*
Honey guides	*Indicatoridae*
Hornbills	*Bucerotidae*
House finch	*Carpodacus mexicanus*
House sparrow	*Passer domesticus*
House wren	*Troglodytes aëdon*
Hummingbirds	*Trochilidae*
Jacana	*Jacana spinosa*
Jacanas	*Jacanidae*
Jackdaw	*Corvus monedula*
Kentish plover	*Charadrius alexandrinus*
King eider	*Somateria spectabilis*
Kittiwake	*Rissa tridactyla*
Lapwing	*Vanellus vanellus*
Loggerhead shrike	*Lanius ludovicianus*
Long-billed marsh wren	*Telmatodytes palustris*
Mallard	*Anas platyrhynchos*
Megapodes	*Megapodiidae*
Mourning dove	*Zenaidura macroura*
Murres	*Alcidae*
Night hawk	*Chordeiles minor*
Night heron	*Nycticorax nycticorax*
Noddy (tern)	*Anous stolidus*
Northern phalarope	*Lobipes lobatus*
Ovenbird	*Seiurus aurocapilus*

Pacific eider	*Somateria mollissima*
Partridges	*Phasianidae*
Pelicans	*Pelicanidae*
Penguins	*Spheniscidae*
Petrels	*Hydrobatidae*
Phalaropes	*Phalaropodidae*
Pheasants	*Phasianidae*
Pied-billed grebe	*Podilymbus podiceps*
Pigeons	*Columbidae*
Plovers	*Charadriidae*
Purple martin	*Progne subis*
Rails	*Rallidae*
Raven	*Corvus corax*
Red-backed shrike	*Lanius collurio*
Red-billed weaver	*Quelea quelea*
Redshank	*Tringa totanus*
Red-winged black-bird	*Agelaius phoeniceus*
Ring dove	*Streptopelia risoria*
Ringed plover	*Charadrius hiaticula*
Ring-necked pheas-ant	*Phasianus colchicus*
Rook	*Corvus frugilegus*
Ruff	*Philomachus pugnax*
Ruffed grouse	*Bonasa umbellus*
Sandpipers	*Scolopacidae*
Satin bower bird	*Ptilonorhynchus violaceus*
Serin	*Serinus canaria*
Shearwaters	*Procellariidae*
Shell parakeet	*Melopsittacus undulatus*
Short-tailed shear-water	*Puffinus tenuirostris*
Shrikes	*Laniidae*
Smooth-billed ani	*Crotophaga ani*
Snow bunting	*Plectrophenax nivalis*
Sociable weaverbird	*Philetairus socius*
Sooty tern	*Sterna fuscata*
Song sparrow	*Melospiza melodia*
Starling	*Sturnus vulgaris*
Storks	*Ciconiidae*
Storm petrel	*Hydrobates pelagicus*
Swift	*Apus apus*
Swifts	*Apodidae*
Terns	*Sterninae*
Tinamous	*Tinamidae*
Tricolored red-winged blackbird	*Agelaius tricolor*
Turkey	*Meleagris gallopavo*
Turnstone	*Arenaria interpres*
Valley quail	*Lophortyx californica*
Waders	*Scolopacidae*
Weaver finches	*Ploceidae*
Western gull	*Larus occidentalis*
White-crowned spar-row	*Zonotrichia leucophrys*
White-tailed kite	*Elanus leucurus*
Woodpeckers	*Picidae*
Wrens	*Troglodytidae*
Wryneck	*Jynx torquilla*
Yellow-eyed penguin	*Megadyptes antipodes*
Yellow-headed blackbird	*Xanthocephalus xantho-cephalus*
Zebra finch	*Poephila guttata*

B. MAMMALS

African lion	*Felis leo*
Alaska fur seal	*Callorhinus alascanus*

American beaver	*Castor canadensis*
American bison	*Bison bison*
American buffalo	*Bison bison*
American elk	*Cervus canadensis*
American red squir-rel	*Sciurus hudsonicus*
Antelopes	*Bovidae*
Asiatic squirrel	*Callosciurus leucomus*
Bats	*Vespertilionidae*
Bicolored white toothed shrew	*Crocidura leucodon*
Bottle-nosed dolphin	*Tursiops truncatus*
California sea lion	*Zalophus californianus*
Camels	*Camelidae*
Carnivores	*Carnivora*
Central American opossum	*Marmosa cinerea*
Chimpanzee	*Pan troglodytes*
Common vole	*Microtus arvalis*
Cotton rat	*Sigmodon hispidus*
Dall sheep	*Ovis dalli*
Deer mouse	*Peromyscus maniculatus*
Dusky-footed wood-rat	*Neotoma fuscipes*
Elephant	*Loxodonta africana*
Elephant seal	*Mirounga angustirostris*
European hare	*Lepus europaeus*
European water vole	*Arvicola terrestris*
European yellow-necked mouse	*Apodemus flavicollis*
Field mouse	*Microtus arvalis*
Field vole	*Microtus agrestis*
Galapagos sea lion	*Zalophus wollebaeki*
Golden hamster	*Mesocricetus auratus*
Gorilla	*Gorilla gorilla*
Guanaco	*Lama guanicoe*
Hippopotamus	*Hippopotamus amphibius*
Kangaroos	*Macropodidae*
Llamas	*Camelidae*
Meadow mouse	*Microtus pennsylvanicus*
Moose	*Alces americana*
Northern pigmy mouse	*Baiomys taylori*
Opossum	*Didelphus virginiana*
Orang-utang	*Pongo pygmaeus*
Polecat	*Mustela putorius*
Red deer	*Cervus elaphus*
Red kangaroo	*Macropus rufus*
Rhesus monkey	*Macaca mulatta*
Rice rat	*Oryzomys palustris*
Rodents	*Rodentia*
Seals	*Phocidae*
Sea lions	*Otariidae*
Shrew	*Blarina brevicauda*
Ungulates	*Ungulata*
Wood-mouse	*Peromyscus leucopus*
Wood-rat	*Neotoma albigula*

VI. References

ADAMS, J. S., AND HERRICK, R. B. 1955. Interactions of the gonadal hormones in the chicken. Poult. Sci., **34,** 117–121.

ALLAN, H., AND WILES, P. 1932. The role of the pituitary gland and parturition. I. Hypophysectomy. J. Physiol., **75,** 23–28.

ALLEN, A. A. 1934. Sex rhythm in the ruffed

grouse *(Bonasa umbellus* Linn.) and other birds. Auk, **51**, 180–199.

ALLEN, G. M. 1939. *Bats.* Cambridge: Harvard University Press.

ALLEN, R. P., AND MANGELS, F. P. 1940. Studies of the nesting behavior of the black-crowned night heron. Proc. Linn. Soc. N. Y., No. 50–51, 1–28.

ALLEN, R. W., AND NICE, M. M. 1952. A study of the breeding biology of the purple martin *(Progne subis).* Amer. Midl. Nat., **47**, 606–665.

ALTMANN, M. 1952. Social behavior of elk, *Cervus canadensis,* in the Jackson Hole area of Wyoming. Behaviour, **4**, 116–143.

ALTMANN, M. 1958. Social integration of the moose calf. Anim. Behav., **6**, 155–159.

AMADON, D. 1944a. The genera of Corvidae and their relationships. Amer. Mus. Novit., No. 1251.

AMADON, D. 1944b. Results of the Archbold expeditions. No. 50. A preliminary life history study of the Florida jay, *Cyanocitta c. coerulescens.* Amer. Mus. Novit., No. 1252.

AMANTEA, G. 1928. Sul ritmo di ovulazione normale nella Columba domestica e su un espediente atto ad accelerarlo. Boll. Soc. ital Biol. sper., **3**, 117–119.

ANDERSSON, B. 1951a. Some observations on the neuro-hormonal regulation of milk-ejection. Acta physiol. scand., **23**, 1–7.

ANDERSSON, B. 1951b. The effect and localization of electrical stimulation of certain parts of the brain stem in sheep and goats. Acta. physiol. scand., **23**, 8–23.

ANDERSSON, B. 1953. The effect of injections of hypertonic NaCl solutions into different parts of the hypothalamus of goats. Acta physiol. scand., **28**, 188–201.

ANDERSSON, B., AND MCCANN, S. M. 1955. Drinking, antidiuresis, and milk ejection from electrical stimulation within the hypothalamus of the goat. Acta physiol. scand., **35**, 191–201.

ARMSTRONG, E. A. 1947. *Bird Display and Behaviour.* London: Lindsay Drummond, Ltd.

ARMSTRONG, E. A. 1955. *The Wren.* London: William Collins Sons & Company, Ltd.

ARONSON, L. R. 1959. Hormones and reproductive behavior: some phylogenetic considerations. In *Comparative Endocrinology,* A. Gorbman, Ed., pp. 98–120. New York: John Wiley & Sons.

ASCHEMEIER, C. R. 1922. Beds of the gorilla and chimpanzee. J. Mammal., **3**, 176–178.

ASCHOFF, J. 1955. Jahresperiodik der Fortpflanzung bei Warmblütern. Studium gen., **8**, 742–776.

ASDELL, S. A. 1946. *Patterns of Mammalian Reproduction.* Ithaca: Comstock Publishing Company.

AVERY, G. T. 1925. Notes on reproduction in guinea pigs. J. comp. Psychol., **5**, 373–396.

BACQ, Z. M. 1932a. The effect of sympathectomy on sexual functions, lactation, and the maternal behavior of the albino rat. Amer. J. Physiol., **99**, 444–453.

BACQ, Z. M. 1932b. Observation du comportement maternel du rat albino sympathectomisé. J. Psychol. morm. path., **29**, 254–257.

BAERENDS, G. P. 1959. The ethological analysis of incubation behavior. Ibis, **101**, 357–368.

BAGGERMAN, B., BAERENDS, G. P., HEIKENS, H. S., AND MOOK, J. H. 1956. Observations on the behaviour of the black tern, *Chlidonias n. niger* (L.), in the breeding area. Ardea, **44**, 1–71.

BAGSHAWE, T. W. 1938. Notes on the habits of the gentoo and ringed or Antarctic penguins. Trans. zool. Soc. Lond., **24**, 185–306.

BAILEY, R. E. 1950. Inhibition with prolactin of light-induced gonad increase in white-crowned sparrows. Condor, **52**, 247–251.

BAILEY, R. E. 1952. The incubation patch of passerine birds. Condor, **54**, 121–136.

BAILEY, V. 1924. Breeding, feeding and other life habits of meadow mice *(Microtus).* J. agric. Res., **27**, 523–536.

BAKER, J. R. 1938. The evolution of breeding seasons. In *Evolution: Essays on Aspects of Evolutionary Biology,* G. R. de Beer, Ed., pp 161–177. Oxford: Oxford University Press.

BALDWIN, S. P., AND KENDEIGH, S. C. 1932. Physiology of the temperature of birds. Sci. Publ Cleveland Mus. nat. Hist., **3**, 1–196.

BARTELMEZ, G. W. 1912. The bilaterality of the pigeon's egg. A study in egg organization from the first growth of the oocyte to the beginning of the cleavage. J. Morph., **23**, 269–328.

BARTH, E. K. 1955. Egg-laying, incubation and hatching of the common gull *(Larus canus).* Ibis, **97**, 222–239.

BARTHOLOMEW, G. A. 1952. Reproductive and social behavior of the northern elephant seal. Univ. Calif. Publ. Zool., **47**, 369–472.

BARTHOLOMEW, G. A. 1953. Behavioral factors affecting social structure in the Alaska fur seal. Trans. N. Amer. Wildl. Conf., **18**, 481–502.

BARTHOLOMEW, G. A. 1959. Mother-young relations and the maturation of pup behaviour in the Alaska fur seal. Anim. Behav., **7**, 163–171.

BARTHOLOMEW, G. A., AND DAWSON, W. R. 1952. Body temperatures in nestling western gulls. Condor, **54**, 58–60.

BARTHOLOMEW, G. A., AND DAWSON, W. R. 1954. Temperature regulation in young pelicans, herons, and gulls. Ecology, **35**, 466–472.

BARTHOLOMEW, G. A., AND HOEL, P. G. 1953. Reproductive behavior of the Alaska fur seal, *Callorhinus ursinus.* J. Mammal., **34**, 417–436.

BATEMAN, N. 1957. Some physiological aspects of lactation in mice. J. agric. Sci., **49**, 60–77.

BATES, R. W., LAHR, E. L., AND RIDDLE, O. 1935. The gross action of prolactin and follicle-stimulating hormone on the mature ovary and sex accessories of fowl. Amer. J. Physiol., **111**, 361–368.

BATES, R. W., RIDDLE, O., AND LAHR, E. L. 1937. The mechanism of the anti-gonad action of prolactin. Amer. J. Physiol., **119**, 610 614.

BATES, R. W., RIDDLE, O., AND LAHR, E. L. 1939. The racial factor in the pigeon crop-sac method of bioassay of prolactin. Amer. J. Physiol., **125**, 722–729.

BATES, R. W., RIDDLE, O., LAHR, E. L., AND SCHOOLEY, J. P. 1937. Aspects of splanchnomegaly associated with the action of prolactin. Amer. J. Physiol., **119**, 603–609.

BEACH, F. A. 1937. The neural basis of innate behavior. I. Effects of cortical lesions upon the maternal behavior pattern in the rat. J. comp. Psychol., **24**, 393–439.

BEACH, F. A. 1938. The neural basis of innate behavior. II. Relative effects of partial decortication in adulthood and infancy upon the maternal behavior of the primiparous rat. J. genet. Psychol., **53**, 109–148.

BEACH, F. A. 1939a. The neural basis of innate behavior. III. Comparison of learning ability and instinctive behavior in the rat. J. comp. Psychol., **28**, 225–262.

BEACH, F. A. 1939b. Maternal behavior of the pouchless marsupial, *Marmosa cinerea*. J. Mammal., **20**, 315–322.

BEACH, F. A. 1942. Analysis of factors involved in the arousal, maintenance and manifestation of sexual excitement in male animals. Psychosom. Med., **4**, 173–198.

BEACH, F. A. 1947a. A review of physiological and psychological studies of sexual behavior in mammals. Physiol. Rev., **27**, 240–307.

BEACH, F. A. 1947b. Evolutionary changes in the physiological control of mating behavior in mammals. Psychol. Rev., **54**, 297–315.

BEACH, F. A. 1948. *Hormones and Behavior*. New York: Paul B. Hoeber, Inc.

BEACH, F. A. 1951. Instinctive behavior: reproductive activities. In *Handbook of Experimental Psychology*, S. S. Stevens, Ed., pp. 387–434. New York: John Wiley & Sons.

BEACH, F. A. 1958a. Evolutionary aspects of psychoendocrinology. In *Behavior and Evolution*, A. Roe and G. G. Simpson, Eds., pp. 81–102. New Haven: Yale University Press.

BEACH, F. A. 1958b. Normal sexual behavior in male rats isolated at fourteen days of age. J. comp. physiol. Psychol., **51**, 37–38.

BEACH, F. A., AND JAYNES, J. 1954. Effects of early experience upon the behavior of animals. Psychol. Bull., **51**, 239–263.

BEACH, F. A., AND JAYNES, J. 1956a. Studies of maternal retrieving in rats. II. Effects of practice and previous parturitions. Amer. Nat., **90**, 103–109.

BEACH, F. A., AND JAYNES, J. 1956b. Studies of maternal retrieving in rats. III. Sensory cues involved in the lactating female's response to her young. Behaviour, **10**, 104–125.

BEACH, F. A., AND JAYNES, J. 1956c. Studies of maternal retrieving in rats. I. Recognition of young. J. Mammal., **37**, 177–180.

BEACH, F. A., AND LEVINSON, G. 1950. Effects of androgen on the glans penis and mating behavior of castrated male rats. J. exp. Zool., **114**, 159–172.

BEAMS, H. W., AND MEYER, R. K. 1931. The formation of pigeon "milk." Physiol. Zoöl., **4**, 486–500.

BEEBE, W. 1936. *Pheasants, Their Lives and Homes*. New York: Doubleday, Doran & Company, Inc.

BEER, C. G. 1961. Incubation and nest-building behaviour of black-headed gulls I: Incubation behaviour in the incubation period. Behaviour, **17**, *in press*.

BENIEST-NOIROT, E. 1958. Analyse du comportement dit maternel chez la souris. Monogr. franç. Psychol., No. 1.

BENJAMIN, R. M., AND THOMPSON, R. F. 1959. Differential effects of cortical lesions in infant and adult cats on roughness discrimination. Exp. Neurol., **1**, 305–321.

BENNETT, M. A. 1940. The social hierarchy in ring doves. II. The effect of treatment with testosterone propionate. Ecology, **21**, 148–165.

BENOIT, J. 1956. Etats physiologiques et instinct de reproduction chez les oiseaux. In *L'Instinct dans le Comportement des Animaux et de l'Homme*, P.-P. Grassé, Ed., pp. 177–260. Paris: Masson & Cie.

BENOIT, J., AND ASSENMACHER, I. 1955. Le controle hypothalamique de l'activité préhypophysaire gonadotrope. J. Physiol. Path. gén., **47**, 427–567.

BENSON, G. K., AND COWIE, A. T. 1956. Lactation in the rat after hypophysial posterior lobectomy. J. Endocrin., **14**, 54–65.

BENSON, G. K., AND FOLLEY, S. J. 1956. Oxytocin as stimulator for the release of prolactin from the anterior pituitary. Nature, **177**, 700.

BENSON, G. K., AND FOLLEY, S. J. 1957. The effect of oxytocin on mammary gland involution in the rat. J. Endocrin., **16**, 189–201.

BENT, A. C. 1922. Life histories of North American petrels and pelicans and their allies. Bull. U. S. nat. Mus., No. 121.

BENT, A. C. 1923. Life histories of North American wild fowl (Part 1). Bull. U. S. nat. Mus., No. 126.

BENT, A. C. 1925. Life histories of North American wild fowl (Part 2). Bull. U. S. nat. Mus., No. 130.

BENT, A. C. 1939. Life histories of North American woodpeckers. Bull. U. S. nat. Mus., No. 174.

BENT, A. C. 1942. Life histories of North American flycatchers, larks, swallows and their allies. Bull. U. S. nat. Mus., No. 179.

BERG, I. A. 1944. Development of behavior: the micturition pattern in the dog. J. exp. Psychol., **34**, 343–368.

BERGMAN, G. 1946. Der Steinwälzer, *Arenaria i. interpres*, (L.), in seiner Beziehung zur Umwelt. Acta zool. fenn., **47**, 1–152.

BERRY, J. 1943. Artificial goose nests. An experiment on the breeding psychology of wild geese. Avicult. Mag., 5th ser., **8**, 55–59.

BERRY, J. 1944. Artificial goose nests again. Further observations on the breeding psychology of wild geese. Avicult. Mag., 5th ser., **9**, 75–79.

BIRCH, H. G. 1956. Sources of order in the maternal behavior of animals. Amer. J. Orthypsychiat., **26**, 279–284.

BIRCH, H. G., AND CLARK, G. 1946. Hormonal modification of social behavior: II. The effects of sex-hormone administration on the social dominance status of the female-castrate chimpanzee. Psychosom. Med., **8**, 320–331.

BIRCH, H. G., AND CLARK, G. 1950. Hormonal modification of social behavior: IV. The mechanism of estrogen-induced dominance in chimpanzees. J. comp. physiol. Psychol., **43**, 181–193.

BISSONNETTE, T. H. 1937. Photoperiodicity in birds. Wilson Bull., **49**, 241–270.

BISSONNETTE, T. H. 1939. Sexual photoperiodicity in the blue jay (*Cyanocitta cristata*). Wilson Bull., **51**, 227–232.

BISSONNETTE, T. H., AND ZUJKO, A. J. 1936. Normal progressive changes in the ovary of the starling (*Sturnus vulgaris*) from December to April. Auk, **53**, 31–50.

BLAIR, W. F. 1941. Observations on the life history of Baiomys taylori subater. J. Mammal., **22**, 378–383.

BLAKELY, R. M., ANDERSON, R. W., AND MACGREGOR, H. I. 1951. The estrogen interruption of broodiness in turkeys. Poult. Sci., **30**, 907.

BLANCHARD, B. D. 1941. The white-crowned sparrows (*Zonotrichia leucophrys*) of the Pacific seaboard: environment and annual cycle. Univ. Calif. Publ. Zool., **46**(1), 1–178.

BLAUVELT, H. 1955. Dynamics of the mother-newborn relationship in goats. In *Group Processes. Transactions of the First Conference*, B. Schaffner, Ed., pp. 221–258. New York: Josiah Macy, Jr. Foundation.

BOURLIÈRE, F. 1954. *The Natural History of Mammals.* New York: Alfred A. Knopf, Inc.

BRACKBILL, H. 1958. Nesting behavior of the wood thrush. Wilson Bull., **70**, 70–89.

BRADLEY, T. R., AND CLARKE, P. M. 1956. The response of rabbit mammary glands to locally administered prolactin. J. Endocrin., **14**, 28–36.

BRANT, J. W. A., AND NALBANDOV, A. V. 1956. Role of sex hormones in albumen secretion by the oviduct of chickens. Poult. Sci., **35**, 692–700.

BRAUDE, R., AND MITCHELL, K. G. 1952. Observations on the relationship between oxytocin and adrenaline in milk ejection in the sow. J. Endocr., **8**, 238–241.

BREITENBACH, R. P., AND MEYER, R. K. 1959. Pituitary prolactin levels in laying, incubating and brooding pheasants (*Phasianus colchicus*). Proc. Soc. exp. Biol., N. Y., **101**, 16–19.

BROADHURST, P. L. 1958. Determinants of emotioality in the rat. III. Strain differences. J. comp. physiol. Psychol., **51**, 55–59.

BROWN, R. Z. 1953. Social behavior, reproduction, and population changes in the house mouse (*Mus musculus* L.). Ecol. Monogr., **23**, 217–240.

BULLOUGH, W. S. 1951. *Vertebrate Sexual Cycles.* London: Methuen & Company, Ltd.

BURGER, J. W. 1942. The influence of some external factors on the ovarian cycle of the female starling. Anat. Rec., **84**, 518.

BURGER, J. W. 1949. A review of experimental investigations on seasonal reproduction in birds. Wilson Bull., **61**, 211–230.

BURGER, J. W. 1953. The effect of photic and psychic stimuli on the reproductive cycle of the male starling, *Sturnus vulgaris.* J. exp. Zool., **124**, 227–239.

BURROWS, W. H., AND BYERLY, T. C. 1936. Studies of prolactin in the fowl pituitary. I. Broody hens compared with laying hens and males. Proc. Soc. exp. Biol., N. Y., **34**, 841–844.

BURROWS, W. H., AND BYERLY, T. C. 1938. The effect of certain groups of environmental factors upon the expression of broodiness. Poult. Sci., **17**, 324–330.

BURROWS, W. H., AND BYERLY, T. C. 1940. Premature expulsion of eggs by hens injected with posterior pituitary substances. Poult. Sci., **19**, 346.

BURROWS, W. H., AND BYERLY, T. C. 1942. Premature expulsion of eggs by hens following injection of whole posterior pituitary preparations. Poult. Sci., **21**, 416–421.

BYERLY, T. C., AND BURROWS, W. H. 1936. Studies of prolactin in the fowl pituitary. II. Effects of genetic constitution with respect to broodiness on prolactin content. Proc. Soc. exp. Biol., N. Y., **34**, 844–846.

CAMPBELL, B., AND PETERSEN, W. E. 1953. Milk "let-down" and the orgasm in the human female. Hum. Biol., **25**, 165–168.

CANNON, W. B. 1929. *Bodily Changes in Pain, Hunger, Fear, and Rage.* New York: Appleton-Century, Inc.

CANNON, W. B. 1930. Quelques observations sur le comportement maternel d'animaux privés du système sympathique. J. Psychol. norm. path., **27**, 486–488.

CANNON, W. B. 1934. Hunger and thirst. In *A Handbook of General Experimental Psychology*, C. Murchison, Ed., pp. 247–263. Worcester, Mass.: Clark University Press.

CANNON, W. B., AND BRIGHT, E. M. 1931. A belated effect of sympathectomy on lactation. Amer. J. Physiol., **97**, 319–321.

CANNON, W. B., NEWTON, H. F., BRIGHT, E. M., MENKIN, V., AND MOORE, R. M. 1929. Some aspects of the physiology of animals surviving complete exclusion of sympathetic nerve impulses. Amer. J. Physiol., **89**, 84–107.

CARPENTER, C. R. 1933a. Psychobiological studies of social behavior in Aves. I. The effect of complete and incomplete gonadectomy on the primary sexual activity of the male pigeon. J. comp. Psychol., **16**, 25–57.

CARPENTER, C. R. 1933b. Psychobiological studies of social behavior in Aves. II. The effect of complete and incomplete gonadectomy on secondary sexual activity with histological studies. J. comp. Psychol., **16**, 59–97.

CARPENTER, C. R. 1934. A field study of the behavior and social relations of howling monkeys. Comp. Psychol. Monogr., **10**, No. 48.

CARR, R. M., AND WILLIAMS, C. D. 1957. Exploratory behavior of three strains of rats. J. comp. physiol. Psychol., **50**, 621–623.

CARSON, J. R., BACON, B. F., BEALL, G., AND RYAN, F. A. 1960. Breed differences in the relationship between broodiness and egg production in the chicken. Poult. Sci., **39**, 538–544.

CARSON, J. R., EATON, R. D., AND BACON, B. F. 1956. Termination of broodiness in the chicken. Bull. Storrs agric. Exp. Sta., **323**, 3–10.

CAUSEY, D., AND WATERS, R. H. 1936. Parental care in mammals with especial reference to the carrying of young by the albino rat. J. comp. Psychol., **22**, 241–254.

CHAMPY, C., AND COLLE, P. 1919. Sur une corrélation entre la glande du jabot du pigeon et les glandes génitales. C. R. Soc. Biol., Paris, **82**, 818–819.

CHAMPY, C., COUJARD, R., AND DEMAY, M. 1950. La sensibilité aux hormones. Ses caractéristiques et son mécanisme. Ire Partie. Ann. Endocr., Paris, **11**, 195–211.

CHANCE, E. 1940. *The Truth about the Cuckoo*. London: Country Life, Ltd.

CHAPMAN, F. M. 1935. The courtship of Gould's manakin (*Manacus vitellinus vitellinus*) on Barro Colorado Island, Canal Zone. Bull. Amer. Mus. nat. Hist., **68**, 471–525.

CHU, J. F. 1945. The influence of thyroid on pregnancy and parturition in the rabbit. J. Endocrin., **4**, 109–114.

CLARK, G., AND BIRCH, H. G. 1946. Hormonal modification of social behavior: III. The effects of stilbestrol therapy on social dominance in the female-castrate chimpanzee. Bull. Canad. psychol. Ass., **6**, 15–18.

CLAUSEN, D.-M. 1959. Hormonale Regulation des Nestbaus der Brieftaube. Verh. dtsch. zool. Ges., **1959**, 297–308.

COLE, L. J. 1917. Determinate and indeterminate laying cycles in birds. Anat. Rec., **11**, 504–505.

COLE, L. J. 1930. The laying cycle in the house wren. Wilson Bull., **42**, 78.

COLE, L. J. 1933. The relation of light periodicity to the reproductive cycle, migration, and distribution of the mourning dove (*Zenaidura macroura carolinensis*). Auk, **50**, 284–296.

COLE, L. J., AND KIRKPATRICK, W. F. 1915. Sex ratios in pigeons, together with observations on the laying, incubation and hatching of the eggs. Bull. R. I. agric. Exp. Sta., **162**, 461–512.

COLE, R. K., AND HUTT, F. B. 1953. Normal ovulation in non-laying hens. Poult. Sci., **32**, 481–492.

COLES, C. 1937. Some observations on the habits of the brush turkey (*Alectura lathami*). Proc. zool. Soc. Lond., **107**, 261–273.

COLLIAS, E. C., AND COLLIAS, N. E. 1957. The response of chicks of the Franklin's gull to parental bill-color. Auk, **74**, 371–375.

COLLIAS, N. E. 1940. Some effects of sex hormones on broodiness in fowl and pigeon. Anat. Rec. (suppl.), **78**, 146–147.

COLLIAS, N. E. 1946. Some experiments on brooding behavior in fowl and pigeon. Anat. Rec., **96**, 572.

COLLIAS, N. 1950. Hormones and behavior with special reference to birds and the mechanisms of hormone action. In *A Symposium on Steroid Hormones*, E. S. Gordon, Ed., pp. 277–329. Madison: University of Wisconsin Press.

COLLIAS, N. E. 1952. The development of social behavior in birds. Auk, **69**, 127–159.

COLLIAS, N. E. 1956. The analysis of socialization in sheep and goats. Ecology, **37**, 228–239.

COLLIAS, N. E., AND COLLIAS, E. C. 1956. Some mechanisms of family integration in ducks. Auk, **73**, 378–400.

COLLIP, J. B., SELYE, H., AND THOMSON, D. L. 1933. Gonad-stimulating hormones in hypophysectomized animals. Nature, **131**, 56.

COOMBS, C. J. F., AND MARSHALL, A. J. 1956. The effects of hypophysectomy on the internal testis rhythm in birds and mammals. J. Endocrin., **13**, 107–111.

COOPER, J. B. 1942. An exploratory study on African lions. Comp. Psychol. Monogr., **17**, No. 7.

COOPER, J. B. 1944. A description of parturition in the domestic cat. J. comp. Psychol., **37**, 71–79.

COTES, P. M., AND CROSS, B. A. 1954. The influence of suckling on food intake and growth of adult female rats. J. Endocrin., **10**, 363–367.

COUJARD, R. 1943. Le role du sympathique dans les actions hormonales. Bull. biol., **77**, 120–223.

COWIE, A. T. 1957. The maintenance of lactation in the rat after hypophysectomy. J. Endocrin., **16**, 135–147.

COWIE, A. T., FOLLEY, S. J., CROSS, B. A., HARRIS, G. W., JACOBSOHN, D., AND RICHARDSON, K. C. 1951. Terminology for use in lactational physiology. Nature, **168**, 421.

CRAIG, W. 1908. The voices of pigeons regarded as a means of social control. Amer. J. Sociol., **14**, 86–100.

CRAIG, W. 1911. Oviposition induced by the male in pigeons. J. Morph., **22**, 299–305.

CRAIG, W. 1913. The stimulation and the inhibition of ovulation in birds and mammals. J. Anim. Behav., **3**, 215–221.

CRAIG, W. 1914. Male doves reared in isolation. J. Anim. Behav., **4**, 121–133.

CRAIG, W. 1918. Appetites and aversions as constituents of instincts. Biol. Bull., Wood's Hole, **34**, 91–107.

CRISPENS, C. G., JR. 1956. Prolactin: an evaluation of its use in ring-necked pheasant propagation. J. Wildlife Mgmt, **20**, 453–455.

CRISPENS, C. G., JR. 1957. Use of prolactin to induce broodiness in two wild turkeys. J. Wildlife Mgmt, **21**, 462.

CROSS, B. A. 1950. Suckling antidiuresis in rabbits. Nature, **166**, 612–613.

CROSS, B. A. 1951. Suckling antidiuresis in rabbits. J. Physiol., **114**, 447–453.

CROSS, B. A. 1952. Nursing behaviour and the milk ejection reflex in rabbits. J. Endocrin., **8**, xiii–xiv.

CROSS, B. A. 1953. Sympathetico-adrenal inhibition of the neurohypophysial milk-ejection mechanism. J. Endocrin., **9**, 7–18.

CROSS, B. A. 1954. Milk ejection resulting from mechanical stimulation of mammary myoepithelium in the rabbit. Nature, **173**, 450.

CROSS, B. A. 1955a. The hypothalamus and the mechanism of sympathetico-adrenal inhibition of milk ejection. J. Endocrin., **12**, 15–28.

CROSS, B. A. 1955b. Neurohumoral mechanisms in emotional inhibition of milk ejection. J. Endocrin., **12**, 29–37.

CROSS, B. A. 1957. Physiological foundations of milk production and lactational disorders. Vet. Rec., **69**, 1216–1226.

CROSS, B. A. 1959. Neurohypophyseal control of parturition. In *Recent Progress in the Endocrinology of Reproduction*, C. W. Lloyd, Ed., pp. 441–455. New York: Academic Press, Inc.

CROSS, B. A. 1960. Neural control of lactation. In *Milk: The Mammary Gland and Its Secretion*, A. T. Cowie and S. K. Kon, Eds., pp. 229–277. New York: Academic Press, Inc.

CROSS, B. A., AND GREEN, J. D. 1959. Activity of single neurones in the hypothalamus: effect of osmotic and other stimuli. J. Physiol., **148**, 554–569.

CROSS, B. A., AND HARRIS, G. W. 1950. Milk ejection following electrical stimulation of the pituitary stalk in rabbits. Nature, **166**, 994–995.

CROSS, B. A., AND HARRIS, G. W. 1951. The neurohypophysis and "let-down" of milk. J. Physiol., **113**, 35P.

CROSS, B. A., AND HARRIS, G. W. 1952. The role of the neurohypophysis in the milk-ejection reflex. J. Endocrin., **8**, 148–161.

CROSS, B. A., AND SILVER, I. A. 1956. Milk ejection and mammary engorgement. Proc. roy. Soc. Med., **49**, 978–979.

CULLEN, E. 1957. Adaptations in the kittiwake to cliff-nesting. Ibis, **99**, 275–302.

CURIO, E. 1955. Der Jugendtransport einer Gelbhalsmaus (*Apodemus f. flavicollis* Melch.). Z. Tierpsychol, **12**, 459–462.

CUSHING, J. E. 1941. Non-genetic mating preference as a factor in evolution. Condor, **43**, 233–236.

CUSHING, J. E., AND RAMSAY, A. O. 1949. The non-heritable aspects of family unity in birds. Condor, **51**, 82–87.

CUTHBERT, N. L. 1945. The ovarian cycle of the ring dove (*Streptopelia risoria*). J. Morph., **77**, 351–377.

CUTHBERT, N. L. 1954. A nesting study of the black tern in Michigan. Auk, **71**, 36–63.

DAANJE, A. 1941. Über das Verhalten des Haussperlings (*Passer domesticus* (L)). Ardea, **30**, 1–42.

DANIEL, J. C., JR. 1957. An embryological comparison of the domestic fowl and the redwinged blackbird. Auk, **74**, 340–358.

DANNEEL, R., AND KAHLO, L. 1947. Untersuchungen über die dominant erbliche Haarlosigkeit bei der Hausmaus. Z. Naturf., **2b**, 215–222.

DARLING, F. F. 1938. *Bird Flocks and the Breeding Cycle*. Cambridge: Cambridge University Press.

DARLING, F. F. 1956. *A Herd of Red Deer*, corrected ed. Oxford: Oxford University Press.

DATHE, H. 1934. Eine neue Beobachtung des Känguruhgeburtsaktes. Zool. Gart., Lpz., **7**, 223–224.

DAVIS, D. E. 1940a. Social nesting habits of the smooth-billed ani. Auk, **57**, 179–218.

DAVIS, D. E. 1940b. Social nesting habits of *Guira guira*. Auk, **57**, 472–484.

DAVIS, D. E. 1941. The belligerency of the kingbird. Wilson Bull., **53**, 157–168.

DAVIS, D. E. 1942a. The number of eggs laid by cowbirds. Condor, **44**, 10–12.

DAVIS, D. E. 1942b. The phylogeny of social nesting habits in the Crotophaginae. Quart. Rev. Biol., **17**, 115–134.

DAVIS, D. E. 1945. The occurrence of the incubation patch in some Brazilian birds. Wilson Bull., **57**, 188–190.

DAVIS, D. E. 1955. Determinate laying in barn swallows and black-billed magpies. Condor, **57**, 81–87.

DAVIS, D. E. 1958. Relation of "clutch-size" to number of ova ovulated by starlings. Auk, **75**, 60–66.

DAVIS, P. 1957. The breeding of the storm petrel. Brit. Birds, **50**, 85–101, 371–384.

DAWSON, A. B. 1946. Some evidences of specific activity of the anterior pituitary gland of the cat. Amer. J. Anat., **78**, 347–409.

DAWSON, W. R., AND EVANS, F. C. 1957. Relation of growth and development to temperature regulation in nestling field and chipping sparrows. Physiol. Zoöl., **30**, 315–327.

DELACOUR, J. 1951. *The Pheasants of the World*. New York: Charles Scribner's Sons.

DELACOUR, J., AND MAYR, E. 1945. The family Anatidae. Wilson Bull., **57**, 3–55.

DELL, P. C. 1958a. Some basic mechanisms of the translation of bodily needs into behaviour. In *Ciba Foundation Symposium on the Neurological Basis of Behaviour*, G. E. W. Wolstenholme and C. M. O'Connor, Eds., pp. 187–203. London: J. & A. Churchill, Ltd.

DELL, P. C. 1958b. Humoral effects on the brain stem reticular formations. In *Reticular Formation of the Brain*, H. H. Jasper *et al.*, Eds., pp. 365–379. Boston: Little, Brown & Company.

DENENBERG, V. H., SAWIN, P. B., FROMMER, G. P., AND ROSS, S. 1958. Genetic, physiological, and behavioral background of reproduction in the rabbit. IV. An analysis of maternal behavior at successive parturitions. Behaviour, **13**, 131–142.

DENNISTON, R. H. 1956. Ecology, behavior and population dynamics of the Wyoming or rocky mountain moose, *Alces alces shirasi*. Zoologica, N. Y., **41**, 105–118.

DESCLIN, L. 1936. A propos de l'influence de la lactation sur la structure du lobe antérieur de l'hypophyse du rat blanc. C. R. Soc. Biol., Paris, **122**, 447–449.

DESCLIN, L. 1940. Influence de la section de la tige hypophysaire sur la lactation chez le rat blanc. C. R. Soc. Biol., Paris, **134**, 267–269.

DESCLIN, L. 1947. Concerning the mechanism of

diestrum during lactation in the rat. Endocrinology, **40**, 14–29.

DESCLIN, L. 1956a. Hypothalamus et libération d'hormone lutéotrophique. Expériences de greffe hypophysaire chez le rat hypophysectomizé. Action lutéotrophique de l'ocytocine. Ann. Endocr., Paris, **17**, 586–595.

DESCLIN, L. 1956b. L'ocytocine peut-elle déclencher la libération de lutéotrophine hypophysaire chez le rat? C. R. Soc. Biol., Paris, **150**, 1489–1490.

DEUSING, M. 1939. Nesting habits of the pied-billed grebe. Auk, **56**, 367–373.

DEUTSCH, J. A. 1957. Nest-building behaviour of domestic rabbits under seminatural conditions. Brit. J. Anim. Behav., **5**, 53–54.

DIETERLEN, F. 1959. Das Verhalten des syrischen Goldhamsters (*Mesocricetus auratus* Waterhouse). Untersuchungen zur Frage seiner Entwicklung und seiner angeborenen Anteile durch geruchsisolierte Aufzuchten. Z. Tierpsychol., **16**, 47–103.

DISNEY, H. J., DE S., AND MARSHALL, A. J. 1956. A contribution to the breeding biology of the weaver-finch *Quelea quelea* (Linnaeus) in East Africa. Proc. zool. Soc. Lond., **127**, 379–387.

DISPENSA, J., AND HORNBECK, R .T. 1941. Can intelligence be improved by prenatal endocrine therapy? J. Psychol., **12**, 209–224.

DIXON, K. 1949. Behavior of the plain titmouse. Condor, **51**, 110–136.

DONOVAN, B. T., AND VAN DER WERFF TEN BOSCH, J. J. 1957. The hypothalamus and lactation in the rabbit. J. Physiol., **137**, 410–420.

EAYRS, J. T., AND BADDELEY, R. M. 1956. Neural pathways in lactation. J. Anat., Lond., **90**, 161–171.

ECKSTEIN, P. 1949. Patterns of the mammalian sexual cycle. Acta anat., **7**, 389–410.

EIBL-EIBESFELDT, I. 1950. Beiträge zur Biologie der Haus-und Ährenmaus nebst einigen Beobachtungen an anderen Nagern. Z. Tierpsychol., **7**, 558–587.

EIBL-EIBESFELDT, I. 1955a. Angeborenes und Erworbenes im Nestbauverhalten der Wanderratte. Naturwissenschaften, **42**, 633–634.

EIBL-EIBESFELDT, I. 1955b. Zur Biologie des Iltis (*Putorius putorius* L.). Verh. dtsch. zool. Ges., **1955**, 304–314.

EIBL-EIBESFELDT, I. 1955c. Ethologische Studien am Galapagos-Seelöwen, *Zalophus wollebaeki* Sivertsen. Z. Tierpsychol., **12**, 286–303.

EIBL-EIBESFELDT, I. 1956. Fortschritte der vergleichenden Verhaltensforschung. Naturw. Rdsch., **1956**, 86–90, 136–142.

EIBL-EIBESFELDT, I. 1958. Das Verhalten der Nagetiere. In *Handbuch der Zoologie*, J.-G. Helmcke, H. v., Lengerken, and D. Starck, Eds., Vol. 8, Lief. 12, Teil 10, 88 pp. Berlin: Walter de Gruyter & Company.

EIBL-EIBESFELDT, I., AND KRAMER, S. 1958. Ethology, the comparative study of animal behavior. Quart. Rev. Biol., **33**, 181–211.

EIGEMANN, M. 1937. Experimentelle Untersuchungen über die Brutigkeit der Hühner. Arch. Geflügelk., **11**, 273–342.

EISENTRAUT, M. 1928. Über die Baue und der Winterschlaf des Hamsters (*Cricetus cricetus* L). Z. Säugetierk., **3**, 172–208.

EISNER, E. 1958. Incubation and clutch size in gulls. Anim. Behav., **6**, 124–125.

EISNER, E. 1960. The relationship of hormones to the reproductive behaviour of birds, referring especially to parental behaviour: a review. Anim. Behav., **8**, 155–179.

ELDER, W. H., AND WELLER, M. W. 1954. Duration of fertility in the domestic mallard hen after isolation from the drake. J. Wildlife Mgmt, **18**, 495–502.

ELSBERG, C. A., BREWER, E. D., AND LEVY, I. 1935. The sense of smell. IV. Concerning conditions which may temporarily alter normal olfactory acuity. Bull. neurol. Inst. N. Y., **4**, 31–44.

ELY, F., AND PETERSEN, W. E. 1941. Factors involved in the ejection of milk. J. Dairy Sci., **24**, 211–223.

EMLEN, J. T. 1941. An experimental analysis of the breeding cycle of the tricolored redwing. Condor, **43**, 209–219.

EMLEN, J. T. 1954. Territory, nest building, and pair formation in the cliff swallow. Auk, **71**, 16–35.

EMLEN, J. T., AND LORENZ, F. W. 1942. Pairing responses of free-living valley quail to sex-hormone implants. Auk, **59**, 369–378.

ENGELS, W. L., AND JENNER, C. W. 1956. The effect of temperature on testicular recrudescence in juncos at different photoperiods. Biol. Bull., Wood's Hole, **110**, 129–137.

ERHARDT, K. 1929. Beitrag zur Hypophysen-Vorderlappenreaktion unter besonderer Berücksichtigung der Aschheim-Zondekschen Schwangerschaftsreaktion. Klin. Wschr., **8**, 2044–2047.

ERNST, M. 1929. Experimentelle Untersuchungen und klinische Beobachtungen über Entnervung der Weiblichen Brustdruse. Dtsch. Z. Chir., **215**, 302–308.

EVERETT, J. W. 1954. Luteotrophic function of autografts of the rat hypophysis. Endocrinology, **54**, 685–690.

EVERETT, J. W. 1956. Functional corpora lutea maintained for months by autografts of rat hypophysis. Endocrinology, **58**, 786–796.

EWER, R. F. 1959. Suckling behaviour in kittens. Behaviour **15**, 146–162.

FALCONER, D. S. 1953. Asymmetrical response in selection experiments. Gen. Ass. int. Un. biol. Sci., Naples, series B, **15**, 16–41.

FARNER, D. 1955. The annual stimulus for migration. In *Recent Studies in Avian Biology*, A. Wolfson, Ed., pp. 198–237. Urbana: University of Illinois Press.

FARNER, D. S. 1958. Incubation and body temperatures in the yellow-eyed penguin. Auk, **75**, 249–262.

FAUTIN, R. W. 1941. Incubation studies of the

yellow-headed blackbird. Wilson Bull., **53,** 107–122.

FICKEN, R. W., VAN TIENHOVEN, A., FICKEN, M. S., AND SIBLEY, F. C. 1960. Effect of visual and vocal stimuli on breeding in the budgerigar (*Melopsitacus undulatus*). Anim. Behav., **8,** 104–106.

FISHER, A. E. 1956. Maternal and sexual behavior induced by intracranial chemical stimulation. Science, **124,** 228–229.

FISHER, E. M. 1940. Early life of a sea otter pup. J. Mammal., **21,** 132–137.

FISHER, J. 1952. *The Fulmar.* London: William Collins Sons & Company, Ltd.

FLEAY, D. H. 1937. Nesting habits of the brush-turkey. Emu, **36,** 153–163.

FLERKO, B., AND SZENTOGOTHAI, J. 1957. Oestrogen sensitive structures in the hypothalamus. Acta endocr., **26,** 121–127.

FOLLEY, S. J. 1947. The nervous system and lactation. Brit. med. Bull., **5,** 142–148.

FOLLEY, S. J. 1956. *The Physiology and Biochemistry of Lactation.* London: Oliver and Boyd, Ltd.

FRANK, F. 1952. Adoptionsversuche bei Feldmäusen (*Microtus arvalis* Pall.). Z. Tierpsychol., **9,** 415–423.

FRANKLIN, K. J., AND WINSTONE, N. E. 1954. Further notes on parturition in the rabbit. J. Physiol., **125,** 43–50.

FRAPS, R. M. 1955. The varying effects of sex hormones in birds. Mem. Soc. Endocrin., **4,** 205–219.

FRAPS, R. M., HOOKER, C. W., AND FORBES, T. R. 1948. Progesterone in blood plasma of the ovulating hen. Science, **108,** 86–87.

FRAPS, R. M., HOOKER, C. W., AND FORBES, T. R. 1949. Progesterone in blood plasma of cocks and nonovulating hens. Science, **109,** 493.

FREUD, J., AND UYLDERT, I. E. 1948a. Mamma and lactation in rats and other species. Arch. int. Pharmacodyn., **76,** 74–94.

FREUD, J., AND UYLDERT, I. E. 1948b. Micturition and copulation behavior patterns in dogs. Acta brev. neerl. Physiol., **16,** 49–53.

FRIEDMANN, H. 1929. *The Cowbirds. A Study in the Biology of Social Parasitism.* Springfield, Ill.: Charles C Thomas.

FRIEDMANN, H. 1930. The sociable weaverbird of South Africa. Nat. Hist., N. Y., **30,** 205–212.

FRIEDMANN, H. 1949. The breeding habits of the weaver birds. A study in the biology of behavior patterns. Rep. Smithson. Instn, **1949,** 293–316.

FRIEDMANN, H. 1955. The honey-guides. Bull. U. S. nat. Mus., No. 208.

FRISCH, O. v. 1959. Kiebitzbruten in Gefangenschaft mit Aufzucht von Rotschenkeln durch ein Kiebitzpaar. J. Orn. Lpz., **100,** 307–312.

FRISCH, O. v., AND KAHMANN, H. 1952. Über die Beziehungen von Muttertier und Nestling bei kleinen Säugetieren. Experientia, **8,** 221–223.

FRITH, H. J. 1956a. Temperature regulation in the nesting mounds of the mallee-fowl, *Leipoa*

ocellata Gould. C. S. I. R. O. Wildlife Res., **1,** 79–95.

FRITH, H. J. 1956b. Breeding habits in the family Megapodiidae. Ibis., **98,** 620–640.

FULLER, J. L. 1960. Behavior genetics. Annu. Rev. Psychol., **11,** 41–70.

FULLER, J. L., AND THOMPSON, W. R. 1960. *Behavior Genetics.* New York: John Wiley & Sons, Inc.

GAINES, W. L. 1915. A contribution to the physiology of lactation. Amer. J. Physiol., **38,** 285–312.

GLOVER, F. A. 1953. Nesting ecology of the pied-billed grebe in northwestern Iowa. Wilson Bull., **65,** 32–39.

GODFREY, E. F., AND JAAP, R. G. 1950. Estrogenic interruption of broodiness in the domestic fowl. Poult. Sci., **29,** 356–361.

GOETHE, F. 1937. Beobachtungen und Untersuchungen zur Biologie der Silbermöwe auf der Vogelinsel Memmertsand. J. Orn., Lpz., **85,** 1–119.

GOODALE, H. D. 1916. Note on the behavior of capons when brooding chicks. J. Anim. Behav., **6,** 319–324.

GOODALE, H. D. 1918. Feminized male birds. Genetics, **3,** 276–299.

GOODALE, H. D., SANBORN, R., AND WHITE, D. 1920. Broodiness in domestic fowl. Bull. Mass. agric. Exp. Sta. No. **199,** 93–116.

GOODWIN, D. 1948. Incubation habits of the golden pheasant. Ibis, **90,** 280–284.

GOODWIN, D. 1951. Some aspects of the behaviour of the jay *Garrulus glandarius*. Ibis, **93,** 414–442.

GOODWIN, D. 1955. Notes on European wild pigeons. Avicult. Mag., **1955,** 54–85.

GRACHEV, I. I. 1952. (The development of a conditioned milk ejection reflex on the basis of mechanical stimulation of the teat) (in Russian). C. R. Acad. Sci. U.R.S.S., **86,** 441–444.

GRANIT, R. 1955. *Receptors and Sensory Perception.* New Haven: Yale University Press.

GRASSÉ, P.-P., ED. 1955. *Traité de Zoologie*, vol. **17,** Mammiféres. Paris: Masson & Cie.

GRASSÉ, P.-P., BOURLIÈRE, F., AND VIRET, J. 1955. Ordre des marsupiaux. In *Traité de Zoologie*, P.-P. Grassé, Ed., vol. **17,** pp. 93–185. Paris: Masson & Cie.

GRASSÉ, P.-P., AND DEKEYSER, P. L. 1955. Ordre des rongeurs. In *Traité de Zoologie*, P.-P. Grassé, Ed., vol. **17,** pp. 1321–1573. Paris: Masson & Cie.

GREEN, J. D. 1951a. The comparative anatomy of the hypophysis, with special reference to its blood supply and innervation. Amer. J. Anat., **88,** 225–312.

GREEN, J. D. 1951b. Innervation of the pars distalis of the adenohypophysis studied by phase microscopy. Anat. Rec., **109,** 99–108.

GREEN, J. D., AND HARRIS, G. W. 1947. The neurovascular link between the neurohypophysis and adenohypophysis. J. Endocrin., **5,** 136–146.

GRÉGOIRE, C. 1947a. Factors involved in maintaining involution of the thymus during suckling. J. Endocrin., **5**, 68–87.

GRÉGOIRE, C. 1947b. Failure of lactogenic hormone to maintain pregnancy involution of the thymus. J. Endocrin., **5**, 115–120.

GREULICH, W. W. 1934. Artificially induced ovulation in the cat (*Felis domestica*). Anat. Rec., **58**, 217–224.

GROSSKOPF, G. 1958. Zur Biologie des Rotschenkels (*Tringa t. totanus*) I. J. Orn., Lpz., **99**, 1–17.

GROSVENOR, C. E., AND TURNER, C. W. 1957. Release and restoration of pituitary lactogen in response to nursing stimuli in lactating rats. Proc. Soc. exp. Biol., N. Y., **96**, 723–725.

GRZIMEK, B. 1945. Ein Fohlen, des kein Pferd kannte. Z. Tierpsychol., **6**, 391–405.

GULLION, G. W. 1954. The reproductive cycle of American coots in California. Auk, **71**, 366–412.

GURR, L. 1954. A study of the blackbird *Turdus merula* in New Zealand. Ibis, **96**, 225–261.

HAARTMAN, L. v. 1957. Adaptation in hole-nesting birds. Evolution, **11**, 339–347.

HAFEZ, E. S. E. 1959. Nursing-suckling interactions in the domestic pig. Bull. ecol. Soc. Amer., **40**, 65.

HAIN, A. M. 1935. The effect of (a) litter size on growth and (b) of estrone administered during lactation (rat). Quart. J. exp. Physiol., **25**, 303–313.

HAMILTON, W. J. 1939. *American Mammals: Their Lives, Habits and Economic Relations.* New York: McGraw-Hill Book Company.

HAMMOND, J., AND MARSHALL, F. H. A. 1925. *Reproduction in the Rabbit.* London: Oliver and Boyd, Ltd.

HANN, H. W. 1937. Life history of the ovenbird in Southern Michigan. Wilson Bull., **49**, 145–237.

HANN, H. W. 1941. The cowbird at the nest. Wilson Bull., **53**, 211–221.

HARDY, J. W. 1957. The least tern in the Mississippi valley. Publ. Mus., Mich. State Univ., biol. Ser., **1**, 1–60.

HARLOW, H. F. 1959. Love in infant monkeys. Sci. Amer., **200** (6), 68–74.

HARLOW, H. F., AND ZIMMERMANN, R. R. 1958. The development of affectional responses in infant monkeys. Proc. Amer. phil. Soc., **102**, 501–509.

HARLOW, H. F., AND ZIMMERMANN, R. R. 1959. Affectional responses in the infant monkey. Science, **130**, 421–432.

HARPER, E. H. 1904. The fertilization and early development of the pigeon's egg. Amer. J. Anat., **3**, 349–386.

HARRIS, G. W. 1947a. The blood-vessels of the rabbit's pituitary gland and the significance of the pars and zona tuberalis. J. Anat., Lond., **81**, 343–351.

HARRIS, G. W. 1947b. The innervation and actions of the neurohypophysis; an investigation using the method of remote-control stimulation. Phil. Trans., **232B**, 385–441.

HARRIS, G. W. 1948. Electrical stimulation of the hypothalamus and the mechanism of neural control of the adenohypophysis. J. Physiol., **107**, 418–429.

HARRIS, G. W. 1955. *Neural Control of the Pituitary Gland.* London: Edward Arnold & Company.

HARRIS, G. W. 1958. The central nervous system, neurohypophysis, and milk ejection. Proc. roy. Soc., **149B**, 336–353.

HARRIS, G. W. 1959. The nervous system—follicular ripening, ovulation, and estrous behavior. In *Recent Progress in the Endocrinology of Reproduction*, C. W. Lloyd, Ed., pp. 21–52. New York: Academic Press, Inc.

HARRIS, G. W., AND JACOBSOHN, D. 1952. Functional grafts of the anterior pituitary gland. Proc. roy. Soc., **139B**, 263–276.

HARRIS, G. W., MICHAEL, R. P., AND SCOTT, P. P. 1958. Neurological site of action of stilboestrol in eliciting sexual behaviour. In *Ciba Foundation Symposium on the Neurological Basis of Behaviour*, G. E. W. Wolstenholme and C. M. O'Connor, Eds., pp. 236–254. London: J. & A. Churchill, Ltd.

HARTMAN, C. G. 1920. Studies in the development of the opossum, *Didelphys virginiana* L. V. The phenomena of parturition. Anat. Rec., **19**, 250–261.

HARTMAN, C. G. 1939. Ovulation, fertilization and the transport and viability of eggs and spermatozoa. In *Sex and Internal Secretions*, 2nd ed., E. Allen, C. H. Danforth and E. A. Doisy, Eds., pp. 630–719. Baltimore: The Williams & Wilkins Company.

HATT, R. T. 1929. The red squirrel: its life history and habits, with special reference to the Adirondacks of New York and the Harvard forest. Roosevelt Wild Life Ann., **2**, 1–145.

HAUSCHKA, T. S. 1952. Mutilation patterns and hereditary cannibalism in mice. J. Hered., **43**, 117–123.

HAWBECKER, A. C. 1942. A life history study of the white-tailed kite. Condor, **44**, 267–276.

HAYS, F. A. 1940. Inheritance of broodiness in Rhode Island Reds. Bull. Mass. agric. Exp. Sta., No. **377**, 1–11.

HEAPE, W. 1905. Ovulation and degeneration of ova in the rabbit. Proc. roy. Soc., **76B**, 260–268.

HEBB, D. O. 1949. *The Organization of Behavior.* New York: John Wiley & Sons, Inc.

HEBB, D. O. 1953. Heredity and environment in mammalian behaviour. Brit. J. Anim. Behav., **1**, 43–47.

HEDIGER, H. 1942. Der Geburtsvorgang beim Bison americanus. Ciba-Z., No. **84**, 2955–2956.

HEDIGER, H. 1950. *Wild Animals in Captivity.* London: Butterworth & Company, Ltd.

HEDIGER, H. 1952. Brutpflege bei Säugetieren. Ciba-Z., **11**, 4749–4757.

HEDIGER, H. 1955. *Studies of the Psychology and Behaviour of Captive Animals in Zoos and Circuses.* London: Butterworth & Company, Ltd.

HEDIGER, H. 1958. Verhalten der Beuteltiere

(Marsupialia). In *Handbuch der Zoologie*, J.-G. Helmcke, H. v. Lengerken, and D. Starck, Eds., vol. **8**, Lief. 18, Teil 10. Berlin: Walter de Gruyter & Company.

HEDIGER, H. 1959. Wie Tiermütter ihre Jungen tragen. Ernte, **1959**, 33–46.

HEINROTH, O. 1922. Die Beziehungen zwischen Vogelgewicht, Eigewicht, Gelegegewicht und Brutdauer. J. Orn., Lpz., **70**, 172–285.

HENDERSON, I. D. 1956. Cyclical changes in female nasal mucus. J. clin. Endocrin., **16**, 905–909.

HEROLD, L. 1939. Einfluss der Hypophysenstieldurchtrennung auf die Lactation. Arch. Gynaek., **168**, 534–538.

HEROLD, W. 1954. Über eine nicht gravid gewesene Ratte, die Mäuse säugt. Z. Tierpsychol., **11**, 138–140.

HERRICK, F. 1911. Nests and nest-building in birds. J. Anim. Behav., **1**, 159–192, 244–277, 336–373.

HERSHER, L., MOORE, A. U., AND RICHMOND, J. B. 1958. Effect of post partum separation of mother and kid on maternal care in the domestic goat. Science, **128**, 1342–1343.

HERTER, K. 1936. Das thermotaktische Optimum bei Nagetieren, ein mendelndes Art- und Rassenmerkmal. Z. vergl. Physiol., **23**, 605–650.

HERTER, K. 1941. Die Vorzugstemperaturen bei Landtieren. Naturwissenschaften, **29**, 155–164.

HERTER, K. 1952. *Der Temperatursinn der Säugetiere*. Leipzig: Geest & Portig.

HERTER, K., AND HERTER, M. 1955. Über eine scheinträchtige Iltisfähe mit untergeschobenem Katzenjungen. Zool. Gart., Lpz., **22**, 33–46.

HERTER, K., AND SGONINA, K. 1939. Vorzugstemperatur und Hautbeschaffenheit bei Mäusen. Z. vergl. Physiol., **26**, 366–415.

HESS, E. H. 1959. Imprinting. Science, **130**, 133–141.

HESSELBERG, C., AND LOEB, L. 1937a. The retrogression of the lactating mammary gland in the guinea pig. Amer. J. Physiol., **118**, 528–531.

HESSELBERG, C., AND LOEB, L. 1937b. The structure of the secreting and retrogressing mammary gland in the guinea pig. Anat. Rec., **68**, 103–112.

HINDE, R. A. 1952. The behaviour of the great tit (*Parus major*) and some related species. Behaviour (Suppl.), **2**, 1–201.

HINDE, R. A. 1958. The nest-building behaviour of domesticated canaries. Proc. zool. Soc. Lond., **131**, 1–48.

HINDE, R. A. 1959. Unitary drives. Anim. Behav., **7**, 130–141.

HINDE, R. A., THORPE, W. H., AND VINCE, M. A. 1956. The following response of young coots and moorhens. Behaviour, **9**, 214–242.

HINDE, R. A., AND WARREN, R. P. 1959. The effect of nest building on later reproductive behaviour in domestic canaries. Anim. Behav., **7**, 35–41.

HOFFMANN, A. 1949. Über die Brutpflege des

polyandrischen Wasserfasans, *Hydrophasianus chirurgus* (Scop.). Zool. Jb., **78**, 367–403.

HÖHN, E. O. 1957. Observations on display and other forms of behavior of certain arctic birds. Auk, **74**, 203–214.

HÖHN, E. O. 1959. Prolactin in the cowbird's pituitary in relation to avian brood parasitism. Nature, **184**, 2030.

HOOKER, C. W., AND WILLIAMS, W. L. 1940. Retardation of mammary involution in the mouse by inhibition of the nipples. Yale J. Biol. Med., **12**, 559–564.

HOOKER, C. W., AND WILLIAMS, W. L. 1941. Retardation of mammary involution in mice by injection of lactogenic hormone. Endocrinology, **28**, 42–47.

HORNER, B. E. 1947. Paternal care of young mice of the genus *Peromyscus*. J. Mammal., **28**, 31–36.

HOWARD, H. E. 1920. *Territory in Bird Life*. London: Chatto and Windus, Ltd.

HOWARD, H. E. 1940. *A Waterhen's Worlds*. Cambridge University Press.

HOWELL, T. R. 1952. Natural history and differentiation in the yellow-bellied sapsucker. Condor, **54**, 237–282.

HUBBS, C. L. 1953. Dolphin protecting dead young. J. Mammal., **34**, 498.

HURST, V., MEITES, J., AND TURNER, C. W. 1943. Lactogenic hormone content of the AP of the pigeon. Proc. Soc. exp. Biol., N. Y., **53**, 89–91.

HUSTON, T. M., AND NALBANDOV, A. V. 1953. Neurohumoral control of the pituitary in the fowl. Endocrinology, **52**, 149–156.

INGELBRECHT, P. 1935. Influence du système nerveux central sur la mamelle lactente chez le rat blanc. C. R. Soc. Biol., Paris, **120**, 1369–1371.

IRVING, L., AND KROG, J. 1956. Temperature during the development of birds in arctic nests. Physiol. Zoöl., **29**, 195–205.

JACOBSOHN, D. 1949. The effect of transection of the hypophysial stalk on the mammary glands of lactating rabbits. Acta physiol. scand., **19**, 10–18.

JACOBSOHN, D., AND WESTMAN, A. 1945. On the structure and function of the mammary glands after hypophysectomy and transection of the hypophyseal stalk in rats. Acta physiol. scand., **9**, 284–295.

JAMES-VEITCH, E., AND BOOTH, E. S. 1954. Behavior and life history of the glaucous-winged gull. Walla Walla Coll. Publ. Dep. biol. Sci., No. 12.

JOHNSTON, D. W. 1956. The annual reproductive cycle of the California gull. Condor, **58**, 134–162, 206–221.

JOHNSTON, D. W. 1958. Sex and age characters and salivary glands of the chimney swift. Condor, **60**, 73–84.

KABAT, C., BUSS, I. O., AND MEYER, R. K. 1948. The use of ovulated follicles in determining eggs laid by the ring-necked pheasant. J. Wildlife Mgmt, **12**, 399–416.

KAGAN, J., AND BEACH, F. A. 1953. Effects of early

experience on mating behavior in male rats. J. comp. physiol. Psychol., **46**, 204–208.

KAHMANN, H., AND VON FRISCH, O. 1952. Über die Beziehungen von Muttertier und Nestling bei kleinen Säugetieren. Experientia, **8**, 221–223.

KAHN, M. W. 1954. Infantile experience and mature aggressive behavior of mice: some maternal influences. J. genet. Psychol., **84**, 65–75.

KALTENBACH, J. C. 1953a. Local action of thyroxin on amphibian metamorphosis. I. Local metamorphosis in *Rana pipiens* larvae effected by thyroxin-cholesterol implants. J. exp. Zool., **122**, 21–40.

KALTENBACH, J. C. 1953b. Local action of thyroxin on amphibian metamorphosis. II. Development of the eyelids, nictitating membrane, cornea and extrinsic ocular muscles in *Rana pipiens* larvae effected by thyroxin-cholesterol implants. J. exp. Zool., **122**, 41–52.

KATZ, D. 1937. *Animals and Men: Studies in Comparative Psychology*. London: Longmans, Green & Co., Inc.

KAUFMAN, L. 1932. Quelques expériences sur les hormones determinant la sécrétion lactée du jabot des pigeons. C. R. Soc. Biol., Paris, **111**, 881–883.

KAUFMAN, L. 1948. On the mode of inheritance of broodiness. Proc. World's Poult. Cong., Copenhagen, **8**(1), 301–304.

KAUFMAN, L., AND DABROWSKA, L. 1931. L'influence des hormones sur la "lactation" du pigeon. C. R. Ass. Anat., **26**, 295–299.

KAWAKAMI, M., AND SAWYER, C. H. 1959a. Induction of behavioral and electroencephalographic changes in the rabbit by hormone administration or brain stimulation. Endocrinology, **65**, 631–643.

KAWAKAMI, M., AND SAWYER, C. H. 1959b. Neuroendocrine correlates of changes in brain activity thresholds by sex steroids and pituitary hormones. Endocrinology, **65**, 652–668.

KEAST, J. A., AND MARSHALL, A. J. 1954. The influence of drought and rainfall on reproduction in Australian desert birds. Proc. zool. Soc. Lond., **124**, 493–499.

KENDEIGH, S. C. 1941. Territorial and mating behavior of the House Wren. Illinois biol. Monogr., **18**, No. 3.

KENDEIGH, S. C. 1952. Parental care and its evolution in birds. Illinois biol. Monogr., **22**, Nos. 1–3.

KENDEIGH, S. C., AND BALDWIN, S. P. 1928. Development of temperature control in nestling house wrens. Amer. Nat., **62**, 249–278.

KENNEDY, J. S. 1954. Is modern ethology objective? Brit. J. Anim. Behav., **2**, 12–19.

KINDER, E. F. 1927. A study of the nest building activity of the albino rat. J. exp. Zool., **47**, 117–161.

KING, J. A. 1958. Maternal behavior and behavioral development in two subspecies of *Peromyscus maniculatus*. J. Mammal., **39**, 177–190.

KLEIN, M. 1952. Uterine distension, ovarian hormones and maternal behavior in rodents. Ciba Colloq. Endocrin., **3**, 84–88.

KLEIN, M. 1956. Aspects biologiques de l'instinct reproducteur dans le comportement des mammifères. In *L'Instinct dans le Comportement des Animaux et de l'Homme*, P.-P. Grassé, Ed., pp. 287–344. Paris: Masson & Cie.

KLOMP, H. 1951. Over de achteruitgang van de Kievit, *Vanellus vanellus* (L.) in Nederland en gegevens over het legmechanisme en het eiproductie-vermogen. Ardea, **39**, 143–182.

KLUYVER, H. N. 1955. Das Verhalten des Drosselrohrsängers, *Acrocephalus arundinaceus* (L), am Brutplatz mit besonderer Berücksichtigung der Nestbautechnik und der Revierbehauptung. Ardea, **43**, 1–50.

KOBAYASHI, H. 1952. Effects of hormonic steroids on molting and broodiness in the canary. Annot. zool. jap., **25**, 128–134.

KOBAYASHI, H. 1953a. Studies on molting in the pigeon. IV. Molting in relation to reproductive activity. Jap. J. Zool., **11**, 11–20.

KOBAYASHI, H. 1953b. Studies on molting in the pigeon. VII. Inhibitory effect of lactogen on molting. Jap. J. Zool., **11**, 21–26.

KOBAYASHI, H., AND OKUBO, K. 1954. Effects of desoxycorticosterone acetate on broodiness, molting and pituitary lactogen content in the canary, and on metamorphosis of the toad tadpole. Annot. zool. jap., **27**, 173–179.

KOEHLER, O. 1954. Review of Lehrman, 1953. Z. Tierpsychol., **11**, 330–334.

KOFORD, C. B. 1957. The vicuna and the puna. Ecol. Monogr., **27**, 153–219.

KOLLER, G. 1952. Der Nestbau der weissen Maus und seine hormonale Auslösung. Verh. dtsch. zool. Ges., Freiburg, **1952**, 160–168.

KOLLER, G. 1956. Hormonale und psychische Steuerung beim Nestbau weiser Mäuse. Zool. Anz. (Suppl.), **19**, (Verh. dtsch. zool. Ges., 1955), 123–132.

KOLLROS, J. 1942. Experimental studies on the development of the corneal reflex in Amphibia. I. The onset of the reflex and its relationship to metamorphosis. J. exp. Zool., **89**, 37–67.

KOLLROS, J. 1943. Experimental studies on the development of the corneal reflex in Amphibia. II. Localized maturation of the reflex mechanism effected by thyroxin-agar implants into the hind-brain. Physiol. Zoöl., **16**, 269–279.

KORNOWSKI, G. 1957. Beiträge zur Ethologie des Blässhuhns (*Fulica atra* L.). J. Orn., Lpz., **98**, 318–355.

KORTLANDT, A. 1940. Eine Übersicht der angeborenen Verhaltungsweisen des mittel-europäischen Kormorans (*Phalacrocorax carbo sinensis* [Shaw & Wood], ihre Funktion, ontogenetische Entwicklung und phylogenetische Herkunft. Arch. néerl. Zool., **4**, 401–442.

KOSIN, I. L. 1948. The use of testosterone propionate in controlling broodiness in turkeys. Poult. Sci., **27**, 671.

KOSSACK, C. W. 1947. Incubation temperatures

of Canada geese. J. Wildlife Mgmt, **11**, 119–126.

KRAMER, G. 1950. Der Nestbau beim Neuntöter (*Lanius collurio* L.). Orn. Ber., **3**, 1–14.

KRUMBIEGEL, I. 1954–1955. *Biologie der Säugetiere*, 2 Vols. Krefeld, Germany: Agis-Verlag.

KURAMITSU, C., AND LOEB, L. 1921. The effect of suckling and castration on the lactating mammary gland in rat and guinea pig. Amer. J. Physiol., **56**, 40–59.

KURODA, N. 1956. Observations and experiments on carrier pigeon II. Zool. Mag., Tokyo, **65**, 22–26.

LABATE, J. S. 1940. Influence of uterine and ovarian nerves on lactation. Endocrinology, **27**, 342–344.

LABRIOLA, J. 1953. Effects of caesarean delivery upon maternal behavior in rats. Proc. Soc. exp. Biol., N. Y., **83**, 556–557.

LACK, D. 1933. Nesting conditions as a factor controlling breeding time in birds. Proc. zool. Soc. Lond., **1933**, 231–237.

LACK, D. 1940. Observations on captive robins. Brit. Birds, **33**, 262–270.

LACK, D. 1941. Notes on territory, fighting, and display in the chaffinch. Brit. Birds, **34**, 216–219.

LACK, D. 1946. *The Life of the Robin*, rev. ed. London: H. F. & G. Witherby.

LACK, D. 1947. The significance of clutch-size. Ibis, **89**, 302–352.

LACK, D. 1956a. A review of the genera and nesting habits of swifts. Auk, **73**, 1–32.

LACK, D. 1956b. *Swifts in a Tower*. London: Methuen & Company, Ltd.

LACK, D., AND EMLEN, J. T. 1939. Observations on breeding behavior in tricolored redwings. Condor, **41**, 225–230.

LAHR, E. L., AND RIDDLE, O. 1938. Proliferation of crop-sac epithelium in incubating and in prolactin-injected pigeons studied with the colchicine method. Amer. J. Physiol., **123**, 614–619.

LAMOND, D. R. 1958. Infertility associated with extirpation of the olfactory bulbs in female albino mice. Aust. J. exp. Biol., **36**, 103–108.

LAMOND, D. R. 1959. Effect of stimulation derived from other animals of the same species on oestrous cycles in mice. J. Endocrin., **18**, 343–349.

LANDRY, S. O. 1959. Lactation hair in the Asiatic squirrel and relationship of lactation hair to mammary hair. Science, **130**, 37.

LANG, H. B. 1931. A note on maternal behavior in two female virgin dogs. Psychiat. Quart., **5**, 649–651.

LASHLEY, K. S. 1915. Notes on the nesting activities of the noddy and sooty terns. Pap. Tortugas Lab., **7**, 61–83.

LASHLEY, K. S. 1929. *Brain Mechanisms and Intelligence*. Chicago: University of Chicago Press.

LASHLEY, K. S. 1933. Integrative functions of the cerebral cortex. Physiol. Rev., **13**, 1–42.

LASHLEY K. S. 1938. Experimental analysis of

instinctive behavior. Psychol. Rev., **45**, 445–471.

LAVEN, B. 1941. Beobachtungen über Balz und Brut beim Kiebitz (*Vanellus vanellus* L.). J. Orn. Lpz., Ergänzungsband **3**, 1–64.

LAVEN, H. 1940a. Beiträge zur Biologie des Sandregenpfeifers (*Charadrius hiaticula* L.). J. Orn., Lpz., **88**, 183–287.

LAVEN, H. 1940b. Über Nachlegen und Weiterlegen. Orn. Mber., **48**, 131–136.

LAYNE, D. S., COMMON, R. H., MAW, W. A., AND FRAPS, R. M. 1957. Presence of progesterone in extracts of ovaries of laying hens. Proc. Soc. exp. Biol., N. Y., **94**, 528–529.

LEA, R. B. 1942. A study of the nesting habits of the cedar waxwing. Wilson Bull., **54**, 225–237.

LEBLOND, C. P. 1937. L'instinct maternel: Nature et relations avec la glande mammaire, l'hypophyse et le systeme nerveux. Rev. franç. Endocr., **15**, 457–475.

LEBLOND, C. P. 1938. Extra-hormonal factors in maternal behavior. Proc. Soc. exp. Biol., N. Y., **38**, 66–70.

LEBLOND, C. P. 1940. Nervous and hormonal factors in the maternal behavior of the mouse. J. genet. Psychol., **57**, 327–344.

LEBLOND, C. P., AND ALLEN, E. 1937. Emphasis of the growth effect of prolactin on the crop gland of the pigeon by arrest of mitoses with colchicine. Endocrinology, **21**, 455–460.

LEBLOND, C. P., AND NELSON, W. O. 1936. L'instinct maternel après hypophysectomie. C. R. Soc. Biol., Paris, **122**, 548–549.

LEBLOND, C. P., AND NELSON, W. O. 1937a. Maternal behavior in hypophysectomized male and female mice. Amer. J. Physiol., **120**, 167–172.

LEBLOND, C. P., AND NELSON, W. O. 1937b. Présence d'instinct maternel sans stimulation hormonale. C. R. Soc. Biol., Paris, **124**, 1064.

LEHRMAN, D. S. 1953. A critique of Konrad Lorenz's theory of instinctive behavior. Quart. Rev. Biol., **28**, 337–363.

LEHRMAN, D. S. 1955. The physiological basis of parental feeding behavior in the ring dove (*Streptopelia risoria*). Behaviour, **7**, 241–286.

LEHRMAN, D. S. 1956a. Comparative physiology (behavior). Annu. Rev. Physiol., **18**, 527–542.

LEHRMAN, D. S. 1956b. On the organization of maternal behavior and the problem of instinct. In *L'Instinct dans le Comportement des Animaux et de l'Homme*, P.-P. Grassé, Ed., pp. 475–520. Paris: Masson & Cie.

LEHRMAN, D. S. 1958a. Induction of broodiness by participation in courtship and nest-building in the ring dove (*Streptopelia risoria*.). J. comp. physiol. Psychol., **51**, 32–36.

LEHRMAN, D. S. 1958b. Effect of female sex hormones on incubation behavior in the ring dove (*Streptopelia risoria*). J. comp. physiol. Psychol., **51**, 142 145.

LEHRMAN, D. S. 1959a. Hormonal responses to external stimuli in birds. Ibis, **101**, 478–496.

LEHRMAN, D. S. 1959b. On the origin of the reproductive behavior cycle in doves. Trans. N. Y. Acad. Sci., **21**, 682–688.

LEHRMAN, D. S., AND BRODY, P. 1957. Oviduct response to estrogen and progesterone in the ring dove (*Streptopelia risoria*). Proc. Soc. exp. Biol., N. Y., **95**, 373–375.

LEHRMAN, D. S., BRODY, P. N., AND WORTIS, R. P. 1961. The presence of the mate and of nesting material as stimuli for the development of incubation behavior and for gonadotropin secretion in the ring dove (*Streptopelia risoria*). Endocrinology, **68**, 507–516.

LEHRMAN, D. S., AND WORTIS, R. P. 1960. Previous breeding experience and hormone-induced incubation behavior in the ring dove. Science, **132**, 1667–1668.

LE MAGNEN, C. 1953. L'olfaction: le fonctionnement olfactif et son intervention dans les regulations psycho-physiologiques. J. Physiol. Path. gén., **45**, 285–326.

LEOPOLD, A. S. 1944. The nature of heritable wildness in turkeys. Condor, **46**, 133–197.

LEVINE, S. 1959a. Emotionality and aggressive behavior in the mouse as a function of infantile experience. J. gen. Psychol., **94**, 77–83.

LEVINE, S. 1960. Stimulation in infancy. Sci. Amer., **202** (5), 80–86.

LEVY, D. M. 1934. Experiments on the suckling reflex and social behavior of dogs. Amer. J. Orthopsychiat., **4**, 203–224.

LEYHAUSEN, P. 1956. Verhaltensstudien an Katzen. Z. Tierpsychol., Beiheft **2**, 1–120.

LIENHART, R. 1927. Contribution a l'étude de l'incubation. C. R. Soc. Biol., Paris, **97**, 1296–1297.

LINSDALE, J. M. 1938. Environmental responses of vertebrates in the Great Basin. Amer. Midl. Nat., **19**, 1–206.

LINSDALE, J. M., AND TEVIS, L. P. 1951. *The Dusky-footed Wood Rat, a Record of Observations Made on the Hastings Natural History Reservation*. Berkeley: University of California Press.

LINZELL, J. L. 1955. Some observations on the contractile tissue of the mammary glands. J. Physiol., **130**, 257–267.

LINZELL, J. L. 1959. The innervation of the mammary glands in the sheep and goat with some observations on the lumbosacral autonomic nerves. Quart. J. exp. Physiol., **44**, 160–176.

LOFTS, B., AND MARSHALL, A. J. 1956. The effects of prolactin administration on the internal rhythm of reproduction in male birds. J. Endocrin., **13**, 101–106.

LOFTS, B., AND MARSHALL, A. J. 1957. The interstitial and spermatogenetic tissue of autumn migrants in southern England. Ibis, **99**, 621–627.

LOISEL, G. 1906. Relations entre les phénomènes du rut, de la lactation, de la mue et de l'amour maternel chez une chienne hybride. C. R. Soc. Biol., Paris, **60**, 255–258.

LORENZ, K. Z. 1935. Der Kumpan in der Umwelt des Vogels. J. Orn., Lpz., **83**, 137–213, 289–413.

LORENZ, K. Z. 1937. Über die Bildung des Instinktbegriffes. Naturwissenschaften, **25**, 289–300, 307–318, 324–331.

LORENZ, K. Z. 1950. The comparative method in studying innate behaviour patterns. Symp. Soc. exp. Biol., **4**, 221–268.

LYONS, W. R. 1937. Preparation and assay of mammotropin. Cold Spr. Harb. Symp. quant. Biol., **5**, 198–209.

LYONS, W. R., LI, C. H., AND JOHNSON, R. E. 1958. The hormonal control of mammary growth and lactation. Recent Progr. Hormone Res., **14**, 219–254.

LYTLE, I. M., AND LORENZ, F. W. 1958. Progesterone in the blood of the laying hen. Nature, **182**, 1681.

MAGOUN, H. W. 1952a. An ascending reticular activating system in the brain stem. Arch. Neurol. Psychiat., Chicago, **67**, 145–154.

MAGOUN, H. W. 1952b. The ascending reticular activating system. Res. Publ. Ass. nerv. ment. Dis., **30**, 480–492.

MAIER, N. R. F., AND SCHNEIRLA, T. C. 1942. Mechanisms in conditioning. Psychol. Rev., **49**, 117–134.

MAKATSCH, W. 1937. *Der Brutparasitismus der Kuckucksvogel*. Leipzig: Quelle & Meyer.

MARKEE, J. E., SAWYER, C. H., AND HOLLINSHEAD, W. H. 1946. Activation of the anterior hypophysis by electrical stimulation in the rabbit. Endocrinology, **38**, 345–357.

MARLER, P. 1956. Behaviour of the chaffinch, *Fringilla coelebs. Behaviour* (Suppl.) **5**, 1–184.

MARSHALL, A. J. 1951. The refractory period of testis rhythm in birds and its possible bearing on breeding and migration. Wilson Bull., **63**, 238–261.

MARSHALL, A. J. 1952. Display and the sexual cycle in the spotted bowerbird (*Chamydera maculata*, Gould). Proc. zool. Soc. Lond., **122**, 239–252.

MARSHALL, A. J. 1954. *Bower-Birds. Their Displays and Breeding Cycles*. Oxford: Oxford University Press.

MARSHALL, A. J. 1959. Internal and environmental control of breeding. Ibis, **101**, 456–478.

MARSHALL, A. J., AND COOMBS, C. J. F. 1952. Lipoid changes in the gonads of wild birds. Nature, **169**, 261–264.

MARSHALL, A. J., AND COOMBS, C. J. F. 1957. The interaction of environmental, internal and behavioural factors in the rook, *Corvus f. frugilegus* Linnaeus. Proc. zool. Soc. Lond., **128**, 545–589.

MARSHALL, A. J., AND DISNEY, H. J. DE S. 1956. Photostimulation of an equatorial bird (*Quelea quelea*, Linnaeus). Nature, **177**, 143–144.

MARSHALL, A. J., AND DISNEY, H. J. DE S. 1957. Experimental induction of the breeding season in a xerophilous bird. Nature, **180**, 647–649.

MARSHALL, A. J., AND SERVENTY, D. L. 1956. The breeding cycle of the short-tailed shearwater, *Puffinus tenuirostris* (Temminck) in relation to transequatorial migration and its environment. Proc. zool. Soc. Lond., **127**, 489–510.

MARSHALL, F. H. A. 1936. Sexual periodicity and the causes which determine it. Phil. Trans., **226B**, 423–456.

MARSHALL, F. H. A. 1942. Exteroceptive factors in sexual periodicity. Biol. Rev., **17**, 68–90.

MARSHALL, F. H. A. 1956. The breeding season. In *Marshall's Physiology of Reproduction*, 3rd ed., A. S. Parkes, Ed., Vol. 1, Part 1, pp. 1–42. London: Longmans, Green & Company, Inc.

MARTINEZ, C., AND BITTNER, J. J. 1956. A non-hypophyseal sex difference in estrous behavior of mice bearing pituitary glands. Proc. Soc. exp. Biol., N. Y., **91**, 506–509.

MARTINS, T. 1949. Disgorging of food to the puppies by the lactating dog. Physiol. Zoöl., **22**, 169–172.

MARTINS, T., AND VALLE, J. R. 1948. Hormonal regulation of the micturition behavior of the dog. J. comp. physiol. Psychol., **41**, 301–311.

MARZA, V. D., AND MARZA, E. V. 1935. The formation of the hen's egg. Quart. J. micr. Sci., **78**, 133–249.

MASCHKOWZEW, A. 1940. Bedeutung des geschlechtsdimorphismus bei den Wirbeltieren (die neuroemotionale Theorie des Geschlechtszyklen). C. R. Acad. Sci. U.R.S.S., **27**, 89–93.

MASON, R. C. 1952. Synergistic and antagonistic effects of progesterone in combination with estrogens on oviduct weight. Endocrinology, **51**, 570–572.

MASSON, G. M. C. 1948. Effects of estradiol and progesterone on lactation. Anat. Rec., **102**, 513–521.

MATTHEWS, L. H. 1939. Visual stimulation and ovulation in pigeons. Proc. roy. Soc., **126B**, 557–560.

MAYAUD, N. 1950. Biologie de la reproduction. In *Traité de Zoologie*, P.-P. Grassé, Ed., Tome **15** (Oiseaux), pp. 539–653. Paris: Masson & Cie.

MAYER, G., AND CANIVENC, R. 1951. Mécanismes de la montée laiteuse. J. Physiol. Path. gén., **43**, 804–807.

MAYR, E., AND BOND, J. 1943. Notes on the generic classification of the swallows, Hirundinidae. Ibis, **85**, 334–341.

McBRIDE, A. F., AND HEBB, D. O. 1948. Behavior of the captive bottle-nosed dolphin, *Tursiops truncatus*. J. comp. physiol. Psychol., **41**, 111–123.

McBRIDE, A. F., AND KRITZLER, H. 1951. Observations on pregnancy, parturition and postnatal behavior in bottlenose dolphin. J. Mammal., **32**, 251–266.

McCANN, S. M., MACK, R., AND GALE, C. 1959. The possible role of oxytocin in stimulating the release of prolactin. Endocrinology, **64**, 870–889.

McCLEARN, G. E. 1959. The genetics of mouse behavior in novel situations. J. comp. physiol. Psychol., **52**, 62–67.

McHUGH, T. 1958. Social behavior of the American buffalo (*Bison bison bison*). Zoologica, N. Y., **43**, 1–40.

McILHENNY, E. A. 1937. Life history of the boat-tailed grackle in Louisianna. Auk, **54**, 274–295.

McQUEEN-WILLIAMS, M. 1935a. Decreased mammotropin in pituitaries of thyroidectomized (maternalized) male rats. Proc. Soc. exp. Biol., N. Y., **33**, 406–407.

McQUEEN-WILLIAMS, M. 1935b. Maternal behavior in male rats. Science, **82**, 67–68.

MEISE, W. 1934. Zur Brutbiologie der Ralle, *Laterallus leucopyrrhus* (Vieill.). J. Orn., Lpz., **82**, 257–268.

MEITES, J. 1954. Recent studies on the mechanisms controlling the initiation of lactation. Rev. canad. Biol., **13**, 359–370.

MEITES, J., BERGMAN, A. J., AND TURNER, C. W. 1941. Relation of size of litter to AP lactogen content of nursing rabbits. Proc. Soc. exp. Biol., N. Y., **46**, 670–671.

MEITES, J., AND SHELESNYAK, M. C. 1957. Effects of prolactin on duration of pregnancy, viability of young, and lactation in rats. Proc. Soc. exp. Biol., N. Y., **94**, 746–749.

MEITES, J., AND TURNER, C. W. 1942a. Studies concerning the mechanism controlling the initiation of lactation at parturition. I. Can estrogen suppress the lactogenic hormone of the pituitary? Endocrinology, **30**, 711–718.

MEITES, J., AND TURNER, C. W. 1942b. Studies concerning the mechanism controlling the initiation of lactation at parturition. III. Can estrogen account for the precipitous increase in the lactogen content of the pituitary following parturition? Endocrinology, **30**, 726–733.

MEITES, J., AND TURNER, C. W. 1942c. Studies concerning the mechanism controlling the initiation of lactation at parturition. IV. Influence of suckling on lactogen content of pituitary of postpartum rabbits. Endocrinology, **31**, 340–344.

MEITES, J., AND TURNER, C. W. 1947. Effect of sex hormones on pituitary lactogen and crop glands of common pigeons. Proc. Soc. exp. Biol., N. Y., **64**, 465–468.

MEITES, J., AND TURNER, C. W. 1948. Studies concerning the induction and maintenance of lactation. II. The normal maintenance and experimental inhibition and augmentation of lactation. Res. Bull. Mo. agric. Exp. Sta., No. 416.

MENDELL, H. L. 1936. The home-life and economic status of the double-crested cormorant, *Phalacrocorax auritus auritus* (Lesson). Univ. Me. Stud., No. **38** (Ser. 2), 1–159.

MENZEL, R., AND MENZEL, R. 1953. Einiges aus der Pflegewelt der Mutterhündin. Behaviour, **5**, 289–304.

MESSMER, E., AND MESSMER, I. 1956. Die Entwicklung der Lautäusserungen und einiger Verhaltensweisen der Amsel (*Turdus merula merula* L.) unter natürlichen Bedingungen und nach Einzelaufzucht in schalldichten Räumen. Z. Tierpsychol., **13**, 341–441.

MEWALDT, L. R. 1952. The incubation patch of the Clark nutcracker. Condor, **54**, 361.

MEWALDT, L. R. 1956. Nesting behavior of the Clark nutcracker. Condor, **58**, 3–23.

MEYER, B. J., AND MEYER, R. K. 1944. Growth and reproduction of the cotton rat, *Sigmodon hispidus hispidus*, under laboratory conditions. J. Mammal., **25**, 107–129.

MEYERRIECKS, A. J. 1960. Comparative breeding behavior of four species of North American herons. Publ. Nuttall orn. Club, No. 2.

MILLER, A. H. 1931. Systematic revision and natural history of the American shrikes (*Lanius*). Univ. Calif. Publ. Zool., **38**, 11–242.

MILLER, L. 1921. The biography of Nip and Tuck. A study of instincts in birds. Condor, **23**, 41–47.

MILLER, N. E. 1957a. Objective techniques for studying motivational effects of drugs on animals. In *Psychotropic Drugs*, S. Garattini and V. Ghetti, Eds., pp. 83–103. Amsterdam: Elsevier Press, Inc.

MILLER, N. E. 1957b. Experiments on motivation. Science, **126**, 1271–1278.

MIXNER, J. P., AND TURNER, C. W. 1941. Influence of local applications of turpentine on mammary gland growth and involution. Proc. Soc. exp. Biol., N. Y., **46**, 437–440.

MOHN, M. P. 1958. The effects of different hormonal states on the growth of hair in rats. In *The Biology of Hair Growth*, W. Montagna and R. A. Ellis, Eds., pp. 335–398. New York: Academic Press, Inc.

MOORE, C. R. 1919. On the physiological properties of the gonads as controllers of somatic and psychical characteristics. I. The rat. J. exp. Zool., **28**, 137–160.

MOORE, C. R. 1920. Sex gland transplantation and the modifying effect in rats and guinea pigs. Anat. Rec., **20**, 194.

MOORE, C. R. 1921. On the physiological properties of the gonads as controllers of somatic and psychical characteristics. IV. Gonad transplantation in the guinea pig. J. exp. Zool., **33**, 365–389.

MOORE, J. C. 1955. Bottle-nosed dolphins support remains of young. J. Mammal., **36**, 466–467.

MORGAN, C. T. 1943. *Physiological Psychology*. New York: McGraw-Hill Book Company.

MORGAN, C. T. 1957. Physiological mechanisms of motivation. Neb. Symp. Motiv., **1957**, 1–35.

MORGAN, C. T. 1959. Physiological theory of drive. In *Psychology: A Study of a Science*, Vol. 1, S. Koch, Ed., pp. 644–671. New York: McGraw-Hill Book Co.

MORRIS, D. 1954. The reproductive behaviour of the zebra finch (*Poephila guttata*), with special reference to pseudofemale behaviour and displacement activities. Behaviour, **6**, 271–322.

MORRIS, D. 1957. The reproductive behaviour of the bronze mannikin, *Lonchura cucullata*. Behaviour, **11**, 156–201.

MOYNIHAN, M. 1953. Some displacement activities of the black-headed gull. Behaviour, **5**, 58–80.

MURIE, A. 1944. *The Wolves of Mount McKinley*. Washington: Fauna National Parks U. S., No. 5.

MURIE, O. J. 1951. *The Elk of North America*. Washington: Wildlife Management Institute.

NAKAJO, W., AND TANAKA, K. 1956. Prolactin potency of the cephalic and the caudal lobe of the anterior pituitary in relation to broodiness in the domestic fowl. Poult. Sci., **35**, 990–994.

NALBANDOV, A. V. 1945. A study of the effect of prolactin on broodiness and on cock testes. Endocrinology, **36**, 251–258.

NALBANDOV, A. V. 1953. Endocrine control of physiological functions. Poult. Sci., **32**, 88–103.

NALBANDOV, A. V., AND CARD, L. E. 1945. Endocrine identification of the broody genotype of cocks. J. Hered., **36**, 34–39.

NAY, T., AND FRASER, A. S. 1955. Growth of the mouse coat. V. Effects of pregnancy and lactation. Aust. J. biol. Sci., **8**, 428–433.

NEFF, J. A. 1937. Nesting distribution of the tri-colored redwing. Condor, **39**, 61–81.

NELSON, W. O., AND SMELSER, G. K. 1933. Studies on the physiology of lactation. II. Lactation in the male guinea pig and its bearing on the corpus luteum. Amer. J. Physiol., **103**, 374–381.

NEW, D. A. T. 1957. A critical period for the turning of hens' eggs. J. Embryol. exp. Morph., **5**, 293–299.

NEWTON, M., AND NEWTON, N. R. 1948. The letdown reflex in human lactation. J. Pediat., **33**, 698–704.

NEWTON, N. R., AND NEWTON, M. 1950. Relation of the let-down reflex to the ability to breast feed. Pediatrics, **5**, 726–733.

NICE, M. M. 1937. Studies in the life history of the song sparrow. I. A population study of the song sparrow. Trans. Linn. Soc. N. Y., **4**, 1–247.

NICE, M. M. 1943. Studies of the life history of the song sparrow. II. The behavior of the song sparrow and other passerines. Trans. Linn. Soc. N. Y., **6**, 1–328.

NICE, M. M. 1949. The laying rhythm of cowbirds. Wilson Bull., **61**, 231–234.

NICE, M. M. 1954. Problems of incubation periods in North American birds. Condor, **56**, 173–197.

NICE, M. M., AND THOMAS, R. H. 1948. A nesting of the Carolina wren. Wilson Bull., **60**, 139–158.

NICHOLSON, A. J. 1941. The homes and social habits of the wood-mouse (*Peromyscus leucopus noveboracensis*) in southern Michigan. Amer. Midl. Nat., **25**, 196–223.

NICOLAI, J. 1956. Zur Biologie und Ethologie des

Gimpels (*Pyrrhula pyrrhula* L.). Z. Tierpsychol., **13,** 93–132.

NICOLL, C. S., AND MEITES, J. 1959. Prolongation of lactation in the rat by litter replacement. Proc. Soc. exp. Biol., N. Y., **101,** 81–82.

NIKITOVITCH-WINER, M., AND EVERETT, J. W. 1958. Comparative study of luteotropin secretion by hypophysial autotransplants in the rat. Effects of site and stages of the estrous cycle. Endocrinology, **62,** 522–532.

NISSEN, H. W. 1931. A field study of the chimpanzee: observations of chimpanzee behavior and environment in western French Guinea. Comp. Psychol. Monogr., **8,** No. 36.

NISSEN, H. W., AND YERKES, R. M. 1943. Reproduction in the chimpanzee: report on forty-nine births. Anat. Rec., **86,** 567–578.

NOBLE, G. K., AND WURM, M. 1940. The effect of testosterone propionate on the black-crowned night heron. Endocrinology, **26,** 837–850.

NOBLE, G. K., AND WURM, M. 1942. Further analysis of the social behavior of the black-crowned night heron. Auk, **59,** 205–224.

NOBLE, G. K., WURM, M., AND SCHMIDT, A. 1938. Social behavior of the black-crowned night heron. Auk, **55,** 7–40.

OBIAS, M. D. 1957. Maternal behavior of hypophysectomized gravid albino rats and the development and performance of their progeny. J. comp. physiol. Psychol., **50,** 120–124.

ODUM, E. P. 1942. Annual cycle of the black-capped chickadee-2. Auk, **58,** 518–535.

PALMER, R. S. 1941. A behavior study of the common tern. Proc. Boston Soc. nat. Hist., **42,** 1–119.

PALUDAN, K. 1951. Contributions to the breeding biology of *Larus argentatus* and *Larus fuscus* Vidensk. Medd. dansk naturh. Foren. Kbh., **114,** 1–128.

PARKES, K. C. 1953. The incubation patch of males of the suborder Tyranni. Condor, **55,** 218–219.

PATEL, M. D. 1936. The physiology of the formation of the pigeon's milk. Physiol. Zoöl., **9,** 129–152.

PAYNE, F. 1943. The cytology of the anterior pituitary of broody fowls. Anat. Rec., **86,** 1–13.

PEARL, R. 1912. The mode of inheritance of fecundity in the domestic fowl. J. exp. Zool., **13,** 153–268.

PEARL, R. 1914. Studies on the physiology of reproduction in the domestic fowl. VII. Data regarding the brooding instinct in its relation to egg production. J. Anim. Behav., **4,** 266–288.

PEARSON, A. K., AND PEARSON, O. P. 1955. Natural history and breeding behavior of the tinamou, *Nothoprocta ornata.* Auk. **72,** 113–127.

PEARSON, O. P. 1944. Reproduction in the shrew (*Blarina brevicauda* Say). Amer. J. Anat., **75,** 39–93.

PETERSEN, A. J. 1955. The breeding cycle in the bank swallow. Wilson Bull., **67,** 235–286.

PETERSEN, W. E. 1948. The hormonal control of lactation. Recent Progr. Hormone Res., **2,** 133–158.

PETERSEN, W. E., AND LUDWICK, T. M. 1942. The humoral nature of the factor causing the let down of milk. Fed. Proc., **1,** 66–67.

PFEIFFER, C. A. 1936. Sexual differences of the hypophyses and their determination by the gonads. Amer. J. Anat., **58,** 195–225.

PFEIFFER, C. A. 1937. Hypophyseal gonadotropic hormones and the luteinization phenomenon in the rat. Anat. Rec., **67,** 159–175.

PHILLIPS, C. A. 1887. Egg-laying extraordinary in *Colaptes auratus.* Auk, **4,** 346.

PHOENIX, C. H., GOY, R. W. GERALL, A. A., AND YOUNG, W. C. 1959. Organizing action of prenatally administered testosterone propionate on the tissues mediating mating behavior in the female guinea pig. Endocrinology, **65,** 369–382.

PILTERS, H. 1954. Untersuchungen über angeborene Verhaltensweisen bei Tylopoden, unter besonderer Berücksichtigung der neuweltlichen Formen. Z. Tierpsychol., **11,** 213–303.

PITELKA, F. A. 1942. Territoriality and related problems in North American hummingbirds. Condor, **44,** 189–204.

PITT, F. 1929. Notes on the effect of temperature upon the breeding behaviour of birds, with especial reference to the northern golden plover (*Charadrius apricarius altifrons*), and the fieldfare (*Turdus pilaris*). Ibis (ser. 12), **5,** 53–71.

POLIKARPOVA, E. 1940. Influence of external factors upon the development of the sexual gland of the sparrow. C. R. Acad. Sci. U.R.S.S., **26,** 91–95.

PORTER, R. W., CAVANAUGH, E. B., CRITCHLOW, B. V., AND SAWYER, C. H. 1957. Localized changes in electrical activity of the hypothalamus in estrous cats following vaginal stimulation. Amer. J. Physiol., **189,** 145–151.

POULSEN, H. 1953a. Inheritance and learning in the song of the chaffinch (*Fringilla coelebs* L.). Behaviour, **3,** 216–228.

POULSEN, H. 1953b. A study of incubation responses and some other behaviour patterns in birds. Vidensk. Medd. dansk. naturh. Foren. Kbh., **115,** 1–131.

PRECHTL, H. F. R. 1956. Neurophysiologische Mechanismen des formstarren Verhaltens. Behaviour, **9,** 244–319.

PRÉVOST, J. 1953. Formation des couples, ponte et incubation chez le manchot empereur. Alauda, **21,** 141–156.

PRICE, J. B. 1936. The family relations of the plain titmouse. Condor, **38,** 23–28.

PUNNETT, R. C., AND BAILEY, P. G. 1920. Genetic studies in poultry. II. Inheritance of egg-colour and broodiness. J. Genet., **10,** 277–299.

PUTNAM, L. S. 1949. The life history of the cedar waxwing. Wilson Bull., **61,** 141–182.

QUILLIGAN, E. J., AND ROTHCHILD, I. 1960. The corpus luteum-pituitary relationship: the luteotrophic activity of homotransplanted pituitaries in intact rats. Endocrinology, **67**, 48–53.

RABAUD, E. 1921a. L'instinct maternel chez les mammifères. Bull. Soc. zool. Fr., **46**, 73–81.

RABAUD, E. 1921b. L'instinct maternal chez les mammifères. J. Psychol. norm. path., **18**, 487–495.

RAMAKRISHNA, P. A. 1950. Parturition in certain Indian bats. J. Mammal., **31**, 274–278.

RAMSAY, A. O. 1951. Familial recognition in domestic birds. Auk, **68**, 1–16.

RAMSAY, A. O. 1953. Variations in the development of broodiness in fowl. Behaviour, **5**, 51–57.

RAND, A. L. 1940. Results of the Archbold expeditions. No. 26. Breeding habits of the birds of paradise: *Macgregoria* and *Diphyllodes*. Amer. Mus. Novit., No. 1073.

RAND, A. L. 1941. Results of the Archbold expeditions. No. 34. Development and enemy recognition of the curve-billed thrasher *Toxostoma curvirostre*. Bull. Amer. Mus. nat. Hist., **78**, 213–242.

RAND, A. L. 1942. Results of the Archbold expeditions. No. 44. Some notes on bird behavior. Bull. Amer. Mus. nat. Hist., **79**, 517–524.

RASMUSSEN, A. T. 1938. Innervation of the hypophysis. Endocrinology, **23**, 263–278.

REECE, R. P., AND TURNER, C. W. 1936. Influence of suckling upon galactin content of the rat pituitary. Proc. Soc. exp. Biol., N. Y., **35**, 367–368.

REECE, R. P., AND TURNER, C. W. 1937a. Effect of stimulus of suckling upon galactin content of the rat pituitary. Proc. Soc. exp. Biol., N. Y., **35**, 621–622.

REECE, R. P., AND TURNER, C. W. 1937b. The lactogenic and thyrotropic hormone content of the anterior lobe of the pituitary gland. Res. Bull. Mo. agric. Exp. Sta., No. 266.

REICHENOW, E. 1921. Über die Lebensweise des Gorillas und des Schimpansen. Naturwissenschaften, **9**, 73–77.

RENNELS, E. G., AND CALLAHAN, W. P. 1959. The hormonal basis for pubertal maturation of hair in the albino rat. Anat. Rec., **135**, 21–32.

(REYNIERS, J. A.) 1953. Germ-free life. Lancet, **1953**, (Vol. II), 933–934.

RICHARDSON, K. S. 1949. Contractile tissues in the mammary gland, with special reference to myoepithelium in the goat. Proc. roy. Soc., **136B**, 30–45.

RICHARDSON, W. B. 1943. Wood rats (*Neotoma albigula*): their growth and development. J. Mammal., **24**, 130–143.

RICHTER, C. P. 1937. Hypophyseal control of behavior. Cold Spr. Harb. Symp. quant. Biol., **5**, 258–268.

RICHTER, C. P. 1941. Behavior and endocrine regulations of the internal environment. Endocrinology, **2**, 193–195.

RICHTER, C. P. 1943. Total self-regulatory functions in animals and human beings. Harvey Lect., **38**, 63–103.

RICHTER, C. P., AND BARELARE, B. 1938. Nutritional requirements of pregnant and lactating rats studied by the self-selection method. Endocrinology, **23**, 15–24.

RICHTER, C. P., AND ECKERT, J. F. 1936. Behavior changes produced in the rat by hypophysectomy. Proc. Ass. Res. nerv. Dis., **17**, 561–571.

RICHTER, C. P., AND WISLOCKI, G. B. 1930. Anatomical and behavior changes produced in the rat by complete and partial extirpation of the pituitary gland. Amer. J. Physiol., **95**, 481–492.

RIDDLE, O. 1911. On the formation, significance and chemistry of the white and yellow yolk of ova. J. Morph., **22**, 455–491.

RIDDLE, O. 1916. Studies on the physiology of reproduction in birds. I. The occurrence and measurement of a sudden change in the rate of growth of avian ova. Amer. J. Physiol., **41**, 387–396.

RIDDLE, O. 1935. Aspects and implications of the hormonal control of the maternal instinct. Proc. Amer. phil. Soc., **75**, 521–525.

RIDDLE, O. 1937. Physiological responses to prolactin. Cold Spr. Harb. Symp. quant. Biol., **5**, 218–228.

RIDDLE, O., AND BATES, R. W. 1933. Concerning anterior pituitary hormones. Endocrinology, **17**, 689–698.

RIDDLE, O., AND BATES, R. W. 1939. The preparation, assay and actions of lactogenic hormone. In *Sex and Internal Secretions*, 2nd ed., E. Allen, C. H. Danforth and E. A. Doisy, Eds., pp. 1088–1117. Baltimore: The Williams & Wilkins Company.

RIDDLE, O., BATES, R. W., AND LAHR, E. L. 1935. Prolactin induces broodiness in fowl. Amer. J. Physiol., **111**, 352–360.

RIDDLE, O., AND BEHRE, E. H. 1921. Studies on the physiology of reproduction in birds. IX. On the relation of stale sperm to fertility and sex in ring-doves. Amer. J. Physiol., **57**, 228–249.

RIDDLE, O., AND BRAUCHER, P. F. 1931. Studies on the physiology of reproduction in birds. XXX. Control of the special secretion of the crop-gland in pigeons by an anterior pituitary hormone. Amer. J. Physiol., **97**, 617–625.

RIDDLE, O., AND BURNS, F. H. 1931. A conditioned emetic reflex in the pigeon. Proc. Soc. exp. Biol., N. Y., **28**, 979–981.

RIDDLE, O., AND DYKSHORN, S. W. 1932. Secretion of crop-milk in the castrate male pigeon. Proc. Soc. exp. Biol., N. Y., **29**, 1213–1215.

RIDDLE, O., HOLLANDER, W. F., MILLER, R. A., LAHR, E. L., SMITH, G. C., AND MARVIN, H. N. 1942. Endocrine studies. Yearb. Carneg. Instn, **41**, 203–211.

RIDDLE, O., AND LAHR, E. L. 1944. On broodiness of ring doves following implants of certain steroid hormones. Endocrinology, **35**, 255–260.

RIDDLE, O., LAHR, E. L., AND BATES, R. W. 1935a.
Effectiveness and specificity of prolactin in the
induction of the maternal instinct in virgin
rats. Amer. J. Physiol., 113, 109.

RIDDLE, O., LAHR, E. L., AND BATES, R. W. 1935b.
Prolactin-induced activities which express ma-
ternal behavior in virgin rats. Amer. J.
Physiol., 113, 110.

RIDDLE, O., LAHR, E. L., AND BATES, R. W. 1935c.
Maternal behavior induced in virgin rats by
prolactin. Proc. Soc. exp. Biol., N. Y., 32,
730-734.

RIDDLE, O., LAHR, E. L., AND BATES, R. W. 1936.
Endocrine studies. Yearb. Carneg. Instn, 35,
49-56.

RIDDLE, O., LAHR, E. L., AND BATES, R. W. 1942.
The role of hormones in the initiation of
maternal behavior in rats. Amer. J. Physiol.,
137, 299-317.

RIESS, B. F. 1950. The isolation of factors of
learning and native behavior in field and laboratory studies. Ann. N. Y. Acad. Sci., 51,
1093-1102.

RIESS, B. F. 1954. The effect of altered environments and of age in mother-young relationships among animals. Ann. N. Y. Acad. Sci.,
57, 606-610.

RILEY, G. M., AND WITSCHI, E. 1938. Comparative effects of light stimulation and administration of gonadotropic hormones on female
sparrows. Endocrinology, 23, 618-624.

RITTINGHAUS, H. 1956. Untersuchungen am See-
regenpfeifer (Charadrius alexandrinus L.) auf
der Insel Oldeoog. J. Orn., Lpz., 97, 117-155.

RIVOLIER, J. 1956. Emperor Penguins. London:
Elek Books, Ltd.

ROBERTS, B. 1940. The breeding behaviour of
penguins with special reference to Pygoscelis
papua (Forster). Sci. Rep. Brit. Grahamld
Exped., 1, 195-254.

ROBERTS, E., AND CARD, L. E. 1934. Inheritance
of broodiness in the domestic fowl. Proc.
World's Poult. Cong., Rome, 5(2), 353-358.

ROBERTS, N. L. 1937. Some ecological aspects of
bird life. Emu, 37, 48-55.

ROMANOFF, A. L. 1943. Growth of avian ovum.
Anat Rec., 85, 261-267.

ROMANOFF, A. L. 1949. Critical periods and
causes of death in avian embryonic development. Auk, 66, 264-270.

ROMANOFF, A. L., AND ROMANOFF, A. J. 1949. The
Avian Egg. New York: John Wiley & Sons,
Inc.

ROSENBLATT, J. S., AND ARONSON, L. R. 1958a.
The influence of experience on the behavioural
effects of androgen in prepuberally castrated
male cats. Anim. Behav., 6, 171-182.

ROSENBLATT, J. S., AND ARONSON, L. R. 1958b. The
decline of sexual behavior in male cats after
castration with special reference to the role
of prior sexual experience. Behaviour, 12, 285-
338.

ROSS, S., DENENBERG, V. H., FROMMER, G. P., AND
SAWIN, P. B. 1959. Genetic, physiological

and behavioral background of reproduction in
the rabbit. V. Nonretrieving of neonates. J.
Mammal., 40, 91-96.

ROSS, S., DENENBERG, V. H., SAWIN, P. B., AND
MEYER, P. 1956. Changes in nest building
behaviour in multiparous rabbits. Brit. J.
Anim. Behav., 4, 69-74.

ROTHCHILD, I. 1960a. The corpus luteum-pituitary relationship: the association between the
cause of luteotrophin secretion and the cause
of follicular quiescence during lactation; the
basis for a tentative theory of the corpus luteum-pituitary relationship in the rat. Endocrinology, 67, 9-41.

ROTHCHILD, I. 1960b. The corpus luteum-pituitary relationship: the lack of an inhibiting
effect of progesterone on the secretion of pituitary luteotrophin. Endocrinology, 67, 54-
61.

ROTHCHILD, I., AND DICKEY, R. 1960b. The corpus luteum-pituitary relationship: a study of
the compensatory hypertrophy of the ovary
during pseudopregnancy and lactation in the
rat. Endocrinology, 67, 42-47.

ROTHCHILD, I., AND FRAPS, R. M. 1944. Relation
between light-dark rhythms and hour of lay
of eggs experimentally retained in the hen.
Endocrinology, 35, 355-362.

ROTHCHILD, I., AND FRAPS, R. M. 1949. The induction of ovulating hormone release from the
pituitary of the domestic hen by means of
progesterone. Endocrinology, 44, 141-149.

ROTHCHILD, I., AND QUILLIGAN, E. J. 1960. The
corpus luteum-pituitary relationship: on the
reports that oxytocin stimulates the secretion
of luteotrophin. Endocrinology, 67, 122-125.

ROWAN, W. 1926. On photoperiodism, reproductive periodicity, and the annual migration of
birds and certain fishes. Proc. Boston Soc. nat.
Hist., 38, 147-189.

ROWAN, W. 1931. The Riddle of Migration.
Baltimore: The Williams & Wilkins Company.

ROWELL, T. E. 1960a. The family group in golden
hamsters: its formation and breakup. Anim.
Behav., 9, in press.

ROWELL, T. E. 1960b. Maternal behaviour in
non-maternal animals. Behaviour, 16, in press.

ROWELL, T. E. 1960c. On the retrieving of young
and other behaviour in lactating golden hamsters. Proc. zool. Soc. Lond., 135, 265-282.

RYVES, B. H. 1934. The breeding habits of the
corn-bunting as observed in North Cornwall:
with special reference to its polygamous habit.
Brit. Birds, 28, 2-26.

RYVES, B. H. 1943a. An investigation into the
roles of males in relation to incubation. Brit.
Birds, 37, 10-16.

RYVES, B. H. 1943b. An examination of incubation in its wider aspects based on observations in North Cornwall. Brit. Birds, 27, 42-
49.

SAEKI, Y., AND TANABE, Y. 1954. Changes in prolactin potency of the pituitary of the hen

during nesting and rearing in her broody period. Bull. nat. Inst. agric. Sci., Tokyo, Ser. G., **8**, 101–109.

SAEKI, Y., AND TANABE, Y. 1955. Changes in prolactin content of fowl pituitary during broody periods and some experiments on the induction of broodiness. Poult. Sci., **34**, 909–919.

SALOMONSEN, F. 1939. Oological studies in Gulls. I. Egg-producing power of *Larus argentatus* Pont. Dansk. orn. Foren. Tidsskr., **33**, 113–133.

SAWIN, P. B., AND CRARY, D. D. 1953. Genetic and physiological background of reproduction in the rabbit. II. Some racial differences in the pattern of maternal behavior. Behaviour, **6**, 128–146.

SAWIN, P. B., AND CURRAN, R. H. 1952. Genetic and physiological background of reproduction in the rabbit. I. The problem and its biological significance. J. exp. Zool., **120**, 165–201.

SAWIN, P. B., DENENBERG, V. H., ROSS, S., HAFTER, E., AND ZARROW, M. X. 1960. Maternal behavior in the rabbit: hair loosening during gestation. Amer. J. Physiol., **198**, 1099–1102.

SAWYER, C. H. 1949. Reflex induction of ovulation in the estrogen-treated rabbit by artificial vaginal stimulation. Anat. Rec., **103**, 502.

SAWYER, C. H. 1958. Activation and blockade of the release of pituitary gonadotropin as influenced by the reticular formation. In *Reticular Formation of the Brain*, H. H. Jasper *et al.*, Eds., pp. 223–230. Boston: Little, Brown & Company.

SAWYER, C. H. 1959. Nervous control of ovulation. In *Recent Progress in the Endocrinology of Reproduction*, C. W. Lloyd, Ed., pp. 1–20. New York: Academic Press, Inc.

SAWYER, C. H., AND KAWAKAMI, M. 1959. Characteristics of behavioral and electroencephalographic after-reactions to copulation and vaginal stimulation in the female rabbit. Endocrinology, **65**, 622–630.

SAWYER, C. H., AND MARKEE, J. E. 1959. Estrogen facilitation of release of pituitary ovulating hormone in the rabbit in response to vaginal stimulation. Endocrinology, **65**, 614–621.

SCHANTZ, W. E. 1937. A nest-building male song sparrow. Auk, **54**, 189–191.

SCHJELDERUP-EBBE, T. 1924. Fortgesetzte biologische Beobachtungen des Gallus domesticus. Psychol. Forsch., **5**, 343–355.

SCHNEIDER, R. A., COSTILOE, J. P., HOWARD, R. P., AND WOLF, S. 1958. Olfactory perception thresholds in hypogonadal women: changes accompanying administration of androgen and estrogen. J. clin. Endocrin. Metab., **18**, 379–390.

SCHNEIRLA, T. C. 1950. A consideration of some problems in the ontogeny of family life and social adjustment in various infra-human animals. In *Problems of Infancy and Childhood. Transactions of the Fourth (1950) Conference*, M. J. E. Senn, Ed., pp. 81–124. New York: Josiah Macy, Jr. Foundation.

SCHNEIRLA, T. C. 1956. Interrelationships of the "innate" and the "acquired" in instinctive behavior. In *L'Instinct dans le Comportement des Animaux et de l'Homme*, P.-P. Grassé, Ed., pp. 387–452. Paris: Masson & Cie.

SCHNEIRLA, T. C. 1959. An evolutionary and developmental theory of biphasic processes underlying approach and withdrawal. Neb. Symp. Motiv., **1959**, 1–42.

SCHOOLEY, J. P. 1937. Pituitary cytology in pigeons. Cold Spr. Harb. Symp. quant. Biol., **5**, 165–179.

SCHOOLEY, J. P., AND RIDDLE, O. 1938. The morphological basis of pituitary activity in pigeons. Amer. J. Anat., **62**, 313–349.

SCHÜZ, E. 1943. Über die Jungenaufzucht des weissen Storches (*C. ciconia*). Z. Morph. Ökol. Tiere, **40**, 181–237.

SCOTT, J. P. 1945. Social behavior, organization and leadership in a small flock of domestic sheep. Comp. Psychol. Monogr., **18**, 1–29.

SCOTT, J. P. 1953. The process of socialization in higher animals. Proc. Milbank Memor. Fund, **29**, 82–103.

SCOTT, J. P. 1958. *Aggression*. Chicago: University of Chicago Press.

SEITZ, P. F. D. 1954. The effects of infantile experiences upon adult behavior in animal subjects: I. Effects of litter size during infancy upon adult behavior in the rat. Amer. J. Psychiat., **110**, 916–927.

SEITZ, P. F. D. 1958. The maternal instinct in animal subjects: I. Psychosom. Med., **20**, 215–226.

SEITZ, P. F. D. 1959. Infantile experience and adult behavior in animal subjects. II. Age of separation from the mother and adult behavior in the cat. Psychosom. Med., **21**, 353–378.

SELANDER, R. K. 1960. Failure of estrogen and prolactin treatment to induce brood patch formation in brown-headed cowbirds. Condor, **62**, 65.

SELYE, H. 1934. On the nervous control of lactation. Amer. J. Physiol., **107**, 535–538.

SELYE, H., COLLIP, J. B., AND THOMSON, D. L. 1934. Nervous and hormonal factors in lactation. Endocrinology, **18**, 237–248.

SELYE, H., AND MCKEOWN, T. 1934a. Further studies on the influence of suckling. Anat. Rec., **60**, 323–332.

SELYE, H., AND MCKEOWN, T. 1934b. Production of pseudo-pregnancy by mechanical stimulation of the nipples. Proc. Soc. exp. Biol., N. Y., **31**, 683–687.

SEUBERT, J. L. 1952. Observations on the renesting behavior of the ring-necked pheasant. Trans. N. Amer. Wildl. Conf., **17**, 305–329.

SEWARD, J. P., AND SEWARD, G. H. 1940. Studies on the reproductive activities of the guinea pig. I. Factors in maternal behavior. J. comp. Psychol., **29** 1–24.

SGOURIS, J. T., AND MEITES, J. 1952. Inactivation of prolactin by body tissues *in vitro*. Amer. J. Physiol., **169**, 301–304.

SHADLE, A. R. 1945. Rat foster mother of mice. J. Mammal., **26**, 193–194.

SHIMIZU, S., BAN, T., AND KUROTSU, T. 1956. Studies on the milk-ejection response induced by the electrical stimulation of the hypothalamus of rabbits. Med. J. Osaka Univ., **7**, 79–99.

SHIRLEY, H. V., AND NALBANDOV, A. V. 1956a. Effects of neurohypophysectomy in domestic chickens. Endocrinology, **58**, 477–483.

SHIRLEY, H. V., AND NALBANDOV, A. V. 1956b. Effects of transecting hypophyseal stalks in laying hens. Endocrinology, **58**, 694–700.

SHOEMAKER, H. H. 1939. Effect of testosterone propionate on behavior of the female canary. Proc. Soc. exp. Biol., N. Y., **41**, 299–302.

SIMEONE, F. A., AND ROSS, J. F. 1938. The effect of sympathectomy on gestation and lactation in the rat. Amer. J. Physiol., **122**, 659–667.

SIMMONS. K. E. L. 1954. The behaviour and general biology of the graceful warbler *Prinia gracilis*. Ibis, **96**, 262–292.

SIMMONS, K. E. L. 1955a. Studies on great crested grebes. 5. Platform-behaviour. Avicult. Mag., **61**, 235–253.

SIMMONS, K. E. L. 1955b. Studies on great crested grebes. 6. Notes on some aspects of parental-behaviour. Avicult. Mag., **61**, 294–316.

SIMPSON, S. 1911. Observations on the body temperature of the domestic fowl (*Gallus gallus*) during incubation. Trans. roy. Soc. Edinb., **47**, 605–617.

SKEAD, C. J. 1947. A study of the Cape weaver. Ostrich, **18**, 1–42.

SKUTCH, A. F. 1953a. Life history of the southern house wren. Condor, **55**, 121–149.

SKUTCH, A. F. 1953b. How the male bird discovers the nestlings. Ibis, **95**, 1–37, 505–543.

SKUTCH, A. F. 1957. The incubation patterns of birds. Ibis, **99**, 69–93.

SLADEN, W. J. L. 1953. The Adelie penguin. Nature, **171**, 952–955.

SLIJPER, E. J. 1956. Some remarks on gestation and birth in Cetacea and other aquatic mammals. Hvalråd. Skr., No. 41.

SLIJPER, E. J. 1960. Die Geburt der Säugetiere. In *Handbuch der Zoologie*, J.-G. Helmcke, H. v. Lengerken, and D. Starck, Eds., Vol. 8, Lief. 25, Teil 9, 108 pp. Berlin: Walter de Gruyter & Company.

SLONAKER, J. R. 1925. The effect of copulation, pregnancy, pseudopregnancy, and lactation on the voluntary activity and food consumption of the albino rat. Amer. J. Physiol., **71**, 362–394.

SMITH, P. E. 1954. Continuation of pregnancy in rhesus monkey following hypophysectomy. Endocrinology, **55**, 655–664.

SOUTHERN, H. N. 1954. Mimicry in cuckoos' eggs. In *Evolution as a Process*, J. Huxley, A. C. Hardy, and E. B. Ford, Eds., pp. 219–232. London: Allen and Unwin.

SOWLS, L. 1949. A preliminary report on renesting in waterfowl. Trans. N. Amer. Wildl. Conf., **14**, 260–274.

SPENCE, K. W. 1937. Réactions des mères chimpanzés a l'égard des enfants chimpanzés après séparation. J. Psychol. norm. path., **34**, 475–493.

STAMM, J. S. 1954. Genetics of hoarding. I. Hoarding differences between homozygous strains of rats. J. comp. physiol. Psychol., **47**, 157–161.

STAMM, J. S. 1955. The functions of the median cerebral cortex in maternal behavior of rats. J. comp. physiol. Psychol., **48**, 347–356.

STAMM, J. S. 1956. Genetics of hoarding. II. Hoarding behavior of hybrid and back-crossed strains of rats. J. comp. physiol. Psychol., **49**, 349–352.

STANFORD, J. A. 1952. An evaluation of the adoption method of bobwhite quail propagation. Trans. N. Amer. Wildl. Conf., **17**, 330–337.

STELLAR, E. 1954. The physiology of motivation. Psychol. Rev., **61**, 5–22.

STIEVE, H. 1919. Die Entwicklung des Eierstockseies der Dohle (*Colaeus monedula*). Ein Beitrag zur Frage nach den physiologischerweise im Ovar stattfindenden Rückbildungsvorgängen. Arch. mikr. Anat., Abteil. II, **92**, 137–288.

STONE, C. P., AND KING, F. A. 1954. Effects of hypophysectomy on behavior in rats: I. Preliminary survey. J. comp. physiol. Psychol., **47**, 213–219.

STONE, C. P., AND MASON, W. A. 1955. Effects of hypophysectomy on behavior in rats: III. Thermoregulatory behavior. J. comp. physiol. Psychol., **48**, 456–462.

STONEHOUSE, B. 1953. The Emperor Penguin (*Aptenodytes forsteri* Gray). I. Breeding behaviour and development. Sci. Rep. Falkld I. Depend. Surv., No. 6, 1–33.

STORER, R. W. 1952. A comparison of variation, behavior and evolution in the sea bird genera Uria and Cepphus. Univ. Calif. Publ. Zool., **52**, 121–222.

STRESEMANN, E. 1934. Aves. In *Handbuch der Zoologie*, W. Kuckenthal, Ed., vol. 7, part 2, pp. 1–899. Berlin: Walter de Gruyter & Company.

STURMAN-HULBE, M., AND STONE, C. P. 1929. Maternal behavior in the albino rat. J. comp. Psychol., **9**, 203–237.

SVIHAL, A. 1931. Life history of the Texas rice rat (*Oryzomys palustris texensis*). J. Mammal., **12**, 238–242.

SWANBERG, P. O. 1950. On the concept of "incubation period." Vår. Fågelv., **9**, 63–80.

TAIBELL, A. 1928. Risveglio artificiale di istinti tipicamenta femminili nei maschi di taluni uccelli. Atti Soc. Nat. Mat. Modena, **59**, 93–102.

TAVOLGA, M. C., AND ESSAPIAN, F. S. 1957. The behavior of the bottle-nosed dolphin (*Tursiops truncatus*): mating, pregnancy, parturition and mother-infant behavior. Zoologica, N. Y., **42**, 1–31.

TEDFORD, M. D., AND YOUNG, W. C. 1960. Ovarian structure in guinea pigs made hermaphroditic by the administration of androgen prenatally (abstr.). Anat. Rec., *in press*.

TEMBROCK, G. 1957. Zur Ethologie des Rotfuchses (*Vulpes vulpes* (L.)), unter besonderer Berücksichtigung der Fortpflanzung. Zool. Gart., Lpz., **23**, 289–532.

TGETGEL, B. 1926. Untersuchungen über den Sekretionsdruck und über das Einschiessen der Milch im Euter-Rindes. Schweiz. Arch. Tierheilk., **68**, 335–348, 369–387.

THOMSON, A. L. 1950. Factors determining the breeding seasons of birds: an introductory review. Ibis, **92**, 173–184.

THORPE, W. H. 1954. The process of song-learning in the chaffinch as studied by means of the sound spectrograph. Nature, **173**, 465–469.

THORPE, W. H. 1956. *Learning and Instinct in Animals*. Cambridge: Harvard University Press.

THORPE, W. H. 1958. The learning of song patterns by birds, with especial reference to the song of the chaffinch *Fringilla coelebs*. Ibis, **100**, 535–570.

TIETZ, E. G. 1933. The humoral excitation of the nesting instincts in rabbits. Science, **78**, 316.

TINBERGEN, N. 1935. Field observations of East Greenland birds. I. The behaviour of the red-necked phalarope (*Phalaropus lobatus* L.) in spring. Ardea, **24**, 1–42.

TINBERGEN, N. 1939a. On the analysis of social organization among vertebrates, with special reference to birds. Amer. Midl. Nat., **21**, 210–234.

TINBERGEN, N. 1939b. The behavior of the snow bunting in spring. Trans. Linn. Soc. N. Y., **5**, 1–94.

TINBERGEN, N. 1951. *The Study of Instinct*. Oxford: Oxford University Press.

TINBERGEN, N. 1952. "Derived" activities; their causation, biological significance, origin, and emancipation during evolution. Quart. Rev. Biol., **27**, 1–32.

TINBERGEN, N. 1953. *The Herring Gull's World*. London: William Collins Sons & Company, Ltd.

TINBERGEN, N. 1955. Psychology and ethology as supplementary parts of a science of behavior. In *Group Processes: Transactions of the First Conference*, B. Schaffner, Ed., pp. 75–167. New York: Josiah Macy, Jr. Foundation.

TINBERGEN, N., AND KUENEN, D. J. 1939. Über die auslösenden und die richtunggebenden Reizsituationen der Sperrbewegung von jungen Drosseln (Turdus m. merula L. und T. e. ericetorum Turton). Z. Tierpsychol., **3**, 38–60.

TINBERGEN, N., AND PERDECK, A. C. 1950. On the stimulus situation releasing the begging response in the newly hatched herring gull chick (*Larus argentatus* Pont). Behaviour, **3**, 1–39.

TINKLEPAUGH, O. L., AND HARTMAN, C. G. 1930. Behavioral aspects of parturition in the monkey, *M. rhesus*. J. comp. Psychol., **11**, 63–98.

TINKLEPAUGH, O. L., AND HARTMAN, C. G. 1932. Behavior and maternal care of the newborn monkey (*Macaca mulatta* = "*M. rhesus*"). J. genet. Psychol., **40**, 257–286.

TUCKER, B. W. 1943. Brood-patches and the physiology of incubation. Brit. Birds, **37**, 22–28.

TURNER, C. D. 1939. The modification of sexual differentiation in genetic female mice by the prenatal administration of testosterone propionate. J. Morph., **65**, 353–381.

TURNER, C. W., AND REINEKE, E. P. 1936. A study of the involution of the mammary gland of the goat. Res. Bull. Mo. agric. Exp. Sta., No. 235.

TVERSKOY, G. B. 1953. The nature of sensory stimuli from the udder, participating in reflex regulation of milk secretion (in Russian). J. gen. Biol., Moscow, **14**, 349–359.

UYLDERT, I. E. 1943. Investigations on the mammary gland and the lactation process in rats. Acta brev. neerl. Physiol., **13**, 17–20.

UYLDERT, I. E. 1946. A conditioned reflex as a factor influencing the lactation of rats. Acta brev. neerl. Physiol., **14**, 86–89.

VALENSTEIN, E. S., RISS, W., AND YOUNG, W. C. 1955. Experiential and genetic factors in the organization of sexual behavior in male guinea pigs. J. comp. physiol. Psychol., **48**, 397–403.

VALENSTEIN, E. S., AND YOUNG, W. C. 1955. An experiential factor influencing the effectiveness of testosterone propionate in eliciting sexual behavior in male guinea pigs. Endocrinology, **56**, 173–177.

VAN OORDT, G. J. 1934. Über einen biologischen Unterschied zwischen Fluss-und Kustenseeschwalben (*Sterna hirundo* und *Sterna paradisaea*). Beitr. FortPflBiol. Vögel, **10**, 5–6.

VAN TIENHOVEN, A. 1958. Effect of progesterone on broodiness and egg production of turkeys. Poult. Sci., **37**, 428–433.

VAUGIEN, L. 1948. Recherches biologiques et expérimentales sur le cycle reproducteur et la mue des oiseaux passeriformes. Bull. biol., **82**, 166–213.

VAUGIEN, L. 1951. Ponte induite chez la Perruche ondulée maintenue a l'obscurité et dans l'ambience des volières. C. R. Acad. Sci., Paris, **232**, 1706–1708.

VERLAINE, L. 1934. L'instinct et l'intelligence chez les oiseaux. Rech. Phil., **3**, 285–305.

VERWEY, J. 1930. Die Paarungsbiologie des Fischreihers (*Butorides v. virescens*). Zool. Jb., **48**, 1–120.

VON PFEFFER-HÜLSEMANN, K. 1955. Die angeborenen Verhaltensweisen der Sturmmöwe (*Larus c. canus* L.). Z. Tierpsychol., **12**, 434–451.

WAHLSTRÖM, A. 1929. Beiträge zur Biologie von *Crocidura leucodon* (Herm). Z. Säugetierk., **4**, 157–185.

WALLER, H. 1938. *Clinical Studies in Lactation.* London: William Heinemann, Ltd.

WARREN, D. C., AND CONRAD, R. M. 1939. Growth of the hen's ovum. J. agric. Res., **58**, 875–893.

WARREN, E. R. 1927. *The Beaver.* Baltimore: The Williams & Wilkins Co.

WARREN, R. P., AND HINDE, R. A. 1959. The effect of oestrogen and progesterone on the nest-building of domesticated canaries. Anim. Behav., **7**, 209–213.

WARREN, R. P., AND HINDE, R. A. 1961. Roles of the male and the nest-cup in controlling the reproduction of female canaries. Anim. Behav., **9**, in press.

WATSON, J. B. 1908. The behavior of noddy and sooty terns. Publ. Carneg. Instn, No. **103**, 189–255.

WEICHERT, C. K. 1939. The experimental shortening of prolonged gestation in the lactating albino rat. Anat. Rec., **75**, (suppl.), 72–73.

WEICHERT, C. K. 1942. Selection of nipples by suckling rats and its effect upon mammary system. Endocrinology, **31**, 349–353.

WEICHERT, C. K., AND KERRIGAN, S. 1942. Effects of estrogen upon the young of injected lactating rats. Endocrinology, **30**, 741–752.

WEIDMANN, U. 1956. Observations and experiments on egg-laying in the black-headed gull (*Larus ridibundus* L.). Brit. J. Anim. Behav., **4**, 150–161.

WEININGER, O. 1956. The effects of early experience on behavior and growth characteristics. J. comp. physiol. Psychol., **49**, 1–9.

WEISS, P., AND ROSSETTI, F. 1951. Growth responses of opposite sign among different neuron types exposed to thyroid hormone. Proc. nat. Acad. Sci., Wash., **37**, 540–556.

WELLER, M. W. 1958. Observations on the incubation behavior of a common nighthawk. Auk, **75**, 48–59.

WELLER, M. W. 1959. Parasitic egg laying in the redhead (*Aythya americana*) and other North American Anatidae. Ecol. Monogr., **29**, 333–365.

WELTER, W. A. 1935. The natural history of the long-billed marsh wren. Wilson Bull., **47**, 3–34.

WESTERSKOV, K. 1956. Incubation temperatures of the pheasant *Phasianus colchicus*. Emu, **56**, 405–420.

WESTON, H. G. 1947. Breeding behavior of the Black-headed Grosbeak. Condor, **49**, 54–73.

WHITEHOUSE, H. L. K., AND ARMSTRONG, E. A. 1953. Rhythms in the breeding behaviour of the European wren. Behaviour, **5**, 261–288.

WHITELEY, H. J. 1958. Studies on hair growth in the rabbit. J. Anat., Lond., **92**, 563–567.

WHITMAN, C. O. 1919. The behavior of pigeons. Publ. Carneg. Instn, No. 257.

WHITTEN, W. K. 1956a. Modification of the oestrous cycle of the mouse by external stimuli associated with the male. J. Endocrin., **13**, 399–404.

WHITTEN, W. K. 1956b. The effect of removal of the olfactory bulbs on the gonads of mice. J. Endocrin., **14**, 160–163.

WHITTEN, W. K. 1959. Occurrence of anoestrus in mice caged in groups. J. Endocrin., **18**, 102–107.

WHITTLESTONE, W. G. 1954. The effect of adrenaline on the milk-ejection response of the sow. J. Endocrin., **10**, 167–172.

WIESNER, B. P., AND SHEARD, N. M. 1933. *Maternal Behaviour in the Rat.* London: Oliver and Boyd, Ltd.

WILLIAMS, L. 1952. Breeding behavior of the Brewer blackbird. Condor, **54**, 3–47.

WILLIAMS, W. L. 1941. The effect of non-suckling and the non-removal of milk upon individual mammary glands in the lactating mouse. Yale J. Biol. Med., **14**, 201–208.

WILLIAMS, W. L. 1945. The effects of lactogenic hormone on post parturient unsuckled mammary glands of the mouse. Anat. Rec., **93**, 171–183.

WIMSATT, W. A. 1945. Notes on breeding behavior, pregnancy, and parturition in some vespertilionid bats of the eastern United States. J. Mammal., **26**, 23–33.

WIMSATT, W. A. 1960. An analysis of parturition in Chiroptera, including new observations on *Myotis l. lucifugus*. J. Mammal., **41**, 183–200.

WINGSTRAND, K. G. 1943. Zur Diskussion über das Brüten des Hühnerhabichts *Accipiter gentilis* (L.). K. fysiogr. Sällsk. Lund Förh., **13**, 220–228.

WINGSTRAND, K. G. 1951. *The Structure and Development of the Avian Pituitary.* Lund: C. W. K. Gleerup Publishers.

WITSCHI, E. 1935. Seasonal sex characters in birds and their hormonal control. Wilson Bull., **47**, 177–188.

WITSCHI, E. 1938. Hormonal control of seasonal phenomena in birds. Proc. int. orn. Congr., **9**, (Rouen), 431–435.

WOLBURG, I. 1952. Über Vorzugstemperaturen von Muriden. Biol. Zbl., **71**, 601–617.

WUNDER, W. 1937. Brutpflege und Nestbau bei Säugetieren. Ergebn. Biol., **14**, 280–348.

YAMASHINA, Y. 1952. Notes on experimental brooding induced by prolactin injections in the domestic cock. Annot. zool. jap., **25**, 135–142.

YAMASHINA, Y. 1956a. Studies on the elimination of broodiness in domestic fowl by the use of prolactin. IV. Studies on the hybrid between male White Leghorn and female Barred Plymouth Rock (Japanese with English summary). Misc. Rep. Yamashina's Inst. Orn. Zool., **30**, 271–276.

YAMASHINA, Y. 1956b. Studies on the elimination of broodiness in domestic fowl by the use of prolactin. V. Broodiness in the Plymouth Rocks obtained from the cross with the cocks which were proved unbroody by prolactin-injection. Misc. Rep. Yamashina's Inst. Orn. Zool., **30**, 311–317.

YASUDA, M. 1953. Cytological studies of the anterior pituitary in the broody fowl. Proc. imp. Acad. Japan, **29,** 586–594.

YAZAKI, I. 1956. Effect of adrenalectomy on regrowth of hair in pregnant and lactating rats. Annot. zool. jap., **29,** 121–128.

YERKES, R. M. 1915. Maternal instinct in a monkey. J. Anim. Behav., **5,** 403–405.

YERKES, R. M. 1935. A second-generation captive-born chimpanzee. Science, **81,** 542–543.

YERKES, R. M., AND CHILD, M. S. 1927. Anthropoid behavior. Quart. Rev. Biol., **2,** 37–57.

YERKES, R. M., AND ELDER, J. H. 1937. Concerning reproduction in the chimpanzee. Yale J. Biol. Med., **10,** 41–48.

YERKES, R. M., AND TOMILIN, M. I. 1935. Mother-infant relations in chimpanzee. J. comp. Psychol., **20,** 321–359.

YOKOYAMA, A. 1956. Milk-ejection responses following administration of "tap" stimuli and posterior pituitary extracts. Endocr. jap., **3,** 32–37.

YOUNG, P. T. 1949. Food-seeking drive, affective process and learning. Psychol. Rev., **56,** 98–121.

YOUNG, P. T. 1959. The role of affective processes in learning and in motivation. Psychol. Rev., **66,** 104–125.

YOUNG, W. C. 1957. Genetic and psychological determinants of sexual behavior patterns. In *Hormones, Brain Function, and Behavior,* H. Hoagland, Ed., pp. 75–98. New York: Academic Press, Inc.

YTREBERG, N.-J. 1956. Contribution to the breeding biology of the black-headed gull (*Larus ridibundus* L.) in Norway. Nytt Mag. Zool., **4,** 5–106.

ZARROW, M. X., SAWIN, P. B., ROSS, S., AND DENENBERG, V. H. 1962. Maternal behavior in the rabbit and a consideration of its endocrine basis. In *The Roots of Behavior,* E. L. Bliss, Ed., *in press.* New York: Paul B. Hoeber, Inc.

ZIPPELIUS, H.-M. 1957. Zur Karawanenbildung bei der Feldspitzmaus (*Crocidura leucodon*). Bonner zool. Beitr., **8,** 81–85.

ZIPPELIUS, H.-M., AND SCHLEIDT, W. M. 1956. Ultraschall-Laute bei Mäusen. Naturwissenschaften, **43,** 502.

Acknowledgments. Work from the author's laboratory, described in this chapter, was accomplished with the support of research grants from the National Science Foundation (G2546), the National Institutes of Health of the United States Public Health Service (M2271 and C3617), the Rockefeller Foundation, and the Rutgers University Research Council (261), to all of whom grateful acknowledgment is made.

Dr. I. Eibl-Eibesfeldt, Dr. R. A. Hinde, and Dr. J. S. Rosenblatt each read various parts of the chapter, and made many helpful suggestions.

Miss June Thomas typed the manuscript. Miss Thomas and Miss Nina Lehrman assisted with the difficult task of proof-reading.

22

SEX HORMONES AND OTHER VARIABLES IN HUMAN EROTICISM[1]

John Money, Ph.D.

ASSOCIATE PROFESSOR OF MEDICAL PSYCHOLOGY AND PEDIATRICS,
THE JOHNS HOPKINS UNIVERSITY, BALTIMORE

[1] From the Departments of Psychiatry and Pediatrics, The Johns Hopkins University. The research program from which many of the data discussed in this chapter were derived has been supported since 1951 by a grant from the Josiah Macy, Jr. Foundation. Since 1957 it has been supported also by research grant M-1557 from the National Institute of Mental Health of the National Institutes of Health. The research, formerly under the aegis of Dr. John C. Whitehorn, Professor Emeritus of Psychiatry, is dependent on the unfailing good will of Dr. Lawson Wilkins, Professor of Pediatrics, whose endocrine clinic has provided an indispensable wealth of clinical material.

I. Introduction

Investigators of the role of gonadal hormones in human eroticism are more restricted by the mores of our culture than are students in other areas of biologic and medical research. Partly for this reason, our knowledge of the relationship between hormones and reproductive behavior in man is not as advanced as it is for the lower animals generally. There is, however, one compensating factor. Unlike studies of lower mammals which must be on the basis of gestural and nonverbal signs alone, the study of human eroticism is not limited in this way. Eroticism[2] in man is a complex of signs and signals including physiosomatic signs from the reproductive system, behavioral gestures of premating and mating endeavors, and language messages about sexual sensations, imagery, and expectancy. In the study of human eroticism, therefore, linguistic, verbal signs may be added to the gestural ones, and when interviews are conducted with sufficient skill, objectivity, and regard for the importance of suitable controls, information can be obtained which supplements invaluably that gathered from naturalistic observations and experiments on lower mammals.

The availability of pathologic subjects

[2] Conceptually, eroticism is a more inclusive term than libido in its traditional sense of sexual desire. In Freudian or Jungian usage, however, libido is vastly more comprehensive a concept than eroticism. To avoid ambiguity the term libido is little used in this chapter.

TABLE 22.1

Sex hormone anomalies and numbers of patients

Unmatured boys aged 16 or older, not dwarfed, with hypogonadism and sex-hormone deficiency.... 11
Unmatured girls over 16, dwarfed in stature, with gonadal aplasia and sex-hormone deficiency:
  (a) Male sex chromatin... 7
  (b) Female sex chromatin.. 2
Woman, sex-hormone deficiency secondary to pituitary deficiency............................... 1
Female hyperadrenocortical hermaphrodites precociously virilized, studied when feminized on
    cortisone therapy:
  (a) Between ages 8 and 14 years.. 9
  (b) Between ages 15 and 53 years... 12
Boys with idiopathic sexual precocity... 9
Girls with idiopathic sexual precocity.. 16
Boys with precocious puberty of hyperadrenocortical onset, not arrested by treatment........... 8

Various anatomic anomalies affecting eroticism and numbers of patients

Paraplegic men.. 1
Clitorectomized hermaphrodites.. 9
Men with penectomy.. 4
Woman with radical vulvectomy... 1

has been important for the furtherance of investigation and development of concepts in human eroticism. It is a well known principle that pathology, by its very exaggerations, helps to sharpen one's acuity for perception of the normal.

On the basis of these principles, this chapter presents material on human eroticism. A part is a review of the many published reports. Much of it, on the other hand, was obtained from people who had some pathologic condition that affected their sexual functioning. More than 100 were patients of a variety of ages and types of hermaphroditism and for whom a psychologic study had been completed, the same patients whose histories were the basis of Chapter 23 on the ontogenesis of sexual behavior by the Hampsons. Full details of the endocrine conditions in these patients will be found in Wilkins (1957), the method of psychologic study in Money (1957). Other patients were paraplegics and quadriplegics whose study was made possible through the kindness of Dr. John Neustadt at Baltimore City Hospitals and Dr. Alexander Dowling, Medical Director of Maryland State Chronic Disease Hospitals. The numbers of patients in the different groups are shown in Table 22.1.

Historically, the medical management of hermaphroditism followed the common assumption that masculine eroticism is an

attribute of male-hormone functioning and female eroticism of female-hormone functioning. This view receives considerable support in the phenomena of reproductive or sexual behavior in subhuman mammals (see chapter by Young). It was not until 1945 that the significance of hermaphroditism for psychosexual theory was given serious consideration. In that year Ellis published a review of 84 case reports in the periodical literature. In these reports psychologic information was for the most part anecdotal rather than systematically collected. An important exception was a case study in 1942 by Finesinger, Meigs and Sulkowitch, which still remains the sole example of psychoanalysis applied to an hermaphrodite. The patient was a male hermaphrodite, aged 17, boyish in build and hormonally unfeminized, who had always lived as a girl. Psychoanalytic sessions were conducted daily for 6 months, as a matter of research interest. In a personal communication, Finesinger confirmed that, without exception, the patient's free associations were typically those of a teen-aged girl.

In 1950 Money began a series of hermaphroditic studies[3] that have since been expanded in a continuous program in col-

[3] Money, 1952, 1955; Money, Hampson and Hampson, 1955a, 1955b, 1956, 1957; Hampson, 1955; Hampson, Hampson and Money. 1955; Hampson, Money and Hampson, 1956.

laboration originally with Dr. Joan G. Hampson and latterly with Dr. John L. Hampson and Dr. John W. Shaffer also. Seven variables of sex were examined for incongruities that might exist among them in hermaphroditic patients: (1) nuclear sex, *i.e.*, the sex-chromatin pattern of cell nuclei (Barr, 1957), or the actual chromosome count (Ferguson-Smith, 1960); (2) gonadal sex; (3) hormonal sex and pubertal feminization or virilization; (4) the internal accessory reproductive structures; (5) external genital morphology; (6) sex of assignment and rearing; (7) gender role and sexual orientation established while growing up.

From the evidence these investigators collected, it became quite clear that, among other incongruities in hermaphrodites, the gender role and erotic orientation as man or woman may be independent of hormonal sex. Full elucidation of the relationship between functioning of the sex hormones and of eroticism in men and women is far from complete, however. It is the aim of this chapter to contribute to the elucidation of this problem.

II. Empiric Endocrine Restrictions

Unraveling of erotic-hormonal relationships is subject to three restrictions imposed by the biochemical nature of the sex hormones. The first pertains to study of the effects of hormone administration. It arises from the possible biotransformation of androgens into estrogens, in the male, and of gestagens into androgens in the female. The possibility of such transformations restricts what may be inferred from the results of experimental administration of the sex hormones. It cannot, for instance, be assumed after injection of a specific hormone, say testosterone, that the observed sequelae are direct effects of the testosterone. Some of the hormonal substance may have been converted into an estrogen after its absorption into the blood. Thus, conversion of androgen into estrogen may explain duct proliferation in the breasts (gynecomastia) of a male castrate treated with large doses of testosterone, or in some untreated rapidly maturing, ordinary adolescent males.

The second restriction in the unraveling of erotic-hormonal relationships pertains to determinations of blood and urinary hormone levels. It arises from the fact that the sex hormones, *in vivo*, are unstable chemical compounds. From a given androgenic steroid, related forms may be derived by molecular rearrangement, addition, or reduction (see chapter by Villee). These changes appear to take place constantly in the biosynthesis and metabolism of androgen in the living body. The same holds true for estrogens and gestagens.

It is impossible at the present stage of scientific knowledge to identify the full variety of related forms of the sex hormones that are functionally active in the body, or to estimate their quantity. Quantitative assessments of androgens or estrogens in routine laboratory practice are not assessments of the hormones actually circulating in the blood and stimulating the cells of the various tissues and organs. Determinations of hormone levels in blood and urine are, in general, determinations of derivative forms and metabolic end-products of the actual compounds active in the body, some of them biologically inert.

Biochemical instability of the sex hormones does not mean that laboratory hormonal measures are useless. What it does mean is that the level of biologically active circulating hormone must be inferred from the laboratory findings. The inference may not be made unless appropriate norms and criteria have been empirically established. In individual cases the further significance of laboratory findings can be pinned down only when they are appraised within the context of clinical and other findings about the patient or subject concerned. To illustrate, an above-average level of urinary ketosteroids in a male may be without specific significance. It would be highly significant, however, if the sample came from a patient who showed other signs such as tumorous enlargement of the adrenal gland or testis, or, in a younger patient, signs of precocious virilism.

The third restriction in unraveling erotic hormonal relationships pertains to bioassays as they are routinely performed. A sex-hormone compound which is judged biologically active, and not inert, is so judged on the basis of its stimulating effect on appropriate morphologic sexual characteristics in test animals. Thus, a biologically active androgen is one that stimulates comb growth in the capon, or prostatic and seminal vesicle secretion in the castrate or immature rat. Similarly, estrogen induces changes in the vaginal epithelium in adult spayed mice or maturation of the uterus in juvenile mice. Gestagens induce the appropriate gestational changes in the endometrium of the uterus. It does not follow that a specified biologically active compound will be equally potent in its stimulating effect on all secondary sexual characteristics. For example, in hypopituitary, eunuchoid youths testosterone induces a fair degree of virilization, except for growth of the beard, although in castrated boys the effect of testosterone on beard growth is excellent. Within a species, some individuals are more sensitive, some more resistant to a prescribed amount of hormone. Within an individual, some target organs are more sensitive or more resistant than others. Examples of such variations are mentioned from time to time in the ensuing text. Because of such variations, there is the possibility that an otherwise biologically active synthetic hormone may fail or partially fail to evoke signs of eroticism, or that it may evoke seemingly incongruous effects.

III. Morphologic and Behavioral Maturation

Androgens are specific for bringing about adult growth of the genital tract in males. Estrogens are similarly specific for females. Further, androgens are antagonistic to feminized genital maturation in females, the classic example being virilizing hyperadrenocorticism in girls.[4] These girls, hermaphroditic if born with their adrenal dysfunction, have a precocious and exclusively virilizing puberty. Their ovaries fail to mature and the clitoris becomes hypertrophied to resemble a penis in size. Estrogens are antagonistic to virilized genital maturation in males. They inhibit androgen production in the testes and thus simulate castration. Simultaneously, they stimulate enlargement of the breasts.

Hormonal failure of the gonads, whether through castration or hypofunction of the

gonadal endocrine cells, results in persistence of infantile sexual and body morphology. Patients who reach the middle teenage, or beyond, with sex hormone failure untreated, demonstrate how far-reaching is the morphologic function of the sex hormones.

Teen-agers with morphologically prepubertal bodies are invariably identified by strangers as younger than their age. Old friends, family, and social intimates fall with perilous ease into the custom of treating them as preadolescent juveniles. It is difficult for them to remain persona grata with their age-mates. The boys are worse off than the girls, for it is more feasible for a girl with facial make-up and built-in "falsies" to disguise some of the stigmata of sexual infantilism than it is for a beardless, high-voiced boy. Many girls as well as boys, however, fall by the wayside, physically too immature for their own age group, yet socially too mature for younger children of similar physique. Among the 10 girls and 11 boys of Table 22.1 who were over 16 and still physically unmatured, only 1 girl and 1 boy had a history of a teen-age social and dating life that approached the norm for their group.

When a teen-ager with sex-hormonal failure is responded to as a juvenile from all quarters, the chances are very great that he or she will respond as a juvenile and lag behind in psychologic and behavioral development as he or she gets older.[5] The longer this lag persists, the more difficult becomes the problem of social and psychologic adjustment as a maturing and mature adult, after hormonal substitution therapy has been instituted.[6] Adolescent psychologic growth cannot be properly achieved in the absence of adolescent physical growth, but it also cannot be properly achieved in the absence of age-mates who are also in the adolescent growth phase. The early teen-years appear

[4] These actions of androgens and estrogens are described and discussed fully in the chapter by Burns.

[5] This lag is seen even more acutely in dwarfed children whose size belies their age. The converse, an acceleration of psychologic and behavioral development, is possible in children with precocious physical and sexual maturation.

[6] The same kind of adjustment problem has been seen almost without exception in the post-teen-age women with virilized hyperadrenocortical hermaphroditism, after they have begun to feminize in body morphology following institution of cortisone therapy.

to be the critical period for optimal, all-round adolescent development.

The behavioral immaturity that matches sexual immaturity is not necessarily reversible. It may establish itself as a chronic handicap, especially if puberty is too long delayed into and beyond the late teens. Chronic behavioral immaturity then defeats the success of hormonal substitution therapy by militating against success in mating and in adult erotic relationships.

Androgens and estrogens both mature the body, the one in a virilizing, the other in a feminizing way. Androgens, in addition, have a strong positive influence on nitrogen metabolism and so on muscular strength and energy. This muscular effect was particularly noted by two hypogonadal males in the series who worked as manual laborers. Before treatment began they made euphemistic statements about their fatigue threshold. After treatment they were able to make a comparison and so to realize how easily they had tired formerly. The converse effect of androgen suppression producing a diminution of muscular strength and energy is well observed in hyperadrenocortical females when their androgen excesses are first suppressed by cortisone therapy. Two patients have remarked on this phenomenon.

The androgenic effect of stepped-up nitrogen metabolism and increased general muscular size and strength (Kochakian, 1946; Kochakian and Tillotson, 1957) does not seem to have any direct effect on eroticism. The hypogonadal men (Table 22.1) on androgen-substitution therapy became sexually more active and participative, but not because they had formerly been invalids too weak to participate. They did not become more violent, assaultive, or aggressive, even though they had more muscle power at their disposal.

Rather than being spread generally over the nervous system and musculature, the specifically erotic action of androgen, insofar as it can be identified, seems to be anatomically localized. In particular, the undeveloped penis or clitoris responds to initial androgen administration with extensive dilation of its vasculature and with growth in size. Thereafter, maintenance of an erection by complete engorgement of the organ with

blood is facilitated by androgen. Tumescence of the penis can occur in the absence of androgen, but the erection is generally not complete and long lasting.

The seminal vesicles and prostate remain immature in a male until they are stimulated into growth by androgen. Thereafter, their fluids, which form the medium of sperm conveyance and nourishment, are secreted only so long as there is sufficient androgen in the body.

IV. Eroticism and the Supply of Sex Hormone

A. PREPUBERTAL AND POSTPUBERTAL CASTRATION

Much of the literature bearing on this subject was reviewed by Kinsey, Pomeroy, Martin and Gebhard (1953). Their summary of the effects of gonadectomy performed prepubertally, as well as the summaries of their predecessors (Lipschütz, 1924; Commins and Stone, 1932; Beach, 1948), contains abundant evidence for the importance of gonadal hormones in the development of sexual responsiveness in man. The repeated emphasis by Kinsey, Pomeroy, Martin and Gebhard that damage to other endocrine glands such as the pituitary, thyroid, adrenals, and islands of Langerhans, may have similar disastrous effects on the development of the capacity to respond sexually does not weaken the case for the specific role of the gonadal hormones in such development. Debilitating effects on vital functions including reproduction do follow ablation of these other glands, but when the gonads are removed the damaging effects, although general, are nevertheless most sharply focused on reproductive function. The damage is clearly evident in the chronic infantilism that follows prepubertal castration.

The results of postpubertal castration are more variable as Bremer's excellent study (1959) and the reviews by Tauber (1940), Engle (1942), Beach (1948), and Kinsey, Pomeroy, Martin and Gebhard (1953) indicate, some males and females report that the retention of sexual capacities and responsiveness is ostensibly complete following castration, others that decrease or total loss occurs. The most serious obstacle to clarification is the inadequacy of detail in most of the reports available for evaluation, although some reports are exemplary, like those of Foss (1937) and Hamilton (1943). Another part of the difficulty is that the effects of gonadectomy may vary with age, being less marked in older than younger men, with respect to behavior as well as to physical characters. More important, as many writers have emphasized, is the dominance of cognitional and learned factors in the overt expression of eroticism in man. These may include type and extent of prior sexual experience, preference for a given partner, freedom from fear of pregnancy, the degree of respect and affection in the marital relationship, the background of cultural expectancy regarding castration, and so forth.

In efforts to ascertain the effects of castration, as well as in other efforts to determine the role of the gonads in erotic functioning, past experience is always a complicating factor in any type of subject under study. As lower animals and presumably man develop and mature, psychologic or experiential as well as genic factors mold the substrate on which the hormones act in such a way that diversity rather than similarity in response is seen during adulthood (see chapter on hormones by Young). The range may extend from absence of a response to intense reactions verging on the pathologic in their deviation from what is typical for the species. For the investigator who is expecting a uniformity of response to a given quantity of a hormone, this diversity in response may mask the effect of the hormone and prompt him to minimize the degree of its effectiveness. Or, atypical patterns of behavior such as homosexuality may be seen in individuals in whom there is no evidence of gonadal pathology or of abnormality of secretory function (Kinsey, 1941; Sevringhaus and Chornyak, 1945). Cases of this kind do not justify rejection of the concept of hormonal participation in human erotic behavior. They give emphasis instead to the importance of the character of the tissues mediating the behavior, by whatever mechanisms it is brought to expression.

B. HYPOGONADISM

Surgical castration has a functional counterpart in hypogonadism which, like castration, may be of either prepubertal or postpubertal occurrence. Unlike castration, hypogonadism may be partial, with only partial and not complete deficiency of gonadal hormones. Published reports sometimes confuse one type of patient with another, so that findings are somewhat difficult to evaluate. The difficulty is enhanced by the fact that new diagnostic advances in endocrinology and nuclear sexing permit greater precision in the grouping of patients, not possible in the older studies. In general, however, there has been a consensus of opinion that erotic drive in hypogonadal and eunuchoid males of various types is likely to be heightened by androgen administration (McCullagh, McCullagh and Hicken, 1933; Vest and Howard, 1938; Howard and Vest, 1939; Pratt, 1942; Heller and Nelson, 1945; Heller and Maddock, 1947). In cases of partial gonadal failure, control studies with a placebo would have validated the results more convincingly, but in cases of total gonadal failure the results of hormonal substitution therapy are quite dramatic enough to be convincing in themselves. Definitive reports on eroticism in treated hypogonadal females are lacking in the literature.

C. GONADAL FAILURE

Fresh evidence on hypogonadism was obtained from the hypogonadal patients listed in Table 22.1. These patients were completely hypogonadal, that is totally hormone deficient at the age of 16 or older, before treatment began. They were prepubertal, functional castrates.

Juveniles, who are by definition hypogonadal, play erotically together, but it is quite a different matter for a person who has reached the adult years with unmatured genitals to engage in an erotic relationship. Metaphorically speaking, this fact suggests that the first job of the sex hormones is to set the stage properties in order so that the drama of eroticism can be enacted. Support for such a view comes from the circumstance that among the hypogonadal patients entered in Table 22.1, advancing age alone did not change childhood eroticism to adulthood eroticism when sex-hormone failure persisted beyond the age of 16. There were 11 such who were candidates for androgen-substitution treatment and 10 for estrogen-substitution treatment. They evidenced a wide range of variability in their pretreatment erotic development, concomitant with such individual differences as dwarfed stature (among the girls only),[7] inhibitory training in sexual matters, restricted opportunities for social development, and amount of close contact with dating or marriage partners.

Response to treatment may be summed up by saying that these 21 patients went through an erotic development not unlike that of normal boys and girls. It is of interest in addition that they exhibited the same wide range of variability of erotic development and activity after treatment that they had before. It is worth reporting that, among the girls with gonadal aplasia the 2 with a female sex-chromatin pattern (and 1 younger girl like them) did not respond to estrogens in a way conspicuously different from the 7 with a male chromatin pattern.

Eroticism following induced puberty turned out, then, to be not so different from eroticism following ordinary puberty in its character and in its dependence on the presence of sex hormones.

The patients requiring induction of puberty proved more instructive in another way. These individuals, if they omitted their substitution therapy for a period, were in a position to give information about adult eroticism in the absence of sex hormones.

D. SUBSTITUTION THERAPY DISCONTINUED

Of the 11 hypogonadal men entered in Table 22.1, there were 5 who discontinued androgen medication for 3 months or longer. In each case, the absence of androgen from the tissues made a decided difference. The most sensitive indicator was the ejaculate.

[7] Dwarfed boys who also had gonadal failure secondary to hypopituitarism were not included in this study. Dwarfed girls were of necessity included, since dwarfism is a frequent accompaniment of gonadal aplasia in girls. Except for one juvenile surgical castrate, there were in the clinic files no nondwarfed girls with sex-hormone failure.

It gradually diminished in volume until no fluid was emitted. In addition, the men reported that they had fewer erections and a lessened initiative to masturbate or to make coital advances. With loss of ejaculation, they also lost erotic ejaculatory dreams. They considered that waking erotic imagery and daydreams diminished in frequency of appearance.

One may generalize and say that these men did not lose completely their erotic imagery, their erotic sensations, or their erotic actions and behavior. What did happen was that eroticism, whether in imagery, sensation, or activity, was not initiated with the same frequency as before. This failure of initiation showed up in the involuntary failure of the penis to erect or to hold an erection, and in the failure of other, more voluntary erotic actions and coordinated endeavors, as well.

The man who was married when he discontinued treatment had a good barometer of the failure of his erotic initiative, namely his wife's comments and complaints. In fact, this man, and the two others who married, found that it paid them not to become lax about their injections. They reported a slackening of erotic initiative, including erectile potency, if they delayed even a week in getting their monthly injection of long-acting testosterone.

The conclusion to be drawn from periods of interrupted treatment in men with sex-hormone failure is that androgen is necessary, not only to induce morphologic maturity, but also for the maintenance of a well functioning eroticism.

There were four hypogonadal women who discontinued estrogen medication for 3 months or longer. One of them was off treatment for 3 months by request. She married during the first month. Two others were single and celibate. One of the latter discontinued treatment with stilbestrol for 18 months, before resuming on Premarin, because stilbestrol produced unpleasant gastric symptoms. The other single woman had been off treatment for 2 years, having discovered that the only sequel of significance was cessation of the menses. The fourth woman was divorced. She discontinued treatment after a doctor scared her about the carcinogenic dangers of estrogen. She continued to have sexual liaisons during the 5 years off treatment, although eventually she discovered that vaginal tightness and dryness due to lack of estrogen-stimulated secretions was a handicap.

The four women had been on cyclic estrogen therapy so that they menstruated on withdrawal of estrogen for a week each month. Following total withdrawal of estrogen, they ceased to menstruate. Vaginal smears showed that the vaginal mucosa underwent involutional changes as in postmenopausal women. There were no definitive reports of hot flashes or malaise typical of the climacteric, however.

The women reported nothing to indicate any change in their erotic imagery, sensations, or actions. The two who were having intercourse claimed that they reached the climax of orgasm, the same as when taking estrogen.

The evidence from these women fits in with common knowledge concerning postmenopausal disappearance of estrogen in ordinary women. Although there are exceptions, erotic imagery, sensations, and actions are not abolished, often not even lessened, in the usual course of diminished estrogen production at the menopause.

E. IMPOTENCE AND FRIGIDITY

Except in hormone-deficient patients of the hypogonadal and castrate type, impotence in men and frigidity in women are usually unresponsive to treatment with gonadal hormones (Rennie, Vest and Howard, 1939; Creevy and Rea, 1940; Spence, 1940; Carmichael, Noonan and Kenyon, 1941; Kenyon, 1941; Heller and Maddock, 1947; Perloff, 1949). An exception is that a small proportion of frigid women have responded to androgen therapy (Salmon and Geist, 1943). Impotence not due to hormonal insufficiency may be due to vascular and circulatory impairment of the genital organs. Impotence has also been found associated with diabetes mellitus (Rubin and Babbott, 1958). Usually, impotence and frigidity not responsive to hormonal treatment are said to be psychogenic in origin, and the argument for psychogenesis is supported when the disorders are not constant but dependent on time, place, and partner.

The possibility that inherited constitutional variations among individuals play a part in impotence and frigidity is suggested by the data of Grunt and Young (1952) and Riss and Young (1954) obtained from studies of the male guinea pig. When high-score and low-score animals were castrated and injected with different quantities of testosterone propionate, the behavior that was exhibited by individual animals was similar to that displayed before gonadectomy and replacement therapy. Furthermore, the administration of large quantities of the hormone did not alter this relationship. Apparently in this species individuals have a characteristic level of responsiveness. Human males may be similar. The tissues that are generally acknowledged to be responsive to sex hormones, such as peripheral receptors (see below), probably do not have the same threshold of responsiveness in all persons, and these threshold differences are probably inherited. In such cases as those of impotence and frigidity due to psychic inhibition, where hormone levels are not deficient, additional, exogenous hormone has no effect on a response threshold already well primed with hormone.

F. ANDROGEN, ESTROGEN, AND EROTICISM IN MEN AND WOMEN

The relationship of estrogen to eroticism in the adult female seems, after the pubertal estrogenic function of maturing the reproductive tract and feminizing the body morphology in general, to be restricted to maintaining the lubricant secretions of the vagina preparatory to copulation. The primary estrogenic function would seem to be monitoring endometrial growth in close coordination with the gestagenic function of monitoring nidation and gestation.[8]

Inasmuch as maintenance of well functioning eroticism in men appears to be dependent on androgen, it would be an odd

---

[8] Benedek and Rubenstein (1942) defended the thesis that the content of the dreams and psychoanalytic free-associations of 15 women patients could be used to predict which phase their menstrual cycles had reached, as determined by vaginal smear tests. Their hypothesis has not received general acceptance (see chapter by Hampson and Hampson); the collection of additional data and a reconsideration of the problem would be appropriate.

biologic discontinuity if erotic imagery, sensations, and actions in the female of the human species should be, by contrast with estrous behavior of lower animals, independent of hormonal functioning. A tenable hypothesis is that erotic imagery, sensations, and actions are maintained well functioning in both men and women by androgens. In women, the androgens of eroticism might conceivably be of adrenal origin, or they may be derived from gestagens, or they may be of an origin as yet unknown. The most likely explanation is that these androgens are of adrenal origin. Waxenberg, Drellich and Sutherland (1959) reported an excellent study of eroticism in 29 women who had both ovaries and both adrenals removed in the treatment of breast cancer. Loss of only the ovaries and ovarian hormones had no definite adverse effect on sexual drive, activity, and response, but all three were diminished or abolished in most of the women after their adrenals also had been removed. The adrenals secrete some estrogen, but larger amounts of androgen. The authors concluded that the loss of adrenal androgens was the responsible factor in the women's lessened or abolished eroticism.

Other evidence can be marshaled to support the hypothesis that androgen is the hormone of eroticism in men and women. Many women for whom androgen therapy is prescribed report an increase of sexual desire as a side-effect (Shorr, Papanicolaou and Stimmel, 1938; Salmon, 1941; Greenblatt, Mortara and Torpin, 1942; Greenblatt, 1943; Salmon and Geist, 1943; Foss, 1951; Kupperman and Studdiford, 1953; Dorfman and Shipley, 1956). In the clinical lore of urology, conversely, many men for whom estrogen is prescribed report great diminution or total abolition of sexual desire and activity (Focte, 1944; Paschkis and Rakoff, 1950).

The role of gonadal hormones in stimulating eroticism in males and females is discussed by Carter, Cohen and Shorr (1947) in a review of the use of androgens in women and by Perloff (1949). It is noted in both articles (1) that the return of normal libido in certain menopausal women under treatment with estrogens may perhaps be related to increased vascularity and epithelial proliferation of the genital tract, and (2) that the increased libido in women who receive testosterone occurs coincidentally with hypertrophy of the clitoris. From these observations, the hypothesis follows that the hormones, especially androgens, although not the exclusive basis of libidinous urge which is multidetermined, may influence the libido by affecting end-organ sensitivity.

Whatever its nature, the androgen-eroticism relationship is far from being a simple linear correlation. There are irregularities that cannot at present be explained. Such irregularities show up in the different reactions in hyperadrenocortical female hermaphrodites before and after their gross excess of adrenal androgens is lowered by cortisone therapy.

G. HYPERADRENOCORTICAL DIVERSITIES

There were 21 hyperadrenocortical, hermaphroditic females in the larger series in Table 22.1 who satisfied the triple conditions: (a) they had been brought up and lived as girls and women; (b) they were over the age of 8 and, therefore, precociously virilized before cortisone treatment was instituted; (c) they were interviewed after (in some instances before, also) their virilism had been suppressed and their feminization established by cortisone treatment. Among the 21, 9 were hormonally treated and psychologically studied before the age of 14; 12 were between the ages of 15 and 53.

Erotically, 4 of these 21 patients were noteworthy as follows. One of the younger patients suffered from painful priapism of her enlarged clitoris and, postsurgically, from persistent erections of its stump; the clitoral stump became flaccid and unbothersome after cortisone therapy. Two of the older patients manifested extreme hypereroticism, including compulsory copulatory episodes, before cortisone treatment. Although they reported mild lowering of erotic drive after treatment, they continued to rate higher than all but 1 other of the 21 in posttreatment erotic participation. There was one older patient who showed no evidence of erotic activity, and claimed no erotic sensations or inclinations either before or after the cortisone treatment. Her absence of eroticism is unique in this series of patients and remains a puzzle without explanation.

Between the extremes of hypereroticism and hypo-eroticism, the majority of the patients showed a more moderate eroticism. In the majority group, comprising 17 patients, 8 stated that they had fewer clitoral-stump erections or that they masturbated less frequently after cortisone treatment. In the interviews with the other 9, no evidence of change was obtained, but the possibility of change could not be retrospectively excluded with certainty.

None of the 21 patients gave evidence of loss or change of sensitivity of erotic zones, other than the clitoral, while their hormonal feminization was maintained by cortisone treatment, except that sporadically the breasts were reported more sensitive. It is noteworthy that none reported a post-treatment cessation of erotic sensitivity in the clitoral zone—only of erectile autonomy and hypersensitivity of the clitoris, or of its amputated stump. What they lost, therefore, was that autonomous initiatory eroticism of the phallus which seems to be so basic in the eroticism of men. The women were all unequivocally pleased to be relieved of clitoral hypersensitivity; it was the pleasure of being able to feel like a normal woman, several of them explained. In some cases, the clitoris had been amputated in early childhood. Only one of the older patients elected against, and none regretted a decision in favor of this feminizing surgical procedure.

H. EROTICISM IN PRECOCIOUS PUBERTY

An unusual group of children of special interest in the study of childhood eroticism are those with precocious puberty. In children with this diagnosis, the sex hormones function prematurely in relation to the scope and maturity of cognitional functioning as well as to the variety and extent of learning and behavior (Doe-Kulmann and Stone, 1927; Keene and Stone, 1937; Werner, Spector, Vitt, Ross and Anderson, 1942).

In sexual precocity of the idiopathic type, the children are anatomically and physiologically normal in all respects except that the pubertal alarm clock has, so to speak, sounded too early. With respect to the 25 children with idiopathic sexual precocity (Table 22.1), it can only be said that they showed the same range of variation between sexual expression—childhood sex play and masturbation—and sexual inhibition and self-discipline as one might ordinarily find in a randomly assembled group of sexually immature children matched for age and social background. At least, it would be very easy to find nonprecocious children with matching sexual behavior. The frequency of masturbation seemed increased in some of the boys with idiopathic sexual precocity, as a direct function of their ability to ejaculate. Others who did not masturbate had sleep emissions. In none of the children did premature hormonal function, *ipso facto*, lead to premature attempts at mating. As in normal children, the latter appears only when it is encouraged by social experiences and opportunities to learn.[9]

V. Cognitional Rehearsals

A. DEFINITION

Erotic thought and imagery, fantasies and dreams, may all be referred to, for want of a better generic term, as cognitional rehearsals. They may be on-the-spot responses to perceptual images—sights, sounds, smells, touches, tastes—pertaining to sex. The sexy blonde and the lecherous thoughts of boys on the corner as she passes are a stereotyped example. Verbal or graphic reports at second hand may be

[9] A recent report (Gerall, 1958) containing a review of the relevant literature is of interest for the point made in this section. In the guinea pig, but not in the rat, the administration of testosterone propionate to castrated young animals did not advance the appearance of the copulatory pattern or ejaculatory response. In both species injections of testosterone propionate produced greater than normal weights of the seminal vesicles, prostate, and coagulating gland. On the other hand, a difference between the species is reflected in the amount of secretory activity. The level of fructose and citric acid in the prostate gland and seminal vesicles of rats injected with testosterone propionate was several times greater than that in normal rats. In the guinea pig testosterone propionate did not produce precocious secretion of these substances.

stimuli that trigger off the derivative sexual imagery and ideas. Erotic thoughts, imagery, and fantasy are not necessarily followed by sexual acts. The rehearsal in thought or in dream may be an entity unto itself, carried no further. Moreover, the rehearsal may also be far removed in time from the day when it will be put into performance.

Erotic rehearsals in dreams and daydreams appear to be spontaneously initiated in many instances. The stimulus may conceivably be a proprioceptive, somesthetic one from the pelvic reproductive system. A memory stimulus may also be the activator of erotic dreams and daydreams, its arousal not manifestly dependent on perceptual signals from the pelvis or elsewhere. The degree of dependence of these rehearsals on gonadal secretions will be considered here.

B. CHILDHOOD REHEARSALS

It is a matter of everyday knowledge that young children, hormonally immature, have thoughts and fantasies, often disclosed in play, that are cognitional rehearsals of eroticism in its broadest sense. Kindergarten children play their way through romantic flirtations, love affairs, and promises to marry when they grow up. Some of these affairs are developed in elaborate make-believe detail and are viable for months. Explicit genital and copulatory imagery is not a necessary or regular part of these romantic rehearsals. Genital play, however, including copulatory play, is not alien to the play repertory of young children. The frequency of its occurrence seems to depend largely on local cultural and social sanctions. The field studies of cultural anthropologists among ethnic groups geographically as far apart as Africa, Oceana, and the American continents have shown that genital play of all types including copulatory play may be regarded and permitted or encouraged as an expected part of the behavior of normal childhood (Chapter by Mead; Ford and Beach, 1951).

Here is a brief report on the cognitional rehearsals in the 14 of the 25 children in Table 22.1 (12 girls and 2 boys) who had sexually matured physically at or before the age of 8, who were available for psychologic study between the ages of 5 and 12, and who were not too young to be coherent informants.

Among the 14, the occurrence and reporting of sexual dreams and daydreams was variable. Five of the 12 girls said that they had daydreams of boy-friends and romance, and recounted examples—all very stereotyped, Prince-Charming adventures—that excluded genital sex. Romantic sleep-dreams were characterized by the same stereotypy in the 2 girls reporting them. None of the girls gave any evidence of orgasm dreams. In fact, there was no evidence that any of them had experienced orgasm, asleep or awake.

Of the 2 older boys, 1 could not recall dreams or daydreams, although he had seen ejaculation stains on his pajamas. He was seen only once, at the age of 7. The other boy (Money and Hampson, 1955) was seen annually between the ages of 5 and 11. He had florid sexy dreams and daydreams of seeing and kissing naked women that were more freely reported before he was 6 and again after he was 9 years old than during the intervening period. He could not produce a specimen of ejaculate at the age of 7. He was 10 before he gave unequivocal accounts of ejaculation. At that time, the erotic imagery of wet dreams and masturbation fantasies was primarily pictorial and represented couples in various copulatory poses and actions.

The data of these too few male cases can be augmented by adding 8 cases (Table 22.1) of precocity in boys that began as hyperadrenocortical and then became testicular precocity after adrenal overactivity was corrected. It is usual for maturational precocity to continue, as in these cases, once a certain level of somatic maturity has been achieved, even after the original stimulus to precocity has been removed.

The 8 boys were all well advanced into puberty by the age of 8. Two of them reported emissions. These 2 had erotic daydreams and, at night, wet dreams, with imagery of erotic play with girls; the older of the 2, aged 8, also had imagery of intercourse. Two other boys told of daydreams of kissing and petting with girls, accompanied by erection. A fifth boy reported nonerotic mystery and adventure fantasies accompanied by erection.

Reviewing now the histories of the 22 older children with precocious hormonal puberty, it is noteworthy that like their erotic play, the thematic content of their dreams and daydreams directly reflected not the hormonal age but the social age that each child had achieved (see also Rafferty and Stein, 1958). The social age agreed with or was in advance or arrears of the birthday age, dependent on the variety and extent of life experiences the child had encountered and, in turn, transacted. Premature puberty made a difference not in the content and imagery of erotic play, dreams and daydreams, but in the frequency of their occurrence.

C. HYPOGONADAL ADULTS AND CASTRATES

Orgasm dreams are ordinarily regarded as postpubertal phenomena exclusively. None of the hypogonadal patients of both sexes reported in Table 22.1 reported orgasm dreams before puberty was induced with hormonal substitution therapy. Some of them, however, gave examples of sexy daydreams and fantasies. Hormonal therapy did not unconditionally guarantee the onset or the increased occurrence of erotic dreams or daydreams in these hypogonadal patients, although it had such an effect in most instances.

VI. Sex Hormones, Neural Tissues, and Behavior

In lower animals and presumably in man gonadal hormones act on many target organs or tissues of the body and bring to expression the responses characteristic of those tissues: growth, secretions, motility, sensitization for implantation, alterations in behavior, and others, depending on the tissue. Each tissue in its way, therefore, is with the hormones a coordinate of sexual function. In the case of behavior, neural tissues are in this category. Of these, peripheral receptors have been and are the object of especial attention, for as noted above, the possibility exists that, when sensitized by gonadal hormones, they have a role in the mediation of behavior (see also chapter by Young). For the elucidation of

this problem, the verbal reports of human subjects in whom there has been deafferentation of the genital and other erotic areas of the body have provided information which cannot be obtained from lower animals.

In paraplegics, and following penectomy and vulvectomy cognitional eroticism can be studied independently of sensations generated in the genitopelvic area.

A. PARAPLEGIC COGNITIONAL EROTICISM

The complete independence of erotic cognition and pelvic signals is demonstrated in the case of paraplegia. The physiologic state in such patients is variable, as is the level of gonadal hormone secretion (Cooper, Rynearson, MacCarty and Power, 1950; Cooper and Hoen, 1952; Bors, Engle, Rosenquist and Holliger, 1950). It was found that approximately two-thirds of 500 paraplegic and quadriplegic patients were capable of achieving erection, and of these one-third had successful intromission (Talbot, 1955; Zeitlin, Cottrell and Lloyd, 1957), without, however, the gratification obtained before the injury. The dream eroticism of 34 patients was reported by Bors, Engle, Rosenquist and Holliger. Ten patients did not recall any sexual dreams, 14 remembered dreams lacking orgasm, and 10 had complete dry dreams, i.e., including the feelings of orgasm, but without erection or ejaculation.

The independence of erotic cognition and pelvic signals is further demonstrated by an interview with a paraplegic patient (Table 22.1). He was 19 years old and had a paraplegia of 10 months duration. Spinal destruction was at C4 and C5. Loss of feeling and motor function was absolute below the nipples.

In the interview, the man described with exceptional clarity his feelings when his girl-friend kissed him. It seemed as though his penis would be getting into an erection and throbbing, he said. "But when I would look down, nothing was there—it was all in my mind, or something". The phenomenon was similar when he had sexy daydreams, he said. Then he went on, again documenting the discontinuity of cognitional and genitopelvic eroticism. He would think of a time when he had actually had intercourse, he said, as he might formerly have done in a masturbation fantasy. Again he would get a feeling that something was building up pelvically, whereas, in fact, nothing was happening.

The patient introduced the topic of sleeping dreams in which he dreamed of intercourse and orgasm. The dream-orgasm was not accompanied by an erection or ejaculation, but the feeling was the same as it had been in an ordinary nocturnal emission, the man said.

The sexy thoughts and fantasies of a paraplegic patient may serve the literal purpose of rehearsals and lead to attempts at intercourse. Then one has the exceptional phenomenon of cognitional eroticism occurring simultaneously with involuntary, reflex action of the pelvic genitalia, the only possible connection between the two being via the eyes and hands.

So much for paraplegics, the accidental experimental subjects in whom the genital tactile receptors remain intact while their distant connections with the brain are broken. Turn now to the obverse case, patients whose external genitals have been damaged or resected so that, whatever the extent of neural damage, it is local only.

B. CLITORECTOMY IN HERMAPHRODITES

Genital resection, in the course of surgical reconstruction, is desirable in the management of certain cases of hermaphroditism (Jones and Scott, 1958). An enlarged clitoris of penis-like proportions is incompatible with complete femininity in the experience of the majority of hermaphrodites living as girls and women. They desire that their masculinized clitoris be amputated.

Such an operation is usually performed on hyperadrenocortical hermaphrodites if they are to be reared as girls, or if they are already psychosexually established as females. For present purposes, the older patients with this adrenogenital type of hermaphroditism (Table 22.1) are of particular interest. Before the introduction of cortisone therapy in 1950, these patients had undergone a precocious but virilizing puberty in early childhood, under the influence of an excessive supply of adrenal androgen. Under the impact of these androgens, the enlarged, unamputated clitoris was erotically very

sensitive. At the same time, the vagina remained unestrogenized and immature. In most instances the vaginal opening was congenitally misplaced in a urogenital sinus and needed surgical reconstruction.

Among 17 older potential informants in this category of hyperadrenocortical hermaphrodites, there were 9 who satisfied the triple condition: (a) they had been brought up as girls and lived as women; (b) they were older than 16 at the time of reporting on eroticism; (c) they had been clitorectomized and reported on their postsurgical eroticism.

The breakdown of findings in these 9 cases was as follows: in 4 the data indicated the patient had not experienced orgasm; in 5 the evidence was that the patient had experienced orgasm, in 2 masturbatory, in 3 coital.

The 9 women were receiving cortisone when they reported on eroticism. There was no evidence, however, to suggest that orgasm might have been lost following clitorectomy only to reappear after hormonal feminization had been established under cortisone therapy, or that orgasm was lost under the influence of cortisone.

There is no ready explanation for the lack of orgasm in the 4 patients where such appeared to be the case. So far as could be ascertained from unstandardized operative notes, lack of orgasm did not correlate with the amount of clitoral tissue removed, or with any other surgical factor.

The point of these data on orgasm and clitorectomy is not, however, that some clitorectomized patients did not experience orgasm. On the contrary, the point is that capacity for orgasm proved compatible with clitorectomy and surgical feminization of the genitalia in some of these patients. Erotically sensitive though it had been, the main body of the clitoris, including the glans of the clitoris, was dispensable with respect to orgasm.

C. PENECTOMY

Four patients with an amputated penis (Table 22.1) were available for psychologic study. All reported retention of the capacity for orgasm.

One of the patients lost his penis at the age of 30. Ten years later the prostate was removed and the urethral orifice was re-located near the anus, requiring urination from a sitting position. He was interviewed psychologically at the age of 42. After his injury, he frequently had erection of his penile stump in response to seeing or joking with an attractive woman. In sexual rela-tions, mutual genital friction sufficient to induce mutual orgasm was produced.

Another patient reported loss of the ca-pacity for ejaculation, although he retained the sensation of orgasm in dreams. His was a case of penectomy due to malignancy. There were metastases to both groins re-quiring radical bilateral groin dissection. The man was 56 when interviewed and had been in the hospital a year. He said he continued to feel sexually aroused, the feel-ings being the same as they always had been, as for example when his wife came to visit him.

D. VULVECTOMY

It is roughly accurate to say that the fe-male equivalent of penectomy is radical vulvectomy. An interview was obtained with one patient who had this operation. Fifteen years earlier she had had an epi-dermoid carcinoma of the vulva which en-tailed complete resection of the clitoris, labia majora, labia minora, and the mucosa of the introitus. The patient was 45 years old and still premenopausal when she re-turned, through the courtesy of Dr. Howard W. Jones, Jr., for an interview. She was very frank and spontaneous about her sex life postoperatively. She said that, although she was still self-conscious about her genital appearance, so far as sexual feeling was concerned there was no difference. The feel-ing or orgasm occurred sometimes in dreams, she said, as well as in coitus.

Summarizing, it is seen that from patients who have undergone extensive surgical re-section of the genitals, erotic arousal can be initiated and carried to the completion of orgasm despite the loss of large zones of erotic sensory tissue, including the vulva or the penis itself. From paraplegics one learns that cognitional arousal is possible in sub-jects in whom the genital tactile receptors are intact while their connections with the brain are broken. From eunuchs and hypo-gonadal patients (their detailed case illus-

trations omitted at this point) one learns that erotic arousal and climax can some-times occur despite hormonal deficiency that in men causes absence of seminal fluid. Thus, among the coordinates of sexual func-tion there are three: local genital surfaces, the brain, the hormones, any one of which can fail in its contribution without total destruction of sexual function. No one of the three can be said to be indispensable more than the others, except insofar as the hor-mones are indispensable to fertility. None-theless, it is evident that loss of any one of the three constituents is an immense handi-cap to effective sexual functioning.

VII. Concluding Remarks

The sex hormones, it appears, have no direct effect on the direction or content of erotic inclination in the human species. These are assumed to be experientially de-termined. The importance of experiential factors is nowhere better revealed than in hermaphrodites.

To refer back to the beginning of the chapter, the gender role and gender ori-entation of hermaphrodites became estab-lished in accordance with the sex of assign-ment and rearing. One may say that all through childhood these people accumulated a continuous sequence of cognitional re-hearsals in accordance with the encounters and transactions of their sex of assignment. This accumulation exerted its formative in-fluence irrespective of contradictory chro-mosomal sex, gonadal sex, hormonal sex, or morphologic sex.

Even in those few cases where the gender role and orientation developed ambiguously or contradicted the sex of rearing, the sig-nificance of cognitional rehearsals emerged as paramount. In the first place, these were never cases of children who, irrespective of hidden hermaphroditic incongruities, had external genitals that looked perfectly male or perfectly female. The external genitals looked ambiguous, thereby permitting the child from infancy onwards to make com-parisons and conjectures about being a boy or a girl. Many of the children had am-biguous external genitals. The few who de-veloped an ambiguous gender role and ori-entation experienced a reinforcement of ambiguity in the social environment. The parents remained basically unconvinced that they had a son, or a daughter. In some instances there had been also a reassignment of sex. Neighbors remembered and talked about the boy who turned into a girl, and playmates made verbal ammunition of the accusation of being half boy, half girl, or a freak. Even before school age, clear evidence might emerge of a child's personal conviction that everyone was making a mistake and that it was time to begin immediate rehearsals for living as a member of the opposite sex.

It may well be that homosexuality, and other behavioral disorders of sex, are fundamentally disorders of cognitional eroticism, early established and deeply ingrained, their relation to other variables of sex being peripheral at most.

It may be also that disorders of cognitional eroticism should be regarded as imprinting phenomena (chapter by the Hampsons; Fletcher, 1957; Schiller, 1957), imprints that are actually misprints. In accordance with the principles of imprinting, it would be the case that these misprint disorders can be established only at a specified critical period in the life history. The early age, between 18 months and 3 years, after which it becomes psychologically hazardous to make sex reassignments of hermaphrodites suggests that the critical period for the imprinting of gender role and orientation corresponds with the critical period for the establishment of native language. There may conceivably be another critical period for limited modification of gender imprints at the time of puberty.

The phenomenon of the critical imprinting period allows an explanation of the fact that, in the case of homosexuality, a person can engage in a homosexual act when safely past the critical period without becoming a chronic homosexual. Effectively imprinted at the critical period to respond to homosexual stimuli, however, a person becomes a chronic homosexual. Effective stimuli may be extremely specific, and variable from person to person, which may account for the varieties of homosexual preference.

The phenomenon of the critical imprinting period allows an explanation not only of disorders of cognitional eroticism, but also of normal and healthy cognitional erot-

icism. Just as nonhealthy eroticism may become indelibly imprinted, so also · may healthy eroticism, masculine and feminine. Indeed, so fixed is masculinity and femininity of outlook in healthy men and women, respectively, that it has always been assumed that sexual orientation must be determined in some automatic fashion utterly independent of life experience, for example, by genes or hormones. Now it becomes necessary to allow that erotic outlook and orientation is an autonomous psychologic phenomenon independent of genes and hormones and, moreover, a permanent and ineradicable one as well.

The idea of a psychologic phenomenon being autonomous is not new in psychologic theory, but the idea that a psychologic phenomenon may be permanent and ineradicably imprinted is not always hospitably received in the company of present day theories. It is a challenging concept, and one worthy of extensive research within and beyond its application to sex.

The stimuli that bring eroticism to expression remain to be discussed. Are these, too, purely perceptual and learned or do the sex hormones automatically trigger behavior in man as they may do in the lower animals? From the histories of the patients listed in Table 22.1 and the reports herein cited, it is clear that certain changes in behavior are associated with hormone administration: the increased sexual activity of the hypogonadal men who received androgen therapy, the diminution in sexual activity they reported in periods when treatment was discontinued, the increased sexual desire in women following androgen therapy.

Some writers have suggested that psychologic stimuli are sufficient, that in man there has been an emancipation from hormonal control. If it is true, however, as a number of the same writers have postulated, that the sex hormones have a direct effect on the genitalia, maintaining them erotically functional, and on the generation of genitopelvic tactile and somesthetic signals that are relayed to the brain, the role of sex hormones in erotic arousal cannot properly be claimed to have been completely replaced by psychologic stimuli, for indeed the two are not mutually separable.

Tactile and somesthetic signals relayed to the brain from both the genitopelvic area and from other parts of the body may have erotic significance and promote erotic arousal. Erotic arousal may be generated also by signals sent to the brain from the eyes, the ears, and the sense of smell, which signals may be erotically just as potent as genitopelvic tactile signals. An action of sex hormones on certain of these modalities has been claimed (Torda and Wolff, 1944; Beach, 1948; Le Magnen, 1952a, 1952b; Harris, Michael and Scott, 1958; Schneider, Costiloe, Howard and Wolf, 1958), but the area is largely unexplored, especially in man.

Erotic arousal may be triggered not only by sensory signals but also by memory signals from the brain, witness the erotic dreams of paraplegic patients who are incapable of pelvic sensation and who presumably do not, while sleeping, see, hear, smell or feel anything erotic that induces the dreams. Primarily the function of the brain in eroticism is to coordinate and record signals that arrive by way of the different sensory modalities. Messages so received may then be either inhibited or further processed and transmitted in the service of erotic arousal. The brain can perform its erotic function independently of pelvic participation, witness again the dreams and fantasies of paraplegic patients whose genitalia function only through spinal reflexes and without any neural connection with the brain. The brain may record erotic signals and store them as memories for indefinite periods of time, so that past experiences of critical significance in the life history exert a constant and indelible influence on an individual's erotic inclinations and choices.

VIII. References

BARR, M. L. 1957. Cytologic tests of chromosomal sex. Progr. Gynec., 3, 131–141.
BEACH, F. A. 1948. *Hormones and Behavior.* New York: Paul B. Hoeber, Inc.
BENEDEK, T., AND RUBENSTEIN, B. B. 1942. The sexual cycle in women; the relation between ovarian function and psychodynamic processes. Psychosom. Med. Monogr., 3.
BORS, E., ENGLE, E. T., ROSENQUIST, R. C., AND HOLLIGER, V. H. 1950. Fertility in paraplegic males: a preliminary report on endocrine studies. J. Clin. Endocrinol., 10, 381–398.
BREMER, J. 1959. *Asexualization, a Follow-up Study of 244 Cases.* New York: Macmillan Company.
CARMICHAEL, H. T., NOONAN, W. J., AND KENYON, A. T. 1941. The effects of testosterone propionate in impotence. Am. J. Psychiat., 97, 919–943.
CARTER, A. C., COHEN, E. J., AND SHORR, E. 1947. The use of androgens in women. Vitamins & Hormones, 5, 317–391.
COMMINS, W. C., AND STONE, C. P. 1932. Effects of castration on the behavior of mammals. Psychol. Bull., 29, 493–508.
COOPER, I. S., RYNEARSON, E. H., MacCARTY, C. S., AND POWER, M. H. 1950. Metabolic consequences of spinal cord injury. J. Clin. Endocrinol., 10, 858–870.
COOPER, I. S., AND HOEN, T. I. 1952. Metabolic disorders in paraplegics. Neurology, 2, 332–340.
CREEVY, C. D., AND REA, C. E. 1940. The treatment of impotence by male sex hormone. Endocrinology, 27, 392–394.
DOE-KULMANN, L., AND STONE, C. P. 1927. Notes on the mental development of children exhibiting the somatic signs of puberty praecox. J. Abnormal & Social Psychol., 22, 291–324.
DORFMAN, R. I., AND SHIPLEY, R. A. 1956. *Androgens: Biochemistry, Physiology and Clinical Significance.* New York: John Wiley & Sons, Inc.
ELLIS, A. 1945. The sexual psychology of human hermaphrodites. Psychosom. Med., 7, 108–125.
ENGLE, E. T. 1942. The testes and hormones. In *Problems of Ageing*, 2nd ed., C. V. Cowdry, Ed., pp. 475–494. Baltimore: The Williams & Wilkins Company.
FERGUSON-SMITH, M. A. 1960. Nuclear sex and the sex chromosomes. J. Chronic Dis., 12, 203–210.
FINESINGER, J. E., MEIGS, J. V., AND SULKOWITCH, H. W. 1942. Clinical, psychiatric and psychoanalytic study of a case of male pseudohermaphroditism. Am. J. Obst. & Gynec., 44, 310–316.
FLETCHER, R. 1957. *Instinct in Man in the Light of Recent Work in Comparative Psychology.* New York: International Universities Press.
FOOTE, R. M. 1944. Diethylstilbestrol in the management of psychopathologic states in males. J. Nerv. & Ment. Dis., 99, 928–935.
FORD, C. S., AND BEACH, F. A. 1951. *Patterns of Sexual Behavior.* New York: Paul B. Hoeber, Inc.
FOSS, G. L. 1937. Effect of testosterone propionate on a postpubertal eunuch. Lancet, 2, 1307–1309.
FOSS, G. L. 1951. The influence of androgens on sexuality in women. Lancet, 1, 667–669.
GERALL, A. A. 1958. An attempt to induce precocious sexual behavior in male guinea pigs by injections of testosterone propionate. Endocrinology, 63, 280–284.
GREENBLATT, R. B. 1943. Testosterone propionate pellet implantation in gynecic disorders. J. A. M. A., 121, 17–24.

GREENBLATT, R. B., MORTARA, F., AND TORPIN, R. 1942. Sexual libido in the female. Am. J. Obst. & Gynec., **44,** 658–663.

GRUNT, J. A., AND YOUNG, W. C. 1952. Differential reactivity of individuals and the response of the male guinea pig to testosterone propionate. Endocrinology, **51,** 237–248.

HAMILTON, J. B. 1943. Demonstrated ability of penile erection in castrate men with markedly low titers of urinary androgens. Proc. Soc. Exper. Biol. & Med., **54,** 309–312.

HAMPSON, J. G. 1955. Hermaphroditic genital appearance, rearing and eroticism in hyperadrenocorticism. Bull. Johns Hopkins Hosp., **96,** 265–273.

HAMPSON, J. L., HAMPSON, J. G., AND MONEY, J. 1955. The syndrome of gonadal agenesis (ovarian agenesis) and male chromosomal pattern in girls and women: psychologic studies. Bull. Johns Hopkins Hosp., **97,** 207–226.

HAMPSON, J. G., MONEY, J., AND HAMPSON, J. L. 1956. Teaching clinic: hermaphroditism, recommendations concerning case management. J. Clin. Endocrinol., **16,** 547–556.

HARRIS, G. W., MICHAEL, R. P., AND SCOTT, P. P. 1958. Neurologic site of action of stilbestrol in eliciting sexual behavior. In *Ciba Foundation Symposium on the Neurologic Basis of Behavior.* Boston: Little, Brown & Company.

HELLER, C. G., AND NELSON, W. O. 1945. Hyalinization of seminiferous tubules and clumping of Leydig cells. Notes on treatment of clinical syndrome with testosterone propionate, methyl testosterone, and testosterone pellets. J. Clin. Endocrinol., **5,** 27–33.

HELLER, C. G., AND MADDOCK, W. O. 1947. The clinical uses of testosterone in the male. Vitamins & Hormones, **5,** 393–432.

HOWARD, J. E., AND VEST, S. A. 1939. Clinical experiments with male sex hormones. II. Further observations on testosterone propionate in adult hypogonadism, and preliminary report on the implantation of testosterone. Am. J. Med. Sc., **198,** 823–837.

JONES, H. W., JR., AND SCOTT, W. W. 1958. *Hermaphroditism, Genital Anomalies and Related Endocrine Disorders.* Baltimore: The Williams & Wilkins Company.

KEENE, C. M., AND STONE, C. P. 1937. Mental status as related to puberty praecox. Psychol. Bull., **34,** 123–133.

KENYON, A. T. 1941. Problems in the recognition and treatment of testicular insufficiency. New England J. Med., **225,** 714–719.

KINSEY, A. C. 1941. Homosexuality. Criteria for a hormonal explanation of the homosexual. J. Clin. Endocrinol., **1,** 424–428.

KINSEY, A. C., POMEROY, W. B., MARTIN, C. F., AND GEBHARD, P. H. 1953. *Sexual Behavior in the Human Female.* Philadelphia: W. B. Saunders Company.

KOCHAKIAN, C. D. 1946. The protein anabolic effects of steroid hormones. Vitamins & Hormones, **4,** 255–310.

KOCHAKIAN, C. D., AND TILLOTSON, C. 1957. Influence of several C_{19}-steroids on the growth of individual muscles of the guinea pig. Endocrinology, **60,** 607–618.

KUPPERMAN, H. S., AND STUDDIFORD, W. E. 1953. Endocrine therapy in gynecologic disorders. Postgrad. Med., **14,** 410–425.

LE MAGNEN, J. 1952a. Les phénomènes olfacto-sexuels chez l'homme. Arch. Sc. Physiol., **6,** 125–150.

LE MAGNEN, J. 1952b. Les phénomènes olfacto-sexuels chez le rat blanc. Arch. Sc. Physiol., **6,** 295–331.

LIPSCHÜTZ, A. 1924. *The Internal Secretions of the Sex Glands.* Baltimore: The Williams & Wilkins Company.

MCCULLAGH, E. P., MCCULLAGH, D. R., AND HICKEN, N. F. 1933. Diagnosis and treatment of hypogonadism in the male. Endocrinology, **17,** 49–63.

MONEY, J. 1952. Hermaphroditism: an inquiry into the nature of a human paradox. Unpublished doctoral dissertation, Harvard University Library.

MONEY, J. 1955. Hermaphroditism, gender and precocity in hyperadrenocorticism: psychologic findings. Bull. Johns Hopkins Hosp., **96,** 253–264.

MONEY, J. 1957. *The Psychologic Study of Man.* Springfield, Ill.: Charles C Thomas.

MONEY, J., AND HAMPSON, J. G. 1955. Idiopathic sexual precocity in the male: Management, report of a case. Psychosom. Med., **17,** 1–15.

MONEY, J., HAMPSON, J. G., AND HAMPSON, J. L. 1955a. Hermaphroditism: recommendations concerning assignment of sex, change of sex and psychologic management. Bull. Johns Hopkins Hosp., **97,** 284–300.

MONEY, J., HAMPSON, J. G., AND HAMPSON, J. L. 1955b. An examination of some basic sexual concepts: the evidence of human hermaphroditism. Bull. Johns Hopkins Hosp., **97,** 301–319.

MONEY, J., HAMPSON, J. G., AND HAMPSON, J. L. 1956. Sexual incongruities and psychopathology: the evidence of human hermaphroditism. Bull. Johns Hopkins Hosp., **98,** 43–57.

MONEY, J., HAMPSON, J. G., AND HAMPSON, J. L. 1957. Imprinting and the establishment of gender role. A. M. A. Arch. Neurol. & Psychiat., **77,** 333–336.

PASCHKIS, K. E., AND RAKOFF, A. E. 1950. Some aspects of the physiology of estrogenic hormones. Recent Progr. Hormone Res., **5,** 115–149.

PERLOFF, W. H. 1949. Role of the hormones in human sexuality. Psychosom. Med., **11,** 133–139.

PRATT, J. P. 1942. A personal note on methyl testosterone in hypogonadism. J. Clin. Endocrinol., **2,** 460–464.

RAFFERTY, F. T., AND STEIN, E. S. 1958. A study of the relationship of early menarche to ego development. Am. J. Orthopsychiat., **28,** 170–179.

RENNIE, T. A. C., VEST, S. A., AND HOWARD, J. E. 1939. The use of testosterone propionate in impotence: clinical studies with male sex hormones. South. M. J., **32,** 1004–1007.

RISS, W., AND YOUNG, W. C. 1954. The failure of large quantities of testosterone propionate to activate low drive male guinea pigs. Endocrinology, **54**, 232–235.

RUBIN, A., AND BABBOTT, D. 1958. Impotence and diabetes mellitus. J. A. M. A., **168**, 498–500.

SALMON, U. J. 1941. Rationale for androgen therapy in gynecology. J. Clin. Endocrinol., **1**, 162–179.

SALMON, U. J., AND GEIST, S. H. 1943. Effect of androgens upon libido in women. J. Clin. Endocrinol., **3**, 235–238.

SCHILLER, C. H. (Ed). 1957. *Instinctive Behavior*. New York: International Universities Press.

SCHNEIDER, R. A., COSTILOE, J. P., HOWARD, R. P., AND WOLF, S. 1958. Olfactory perception thresholds in hypogonadal women: changes accompanying administration of androgen and estrogen. J. Clin. Endocrinol., **18**, 379–390.

SEVRINGHAUS, E. J., AND CHORNYAK, J. 1945. A study of homosexual adult males. Psychosom. Med., **7**, 302–305.

SHORR, E., PAPANICOLAOU, G. N., AND STIMMEL, B. F. 1938. Neutralization of ovarian follicular hormone in women by simultaneous administration of male sex hormone. Proc. Soc. Exper. Biol. & Med., **38**, 759–762.

SPENCE, A. W. 1940. Testosterone propionate in functional impotence. Brit. Med. J., **2**, 411–413.

TALBOT, H. S. 1955. The sexual function in paraplegics. J. Urol., **73**, 91–100.

TAUBER, E. S. 1940. Effects of castration upon the sexuality of the adult male: a review of relevant literature. Psychosom. Med., **2**, 74–87.

TORDA, C., AND WOLFF, H. G. 1944. Effect of steroid substances on synthesis of acetylcholine. Proc. Soc. Exper. Biol. & Med., **57**, 327–330.

VEST, S. A., JR., AND HOWARD, J. E. 1938. Clinical experiments with the use of male sex hormones. I. Use of testosterone propionate in hypogonadism. J. Urol., **40**, 154–183.

WAXENBERG, S. E., DRELLICH, M. G., AND SUTHERLAND, A. M. 1959. Changes in female sexuality after adrenalectomy. J. Clin. Endocrinol., **19**, 193–202.

WERNER, A. A., SPECTOR, H. I., VITT, A. E., ROSS, W. L., AND ANDERSON, W. A. D. 1942. Pubertas praecox in a six-year-old boy produced by a tumor of the testis, probably of interstitial cell origin. J. Clin. Endocrinol., **2**, 527–530.

WILKINS, L. 1957. *The Diagnosis and Treatment of Endocrine Disorders in Childhood and Adolescence*, 2nd ed. Springfield, Ill.: Charles C Thomas.

ZEITLIN, A. B., COTTRELL, T. L., AND LLOYD, F. A. 1958. Sexology of the paraplegic male. Fertil. & Steril., **8**, 337–344.

23

THE ONTOGENESIS OF SEXUAL BEHAVIOR IN MAN

John L. Hampson, M.D.

ASSOCIATE PROFESSOR OF PSYCHIATRY AND PEDIATRICS, THE JOHNS
HOPKINS UNIVERSITY, BALTIMORE, MARYLAND

and

Joan G. Hampson, M.D.

ASSISTANT PROFESSOR OF PSYCHIATRY AND PEDIATRICS, THE JOHNS
HOPKINS UNIVERSITY, BALTIMORE, MARYLAND

I. Introduction

Adam and Eve—the ancient account of their creation is firmly anchored in our cultural traditions as symbolic of the primeval separateness of male and female. Plato, it is true, re-endorsed an ancient legend of the original hermaphroditism of Man, and Freud rehabilitated for Science a bisexual concept of the human psyche. Yet the dichotomy of male and female is so entrenched in colloquial philosophy that even in rigorous scientific thinking it is difficult to transcend.

Embryologists have long known of the original developmental hermaphroditism of the human fetus. It is well established by biochemists that the sex hormones are closely akin in their chemical structure. Although the overlap between male and female has been conceded, psychosexual orientation in the two sexes has, in the final analysis, been attributed to two separate instincts. These instincts have been vaguely ascribed to innate and constitutional sources. The idea of a complete psychosexual neutrality in the human infant seemed too farfetched to be entertained seriously.

II. Heredity, Environment and the Instinct Controversy

Since the beginning of history man has assumed himself to be separate and apart

1401

from other creatures in a myriad of ways. The theologians of our time, no less than the Greek philosophers of the fourth century B.C. have held to a view that infrahuman creatures function instinctively, reserving intellect, reasoning, and will power for Man alone. But as Beach (1955) has written: "prescientific concepts of instinct were not deduced from the facts of nature; they were necessitated by the demands of philosophic systems based on supernatural conceptions of nature."

It would be foolish to quibble here about the place of Man in Nature; it is assumed, *a priori*, the Man belongs in the system of biologic continuities. It is also assumed that a student of behavior, even as a student of biochemistry or anatomy, can expect to observe differences both between species and within a species. These differences do not in themselves contradict the assumption of a system of continuities.

The concept of instinct, quite apart from having served to set the other animals apart from man, has been used also as a means of explaining and understanding behavioral phenomena which emerged so spontaneously and with such predictability that they *seemed* to have arisen preformed from some inner source. At the same time the terms *innate, constitutional*, and *genetically determined* attained explanatory significance in some quarters. Although the instinctive explanation of behavior still enjoys currency, the concept has not gone unchallenged (Beach and Jaynes, 1954, 1955). Experimental and clinical psychology embrace a theory of instincts; psychoanalytic theory of personality relies heavily on instinctive explanations and commonly regards psychologic disorder as due to some disorganization of instinctual life. There is, however, an accumulating body of evidence which strongly suggests that the usual instinctual explanation of behavior is a gross oversimplification; as an adequate foundation for a science of behavior the traditional form of the concept of instinct has proven less than adequate.

One factor in this inadequacy is the regrettable alliance of the term *innate* with the concept of instinct. *Innate* and *instinctive* have come to be equated in common usage in a way that excludes the influence of experience and learning. The more rigorous scientific viewpoint holds that a distinction between learned and unlearned behavior is not only impossible to dichotomize in any meaningful way but is, in any case, not a very useful distinction. For as Beach (1955) has pointed out: "the final form of any response is affected by a multiplicity of variables only two of which are genetical and experiential factors." Thus in considering any behavior pattern one is obliged to take cognizance of the interplay between two broad categories of variables: (1) those variables which are *intrinsic* to the organism, and (2) those variables which are *extrinsic*. Much of the present volume deals in detail with the intrinsic variables which one must consider in studying sexual behavior. In his chapter on hormones, Young takes into account one of these intrinsic variables, gonadal hormones, and the influence on reproductive behavior in infrahuman species. Cultural influence is an important extrinsic variable dealt with in the chapter by Mead.

A. ANIMAL STUDIES AND HUMAN SEX BEHAVIOR

Social behavior in man, including sexual behavior, is undeniably complex and frequently baffling. It is not a new observation that many of the social attitudes and behavior patterns in man are acquired through one or another process of learning during an individual's lifetime. It is relatively recent, however, that scientifically sound evidence has been collected which spotlights the earliest months and years of life as a highly critical learning period of inexorable importance to later psychologic functioning. As yet the bulk of the experimental evidence for this has come from animal experimentation; experimentation in humans has of necessity been limited to chance occurrences and the "experiments of Nature."

In the area of social perception and social responses some of the most important work in recent years has been done by the European zoologists who have elected to be called ethologists. These experimentalists, notably Lorenz and Tinbergen, have devoted much attention to the observation that, in many animal species, virtually all social behavior is based on, or is an elaboration of, specific stereotyped behavior that can be elicited by *specific sign stimuli*. These stereotyped behavior patterns they consider to be innate in the traditional sense of "instinctive." It has been postulated that special neurophysiologic brain mechanisms, referred to as Innate Releasing Mechanisms (IRM), operate to release the impounded "innate reaction." Operation of an IRM is a response to specific sign stimuli (the terms *cue stimuli* and *social releasers* have also been applied) in the environment. In the herring gull, for example, the red spot on the beak of the adult has been found to serve as a trigger stimulus which elicits food-begging behavior in the fledgling.

Systematic study of similar phenomena in humans has not yet been undertaken. A well known human example is the smiling response in infants (Spitz and Wolf, 1946). The smiling response becomes active somewhere between the fourth and tenth week of life and is elicited by the sign stimulus of a slowly moving human face or, alternatively, the essential elements comprising the gestalt of the human face. Thus a drawing of two circles for eyes and a mark for a nose and mouth moved slowly in the infant's visual field will suffice.

A word about terminology is in order at this point. Some psychiatrists, knowing the importance of the theory of instinct in psychoanalytic doctrine, have been eager to construe ethologic findings as an experimental validation of this theory. Doubtless the overlap in terminology in the two fields has encouraged this not entirely justifiable practice and the result has been a semantic entente rather than an identity of operational definitions. In writing this chapter, we have been in no position to be laboratory purists in the matter of operational definitions; on the other hand, in pointing up the similarity, where it occurs, between concepts derived from ethology and from our own work we have endeavored to avoid the worst sins of argument by analogy. In the context of human psycholology, we have deliberately avoided some of the ethologic vocabulary as being arbitrarily mechanistic and too likely to breed anachronistic misunderstanding among those chiefly acquainted with psychodynamic concepts.

The premise that behavior is based primarily on instincts is gradually disappearing from scientific writing and the traditional concept of instinct is undergoing revision and modification.[1] In its place has emerged the view that early experience importantly structures subsequent behavior. This is not to say, lest misunderstanding arise, that the animal organism, human or subhuman, is merely a blank slate to be written upon by the capricious finger of life experiences. Quite the contrary, for there are now many studies in the literature dealing with genetic constitution and the inheritance of basic capacities affecting later learning, temperament and personality (Medawar, 1947; Scott, 1953; Scott and Charles, 1953, 1954; Palowski and Scott, 1956; Goy and Young, 1957).

With increasing sophistication in these matters behavioral scientists have begun to abandon the fruitless effort to determine what proportion environmental or hereditary factors contribute to a given behavior pattern. Instead, greater attention is being given to the question, "*how* do these factors operate in structuring behavior?"

Anastasi (1958) has recently appraised the heredity-environment issue and the multifocal research approaches required to investigate the question "how?" That author rightly points out that the influence of hereditary or environmental factors is always indirect; the more indirect the connection the wider the range of variation of possible outcomes.

With respect to early experience Beach and Jaynes (1954) see three possible answers to the question of how its influence is mediated: (1) habits formed in early life may persist in adult behavior; (2) the individual's perceptual capacities may be so structured by early experience as to affect adult behavior; and (3) during specific

[1] Two extensive reviews dealing with instinctive behavior have recently been published. In the one, Fletcher (1957) has surveyed the work in ethology, comparative psychology, and social and educational theory. Fletcher endeavors to integrate these new insights with psychoanalytic instinct theory; regrettably he omits mention of such important American and Canadian work as that of Scott, Nissen, Skinner, Hebb, and Young, to mention only a few. The other review (Schiller, 1957) is more narrowly restricted to a presentation of a few important, perhaps classic, studies in animal behavior.

stages in ontogeny ("critical periods") certain types of behavior are indelibly shaped and molded for the life of the animal.

B. THE CRITICAL PERIOD HYPOTHESIS

Research advances in psychology during the past decade have added so much information relevant to the establishment of the modalities of social behavior that it may be anachronistic to discuss the "critical period" for learning as merely an hypothesis. Stated briefly, it is now well established that there are limited and often highly specific periods during the early life of an animal during which important social learning takes place, more or less permanently affecting the subsequent social behavior of the individual. There is known to be considerable species variation in the occurrence and duration of these critical learning periods. In the graylag goose, for example, one critical period can be identified as beginning immediately after hatching (Lorenz, 1935, 1950, 1952). Scott and his co-workers (Scott, Fredericson and Fuller, 1951; Scott and Marston, 1950; Scott, 1958) in a meticulously detailed series of observations have identified five distinct periods in the life history of the dog. In this species, the period from 3 to 7 weeks (Period III, Primary Socialization) is the time when primary social modalities become established. Physiologically this period is characterized by advancing but incomplete myelinization and development of the central nervous system and associated sense organs; for the first time conditioning becomes possible. Critical periods have also been identified and studied in the mouse (Williams and Scott, 1953), sheep (Scott, 1945), howling monkey (Carpenter, 1934), and red deer (Darling, 1937).

The finding that a critical period for primary socialization is such a widespread phenomenon in animals gives us reason to expect a continuity of this situation in the human species. Scott (1958) speculates, on the basis of his findings in dogs, that one might expect the earliest critical period in humans to begin between the 6th to 24th week of life and to last two years or possibly longer. Needless to say, much has already been written in the psychiatric and psychoanalytic literature to support a contention

that these earliest years of life are crucial ones in personality development. The findings in regard to the establishment of psychologic sex reported in detail on the pages to follow are in substantial agreement with the view that critical learning periods in the human are indeed an established reality.

C. IMPRINTING

There is a particular phenomenon well described by the ethologists which deserves special mention, namely, the phenomenon of *imprinting*. Our work (Hampson and Money, 1955; Money, 1955; Money and Hampson, 1955; Money, Hampson and Hampson, 1955a, b, 1957; Hampson, 1955; Hampson, Hampson and Money, 1955; Hampson, Money and Hampson, 1956) with hermaphroditic children has led us to see an analogy between establishment of gender role in early childhood and the phenomenology of imprinting as described in lower animals.[2]

The following are two examples which illustrate the basic similarities involved.

1. In years past the sight of a string of day-old goslings following their parent would have been cited as an example of innate, unlearned instinctive behavior. Heinroth (1910), Lorenz (1935), and others have shown how, in birds, species recognition as well as appropriate behavior in response to another member of its species, is not pre-established but is subject to modification through early life experience. A greylag gosling, for example, that has lived a few days with its parents will never respond to a human as if the human were its parent. On the other hand, to quote Lorenz (in Schiller, 1953), "if a greylag gosling is taken into human care immediately after hatching, all the behavior patterns which are slanted to the parents respond at once to the human being. In fact, only very careful treatment can induce incubator-hatched

---

[2] Lorenz (in Schiller, 1957) specified two features characteristic of the phenomenon of imprinting which differentiate it from other types of learning. (1) Imprinting is limited to a very definite and often extremely short phase of ontogeny, the "critical period." (2) The result of this process of determination is irreversible. In this context the term learning is used in the broad sense referring to a family of processes inferred from the observation that animals learn. To quote Verplanck (1957): "When we say that an animal learns, we are stating that, other things being equal, some behavior now occurs in a situation in which it had not occurred previously, or that the behavior now occurring in a given situation is different from the behavior that occurred on the last occasion the animal was in that situation."

TABLE 23.1
Varieties of ambisexual incongruities

1. *Congenital hyperadrenocortical females:* externally hermaphroditic; normal internal reproductive organs; female sex chromatin pattern... 66

2. *Hermaphrodites with ambiguous or masculinized external genitals:* normal functional female internal reproductive structures and ovaries; female sex chromatin pattern.................... 6

3. *Classical true hermaphroditism:* testicular and ovarian tissue both present; enlarged phallus; variable development of the genital ducts; male or female sex chromatin pattern............... 1

4. *Cryptorchid hermaphrodites with relatively complete Müllerian differentiation:* penis hypospadic or normal; possibly virilizing at puberty; male sex chromatin pattern...................... 7

5. *Cryptorchid hermaphrodites with relatively incomplete Müllerian differentiation:* hypospadic or clitoral phallus; possibly virilizing at puberty; male sex chromatin pattern
   a. With urogenital sinus.. 18
   b. With blind vaginal pouch... 2

6. *Simulant females with feminizing inguinal testes and vestigial Müllerian differentiation:* blind vaginal pouch; male sex chromatin pattern... 13

greylag goslings to follow a grey mother goose. They must not be allowed to see a human being from the moment they break their shell to the time they are placed under the mother goose. If they do, they follow the human being at once." It is also remarkable that almost any object between the size of a small chicken and a human being which moves and makes a noise can imprint the following-response in a newborn greylag.

In the experimental goslings the imprint of filial response to a decoy parent, with a human-being as parental model, was fixed and irreversible.

2. There is a relatively rare variety of hermaphroditism (Variety 2, Table 23.1) in which a baby is born in every respect a regular, normal female except that the labia are fused to look like a scrotum and the clitoris is enlarged to look like an unfinished penis; there is a gutter in the place of a penile urethra so that urination is accomplished in a sitting position (Fig. 23.1). So confusing is the ambiguity of such genitalia that the baby may be considered either a boy or a girl. Studies have been made, one of which has been reported by Money, Hampson, and Hampson (1956), of two such people reared as boys who have now reached adulthood. We have also studied three similar people, still juvenile, being reared as girls. It is not surprising that the latter are growing up as ordinary girls psychologically undifferentiable from their normal sisters and schoolgirl friends. What is quite remarkable, however, is that two individuals reared as boys matured with a regular, masculine psychology, and sexual orientation. At the time of the first signs of pubertal feminization they had recoiled from any suggestion that they change to live as a girl and subsequently they had been pleased and benefited by surgical and hormonal masculinization. Erotically they have been beset by the handicap of an undersized and malformed penis and scrotum. Nonetheless they were living happy, successful lives as men, one of them old enough to be a husband and an adoptive father. The imprint of

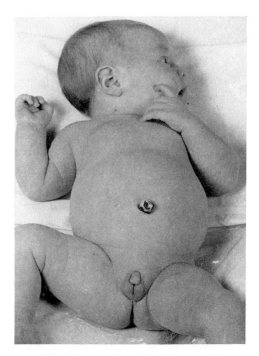

Fig. 23.1. Six-day-old female infant with masculinized external genitals, female sex chromatin pattern. (Courtesy of Dr. Lawson Wilkins.)

psychologic masculinity, from multiple male models and examples, was fixed and irreversible.

Psychiatrists have long realized that some modalities and disorders of psychologic functioning in humans resist all efforts at modification. The traditional explanation of this has rested heavily on constitutional and genetic considerations. In recent years animal studies such as these cited, together with new findings in the fields of psychiatry and clinical psychology, suggest possible alternative explanations.[3] The investigations into the nature of psychologic sex provide an example in point, for a person's psychosexual orientation, once established, becomes an ineradicable part of personality functioning.

III. The Establishment of Psychologic Sex

In the human psychologic sexuality is not differentiated when the child is born. Rather, psychologic sex becomes differentiated during the course of the many experiences of growing up, including those experiences dictated by his or her own bodily equipment. Thus, in the place of the theory of an innate, constitutional psychologic bisexuality such as that proposed by Freud— a concept already questioned on theoretical grounds by Rado (1940), among others—we must substitute a concept of psychologic sexual neutrality in humans at birth. Such psychosexual neutrality permits the development and perpetuation of divers patterns of psychosexual orientation and functioning in accordance with the life experiences each individual may encounter and transact.

A. THE EVIDENCE OF HUMAN HERMAPHRODITISM

The evidence for the foregoing statement has, in part, emerged from the study of human hermaphroditism.[4] The sexual incongruities which occur in hermaphroditism involve contradictions, singly or in combination, between six variables of sex. These variables, the first five of which are dealt with in specific detail by other writers in this volume, are: (a) chromosomal sex: (b) gonadal sex; (c) hormonal sex; (d) internal accessory reproductive structures; (e) external genital morphology; (f) the sex of assignment and rearing. Hermaphroditic patients, showing various combinations of these six sexual variables, may be appraised with respect to a seventh variable. (g) Gender role[5] or psychologic sex. In this way one can ascertain something about the relative importance of each of the six variables in relation to the seventh.

A nineteenth century classification of hermaphrodites was based on the assumption that the microscopic structure of the gonads was the ultimate criterion for purposes of

---

[3] Others have also pointed out analogies between the ethologic findings in lower animals and certain psychologic and behavioral phenomena in humans. Lorenz, Bowlby and Walter, to name but a few (see Tanner and Inhelder, 1953, 1954, 1955), have discussed possible relationships implicit in animal findings to the ontogeny and phylogeny of psychologic development in children. Russell and Russell (1957) have made the suggestion that certain aspects of human behavior might best be approached and studied from an ethologic point of view.

[4] The term hermaphrodite is used here to describe not only those individuals with completely ambiguous external genital development but also to include all instances in which a contradiction exists between the predominant external genital appearance on the one hand and the sex chromatin pattern, gonads, hormones, or internal accessory structures, singly or severally, on the other. In this sense the older terms *pseudohermaphrodite* and *intersexuality* are superfluous and unnecessarily confusing and have not been retained. Undeniably no classificatory scheme is perfect or sacrosanct; other classifications of the hermaphroditic anomalies have been published (*cf.* Wilkins 1957, Jones and Scott, 1958).

[5] By the term, *gender role*, is meant all those things that a person says or does to disclose himself or herself as having the status of boy or man, girl or woman, respectively. It includes, but is not restricted to sexuality in the sense of eroticism. Gender role is appraised in relation to the following: general mannerisms, deportment and demeanor; play preferences and recreational interests; spontaneous topics of talk in unprompted conversation and casual comment; content of dreams, daydreams, and fantasies; replies to oblique inquiries and projective tests; evidence of erotic practice and finally, the person's own replies to direct inquiry. Lest there be misunderstanding, the term *gender role* is not identical and synonymous with the term *sex of assignment and rearing*. Sex status can be assigned to a child by parental, medical, or legal decision. The psychologic phenomenon which we have termed gender role, or psychosexual orientation, evolves gradually in the course of growing up and cannot be assigned or discarded at will. The components of gender role are neither static nor universal. They change with the times and are an integral part of each culture and subculture. Thus one may expect important differences in what is to be considered typical and appropriate masculine or feminine gender role as displayed by a native of Thailand and a native of Maryland, or as displayed by the pioneer contemporaries of Peter Stuyvesant and by their descendants in Westchester County suburbia of the 1960's.

differentiation (Klebs, 1876). In his classification Klebs recognized *true hermaphrodites*, who possessed both ovarian and testicular tissue, *male pseudohermaphrodites* with only testicular tissue and *female pseudohermaphrodites* with only ovarian tissue. In studying the determinants of the psychologic phenomena of sexual outlook and orientation—gender role—Kleb's classification has proven too anachronistic to be useful, for modern discoveries in endocrinology, including recent work in sex chromatin determination (Moore and Barr, 1953; Moore, Graham, and Barr, 1953; Grumbach and Barr, 1958) make it clear that multiple variables are involved. The following list of the varieties of ambisexual incongruities was drawn up with these considerations in mind and is based in part on Dr. John Money's unpublished doctoral thesis in which he reviewed the medical literature of over 300 cases of hermaphroditism.

It would be inappropriate here to expound at length on the differential diagnosis of the various clinical types of ambisexual incongruities but it may be relevant to comment briefly on the six varieties listed in Table 23.1.

Variety 1. Congenital hyperadrenocortical females. In this group of patients the external genitals may appear almost normally female with slight to medium enlargement of the clitoris; or there may be a single urogenital orifice with enlargement of the clitoris. Rarely, a penile urethra and a fused empty scrotal sac are found. Without benefit of suppressive cortisone therapy physical growth and development is precocious and virilizing. Diagnosis is now possible during the neonatal period by means of urinary 17-ketosteroid assessment, without laparotomy. Plural incidence in a family is common, but is usually restricted to a single generation and a single marriage (Childs, Grumbach and Van Wyk, 1956). The Müllerian system and ovaries are normal; the sex chromatin pattern is female.

Variety 2. Hermaphrodites with ambiguous or masculinized external genitals. Unlike females with hyperadrenocorticism, the hermaphrodites in this group, although born with varying degrees of ambiguous or masculinized genitals, do not show progressive virilization. On the contrary, since the ovaries and accessory internal reproductive structures are normal, secondary feminization at puberty is the rule and reproduction is possible. The enlarged phallus usually resembles a hypospadic penis with chordee. Labial fusion may be pronounced or even complete. The vagina usually opens into a urogenital sinus but occasionally opens independently. The sex chromatin pattern is female. Wilkins, Jones, Holman and Stempfel (1958) have published a report on 21 such hermaphrodites; in all but 3 the mother had received progestinic medication (usually 17-ethinyltestosterone) beginning in the first trimester of pregnancy.

Variety 3. Classical true hermaphroditism. Ovarian and testicular tissue is present, in one ovotestis, the other gonad being an ovary or a testis, in two ovotestes, or in one ovary and one testis. The internal genital structures as well as the external genitalia show various degrees of ambiguity. Pubertal development of the secondary sexual characteristics may be masculine, feminine, or ambiguous. Diagnosis requires laparotomy and biopsy of the gonads. In an unpublished study of 20 patients with classical true hermaphroditism, M. L. Barr found that 15 had a female sex chromatin pattern.

Variety 4. Cryptorchid hermaphrodites with relatively complete Müllerian differentiation. The penis may be fully formed with a penile urethra or it may be hypospadic. One or both testes may by cryptorchid; one testis may be atrophic. Müllerian structures not infrequently herniate into the groin or scrotum in the company of one testis. At puberty the secondary sexual development is nearly always masculine although a eunuchoid habitus is sometimes observed, especially in those instances of bilateral cryptorchidism and hypospadias. Diagnosis requires surgical exploration; the sex chromatin pattern is probably always male although it is conceivable that a female pattern may be possible.

Variety 5. Cryptorchid hermaphrodites with relatively incomplete Müllerian differentiation. Historically, hypospadiacs have not been called hermaphrodites unless the hypospadias is severe, the scrotum bifid, and the testes undescended. Careful examination, however, often reveals that such hypospadiacs have a blind vaginal pouch hidden beyond the single external urogenital orifice; or there may be a separate external orifice for a blind vaginal pouch. In some instances the phallus may be only slightly larger than a clitoris. The Müllerian and Wolffian systems are malformed or vestigial. A virilizing puberty cannot be predicted; in some patients pubertal development may be weakly feminine resulting in breast enlargement. Plural incidence within a family may occur. Diagnosis requires testicular biopsy; the sex chromatin pattern is probably always male although future findings may require a revision of this assumption.

Variety 6. Simulant females with feminizing inguinal testes and vestigial Müllerian differentiation. In this group of patients the external genital appearance completely simulates the normal female. The vagina is a blind pouch and, with few exceptions, the Müllerian system is a cord-like vestige; the Wolffian system is malformed or vestigial. The testes may remain intra-abdominal or herniate into the groin; even in adults the microscopic appearance of the testes is best described as immature and poorly differentiated. At puberty the development of the female secondary sexual characteristics is nearly always complete except that menstruation does not occur. In about one-

TABLE 23.2

Sex chromatin pattern and rearing contradictory: 20 cases

Variety of Ambisexual Incongruities	Sex Chromatin Pattern	Assigned Sex and Rearing	Gender Role
Hyperadrenocortical females (variety 1): total, 3	3 ♀	3 ♂	3 ♂
Hermaphrodites with ambiguous or masculinized external genitals (variety 2): total, 1	1 ♀	1 ♂	1 ♂
Classical true hermaphroditism (variety 3): total, 1	1 ♀	1 ♂	1 ♂
Cryptorchid hermaphrodites (varieties 4, 5): total, 8	8 ♂	8 ♀	8 ♀
Simulant females with feminizing testes (variety 6): total, 6	6 ♂	6 ♀	6 ♀

Additional Data

Gonads	Endogenous Hormonal Sex	Internal Accessory Organs	External Genital Morphology
3 ♀	3 ♂	3 ♀	3 ⚥
1 ♀	1 ♀	1 ♀	1 ⚥
♀ left ♂ right	1 ⚥	1 ⚥	1 ⚥
8 ♂	2 ♂, 1 ♀ 5 juvenile	4 ♂, 3 ♀ 1 ⚥	8 ⚥
6 ♂	2 ♀ 4 juvenile	6 vestigial	6 ♀

third of the cases sexual hair fails to appear despite normal adult estrogen levels. Diagnosis requires gonadal biopsy and the demonstration of a male sex chromatin pattern. Familial incidence in several generations is common.

The following findings and conclusions emerged from the study[6] of a series of over 110 hermaphroditic individuals. The tables do not include an entry for every single patient. Some of the patients were too young at the time of study for meaningful conclusions to be drawn; others failed in one or another detail to fulfill the criteria necessary for inclusion. On the other hand, some patients, because of their multiple hermaphroditic manifestations, qualified for inclusion in more than one of the following tables.

1. Chromosomal Sex

There were 20 patients in this series of hermaphroditic individuals who had been assigned to and reared in a sex contrary to

[6] Under the aegis of John C. Whitehorn, Professor of Pediatrics, The Johns Hopkins University. The research was supported by grants from the Josiah Macy, Jr., Foundation, and the Public Health Service (USPHS Grant M-1557).

their sex chromatin pattern as established by skin biopsy or the buccal smear technique (Grumbach and Barr, 1958).[7] Without a single exception, it was found that the gender role and orientation as man or woman, boy or girl was in accordance with the assigned sex and rearing rather than in accord with the chromosomal sex (Table 23.2). It seems convincingly clear, therefore, that gender role, orientation as male or female, does not correspond automatically with the chromosomal sex; rather, it is in some way related to assigned sex and rearing.

2. Gonadal Sex

There were 30 hermaphroditic patients in whom a contradiction was found between

[7] Tables 23.2 through 23.7 are revisions of tabular material published earlier (Money, Hampson and Hampson, 1955b) and include patients studied since the original report. The authors are indebted to John Money, Ph.D., for his part in collecting psychologic data on which the tables are based. The responsibility, however, for the additions to and modifications of the earlier tables was assumed by the authors of this chapter.

TABLE 23.3

Gonads and rearing contradictory: 30 cases

Variety of Ambisexual Incongruity	Gonads	Assigned Sex and Rearing	Gender Role
Hyperadrenocortical females (variety 1): total, 5	5 ♀	5 ♂	5 ♂
Hermaphrodites with ambiguous or masculinized external genitals (variety 2): total, 2	2 ♀	2 ♂	2 ♂
Cryptorchid hypospadic hermaphrodites (varieties 4, 5): total, 14	14 ♂	13 ♀ 1 ♀ → ♂	11 ♀ 3 ⚥
Simulant females with feminizing testes (variety 6): total, 9	9 ♂	9 ♀	9 ♀

Additional Data

Sex Chromatin Pattern	Endogenous Hormonal Sex	Internal Accessory Organs	External Genital Morphology
5 ♀	5 ♂	5 ♀	5 ⚥
1 ♀ 1 ♀ (?)	2 ♀	2 ♀	2 ⚥
9 ♂ 5 ♂ (?)	6 ♂ 1 ♀ 7 juvenile	8 vestigial 1 ⚥ 5 ♀	14 ⚥
7 ♂ 2 ♂ (?)	2 ♀ 7 juvenile	9 vestigial	9 ♀

the sexual status of the gonads and the sex of assignment and rearing (Table 23.3). In all but 3, psychologic studies revealed a gender role fully concordant with the sex of rearing. As a prognosticator of a person's gender role and orientation, gonadal structure, *per se*, thus proved to be unreliable; again gender role was in greatest accord with the assigned sex and rearing.

3. Hormonal Sex

It is of course necessary to consider hormonal sex separately from gonadal histology, for ovaries do not always secrete effective estrogens, nor testes effective androgens. The ovaries of *females with hyperadrenocorticism* are suppressed in function and, although their adrenals produce an excess of estrogens as well as of androgens, the androgenic activity dominates, inducing excessive virilization of the body. The gonads of *simulant females with inguinal testes* produce, in most instances, estrogens which feminize the body.

The data on 31 patients who went into or beyond puberty or, in the cases of patients

with hyperadrenocorticism, a precocious puberty-equivalent in which hormonal influences induced secondary sexual changes contradictory of the sex in which the individual had been living, are summarized in Table 23.4. In all patients the contradiction was subsequently corrected with hormonal therapy and with plastic surgery when indicated.

Of the 31 patients whose sex hormones and secondary sexual body development contradicted their assigned sex and rearing, only 5 became ambivalent with respect to their gender role. Four of the 5 had been reared as girls. One of these, a man in his thirties when studied by Dr. John Money, had acted on his own initiative and changed to live as a man from the age of 16 onward. The other four, although living as women, displayed disordered gender role as evidenced by some degree of bisexual erotic inclination. The impracticability of publishing here the extensive psychiatric and psychologic records of these 5 patients requires the authors to submit, instead, their considered opinion that these 5 patients do not.

TABLE 23.4

Endogenous hormonal sex and rearing contradictory: 31 cases

Variety of Ambisexual Incongruity	Endogenous Hormonal Sex	Assigned Sex and Rearing	Gender Role
Hyperadrenocortical females (variety 1): total, 21	21 ♂	21 ♀	19 ♀ 2 ♂
Hermaphrodites with ambiguous or masculinized external genitals (variety 2): total, 2	2 ♀	2 ♂	2 ♂
Classical true hermaphroditism (variety 3): total, 1	1 ⚥	1 ♂	1 ♂
Cryptorchid hermaphrodites with relatively complete Müllerian differentiation (variety 4): total, 2	2 ♂	2 ♀	2 ♀
Cryptorchid hermaphrodite, feminizing (variety 5): total, 1	1 ♀	1 ♂	1 ♂
Cryptorchid hermaphrodite, virilizing (variety 5): total, 4	4 ♂	4 ♀	1 ♀ 3 ♂

Additional Data

External Genital Morphology	Sex Chromatin Pattern	Gonads	Internal Accessory Organs
21 ⚥	21 ♀ (?)	21 ♀	21 ♀
2 ⚥	1 ♀ 1 ♀ (?)	2 ♀	2 ♀
1 ⚥	1 ♀	1 ⚥	1 ⚥
2 ⚥	1 ♂ 1 ♂ (?)	2 ♂	2 ♀
1 ⚥	1 ♂ (?)	1 ♂	1 vestigial
4 ⚥	1 ♂ 3 ♂ (?)	4 ♂	4 vestigial

in themselves, seem to offer any convincing evidence that sex hormones act as a single causal agent in the establishment of an individual's gender role and psychosexual orientation. Restoration of normal female estrogen balance did not alter the psychosexual functioning of the 4 patients who had lived as women; the patient who had changed to live as a man declined androgen treatment after surgical castration for malignancy. The remaining 26 patients in the group established a gender role consistent with their assigned sex and rearing, despite the embarrassment and difficulties of living with contradictory secondary sexual development.

4. Internal Accessory Organs

The fourth sex variable embraces the internal derivatives of the Müllerian and Wolffian duct systems. The uterus, as the organ of menstruation, and the prostate and seminal vesicles as organs concerned with the secretion of seminal fluid, are of particular theoretic importance psychologically.

There were 25 instances in the group of patients studied in whom the assigned sex and rearing was not in accord with the predominant male or female internal accessory structures (Table 23.5). In 22 of the 25 the individual's gender role agreed with the assigned sex and rearing. The 3 remaining were the same three who deviated in Table 23.3; they appeared again as deviants in Table 23.4.

It is rare in hermaphroditism for either the uterus or the prostate to reach functional maturity without medical intervention. There were 3 patients among the 25 in Table 23.5 for whom this statement did not hold; despite the fact that the 3 had grown up with a normal uterus, they had been reared as boys and had a thoroughly masculine gender role. In view of these findings there seems no reason to suspect any correlation between gender role and the internal accessory organs.

5. External Genital Appearance

The appearance at birth of the external genitals usually dictates the sex to which a baby is assigned and in which it is reared. As a child grows older the appearance of the external genitals is a bodily feature of importance to the child's private assuredness of being a boy or a girl.

When a hermaphroditic baby is born the medical attendants are likely to be less casual in declaring its sex from external appearance alone. Nevertheless in reviewing the histories of a large number of babies born with anomalous external genitalia it was our impression that in the majority of cases the external genital appearance was a primary consideration in the initial assignment of sex. It is perhaps remarkable that some children, in fact, are reared in a sex contradicting their predominant external genital appearance. Moreover, it is even possible for such hermaphrodites to establish a gender role entirely in agreement with assigned sex and rearing, despite the para-

TABLE 23.5

Internal accessory organs and rearing contradictory: 25 cases

Variety of Ambisexual Incongruity	Internal Accessory Organs	Assigned Sex and Rearing	Gender Role
Hyperadrenocortical females (variety 1): total, 5	5 ♀	5 ♂	5 ♂
Hermaphrodites with ambiguous or masculinized external genitals (variety 2): total, 2	2 ♀ > ♂	2 ♂	2 ♂
Classical true hermaphroditism (variety 3): total, 1	1 ⚥	1 ♂	1 ♂
Cryptorchid hermaphrodites with incomplete Müllerian differentiation (variety 5): total, 8	8 ♂ > ♀ (vestigial)	6 ♀ 1 ♂ → ♀ 1 ♀ —	5 ♀ 3 ⚥
Simulant females with feminizing testes (variety 6): total, 9	9 ♂ > ♀	9 ♀	9 ♀

Additional Data

Sex Chromatin Pattern	Gonads	Endogenous Hormonal Sex	External Genital Morphology
5 ♀ (?)	5 ♀	5 ♂	4 ⚥ 1 ♂
1 ♀ 1 ♀ (?)	2 ♀	2 ♀	2 ⚥
1 ♀	1 ⚥	1 ⚥	1 ⚥
4 ♂ 4 ♂ (?)	8 ♂	4 ♂ 4 juvenile	8 ⚥
7 ♂ 2 ♂	9 ♂	2 ♀ 7 juvenile	9 ♀

doxical appearance of their external genitalia.

In our series of hermaphrodites there were 25 with a marked degree of contradiction between their external genital appearance and their assigned sex and rearing (Table 23.6). Of the 16 older patients, all had lived at least to teen-age (in one case as long as 47 years!) with ambiguous or contradictory genital appearance. Of the 9 under 12 years of age all had lived for at least 8 years of their life surgically uncorrected. All but 2 of the 25 individuals had been able to come to terms with his or her anomalous appearance and had established a gender role wholly consistent with assigned sex and rearing. The exceptions, one a young adult, the other a middle-aged man, had profound psychologic problems, some of which were clearly concerned with an ambivalent gender identification. It is of interest that both

of these patients had had a reassignment of sex, the one by medical decision at the age of 5 from female to male; the other, at the age of 16, of his own initiative changed to live as a male.

Lest the foregoing be misunderstood, the table documents the possibility of a person's establishing a gender role consistent with the sex of assignment and rearing despite ambiguous looking or even contradictory-looking genitals. The Table does not, however, document the enormity of the problem these people had to surmount in coming to terms psychologically with their paradoxical appearance. It has been our experience that more than anything else, the *visible* anatomic genital or bodily contradictions occasion the grestest psychologic distress. Although none of this group of patients had ever had a psychotic illness, many displayed a moderate degree of psy-

TABLE 23.6

External genital appearance and rearing contradictory: 25 cases

Variety of Ambisexual Incongruity	Predominant External Genital Appearance	Assigned Sex and Rearing	Gender Role
Hyperadrenocortical females (variety 1): total, 16	♂ > ♀	16 ♀	16 ♀
Cryptorchid hermaphrodites with relatively complete Müllerian differentiation (variety 4): total, 3	♂ > ♀	3 ♀	3 ♀
Cryptorchid hermaphrodites with relatively incomplete Müllerian differentiation (variety 5): total, 3	♀ > ♂	1 ♂ 2 ♀ → ♂	1 ♂ 2 ♀
Cryptorchid hermaphrodites with relatively incomplete Müllerian development (variety 5): total, 2	♂ > ♀	2 ♀	2 ♀
Cryptorchid hermaphrodites, etc., feminizing (breasts) variety 5): total, 1	♀ > ♂	1 ♂	1 ♂

Additional Data

Sex Chromatin Pattern	Gonads	Endogenous Hormonal Sex	Internal Accessory Organs
16 ♀ (?)	16 ♀	16 ♂	16 ♀
1 ♂ 2 ♂ (?)	3 ♂	1 ♂ 2 juvenile	3 ♀
1 ♂ 2 ♂ (?)	3 ♂	1 ♂ 2 juvenile	3 vestigial
2 ♂	2 ♂	1 ♂ 1 juvenile	2 vestigial
1 ♂ (?)	1 ♂	1 ♀	1 vestigial

chologic nonhealthiness. The importance of body appearance in the establishment of gender role is dealt with more fully in a later section.

6. Assigned Sex and Rearing

In the foregoing tables, chromosomal sex, gonadal sex, hormonal sex, internal reproductive organs, and external genital appearance have been considered in turn with respect to (1) the assigned sex and rearing, and (2) the gender role established by each individual. In only 7 of the cases represented in these tables was there any inconsistency between the sex of rearing and gender role despite other incongruities between these and the other variables of sex. Parenthetically, it is to be noted that 3 of the 7 appear in more than one of the tables.

Thus it appears legitimate, once again, to conclude that there is a very close relationship between the sex of assignment and rearing and the establishment of a masculine or feminine gender role and psychosexual orientation.

7. Psychologic Sex: Gender Role

The evidence of human hermaphroditism indicates that psychologic maleness or femaleness in the human is not to be attributed to any single one of the physical variables of sex, i.e., the gonads, sex hormones, sex chromatin pattern, or the morphology of the external genitals and internal reproductive structures. It is, of course, conceivable that some other intrinsic body factor could have an important bearing on psychosexual development. Anthropometrists in Europe (Vague, 1953) and in this country (Sheldon and Stevens, 1942) have suggested a relationship between body build and psychosexual orientation. Their data, however, are not beyond alternative interpretation insofar as the psychologic importance of body structure is concerned.

In the late nineteenth century von Krafft-Ebing (1890) suggested special bisexual brain centers as an explanation of the psychologic differences between men and women. There have never been established any anatomic or neurophysiologic data to support such a conjecture. From 1890 to the present day, however, von Krafft-Ebing's views on the bisexual na-

TABLE 23.7

Gender role in patients with same diagnosis reared male or female: 65 cases

Variety of Ambisexual Incongruity	Assigned Sex and Rearing	Gender Role
Hyperadrenocortical females (variety 1)	39 ♀ 5 ♂	37 ♀ 2 ♂ 5 ♂
Cryptorchid hermaphrodites (varieties 4, 5)	15 ♀ 6 ♂	12 ♀ 3 ♂ 6 ♂

ture of man have been taken up in turn by such theorists as H. Ellis, Hirschfeld, Freud and others in a way that has shaped psychiatric theory (see also Rado, 1940). The presence of chromosomal, hormonal, gonadal, or genital incongruities in an individual does not automatically confer incongruous or disordered masculine or feminine psychologic development. It would seem that the theory of bisexuality must be laid to rest when one considers the evidence of hermaphroditic individuals *with the same diagnosis* some of whom have been reared as boys and some as girls (Table 23.7).

There are 65 cases represented in Table 23.7 including 5 of the 7 in the entire series studied in whom ambivalence of gender role was found. These 5 had all been reared as girls. Of the 60 remaining, the 49 patients reared as girls had established an entirely feminine gender role, whereas the 11 reared as boys had established a masculine gender role and orientation.

One can conclude that an individual's gender role and orientation as boy or girl, man or woman does not have an innate, preformed instinctive basis as some have maintained. Instead the evidence supports the view that psychologic sex is undifferentiated at birth, a sexual neutrality in the place of the Freudian bisexuality, and that the individual becomes differentiated as masculine or feminine, psychologically, in the course of the many experiences of growing up.

The compelling quality of the genital erotic component of sex role has led to the utilization of a concept of *drive* as an explanation of sex role differences. In that event sex drive should be considered genderless at birth and can be assumed to have no somatic basis other than the highly innervated and erotically sensitive areas of the body. As an alternative to a drive concept some will find it preferable to say simply that the erotically sensitive parts of the human body can be used and stimulated by oneself or another person and that during the process of psychologic growth and development erotic sensations become firmly associated with and inextricably a part of adult gender role.

B. THE INFLUENCE OF THE PHYSICAL SEX VARIABLES ON THE ESTABLISHMENT OF GENDER ROLE: BODY IMAGE

To say that a person's gender role is a correlation of the kind of learning experiences encountered and transacted is not to endorse an oversimplified version of social and environmental determinism. It is readily seen that in a very real sense the somatic variables of sex constitute an important part of a person's environment.

For example, although hormonal functioning does not directly or automatically determine maleness or femaleness of gender role an important relationship is involved, namely, the effect of hormones on body morphology and their sensitizing influence on genital sensory structures. Before birth hormonal functioning has a major role to play in embryonic differentiation of both the internal and external genital structures. When a child is born, needless to say, it is the morphology of the external genitalia which dictates or guides the assignment of sexual status. Although we have found that most children can overcome the quandary of anomalous or ambiguous genital appearance and grow up with a sexual orientation appropriate to the sex in which they were reared, it is by no means true that they do so without difficulty or with complete success. Broadly speaking, the more pronounced and obvious the anomaly the greater the concomitant feelings of bashfulness, shame, and differentness with which the person must contend. Some children, in the face of ambiguous genital appearance, may privately construe that an error has been made; they are then able to adapt to a psychosexual orientation appropriate to their assigned sex only by paying the penalty of one or another kind of psychologic

symptomatology. Parents, too, react to their child's ambiguous genital development with concerns and worries about the correctness of the child's sexual identity thus importantly structuring the family environment in which gender learning has its experiential origins.

The sex hormones also play an important role at puberty in establishing the secondary sexual characteristics of the body. Ordinarily the transition from prepuberty to adolescence is a gradual one that occurs in the setting of pubertal physical changes and social interaction. A child's anticipation of being grown up and of being considered grown up by others directs attention to body appearance. More than any other indicator the physical changes at puberty indicate to other people that this person is now ready for the social transactions of adolescence. Thus prepubertal children usually anticipate eagerly the first signs of breast development, of beard growth or voice change, as evidence that they are growing up, and they compare their progress with that of their age-mates. The appearance of menses in girls and nocturnal emissions in boys are important private signs which enhance a child's sense of confidence in his or her masculinity or femininity. In the absence of visible bodily signs of maturity the youngster suffers not only in lowered self-esteem but equally important is excluded by his contemporaries from a host of adolescent activities which are indispensable to psychologic and social maturation. Secondary sexual development may, however, be incongruous (as in hyperadrenocortical female hermaphrodites), precocious (as in cases of idiopathic sexual precocity), or delayed (as in hypogonadal males and girls with gonadal dysgenesis). Incongruity, precocity, and delay in secondary sexual development inevitably have important effects psychologically. The more publicly evident the incongruity the more distressing the person finds it. Thus hirsute girls and women with hyperadrenocorticism have almost invariably reported to us that they would, more than anything else like to be rid of their unfeminine-looking body hair; their hyperplastic clitoris and deep voice assumed a secondary importance beside the hirsutism. Precocious appearance of the hormonally induced signs of puberty may, on the one hand, open the doors to adolescent social encounters before a child is psychologically ready and able to cope with such learning experiences (see Hampson, 1955; Money, 1955). On the other hand pubertal delay permits a lag in social and psychologic development by making the child so out of step with his contemporaries that the job of catching up may be slow or even impossible. Without belaboring the point, body appearance does have an important, indirect bearing on the development of psychologic functioning, including that which we term gender role or psychosexual orientation.

There is yet another link between hormonal functioning and gender role which is specifically relevant to the genital erotic component of psychologic sex. To be brief, for this topic is taken up more fully in Money's chapter on sex hormones and eroticism, both androgens and estrogens can act on external genital structures so as to intensify genital erotic sensation. In the absence of one or the other sex hormone genital erotic sensation is relatively weak. We would stress that genital eroticism, however important, is but one facet of the constellation of elements comprising psychosexual functioning. One may, therefore, expect to find individual differences, both pathologic and nonpathologic, in this component alone, or in combination with the other components of gender role behavior.

C. SOCIAL LEARNING AND GENDER ROLE

It is not a new idea that humans learn a great deal during their earliest years. From the beginning of psychodynamic research, much information has been collected about the importance of learning experiences in man and the influence of such experience in shaping those psychologic modalities broadly spoken of as personality.[8]

Freud (1910) was among the first to pre-

[8] It is beyond the scope of this chapter to discuss the many theories of personality extant in psychology and psychiatry. The interested reader will find an excellent review of the more important of these theories in *Theories of Personality* by Hall and Lindsey (1957). Murphy (1947), with considerable appropriateness, defined personality as "the integration of all the roles that a particular person has to enact."

sent a comprehensive theory of psychosexuality. Freud apparently based his views on a postulate von Krafft-Ebing had also embraced some years before, namely, that every person is inherently bisexual, or, in another sense, homosexual as well as heterosexual tendencies are originally present in everyone. The Freudian theory of psychosexual development embodied a succession of oral, anal, and genital phases and held that the psychologic differences between the sexes emerged during the first 5 years of life.[9] Freud saw the third to the fifth year

[9] Freud (1949) attached great importance to a biologic hypothesis that "man is descended from a mammal which reached maturity at the age of five, but that some great external influence was brought to bear upon the species and interrupted the straight line of development of sexuality. This may also have been related to some other transformations in the sexual life of man as compared with that of animals, such as the suppression of the periodicity of the libido and the exploitation of the part played by menstruation in the relation between the sexes." Freud (1927) gave the following account of the maturation and development of infantile sexuality: "The sexual function . . . is in existence from the very beginning of the individual's life, though at first it is assimilated to the other vital functions and does not become independent of them until later; it has to pass through a long and complicated process of development before it becomes what we are familiar with as the normal sexual life of the adult. It begins by manifesting itself in the activity of a whole number of component instincts. These are dependent upon erotogenic zones in the body; some of them make their appearance in pairs of opposite impulses (such as sadism and masochism or the impulse to look and to be looked at) they operate independently of one another in their search for pleasure, and they find their object for the most part in the subject's own body. Thus to begin with they are noncentralized and predominantly auto-erotic. Later they begin to be co-ordinated; a first step of organization is reached under the dominance of the oral components, an anal-sadistic stage follows and it is only after the third stage has at last been reached that the primacy of the genitals is established and that the sexual function begins to serve the ends of reproduction."

In Freud's view it was the phallus which dictated the organization of infantile sexuality: "The difference between the two—the infantile genital organization and the final genital organization of the adult—constitutes at the same time the main characteristic of the infantile form, namely that for both sexes in childhood only one kind of genital organ comes into account, the male. The primacy reached is, therefore, not a primacy of genital but of the phallus" (Freud, 1924). Freud considered there was no distinction between maleness and femaleness in the anal-sadistic stage; in the in-of life as largely occupied by Oedipal[10] operations culminating in the resolution of the innate bisexual conflict.

Despite the fact that the concept of innate bisexual instincts has been repeatedly challenged on theoretical grounds (Rado, 1940) during the past two decades, the notion continues to enjoy doctrinaire status. That this is so is rather remarkable, for the bulk of modern research, both in animals and man, points unequivocally to the importance of learning in the establishment of those behavioral and psychologic characteristics which in humans we speak of as personality. Thus an individual learns ways of behaving through the experiences he encounters and transacts and not by virtue of an endowment of inbuilt imperatives for one or another mode of functioning and behaving. The evidence of human hermaphroditism, as cited earlier, is substantially in agreement with this point of view provided it be allowed that learning includes an individual's experiences, as mediated by his own uniquely individual perceptual-cognitional capacities, with his own body morphology and physiologic functioning.

The accrued evidence strongly suggests that the beginnings of gender-specific psychologic characteristics are, to an important extent, acquired, and so become manifest, very early in life, probably during the first 2½ or 3 years. This early period for gender role learning may quite legitimately, it is thought, be designated a *critical period*, the effects of which persist throughout the life of the individual. One item of evidence for this comes from the psychologic studies (Hampson, 1955) of children and adults who had undergone a reassignment of sex status at some time in their lives. Some, but not all of these hermaphroditic individuals

were hyperadrenocortical hermaphrodites. Data on 12 of these patients are shown in Figure 23.2. Only patients who had been studied at least 6½ years and up to a maximum of 20 years after the reassignment of sex were included. In each instance an appraisal was made of the pervasive thoroughness of sexual orientation in the sex assigned at the change using the criteria for gender role discussed earlier in this chapter. An appraisal was also made in each case of the successfulness and stability of day-to-day adjustment with deliberate intention, if any doubt existed, of erring on the side of over-scrupulousness rather than allowing any benefit of the doubt.

Of the 5 who were reassigned before their first birthday all but 1 had no subsequent disturbance psychologically. This one child, living as a girl, growing up in circumstances of family turmoil and chaos, and subjected to repeated thoughtless comments about the time "when you were a boy" had begun to display truant behavior at school and some degree of uncertainty about her gender status. With only 1 exception the 7 patients reassigned later than the first birthday were rated as inadequately adjusted. The exception was a boy who, in all fairness, had to be rated as adequately adaptive, inasmuch as the problems he had were typical for many boys of his religious and moral upbringing, and likely to be transient. The three patients reassigned at the age of 4 or after had varying degrees of confusion and ambivalence with regard to their gender status.

The importance of the earliest years of life for gender role learning is illustrated in Figure 23.2. However, one should not infer from such data any hard and fast date-line for either the beginning or the ending of the early critical period for gender orientation but merely the broad limits. Such a view is in agreement with the findings of other investigators who have seen gender-role differentiation beginning about the second year of life and becoming firmly established by the third year, by which age roughly 75 per cent of children can distinguish between the sexes and identify themselves as boys or girls (Gesell, Ilg and Ames, 1940; Seward, 1946). Although the development of gender role is a continuing process throughout the

---

fantile genital stage maleness had emerged but no femaleness. Not until puberty was the polarity of male and female established.

[10] Stated briefly, the Freudian Oedipus complex consists of a sexual attraction for the parent of the opposite sex and a hostile dislike for the parent of the same sex. The child's sexual identification is then thought to occur as a defense against his projected hostile impulses and a fear of retaliation. Although it cannot be denied that this sequence of events may sometimes occur it is contrary to the facts to consider seriously that this is the only, or even the most important means by which a child establishes his gender identity.

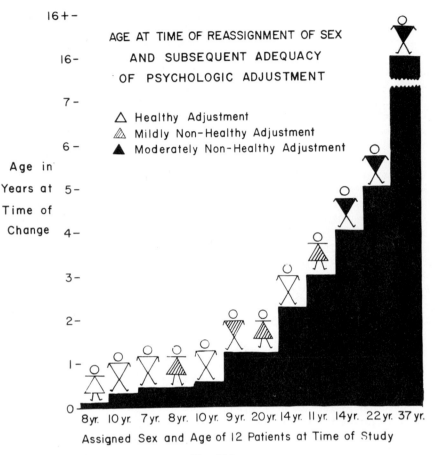

16+ -

AGE AT TIME OF REASSIGNMENT OF SEX

16 -

AND SUBSEQUENT ADEQUACY

OF PSYCHOLOGIC ADJUSTMENT

7 -

△ Healthy Adjustment
△ Mildly Non-Healthy Adjustment

6 -

▲ Moderately Non-Healthy Adjustment

Age in

Years at 5 -

Time of

Change 4 -

3 -

2 -

1 -

0

8 yr. 10 yr. 7 yr. 8 yr. 10 yr. 9 yr. 20 yr. 14 yr. 11 yr. 14 yr. 22 yr. 37 yr.

Assigned Sex and Age of 12 Patients at Time of Study

FIG. 23.2

growing up years and into adulthood, the first few years of a child's life are significantly characterized by mutually reciprocating expectancies on the part of parents and child alike regarding gender-appropriate behavior which are particularly influential in structuring personality functioning. Speaking metaphorically, the learning experiences during the first 2 to 3 years appear to be critical in that they set the stage for the dramatization to follow.

1. Social Environment and the Establishment of Gender Role

In working with hermaphroditic children and their parents, it has become clear that the establishment of a child's psychosexual orientation begins not so much with the child as with his parents. Faced with the dilemma of a sexually ambiguous-looking baby it is next to impossible for parents to avoid assigning sex status to the child. If medical indecision about the child's sex status is delayed too long such parents, understandably, find it difficult to refer to their baby as "it" indefinitely. Under ordinary circumstances, there is no such quandary about the sex status of a newborn and appropriate pronouns are used from the outset. From cigars, which announce a new son, to a mother's insistence on sex-appropriate pink or blue cradle accessories, our cultural folkways provide ample evidence that parental attitudes and expectancies are set in operation virtually the moment a child is born. Thus the assigned sex-status, as well as such body signs as the external genitals,[11]

[11] It is only partly facetious to say that even the hair-cut is important. In a clear and unmistakable way the short hair-cut of a boy and the long tresses of the girl provide a clear sign to others which in effect announces "I am a boy (girl)—treat me as such." Many preschool youngsters when

provides an important stimulus to parents which helps determine the gender-species role training they will provide.

Rabban (1950) studied the influence of social class status on sex-role identification in children and reported that boys are more clearly aware of sex-appropriate behavior than girls in both middle- and working-class groups. On the other hand, he found that boys and girls of the working-class group were not only earlier, but more clearly, aware of gender-appropriate behavior than were either boys or girls of the middle-class group. Clearly class level provides the social frame of reference within which such diverse influences as parental models, playmates, social mores, attitudes, and opportunities can operate to structure gender role and personality structure.

In their excellent study of how 379 American mothers brought up their children from birth to kindergarten, Sears, Maccoby and Levin (1957) correctly point out that, although sex role in modern American culture is constantly changing and shifting in terms of what the culture regards as appropriate, there is no culture that does not make some distinction between masculine or feminine role behavior (see also the Mead's chapter, in this volume). Although it may not be a logical absurdity to regard masculine and feminine behavior as biologically innate phenomena, the study of sex role in other cultures makes it clear that all too often we have wrongly identified that which is current and prevalent in our own culture as the natural and normal state of affairs. It seems more in accord with the findings in both humans and other animal forms to regard humans, male and female alike, as capable of acquiring, during early life, an almost infinite variety of behavior patterns some of which will be approved of as serving the individual and society well, whereas others will be considered unfortunate, if not actually detrimental, both biologically and culturally (*cf.* Mead's comments on the folkways of the Mundugumors).

Sears, Maccoby and Levin (1957) distinguished three kinds of learning occurring in association with the development of social

behavior appropriate to the child's own sex: (1) trial and error, (2) direct tuition by the parents, and (3) role practice or rehearsals. From their experience these authors were inclined to believe that very little learning of social behavior and social values ever occurs by simple trial and error. They point out an important difference between learning by direct tuition and guidance and learning through role rehearsal, namely that, in the latter, the child selects the actions to perform from his own observations of what the role requires rather than from what the instructions of his parents may be. This being so one must immediately consider individual differences in cognitional and perceptual inheritance as important variables affecting the final outcome of such learning.

In studying the intentional teaching of gender-appropriate behavior by the 379 parents in their study, Sears, Maccoby and Levin found important differences in the kind of rearing meted out to the two sexes. Among the items studied it was with respect to aggressive behavior that the greatest distinctions were made by parents; boys were allowed significantly more freedom than girls to fight back in encounters with nonsiblings. Many mothers actively encouraged their sons to be aggressive and provided ample opportunity for learning aggressive behavior and, as one parent put it, to be a "real boy." Parental attitude toward such diverse things as household tasks and chores and school achievement differed, too, with respect to sons and daughters. Of the 91 mothers of boys and the 83 mothers of girls who were most strongly inclined to differentiate sex-role in their rearing practices, it was found that definitely higher expectations were put on girls for *table manners, neatness and orderliness*, and *instant obedience*. Techniques of child training differed too: even with the nonaggressive group of children, boys were more commonly administered physical punishment than girls. Girls were disciplined more often by so-called love-oriented techniques of praise for good behavior and the display of disappointment at unacceptable behavior. Interestingly, many of the mothers did not recognize any efforts they were making to evoke appropriate sex-role behavior in their child and those

asked about the difference between boys and girls will give an answer in terms of the hair-cut rather than the genitals.

who did were inclined to interpret the difference as their natural reaction to the "innate" sex-determined temperament of the child.

2. Gender Role Rehearsal

Role rehearsal stands apart as being of unique importance to the acquisition of role behavior. Needless to say this mode of learning operates hand in hand with parental expectancies and experiential opportunities.

Gender role rehearsals in childhood occur as pretend operations. Much of the time these rehearsals occur in fantasy only, although it is but a short step for a child from fantasy and daydreams to active play. Sears, Maccoby and Levin (1957) point out that such role practice involves more than simple imitation of single aspects of the model's behavior in that the child "takes on the role itself, at least momentarily, with all the feelings, attitudes, values and actions that he attributes to the person who actually occupies the role."[12] In this way a child "tries out" many roles, some of which he will keep and others discard. Thus, typically, a child does not lose his sexual identity by switching from pretending to be a nurse or a mother one time and a fireman sometime later. The available evidence strongly suggests, moreover, that it is social endorsement and approbation of any given pattern of identification which governs the final constitution of gender role. A boy, for instance, will therefore come to share many of his mother's attitudes and values while abhorring for himself the use of feminine cosmetics.

In the absence of the possibility for controlled experimental studies in this area with humans, questions as to the determinants of gender-specific adolescent phenomena have remained matters of conjecture. The temporal coincidence of bodily maturational changes with the emergence of psychologic signs of heterosexual interest

[12] This mode of learning is usually referred to as *identification* in the psychiatric literature. Kagan (1958) has attempted an analysis of the concept of identification in an effort to place the concept within the framework of learning theory. In this he defined identification as an acquired cognitive response within a person which can lead to similarities in behavior between a subject and a model.

has been taken by some as evidence of a common origin in sex-specific instincts or gonadal hormones. As pointed out earlier, there are undeniably physiologic correlates of gender role in that body image and body functioning are an inevitable ingredient of experience. The development of breasts and a more feminine figure in adolescence, for example, increases the likelihood of a girl's being included in teen-age social activities such as dating. Nonetheless, role enactment is preceded by role rehearsal in games of pretend, daydreams, and fantasies during the childhood and pre-adolescent years in the course of which gender role becomes initially structured and, usually, indelibly so.

The girls and women born with the condition known as gonadal dysgenesis provide an unplanned experiment-of-Nature which sheds some light on the origins of gender role fantasies and sexual enactment. This group of patients, reported on earlier by Hampson, Hampson and Money (1955), and now found to have an XO chromatin pattern rather than a typical female XX pattern, is of relevance in that despite normal female external genital appearance their gonads are dysplastic and do not secrete female sex hormones. A measure of control over the timing of puberty is possible, for at the socially appropriate age, treatment with estrogens is begun so that secondary sexual physical development proceeds along typically feminine lines.

Table 23.8 summarizes the psychosexual data on 13 such individuals; in four instances psychiatric and psychologic studies were obtained both before and after the administration of estrogens to induce somatic puberty. Without exception all 13 had established an unequivocally feminine gender role and psychosexual orientation. Also without exception daydreams and fantasies of heterosexual courtship, romance, and sometimes of marriage, motherhood and erotic play had not only occurred but in most cases were a conspicuous feature of their psychosexual expression. The daydreams and fantasies of these individuals were recognizably feminine in quality and content whether or not treatment with estrogen had been instituted, although, to be sure, increasing age and experience seemed

TABLE 23.8

Psychosexual data for 13 patients with gonadal dysgenesis and XO sex chromatin pattern

	Patient and Age at Time of Study	Daydreams and Fantasies of Heterosexual Courtship, Motherhood and Erotic Play	Auto-erotic Genital Practices	Heterosexual Social Dating	Heterosexual Erotic Activity: Kissing, Petting, etc.	Heterosexual Intercourse	Homosexual Eroticism of Any Sort
Before estrogen substitution therapy	1, age 9½	+	+	−	−	−	−
	2, age 12	+	−	−	−	−	−
	3, age 12½	+	+	−	−	−	+
	4, age 13	+	Inconclusive data	−	−	−	−
	5, age 13	+	+	+	−	−	−
	6, age 14	+	−	−	−	−	−
	7, age 15½	+	+	+	−	−	−
	8, age 16	+	−	+	+	−	−
	9, age 17	+	Inconclusive data	+	−	−	−
After estrogen substitution therapy	3, age 15	+	+	−	−	−	−
	4, age 17	+	+	+	−	−	−
	6, age 17	+	+	+	+	−	−
	8, age 17	+	+	+	+	−	−
	10, age 19	+	−	+	+	Inconclusive data	−
	11, age 23	+	+	+	+	−	−
	12, age 26	+	+	+	+	−	−
	13, age 27	+	−	+	+	+	−

to result in more sophisticated fantasy material. The data also show that, although auto-erotic genital activity, usually masturbatory, occurred more often among girls who had been supplied with estrogen, such activity was by no means precluded by the total absence of gonadal hormones. The one patient noted in the column for homo-erotic activity of any sort had engaged in transient homo-erotic play during her preteen years; this girl has been described in greater detail elsewhere (Hampson, Hampson and Money, 1955). In a general way, it appeared that with increasing age, the likelihood of at least some heterosexual social and erotic encounters was increased even in the absence of estrogen therapy. In this regard, however, both qualitative and quantitative differences were observed before and after the secondary sexual changes of puberty had been induced with estrogen treatment. It seemed likely that this difference could be accounted for by the increased social opportunities opened up by a maturing body appearance.

3. Gender Role Identification and Gender Role Preference

It is a common observation, substantiated by clinical and experimental findings (Brown, 1956; Rabban, 1950), that beginning as early as the third year of life some children express a preference to have been born, or even to be, of the sex opposite that in which they are being reared. This unexpected role preference, in our western civilization at least, is encountered far more frequently in girls than in boys. In Brown's (1958) study of middle-class children between the ages of 3½ to 11½ years, the boys expressed a considerably stronger preference for the masculine role than did the girls for the feminine role. A number of studies have shown that even among adults, up to 12 times as many women as men report sometimes wishing that they were of the opposite sex (Terman, 1938; Gallup, 1955). Unless one is aware of this phenomenon and the reasons for its occurrence it may be a major source of error in the evaluation of psychosexual functioning and its origins and development.

One explanation (and one which has had little or no scientific evidence to support it) was Freud's proposal that the young girl regularly felt envious of the male phallus ("penis envy") in the absence of a similar organ herself. The resolution of "penis envy" was held by Freud to be an essential part of psychosexual development during childhood. The psychoanalytic position on this matter has changed considerably over the years, however, and at present seems more in accord with the sociologic findings (Thompson, 1943).

Two factors seem to have an important bearing on expressed role preference. For one, our western culture is more apt to permit a girl to express a contrary gender role preference than it is a boy. Parents may permit, even encourage, tomboyishness in a daughter; a sissy son would likely evoke concern or even embarrassment. Secondly, and more important, is the child's growing awareness of the favored position of the male in the culture, a position carrying with it greater prestige and privilege than does being a female. Children may very early in life see that this is so and, unless wise parental guidance intervenes, the young girl becomes understandably envious of the masculine *status* which she does not have.

Although in typical, healthy psychosexual development gender role *identification* and gender role *preference* do not come into serious or permanent conflict, it is important to recognize that this may not invariably be so. Brown (1958a), writing of nonhermaphroditic girls and women, cites three major gender role patterns: (a) identification with and preference for the gender role of one's own sex, (b) identification with the gender role of one's own sex but preference for the gender role of the opposite sex, and (c) identification with the gender role of the opposite sex but preference for the gender role of one's own sex. One could find clinical justification for yet a fourth pattern, namely (d) identification with the gender role of the opposite sex combined with a solidly pervasive preference for the gender role of the opposite sex.

The relevance of this diversity of possible gender role patterns for such disorders of psychologic sex as homosexuality and transvestism is obvious and is dealt with in another section.

Although reliable well documented evidence has only in recent years begun to appear in the scientific literature, it is probably safe to say that gender role development during childhood is continuously and directly related to adult sexual behavior in humans.

IV. Parental Behavior in Humans

Ahead of the human infant at birth lies the prospect of a more protracted period of immature dependency than for any other neonatal animal. That the human race has survived at all is testimony to the fact that in some way humans are capable of nurturing their young through this period of dependent immaturity. As with other human activities, parental behavior has been variously ascribed to innate, automatic instincts or drives, or, alternatively, considered by some to be largely determined by experience and social learning.

In other animal species maternal care has been considered the paradigm of instinctive behavior. Without belaboring the point, it may safely be said that both experimental biologists and comparative psychologists have come to see the problem as vastly more complex than the traditional assumptions have previously allowed. Whenever a species has been systematically and properly observed and studied, that behavior previously ascribed, by default, to "instinct" has been revealed as being the product of a great many variables. In this respect maternal behavior in infrahuman species has proven no exception and the concept of a "maternal instinct" operating without prior learning or experience now lacks scientific endorsement.

Insofar as maternal behavior in the human species is concerned, much the same predicament has prevailed as for other species; inadequate or improper study and experimentation had left a gap between common observation and scientifically established fact which the concept of a maternal instinct seemed to bridge. One of the chief difficulties in studying humans has been the practical one of observing individuals systematically and carefully over a long period of years. Moreover, many psychoanalytic and psychiatric studies have dealt with maternal *attitudes* rather than with mothering *behavior* in its broadest sense. Brody (1956) made a scholarly and comprehensive review of the literature pertaining to maternal behavior as of that date, dividing her survey into three main categories: (1) experimental studies in subhuman species, (2) anthropologic reports, particularly as they pertain to the feeding and handling of young children, and (3) clinical data culled from the literature of pediatrics, clinical psychology, psychiatry, and psychoanalysis. She noted with considerable relevance that the bulk of the material in the literature on human maternal behavior pointed to the interest of investigators in finding etiologic factors for the character disturbances and other psychopathologies,[13] and that there was a dearth of systematic investigation of the mothers themselves.

In an effort to devise a systematic method for the investigation of some significant aspects of maternal behavior, Brody made a content analysis of the behavioral records of 32 mothers whose behavior with their infants was observed for an approximately 4-hour period under standard conditions. Her research was also intended to test the hypothesis, namely, that the mother-infant interaction during feeding is the salient index of maternal behavior, "serving better than any other activity as a model of a mother's over-all behavior toward a given infant." Making use of explicitly defined quantitative methods, the observational records were subjected to systematic classification and comparison. The 32 maternal records lent themselves to classification into four groups, each group having a statistically distinctive pattern of general maternal behavior. From this general typology four types of maternal feeding behavior were described. Although the hypothesis regarding feeding as an index of general maternal behavior was not proven for mothers of infants as young as 4 weeks of age, it was convincingly proven for mothers of older infants. Brody's work demonstrates the feasibility of quantitative examination and evaluation of parental behavior.

Sears, Maccoby, and Levin's (1957) study of the child rearing practices of 379 American mothers is another important recent contribution toward filling the hiatus in our knowledge of parental behavior in humans. The relevance of such studies to a better understanding of psychosexual development was referred to in an earlier section.

Present day psychiatric thinking about parental behavior has been importantly structured by psychoanalytic theory. Freud regarded motherhood as the culmination of psychosexual development, the course of which he considered to be impelled by instinctual drives. Subsequent workers operating in the psychoanalytic frame of reference using, *a priori*, a concept of a maternal instinctual drive have further developed these ideas (*e.g.*, Bonaparte, 1953; Deutsch, 1945).

On the other hand, there have been workers who have sought to prove that the psychologic manifestations of the maternal state are to be understood only in terms of the influence of social institutions and ideologies. Briffault (1931), representing an extreme in this point of view, maintained that all social feelings are derived from the mother-child relationship and considered the complexity of human social organization to be a direct correlate of the prolonged period of dependency of the human infant on his mother.

Until recently, the purely biologic factors in human maternal behavior have been subjected to very little direct scrutiny. Benedek (1949) postulated that the mother-child symbiosis begins at conception and continues through and beyond parturition

[13] The empiric data bearing on those theories alleging that certain features of parental care of infants determine adult personality was reviewed, as of 1949, by Orlansky (1949). Orlansky found much to doubt and criticize in the widely popular psychoanalytic opinions and emphasized instead the importance of constitutional and cultural factors as well as post-infantile experience in personality formation. In recent years, however, so much has been published concerning the inter-relatedness of parental and child behavior that cognizance must be taken of this variable in personality development. The question is no longer *whether* but *how* such influences act to structure personality.

to lactation. Progestin and/or prolactin are seen by Benedek as inducing not only somatic changes but also the "registering of these changes in the psychic apparatus"; she viewed motherliness as stemming from the biologic effects and specific concomitants of these hormones. Such a view cannot be substantiated in the present state of knowledge concerning the specificities of psychologic-hormonal relationships.

Levy (1942) attempted to tease out some of the psychosomatic correlates of maternal behavior. Based on interviews involving much self-appraisal, his finding that there is "a rather high and significant positive correlation between maternal behavior and duration of menstrual flow" (r = 0.579) would have to be challenged on several grounds, the most significant of which is that the study on which the findings were based did not include any direct observations of maternal behavior. A decade later (Levy and Hess, 1952) Levy himself established the lack of positive correlation between interview and self-appraisal data on the one hand and direct observational ratings on the other.

The ethologists, having identified seemingly ready-made neurophysiologic pathways or releasing mechanisms for certain social responses in lower animals, have suggested that parental behavior can be viewed in much the same light. Lorenz is quoted by Tinbergen (1951) as considering that "parental behavior, a subinstinct of the major reproductive instinct, is responsive to sign-stimuli provided by the human baby." Although no controlled experimentation has been done in this area, Lorenz suggested that the human parental instinct, or IRM, responds to the gestalt of (1) a short face in relation to a large forehead, (2) protruding cheeks, and (3) maladjusted limb movements. Engaging though such a concept may be, no one acquainted with the complexity of human psychologic development and functioning would seriously embrace such a view as adequately explaining the totality of parental or maternal behavior.

Without intending to oversimplify an obviously complex feature of human behavior the authors submit that parental behavior may be considered to be a facet of and an extension of gender role. Like the other as-

pects of gender role that have been considered, parental role behavior does not require and is not dependent on innate sex-specific mechanisms. That it is teleologically purposive is fortuitous rather than directly causal. Like other aspects of gender role, parental behavior is acquired largely through a process of learning during childhood. Direct tuition, identification with single or multiple parental models, rehearsals through play and fantasy—all come to be involved in the learning process. Like other aspects of gender role, the acquisition of parental role behavior may go smoothly and normally, or become disordered.[14]

V. The Sexual Cycle in Women: Psychosexual Concomitants

Cyclic variations in the sexual behavior of lower mammals and infrahuman primates as they relate to the hormonal events of the reproductive cycle have received much attention. Clearcut rhythms of heightened sexual activity have been described in the females not only of the lower mammalian species but of monkeys and apes as well. The occurrence of heightened sexual responsiveness and activity coinciding with the follicular (high estrogen) phase of the cycle in these subhuman species has been viewed as biologically purposeful in that it serves in the perpetuation of the species. The quest for evidences of similar estral correlates in the human female has been an inevitability.

It is probably safe to say that in terms of the complexity of motivation of behavior Man presents a considerably wider range of variables than any infrahuman species. It has become apparent, even in infrahuman species, however, that a single index, such as coital frequency, is unsatisfactory in studying over-all sexual behavior.

In studying Man one difficulty has been in getting agreement as to the components encompassed by the totality of sexual behavior. A second difficulty has been the es-

[14] A discussion of disordered parental behavior is beyond the scope of this chapter. Brief reference here to "maternal overprotectiveness," "maternal underprotectiveness" (see Levy, 1943), and to allegedly "schizophrenogenic" parental behavior (Tietze, 1949; Reichard and Tillman, 1950) will serve to illustrate the point.

tablishment of generally acceptable indices for the measurement of these components. Benedek and Rubinstein (1942) sought to circumvent these difficulties in the study of cyclic sexual behavior in the human female. They argued that: "Sexual desire, urge, and tenderness alternate with affective behavior of other sorts or may find substitution in activities and fantasies which are far different from overt sexual behavior, although all may be consequences of sexual stimulation." They made the assumption that the sexual rhythm of woman can be detected *only* "by psychoanalytic interpretation of the various preconscious and unconscious representations of the sexual drive" and therefore regarded the analysis of dreams, fantasies, and free-associative material as the primary data to be correlated with the cyclic physiologic changes. In brief, their study of 15 neurotic women by this approach revealed: (1) the estrogenic phase of the cycle corresponds to active heterosexual tendencies, the object of which is the sexual partner and coitus, fusing with (2) a passive receptive tendency correlated with progesterone activity, (3) a sudden decrease of active libido following ovulation which is assumed to correlate with the increase in progesterone levels, with interest for the sexual partner diminishing and with "emotional preparation for the function of motherhood" becoming the object of the sexual drive, and (4) disappearance of the emotional concentration on motherhood if pregnancy did not occur (decreased production of progesterone). Benedek and Rubinstein allowed that basic capacities for love, motherliness, constructive activity or their lack are present before the maturation of sexual functioning and that they do not cease to exist after the decline of hormone regulation. They acknowledged further that the processes which they described are "like faint ripples on a large body of water as compared with the constitutional basis of personality." For those who were able to accept the basic premises of this approach, Benedek and Rubinstein's work can be considered to verify the biologic assumptions implicit in Freud's concept of sexual drive.

On the other hand the many other workers (*e.g.*, Davis, 1926; Hamilton, 1929; Dickinson and Bean, 1931) who have given more consideration to the statements of women regarding their *conscious* awareness of erotic desire and readiness for sexual activity as well as the reports of these women regarding overt sexual activity, do not agree with the findings of Benedek and Rubinstein. Although women show great individual diversity, their testimony in general is that erotic feeling and desire increase immediately before and again immediately after menstruation. Aware of the possible pitfalls in questionnaire type of data-gathering, where failures and inaccuracies in both memory and reporting may seriously impair the validity of the conclusions, McCance, Luff and Widdowson (1937) analyzed the daily entries in the special diary-type records of 780 complete menstrual cycles kept for them by 167 women. They found that nearly half of the subjects reported some degree of variation in sexual feeling during a menstrual cycle. The main peak of heightened eroticism occurred about the 8th day following the onset of menstrual flow (average duration of flow, 4.5 days) with a second smaller peak just preceding the onset of the next menstrual flow. These authors also systematically surveyed other menstrual molimina, recording the periodicity of each subjective phenomenon.

Kinsey, Pomeroy, Martin and Gebhard (1953) seeking a still more objective measure of female erotic arousal and responsiveness than that provided by a woman's subjective self-appraisal, collected data concerning variations in the quantity of mucous vaginal secretions (both Bartholin's and cervical glands) during the menstrual cycle. Their data indicated that "there is considerable variation in the quantity of the vaginal secretions among different females. There may also be variation in the quantity of secretion at different times in the same individual." Further, their data indicated that "the time of maximal mucous secretion and the time of maximal erotic responsiveness are almost always the same." About 59 per cent of their sample of women with coital experience recognized a monthly fluctuation in their vaginal secretions during erotic arousal. In general, these women reported increases to occur premenstrually, and, somewhat less generally, postmenstrually. The data are in accord with the consensus of earlier workers pointing to evidence of pre- and postmenstrual enhancement of sexual responsiveness.

These findings have been puzzling in that they seemed contrary to biologic ends and to the observed increase in coital frequency just before ovulation in lower primates. Several explanations for the differences between these findings in humans and those in lower mammals have been suggested, important among which are the social attitudes bearing on sexual activity. In the majority of human societies sexual intercourse during active menstrual bleeding is contravened by prohibitions ranging from esthetic distaste to rigidly ritualized taboo. Moreover, the human female is probably alone among menstruating creatures in being able to anticipate and plan in terms of menstruation. The significance of the intermenstrual period and its association with ovulation and pregnancy is, in more sophisticated societies, so widely known as to constitute yet another variable that must be taken into account. In this sense it is even possible that the observed "peaks" of heightened eroticism are artifacts dependent on many factors other than variations in the supply of female sex hormones. It is in any case apparent that the increasing importance of nonhormonal control of sexual functioning through agencies of social learning and cognitional functioning to be observed even in monkeys and apes has reached its highest development in the human species.

VI. Disorders of Psychologic Sex: Psychopathology

A. GENDER ROLE DISTORTIONS

Of all the disorders of psychologic sex, homosexuality and transvestism have seemed to be the most baffling and difficult to explain. As is common when ignorance prevails, causal theories have grown up, some outrageous, some fanciful, some provocative, but none that has received the universal endorsement of medical science. Terms such as intersexuality, psychologic hermaphroditism, and others have found their way into the literature, often being used as if the words themselves constituted a scientific explanation.

One of the common errors made in considering the problem of psychologic sex disorders, particularly homosexuality, has been to conceive of men and women as divided each into two camps: those who are heterosexual, and therefore spoken of as normal, and those who are homosexual. Such a notion is both conceptually and statistically incorrect and unwarranted. The comprehensive studies on sex behavior in American men and women (Kinsey, Pomeroy and Martin, 1948; Kinsey, Pomeroy, Martin and Gebhard, 1953) have produced some of the best evidence relative to the incidence of homosexual behavior. According to those authors, 37 per cent of the white male population and 13 per cent of the white female population have had at least some overt homosexual experience to the point of orgasm between adolescence and old age. On the other hand, only 4 per cent of the white males and 1 to 3 per cent of the white females were found to be exclusively homosexual in their erotic activities throughout their lives. Between these extremes these authors found a wide range of sexual behavior involving varying proportions of heterosexual and homosexual orientation and activity which could, with good justification, be arranged on, and described by, a 7-point (0 to 6) rating scale. Such findings make it clear that one is never justified in speaking of homosexuality as if it were a single descriptive or clinical entity as some authors have done. The point is well taken (Kinsey, Pomeroy and Martin, 1948, p. 617) that: "It would encourage clearer thinking on these matters if persons were not characterized as heterosexual or homosexual, but as individuals who have had certain amounts of heterosexual experience and certain amounts of homosexual experience. Instead of using these terms as substantives which stand for persons, or even as adjectives to describe persons, they may better be used to describe the nature of the overt sexual relations, *or, of the stimuli to which an individual erotically responds*" (italics ours). For the purposes of the study, Kinsey, Pomeroy, Martin and Gebhard deliberately restricted themselves to an investigation of those sexual activities which culminate in orgasm. They doubtless would have allowed that, although overt homosexual stimulation to the point of orgasm, is one index of homosexuality it is not the only index. Psychologic sex is not restricted to sexuality in the sense of genital eroticism, but includes, for example, wishes and fantasies, demeanor and interests.

By way of illustrating this point as it pertains to homosexuality, we cite an excerpt from the letter to the authors from a 24-year-old woman. A Latin-American university student, the woman was not fluent in idiomatic English, but nonetheless, clearly expressed her dilemma.

"...I want to add that my attitudes, my way of thinking and feeling, my viewpoints regarding life, love, and everything else that make up and define the personality toward a specific sex have been masculine since I can remember. Later on, when a person reaches that complicated and difficult age when he discovers the difference between men and women, I suddenly realized that I liked girls very much, but not precisely as friends. I have never practiced homosexualism, which I consider dishonest and abnormal. I have struggled to adapt myself to the behavior of girl friends, in an endeavor to be like them, but I have failed completely. I know it is useless to pretend to adjust myself to a feminine life because the problems, behavior, and attitudes of such sex are so strange and far away from me that I could not make them a part of my everyday life .... I have used lipstick; I have tried to dress differently—more like other girls, but I have not known how to select a more attractive dress; and to go to a dress-maker fills me with an anger that I do not understand. I have tried to widen the circle of my acquaintances by joining a girls' club, but I have dropped out because I cannot bear their small talk, which, even if I respect, I cannot share. I have gone out with some good male friends who have shown themselves to be interested in talking with me about the current things, but I have not been able to dance once, and one night I made myself ridiculous by leaving without any explanations because of my deep feelings of inadequacy...."

This patient, like many others seen clinically, displayed a host of signs characteristic of a pervasive identification with a male model. Such a person may be said to have acquired what Brown (1958b) regards as an *inverted gender identification*. Almost invariably[15] the person with inverted gender identification desires sexual activity with a person of the same anatomic sex and in that sense can be regarded as homosexual in his

or her preference of sex partner whether or not homosexual activity has actually taken place. In this light homosexuals as a group have as their common denominator only an erotic preference for sexual partners of the same anatomic or biologic sex. Brown has proposed the terms *inverted homosexual* and *noninverted homosexual* as more accurately describing the psychologic features in the gender role identification of these individuals. Such terminology does have the undoubted advantage of avoiding the imprecision inherent in the older and more commonly used adjectives "active" and "passive," which refer only to erotic behavior as such.

With the identification of the sex hormones, it was doubtless unavoidable that homosexuality, transvestism and other deviant patterns of sexual behavior in humans came to be ascribed, popularly, to an imbalance of androgen or estrogen. Such a belief was fostered and kept alive by reports of studies in lower animals revealing that injection of sex hormones of the opposite sex could evoke inverted sex behavior; that is to say, such animals failed to conform to the usual pattern of sexual aggressiveness or receptiveness and, further, assumed coital positions typical of the opposite sex (Young and Rundlett, 1939; Ball, 1940; Beach, 1941, 1942a, 1942b, 1945). But anthropomorphic interpretations are always risky and in this instance have proven deceptive and unwarranted insofar as the psychologic sex disorders in humans is concerned. Studies purporting to demonstrate an excess of estrogen in the urinary androgen-estrogen levels of homosexual men (Glass, Deuel and Wright, 1940) have not been verified (Perloff, 1949). It is common clinical experience that the treatment of homosexual persons with sex hormones, although often intensifying erotic genital sensation, does not bring about any change in sex-role or psychosexual orientation. This is not particularly surprising because, as previously stated, androgens and estrogens have an indirect, rather than a direct influence on gender role and erotic orientation. There does not seem to be a valid basis for the endorsement of any theory of a simple and direct hormonal determination of human sexual behavior, either typical or atypical.

---

[15] One exception would seem to be the case of *transvestism*. Transvestites often eschew homosexual sex activity and may have established a heterosexual adjustment of sorts (Hamburger, Stürup and Dahl-Iversen, 1953; Benjamin, 1954).

Several investigators have studied homosexuality from the hereditary point of view. Lang (1940) reported findings which suggested to him that male homosexuals were genotypically female; he considered such individuals to be "male sex intergrades which are genetically female but have lost all morphologic sex characteristics except their chromosome formula." Kallman (1952a, b, 1953) expressed himself as substantially in agreement with this, basing his agreement on his findings in twin studies that 60 per cent of the co-twins of homosexuals displayed no evidence of homosexual behavior, whereas 100 per cent of 44 pairs of one egg twins were concordant "as to overt practice and quantitative rating of homosexual behavior after adolescence." Kallman thus concluded that homosexuality is "a gene controlled disarrangement between male and female maturation (hormonal) tendencies," and that "overt homosexual behavior in the adult male may be viewed as an alternative minus variant in the integrative process of psychosexual maturation, comparable in the sexually reproductive human species to the developmental aspects of left handedness in a predominantly right-handed human world."

Pare (1956), using Barr's technique for the identification of the sex chromatin pattern of cells, adduced strong evidence against Lang's theory that male homosexuals are genotypically female. In a series of 50 markedly homosexual men (average rating on the Kinsey 6-point rating scale was 4.5), the sex chromatin pattern was male in all cases and the incidence of sex chromatin spots did not differ from that of normal male controls. Barr and Hobbs (1954) reported similar findings in a series of transvestites; the sex chromatin pattern was always in accord with the external genital morphology. The studies of Bleuler and Wiedemann (1956), Raboch (1957), and Raboch and Nedoma (1958) are in agreement with these other investigations. Thus the case is clear that, so far as homosexuality and transvestism are concerned, there is no correlation with the sex chromatin pattern of the body cells. Admittedly, it can still be argued that sex chromatin determinations give no direct information regarding genes and further elucidation of this aspect of the problem must await further developments in cytologic techniques.

In the past several years there is increasing evidence from psychiatric and psychologic research to support a view that homosexuality and certain other disorders of psychologic sex have their origins in social learning. The phenomenon of gender role inversion mentioned earlier provides some insight into some of the factors influencing such atypical and disordered learning. Brown (1958a), for example, postulated that males displaying gender role inversion the early years of life characteristically "involve a father who is psychologically ineffective and socially distant so far as the boy is concerned; or a father who is chronically abusive and cruel to the boy. In addition such a family constellation will involve a mother or a mother substitute who is 'idolized' by the boy and to whom he is excessively close and attached." Brown further postulated two additional parent-child relationships which could provide the basis for inversion: (1) "a family in which the same-sex parent himself or herself is predominantly or considerably inverted in sex-role structure, thus exposing the child to a distorted model with which to identify," and (2) "a family in which the parent or parents actually encourage and rear a child of one biologic sex to feel and think and behave like the opposite sex."

The clinical findings of Kolb and Johnson (1955) and of Litin, Giffin and Johnson (1956), although couched in the loosely defined language of psychoanalysis, are in essential agreement with Brown's view. These authors explain deviant sex behavior such as homosexuality in terms of "subtle attitudes within the family" developing from "unconscious or, less frequently, conscious fostering of deviant sexual behavior early in life within the family setting."

It is the opinion of the authors of this chapter that neither the purely genetic explanation nor the purely environmental explanation supplies all the answers to the questions posed by the disorders of psychologic sex. Certainly the evidence of human hermaphroditism points strongly to the tremendous influence of rearing and social learning in the establishment of normal gender role (psychologic sex) and, by analogy, disordered psychologic sex. As stated earlier, however, to make such a statement is not to endorse an oversimplified theory of environmental determinism. The experiences entering into social learning require the active presence of a person—a person whose body morphology, physiologic functioning and cerebral and cognitive equipment are the heritage of genetic factors.[16] It can also be allowed that some as yet unidentified inherited perceptual or cognitive factor may reinforce or make it easier for disorders of psychologic sex to evolve during the course of a person's growing up. Nonetheless, life experience and social learning must be accorded an important place in the establishment of psychologic sex, either ordered or disordered, for the evidence militates too strongly against a theory of innate, preformed, and inherited behavioral imperatives, hormonal or otherwise.

[16] An important difficulty facing an investigator of genetic factors in behavior is the one of knowing precisely what to look for. Such gross items as "intelligence" or "over-all adaptability," although much studied in the past, have proven inadequate as measures of genic influence on behavior. The work of such students of animal behavior as Lorenz, Beach, W. C. Young, J. P. Scott, Guhl, and others, shows clearly that the picture is not as simple as earlier believed. There seems to be general agreement among such investigators that the inherited aspects of a given type of behavior are simple behavioral units often related to basic physiologic and neurophysiologic processes; for the human, at least, it is evident that such anatomic considerations as body morphology must be added. Lower animals display different capacities to learn and to respond emotionally and physiologically according to the nature of the stimulus; such capacities are clearly related to genetic endowment. An example is the finding by Scott and Charles (1953, 1954) that the ease with which beagles could be taught to track a rabbit, terriers to fight, and spaniels to retrieve and socialize could be broken down into a step-wise sequence of learning processes. Scott (1953) suggested that the study of genic influences on behavior is likely to be most fruitful if approached in terms of these smaller units or processes. In Scott's words: "A gene can act only by modifying some physiologic process, whether it be growth in the embryo or pigment formation in the adult, and clear-cut genetic results can be expected in the study of behavior only where a trait is measured which is either a physiologic process or largely based on one. If behavior is measured in terms of over-all adjustment, dozens and even hundreds of physiologic processes are likely to be involved and these may be organized so that a deficiency in one is cancelled by an excess in another."

B. HERMAPHRODITISM AND PSYCHOPATHOLOGY

No one acquainted with Freudian libido theory[17] can fail to be aware that sexuality in the broad sense conceived of by Freud has been accorded a position of great importance in theories concerning the origins of psychiatric disorders. For some, the libido theory constitutes an accepted psychiatric doctrine despite the shaky assumptions (see Bieber, 1958) on which it is based.

It was in these respects that the evidence of human hermaphroditism was examined by Money, Hampson and Hampson (1956). Representing the several varieties of hermaphroditism, 94 hermaphroditic patients were studied psychologically and psychiatrically, and their psychologic healthiness was judged on a 4-point scale. Of the 94 patients, 63 were evaluated as healthy, 16 mildly nonhealthy, 14 moderately nonhealthy, and one, a mental defective, severely nonhealthy. Functional psychosis was conspicuously absent in this group of hermaphroditic patients. In general their psychologic nonhealthiness was in the direction of excessive inhibition and reserve. Commonly these pa-

[17] Briefly, the libido theory (see Freud, 1915) assumes the existence of instinctive sexual forces somehow related to "psychic energy" (a dubious concept in any case) and ultimately responsible for all behavior. Freud postulated an "ego" and a "superego" as the psychic apparatus by which libidinal energy is controlled and made socially acceptable and useful. In elaborating his libido theory, Freud envisioned a 3-stage process of psychosexual development consisting of (1) an *oral stage* related to later dependency relationships, (2) an *anal stage* related to authority relationships, and (3) a *genital stage* related to sexuality in the genital erotic sense. Psychopathologic states, he postulated, were simply regressions to earlier stages of psychosexual, or libidinal organization. Thus Freud considered disordered sexuality, or more precisely, disordered libido, as the primary or basic cause for the neuroses and possibly other psychologic conditions as well. Contrary to views held by other scientists, psychoanalysis has classically held the position that all human emotion, whether affection, warmth, aggression, or anger, has its origins in sexuality as elastically encompassed by the libido theory. Bieber (1958) takes to task those who anachronistically continue to espouse such facile explanatory constructs: "Current psychoanalytic thinking is infiltrated with teleology. We are assigning purpose to behavior facilely.... A teleologic theory cannot account for all psychologic mental functioning. It is inaccurate and misleading."

tients tended to lag in psychologic growth and personality development relative to their contemporaries of comparable IQ. Spells of depressed moodiness, sullen and anxious bashfulness and shyness, and extreme diffidence and guardedness in matters pertaining to sexual and romantic situations were noted. With respect to the gender role these individuals had established, in 95 per cent there was an equivocal correspondence between gender role and of the sex of assignment and rearing whether or not a contradiction existed between this pair of variables and 1 or more of the other 5 sexual variables. Only 5 of the 94 gave any evidence of psychologic nonhealthiness on grounds of a demonstrably ambiguous gender role and orientation. None of the patients studied was psychotic and none required psychiatric hospitalization. This low incidence of seriously incapacitating mental disorder is corroborated by Money's unpublished survey of the literature on hermaphroditism in which he found a 2 per cent incidence of psychosis among 248 postadolescent hermaphrodites.

In the 94 hermaphroditic patients referred to above, several factors stood out as having important bearing on psychologic healthiness, including psychosexual orientation. The first important factor was the nature and degree of the person's visible genital or secondary sexual ambiguity; the more publicly conspicuous the individual's ambiguous appearance, the more difficult it proved for him to transcend his handicap and come to terms with it psychologically. In view of the importance of body appearance, as discussed earlier, this finding is not surprising. The surprise is that so many ambiguous-looking patients were able, appearance notwithstanding, to grow up and achieve a rating of psychologically healthy, or perhaps only mildly nonhealthy. The healthy rating was certainly more common in the patients whose body morphology, irrespective of gonads and sex chromatin pattern, was unambiguous looking than it was in the patients whose sexual appearance was equivocal. Thus, patients whose sex of rearing was contradicted by their gonadal and chromosomal sex were not necessarily destined to be rated nonhealthy.

A second factor of importance in later psychologic adjustment was the consistence of gender role training and experience which the individual had received during the growing-up years. After the early months of life, reassignment of sex, as commented on in an earlier section, turns out to be extremely conducive to later psychologic nonhealthiness. Corrective surgical, hormonal, or psychologic procedures were of greater benefit if they were instituted during infancy or childhood rather than at a later age. This point is well illustrated by the psychologic difficulties which hyperadrenocortical women in their thirties or forties have experienced when treatment with cortisone permitted, for the first time, some degree of belated body feminization. Having already attained some measure of acceptance of their lot as virilized women physically unattractive to men, these women have found themselves gauche, inexpert, and lacking in the self-assurance required for success in the role of girl-friend or wife. As a result episodes of anxiety and depression were common in such patients. By contrast the girls treated in their pre-teen years to permit feminizing body changes, found it considerably easier, psychologically, to negotiate the transition to adolescence and adulthood.

The observation that a multiplicity of factors is involved in the etiology of psychopathology, where it occurs, in hermaphroditic individuals makes clear the danger of embracing pat explanatory concepts, such as those based on libido theory, for the neuroses or any other psychopathy.

VII. Concluding Remarks

On the foregoing pages the authors have considered only a handful of the issues and problems germane to human sexual behavior. Without doubt many other considerations, and many other research contributions could and perhaps should have been included. The reader who is aware of the vast psychiatric and psychologic literature pertaining to sexual functioning in humans will understand the difficulties of a thoroughly comprehensive discussion of the topic in a limited allotment of pages. On the other hand, it is hoped that a central theme will, nonetheless, have been spelled out, a theme first envisioned in the first edition of this book by Frank Lillie who wrote:

"... There is no such biologic entity as sex. What exists in nature is a dimorphism within species into male and female individuals, which differ with respect to contrasting characters, for each of which in any given species we recognize a male form and a female form, whether these characters be classed as of the biologic, or psychologic, or social orders. Sex is not a force that produces these contrasts; it is merely a name for our total impression of the differences. It is difficult to divest ourselves of the prescientific anthropomorphism which assigned phenomena to the control of personal agencies, and we have been particularly slow in the field of the scientific study of sex-characteristics in divesting ourselves not only of the terminology, but also of the influence of such ideas."

VIII. References

ANASTASI, A. 1958. Heredity, environment, and the question "how?" Psychol. Rev., **65**, 197–208.

BALL, J. 1940. The effect of testosterone on the sex behavior of female rats. J. Comp. Psychol., **29**, 151–165.

BARR, M. L., AND HOBBS, G. E. 1954. Chromosomal sex in transvestites. Lancet, **266**, 1109–1110.

BEACH, F. A. 1941. Female mating behavior shown by male rats after administration of testosterone propionate. Endocrinology, **29**, 409–412.

BEACH, F. A. 1942a. Male and female mating behavior in prepubertally castrated male rats and its modification by estrogen administration. Endocrinology, **31**, 673–678.

BEACH, F. A. 1942b. Copulatory behavior in prepubertally castrated male rats and its modification by estrogen administration. Endocrinology, **31**, 679–683.

BEACH, F. A. 1945. Bisexual mating behavior in the male rat; effects of castration and hormone administration. Physiol. Zool., **18**, 390–402.

BEACH, F. A. 1955. The descent of instinct. Psychol. Rev., **62**, 401–410.

BEACH, F. A., AND JAYNES, J. 1954. Effects of early experience upon the behavior of animals. Psychol. Bull., **51**, 239–263.

BENEDEK, T. 1949. The psychosomatic implications of the primary unit: mother-child. Am. J. Orthopsychiat., **19**, 642–654.

BENEDEK, T., AND RUBINSTEIN, B. B. 1942. The Sexual Cycle in Women. Psychosomatic Medicine Monographs, Vol. III, Nos. I and II. Washington: National Research Council.

BENJAMIN, H. 1954. Transsexualism and transvestism as psychosomatic and somatopsychic syndromes. Am. J. Psychotherapy, **8**, 219–230.

BLEULER, M., AND WIEDEMANN, H. R. 1956. Chromosomengeschlecht und Psychosexualität. Arch. Psychiat., **195**, 14–18.

BIEBER, I. 1958. A critique of the libido theory. Am. J. Psychoanalysis, **18**, 52–68.

BONAPARTE, M. 1953. Female Sexuality. New York: International University Press.

BRIFFAULT, R. 1931. The Mothers. New York: Macmillan Company.

BRODY, S. 1956. Patterns of Mothering. New York: International University Press.

BROWN, D. G. 1956. Sex-role preference in young children. Psychol. Monogr., **70**, No. 14.

BROWN, D. G. 1958a. Sex-role development in a changing culture. Psychol. Bull., **55**, 232–242.

BROWN, D. G. 1958b. Inversion and homosexuality. Am. J. Orthopsychiat., **38**, 424–429.

BUNGE, R. G., AND BRADBURY, J. T. 1956. Genetic sex; chromatin test versus gonadal histology. J. Clin. Endocrinol., **16**, 1117–1119.

CARPENTER, C. R. 1934. A field study of the behavior and social relations of howling monkeys. Comp. Psychol. Monogr., **10**, 1–168.

CHILDS, B., GRUMBACH, M. M., AND VAN WYK, J. J. 1956. Virilizing adrenal hyperplasia; a genetic and hormonal study. J. Clin. Invest., **35**, 213–222.

DARLING, F. F. 1937. A Herd of Red Deer. London: Oxford University Press.

DAVIS, K. B. 1926. Periodicity of sex desire. Am. J. Obst. & Gynec., **12**, 824–836.

DEUTSCH, H. 1945. The Psychology of Women, Vol. II. New York: Grune and Stratton.

DICKINSON, R. L., AND BEAN, L. 1931. A Thousand Marriages. A Medical Study of Sex Adjustment. Baltimore: The Williams & Wilkins Company.

FLETCHER, R. 1957. Instinct in Man. New York: International University Press.

FREUD, S. 1910. Three Contributions to the Sexual Theory. New York: Nervous & Mental Disease Publishing Company.

FREUD, S. 1924. The infantile genital organization of the libido. In Collected Papers, Vol. II. New York: International Psychoanalytic Press.

FREUD, S. 1927. An Autobiographical Study. New York: Brentano.

FREUD, S. 1949. An Outline of Psychoanalysis. New York: W. W. Norton & Company.

GALLUP, G. 1955. (June). Gallup Poll. Princeton: Audience Research, Inc.

GESELL, A. L., ILG, F. L., AND AMES, L. B. 1940. The First Five Years of Life. New York: Harper & Brothers.

GLASS, S. J., DEUEL, H. J., AND WRIGHT, C. A. 1940. Sex hormone studies in male homosexuality. Endocrinology, **26**, 590–594.

GOY, R. H., AND YOUNG, W. C. 1957. Somatic basis of sexual behavior patterns in guinea pigs. Psychosom. Med., **14**, 144–151.

GRUMBACH, M. M., AND BARR, M. L. 1958. Cytologic tests of chromosomal sex in relation to sexual anomalies in man. Recent Progr. Hormone Res., **14**, 255–334.

HALL, C. S., AND LINDSEY, G. 1957. Theories of Personality. New York: John Wiley & Sons.

HAMBURGER, C., STÜRUP, G. K., AND DAHL-IVERSEN, E. 1953. Transvestism. J. A. M. A., **152**, 391–396.

HAMILTON, G. V. 1929. A Research in Marriage. New York: Boni Liveright.

HAMPSON, J. G. 1955. Hermaphroditic appearance, rearing and eroticism in hyperadreno-

ONTOGENESIS OF SEXUAL BEHAVIOR 1431

corticism. Bull. Johns Hopkins Hosp., 96, 265–273.
HAMPSON, J. L., HAMPSON, J. G., AND MONEY, J. 1955. The syndrome of gonadal agenesis (ovarian agenesis) and male chromosomal pattern in girls and women: psychologic studies. Bull. Johns Hopkins Hosp., 97, 43–57.
HAMPSON, J. G., AND MONEY, J. 1955. Idiopathic sexual precocity. Psychosom. Med., 17, 16–35.
HAMPSON, J. G., MONEY, J., AND HAMPSON, J. L. 1956. Hermaphrodism: recommendations concerning case management. J. Clin. Endocrinol., 16, 547–556.
HEINROTH, O. 1910. Beiträge zur Biologie, namentlich Ethologie und Psychologie der Anatiden. In Verhandlung V International Ornithologie Kongress, p. 589–702. Berlin: Deutsche Ornithologische Gesellschaft.
JONES, H. W., AND SCOTT, W. W. 1958. Hermaphroditism, Genital Anomalies and Related Endocrine Disorders. Baltimore: The Williams & Wilkins Company.
KAGAN, J. 1958. The concept of identification. Psychol. Rev., 65, 296–305.
KALLMAN, F. J. 1952a. Twin and sibship study of overt male homosexuality. Am. J. Human Genet., 4, 136–153.
KALLMAN, F. J. 1952b. Comparative twin study on the genetic aspects of male homosexuality. J. Nerv. & Ment. Dis., 115, 283–297.
KALLMAN, F. J. 1953. Heredity in Health and Mental Disorder. New York: W. W. Norton & Company.
KINSEY, A. C., POMEROY, W. B., AND MARTIN, C. E 1948. Sexual Behavior in the Human Male. Philadelphia: W. B. Saunders Company.
KINSEY, A. C., POMEROY, W. B., MARTIN, C. E., AND GEBHARD, P. H. 1953. Sexual Behavior in the Human Female. Philadelphia: W. B. Saunders Company.
KLEBS, E. 1876. Handbuch der Pathologischen Anatomie, Band 1. Berlin: A. H. Hirschwald.
KOLB, L. C., AND JOHNSON, A. M. 1955. Etiology and therapy of overt homosexuality. Psychoanalyt. Quart., 24, 506–515.
LANG, T. 1940. Studies in the genetic determination of homosexuality. J. Nerv. & Ment. Dis., 92, 55–64.
LEVY, D. M. 1942. Psychosomatic studies of some aspects of maternal behavior. Psychosom. Med., 4, 223–227.
LEVY, D. M. 1943. Maternal Over-protection. New York: Columbia University Press.
LEVY, D. M., AND HESS, A. 1952. Problems in determining maternal attitudes towards newborn infants. Psychiatry, 15, 273–286.
LITIN, E. M., GIFFIN, M. E., AND JOHNSON, A. M. 1956. Parental influence in unusual sexual behavior in children. Psychoanalyt. Quart., 25, 37–55.
LORENZ, K. 1935. Der Kumpan in der Umwelt des Vogels. Der Artgenösse als auslösendes Moment sozialer Verhaltungsweisen. J. Ornithol., 83, 137–213.
LORENZ, K. 1950. The comparative method in studying innate behavior patterns. Symp. Soc. Exper. Biol., 4, 221–268.

LORENZ, K. 1952. King Solomon's Ring; New Light on Animal Ways. New York: Thomas Y. Crowell Company.
McCANCE, R. A., LUFF, M. C., AND WIDDOWSON, E. E. 1937. Physical and emotional periodicity in women. J. Hyg., 37, 571–611.
MEDAWAR, P. B. 1947. Cellular inheritance and transformation. Biol. Rev., 22, 360–389.
MONEY, J. 1955. Hermaphroditism, gender and precocity in hyperadrenocorticism: psychologic findings. Bull. Johns Hopkins Hosp., 96, 253–264.
MONEY, J., AND HAMPSON, J. G. 1955. Idiopathic sexual precocity in the male. Psychosom. Med., 17, 1–15.
MONEY, J., HAMPSON, J. G., AND HAMPSON, J. L. 1955a. Hermaphroditism: recommendations concerning assignment of sex, change of sex, and psychologic management. Bull. Johns Hopkins Hosp., 97, 284–300.
MONEY, J., HAMPSON, J. G., AND HAMPSON, J. L. 1955b. An examination of some basic sexual concepts: the evidence of human hermaphroditism. Bull. Johns Hopkins Hosp., 97, 301–319.
MONEY, J., HAMPSON, J. G., AND HAMPSON, J. L. 1956. Sexual incongruities and psychopathology: the evidence of human hermaphroditism. Bull. Johns Hopkins Hosp., 98, 43–57.
MONEY, J., HAMPSON, J. G., AND HAMPSON, J. L. 1957. Imprinting and the establishment of gender role. A. M. A. Arch. Neurol. & Psychiat., 77, 333–336.
MOORE, K. L., AND BARR, M. L. 1953. Morphology of the nerve cell nucleus in mammals with special reference to sex chromatin. J. Comp. Neurol., 98, 213–227.
MOORE, K. L., GRAHAM, M. A., AND BARR, M. L. 1953. The detection of chromosomal sex in hermaphrodites from a skin biopsy. Surg. Gynec. & Obst., 96, 641–648.
MOORE, K. L., AND BARR, M. L. 1954. Nuclear morphology according to sex in human tissues. Acta anat., 21, 197–208.
MURPHY, G. 1947. Personality: a Biosocial Approach to Origins and Structure. New York: Harper & Brothers.
ORLANSKY, H. 1949. Infant care and personality. Psychol. Bull., 46, 1–48.
PARE, C. M. B. 1956. Homosexuality and chromosomal sex. J. Psychosom. Res., 1, 247–251.
PAWLOWSKI, A. A., AND SCOTT, J. P. 1956. Hereditary differences in the development of dominance in litters of puppies. J. Comp. & Physiol. Psychol., 49, 353–358.
PERLOFF, W. H. 1949. Role of the hormones in human sexuality. Psychosom. Med., 11, 133–139.
RABBAN, M. 1950. Sex-role identification in young children in two diverse social groups. Genet. Psychol. Monogr., 42, 81–158.
RABOCH, J. 1957. Thirty-one men with female sex chromatin. J. Clin. Endocrinol., 17, 1429–1439.
RABOCH, J., AND NEDOMA, K. 1958. Sex chromatin and sexual behavior. Psychosom. Med., 20, 55–59.

RADO, S. 1940. A critical examination of the concept of bisexuality. Psychosom. Med., **2**, 459–467.

REICHARD, S., AND TILLMAN, C. 1950. Patterns of parent-child relationships in schizophrenia. Psychiatry, **13**, 247–257.

RUSSELL, C., AND RUSSELL, W. M. S. 1957. An approach to human ethology. Behavioral Sc., **2**, 169–200.

SCHILLER, C. H., Ed. 1957. *Instinctive Behavior.* New York: International University Press.

SCOTT, J. P. 1945. Social behavior, organization and leadership in a small flock of domestic sheep. Comp. Psychol. Monogr., **184**, 1–29.

SCOTT, J. P., AND MARSTON, M. 1950. Critical periods affecting the development of normal and maladjustive social behavior of puppies. J. Genet. Psychol., **77**, 25–60.

SCOTT, J. P., FREDERICSON, E., AND FULLER, J. L. 1951. Experimental exploration of the critical period hypothesis. Personality, **1**, 162–183.

SCOTT, J. P. 1953. New directions in the genetic study of personality and intelligence. Eugenical News, **38**, 97–101.

SCOTT, J. P., AND CHARLES, M. S. 1953. Some problems of heredity and social behavior. J. Gen. Psychol., **48**, 209–230.

SCOTT, J. P., AND CHARLES, M. S. 1954. Genetic differences in the behavior of dogs: a case of magnification by thresholds and by habit formation. J. Genet. Psychol., **84**, 175–188.

SCOTT, J. P. 1958. Critical periods in the development of social behavior in puppies. Psychosom. Med., **20**, 42–54.

SEARS, R. R., MACCOBY, E. E., AND LEVIN, H. 1957. *Patterns of Child Rearing.* Evanston, Ill.: Row, Peterson & Company.

SEWARD, G. H. 1946. *Sex and the Social Order.* New York: McGraw-Hill Book Company, Inc.

SHELDON, W. H., AND STEVENS, S. S. 1942. *The Varities of Temperament: a Psychology of Constitutional Differences.* New York: Harper & Brothers.

SPITZ, R. A., AND WOLF, K. M. 1946. The smiling response: a contribution to the ontogenesis of social relations. Genet. Psychol. Monogr., **34**, 57–125.

TANNER, J. M., AND INHELDER, B., Eds. 1953, 1954, 1955. *Discussions in Child Development,* Vols. I, II, III. New York: International University Press.

TERMAN, L. M. 1938. *Psychological Factors in Marital Happiness.* New York: McGraw-Hill Book Company, Inc.

THOMPSON, C. 1943. "Penis envy" in women. Psychiatry, **6**, 123–125.

TIETZE, T. 1949. A study of mothers of schizophrenic patients. Psychiatry, **12**, 55–65.

TINBERGEN, N. 1951. *The Study of Instinct.* London: Clarendon Press.

VAGUE, J. 1953. *La Différenciation Sexuelle Humaine. Ses incidences en pathologie.* Paris: Masson & Cie.

VERPLANCK, W. S. 1957. A glossary of some terms used in the objective science of behavior. Psychol. Rev., Suppl., **64**, 1.

VON KRAFFT-EBING, R. 1890. *Psychopathia Sexualis.* Stuttgart: F. Enke.

WILKINS, L. 1957. *The Diagnosis and Treatment of Endocrine Disorders in Childhood and Adolescence.* Springfield, Ill.: Charles C Thomas.

WILKINS, L., JONES, H. W., HOLMAN, G. H., AND STEMPFEL, R. S. 1958. Masculinization of the female fetus associated with administration of oral and intramuscular progestins during gestation: nonadrenal female pseudohermaphrodism. J. Clin. Endocrinol., **18**, 559–585.

WILLIAMS, E., AND SCOTT, J. P. 1953. The development of social behavior patterns in the mouse in relation to natural periods. Behavior, **6**, 35–64.

WITSCHI, E., NELSON, W. O., AND SEGAL, S. J. 1957. Genetic, developmental, and hormonal aspects of gonadal dysgenesis and sex inversion in man. J. Clin. Endocrinol., **17**, 737–753.

YOUNG, W. C., AND RUNDLETT, B. 1939. The hormonal induction of homosexual behavior in the spayed female guinea pig. Psychosom. Med., **1**, 449–460.

24

Cultural Determinants of Sexual Behavior

Margaret Mead, Ph.D.,

ASSOCIATE CURATOR OF ETHNOLOGY, AMERICAN MUSEUM OF
NATURAL HISTORY, NEW YORK

I. Introduction

The authors of the preceding chapters on reproductive behavior (Hampson and Hampson, Lehrman, Money, Young) have presented material from which several general conclusions may be deduced. Among the vertebrates as a whole, it is evident that genetic, experiential or psychologic, and physiologic (particularly hormonal) factors participate in the regulation of reproductive behavior. The pattern of behavior displayed by adults is the product of the interaction of these factors from the embryonic period into adulthood, but at no time is the contribution of the several factors equal. During the embryonic and fetal periods genetic factors and fetal morphogenic substances thought to be secreted by the embryonic gonads are believed to be the active agents in the determination and differentiation of all the tissues concerned with sexuality, in-cluding the neural tissues mediating sexual behavior (Phoenix, Goy, Gerall and Young, 1959). The suggestion that in man the effects of these substances on the tissues mediating sexual behavior may be overridden by the manner of rearing is contained in the chapters by Hampson and Hampson and Money, but it may be equally significant that in at least some lower mammals as well, experiential factors help to mold the patterns of sexual behavior displayed after the attainment of adulthood (Young, 1957). This suggests that phylogenetically the apparent rise of the experiential factor to dominance started early. After birth or shortly after birth in lower mammals (the limits have not yet been determined), gonadal hormones cease to be organizational and become purely activational. The extent to which they are activational in man is still equivocal. Most colleagues assign a minor role, if any, to them and hold to the view that the dominant factor is psychic (see chapter by Money).

If this thumbnail sketch may be further abbreviated, it is apparent that experiential or psychologic factors act at two points, the degree depending on the phylogenetic position of the species. Once an animal is born and becomes subject to them, they modify the character of the soma established during embryonic and fetal development by genic factors and hormones. After the attainment of adulthood, they, rather than the hormones alone, give force to the sexual behavior that is exhibited.

To this concept, anthropologists have much to contribute. This chapter will concern itself with their findings from cross-cultural materials,[1] with an effort to test out the universality of certain forms of sex behavior in the human species, and with suggestions of new areas of research.[2]

[1] Cross cultural studies may be classified as: historic studies based entirely on archaeologic and literary evidence, and contemporary studies, in which the data have been collected from living members of the society in question. Among contemporary studies, we may distinguish between studies of preliterate peoples, in which the data have to be collected from nonliterate informants and processed into writing, or through the use of observational techniques, notes by investigators, tapes, film, etc., and studies of literate societies. The latter (because in most cases literacy and social complexity go hand in hand) are limited, on the one hand, because it is less easy to describe the entire culture, but, on the other, are more appropriate for the use of quantitative methods because of the possibility of using questionnaires, selecting respondents from sociologically defined classes, and subjecting individuals to a large number of physiologic tests, anatomic observations, etc., all of which are difficult in primitive societies.

The primary materials for this chapter are studies of primitive cultures or, in a few instances, literate cultures which have been studied by anthropologic methods, oral information, and observation. I will draw heavily on my own studies of six primitive groups in the South Pacific, one exotic literate culture (Bali), one American Indian tribe (the Omaha), and on a systematic attention, within an anthropologic frame of reference (Mead, 1949b; Gorer, 1948; Dollard, 1937; Kluckhohn and Kluckhohn, 1948; Warner, 1941–47) for materials on contemporary American cultural behavior.

[2] One point should be noted. Many, if not most, discussions of sexual behavior, including those in the clinical literature, deal with its physiology and ignore the processes whereby the many varieties of behavior are patterned. The latter is the moiety which, of necessity, has been the particular concern of anthropologists and to which their contribution is so important. "Of necessity," we have added, because nowhere in primitive peoples have there been opportunities for the collection of data bearing "on the physiology" of sexual behavior, i.e., tests of the strength or intensity of sexual desire, gonadectomy, replacement therapy, determination of hormonal levels, etc. Recognition that differences in the strength and duration of sex activity may have a predominantly physiologic basis, in contradistinction to a purely psychologic basis, appears to be given in this chapter by the reference to individual variation in the intensity of libido, and by the references to the "period of endocrine reinforcement of sex drives" (p. 00) and to the "triggering of sex drives into the expected pattern". The path by which animal experimentalists have also arrived at these conclusions, particularly the last conclusion, is traced in the chapter by Young.

II. Methods

The difficulties inherent in the study of sex behavior in any society are generally recognized, but they are complicated by additional factors when primitive peoples are studied, areas of taboo which cannot be breached in any case with safety, refusal of one or both sexes to undergo any form of physical examination, small numbers of cases, the width of the language barrier which has to be overcome, status differences between Caucasian investigator and the aboriginal peoples. From such materials negative statements on such matters as absence of homosexual behavior, or absence of knowledge of the procreative role of the father, can only be accepted with the greatest caution and with very careful analysis of the personality and training of the investigator.

One further general consideration must be advanced about the nature of the data we have on sexual behavior (Bateson, 1947). One characteristic of human sex behavior is the insistence on privacy. This privacy may be of many types; it may be only a demand that others who share the same dwelling may not be able to observe and there may be no objections to nonparticipants hearing what is going on. In certain very rare instances, the only demand for privacy may be that nonparticipants remain at a distance and ignore sex activities. But in most human societies, sex relations are conducted in such a way as to exclude witnesses other than couples or individuals who are engaged in comparable activities. This universal aspect of human sex behavior is variously linked with demands for privacy in connection with other bodily functions, such as eating, excretion, suckling, etc. Crawley (1927) gives an illuminating discussion of the incompatibility of different states of bodily urgency and involvement, either within the same individual or between individuals, so that human beings may be repelled either by the food that is left after hunger is satisfied or by the sight of others eating when they themselves are hungry and debarred from participation in the meal. These human tendencies have serious implications for research in the field of sex. Coupled with demands for privacy, there are found in almost every society whole areas of sex behavior which are characterized by gaps in awareness—taboos against naming parts of the body, taboos against verbalizing activities commonly engaged in, taboos against copulation in daylight or in a lighted room, etc. These gaps emphasize the intricacy of the systems of inhibition and expression which make up learned human sex behavior. In most societies, these gaps also provide areas where pornography, the socially disapproved stimulation of objectless erotic desire, can be developed (Mead, 1953).

The presence of unobservable areas of sex activity presents certain barriers to research which are very difficult to overcome. It is even impossible to make objective or systematic observations of those areas of sex activity which are approved of by a society, such as festivals where sexual license turns everyone into a participant and nonparticipation means enacting a role which is socially unacceptable. Those sex activities that can be observed are in some way in the class of the disapproved, i.e., because a disapproved element of voyeurism is included, as when married couples make moving pictures of themselves which will in turn serve as sexual precipitants for further activity. Re-enactment of sex positions both by children among primitive peoples (such as in those examples obtained by Malinowski, 1929) and by prostitutes is likely to contain elements of conscious or unconscious distortion. Drawings and carvings made for pornographic ends are equally unreliable as data on actual practice. So the student of sex behavior is thrown back upon verbal reports by individuals of activities in which they participated at some previous time under exciting circumstances that were exceedingly unconducive to rigorous observation and exact recording.

Even when it is possible to set the interviewing stage so that it seems sufficiently outside the culture to render ordinary cultural controls nonoperative, or to interview in a specially privileged communication pattern such as physician-patient, or to involve the cooperation of educated members of western societies who are disciplined in scientific methods and will honestly try to describe such matters as duration of inter-course or interval between intromission and ejaculation, these reports, although of scientific value as data on *attitudes* toward sex, have a limited value as accounts of exactly what does take place. Once time has elapsed, the type of retrospective falsification that accompanies all reports on matters of emotional interest to the reporter enters in. Studies of such reports on situations about which independent verification has been possible—self-reporting on dietary intake, mothers' reporting on their infants' achievements (Burks, 1928), or womens' records of menstrual rhythms, for example—have demonstrated how extraordinarily unreliable such restrospective reporting can be. If these considerations apply when we are judging the responses to interviews or questionnaires of the positively motivated members of modern western societies who believe the truth is essential if the physician or psychologist is to be able to advise them, the problem becomes much more difficult in dealing with members of non-European, nonliterate societies, many of whom believe that courtesy demands telling a questioner what he wants to hear. All statements about practices among people untrained in the idea that giving factual accounts of some event can be a moral obligation must be taken with additional caution.

These considerations make it possible to lay down some criteria for evaluating statements about sexual practices among any people, and particularly among people to whom factual reporting is unfamiliar. Denials of a practice cannot be regarded as meaningful if that practice is verbally recognized among a given people, even though a strong taboo exists against it. If a people consistently and independently express both amazement and disgust, or amazement and amusement at the mention of some sexual practice for which they have no name and against which they have no taboo, the probability is reasonably high that it is seldom practiced and then only as an individual discovery, not as an institution.

The matter of institutionalization is important; for example kissing (Nyrop, 1898), in the sense that it is known in the modern West, is relatively unknown either as a salutation or as a conventional piece of sexual foreplay in most of the rest of the world. If, however, any use of the lips exists, as in the sign of affection that is so frequent between mother and child in Oceania, in which the mother breathes lightly with parted lips along the surface of the child's forearm, then it may be expected that some mating pairs, on some occasions, will resort to related practices. This generalization has to be qualified by the possibility that whole areas of the body may be so involved in shame that they will be completely avoided, possibly in all mating for generations. A taboo such as the insistence on clothing or darkness (or on a rigorous separation between food ingestion and elimination) carries its own associated negations. On the other hand, all practices that are named and described with acceptance as something that everybody does, or something that young lovers do, may be accepted as practiced. Again, considerable caution is necessary to distinguish between formal, highly institutionalized statements of what should be done, and what is really done, which is often just as institutionalized in practice. This is so even when elders of the tribe are ritually required to supervise first intercourse, a fairly wide-spread practice in many parts of the world.

For example, in Samoa, a few girls of the families of highest rank (including the girl who bears the title of *taupou*, a titular village princess) were expected to be married in state, as virgins. The official chief orator of the bridegroom's household takes the tokens of virginity before the marriage is consummated, and a white sheet of bark cloth or a fine white mat stained with blood is hung outside the house the day after the wedding. The official version of this ceremony is that the bride who was thus publicly tested and proved not to be a virgin was beaten to death. The actual practice seems to have been that the bride who was not a virgin took pains to confess sufficiently ahead of time so that a proper supply of chicken blood could be provided. If she was ever beaten to death, it was not for not being a virgin, but for not taking precautions against publicly shaming her relatives. The actual behavior is congruent with Samoan culture in a way in which the official proclaimed behavior is not (Mead, 1928, 1960).

Thus even positive statements given in

detail by natives who claim to have been observers of or participants in occasions which the ethnographers cannot witness themselves must be viewed with great caution and subjected to the test of congruity with other aspects of the culture. This is especially true of such customs as bride capture, which may be *described* as a violent abduction of the bride as she screams for help, followed by a pitched battle between the kin of bride and groom, but which is in fact a carefully pre-arranged elopement in which the bride does a little ritual screaming (Bali, Bateson and Mead, 1942). As a field worker in areas where other westerners have lived, I have frequently had situations described to me in which the emotion attributed to the natives (fear, panic, horror, violence) turned out, when I had an opportunity to observe the same ceremony, to have been an emotion felt only by the western observer. The foreign observer may confuse his own and the native response, or, in the case of a bizarre occasion in which he is a participant, for example a postmortem cesarian in an open grave, he may be so horror stricken as to communicate his own feelings to the natives. As an interviewer he may convey by tone of voice expectations or anxieties which will influence the interview, or, through ignorance of the possibility of some nuance of behavior, pattern the response in such a way as to distort it. The respondent may relate events as they are theoretically supposed to have been, like a Victorian woman lamenting the fright she felt on her wedding night; the sexually impotent are notoriously good improvisors of nonexperienced ecstasies. Husbands and wives who have lived in close accord may collaborate in myths about their sexual relationship and repeat identical stories in good faith or, as careful check-ups have shown, two people who have participated in the same sexual event may relate wholly different stories, both of which cannot be accurate descriptions. Where a sexual experience has had a highly negative quality, extreme distortions may occur (Erickson, 1938).

No negative or absolute statements about practice can be made with safety. One can say, "No male member of the tribe questioned showed any recognition of female orgasm, and no word could be found for it; one woman described sex experience in such a way that it suggested that she had herself experienced orgasm, but she had no vocabulary for discussing it" (Arapesh, Mead, 1935). One may not say, "Oral stimulation *invariably* accompanied coitus among the Trukese" (Ford and Beach, 1951), or "The sexual performance of the mature woman results *regularly* in complete and satisfactory orgasm" (Ford and Beach, 1951). (Italics mine.)

A skilled investigator can get a reliable account of the known sex behavior to which each individual in the tribe relates his own behavior (either negatively or positively) and can make an estimate of frequency and probably kinds of deviation in terms of the pattern of distribution of other kinds of behavior which it is possible for him to observe. At a generous estimate, there are perhaps two dozen field workers who have both the necessary skills to do work on sex behavior as such and who have done such work. Comparative discussions thus have a choice between treating reports by the skilled and unskilled as comparable—the method chosen by Ford and Beach (1951) and Ford (1945)—and placing the widespread material we can trust (for instance, the explicit formulation of a taboo forbidding intercourse during lactation) with the few reliable studies which are available. The latter method would be equivalent to discussing nest building, knowing for many species of birds only that they build nests (with no details of the role of each sex, the stage in courtship when the nest was commenced, the conditions which would cause a mated pair to abandon the nest, etc.) and interpreting this sparse knowledge in the light of well described nest-building sequences for a few species. Although it would not be possible to extrapolate directly from the known detailed pattern to a species about which the details were unknown, it would be possible to construct hypotheses about the sorts of behavior one might expect to find in these other nest-building species (the way in which activities of the mating pair might be expected to have been triggered by internal stimuli, related to temperature and rainfall, etc.).

In what follows I shall attempt to provide a bridge between the specificity and detail of the Hampson and Hampson and the Money material and our own by discussing first the light cross cultural materials throw on psychologic sex gender and sex role assignment.[3] Intrasocietal studies, such as those which compare the behavior of middle class and lower class members of our own society, or behavior characteristic of various periods of our own history will only be introduced for theoretic purposes, where the cross cultural materials suggest a different interpretation from that which has been placed on them. The discussion will be introduced with a description of the materials, *i.e.*, the selected cultural patterns to which reference is made most frequently.

III. Materials (Selected Cultural Patterns)

An adequate treatment of the sex pattern of any human society, even the classless primitive society of a few hundred individuals, would involve a whole monograph. It

[3] In attempting to adjust existing cross cultural information on the patterning of sex behavior to the frame of reference provided by the Money and Hampson and Hampson chapters, two limitations must be borne in mind. These authors have confined themselves to the discussion of sex behavior as primarily copulatory behavior, with parental behavior subsumed as an aspect of psychologic sex, or learned sex role, and with early childhood experience bearing an acknowledged but unspecified relationship to later sexual functioning. Field workers who have attempted studies of primitive sex behavior have worked in a broader context; puberty rituals and pregnancy, birth and lactation behavior, at the least, have been specifically included within the study of sex behavior, and in most recent work the specific functions of types of child-rearing have also been included.

The second difficulty is that nowhere in primitive studies do we have determination of chromosomal, gonadal, and hormonal sex, or of somatotype constitutions of the individuals in the society whose sex behavior has been studied. Reports on transvestites can carry only impressionistic statements of mien and stance. The levels of hormonal functioning, the range of anatomic variation, and the specific characteristics of deviants cannot be provided. The single exception to these statements is the collection of somatotypes made on my last expedition among the Manus, in which the impressionistic impression of masculinity among the women is supported by analyses of the somatotypes (Tanner, Heath, Mead, Schwartz and Shargo, to be published; reference in Tanner and Inhelder, Vol. 3.)

must, furthermore, be realized that such information about reproductive and other sexual behavior must always be placed in a setting—size and type of population, technologic level, available food supply, etc. For example, many observers have reported that premarital sex relations are permitted in societies where, when the actual situation has been examined, it was found that there may be only one possible female mate for five unmarried young men, and that the actual practice of premarital love affairs is, in fact, a function of the size of the population (Goodenough, 1949). Age of marriage fluctuates with wars and depressions as do birth-rates; the survival of children and the spacing of children is closely related to the supply of food. It is only possible to indicate the range of subject matter about which it is necessary to have information before any statement can be made, and then to sketch in almost diagrammatically a few types of culture patterns for which this information is available, although it cannot all be given here.

Five illustrations have been selected for the following reasons. They are all based on modern work by field workers having a background of modern psychoanalytic and learning theory as well as training in modern American and British anthropologic methods. Two studies (the Siriono and the Lepchas) were done by men alone and three (Arapesh, Manus, and Bali) by a husband-and-wife team, with the bulk of the work on child-rearing and sex being done by the wife. Economically, they cover a wide span from a nomadic hunting people, a trading-fishing people, a sedentary people depending on horticulture, to the elaborate cultures of the Lepchas and the Balinese. These latter cultures contrast, however, because in one, the Lepchas, the complexities of Tibetan and Indian culture have been superimposed upon, without penetrating into, the culture of a people whose character structure and attitudes toward personal relations are as simple as those of the Arapesh or the Siriono, whereas among the Balinese the simplest peasants partake of the complexities of the series of imported cultures. Thematically, Siriono culture is focused on getting food, and Balinese on plastic elaborations of the human body in the form of art

and ceremonial. Specifically, as far as sex is concerned, the patterns vary from the ample indulgence provided by the system of potential spouses among Siriono and Lepchas, through the preference for affection and safety over passion displayed by the Arapesh, to the extreme prudery and devaluation of sex of the Manus, to the attenuation of sexual activity into a great variety of activities—art, gambling, trance —among the Balinese.

A. THE MOUNTAIN ARAPESH OF NEW GUINEA[4]

The Mountain Arapesh, a primitive people inhabiting the Torricellis Mountains of New Guinea, practice burn-and-slash agriculture, do a limited amount of hunting, depend on trade with other tribes for most of their tools, utensils, and ornaments, and purchase an immunity from physical attack by their more aggressive inland neighbors by providing hospitality to plainsmen traveling to and from the beach. Politically, they are organized in clusters of small hamlets within a patrilineal clan structure. Activities arising from intermarriage, *rites de passage*, gift giving, and so forth, are organized among groups of individuals, these activities being instigated and organized by individuals who have had leadership roles thrust upon them and on whom the others then depend. Conditions of life are hard, food is scarce, the protein intake is very inadequate, and members of the tribe who live under primitive conditions exist well below their potential energy output as compared with those who have had better food and care while working on plantations. They speak a multiple-gender language, make little use of abstractions, and are content to admire and trade for the superior artistic and utilitarian products made by other peoples. Warfare is limited to skirmishes between hamlets or clusters of hamlets in occasional conflicts over the elopement or theft of a woman. Giving and receiving food, help in obtaining food, and protection against sorcery arising from thefts of partly eaten food (and other exuviae) are principal themes throughout the culture.

[4] Based on field work done in 1932 (Mead, 1934b, 1935, 1938, 1947b, 1949b, c). The present tense refers to 1932.

From its earliest days, the Arapesh child experiences passive adaptation to the mother's body as it is carried in a string bag against her back or in a sling directly beneath the breast. It receives generous but increasingly unpredictable suckling, as mothers alternate day-long spells of relaxation, when their infants lie in their laps and are suckled almost continuously, with long journeys up and down steep hills carrying heavy loads suspended from their foreheads, when the infants are suspended in a sling beneath their breasts. If there are other lactating women in any small group, they will suckle the child while its mother is away; after menstrual seclusion is resumed, fathers also take care of young children. Children are carried a great deal and are discouraged from too much activity. For example, creeping is discouraged until a child has several teeth, and children who have learned to carry loads may still be tucked into their mothers' carrying bags when they are tired.

Betrothal occurs when the girl is five or six and the boy in early puberty, so that the girl may move into her future husband's household and he and his father and brothers may "grow" her. If age calculations have been faulty and the betrothed children are too close of an age, magic is resorted to in order to check the girl's growth; if this fails, she may be rebetrothed to some older boy in the betrothed's household, because premature sex activity is believed to stunt growth permanently. As feeding the child establishes parental rights to obedience, so feeding his future wife establishes for the bethrothed boy his right to exact obedience and service from his wife in later years. As soon as the first signs of puberty appear, boys and birls become guardians of their own growth, tabooing certain foods. The boys learn to let blood ceremonially from their penises, and following menarche (which is celebrated by a ceremony in which the betrothed pair ceremonially divides a yam, one-half of which the husband keeps until his wife is pregnant) the girls are taught to rub themselves with stinging nettles and to thrust a rolled stinging nettle into the vagina. These practices, believed to promote growth, are painful and seem to act effectively as deterrants

of masturbation. During this period of pubertal growth, the antithesis between growth and sex is heavily emphasized; after the girl has menstruated several times, her young husband may approach her, consummating the marriage privately without ceremony, but watching carefully to see if his hunting or gardening is affected, in which case he must postpone further sex relations longer. A young couple who have begun sex relations must protect their parents from any contact with their sexuality—as in giving them food from a fire by which they have had intercourse—just as their parents once protected them. The preferred sex activity is thus with a younger wife whom one has "grown" and who has become almost like a member of the family, whereas seduction by stranger women is feared, because it is believed that they will steal some of a man's semen and use it to sorcerize him and, in any event, are bound to endanger him in every sort of way. Orgasm for women is not recognized, but close questioning indicates that an occasional woman seems to have had some climactic experience.

Male ceremonial, which centers about a cult of supernatural patrons (tamberans) into which adolescent boys are initiated in infrequently held ceremonies for large groups or in small ceremonies for individuals, is an elaborate pantomine in which the men make the children (who before this have been made of the blood of the women) into their children, feeding them on blood drawn from the arms of the initiating group. In the initiatory enclosure, the initiates are fed, tended, and grown, the men enacting ceremonially the birth sequence, which they speak of as the "women's tamberan."[5] Women, in addition to being excluded from these ceremonies for their own protection, must avoid sacred places presided over by serpent deities (marsalai); menstruating women or men who have recently engaged in intercourse anger the marsalai and the yams; anything connected with marsalais endangers the pregnant woman, as also do

[5] See Mead (1949b) for an analysis of these ceremonial elaborations of womb envy in New Guinea cultures.

yams. The entire ritual cycle[6] stresses a basic dichotomy between sex on the one hand and food and growth on the other.

Intercourse, before a cessation of the menses indicates the beginning of impregnation, is regarded as play, but once a pregnancy is indicated, the married pair has to copulate assiduously to build up the fetus from semen and blood. Once the child is regarded as established (indicated by discoloration of the breasts), intercourse is forbidden to the expectant mother; the father may still have relationships with another wife. There is no recognition of "life" in the fetus, which is believed to sleep peacefully until the moment of birth when it puts its hands by its sides and dives out.

Males are forbidden to witness birth; the birth must take place over the edge of the village, which is situated on a hilltop, in the "bad place" also reserved for excretion, menstrual huts, and foraging pigs. The mother is attended by the woman who has most recently given birth, recency of experience being regarded as more important than age or skill. Only the mother, who sits during childbirth on a specially prepared bark basin, may touch the child and that with a protective leaf; if she picks up the child with her left hand, it will be left-handed. The father stays within earshot, and when told the sex of the child he gives the signal to save it or to let it die by saying "Wash it" or "Do not wash it." In the case of female children, especially if there is already a young female child in the household, the decision may be made not to keep the child. This decision is viewed as protective in not putting too great a strain on mother and siblings. Also, girls are less preferred because "they will marry away, while a boy stays with his relatives always." When the afterbirth has been expelled and gathered up to be placed in a tree so that pigs will not eat it, the mother goes up to the village and lies down with the new infant placed at her breast. The next morning, father and mother are installed together in a house on the ground, for the birth contamination is still too great for the mother and child to enter the regular dwelling, which is raised on piles, and the

father lies down beside the mother in a modified form of the observance technically called *couvade*. Ceremonies to ensure the safe growth of the child are performed. The father takes a long peeled rod, brought in by one of his brothers' wives (the official nurses of the child), and calls in some of their older children who are loitering about. He rubs the rod over their strong backs and then rubs it against the infant's back reciting a charm: "I give you vertebrae, one from a pig, one from a snake, one from a human being, one from a tree snake, one from a python, one from a viper, one from a child." He breaks the rod into six small pieces and hangs them in the house so that, should his foot break a twig as he walks about, the infant's back will not be hurt.

Child begetting is regarded as being just as exhausting for men as for women, in terms of the arduous copulation necessary to accomplish the initial impregnation and the work of feeding children after they are born. Until the child is weaned, the father is expected to sleep beside mother and child and abstain from intercourse with the child's mother and with his other wife or wives also. The child needs the protection of his father's presence to grow, and parents later in life will reproach children, whose behavior they deplore, by emphasizing how long they kept these protective taboos which are mentioned in the same breath with working sago, growing yams, and hunting to provide food for the child's later growth. There is a special ceremony for the reappearance of the menses, which adolescent boys think corresponds to the resumption of intercourse, but the taboo should be kept until the child can walk. Parents whose children are too closely spaced feel guilty before community gossip.

The incest taboo is phrased as "Your own mother, your own sister, your own pigs, your own yams which you have piled up, you may not eat." Those who have been in contact with birth, puberty, sex, or death are in a state from which they must protect themselves by taking great precautions about food. The ideal male personality, like the ideal female personality, is parental, cherishing, intent on growing things—a young wife, a child, food—unaggressive, reluctant to take the initiative, responsive

[6] The rituals are analyzed in detail in Mead (1940).

rather than initiating, a role into which both some males and some females find it difficult to fit. Aggression between males is handled by strong dependent attachments between little boys and older male relatives, whom they help with hunting and gardening, and by a very early retirement from competition of the young adult men who take over the role of looking for wives for younger male relatives with whom they might otherwise have competed. In social organization, in handling the occasional fights, in sex activity, the phrasing is always one of responsiveness, leading because one is asked to lead, helping another to build a house or dig a garden, throwing a spear because one's cousin has been wounded, responding to direct seduction from the strange woman. Attitudes strongly stressed in early childhood prevail through life. Habit patterns of dependency, responsiveness, and low aggression, and a preference for warm domestic contacts rather than for violent or passionate ones are developed early in life and are expressed in almost every facet of the culture. This degree of internal consistency can only be obtained in very small societies in a culture area like New Guinea, which has very low levels of political organization, a high amount of continuous trait diffusion, and a dependence for cultural integration on emotional consistency rather than on political forms.

B. THE MANUS OF THE ADMIRALTY ISLANDS

The Manus tribe,[7] a group of about the same size as the Arapesh (about 2500 people) lived in houses raised on stilts in the salt lagoons off the south coast of the Great Admiralty Island, northeast of New Guinea, and subsisted on fishing and trading. When first observed by Europeans, the Manus, like the Arapesh, had only stone tools, no system of writing, and no political forms capable of integrating more than about 200 people for any length of time. As among the Arapesh, trade was conducted in a framework of affinal ties within the community, and some manufactured objects were im-

[7] All descriptions as of 1928–29 (Mead, 1930, 1934b, 1949b; Fortune, 1935). Later field work, 1953 (Mead, 1956) not included, but because of the great transformation since 1946 I have used the past tense here.

ported from other groups. Where the Arapesh were able to offer hospitality to travelers who would otherwise have been burdened down with food for the journey, the Manus contribution to the economy of some 13,000 people of the Admiralty Islands was a more active one. In their large ocean-going canoes they undertook many voyages, transporting the various specialized products of different groups from one island to another, combining fishing, which provided a surplus which they traded for raw products of garden and forest, with a middleman role through which they themselves were well supplied with every variety of tool, utensil, and ornament which the entire archipelago provided.

Where Arapesh family life emphasized warmth and diffuseness of response to all relatives, Manus life, which also included early betrothal, sharply differentiated among four classes of persons: relatives with whom one was at ease, relatives with with whom joking and license were permitted, affinal relatives to whom one owed respect and in some cases complete avoidance of any contact, and sex partners—husband and wife, and captors and war captive prostitutes, both of which were relationships involving disrespect and hostility. Children grew up in a world in which time and space, number and quantity, categories and classification were important, speaking a bare and accurate language, learning to climb, swim, handle fire, report accurately on past events, and respond with precision and initiative to the natural world.

From the moment of betrothal, little girls of seven or eight or sometimes a little older were subjected to rigorous supervision, wrapping themselves in raincapes to hide their faces from their betrothed or their future male relatives-in-law, giving up the gay excursions with their fisherman fathers, who took them about with them into men's groups until their betrothal shut them off in an avoidance enforced by shame. Boys at a slightly older age were also bound by these same taboos, but where the taboos operated to segregate a girl who had been active and attached to her father, they simply served to keep the boys more away from women's groups and more intensely occupied in their own world, which before marriage included one-sex groups only, unless a war-captured prostitute was in the village.[8] For the girl, the long, dull, incessantly chaperoned period between betrothal, which ended her childhood, and marriage was broken by one bright event, menarche, which men believed to be the only time a woman menstruated without having had intercourse. All the girls of the same age stayed with the just-nubile girl for a month, and the house party ended with a ceremonial in which she was blessed by a paternal aunt, so:

May fire be to her hand,
May she kindle forehandedly the fire of
   her mother-in-law,
In the house of the noble one who receives
   the exchange,
May she blow the house fire,
Providing well for the funeral feast, the
   marriage feast, the birth feast,
She shall make the fire swiftly,
Her eyes shall see clearly by its light.

Then the group of girls, dressed in skirts of money which would also be used for bridal costumes and marriage ceremonies, paraded the village, leaving fire and food on the doorstep of the nubile girl's relatives.

The boy's parallel ceremony was individual. At puberty his ears were pierced and he went through a period of ritual seclusion, when an older paternal relative pronounced a charm over him, so:

The mouth turn toward shell money
The shell money is not plentiful
Let the taro turn the mouth toward it,
Toward plentifulness,
Toward greatness.

Let it become the making of great economic
   transactions.
Let him overhaul and outstrip the others,

May he become rich in dog's teeth,
Attaining many
Toward the attainment of much shell money ...

Thus the attainment of sexual puberty became the occasion for stressing the principal value of the society, the industrious pursuit of wealth which was to be used continuously in transactions. The boy's charm goes on:

Let him become rich,
Let him walk within the house, virtuously,

---

[8] This practice was forbidden by government in 1928 but was still vividly remembered.

He must not walk upon the center board
   of the house floor,
He must call out for an invitation (to enter)
He must call out announcing his arrival to
   women,
That they may stand up to receive him.

Absolute circumspection of sexual behavior at all times from youth to age was demanded of women under all circumstances and of men except where women from another tribe were involved. Sometimes a captured woman was kept as a prostitute. In this case, the men had to take the prostitute, who was regarded as the property of her captor who hired her services to others, with them wherever they went, lest the women of the village kill her.

Each house was presided over by the ghost of the most recently dead male member who prospered the fishing and the trade and protected the health of his household members as long as they practiced impeccable moral behavior (which included even refraining from gossip about sexual matters) and worked with unflagging industry. Illness, which most frequently took the form of malaria, was regarded as a punishment for some moral defection or economic omission, often very slight, which must be confessed and atoned for by more hard work. People were active, nervous, and driving and lived under great tension. Men died before their eldest sons had children; women were as active and tense as men, playing a vigorous role in economic affairs.

The society grouped together its principal preoccupations, sexual morality for its female members and incessant wealth-getting activities. Several years after puberty, depending almost entirely on the financial exigencies of the older men who were financing the marriage exchanges, the young couple were married. The ceremonies were elaborate and were focused on bringing the over-adorned, property-laden bride into the household of her hostile female relatives-in-law. The bridegroom, overcome with shame, fled from the scene. Consummation of the marriage was expected to take the form of rape, the hymenal bleeding being regarded as first menstruation, whereas menarche was regarded by the men as a ruptured vein. Women were so carefully schooled in shame that they did not know that the men did not know that they menstruated between menarche and marriage. Before a child was born, the married pair were uneasy and uncomfortable. They seldom talked together, they never ate together. The young man felt abased by his position of servitude to his financial backer; the young wife lived miserably under the eyes of her mother-in-law. Both turned toward their own relatives, from whom they expected affection and support. Often the young wife ran away. When she became pregnant she might not tell her husband but instead told her own kindred, who prepared the first of the birth exchange feasts and brought it to the door. When her child was born, she was under the care of her brother in either his house or hers, and the husband was banished from the scene for a month or more. When later children were born, the "knee baby" became permanently attached to the father, with whom it stayed. The mother was granted a month's respite, alone with her child, whom she might care for all day. Then, amid bickering and economic calculating, she was returned to her husband. The infant was not taken out of the house until it could hold on to its carrier; from this time on the father began to take the child away from the mother. He presided officiously over the way his child, the child of *his* spirits (although biologic paternity was recognized, it was not regarded as important), was fed, insisting on the milk itself rather than the suckling. In an ideal marriage, husband and wife were equally matched in intelligence, having engaged in common economic enterprises, and had two children, one to sleep with the father, the other with the mother. Early childhood training focused on control and assertiveness; the child was taught to hold on to the back of the adult's neck, even when the adult fell, to climb, swim, and rigorously control its sphincters. Sexual taboos centered about the heterosexual activities of the women; other forms of sex activity, masturbation and one-sex play, were shrouded in shame but were not sinful. In women's gossip, intercourse was described as acutely painful until after the first child was born, and then the most that a woman hoped for was sufficient lubrication so that intercourse would not be too painful.

The Manus had succeeded in building and maintaining a culture with a high standard of living. They were well fed, enjoying the fruits of the toil of all their neighbors; they disciplined each generation by breaking the mother-child tie early, and they insisted on physical adequacy, but gave little place to the pleasures or the graces of life. Finery was worn at puberty and marriage ceremonies and at ceremonies after birth, but as a daily costume only for mourning. The highest expression of affection was between brother and sister: "She works hard for him, he brings food to her, she weeps for him when he dies." Congruently enough, we found in Manus an early death age for males, frequent enuresis in children, prostitution, and hoboes—men who refused to conform to the exactions of this grim, efficient society.

C. THE SIRIONO OF EASTERN BOLIVIA[9]

The Siriono are a very primitive, semi-nomadic people of Eastern Bolivia, who live a rigorous and deprived life under extreme environmental conditions. They live in bands within which extended families act as the effective economic unit, whereas the band (a group of something less than a hundred people) provides an almost closed social milieu within which young people find mates. Their marriage system is one in which all mother's brothers' daughters and other women in the same classificatory relationship are potential wives. The band, from which small nuclear families or large extended families occasionally wander away for days or weeks, camps together in one large, badly built lean-to constructed around tree trunks. Hammocks are suspended from the trees, and each family has its own space between the hammocks for building a fire. The Siriono are primarily hunters, although they also do considerable food collecting and practice a little supplementary agriculture in temporary camping sites which provide some food, for which they do not have adequate storage arrangements. As the group is almost continuously on the move wandering in search of game, with 4- or 5-day halts, there is little possibility of accumulating food, even though both sexes carry loads of 60 or 70 pounds. Fire is carried from camp to camp, but they have lost the art of fire-making

[9] Based on field work done in 1940–41 by Holmberg (1950).

and will undergo extreme hunger rather than eat raw food. Each man hunts for his own family and his extended family, within a pattern of continued importunity from others which leads to many types of avoidance of food-giving, leaving game in the bush, hiding food, eating surreptitiously at night.

The rhythm of life is determined by the seasons. During the very wet season the group remains stationary and eats little meat, depending for food on the ripening of small garden plots. When wild honey is available it is used for making a mead which is the basis of the 10 or 12 drinking parties a year that provide the only amusement and usually end in a brawl. Life is so organized that men hunt only when they have no meat; as soon as they find meat, they substitute rest in camp for the arduous 15- to 20-mile trek through the insect-ridden, thorn-infested jungle. Although the people wear no clothes, cotton is grown for thread and string, and feathers and animal teeth are used extensively as ornaments. The only weapon is a bow and arrow, the bow being the longest in the world, and the principal tool is a sharpened digging stick. Crude pots are made, one usually sufficing for each family. There is continual in-group quarreling and aggression, but no warfare among the bands, who respect one another's territory and occasionally intermarry, a practice which is discouraged by uxorilocal residence, because a man who marries into another band goes away to live and hunt for his parents-in-law. The religious system consists of an unsystematic set of food taboos (most of which are violated whenever conditions become too rigorous), the separation of age from youth, automatic supernatural penalties for breaking the incest prohibition, which includes all the women in the band except the group of potential spouses, vague fears of the spirits of people who have been evil and difficult during their lives, and a vague hope that the spirits of the good relatives, of whom their preserved skulls are representative, may be somewhat helpful. Political organization is limited to the institution of a single hereditary leader, who should excel the others, who has the right to the center of the house, and who

may, if he personally commands respect, be accorded a few other privileges. Property is limited to those things which an individual has made or collected. There is little inheritance, because intimate belongings are destroyed at death.

Hunting is the central economic theme. The camp is moved in relation to hunting grounds; gardens are planted to sustain hunting parties; prestige is based on hunting ability; a good hunter may have several wives; meat is valued above any other food; and a man who is angry works off his anger by going hunting. The Siriono have a detailed knowledge of the wild life of the forest, including a specialized skill in imitating bird and animal cries, the cry of the young for its mother or a creature for its mate, to bring the quarry within arrow shot. On the hunt they communicate with each other by a sort of codified whistling.

Essentially a forest people, they eke out a living which never fails entirely because of some poorly nutritious foods which are ubiquitous, but they lead a poor, hardworking, miserable life and they are frequently hungry and never sure of the next week's meals. The rain pours through their wretched shelters, thorns scratch and tear at their naked bodies, little children have to walk long distances, and the sick and dying must be abandoned, their bones left for the vultures to pick. Small children very early undergo the cares and pains of life, and even before puberty both boys and girls assume the full burdens of adulthood.

In contrast to their low level of technology and poor provision for food and shelter, sex expression is well provided for. As a man has access both before and after marriage to all of his potential wives, among whom are included his wives' sisters and his brothers' wives, there is little difficulty in finding a sex partner, even though there may occasionally be no appropriate woman for a wife. Children are betrothed early and sex relations begin before marriage. Girls are eligible for sex relations as soon as a special ceremony (which may occur before the actual occurrence of menarche) has been performed. Marriage, the decision of the betrothed pair to set up housekeeping, is marked by no ceremonial whatsoever except the moving of the young husband's hammock from his parents' hammock space to that of his parents-in-law.

Some time later, after the wife has borne a child, both partners are eligible to participate in a ceremony of mutual ritual bloodletting, believed to have a rejuvenative effect. At this ceremony the old blood is let out through a series of punctures made in the flesh of the arms; there is much drinking, old pots are thrown away, ritual food taboos are observed, and hunting is facilitated, it is said, because the animals come near the house to watch the men decked out in feathers and red paint and to hear them sing. This is the only important ceremony in the lives of the Siriono.

During menstruation, women go about the house as usual and can cook, but intercourse is not practiced. Cessation of the menses is recognized as a sign of pregnancy, although swelling of the breasts is believed to be a more reliable sign; morning sickness is not recognized. The relationship between intercourse and pregnancy is recognized, and in the postbirth ceremonial the potential husbands with whom the mother has had relations are decorated together with the husband who will acknowledge his social paternity by cutting the umbilical cord of the child. During pregnancy, the mother observes a number of food taboos, and the father is more strict in tabooing foods reserved for the aged. Intercourse, continued right up to delivery, is believed to stimulate the growth of the child, which is said from the time of conception to be a miniature replica of an infant. When labor begins, the father goes hunting to discover the name of the child, which is named after his first quarry. The mother gives birth alone, in a hammock beneath which she has placed ashes and soft earth onto which the child can fall. Inmates of the house of all ages, but mostly women, gather about and gossip but give no help. The cutting of the cord awaits the father's return. The mother gathers up blood and afterbirth, bathes the baby, gives it the breast, and sits for some hours on the ground before re-entering the hammock. Both father and mother then observe various ritual taboos for three days. On the day after birth each parent in turn stands wearing a newly woven baby sling and is scarified and painted. On this day the infant's forehead is depilated and its eyebrows are removed, an excruciatingly painful event which will be repeated at intervals all its life. On the second day, the parents are decorated with feathers. The couvade is ended when the family (including other children and co-wives) takes a short ceremonial journey into the forest to gather firewood and on the return trip sprinkles ashes and water on the trail.

Infancy is said to be the only secure, unhungry period through which a Siriono passes. With their inadequate techniques, it is only the breast-fed infant, supported in a sling, small enough to be protected from the forest, which can be given any sort of security or freedom from hunger. No fuss is made about toilet training. Small children are permitted to urinate in the house; not until they are about three do they learn to go outside the house by themselves, and then the mother accompanies them and wipes them until they are five or six. (Adults retire to some distance in the daytime, but excrete just outside the shelter at night, avoiding the frightening, insect-ridden, dangerous forest.)

Darkness draws a dividing line between public and private behavior in other respects as well. Except in the dark of night, intercourse takes place in the forest. People eat at night so as to prevent others from seeing them and so as to avoid the hungry importunities of the group which forms around anyone who has food, composed of the continuously hungry children who beg for tidbits and of the old begging for enough food to sustain a few more days of life. Food is a continual preoccupation. People quarrel over food and dream about food, women are seduced by food and rewarded by presents of food, and wives object to their husbands' amours because they divert food from the family larder. A man leaves the shelter pursued by admonitions to bring back food, and returns successful to be greeted warmly and after eating to enjoy a bath and sex intercourse or, if unsuccessful, to be scolded for his failure.

All close relationships except those of parents toward a young infant are heavily tinged with aggression interspersed with grooming. Mothers groom their children, hunt for ticks, pluck out thorns; lovers spend hours together in mutual grooming combined with scratching and pinching, poking fingers into each others' eyes, gluing feathers on each others' hair, and painting each other with red paint. This pattern of aggression runs all through. Children are allowed to strike and abuse their parents; older children poke at the eyes and pinch the genitals of younger children, and this practice is repeated with the dying to ascertain whether they are really dead. In the small boys' play groups, in which they are practicing hunting skills, severe wounds are sometimes dealt each other.

The whole pattern of life is very much what one might expect if a society were constructed by a group of hungry, neglected, undisciplined, just-adolescent children. The alliances which do exist are based on necessity; reciprocity must always be enforced; all members of the group not immediately concerned in an event act as unhelpful, greedy, and jeering spectators. These attitudes are exemplified in the drinking party at which the uninvited cluster about the edges waiting until the participants get so drunk that a drink can be stolen, while the women squat about waiting for the inevitable wounds, meanwhile gloating over the brawling, or in the plight of an unmarried man lost near camp at nightfall for whom no one would venture out. Yet, like the refugee children who have grown up in concentration camps, they are capable of forming alliances, of observing minimal ties of loyalty to sex partner and child, and of protecting and even indulging young children. Considering their desperately depriving environment, their poor technology and low elaboration of life, and their early demands on adolescent children, the rules governing sex behavior are such as to preserve the cohesion of the group and yet allow a large amount of permitted gratification, which Holmberg believes serves as a cushion against the frustration involved in their precarious food situation. Satisfactory and easy sex relations may also account for durability of the ties between parents and children and between siblings, who in adult-

hood share spouses with relative lack of conflict. The extremely early access to women may account in part for the lack of responsible effort and the fact that they have fled from neighboring tribes rather than learned from them.

D. THE BALINESE[10]

Bali is not a primitive society, but a complex traditional culture, with courts and kings, writing, money, and iron tools, the potter's wheel, and animal-drawn plows. Before the conquest of Bali by the Netherlands, a conquest which lasted until Bali became part of Indonesia, the Balinese numbered less than a million people. The economy was based on rice agriculture, and the rice diet was supplemented by fish, vegetables, and a limited amount of meat as garnish. Successive waves of religious influence from Hinduism and Buddhism, economic influence from China, and political conquest by Java had swept over an island with a basically Indonesian population speaking a Malay language. A caste system derivative from India was superimposed on the great bulk of the population who were regarded as casteless rather than outcast people. The society was highly organized in villages with traditional law, peculiar to each village and centuries old. The court of the rajahs and the religious palace and judicial courts connected with the rajahs exacted various forms of tribute from peasants who were regarded as related to them, but on the whole each village maintained its own equilibrium within a continuous impersonal contact, organized around large markets, traveling theatrical companies and religious officiants of all types, and intervillage gambling centering around cockfighting. The arts, especially orchestral music, the dance, and the theatre, were highly developed; religious ceremonial involved the construction of thousands of beautiful perishable objects from flour, leaves, and flowers. The people moved with a relaxed, dream-like quality most of the time and filled their hours with almost in-

[10] Based on field work by Gregory Bateson, Jane Belo, Colin McPhee, and myself, done principally in the 1930's. For a comprehensive bibliography. see Mead (1949b), p. 427 et seq.

cessant, unhurried activity of some sort, seldom acknowledging or showing any fatigue. Religious trance was highly developed and appears to provide an alternative form of expression to excellence in one of the arts; individuals or villages specialized in trance or in painting, sculpture, or music. Within an intricate pattern of festival and religious observance, every member of the society was involved in varieties of artistic and ritual experience.

There is so much variation in Bali between village and village and between caste and caste, that it will be possible only to indicate a few widespread emphases and themes.[11] The Balinese infant is carried all its waking hours by mother, father, child nurse, amused female relative, or neighbor. Secured high on the hip by a cloth sling · or supported by an arm which functions like a sling, the child learns to move with a flexible, relaxed rhythm, adjusting to the activities of its carrier, who may be pounding rice, making offerings, or (if the carrier is a child) playing a vigorous running game or having a temper tantrum. Before the child can walk, its hands are manipulated into ritual and dance positions; before it can talk, elaborate courtesy phrases are uttered in its name. It is treated as a delightful animate toy to be teased, provoked into smiles or tears, frightened into a return from any venture far from its protectors by terrible unreal threats. At 7 months the child, although already showing some signs of withdrawal, is a gay little monarch who is spoiled (as are also rajahs and gods) by its attendants, who carry it high where it can see all that goes on, who participates in every audience and who on its own volition leans over to take the full breast of its mother or some other nursing woman, or the dry breast of a young girl, an old grandmother occasionally, or its father.

As the child reaches 2 or 3, the constant teasing and stimulation, which is never allowed to come to a real climax because the mother turns away from the child's rage or ardor, is met by increasing unresponsiveness. The latter, accompanied by tempestuous misery at the birth of a new baby, is muted only by the number of times in which sibling rivalry has been theatrically enacted with borrowed babies. As third child from the bottom, the 5- or 6-year old becomes a child nurse, watching a new baby, its own charge, dispossess the younger child who dispossessed it. Little girls continue on into puberty as child nurses, combining play and work and slightly antagonistic encounters with the gangs of little boys, who are sent off to the fields, each with a machete and a cow or water buffalo to care for, and who occasionally turn up at ceremonies or theatricals, wild, dirty, and unkempt, until one by one, as puberty sets in, they begin to join the older unmarried youths and seek out girls for themselves. Children of both sexes have experienced much genital play from adults; little boys conduct contests in urinating in the middle of the village street. In the theatrical performances, children see child-birth, played by male actors, in which the newborn is killed by witches, but children actually exposed to childbirth go sound asleep out of fear, as do the Balinese in other experiences of strain, such as waiting for a sentence from a court, a decision of a purchaser, etc.

Young adolescents of both sexes are highly sophisticated about sex, knowing the jokes, the innuendo, the gay plots of the theatre in which the prince in the end is tricked and must marry the ugly sister who looks like a mother or a mother-in-law. Love affairs are conducted by exchanges of glances, and both for adolescents and in later amorous encounters, the moment of highest excitement is the first glance, when "they look at each other like two fighting cocks." The strange is more exciting than the familiar. Weddings are punctuated with elaborate jokes about the expected indifference and therefore impotence of the bridegroom.

Among the high castes hausp-arranged marriages were occasions of great ceremony; the bride might be wrapped as a corpse, laid out in an inner room with a group of women around her while she lay for hours as if

---

[11] I have used the past tense for those practices which were becoming obsolete in 1936–1939 and where changes have occurred, accompanying the establishment of the Republic of Indonesia.

dead. Once her noble husband, as he cut
open the white cloth, gave her a present
of land or jewels, as he saw each part of her
body for the first time. The courts were
organized elaborately with many wives, the
newest and most beautiful just pubescent
little girl dancers, and with a variety of
homoerotic and substitutive practices. Court
and theatre alike provided spectacles of
great secondary elaboration of sex. In the
villages the young people eluded their elders,
who were divided into two groups, the serious and the naughty, vicariously permis-
sive; parents attempted to plan the appropriate marriage, between the children of
brothers, so that property was kept in the
family; all but the most submissive usually
arranged their own marriages, the girls
concealing menstruation as long as possible
for fear of being married off. Many marriages followed pregnancies, ritualized by
postconsummation ceremonies, the most
complicated of which might be postponed
for years.

After marriage, husband and wife lived
lives of graceful avoidance, one attending a
feast or ceremony, the other staying at
home, one on the farm, one in the village.
Eating together is not extensively practiced
except at large feasts in which everyone is
very embarrassed; the streets of even small
villages are filled with vendors' stalls where
old and young go for snacks. The people enjoy groups, the crowded streets, the audience
at a play, the great crowds at a cremation
where ceremonies which take months to prepare, attempt, always in vain, finally to get
rid of the earthly body, itself merely a temporary dwelling for a reincarnated spirit.
Burial and cremation ceremonies stress the
preoccupation with the body, as do trance
and the high development of the plastic arts.

Bali may be regarded as a society in
which individuals' responses to their own
bodies have been highly developed whereas
their relationships to others have been
muted during childhood, so that the theatrical enactment is preferred to actuality; both
old bachelors and old maids are found, and
all sorts of social and religious penalties
are directed against the unmarried, the bar-
ren, and the parents of girls only. It was a
culture in which excessive early sexual preoccupation was met by a series of symbolic

forms of expression which seemed adequate
enough to preserve most of the population
in a balanced contentment, gay, impersonal,
artistically creative.

The worst oath was the word *leprosy*
which was terribly feared, particularly because young girls in the first stages were regarded as having particularly beautiful skin;
the worst ceremonial crimes (for there is no
sin in our sense of the word) were zoolagnia,
incest (widely interpreted), bearing twins of
opposite sex, and sex relations with a woman
of higher caste. From such events the community had to be purified by prolonged ceremonial, and the offenders were banished
to lands of punishment, with ceremonial
and without expressions of anger. The very
infrequent crimes were either theft—and a
thief caught red-handed was killed at once,
after the entire political community was
summoned—or murder, usually committed
after running amok or without any pre-
meditation at all. An existence of mutual
nonresponsiveness, dependence on ritual
and calendrical rhythm, was thus occasionally punctuated by sudden unexplained
small acts of violence. When the Dutch
troops came to take over the southern part of
the island, the rajah and his entire court
went out to be shot down by the Dutch guns,
and when the Dutch soldier's hands paused
before the carnage, they turned their krisses
against themselves. In groups, where they
can sleep in close contact or sit leaning
against each other, the Balinese can go great
distances from their villages, or even from
Bali, but an individual taken away alone becomes frightened and ill. Individuals when
tested showed many schizoid elements, yet
they functioned as members of their communities, planting their rice fields, painting,
carving, acting, officiating, within a view of
life in which virgin children and old people
are closest to heaven, those of reproductive
age farthest away.

E. THE LEPCHAS OF SIKKIM[12]

The Lepchas are a Mongoloid people who
once inhabited the greater part of Sikkim
and are now limited in any pure form to a
few small communities on very rough and
precipitous land reserved and governed by

[12] Based on field work done in 1937 by Geoffrey
Gorer (1938). Present tense as of 1937, present conditions unknown.

officials responsible to the Maharajah. They are exploited by Indian money lenders and are increasingly dependent on imported objects such as cloth. From an examination of some historic sources and of the three parallel religions which exist side by side, it is conjectured that the Lepchas once lived isolated lives as hunters and food gatherers with a little primitive agriculture; they were harassed by slave raiders and only settled into larger communities when the area was pacified. Growing cardamum seed for trade is a recent adjustment to the money lenders who exploit their willingness to replace with imported goods products based on difficult handicrafts.

An external analysis of Lepcha culture would describe it as very complex. Money is used; the lamas (Mahayana Buddhists) learn to read the sacred texts; there is a variety of domestic animals, oxen, goats, pigs, and hens; oxen are used for plowing; houses are built on stone supports and have a somewhat complicated architecture; people wear tailored clothing, in the main similar for both sexes; the customary paraphernalia of peasants in the Far East who live in relation with higher authorities is present, a courtesy language, taxation, centrally deputized power to preserve law and order, and so forth.

Although the activities which would classify the Lepchas as members of a complex culture take up a great deal of time in an endless round of recurrent lamaistic feasts, *rites de passage*, and hard and continuous agricultural work, on inspection the Lepchas prove to be a very simple people who have preserved the attitudes and behavior patterns appropriate to a much less complicated way of life. Remnants of hunting behavior, with a bow and poisoned arrows, still exist. Two religious cults are practiced parallel to lamaism; the beliefs are often contradictory, and where the contrast is too great parallel practices develop; in the conflicting beliefs between a life after death which is a better version of this life and the lamaistic belief in reincarnation, lamas and nuns are treated in one way at death, laymen in another. For both the lamas and the practitioners of the earlier cult, ritual is rigidly in the hands of professionals, leaving the rest of the population free to feast and gossip while ceremonial goes on.

The model on which Lepcha expectations about human relationships are built is the 4-generation household containing some 16 or more members. A man who has slowly attained self-assurance and authority presides over the household, and young men who are themselves diffident and dependent work for it. The young daughters-in-law, who come from outside the community in most cases, are the most put upon and unhappy, and young children are treated kindly but ambivalently as a present expense and burden and a possible dangerous menace in case they die in childhood. Within such a household and within a group of such households, which form a community of houses scattered over the mountainsides and ceremonially focused on a monastery, competition is muted. Young men have sexual access to wives of their elder brothers and of the father's younger brothers, whereas elder brothers have to observe the strictest incest taboo toward their younger brothers' wives, so that within the family the extremes of permission and taboo are present. Marriages are arranged by go-betweens. Childhood, seen as the period when children are learning to work, is followed by a period of sexual freedom except within incest relationships (counted to 9 generations on the father's side and 4 on the mother's) and by an early betrothal for a marriage in which both partners may be unwilling but into which, after 2 or 3 years of difficulty, they are expected to settle down after the first child is born. The birth of the first child results in a name change for the group, the parents and grandparents assuming the name of "the parent of X," "the grandparent of X," and so forth. Cooperative work under the leadership of the housefather, within the household presided over by the housemother, is expected to provide enough materials for a continuously generous diet of food and drink (a beer brewed from rice or millet), enough for abundant sacrifices to the gods and frequent hearty feasting. At the feasts, enormous amounts of food and drink are consumed, people become loud mouthed and gaily obscene, but quarreling is guarded against.

This model for a happy life is seriously interfered with by the very high sterility rate and the uneven death rate, so that families are small rather than large, young boys may be left responsible for 4 or 5 dependent women or children, or old men or women be left with no one to care for them in their old age. The poverty and burden of hard work which accompanies such inequalities, natural disasters, particularly rain and hail, and finally death, to which their response is a series of ceremonies to get rid of the dead as thoroughly as possible, are the principal blemishes on a way of life which otherwise demands little except food, drink, sex, and warm unintense friendliness and tolerant respect from others, all of which the cultural arrangements are adequate to supply.

Sex relations with one's betrothed and with other permitted persons usually begin right after betrothal, around the age of 12. Menstruation is believed to follow intercourse, and intercourse with a betrothed spouse is believed to settle the marriage down. In response to this belief, young girls sometimes resist consummating the marriage for several years, in spite of scolding, shaming, and bludgeoning from their elders. The Lepchas regard sex as comparable to eating, regrets aging which mean diminished appetites, and report remarkable potency in their sex relationships in which there is little foreplay and no romance beyond the excitement of an accidental encounter. After children are born, adultery —that is, copulation with other than potential spouses, which now include wife's younger sisters, real and classificatory— is forbidden as it might endanger the lives of the children.

The child is believed to be constituted initially of semen and vaginal lubricant (which is regarded as the counterpart of semen); blood plays no role except to indicate pregnancy. Intercourse is regarded as beneficial and is continued right up to delivery (and resumed very shortly afterward). At a later period in gestation, the child is believed to absorb food through a sort of nipple in the womb, and its growth is not believed to deplete the mother. After the fifth month it is believed to be completely formed even to hair, and from then on the parents must observe an elaborate set of taboos, notably precautions connected with various work activities. The sex of the child in the womb can be changed by an exchange arranged with another pregnant woman. For the birth itself, only strong millet beer is prepared. The birth takes place in the outer room of the two-room house, the living room-kitchen, and all members of the family may be present, but no strangers. Any relative may assist the woman by squatting behind her and pressing on her breasts and belly. Anyone who knows how may cut the cord. For 3 days after birth the child is treated as if it were still in the womb. The stillborn and infants who die are immediately reincarnated as devils who attack other children. When it is necessary to wean a recalcitrant older child because a younger sibling is born, the breast is smeared with the excreta of the new infant. The older child is told that the new infant is a devil.

Young children under 3, wearing no other clothing than the shawl in which they are loosely wrapped, are carried on the back. Children under 3 are carried a great deal of the time. Toilet training begins at 3 months when infants are taken out to the balcony, but the disgust level is very low and very little effort is put into actually training them. The children are passive, unrestless, pliant. When a child is somewhere between 3 and 5, the mother gives it a little haversack which is kept continually filled with food and from which the child learns to share food with others. This early generosity is in accord with the whole emphasis of the society on giving, sharing, making presents, giving feasts. Sex play is active and open during childhood, but masturbating after puberty is denied.

From the age of 6 or 7 both boys and girls are expected to share in the work of the household, girls somewhat more than boys, and by puberty they are expected to be able to assume an adult's work burden, although genuine maturity, ability to take responsibility and initiative, lack of diffidence and shyness are not expected until a man is about 30. Women mature somewhat earlier under the greater pressure of adjusting themselves to strangers. Respect is accorded to age and to the representatives of external political authority, but among themselves they are extremely egalitarian and even-handed. Shame is the major sanction, and individuals shamed by adverse comment may commit suicide. Talk is the major pleasure, and continual conversation, joking, sexual punning, and story telling take the place of art and intellectual activity of any other sort.

A timid, generous, friendly people, the Lepchas have preserved the habits suitable for survival in an earlier environment in a way which ensures their eventual disappearance in a present environment with which they are quite unfitted to compete. They are, however, somewhat protected by the fact that the Maharajah of Sikkim has made the mountainous area of Zongu a Lepcha preserve in which only people of pure Lepcha blood can own land. While this law is enforced, a small group of perhaps 2000 can continue their way of life.

IV. Psychologic Sex Gender and Sex Role Assignment

All known human societies recognize the anatomic and functional differences between males and females in intricate and complex ways; through insistence on small nuances of behavior in posture, stance, gait, through language, ornamentation and dress, division of labor, legal social status, religious role, etc. In all known societies sexual dimorphism is treated as a major differentiating factor of any human being, of the same order as difference in age, the other universal of the same kind. However, where in contemorary America only two approved sex roles are offered to children, in many societies there are more. The commonest sex careers may be classified as:

1. Married female who will bear children and care for her children.

2. Married male who will beget and provide for his children.

3. Adult male who will not marry or beget children but who will exercise some prescribed social function, involving various forms of celibacy, sexual abstinence, renunciation of procreation, specialized forms of ceremonial sexual license, or exemption from social restrictions placed on other men.

4. Adult female who will neither marry nor bear children and who will have a recognized status in a religious context or in society (nuns, temple prostitutes, spinsters, etc.).

5. Persons whose special, nonprocreative ceremonial role is important, roles in which various forms of transvestism and adoption of the behavior of the opposite sex are expected, so that the external genital morphology is either ignored or denied, e.g., shamans, etc.

6. Adult males who assume female roles, including transvestism, where this adult sexual career is open only to males.

7. Adult females who assume male roles, including transvestism, where this adult sexual career is open only to females.

8. Sexually mutilated persons, where the mutilation may be congenital or socially produced (e.g., eunuchs) and where the sex behavior includes specific expectations of nonmarriage, nonparenthood, relaxation of taboos on ordinary relationships between the sexes, etc. (eunuchs, choir boys, etc.).

9. Prostitution, in which the adult individual maintains herself (or less frequently himself) economically by the exploitation of sex relationships with extramarital partners.

10. Zoolagnia, a social role combined with a sex preference for an animal (shepherd and sheep).

11. Age-determined sex roles, as where homoerotic behavior is expected of adolescents, or withdrawal from all sex relationships expected from older heads of households, etc., or license is expected before marriage and fidelity afterward, or chastity before marriage and indulgence after marriage, or where widows are expected neither to remarry nor to engage in any further sex relationships.

Any or all of these adult roles may occur in the same society, and the possibility of a child's choosing or being thrust into any of these roles will also be present wherever the role is widely recognized, whether or not the recognition is positively or negatively weighted. Preparation for a life of celibacy and religious devotion begins early in those societies where the monastic life is a common choice; among those American Indians who recognized the *berdache*, or transvestite male, as a likely career, male children were watched and tested from an early age

—were they going to be "braves" or "live like women"? Once the choice was made, elaborate prescriptions of correct social behavior were available. But among a people where there is no recognition of any other possibility than 1, 2, and 11, the same sorts of indicators of possible cross sex identification which, among the Plains Indians would assure a boy's being classified and reared as a transvestite, will go unnoticed and uninstitutionalized. The fuller the social repertoire the more possible it is to carry a knowledge of the role in the absence of any person to fill it.

So, I witnessed a case in an American Indian tribe of a single young man who had been classified by the women as a *berdache*. At the time when his bodily candidacy was remarked, there was no living *berdache* in the tribe, but the women began watching this boy and once undressed him to see if he, whose behavior appeared to them as feminine, "really was a male." Having satisfied themselves as to his external sex morphology, they *then* pronounced him to be a *berdache*. He wore male exterior clothing but female underwear, was unmarried and was the butt of a good deal of teasing. His attempts to persuade the tribal prostitute to have sex relations were rebuffed with contempt. During our stay in the field, we were visited by a male friend who had been living an avowed homoerotic life in Japan, who was not transvestite but who had a complete repertoire of homosexual postures. Within an hour of his arrival, the single *berdache* in the tribe turned up and tried to make contact with him.

The American Indians provide our best material on the assignment of the various transvestite roles—male dressed as female among the Plains Indians, complex arrangements including two men living as a pseudo-married pair among the Mohave (Devereux, 1937), a male role in which a man becomes a totally self-sufficient "household" capable of both male and female activities among the Navajo (Hill, 1935) and some Sioux (Mirsky, 1937). The best material on transvestism by both sexes as a function of specialized religious activity comes from Siberia (Czaplicka, 1914), although transvestite priests were also known in the Pueblos (Benedict, 1934).

The possibilities of a role may also be carried by a series of negative sanctions, in which the cultural expectation is that no one will become a spinster, a bachelor, a hermit, a transvestite, etc. Here the cultural teaching becomes not, "If you are so afraid of fighting, you will have to *be* a transvestite," but a flat imperative to all males, "Don't ever under any circumstances put yourself in a situation for anal attack by a male."

Among the Iatmul of New Guinea (Bateson, 1958; Mead, 1949b), there were many words for sodomy used continually and indiscriminately by both males and females, but when little boys attempted to act out the indicated behavior, older children or adults immediately intervened, and the little boys were made to fight instead. The slightest successful attack on the exposed anus of any adult male would result in a riot in the men's house. Among the Iatmul, there then developed a possibility of both active and passive homosexual behavior, which, however, was not allowed to be acted out within the tribe. With the passive possibility heavily tabooed and the active given no expression, when the Iatmul young men were recruited for work on plantations they became notorious for their homosexual advances to young men of other tribes, including people like the Arapesh, among whom the possibility of homosexuality was unrecognized rather than tabooed, but whose learned passivity and receptivity made them appropriate partners.

The cues used in different societies in the assignment of any of these roles vary widely. Where bravery is the determining point, as among Plains Indians, a timid male child might be assigned a transvestite role, to which he would then adjust by identifying, not with either warriors or women, but with other transvestites. Preference for feminine occupation may provide a basis for role assignment or, on the other hand, carry no accompanying pressures except a mild amount of amusement (Samoa, Mead, 1928). Where men and women are differentiated in areas involving possibilities of softness and harshness in clothing, tactile sensitivity in a male child may be the first cue which leads his parents, his peers, or himself to assign him to a feminine role. Where religious behavior provides the cues, "purity" in the face of a child of either sex may suggest the role of priest or nun rather than of a married adult. In those societies in which religious functions are marked by ecstatic trance behavior and transvestism for both sexes, early occurrence of states of catalepsy, disassociation, or hallucinatory experiences may trigger the sex role assignment.

The familiar situation in our own culture in which a parent, disappointed in the sex of a child, may assign the opposite role also occurs in other cultures. In Bali, sex-typed division of labor is very clear, but there is no opposition to the occasional man who wishes to weave or the woman who wishes to play a musical instrument. In 1936 there was one girl who cut her hair and fastened her sarong like a boy and played in a men's orchestra, who would have been identified in western, semitransvestite circles as probably homoerotic. But there was also a case of a father who, having 6 daughters and no sons, had formed an orchestra of his daughters, who played well but conformed in all other respects to a female pattern.

In summary, it may be said that sex role assignment may be far more complex in other cultures than in our own, and it would be a mistake to build too much of a theoretic structure on contemporary American educational efforts to induct every child into an active and exclusively heterosexual role within the bonds of legal, monogamous unions (see below, page 1474).

The scattered evidence of the occurrence of individuals with the behavior patterns of the opposite sex in the absence of any patterned recognition of the possibility of a full homosexual role strongly suggests the presence of a rare constitutional factor less explicit than anomalies of the external genital morphology. It seems safe to assume that any behavior which can be institutionalized in a culture and regarded as a recurrent possible human choice has some hereditary base, and that when a society of any size is found in which there are no instances of the behavior, we may then regard such behavior as entirely cultural inventions. In very small tribal groups, the absence of terminology or recognition of any of the other roles described here, and the absence at the time of observation of any individuals

with inverted behavior has to be treated with caution, as cultural loss in the absence of any individuals to fill a role may be very rapid (cf. the case quoted, above, page 1452, of the assignment of a *berdache* role when there was no living *berdache* and warfare within which the role had been meaningful had disappeared). Moreover, the possibility that knowledge of other sex roles may be carried for a long time in vocabulary, ritual, or drama must not be overlooked. In Bali in 1936 to 1938 there were young male and female dancers who, accompanied by an orchestra, traveled from village to village and were ceremonially courted by the men of the village, who danced with them. Since that period there has been increasing recognition in Indonesia that male behavior which is transvestite or homoerotic is disapproved in the western societies which supply the models for modernization. The male form of this dance called *gandrung* was disapproved in 1957. However, there were many cases in which girls were now dancing in roles which had been exclusively male in 1936.

Comparably, among the Iatmul of the Sepik River (Bateson, 1958), elaborate transvestite ceremonies co-existed with the heavy taboo on any form of male passivity in actual sex relations; men dressed as women, and in ceremonies, a mother's brother, dressed in the bedraggled costume of an old woman, would rub his anus on the shin of his sister's son. Furthermore, the transvestism itself changed emphases; among the villages of Mindimbit, Palimbai, Kankanamun, the emphasis was on males, in their role as mother's brothers, dressing and acting like females, and in Tambunum the emphasis was on father's sisters making themselves splendid in male attire, to honor their brother's sons. Thus in a society in which there were actually very heavy penalties for homoerotic passive behavior, which effectively prevented all forms of active homoeroticism within the tribe, the possibilities of such behavior were carried by vocabulary, continuous watchful awareness, and complex and explicit rituals. Such material draws attention to the need for paying more attention to the fantasies and rituals of disturbed children and adults in our own culture, which by their use of traditional mythologic and religious symbols may throw light on the carriers within our very rich literary and folk tradition of the possibilities of behavior which is officially disapproved at the present time. See also Bettelheim's illuminating discussion (Bettelheim, 1954) of spontaneous rituals among disturbed adolescents which compare in detail with ceremonies reported from New Guinea and Australia and provide examples of womb or vulva envy of as great strength as the more familiar and often reported penis envy among girls in western society where the male role is heavily preferred for sociologic reasons (Brown, 1958).

Almost any item of human behavior may become involved in establishing a child's sex role, and similarly those items on which we depend, especially sex gender in third person pronouns and differentiation of names and clothing, may be completely absent. There are many peoples where male and female names are not differentiated and where there is no sex gender in the language. There are peoples where boys and girls are dressed exactly alike, and peoples where perhaps children go without clothing so that the anatomic differences between the sexes are conspicuous from infancy. There are peoples where males are permitted to be naked but girls must be covered, so that among the Manus, when asked to draw a boy and a girl, no genitals were drawn but girls were differentiated from naked boys by fiber aprons. Activity levels may vary, so that girls, boys, and *women* climb coconut trees, or girls, boys, and *men* go fishing. Where boys are classed with women until initiation, as in Iatmul, a strong tendency toward a female posture may be found in pre-adolescent boys and girls. Where girls are classed with men until betrothal, as in Manus (Mead, 1949b), a strong tendency toward male posture and behavior may be found in both boys and girls.

To explain adequately (Mead, 1935, 1949b) the variety of behavior found, it may well be necessary to invoke all the forms now recognized, including constitutional type, which when culturally institutionalized may mean that a mesomorphic woman, for example, is thought of as masculine, or an endomorphic or ectomorphic male is thought of as feminine. Excessive emphasis on constitutional sex typing in small populations or in groups which recruit their members from outside, like monastic orders, the circus, the theatre, the merchant marine, may result over time in establishing what look like hereditary patterns of similarity or contrast between the men and women in a group, which is partly due to favored breeding or to continuous selection. A disregard of constitutional preference by sex may result in favoring a type with low sex contrast, so in Bali any exaggeration of secondary characteristics of either sex is disliked—pendulous breasts in women, hairiness in men are combined in the evil mien of the witch in the theatre. Balinese are typically ectomorphic, with little muscle development, narrow hips, small breasts in women, and slightly overdeveloped breasts in men.

To the extent that genetically determined constitutional type becomes involved in assignment of sex role and attainment of psychologic sex, the possibilities of varieties of spontaneous inversion of gender choice increase. This is conspicuous in American culture on the very simple variable of height. Tallness is a male characteristic, and small men and large women are likely to be regarded, and to regard themselves, as somehow less male and less female, than is the case with tall men and small women.

Historically there has been an increase in role inversion at periods of high civilization, in cities as opposed to rural areas (Westermarck, 1921). Although there may be as much casual homoerotic behavior between adolescent boys, among sailors or other isolated groups of males or females, among the illiterate and those who share a meager tradition, and this may increase in prison, armies, etc., *genuine* role inversion, where ideas of love and passion and problems of identity enter in, seems to be characteristic of high levels of civilization. It is possible that much subtler aspects of constitutional sex typing enter in, and complicate a child's identification with the parent of the opposite sex, involving such matters as type of imagery, preferred sensory modalities, types of cognitive function, etc., which are not conspicuous as individual differences among primitive peoples or the lower economic groups in a complex society.

Where "logic" is regarded as male, and "intuition" as female, little girls with a capacity for logical thought may be pushed toward inversion as a *preference*, for a socially perceived difference between expectations for men and women, or as an identification with a father whose mind corresponds to the cultural stereotype. The same thing may happen to a boy who has a bent for music, in a society in which playing the piano is seen as feminine or in which his mother is the musical member of the family.

V. Intensity and Duration of Sex Activity

Experience with substitution therapy (chapter by Money) has provided many examples of the range of capacity for erotic behavior among castrated men or hysterectomized women. Cross-cultural material also presents examples of wide diversity in the way in which expectations of active erotic performance are institutionalized (Westermarck, 1921). Erotic activity may be seen as necessary or antithetical to the performance of other activities, so harvest or warfare may be preceded by either increased or decreased or entirely forbidden erotic relationships between husbands and wives. This is paralleled by the contrasts among those peoples who believe that fasting and the use of emetics will help a runner in a race, compared with those who regard "training" as a matter of nutrition. Sex activity may be classified as the appropriate preoccupation almost to the exclusion of other interests (Truk, Goodenough, 1949) of people under 30, or as dangerous to the young, to be avoided until full adult stature is attained (Arapesh, Mead, 1935). Heterosexual desire may be regarded as spontaneously engendered and in need of curbing (Manus, Mead, 1930), or as uncertain and flickering and likely to fail altogether when the strangeness of the first encounter has been dispelled (Bali, Bateson and Mead, 1942). Sex activity may be regarded as more appropriate to certain months of the year, in the winter among some Arctic peoples, or forbidden during special seasons, such as the salmon run among the Yurok Indians (Erikson, 1950). Among the Marind Anim (Wirz, 1922), where adolescents pass through a culturally institutionalized period of homoerotic behavior, the establishment

of heterosexual relationships is seen as so difficult that a ritual sacrifice, in which a copulating youth and maiden are ritually slain, is necessary to establish heterosexual behavior in the other young people of their age grade. Increased intercourse may be regarded as facilitative of gestation; a pair wherein the female is seen to have conceived have to work hard so there will be more deposits of semen essential to "feeding" the child. Or intercourse during pregnancy may be tabooed. Lactation taboos, which may even involve the nonlactating other wife in a polygamous marriage, are found in some societies. The most conspicuous imposition of taboo on all heterosexual relationships that has been reported is from the island of Mentawei (Loeb, 1928) where there were periods of ritual abstention sometimes as long as 12 years. Comparable periods of abstention have been reported for Chinese soldiers, or male Chinese abroad in communities without Chinese women, supported by a strong cultural belief that sex is debilitating.

Analysis of the great variety of ways in which men and women are enjoined to copulate, on certain occasions, in certain situations, at certain periods of the life cycle, will reveal how a culture may institutionalize an assumed greater sexual drive or an assumed lesser drive. With the expected range of individual variation, the men and women with greater intensity of libido will find a satisfactory social situation in one culture and a frustrating situation in the other. In many primitive cultures individual ability to conform to these rigidly established norms of tabooed or enjoined sex behavior is shared knowledge of the entire group, and although the man whose libido fails to meet them may be publicly identified, there will also be public knowledge that great variation does exist, that X is able to impregnate all three wives the same week, that Y's wives are always fighting among themselves because none of them has been visited for many days. The pressure on the individual of low libido, although public and personal, may still be more bearable than the anxiety experienced by men and women in modern societies where each individual is ignorant of the behavior of others and may classify himself as too high or too low in libido against some fanciful and unreal standard, or alternatively be tricked by the publication of statistics on reported erotic behavior to compare himself unrealistically against an average as if it were normative.

Certainly the cross-cultural behavior supports the position that culture can modify, in both directions, behavior the capacity for which is itself highly variable from individual to individual.

However, it is easier for females to conform to demands for more sexual activity than fits their own individual desires, and for men to abstain from sexual activity, than for males to simulate greater erotic feeling than is actually present. Whereas Kinsey, Pomeroy, Martin and Gebhard (1953) have pointed out that females cannot simulate the tumescence of peripheral parts of the body, this inability to simulate is far less conspicuous than the males' inability to produce or to maintain an erection.

VI. Cognitive Rehearsal

In the use of a concept like cognitive rehearsal, or in the statement that parental behavior may be subsumed under the establishment of gender role, Money, Hampson and Hampson, in their chapters in this volume, rely on a shared knowledge of much of the ethnographic material of our own culture, on the ability of the reader to supply concrete materials on child rearing, dress, sports, etc. When, however, material from other cultures is used, it becomes important to spell out in considerable detail the way in which handling and experience during infancy, type of relationship to members of both sexes of different ages, and enjoined relationship to the own body, become involved in the formation of the individual cognitive expectation of certain types of mature sex functioning.

In placing sex behavior within the wider pattern of the total culture, a useful model is the community of all living generations, seen from two points of view (Mead, 1947a, 1949a). From the standpoint of the life cycle, the types of pre-adult behavior which are culturally facilitated may be seen as *prefigurative* of adult sexual roles, and the types of behavior found in old age after sex activity has ceased may be seen as *post-figurative*. Thus, both male and female infants learn in infancy something about the mother's breasts which will be part of the adult pattern of foreplay, tabooed foreplay, etc. And (depending on whether the earlier period has been styled as frightening, zestful, pleasant but effortful, mildly rewarding, or more tantalizing than satisfying) old age and cessation of sex activities may be regarded in such different ways as a surcease from unwanted demands, an unbearable deprivation, a well earned rest, the next step in an orderly progression, or something to be compensated for by continued vicarious participation in the ongoing sexual activities of junior members of the community. In this sense, the period following that of adult sex activity may be said to be *postfigurative* of the reproductive period. Seen longitudinally, any period is prefigurative of what comes after and postfigurative of what went before. However, this method of conceptualizing stages in the life cycle is applicable only to the individual life cycle, seen in isolation. Actually the small child is exposed not only to its own responses of sucking, sphincter release and control, locomotion, etc., but to individuals of both sexes and all ages who are reacting to him and to each other in terms of their individual age-sex positions (Erikson, 1959). The child learns from slightly older children's openly expressed disapproval and disgust, as well as from the bitter, gossiping voice of his grandmother, how attitudes toward the body and sex relationships to other persons are patterned within that society. Each age learns from each other age. The child who is learning self-control and ways of meeting the requirements of modesty is constantly reminded by the immodesty and lack of self-control of a younger child. The old observe again every day the activities of maturity from which they are believed to have desisted, which they fervently regret, etc. In this sense, the behavior of any age group may be said to be *cofigurative* for the members of each other age group. For an understanding of sexual learning, which requires not only the formation, but also the maintenance of habits and attitudes, a systematic knowledge of the whole is necessary. For purposes of this type of discussion, sex will be discussed not as behavior leading to orgasm or detumescence or some other index of termination of a genitally localized tension state, but as the entire manifestation during the whole life of those bodily states and acts of initiation and response which contribute to mating and reproduction by physically mature, child-rearing human beings.

It is also important to take into account the relationship between a cultural pattern and the individual differences among members of the society, whether these individual differences are to be attributed to differences in strength of drive, to differences in constitution (such as size, physical beauty, etc.) which are given social significance in various ways, or to differences in upbringing which may be variously attributed to factors such as birth order, age of parents, class, rank, or accidents such as being orphaned. We may compare here patterns of sex behavior with patterns of linguistic behavior; any natural language, in contrast to various artificial languages and codes, must be of such a nature that it can be used by every individual in a given society (Mead, 1958), except those severely handicapped in hearing or in ability to enunciate or learn. The requirements for the patterning of sex behavior are more complex. The culture must provide for the disciplining of sex behavior so that no behavior at any age, by either sex, disturbs the orderly functioning of the society to a point of social disruption. If males are reared to respond with sexual advances to naked females of any state of maturation, small female children must be disciplined into keeping their clothes on in the presence of males. If the courtship and marriage patterns are such that girls are expected to remain unaware of physiologic indices of sex desire until after first intercourse, then rigorous taboos on the manipulation of female children's genitals by adults, older children, or the female children themselves, must be instituted, (cf. the precaution taken in some Catholic countries to have girls clothed even when bathing). If the system of sex behavior depends on a theory that females do not menstruate except once, at menarche, unless they have had sexual intercourse, then some system (such as a cultivated sense of shame) which will ensure that no

woman ever discusses menstruation with men is necessary to preserve this belief (Manus, Mead, 1930). If individuals from wholly different cultural backgrounds are to mingle in a large city, police protection to prevent rape will be necessary as it would not be in a small homogeneous community in which rape is virtually impossible.

Secondly, if the society is to survive, the culture must provide for the disciplining of female receptivity, either by permitting females no opportunity for unconventional responsiveness or by inculcating standards of modesty and sexual ethics which prevent the majority of females from according sexual access to males to such a degree that they jeopardize the marriage arrangements through which males are persuaded to assume the responsibilities of parenthood. Correspondingly, the culture must channel male activity along socially approved lines, at the same time ensuring types of sexual potency, which will result in the types of reproductivity necessary for that society.[13] Every human society must deal simultaneously with two problems: the need for reducing reproductivity in particular areas, as among unmarried women or in families larger than the economic arrangements will support, and ensuring or increasing reproductivity in other areas, as among certain classes in the population, etc. Stated in individual terms, females must be reared in such ways that they are receptive enough but not too receptive, men so that they are sexually neither too active nor too disinterested for reproductivity within authorized marriage arrangements. These problems may be met in various ways which then define gender roles and differentiation of gender roles: by balancing short periods of sexual license with long periods of marriage fidelity (Sumner and Keller, 1927),

[13] There seems to be no social mechanism which will ensure that a society will develop along lines that make for survival rather than extinction. Although members of the society may recognize the rate of reproductivity which they need, they may pursue some course which is socially suicidal, as, for example, regarding a land shortage as a shortage of people to work the land and so seek population growth when actually population restriction is indicated, or, as is often done by modern states, linking overpopulation and need for more land to a war economy which demands a higher birthrate.

by setting aside certain portions of the population for lives of celibacy or prostitution (Parsons, 1913), or by permitting different types of sex activity to different ages (for example, requiring chastity from the unmarried girl but allowing a greater degree of freedom to the married woman (France, Métraux and Mead, 1954), permitting young people to enjoy a great deal of premarital freedom but requiring fidelity after marriage (Dobu, Fortune, 1932), permitting unmarried young males to establish homosexual liaisons followed by periods of heterosexual pairing (Wirz, 1922), etc. Situations which vary to an extreme degree from the biologically expected serve to point up the requirements of patterning sex behavior under more usual conditions (*cf.* communities which have achieved either a temporary or a permanently abnormal sex ratio: the Mormons during the first generation of the sect, with the compensatory institution of polygamy; the Marquesans with their ratio of two males to one female, with the balancing institution of polyandry or secondary husbands (Linton, 1939)).

In this connection it is necessary to point out that balance and compensation are only potentialities of human societies. We find societies which practice polygamy and female infanticide, as well as societies with the expected association between female infanticide and polyandry (Mead, 1937). We find societies with other incompatible sets of aspirations. The Mountain Arapesh fears the more actively sexed Plains Arapesh woman, who is likely to be disruptive domestically; but each small community desires to acquire as many women as possible, and so runaway Plains women are taken in (Mead, 1935). The American man is reared to value the type of marital sex activity congruent with a high degree of receptivity in a woman who is trained to carry the inhibiting role in premarital contacts between the sexes (Mead, 1949b). This characteristic of American dating behavior in the 1930's and 1940's has now been complicated by the new convention of "going steady" in which Ehrmann (1959) reports a second reversal of courtship pattern among college students. On a date, which is exploratory and exploitive, the young American male initiates as intimate sex behavior as he can, and the young American female refuses and temporizes; once, however, a steady relationship which is expected to end in marriage occurs, the male tends to discontinue his exploitive behavior and the female, with greater trust in the situation begins initiating greater intimacy, putting a new strain on the young male's ability to control his impulses.

Even sharper discrepancies and reversals may occur. So, in traditional Puerto Rican culture, the ideal male was expected to demonstrate his *machismo* by seducing many women, and all females were expected to be chaste and faithful leaving only the prostitute as an unsatisfactory testimony to male powers of attraction (Bonilla, 1958).

Societies may develop such an intricate interlocking of practices and restrictions that any disturbance within the system produces extreme disorganization. For example, the Indian system of child marriage correlates with a lack of protection of young unmarried girls from the males of their own joint households, and any delay in the age of child marriage such as may be introduced by Christian practices may endanger the girl who is left unprotected in a home where the Western Christian teacher might feel she is safe. Or a system of sexual ethics may be so linked with the institution of the menstrual segregation tent and a taboo on sex relations during menstruation that the introduction of frame wooden houses and the abandonment of the traditional menstrual segregation may help precipitate the collapse of the entire system of tribal sexual ethics (Mead, 1932).

A great number of the nonindustrialized peoples of the world outside the high cultures of Europe and Asia and the Europeanized Americas regulate sex relationships by elaborate kinship arrangements in which women in certain categories are the preferred wives of men in certain related categories (Murdock, 1949). The preferred wife may be a mother's brother's daughter, or a daughter of any man belonging to the clan from which one's mother came, or a daughter of any man belonging to the clan from which one's father's mother came, etc. These systems impose demographically unreal expectations on the normal population and may develop in several different directions, *e.g.*, more and more remote definitions of an appropriate "mother's brother's daughter" may be permitted, other forms of marriage may be permitted to exist side by side (in turn producing new complications) (Iatmul, Bateson, 1958), or the system may become completely unworkable, as in the Mundugumor requirement that a man marry his mother's father's mother's father's sister's son's daughter's son's daughter, and that he give his sister in exchange for this man's daughter (Mead, 1935). Among a people with a very low infant survival rate this requirement was so impossible to meet that everyone in the community was married incorrectly, with correlated feelings of shame and delinquency which contributed to the social breakdown of the society under culture contact conditions.

In most societies, especially in large complex modern nations, conditions are such that a very large number of individuals are prepared during childhood and early youth for types of adult sex relations which are not those into which they actually enter in later life, thus reproducing on a large scale with great variations in individual cases the types of maladjustment which are found in a limited degree in every human society. The consulting rooms of modern psychiatrists have been so filled with such individuals that the contemporary climate of opinion in the western world has placed great emphasis on sexual maladjustment as a cause of maladjustment in general. But, although the change in scale and the much greater degree of complexity increase the difficulty of so rearing children of both sexes that they will function within the existing family system, all societies face to some degree the sociologic problem of adjusting the marriage system to the sex ratio, the age distribution, etc., of their population. These problems become acute either through a change in the social system (such as the migration of the males in search of work), or a great change in the sex ratio as the result of war, migration, or a sex differential in the death rate.

There is always, also, the parallel problem of maintaining a system of child rearing and a set of relevant and related practices in other fields such as the arts, religious

ceremonial, etc., which will ensure that the majority of individuals born into that society will be able to function within it, being sexually active where activity is called for and sexually inactive where such inactivity is expected and prescribed.

The problem of permitting the publication of literature likely to inflame the imagination of adolescent boys in a society which makes no provision for legitimate premarital sex activities is an example of a contemporary situation in which a legalized practice may be out of step with a legal prohibition (Mead, 1953).

In considering the detailed presentation which is to follow, it will be useful to keep in mind two antithetical tendencies which human beings display, the tendency toward specificity of responses so that a sex response is only possible under the most highly specialized and idiosyncratic conditions and the tendency toward generalization in which the capacity to respond sexually may be extended to every member of the opposite sex within a very wide age range, or may include both sexes and even animals. Thus zoolagnia may exclude all sexual response to human beings and even to other than the chosen type of animal and so represent a specialization, or it may be one item in a very large range of sexually interchangeable objects of sex desire. At the level of sexual practice, specialization leads to those idiosyncratic demands for rituals which are stimulating only for the actor and not for the partner. It is reported that brothels in large cities sometimes cater to these desires, which are so individual as to be unresolvable in ordinary heterosexual partnerships. At the level of sexual choice, the same capacity for specialization displays itself in the phenomenon which is described in English as "falling in love," a type of behavior which occurs to a limited degree in all societies: the obsessive concentration on one individual whether or not he or she is sociologically appropriate as a mate. Where a whole culture assumes such concentration on single individuals, it becomes necessary to generalize the mechanism involved. In England, a very large proportion of working-class men marry (believing they have fallen in love with her) the first girl they ever court (Gorer, 1955); by another process of generalization, American youths are able to fall in love with a whole series of personally diverse but socially practicable tentative partners before a final selection is made (Mead, 1949b). The Lepchas of Sikkim assume that one will become permanently attached to a spouse if one sleeps with that spouse; young girls, married without any opportunity to exercise selection, may refuse to consummate a marriage for several years (Gorer, 1938).

Thus, in examining in different societies either the whole set of cognitive rehearsals within which individuals function and mature or the range of diverse behaviors around some particular period or stage (such as weaning or first intercourse), it is necessary to keep in mind the changes in cortical control and endocrine functioning through which each individual passes and the extent to which an experience, in infancy or childhood, at first intercourse, or childbirth, is an appropriate prefiguration of some later activity or a fulfillment of some earlier learning or expectation. Throughout, we shall be dealing with the question of fit; whether the period at which first sex activity is socially permitted does or does not coincide with periods of endocrine reinforcement of sex drive, and what supplementary cultural practices there are to mediate these various degrees and types of exact or contrapuntal fit.

It is essential to bear in mind also that man is a domestic animal, displaying the characteristics of domestic animals. Man also shows a conspicuous absence of "races" with reproductive isolation and a corresponding lack of inherent or specifically imprinted species recognition patterns (Hartley, 1950). The cultural patterning of human behavior functions very much like inherent species recognition patterns, in that human beings learn that certain individuals are suitable mates and that others are to be rejected in terms of incest taboos or along caste, class, or other lines of social categorization. Small learned details of behavior, the way a spoon is held, the posture of the body, an accent, may be sufficient to warn a male and a female away from each other or to establish a situation in which a temporary or permanent sexual union is possible. Aristocracies, isolated peasant groups, and primitive peoples often display a highly ritualized type of behavior, reminiscent in precision and style of the courtship and mating behavior of wild birds (Lorenz, 1950; Tanner and Inhelder, 1953), whereas the behavior of mixed, newly urbanized populations shows the lack of fine discriminations and the tendency toward promiscuous search and response which has been described in folk language as "barnyard morals."

Konrad Lorenz's recent detailed small group studies of Greylag geese have revealed a series of anomalies not unlike what is found in highly degenerate rural communities or extreme slum conditions (Lorenz, 1959). When geese are reared in a constricted territory, all treat each other as nest mates, the responses which nest mates give each other are perpetuated into adulthood and the warning behavior which a strange male gives to another male, which indicates his maleness, is absent. Under these conditions homosexual male pairs are formed, in which the superiority of the male triumph ceremony, which occurs between mates and between nest mates, proves a greater attraction than the weaker female display. Also a male may mate with two females whom he cannot tell apart unless they are both together, and the females, inhibited in any display of appropriate aggression, cannot chase each other away.

These analogues between the malfunctioning of highly patterned inherited behavior, under conditions of crowding, and the breakdown of highly sanctioned human learned behavior are exceedingly revealing.

VII. Range of Patterning

We may first consider those aspects of human sex behavior which may be said to be based directly on the biologic nature of *Homo sapiens*. As all living peoples belong to a single species, a single recitation of the biologically given framework within which the most primitive and the most civilized operate is sufficient. At the present stage of research, there is no indication that any people on the earth today have an innate equipment superior or inferior to that of any other people, in ways which have implications for social learning.

In considering the sex behavior of *Homo*

sapiens, then, we may regard all living peoples, however primitive their civilizations, as one group, with allowance for the very minor influence of such physical differences among peoples as the degree of pendulousness of women's breasts, or the amount of male body hair. Whatever the culture, *Homo sapiens* is characterized by a very long period of infancy and by the extreme helplessness of the young at birth. Unlike the primates, a human infant is not able to attach himself to the mother and, unlike the other higher mammals, is not able to move about or to seek food for himself. This long period of dependence includes reliance on the parent for warmth, among those peoples whose knowledge of fire has enabled them to live in cold climates, and for shelter, where artificial shelter is a condition of life.

The prolonged period of dependence on the mother or mother surrogate for food, drink, locomotion, and protection has very definite implications for human development. Early Freudian theory emphasized a series of growth stages which are characterized by the zones, oral, anal, genital, which are at the center of the child's developing libido. Freud's early theory has been elaborated in a form suitable for cross-cultural use by Erikson (1950), who has delineated the stages in a child's growth on a diagram in which zones and modes appropriate to zones can be systematically handled. The designation of the mode, *e.g.*, that of incorporation, or retention, makes it possible to include other sensory modalities in the discussion, in addition to the classical oral, anal, and genital ones, listening is incorporative, grasping is associated with the second oral stage of active incorporation, etc. This systematic treatment can be combined with Gesell-Ilg type of analysis by chronologic age into a scheme which makes it possible to compare culturally expected development, for males and females, in different cultures which select different developmental stages for emphasis (Mead, 1948).

Recent studies of institutionalized children whose physical needs were adequately met but who received no individualized human "mothering" suggest that the human organism needs such individualized care not only for survival but also for development of its abilities to learn to speak and to relate itself to other people (Bowlby, 1951). The studies also suggest that during these periods there are stages or phases, critical periods in which deprivation has more drastic effects than at others. There is strongly suggestive evidence that during the stages of actual physical dependency which precede walking, the two stages of dependent lactation, certain types of learning occur, more like "imprinting" (in birds) than "conditioning," which have important consequences in the subsequent functioning of the individual as a human being (Tanner and Inhelder, 1953; see Hampson and Hampson, also). Until recent times, this dependency included breast feeding, and the only alternative to nursing by the real mother was nursing by another lactating woman.

The point in evolution at which the father was willing to take over the care of the second child (the "knee baby") when the mother became pregnant or after the birth of the younger infant is not known. In the primate societies for which we have any record, the males show protective behavior if the young are in danger. Human male care of females with young children has included some provision of food as well as protection in all societies of which we have any record, in contrast with primate societies in which the females and juveniles must fend for themselves (Carpenter, 1934, 1940).

Until the last decade it was possible to ascribe the willingness of the male to participate in his wife's pregnancy, delivery, and lactation care of the child entirely to learned behavior. However, experience during the last decade in the United States, when males have come to combine care of very young infants with increasing enthusiasm in exercising such care, suggests that there may be in human males a hitherto hardly tapped instinctive response to very young infants, which originally functioned only to ensure protection but now functions to ensure active participation. Previously, without invoking any theory of instinctive behavior, it was possible to account for the participation of the father in observation of pregnancy taboos, in the delivery, in lactation taboos, in the care of the knee baby while the wife was segregated with a new child, as learned behavior.

As long as the infant was dependent upon human milk for nutriment, there was in all societies a biologically given situation which differentiated male infancy from female infancy. The male spent the first prewalking period in the care of a member of the opposite sex, the female in the care of a member of the same sex. The invention of artificial infant feeding is a social interference with this biologically given but not biologically inevitable situation, the consequences of which we as yet know little about, because our social institutions still bear the stamp of the earlier condition.

It may then be said that the strongly grounded institution of infants being cared for by women, and during their early months by lactating women, is almost universal. Isolated case histories of children reared in institutions (Bowlby, 1951) and the adult responses of males reared by nurses of different racial or ethnic origin (Dollard, 1937) suggest that contact with a protecting female during this period may be crucial in setting up the later adult patterns of sexual preference and initiative.

The second stage of dependent lactation, when the child still has very limited mobility but has teeth capable of inflicting pain on his mother's breast, also provides recurrent situations in which attitudes toward pain and self-restraint, attack, and fear of retaliation can be set up. These, if carried over into the later development of sex behavior, could (in the case of aberrant individuals in a society which disapproves of such behavior) become the basis for sadomasochist perversions equivalent to a reproductive disability (Hutchinson, 1959). Alternatively, a culture may institutionalize the learning of this stage in a permitted repetitive foreplay style, in which scratching and biting are regarded as the appropriate precursors of sexual intercourse between man and wife (Mundugumor, Mead, 1935; Trobriands, Malinowski, 1929).

The prewalking stages, necessarily interpersonal, provide in the relationship between mother and child a prefiguration of adult sex behavior: interpersonal, in the relationship between nipple and mouth; complementary, in a "learning in reverse"

for the male who as an adult will have to substitute an intrusive initiatory act for an introceptive act; a direct learning for the female, whose adult sex response must also be introceptive (Mead, 1949b; Erikson, 1950). With mobility, the child's interest is shifted to control over the physical environment, to a variety of tasks which are non-interpersonal. Eating is no longer a direct physical relationship with another human being, but a relationship between the self and a nutritive object, banana, bone, piece of taro root, which the mother gives. The child also learns control over the giving and withholding of his excretions. This period, itself universal, is utilized differently by different cultures. In some, it is the model of all human relationships: copulation is regarded as a necessary form of excretion of substances which would otherwise pile up inside the body (Manus, Mead, 1930; American, Mead, 1949b); patterns of sex behavior stress a close identification between reproductive and excretory functions and attendant and appropriate habits of thrift, self-control, withholding, etc., develop.

The third stage of human childhood is the one in which the child's behavior would seem to be leading directly to sexual maturity, if it is compared with the behavior of young primates. This is the age roughly from 4 to 6, when the young male engages in rough experimental play with age mates, is actively interested in phallic display and in the assertive intrusive manner and voice which re-inforce phallic display. The female child displays a high degree of sexual self-consciousness in response to males, especially older males. A significant aspect of this early development is the tremendous discrepancy in size and degree of maturation between the small, sexually conscious male, who is ready to fight for an adult female (usually his mother), and the adult male whose sexual rights he would invade. If evolution had proceeded in an even line, it might have been expected that human males would be mature by 8 or 9, ready to take on the demands of adult sexuality. Occasionally, in a primitive society, one finds traces of this behavior. Among the cannibalistic, head-hunting Mundugumor (Mead, 1935), son and father are rivals for the sister whom each wishes to exchange for a wife, and a small boy of 7, backed up by his mother, may defy his father if the father attempts to exchange an older sister whom the little boy has been taught is his property. The spectacle of a child of this size defying a grown man serves to emphasize the weakness of the child whose size renders him wholly unfit for sexual competition with males whose protection and care he needs.

However, this continuous maturation toward sexual adequacy in both boys and girls is interrupted during the long period of childhood. The interruption gives children a chance to grow to a size where a capacity for procreation, rivalry with adult males, and responsibility within society is possible for the young males, and an appropriate size for intercourse, child bearing, and social responsibility is possible for young females. Whether one considers the level of society which could be maintained by children with the degree of social maturation it is possible to attain by the age of 6 or regards this as an artificial consideration, because in such a society learning would have been of a completely different kind, there is still a striking contrast between the level of social maturation possible at 6 and at 18. In some very simple societies, in submerged groups in slums, or in some exploited labor groups, small boys of 6 are virtually capable of doing all (except producing and providing for children) that is socially required of males as herders, fishermen, hunters, casual laborers, etc., although of course they lack the physical strength of adults. And under extreme conditions such as life among criminals or guerrillas or in concentration camps (Freud, 1955), children of this age develop an extraordinary maturity from which they are normally protected in an orderly society.

Again citing the headhunting, cannibalistic Mundugumor, the keen and open rivalry permitted between father and son is interestingly enough acompanied by a willingness to expose young children to the terrors and rigors of life as lone hostages in the villages of enemies who have become temporary allies. The child is expected to learn the language and the defenses of the enemy for later use in warfare.

Much of the literature on sexual matura-tion in human beings, based as it is on complex urban cultures, stresses the gap between physical puberty and capacity for full social participation as a complication of human maturation and neglects this even more striking sexual precocity which is attained between 4 and 6 years of age. When early sexuality was recognized by Freud, students of sex in modern society developed a theory that the period between the end of early childhood and puberty was characterized by what has been called "latency," a recession of sexual interest and drive (Fries, 1958). During this period, the child's physical energy is consumed in rapid growth culminating in the prepubertal spurt, and his attention is concentrated on the acquisition of physical and social skills that will fit him to function in a human society. The observation that all manifestations of sexuality were heavily inhibited during this period in middle-class European males who had grown up in the last 50 years was generalized to the human race.

Psychoanalysis developed a theory that the psychodynamic mechanism that brings about repressed sexuality during these years of growth is interaction between parents and children over the child's rivalry with the parent of its own sex (the Oedipus conflict). There are sufficient clinical data from western society to suggest that repression is one way of resolving a situation which every human society must face but comparative studies show that it is not the only way (Mead, 1942). Nor does the comparative material lend any support to a theory that proposes a diminished drive during this period as explanatory. The evidence seems to suggest, rather, that unless interfered with by the society, children of both sexes can maintain some sexual interest relatively steadily until the great reinforcement which accompanies the physiologic changes of puberty. The variations in behavior during this period, whether auto-erotic play is reported to disappear (Arapesh, Mead, 1935), or whether young males are treated as sexual playthings by older women (Kaingang, Henry, 1941), or whether children of the same age engage in experimental sex play together, including such adult activities as copulation, depends on the culture pattern (Trobriand, Malinowski, 1929).

One widespread solution of this delay in maturation is the relative isolation of small boys from the age of 6 to puberty from their parents and from female children of their own age. The boys play in gangs, and what sexual play exists will be with a same-sex partner or will take some form of group auto-eroticism and exhibitionism, often with a strong emphasis on horseplay and rough-house (Manus, Bali, Samoa, Mead, 1949b). The separation of this group from the un-attainable adult females, the dangerous adult male rivals, and the unsatisfactory and usually slightly more precocious fe-males of the same age is frequently empha-sized by the young males' unkemptness, their refusal to wash or observe social forms of etiquette (Bali, Bateson and Mead, 1942; Mead, 1949b). They form a slightly outlaw society within a society, which, significantly enough, is the very type of society in which very young males are able to function al-most like adults (Balint, 1952). Another solution is the insistence that the adult male curb all expression of hostile rivalry toward the son or nephew, as among the Arapesh who move about in small family groups which often contain only one boy of this age (Mead, 1935). Sometimes two methods of control are found together, as in large Iat-mul villages (Mead, 1939b), where the small boys spend a good deal of time as a play group (away from the older men into whose activities they have not yet been initiated) mimicking social activities which involve sex play with slightly older girls. But also a certain constraint on a father's relationship to his son, particularly his old-est son, is imposed by elaborate etiquette. A father may not, for instance, take drink-ing water from the river forward of the place in the canoe where his small son is sitting. Among the Mundugumor (Mead, 1935), father and son do not belong to the same kinship "rope," nor does a boy belong to that of his maternal uncle, and relations between own brothers are stiff and formal.[14]

Human societies, therefore, deal in a va-riety of ways with this "latency" period in boys: isolation into groups, stylized sex play, relationships to adults which are sat-

isfying but are also designed to prevent competition, introduction of strong controls into the rivalry behavior of adult males or of systems of etiquette which prevent open conflict.

For females, the problem is rather differ-ent. The human female is unique among higher mammals in having a hymen (Ford and Beach, 1951), and the hymen itself may be regarded as discouraging complete sex relations with immature males incapable of rupturing it or as making first intercourse for the female sufficiently conspicuous and recognizable so that social regulation is possible. There is the additional complica-tion that the hymen is highly variable. In some females, it is unrecognizable; in many, it can be ruptured by physical exercise of various sorts; in a few, it is so tough that rupture can be accomplished only by a surgical operation. It is possible that this variation may actually have a survival value, the possible presence of a hymen that is thick and painful to rupture acting as a social deterrent on the precocious, at the same time that the relative ease of first in-tercourse, in most cases, prevents the estab-lishment of too much fear in either sex.

Human societies have institutionalized the hymen in many ways. Some identify the bleeding of menstruation with the bleed-ing from the rupture of the hymen, so that menstruation is regarded as being due to intercourse (Manus, Mead, 1930; Lepcha, Gorer, 1938). In societies where sexuality is actively valued, older women may stretch the hymen and distend the labia of little girls, or train little girls to do so. Attempts at preservation of an intact hymen so that the tokens of virginity can be ceremonially taken at marriage or so that officiating rel-atives can verify the virginity is also wide-spread (Westermarck, 1921).

The existence of the hymen does, how-ever, give a clue as to the functional value of prolonging the childhood period well be-yond puberty, although there is a strong suggestion that a second, and possibly a sec-ondary, control has been introduced in the form of a postpubertal female sterility (summarized in Montagu, 1957). Ability to conceive does not follow directly after the menarche, although many societies permit sex relations to begin, or even insist on mar-

---

[14] The Mundgugumor "rope" is a descent line with change of sex in each generation. See above.

riage, as soon as the first menstruation has taken place. Where no overt social interference occurs, young people, maturing at different rates, slowly detach themselves from the younger children's groups or from their association with much older people and begin to pair off. Given an upbringing in human society in which children are part of families based on sexual ties, the endocrine changes at puberty appear to provide the necessary triggering of individual activity into the expected pattern. Whether the endocrine changes would be sufficient to induce sex activity in human adolescents who had been reared without relationships to other human beings and without the explicit and articulate patterns of sex relationships which characterize all known societies, we have no way of estimating. In societies without any means of keeping track of age, adolescents may be permitted to set their own pace or may be subjected to initiation ceremonies which flagrantly disregard physiologic puberty; stressing chronologic age groups, as in modern America, introduces an artificial standardization of behavior, grouping together the mature and the immature in expected social rituals such as dancing and dating (Mead, 1959). The imposition of such artificial patterns of social readiness and postponement may be presumed to be one of the factors making adult sex functioning a less uniform and reliable matter in the upper classes of complex societies.

In addition to extreme dependency and a prolongation of maturation in human beings, the disappearance of cycles of sexual readiness is a distinguishing aspect of human sexuality. Not only is there no rutting season and no period of heat, but the male is capable of sex relations at any time and the female is inversely receptive, displaying (at least according to existing data from our own society, collated by Ford and Beach, 1951) the least desire at the time of ovulation and the greatest desire at the time of menstruation (Kinsey, Pomeroy, Martin and Gebhard, 1953). These specialized human sex responses favor the establishment of family life. Until marriage the male is dependent on the willingness of the female to yield to his advances, so he may be refused at those periods when she is unrecep-

tive. (This situation, together with the probable period of adolescent sterility following menarche, probably partly accounts for the low rate of illegitimacy in societies which permit a period of premarital freedom.) However, once the female has set up housekeeping with a male on whom she depends for food and whom she wishes to attach permanently to the care of her dependent children, then yielding to his advances in the absence of any positive inclination on her part is the logical outcome. As the human male is capable of penetration in the absence of any physiologic receptivity on the part of the female, her compliance involves no physiologic underwriting whatsoever, other than the absence of a vaginal spasm. There is no evidence that sexual pleasure on the part of the female is a necessary or even contributory factor in conception (Ford and Beach, 1951).

A further distinctive characteristic of human sexuality is the capacity of some human females to attain orgasmic sexual pleasure, a manifestation which is absent, as far as observation can tell, among most other species. Elkan (1948, 1950) made an extensive survey of the literature on the subject and advanced the view that the capacity for female orgasm is unnecessary in any species in which the male has a mechanism for maintaining the female in a copulatory position until ejaculation is attained. In the case of human beings, the arms serve this purpose. Elkan also believes that the capacity for orgasm in females is a late evolutionary development, present only in some females. Ford and Beach (1951) suggested that the face-to-face position for sex intercourse, the most widespread position among human beings but an exceedingly aberrant one for primates, may be further responsible for a type of clitoral stimulation leading to female orgasm. Additional factors may be the projection on the female by the male of a demand that her feeling match his and the social invention of a large number of techniques for involving the more diffuse eroticism characteristic of the female. Some human societies regard the female climax as essential to the satisfactoriness of the sexual act; in others (Arapesh, Manus, Mead, 1939a, 1949b), female orgasm is unrecognized as a possibility.

Great stress may be laid on the maintenance of intromission without ejaculation for a very long period, with an attendant emphasis on erotic pleasure for the female rather than on climax, as in highly sophisticated Indian practice. All of the existing evidence suggests that female orgasm is not biologically given, but that it may occur under certain conditions, the most essential of which is the belief that orgasm is possible and desirable. There is a certain amount of evidence suggesting very great variability in the female sex in regard to this capacity, so it may be that societies will disallow the possibility of orgasmic response for all women, stylize vigorous response as appropriate for the prostitute but not for the respectable woman, or insist upon response from all women as a sign of affection or assent to male sex activity (Elkan, 1948, 1950. See also Kinsey, Pomeroy, Martin and Gebhard, 1953, Ch. 14).

Human cultures vary tremendously in the type of situation through which sex activity is initiated (Ford and Beach, 1951). Foreplay may be completely absent, opportunity being sufficient stimulus; the sight of the woman's bare genitals may be all the stimulus needed, or there may be quite elaborate rituals to arouse the male. Initiation of sex activity may come from either sex, as among the Iatmul and Tchambuli, where the male is reared to respond very quickly to female taunts of lack of virility. On the other hand, complete passivity in the female may be demanded, and a passive, nonvirginal female may be so stimulating that if she wanders from her chaperones she may be punished by group rape if a group of men happens to encounter her (Mead, 1932). Preoccupation may center on arousing the female, in cultures where female sex enjoyment is valued. Or the prelude to sex activity may be symmetrical: "He holds her breasts, she holds his cheeks" (Arapesh, Mead, 1935). Similarly, the display elements in courtship and foreplay may all be masculine (headdresses, tattooing, scarification, and elaborate clothing being worn by the male) or all feminine; young people of courtship age of both sexes may adorn themselves, or all display of any sort may be forbidden. Bodily preoccupation seems to be more common at puberty than at any

other age, and possibly there may be a specifically sexual basis for this greater interest at this stage; however, it may be due to the greater self-consciousness engendered by bodily changes as much as to a desire to attract the opposite sex. At any rate, the impulses toward display are very heavily overlaid with cultural learning.

The phenomena of puberty are recognized in all cultures, but their significance is variously interpreted. Although menstruation may be interpreted as the result of intercourse, it may be seen as a form of excretion of "bad blood" (Arapesh, Mead, 1935; Wogeo, Hogbin, 1935). In some cases, this interpretation will be extended to male behavior, and males, having no "natural" way of getting rid of bad blood, will ritually cut their penises to let the bad blood out (Bettelheim, 1954). Menstrual pain may be recognized or may be assimilated to the discomforts of segregation in a badly built hut, etc. In my Samoan sample of 30 girls (Mead, 1928, Table 1) 6 of 30 reported menstruating semimonthly, which is probably a very rare cultural recognition of staining at ovulation and *mittelschmerz*. There were no respondents reporting that they menstruated semimonthly among those who reported no dysmenorrhea. Male puberty signs may be institutionalized as signals for putting on clothes or for initiation, or they may be ignored in favor of social status defined by age grading. The phenomenon of wet dreams is one on which there is very little information in the literature, possibly because of the widespread practice of masturbation and frequency of premarital sexuality. (In a society like the Manus, where premarital intercourse was forbidden except with prostitutes captured from another people, prudery prevents good information on such matters.) The change in the form of a girl's breasts is frequently, but not necessarily, ascribed to the beginning of copulation.

Conception may be regarded as occurring entirely independently of the male, except as he "opens the road," so that the actual children are "spirits" who enter the mother (Australia, Montagu, 1938; Trobriand, Malinowski, 1929), or less commonly the mother may be regarded as merely giving the egg laid by the father shelter during gestation (Rossel, Armstrong, 1928). The child may be thought of as the product of a heaven-sent soul and earth introduced by an angel at the time of intercourse (Palestine Arabs, Granqvist, 1947), or it may be variously compounded of semen and vaginal fluid (Iatmul, Mead, 1935), or semen and blood. The semen may be seen as an irritant (Bali, Mead, 1939b) or as food for the fetus (Arapesh, Mead, 1935). The child may inherit entirely from its mother or different parts of itself from each parent—spirit from its father, flesh from its mother (Ashanti, Rattray, 1923), bone from its father, blood from its mother (Arapesh, Mead, 1935)—or the tie to the mother may depend entirely on the postdelivery tie established by breast feeding (Palestine Arabs, Granqvist, 1947). The regulation of sex activities during gestation has an equal variety; intercourse may be thought necessary for some weeks to build up the child (Arapesh, Mead, 1935), repeated intercourse may be believed to produce twins (Mundugumor, Mead, 1935), or all intercourse may be forbidden with the pregnant woman (Iatmul, Mead, 1935). A woman normally permitted to have sex relations with her husband's brothers may be confined to intercourse with her husband during pregnancy (Baganda, Roscoe, 1911). Recognition of "life" may be highly institutionalized, or there may be no recognition that the fetus moves at all before birth (Arapesh, Mead, 1935). Pregnancy cravings are very widely recognized. Morning sickness may be conventionalized as occurring only for the first 3 months, only for the first child, or as an unusual event which happens to only a few women. However it is viewed, although most women will conform to expectancy, a few women do not, thus providing some evidence for the physiologic basis for this response to pregnancy in some women.

Childbirth itself is so overlaid with ritual and social usage that no biologically given detail can be extricated from the mass of complex, often nonfunctional, behavior (Ford, 1945). The mother may be required to do everything herself, no hand but hers permitted to touch the newborn. Midwives with great experience may be allowed to give manual assistance or may be limited to magical practices. The father may be required to be present and to support his wife, or he may be forbidden to see her for weeks; he may be put to bed with her, or in her place. The infant may be put immediately to the mother's breast, or may be fed by a wet nurse or starved until all trace of colostrum has disappeared from the mother's milk. It may be smeared with clay or butter or oil, and its nose and eyes cleaned by the mouth or hand of the officiant midwife or with some material. The cord may be cut close or far, tied or left hanging; it may be expected to fall off (according to the sacred number of the particular tribe) on the fourth day or the fifth. The infant may be carried close in the mother's arms, or in a tray, bag, basket, cradle board, sling, swing, etc. Wherever we find human beings, at no matter how simple a level, all these matters have already been highly stylized and no simple biologically given pattern is discernible. Pain in childbirth is stressed and expected by some peoples, minimized by others. Legends in which men find women who hitherto have lived without men and teach the women the correct methods of childbirth are widespread. (A modern version of this plot detail is found in the "discovery" of natural childbirth in recent years by British physicians who are now indoctrinating women against the incorrect use of anesthetics (Read, 1953).)

Every society deals with the problem of maintaining marriages; very few insist on monogamy for life after a single choice, as has been the custom in Europe for so many centuries. Premarital experimentation and divorce, permitted if there are no children, are both widespread, and there are many extensions of sexual access: brothers of husband, sisters of wife, members of an age grade, etc. In general, monogamy is the most persistent form of marriage: polygamy is usually patterned as a series of marriages so that a man must build a house or work a garden or construct a canoe for each wife as if she were a single wife. Polyandry is very rare and seems less adapted to the adequate care and production of children than polygamy, in which the wife with a young baby is often relieved of other conjugal and household duties by her co-wife.

The nature of the span of female reproductivity, beginning after menarche and ending at menopause with the possibility of many years of postmenopausal life, is again distinctively human; at least no instances have been reported for any primate species. Many societies recognize the postmenopausal period by giving old women the license of men, permitting them to hold male office or to use language and to make jokes which would be regarded as improper for women of child-bearing age. In some societies menopausal hemorrhages are recognized. The Samoans recognize menopausal psychic instability, but they could have learned of it from Europeans, since it was reported 100 years after the beginning of European contact. Diminution or augmentation of sex pleasure is variously expected. Occasionally, sexual pleasure is regarded as even greater for those past the child-bearing period (Jemez, Harper, n.d.) ; European culture has tended to equate the menopause with loss of capacity for sexual pleasure.

Menstruation may be an occasion for avoiding all sexual contact or an occasion for increased activity. The fear of menstruation as a period of supernatural danger to a man's capacity to hunt or fish or make war is widespread; sometimes, however, these powers are reversed, and only the blood of a menstruating woman can effect a cure of some dread disease. Taboos that keep women away from food preparation or require that they feed themselves with special precautions (Ford and Beach, 1951; Ploss, 1902) may be compared to the attempts in human society to keep the mouth and food separated from excretions of any sort, on the one hand, and to the feeling that it is necessary to protect individuals against absorbing through food the dangers associated with the mysterious qualities of the body, especially those which involve any shedding of blood, on the other. Thus, it is not unusual to find such identifications as the use of similar protective devices for girls at first menstruation and boys at ear-piercing or scarification, and of women who die in childbirth and men who die in battle, whose blood together makes the red in the sunset.

Finally, in any discussion of the cultural patterning of sex activity it is necessary to take into account the attitudes toward death, as these involve the relationships between body and soul and between the living and the dead. Birth, marriage, sex, and death may be identified in *rites de passage* (Van Gennep, 1909) through which each individual passes, or they may be treated as highly antithetical events, so that the pregnant woman must be protected from the newly married, the aging from the springing sexuality of the adolescent, the newly wed from the mourners. Each individual who participates in a ceremony for one event learns also something about another; that brides wear white and widows black or that both brides and widows wear black, that the bride must never see a corpse or that she must be wrapped like one and lie as if dead for hours, that no preparation must be completed for the newborn infant for fear it will cause its death, or that one of the first acts of a newly married pair is to make preparations for their funerals.

These parallel or contrasting treatments of moments of high emotion in human life are among the most important cofigurative methods by which human beings learn the pattern of sex behavior. The tie between the living and the dead spouse has received wide elaboration; long periods of mourning, especially for the widow, are enjoined in many societies; the widow may be slain on her husband's funeral pyre or she may be forbidden ever to marry again; marriage with a widow may be surrounded with a great variety of precautions. Among the Arapesh, male potentiality for great anxiety about any other male who has shared the same woman was complicated into complex beliefs about avenging ghosts (Mead, 1935). Other solutions of the problem are found when the widow is married by a male of the social group of the dead man, so that the brother or cousin takes the dead husband's place. Clinical research on the response of individuals to grief has revealed the psychologic basis, ambivalence toward the dead (Cobb and Lindeman, 1943) and identification with the dead, for the extreme pathologic depressions sometimes found in modern societies where there is no longer a collective ritual within which the individual can act out the situation of bereavement.

Another problem which every known human society has met, the solution of which seems essential to the existence of society as we know it, is the problem of sexual attraction within the biologic family, between parents and children, and between brothers and sisters, which is dealt with by the universal incest taboo. Without the incest taboo, the family as we know it would be impossible. Daughters would succeed their mother in their father's affections, and brothers would fight their father and each other for the possession of their sisters. There seems to be no evidence for any biologic basis for the universal incest prohibition, and it has instead to be explained psychologically and sociologically as necessary for the protection of the family unit (Murdock, 1949; Seligman, 1929; Mead, 1949b; Spiro, 1958). Levi-Strauss (1949) identified the point at which the incest taboo came into existence with the beginning of culture as such, a figurative statement of its importance. A variety of practices around the world testifies to the close connection between incest prohibition and social order; brother-sister and occasionally father-daughter marriage may be permitted or even enjoined as a way of differentiating a royal or noble line from the bulk of the populace who must live by a rule which only the royal can break.

The various social devices used to enforce incest prohibitions may be proliferated, so that a community is divided in two, with one-half of one's age mates classified as sexually unavailable; sex relations with a first cousin twice removed may be treated as incest; the relationships between brothers and sisters may be governed by strict codes of avoidance, coupled with myths which trace the origin of love magic to an incestuous relationship between brother and sister. Equally convincing evidence of the social character of the incest taboo can be found in the occurrence of incest, especially father-daughter incest, under conditions of social breakdown among outcast groups who live in slums or on the periphery of society. Sudden changes in patterns of living (for example, migration from a peasant village in Europe, in which there are strict social sanctions in which the entire community shares, to the anonymity of a large American city) may endanger adolescent daughters left alone with their fathers. Both the precautions which have been elaborated in human societies and the points of break-

down suggest that the father-daughter relationship and the elder-brother and younger-sister relationship which mirrors it, are the key positions, congruent as they are with the attractiveness of the less mature female to the more mature male. The opposite peril, attraction between son and mother, although it seems to have less strength, is also a biologic potentiality. There has even been recorded a marriage system in which grandsons occasionally marry their grandmothers and have children by them (Baiga, Elwin, 1939).

Whatever the arrangements, the universality of the incest taboo within the primary biologic family means that all human beings are reared to recognize forbidden as well as permitted sexual partners, and this experience of prohibition becomes a component (sometimes as incentive, sometimes as deterrent) in subsequent mating behavior. Where the prohibition has been unusually strongly enforced, all attraction to the opposite sex may be inhibited, or a type of promiscuous search for the unattainable incestuous object may be set up. But, always beside the range of forbidden acts, words, thought, which characterize the sex behavior of human beings, we must consider also the specifically forbidden objects, parent and sibling of the opposite sex. In many cultures, especially where all human relationships are highly conventionalized, the regulation of sexual attitudes includes a series of avoidances toward relatives-in-law who may in some way be identified with forbidden relatives, the most conspicuous of which is the taboo between a man and his mother-in-law which functions to reduce rivalry between mother and daughter over the possible attractiveness of the young son-in-law. Thus, before the marriage of the female it is the attitudes of older males toward younger females which must be kept in check; after marriage, the focus shifts to the tension between the older woman and younger mature men between whom a relationship is both tempting and socially disruptive of the marriages of the next generation. Various bizarre arrangements occur; for example, a man may marry a widow with a daughter, and later, when the daughter comes of age, marry the daughter and turn his former wife into a mother-in-law to whom he may never speak again (Navajo, Reichard, 1928). In central Tibet (Prince Peter of Greece, 1948), where polyandry is practiced, a group of brothers may share their father's young wife, their stepmother. These extreme variations all serve to emphasize the fact that, like the relationship between father-daughter, the mother-son relationship, especially in its locus in the relationship of the older woman to the mature son, is one with which human societies have to come to terms. (Urbanization, combined with the development of societies containing many millions of individuals who are no longer held together throughout life in small closed systems, necessarily involves very different ways of handling the early prohibitions which are still maintained within the biologic family. Emotional maladjustment in individuals which accompanies faulty learning of culturally expected organization of emotion is undoubtedly one such adaptation (Bibring, 1953).)

I have discussed the various biologic checks on premature sexuality and reproduction, the hymen, the frequency of adolescent sterility, incest regulations, and the possible inverse relationship between female sexual desire and ovulation. With the development of a social recognition of physiologic paternity, the purposeful avoidance of pregnancy becomes possible. This has taken a variety of forms: postponement of marriage, which leaves the chronology of sex acts in the hands of the female; imposition of long periods of sexual abstinence for all males in the community (of which the 12-year-long periods, reported for Mentawei, are an extreme form (Loeb, 1928)); the imposition of specific taboos during the period of lactation, which may involve only the lactating wife or may extend to other wives also (Arapesh, Mead, 1935); devoting a part of the population of one or both sexes to a life of celibacy; the use of contraceptives designed to prevent conception while permitting acts of copulation; alternative forms of attaining sex satisfaction and various measures of interrupting a pregnancy once initiated, by abortion or infanticide. Here again, the evidence is overwhelmingly in favor of there being insufficient biologic indicators to guide man in his search for a means of reducing population. Mutually incompatible institutions exist side by side, as in the cases of female infanticide and polygamy (Eskimo) or in the beliefs about the hygienic necessity for intercourse and beliefs about the hygienic desirability of spacing children (U. S. A.). It can only be concluded from present evidence that, in spite of the variety of biologic checks on fertility which render *Homo sapiens* relatively infertile, no sufficient automatic check[15] on the birth rate is provided biologically which is compatible with the specific resources of any human society.

So far, we have been concerned with those patterns of sex behavior which assure that men and women will marry and rear families and that their sex desires will not become so unmanageable as to disrupt this orderly process of reproduction and child care. But man, like other mammals (Carpenter, 1942), has capacities for types of sex behavior which do not lead to the formation of permanent unions and the production of children—for auto-eroticism, for sexual play with a partner of the same sex, and for adult forms of polymorphous perversity, in which the object of his sexual behavior is a matter of indifference to him (Mead, 1934a). The insistence in the clinical and experimental literature on animal behavior that special conditions are necessary if individuals are actively to prefer "perverse" behavior (behavior other than heterosexual behavior capable of producing offspring) must be placed in the whole context of human sex behavior. There is no more reason to insist that sexual preference for own sex[16] is learned than that heterosexual behavior is learned. But most human societies are so constituted that it is heterosexual behavior that *is* learned. Beach (Ford and Beach, 1951) has presented persuasive arguments in favor of regarding same-sex behavior and

[15] This statement is made with recognition of how complex any such automatic check would be.
[16] The word *homosexual* is misleading because it fails to distinguish between sex *activities* involving a member of the same sex and a highly developed preference for love objects of the same sex, often involving disturbances in sex identification, transvestism, repugnance toward members of the opposite sex, obsessive and promiscuous pursuit of members of the same sex, etc. See Hampson and Hampson, also.

auto-erotic behavior as "natural" behavior rather than as substitutes for heterosexual behavior. If the term *natural* be taken to mean behavior of which all human beings are potentially capable, then one may also argue that the individual who is wholly incapable of a homosexual response has failed to develop one human potentiality.

In human societies, two trends in the handling of homosexuality may be discerned (Westermarck, 1908). A society may focus on heterosexual behavior and treat all other sex behavior as so peripheral that it will not occur in a sufficiently large number of cases to disturb the social equilibrium, or it may stylize very strictly the age grade at which homosexual pairing is permitted (Marind-Anim, Wirz, 1922), the role of the individual who makes a homosexual choice (Mohave, Devereux, 1937), etc. So periods of adolescent homosexuality may be institutionalized, and homosexuality may be expected among warriors or in certain occupational groups. The boy who fails to display the requisite male bravery may be cast as a transvestite, referred to as "she" and given a special role as story-teller to war parties or go-between in love affairs (Cheyenne, Grinnell, 1923).

A fundamental difficulty, not unrelated to the problems which have been solved by the institution of incest, remains in the incompatibility of a libidinal relationship with competition and aggression among males. The anatomic complexity of the male body, with the analogy between anus and vagina, makes the problem of activity-passivity a recurrent one and one which may be intrinsically antithetical to a procreative heterosexual role. The fear in young males of attack by other stronger males, a danger which all societies have to meet in rigorous methods of protecting children and in incest rules, is met by young primates by presenting (Hamilton, 1914; Maslow, 1936a, b). A survey of the existing knowledge of human societies suggests that if male homosexual tendencies are to be tolerated or encouraged, then social institutions fully as rigorous as those governing incest are desirable, protecting the young from exploitation, prescribing certain types of loyalty, and modulating the competition for new partners which is such a frequent accompaniment of socially unsanctioned male homosexuality. Female homosexuality is a reciprocal of male homosexuality; where male anatomy suggests, lacking the human face-to-face copulatory position, complementary attitudes, female anatomy dictates no choices as to activity, passivity, asymmetry, or complementariness and seems to lend itself much less to institutionalization as a counter-mores activity.

One protection against treating the young male as a sexual object is to take steps to regulate, limit, or defeat altogether his sexual competition with older and stronger men. Initiation ceremonies which involve at first rigid exclusion from and then formal admission to the secrets of adult males, very frequently combined with acts of mutilation (knocking out of teeth, incision, subincision, and circumcision, scarification, and tattooing involving submission to painful attacks on the body), are widespread human variants of the conflicts between the springing sexuality of the young male and the diminishing virility of his seniors (Hambly, 1926). Such conflicts may be handled instead by social divisions which cut across all ages: the more meditative may be inducted into a life of celibacy, so that curbs on the aggressiveness of the more virile are not necessary. Castration of slaves and captives so as to provide a supply of eunuchs also reduces a certain number of males to a noncompetitive status, as do caste and class arrangements by which the males of the lower status groups are denied access to the females of the upper status groups. All such patterns of behavior are learned. Whether the learning is so phrased that certain men choose a life of celibacy as higher or purer, encouraged by the social definition of sexual activity as low and animal-like, or whether they have such a choice thrust upon them by the class or caste group in power will make a difference in the way different roles are accepted and in the psychologic price men pay for denying impulses which they have been taught are natural and necessary or undesirable and unnecessary.

In summary, a survey of cultural patterns reveals intricate systems of learned behavior, within which the sexual capacities of the young child, the inappropriate sexual capacities of the older child, the reinforced sexuality of the adolescent, the slowly diminishing sexuality of the male, and the discontinuous zest of the premenopausal and postmenopausal female manifest themselves. It may be expected that detailed studies of the first years of life will reveal the particular mechanisms by which individuals in a given society are prepared for the sexual roles held appropriate by that society and will throw light on the differential efficiency of these various learning sequences.

VIII. The Study of Sex Behavior in Complex Modern Societies

There are a number of serious difficulties about the study of sex behavior in the United States at the present time. The behavior is diversified by class, ethnic group, region, and various special versions of the culture characteristic of religious groups, occupational groups, areas of cities, etc. A national sample does not necessarily allow for any of these variations in a way which provides enough background for estimating the cultural factor in the behavior of any given individual. National samples such as those used by Kinsey, Pomeroy and Martin (1948), and Kinsey, Pomeroy, Martin and Gebhard (1953) were constructed like Gallup polls, with a very few variables —class, age, sex—although the mere listing of the variables which they took into account is impressive. To take only two of the categories which they list (page 5) "Whites, Negroes, *other races,*" *"various degrees of adherence* to religious groups, or with no religion," the amount of variety which is subsumed under these phrasings is enormous. Yet, their aim was to build a national picture from these samples, so that the picture of American behavior, called the behavior of the *human male* and *human female,* was expected to have representativeness in the end. What we do find is that with the aid of the kind of sample they built they got substantially the same picture obtained by Hohman and Schaffner (1947) from their very much more cursory questioning about sex behavior, based on psychiatric screening for the draft in World War II. Their statistics, furthermore, agree very well with materials collected in North-

ern Europe (Undeutsch, 1955). We may well say that their data are reliable, in that another sample, constructed the same way, within the same narrow range of time, would give answers of the same general type, *e.g.,* lower class behavior would show the same sort of contrast with middle and lower-class-upward-mobile behavior, the lower class seeking immediate complete satisfaction early, the middle and the lower-upward-mobile classes relying more on various substitutive and delaying techniques rather than full consummation.

The second complication is the question of historic period. All the available studies of the polling type—and, although Kinsey's interviews were complex and intricate, the assumptions back of them were still of the polling type, *i.e.,* that 100 cases would stand for many thousands—emphasize that the responses change very rapidly in a country like the United States; behavior approved one year may be disapproved the next, and a large part of the adult population shifts its views accordingly. Kinsey's practice of using the memory of a 50-year-old man of what he did at 15, and the replies of a 16-year-old boy of what *he* did at 15, makes no allowance for the changes in attitudes and values and the differential types of retrospective falsifications which are likely to occur—which makes the lumping of these sets of replies together inadmissible. The inadmissibility cannot be tested by simple statistical means; the results are undoubtedly reliable and adding 1000 more 50-year-old men and questioning them about their adolescent sex activities will not change the picture. They are quite reliable, but they may not, and in all probability do not, give an accurate picture of the past, but rather a picture of how 50-year-old men, living in the period of Kinsey's interviewing, would combine present-day standards and values, the experience of their own younger contemporaries and their children, into a stable and systematic but objectively false image of their own pasts.

With the tremendously rapid changes that are taking place, data for a national sample should be collected within a few months, and retrospective reports should be treated separately from reports on recent experience. There are a number of other criticisms of the Kinsey, Pomeroy and Martin sample, the number of male homosexual prostitutes in their lower class male sample, the inadequacy of the sampling of nonwhite groups, the differential effect of male interviewers on males, and male interviewers on females, which need not concern us further here (see also Cochran, Mosteller and Tukey, 1955).

However, one of their findings, so widely quoted, that definitely needs reconsideration is their statement that the sexual enjoyment and activity of women increases as they grow older and that of men decreases. An examination of their data will show that all they require for a sexual act in their male sample is ejaculation, whereas from their female sample they require orgasm. If they had interviewed their male sample about the strength and completeness of the climax involved in coitus, instead of accepting any "outlet" as a unit of sex activity, their results would have been different, as they would have been equating male *learning* about sex and its possibilities with female *learning* about sex and its possibilities. It is only fair to add, however, that what they did here is the usual American male classification, in which quantitative frequency is treated as a surer sign of sexual adequacy than intensity and duration of coitus and depth of orgasm.[17]

In addition to the Kinsey reports, we also have a number of other attempts to construct a picture of American sex behavior (Davis, 1929; Dickinson and Beam, 1931, etc.) based on questionnaires, interviews (Hamilton, 1929), various sorts of samples, for the most part of the middle class and well educated. All of these studies rely on premises which are essentially sociologic and quantitative in nature, and are concerned with problems of reliability. There is no consistent body of cultural or psychodynamic theory behind them.

In contrast, we have also very intensive studies by research workers and psychotherapists, deeply and narrowly grounded in psychodynamic theory, which seek by the study of a few cases to describe the characteristics of the population concerned and to add to a theory of human behavior

[17] I am indebted to Ray Birdwhistell for pointing out this aspect of Kinsey's analysis.

(Erikson, 1951) on sex differentiation, in the Berkeley study, contrasted with the studies by Sears, Maccoby and Levin (1957) and Brown (1958); Davis (1926) who queried women on the cyclic character of desire, as compared with the Benedek and Rubenstein (1939) attempt to correlate intensive psychoanalytic therapy on 15 women with independent physiologic assays of ovulation; studies of the changing incidence of ulcer in male and female patients (Mittelman, Wolff and Scharf, 1942); psychiatric analysis of special groups, such as Deutsch's (1944) study of prepubertal girls; Levy's (1938–39) study of maternal over-protection; Alexander and Healy's *Roots of Crime* (1935). In these studies, sex behavior is only a small part of the whole psychodynamic process that is being explored, and the reports often lack any specific information on the categories which primarily interested Kinsey and his fellow investigators, on the details and incidence of specific erotic behaviors.

A third type of material centers around the question of social role where neither the details of erotic behavior nor the psychodynamic problems are considered, well exemplified by the work of Seward (1946), who at no point discussed childbirth, and mentioned menstruation only once to suggest that the fact that women menstruate is of no significance.

A final group of materials is of the type presented by Money and the Hampsons in which cases initially identified either through anomalies of structure, precocity or hermaphroditism, or behavior, *e.g.*, practicing homosexuals, are explored for specific erotic patterns of behavior.

These various types of material can be used, as the Hampsons and Money use them, as background for a theoretic point which they wish to make about the overweening importance of the sex of assignment and of gender role, but when we attempt to use them to give a picture of sex behavior in the United States in the last two decades, we are confronted at once with the need for a more integrated frame of reference than a mere patchwork summation of shallow national samples, small special samples, and pieces of research done from many different theoretic positions.

Such a study would start from a series of assumptions about the level at which it is possible to talk of American culture as a whole, and where class and regional breakdowns would have to be introduced (Mead, 1949b; Gorer, 1948). It is possible to construct a national picture of sex behavior, based on the mass media, existing laws and court decisions, practices in national institutions like the armed forces, the Federal agencies, supplemented by the statistical and detailed studies mentioned above. The statistical and detailed studies do not provide the basic data for a national paradigm, but the accuracy of the paradigm can be tested against them. At present the only models we have are those made by anthropologists, trained to extract over-all patterns from material on small, preliterate societies, who attempt to extract the same kind of pattern from the masses of available material on American behavior. In such an analysis the publications of the research workers on American sex behavior, and the responses of critics, reviewers, librarians (cf. Proceedings of American Social Hygiene Association, 1948; Geddes, 1954) become part of the data that the anthropologists use. The check on the accuracy of such an analysis must come from detailed studies, on the one hand, and consistent theoretic approaches, on the other.

With these provisos, I shall attempt a brief sketch of American sex behavior, as it has been developing over the period since World War I. It must be understood that this model refers to no single individual, but the most detailed analysis of any single individual should show a systematic relationship to the model. The case of an American Mennonite, or a Puerto Rican resident in New York, or a Moslem student's encounter with an American middle-class girl in a Southwestern College, although containing many elements of foreign cultural behavior, should nevertheless show a systematic relationship to the over-all patterns of recognized American sexual behavior at the present time.

In contemporary American national attitudes toward sex, sex behavior is regarded as necessary for complete mental and physical health during adulthood, and such be-

havior must be exercised within the married state. All departures from this mode—deferred marriage after maturity, a divorced or widowed state which is not remedied by another marriage, vows of religious celibacy, single-purposed devotion to some intellectual or artistic pursuit, sex relations with more than one partner (of either sex), masturbation as an adult except under special circumstances such as among males isolated from women when it is preferred to homosexual behavior—are regarded as either contributing to poor mental health or as a sign of poor mental health. Unmarried adults are poor risks in any enterprise requiring stability of character; even the astronauts must be married. Within the married state, some kind of normal regular sex life should exist, about which there is the widest possible difference of opinion as to what constitutes an appropriate number of sex contacts. As in American attitudes toward digestion, bad effects may be expected if body products bank up inside the body; they should pass through the body and out (cf. Kinsey, Pomeroy and Martin's (1948) definition of sex outlets). Adolescents are in a difficult position because it is recognized that they are sexually mature, even though they are not psychologically or socially ready for marriage. While in school no social expectation of consummated sex relationships is permitted, although the same-aged boy in the army will be provided with adequate prophylactic information. Earlier and earlier marriage, within narrower social groups, where the future parents-in-law know each other, accompany an increasing parental condoning of premartial sex activities of young people who intend to marry.

Sex activity is good for one, just as sleep, recreation, exercise, food, and excretion are good for one. If indulged in as ends rather than as means they may be bad for one. So people sleep "to be fresh next day," exercise to reduce or keep up their muscle tone, and engage in sex activity, if single to keep themselves in good shape, and if married to "have a good personal relationship with the spouse." Sex engaged in for its own sake, as an end, is regarded as bad. All seeking of stimulation, through pornographic literature, bad company, strip tease burlesque, etc., is bad.

Good sex activity involves face-to-face intercourse and should end in satisfaction, seen as ejaculation for the male, and in satisfaction, seen as orgasm, real or feigned, for the female. Either partner may feel justified in self-reproach, or reproach of the other, if this does not occur. All variations on this full sex act of whatever sort, different position, various types of stimulation of other body parts, coitus interruptus as a contraceptive, are felt to be bad for one, resulting in nervousness and tension. They are also against the law in many states and acceptable causes for divorce.

To stabilize marriage, sex compatibility is not enough; there must also be children, either conceived within marriage, adopted, or produced by artificial insemination. However, inability to conceive is not regarded as a bar to marriage; childlessness is a socially remediable state.

Sex is "natural," but because of the extent to which it is still a taboo subject, it is hard to get enough information about it; one is never sure that the practice of oneself and one's marriage partner is "normal," and information on the subject should be sought from books, experts, lovelorn columns. Sex relations should occur between people who are as near as possible equals in class, race, education, only a few years apart, the male preferably slightly older, and all extreme differences in ages or experience which would put one individual in a teaching position toward the other are disapproved. Technique is permissible if learned from books, but disapproved of as a sign of wide experience.

The old double standard in which a male was expected to sow his wild oats has almost disappeared, as has the double standard for class, although Ehrmann's study (Ehrmann, 1959) shows greater frequency of boys dating a girl of a lower class than of middle-class girls dating below their class level. Interest in technical virginity is also disappearing. In the 1940's a marriageable couple made "a clean breast" to each other and started with "a clean slate." Today, with the convention of early going steady,

neither may have had any sex experience except with the other.

In practice, new double standards have developed. Boys are more protective and more likely to postpone full sex relations with a girl whom they plan to marry than with a casual date. Girls are less self-protective and rejecting with boys whom they plan to marry. As a result, other men's girls are treated with less chivalry, and elaborate protections have grown up against interfering between another man and his girl. Young people without specific heterosexual alliances of some sort are treated as potential sex partners, and unmarried and uncommitted people over 25 may be expected to meet each other's sex needs or run the risk of arousing a great deal of hostility.

Within this narrow and demanding set of formal standards and informal expectations, the anxiety about normality and fear of inversion or inadequacy are very great. The pressure on the young male to assume full sexual activities and accompanying social and psychologic responsibilities is extreme, and his probable adequacy a source of anxiety to his parents. Any anomaly of anatomy, physiology, stance, posture, gesture, voice, preference for any type of activity regarded as female, too strong and persistent friendships for other boys, or enthusiams for the company of older or younger males, anomalies of height—failing to grow fast enough being worse than being unusually tall—are lamented, and medical and psychiatric help is likely to be sought. The pressure is only a little less for girls, but whereas a generation ago it was the tomboy who was disapproved, today prepubertal girls are scrutinized for lack of positive female attractiveness rather than for too much virility. Sexual attractiveness is believed to be something which can be artificially enhanced by grooming, practice in social relations, drugs and medications, and various forms of psychologic devices. All these devices serve to offset the anxieties induced by the constant scrutiny of adults and peers. There is no general allowance for the existence of individuals who naturally have more or less libidinal attraction; male successes are explained by the fact that the fortunate male wears a special hat, and the girls gather around; the less successful young male who fails to attract girls may attribute the failure to the fact that he did not comb his hair or put the right hair oil on it.

This attitude toward sex as something that can be manipulated is consonant with other attitudes toward the body as a machine which should work; if it does not work it should be fixed, and people who fail to get it fixed, to "do something about it," are given neither sympathy nor quarter by the society.

Other bodily manifestations of glandular activity are treated in the same way. A child who fails to grow at the right rate should be given medication; dysmenorrhea as an excuse from a variety of fatiguing and irksome physical activities is no longer allowed—here medication and exercise are believed to remedy the condition; morning sickness during pregnancy is interpreted as either glandular imbalance, when medication is indicated, or psychologic rejection of the pregnancy, when psychotherapy or "change in one's attitude" is indicated. Delivery is likewise to be controlled, either by appropriate drugs or the spreading demand for "natural childbirth," manipulating the body and mind before birth, so that medication will not be needed. Breast feeding, which 25 years ago was disappearing, is now also something which the mother can prepare to do, or if her milk cannot be made adequate, then a controlled formula should be given to the baby while it is held as if it were being breast fed.

It can be seen from all this that early and absolute assignment of sex, continuous therapeutic interference with any anomalies which suggest incomplete or inappropriate sexual maturation, and substitution of therapy whenever a loss of endocrine functioning occurs, are all highly congruent with this contemporary emphasis on the importance of every individual being able to function in the same way. Not only this pressure to seem to conform, but the burden of nonconformity with the attendant sense of sin, or guilt, puts a heavy pressure on the very large proportion of Americans who deviate from the recognized patterns of temperament and behavior.

IX. References[18]

ALEXANDER, F., AND HEALY, W. 1935. *Roots of Crime*. New York and London: Alfred A. Knopf.

American Social Hygiene Association. 1948. *Problems of Sexual Behavior*. New York: American Social Hygiene Association.

ARMSTRONG, W. 1928. *Rossel Island*. Cambridge: Cambridge University Press.

BALINT, M. 1952. *Primary Love and Pschoanalytic Technique*. London: Hogarth Press, Ltd.

BATESON, G. 1947. Sex and culture. Ann. New York Acad. Sc., **47**, 647.

BATESON, G. 1958. *Naven*, 2nd ed. Stanford: Stanford University Press.

BATESON, G., AND MEAD, M. 1942. *Balinese Character*, Special Publications, 2. New York: New York Academy of Sciences.

BENEDEK, T., AND RUBENSTEIN, B. 1939. Correlations between ovarian activity and psychodynamic processes. Psychosom. Med., **1**, 245–270.

BENEDICT, R. 1934. *Patterns of Culture*. Boston and New York: Houghton, Mifflin Company.

BETTELHEIM, B. 1954. *Symbolic Wounds: Puberty Rites and the Envious Male*. Glencoe: Free Press.

BIBRING, G. L. 1953. On the "passing of the Oedipus complex" in a matriarchal family setting. In *Drives, Affects, Behavior*, R. M. Loewenstein, Ed., pp. 278–284. New York: International Universities Press.

BONILLA, E. S. 1958. *The Normative Patterns of the Puerto Rican Family in Various Situational Contexts*. Ann Arbor: University Microfilms.

BOWLBY, J. 1951. *Maternal Care and Mental Health*, Monograph 2. Geneva: World Health Organization.

BROWN, D. G. 1958. Sex role development in a changing culture. Psychol. Bull., **55**, 232–242.

BURKS, B. S. 1928. The relative influence of nature and nurture upon mental development: comparative study of foster parent-foster child resemblance and true parent-true child resemblance. Yearbook Nat. Soc. Study Educ., **27(I)**, 219.

CARPENTER, C. R. 1934. A field study of the behavior and social relations of howling monkeys. Comp. Psychol. Monogr., **10**.

CARPENTER, C. R. 1940. A field study in Siam of the behavior and social relations of the gibbon (*Hylobates lar*). Comp. Psychol. Monogr., **16**, 1.

CARPENTER, C. R. 1942. Sexual behavior of free ranging rhesus monkeys (*Macaca mulatta*).

[18] In the references given in the text I have included tribal names where references to the original publications might add illumination for the student, or where the same people are referred to several times, using the form: (Arapesh, Mead, 1935). Where resort to the primary source is not likely to amplify the point, I have used more general references, *e.g.*, Westermarck, without the tribal name.

II. Periodicity of estrus, homosexual, autoerotic and nonconformist behavior. J. Comp. Psychol., **33**, 113.

COBB, S., AND LINDEMAN, E. 1943. *Neuropsychiatric Observations: Management of the Cocoanut Grove Burns at the Massachusetts General Hospital*. Philadelphia: J. B. Lippincott Company.

COCHRAN, W. G., MOSTELLER, F., AND TUKEY, J. W. 1955. Statistical problems of the Kinsey report. In *Sexual Behavior in American Society*, J. Himelhoch and S. F. Fava, Eds., p. 68. New York: W. W. Norton & Company, Inc.

CRAWLEY, E. 1927. *The Mystic Rose, a Study of Primitive Marriage and of Primitive Thought in Its Bearing on Marriage*, revised Ed. London: Methuen & Company, Ltd.

CZAPLICKA, M. A. 1914. *Aboriginal Siberia*. Oxford: Clarendon Press.

DAVIS, K. B. 1926. Periodicity of sex desire. Am. J. Obst. & Gynec., **12**, 824–836.

DAVIS, K. B. 1929. *Factors in the Sex Life of 2200 Women*. New York and London: Harper & Brothers.

DEUTSCH, H. 1944. *The Psychology of Women: A Psychoanalytic Interpretation*. New York: Grune & Stratton.

DEVEREUX, G. 1937. Institutionalized homosexuality of the Mohave Indians. Human Biol., **47**, 603.

DICKINSON, R. L., AND BEAM, L. 1931. *A Thousand Marriages*. Baltimore: The Williams & Wilkins Company.

DOLLARD, J. 1937. *Caste and Class in a Southern Town*. New Haven: Yale University Press.

EHRMANN, W. 1959. *Premarital Dating Behavior*. New York: Henry Holt & Company, Inc.

ELKAN, E. 1948. The evolution of female orgastic ability—a biological survey. Internat. J. Sex, **2**, Aug., 1; Nov., 84.

ELKAN, E. 1950. The "normal" woman. Internat. J. Sex, **4**, 1.

ELWIN, V. 1939. *The Baiga*. London: John Murray.

ERICKSON, M. 1938. Negation or reversal of legal testimony. Arch. Neurol. & Psychiat., **40**, 548.

ERIKSON, E. 1950. *Childhood and Society*. New York: W. W. Norton & Company, Inc.

ERIKSON, E. 1951. Sex differences in the play configurations of pre-adolescents. Am. J. Orthopsychiat., **21**, 667–692.

ERIKSON, E. 1959. *Identity and the Life Cycle: Selected Papers*, Psychological Issues Monograph Series, Vol. 1, No. 1. New York: International Universities Press.

FORD, C. S. 1945. A comparative study of human reproduction. In *Yale University Publications in Anthropology*, p. 32. New Haven: Yale University Press.

FORD, C. S., AND BEACH, F. A. 1951. *Patterns of Sexual Behavior*. New York: Paul B. Hoeber, Inc.

FORTUNE, R. F. 1932. *Sorcerers of Dobu*. London: Routledge & Kegan Paul, Ltd.; New York: E. P. Dutton & Company, Inc.

FORTUNE, R. F. 1935. *Manus Religion*. Philadelphia: American Philosophical Society.

FREUD, A. 1955. Special experiences of young children, particularly in times of social disturbance. In *Mental Health and Infant Development*, K. Soddy, Ed., Vol. I. London: Routledge & Kegan Paul, Ltd.

FRIES, M. 1958. Review of the literature on the latency period. J. Hillside Hosp., **7**, 3–16.

GEDDES, D. P. 1954. *An Analysis of the Kinsey Reports on Sexual Behavior in the Human Male and Female*. New York: E. P. Dutton & Company, Inc.

GOODENOUGH, W. 1949. Premarital freedom in Truk: theory and practice. Am. Anthropologist, **51**, 615.

GORER, G. 1938. *Himalayan Village*. London: Michael Joseph.

GORER, G. 1948. *The American People*. New York: W. W. Norton & Company, Inc.

GORER, G. 1955. *Exploring English Character*. London: Cresset.

GRANQVIST, H. 1947. *Birth and Childhood among the Arabs*. Helsingfors: Soderstrom.

GRINNELL, G. B. 1923. *The Cheyenne Indians*. New Haven: Yale University Press.

HAMBLY, W. 1926. *Origins of Education among Primitive Peoples: A Comparative Study in Racial Development*. London: The Macmillan Company.

HAMILTON, G. V. 1914. Sexual tendencies of monkeys and baboons. J. Anim. Behav., **4**, 295.

HAMILTON, G. V. 1929. *A Research in Marriage*. New York: A. and C. Boni, Inc.

HARPER, B. n.d. Infancy; childhood; adolescence; pregnancy and birth, Pueblo of Jemez, 1926–1935. MS.

HARTLEY, P. H. T. 1950. An experimental analysis of interspecific recognition. In *Physiological Mechanisms in Animal Behavior*, J. F. Danielli and R. Brown, Eds. Cambridge: Cambridge University Press.

HENRY, J. 1941. *Jungle People, a Kaingang Tribe of the Highlands of Brazil*. New York: J. J. Augustin.

HILL, W. W. 1935. The status of the hermaphrodite and transvestite in Navaho culture. Am. Anthropologist, **37**, 273–279.

HOGBIN, I. 1935. Native culture of Wogeo. Oceania, **5**, 308.

HOHMAN, L., AND SCHAFFNER, B. 1947. The sex lives of unmarried men. Am. J. Sociol., **52**, 501–507.

HOLMBERG, A. R. 1950. Nomads of the long bow, the Siriono of eastern Bolivia. Smithsonian Institution, Institute of Social Anthropology, p. 10.

HUTCHINSON, G. E. 1959. A speculative consideration of certain possible forms of sexual selection in man. Am. Naturalist, **93**, 81–91.

KINSEY, A. C., POMEROY, W. B., AND MARTIN, C. E. 1948. *Sexual Behavior in the Human Male*. Philadelphia: W. B. Saunders Company.

KINSEY, A. C., POMEROY, W. B., MARTIN, C. E., AND GEBHARD, P. H. 1953. *Sexual Behavior in the*

Human Female. Philadelphia: W. B. Saunders Company.

KLUCKHOHN, C., AND KLUCKHOHN, F. 1948. American culture: generalized and class patterns. In *Conflicts of Power in Modern Society*, pp. 106–128. New York: Conference on Science, Philosophy and Religion.

LEVI-STRAUSS, C. 1949. *Les Structures élémentaires de la Parenté*. Paris: Presses Universitaires de France.

LEVY, D. 1938–39. Maternal overprotection. Psychiatry, **1**, 561–591; **2**, 99–109; **3**, 563–597.

LINTON, R. 1939. Marquesan culture. In *The Individual and His Society*, A. Kardiner, Ed. New York: Columbia University Press.

LOEB, A. M. 1928. Mentawei social organization. Am. Anthropologist, **30**, 408.

LORENZ, K. 1950. The comparative method in studying innate behavior patterns. In *Physiological Mechanisms in Animal Behavior*, J. F. Danielli and R. Brown, Eds. Cambridge: Cambridge University Press.

LORENZ, K. 1959. The role of aggression in group formation. In *Group Processes*, B. Schaffner, Ed., Vol. 4, pp. 181–251. New York: Josiah Macy, Jr., Foundation.

MALINOWSKI, B. 1929. *The Sexual Life of Savages in North-Western Melanesia*. New York: Liveright Publishing Corporation.

MASLOW, A. H. 1936a. The role of dominance in the social and sexual behavior of infrahuman primates. III. A theory of sexual behavior. J. Genet. Psychol., **48**, 310.

MASLOW, A. H. 1936b. The role of dominance in the social and sexual behavior of infrahuman primates. IV. The determination of hierarchy in pairs and in a group. J. Genet. Psychol., **49**, 161.

MEAD, M. 1928. *Coming of Age in Samoa*. New York: William Morrow & Company.

MEAD, M. 1930. *Growing Up in New Guinea*. New York: William Morrow & Company.

MEAD, M. 1932. *The Changing Culture of an Indian Tribe*. New York: Columbia University Press.

MEAD, M. 1934a. Sex life of the unmarried adult in primitive society. In *The Sex Life of the Unmarried Adult*, I. Wile, Ed. New York: Vanguard Press.

MEAD, M. 1934b. Kinship in the Admiralty Islands. Anthropol. Papers, Am. Museum Nat. Hist., **34**, 183.

MEAD, M. 1935. *Sex and Temperament in Three Primitive Societies*. New York: William Morrow & Company.

MEAD, M. (Ed.) 1937. *Cooperation and Competition among Primitive Peoples*. New York and London: McGraw-Hill Book Company, Inc.

MEAD, M. 1938. The mountain Arapesh. I. An importing culture. Anthropol. Papers, Am. Museum Nat. Hist., **36**, 141.

MEAD, M. 1939a. *From the South Seas*. New York: William Morrow & Company.

MEAD, M. 1939b. Expeditions to Bali and New Guinea. Unpublished field notes.

MEAD, M. 1940. The mountain Arapesh. II. Supernaturalism. Anthropol. Papers, Am. Museum Nat. Hist., **37**, 319.

MEAD, M. 1942. Educative effects of social environment as disclosed by studies of primitive societies. In *Environment and Education, A Symposium*, Supplement Educational Monographs, No. 54, p. 48. Chicago: University of Chicago.

MEAD, M. 1947a. The implications of culture change for personality development. Am. J. Orthopsychiat., **17**, 633.

MEAD, M. 1947b. The mountain Arapesh. III. Socio-economic life. IV. Diary of events in Alitoa. Anthropol. Papers, Am. Museum Nat. Hist., **40**, 159.

MEAD, M. 1948. On the implications for anthropology on the Gesell-Ilg approach to maturation. Am. Anthropologist, **49**, 69–77.

MEAD, M. 1949a. Character formation and diachronic theory. In *Social Structure, Studies Presented to A. R. Radcliffe-Brown*, M. Fortes, Ed. Oxford: Clarendon Press.

MEAD, M. 1949b. *Male and Female. A Study of the Sexes in a Changing World*. New York: William Morrow & Company.

MEAD, M. 1949c. The mountain Arapesh. V. The record of Unabelin with Rorschach analyses. Anthropol. Papers, Am. Museum Nat. Hist., **41**, 289.

MEAD, M. 1953. Sex and censorship in contemporary society. In *New World Writing*, p. 3 New York: New American Library.

MEAD, M. 1956. *New Lives for Old*. New York: William Morrow & Company; London: Victor Gollancz, Ltd.

MEAD, M. 1958. The childhood genesis of sex differences in behavior. In *Discussions on Child Development. Vol. 3, The Third Meeting of the World Health Organization Study Group on the Psychobiological Development of the Child, Geneva 1955*. J. M. Tanner and B. Inhelder, Eds. pp. 13–90, passim. London: Tavistock Publications, Ltd.

MEAD, M. 1959. Cultural contexts of puberty and adolescence. Bull. Philadelphia A. Psychoanalysis, **9**, 59–79.

MEAD, M. 1960. Weaver of the border. In *In the Company of Man*, J. Casagrande, Ed. New York: Harper & Brothers.

MÉTRAUX, R., AND MEAD, M. 1954. *Themes in French Culture*. Stanford: Stanford University Press.

MIRSKY, J. 1937. The Dakota. In *Cooperation and Competition among Primitive Peoples*, M. Mead, Ed., pp. 382–427. New York: McGraw-Hill Book Company.

MITTELMAN, B., WOLFF, H. G., AND SCHARF, M. P. 1942. Emotions and gastroduodenal function: experimental studies on patients with gastritis, duodenitis, and peptic ulcer. Psychosom. Med., **4**, 5–61.

MONTAGU, A. 1938. *Coming into Being among the Australian Aborigines*. New York: E. P. Dutton & Company, Inc.

MONTAGU, A. 1957. *The Reproductive Development of the Female with Especial Reference to the Period of Adolescent Sterility*, 2nd ed. New York: Julian Press, Inc.

MURDOCK, C. P. 1949. *Social Structure*. New York: The Macmillan Company.

NYROP, C. 1898. *The Kiss and Its History*. Chicago: Stromberg, Allen & Company (1901, London: Sands & Company).

PARSONS, E. C. 1913. *Religious Chastity, an Ethnological Study*, by John Main (pseudonym). New York: Macaulay Company.

PHOENIX, C. H., GOY, R. W., GERALL, A. A., AND YOUNG, W. C. 1959. Organizing action of prenatally administered testosterone propionate on the tissues mediating mating behavior in the female guinea pig. Endocrinology, **65**, 369–382.

PLOSS, H. 1927. Das Weib in der Natur- und Volkerkunde, F. von Reitzenstein, Ed., 11 Aufl., 3 vols. Berlin: Neuseld & Henius.

PRINCE PETER OF GREECE. 1948. Tibetan, Toda, and Tiya polyandry: a report on field investigations. Tr. New York Acad. Sc., **10**, 210.

RATTRAY, R. S. 1923. *Ashanti*. London: Oxford University Press.

READ, G. D. 1953. *Childbirth without Fear*. New York: Harper & Brothers.

REICHARD, G. A. 1928. Social life of the Navajo Indians. Columbia Univ., Contr. Anthropol., **7**, 1.

ROSCOE, J. 1911. *The Baganda*. London: The Macmillan Company.

SEARS, R. R., MACCOBY, E. E., AND LEVIN, H. 1957. *Patterns of Child Rearing*. Evanston: Row, Peterson & Company.

SEDA, E. See Bonilla, E. S.

SELIGMAN, B. Z. 1929. Incest and descent, their influence on social organization. J. Royal Anthropol. Inst. Gr. Brit. and Ireland, **59**, 231.

SEWARD, G. H. 1946. *Sex and the Social Order*. New York and London: McGraw-Hill Book Company, Inc.

SPIRO, M. E. 1958. *Children of the Kibbutz*. Cambridge: Harvard University Press.

SUMNER, W. G., AND KELLER, A. G. 1927. *The Science of Society*. New Haven: Yale University Press.

TANNER, J., AND INHELDER, B. (Eds.) 1956, 1958. *Discussions on Child Development, Meetings of the World Health Organization Study Group on the Psychobiological Development of the Child, 1953, 1954, 1955. Vols. 1 and 2, 1956; Vol. 3, 1958*. London: Tavistock Publications, Ltd.

UNDEUTSCH, U. 1955. Comparative incidence of premarital coitus in Scandinavia, Germany, and the United States. In *Sexual Behavior in American Society*, J. Himelhoch and S. F. Fava, Eds., pp. 360–363. New York: W. W. Norton & Company, Inc.

VAN GENNEP, A. 1909. *Les Rites de Passage*. Paris: E. Nourry. (English translation by M. B. Vizedom and G. L. Caffee, 1960, University of Chicago Press.)

WARNER, W. L., LUNT, P. S., STOLE, L., AND LOW, J. O. 1941–47. Yankee City Series. I. (W. L. W. and P. S. L.) The social life of the modern community. II. (W. L. W. and P. S. L.) The status system of a modern community. III. (W. L. W. and L. S.) The social systems of American ethnic groups. IV. (W. L. W. and J. O. L.) The social system of a modern factory. New Haven: Yale University Press.

WESTERMARCK, E. 1908. *The Origin and Development of the Moral Ideas*, Vol. II. London: Macmillan Company.

WESTERMARCK, E. 1921. *The History of Human Marriage*, 5th ed. London: Macmillan Company.

WIRZ, P. 1922. *Die Marind-Anim von Hollandisch-Sud-New-Guinea*. Hamburg: L. Friederichsen.

YOUNG, W. C. 1957. Genetic and psychological determinants of sexual behavior patterns. In *Hormones, Brain Function, and Behavior*, H. Hoagland, Ed., pp. 75–98. New York: Academic Press, Inc.

AUTHOR INDEX

Bromberg, Y. M., 987
Bronski, M., 118
Brooks, C. McC., 199, 281, 520
Brooks, W., 773
Brossard, G., 1046
Brosseau, G. E., Jr., 23
Brouha, L., 540
Brouwer, R., 1174, 1175, 1178, 1186, 1209
Browman, L. G., 259, 529
Brown, A. D., 222
Brown, C. A., 810
Brown, D. G., 1420, 1421, 1426, 1427, 1454, 1473
Brown, E. R., 391
Brown, F., 681
Brown, J. B., 449, 473
Brown, J. H., 458
Brown, J. H. U., 242
Brown, J. R., 1153
Brown, L. H. V., 176, 183
Brown, L. T., 188, 1098, 1126
Brown, M. M., 346, 347, 669
Brown, M. Mac N., 1210, 1212
Brown, P. S., 245, 257, 267
Brown, R. H., 1179
Brown, R. L., 712, 732
Brown, R. W., 241
Brown, R. Z., 1313
Brown, S. O., 692
Brown, W. E., 250, 461, 517, 529, 530, 538, 539, 984, 985
Brown, W. O., 688
Browne, J. C., 476
Browne, J. S. L., 531, 534, 583, 984
Brown-Grant, K., 479
Browning, W. H., 669
Brozec, J., 261, 262, 668
Bruce, H. M., 480, 771, 959, 998, 999
Bruckner, J. H., 1108, 1134
Brüggemann, H., 626, 627
Brull, L., 1050
Bruner, J. A., 94, 100, 113, 122, 127, 261, 337, 932, 985
Bruns, P., 1017
Brunstad, G. E., 998
Bruzzone, S., 271, 471, 474, 516, 517
Bryan, W. L., 681
Bryans, F., 583, 973
Bryans, F. E., 250, 467, 519, 530, 534, 559, 984
Bryant, H. H., 1015
Bryce, T. H., 856
Bryson, V., 711
Brzezinski, A., 987
Buchanan, G. D., 459, 851
Buchholz, R., 467, 1255
Bucht, H., 994
Buckner, G. D., 1107
Buckner, P. J., 799, 800, 802
Bucy, P. C., 224, 225, 227
Bülbring, E., 1103
Bulbrook, R. D., 467
Bullard, J. F., 1011
Bullough, W. S., 451–453, 805, 1063–1065, 1067, 1174, 1276, 1280
Bulmer, D., 922, 926
Bunce, P. L., 248, 424, 433, 434
Bunde, C. A., 248

Bunding, I., 613
Bunge, R. G., 728
Bunn, J. P., 520
Buño, W., 896
Bunting, H., 814, 888, 937
Bur, G. E., 309, 344, 350
Burch, A. B., 162
Burch, J. C., 510
Burckhard, G., 817, 827, 844
Burdak, V. D., 1069
Burdette, W. J., 17
Burdick, H. O., 822, 823, 827, 859
Burford, T. H., 349, 538, 567
Burgdorf, A. L., 185, 186
Burger, H., 825
Burger, J. F., 1174, 1192
Burger, J. W., 276, 1045, 1046, 1137, 1141, 1143, 1279, 1342
Burger, W. L., 1044
Burgos, M. H., 328, 888, 912, 913
Burkhardt, J., 738
Burkhart, E. Z., 401, 410, 425, 427
Burks, B. S., 1435
Burlend, T. H., 1036
Burmester, B. R., 1091, 1122
Burnasheva, S. A., 756, 764, 767, 768
Burnet, F. M., 746
Burns, F. H., 1346
Burns, R. K., 37, 44, 77, 79–82, 84, 85, 87, 89–91, 94, 105–108, 111–114, 120, 122–124, 127, 132, 136, 138–140, 143, 151, 308, 374, 1007, 1035, 1061, 1065, 1067, 1117, 1122, 1198, 1222, 1223
Burr, G. O., 685
Burr, H. S., 816, 827
Burr, M. M., 685
Burrill, M. W., 100, 262, 375, 423–425, 465, 507, 682, 686
Burrill, W. W., 338
Burrows, H., 143, 241, 251, 261, 264, 267, 276, 399, 426, 427
Burrows, W. H., 253, 681, 728, 1101, 1128, 1142, 1147, 1180, 1198, 1278, 1289, 1301, 1302, 1354
Burstein, L. S., 332
Burt, A. S., 210, 258
Burt, A. W. A., 618
Burt, C. C., 992
Burviana, L. M., 756
Burwell, C. S., 992
Busch, D. W. H., 622
Bush, F. E., 163
Buss, I. O., 1114, 1281
Butcher, E. O., 805
Butenandt, A., 965
Butler, E. J., 1110
Butler, W. W. S., III, 392, 394
Butt, H., 348
Butterworth, C. E., Jr., 397
Butts, J. S., 760, 765
Buu-Hoï, N. P., 343
Buus, O., 392
Buxton, C. L., 457, 514, 582
Buyse, A., 77, 103–105, 127, 132
Buzzati-Traverso, A., 25
Byerly, T. C., 253, 681, 1101,

1128, 1146–1148, 1278, 1289, 1301, 1302, 1354
Byrnes, W. W., 265, 266, 268, 271, 503, 1199, 1209

Cabot, A. T., 429
Cadden, J. F., 994
Cady, P., 608
Caffier, P., 908
Cahane, M., 279
Cahane, T., 279
Cairy, C. F., 600
Calatroni, C. J., 472, 509
Calder, A., 1187, 1191
Caldwell, A. L., 464
Calhoun, J. B., 1245
Caligaris, L. C. S., 979
Callahan, W. P., 1347
Callenbach, E. W., 1137, 1145
Callow, R. C., 372
Calzolari, G., 336
Cameron, A. H., 64
Campbell, B., 622, 1343
Campbell, E. A., 1118
Campbell, H. J., 283
Campbell, J., 57, 62
Campbell, J. A., 741
Campbell, M., 176, 177, 203
Campbell, R. M., 690
Campos, A. C., 1090, 1125
Camus, L., 396
Canale, L., 252
Canivenc, R., 250, 537, 604, 851, 1325
Cannon, W. B., 274, 1331, 1345
Cantarow, A., 449, 475, 476, 479, 508, 670, 673, 680, 683, 691, 1108, 1126
Cantarow, E., 684
Canter, H. Y., 351
Cantwell, G., 52
Caplan, I. J., 987
Cara, J., 344
Card, L. E., 253, 254, 739, 1100, 1107, 1109, 1110, 1122, 1126–1128, 1290, 1291, 1299, 1303, 1354, 1357
Carew, L. B., Jr., 1119
Carey, J. B., 997
Caridroit, F., 1090
Carlisle, D. B., 251
Carlson, A. J., 1189
Carlson, F. D., 766
Carlsten, A., 996
Carmichael, E. S., 245
Carmichael, H. T., 1174, 1390
Carmon, J. L., 308
Carpenter, C. R., 723, 1174, 1176, 1179, 1180, 1190, 1192, 1240–1242, 1254, 1312, 1346, 1404, 1461, 1470
Carpenter, H. M., 319
Carr, C. J., 1015
Carr, R. M., 1355
Carr, W. J., 1208
Carranza, J., 1036
Carroll, K. K., 685
Carroll, W. R., 653
Carson, H. L., 23, 25, 26, 34, 66, 739, 1055
Carson, J. R., 1106, 1107, 1137, 1292, 1354
Carstens, H. P., 731, 734

Jessop, W. J. E., 672
Jewell, P. A., 628
Jewett, T. C., Jr., 315
Joël, C. A., 345, 386, 389, 392, 397, 741, 757
Joel, P. B., 657, 658
Johannson, K.-I., 771
Johnson, A., 381, 382
Johnson, A. M., 1427
Johnson, B. C., 672, 688, 692
Johnson, C. E., 479, 985
Johnson, D. C., 465–467
Johnson, G. E., 500
Johnson, R. B., 762
Johnson, R. E., 250, 602–605, 610, 680, 1328
Johnson, R. H., 332, 1007
Johnson, R. M., 394, 604, 610, 613
Johnson, R. T., 280, 282
Johnson, S. Y., 479
Johnston, A. W., 61–63
Johnston, D. W., 1287, 1288, 1352
Johnston, E. F., 52
Johnston, J. E., 383, 830
Johnston, M. B., 381
Johnston, M. E., 479, 480
Johnston, P. M., 1060
Jolly, J., 800
Jolly, W. A., 1003
Jones, C. C., 692
Jones, E. W., 250
Jones, G. E., 894, 931
Jones, G. E. S., 346, 347, 482, 672, 998, 1211, 1214
Jones, H. W., 1406, 1407
Jones, H. W., Jr., 660, 1395
Jones, J. E., 931, 1007
Jones, J. W., 1036, 1180, 1184
Jones, K. W., 58, 59, 62, 64, 129
Jones, W. G., 712, 714, 715
Jones, W. H., 652
Jones, W. J., 530
Jones-Seaton, A., 810, 811
Jordan, D. S., 1047
Jordan, E. O., 1043, 1055
Jordan, E. S., 849
Jordan, L., 1176, 1177
Jorpes, E., 743, 826
Josimovich, J. B., 322
Jost, A., 82, 83, 100, 104, 108, 112–118, 120–122, 125, 129, 132–134, 143–147, 149–151, 163, 241, 256, 345, 423, 1222, 1223
Jowsey, J. R., 1120
Juhn, M., 1090, 1102, 1121, 1123, 1128, 1132
Junck, E. C., 335, 342, 350
Jungck, E. C., 270, 343
Junge, J. M., 742, 825
Junila, W. A., 1137
Junkmann, K., 189, 540

Kabat, C., 1114, 1281
Kagan, J., 1185, 1215, 1216, 1219, 1340
Kahan, I. H., 350
Kahane, E., 386
Kahlo, L., 1347
Kahlson, G., 996
Kahmann, H., 1320, 1336

Kahn, M. W., 1358
Kahn, R. H., 689
Kahnt, L. C., 472
Kaijser, K., 59, 62, 63, 64
Kaiser, I. H., 561, 584
Kajdi, C., 680
Kallas, H., 503
Kalliala, H., 622
Kallman, F. J., 1427
Kalman, S. M., 660
Kaltenbach, J. C., 151, 1348
Kamell, S. A., 539
Kamemoto, F. I. 1135, 1136
Kammlade, W. G., Jr., 251, 258, 260, 500, 501
Kaneko, T., 1117, 1118, 1134
Kaneo, T., 687
Kang, Y. S., 65
Kann, S., 1047, 1053
Kannas, O., 1153
Kanter, A. E., 1053
Kantor, T. G., 943
Kao, C. Y., 815
Kaplan, N. O., 396, 652, 658
Kaplan, W. D., 1112
Kar, A. B., 346, 480, 1091, 1106, 1123
Kare, M. R., 1091
Karlin, L. J., 884
Karnovsky, M. L., 889
Karplus, J., 281
Karvonen, M. J., 622
Kascht, M. E., 991
Kassavina, B. S., 758
Kasturirangan, L. R., 1058, 1059
Katchalsky, A., 757
Katsh, S., 151, 389, 423, 424, 426, 465, 681, 745, 747, 749
Katsuki, K., 35
Katsuragi, T., 1129
Katz, D., 1294
Katz, L. N., 1117, 1118
Kaufman, L., 1300, 1354
Kaufman, N., 679
Kaufmann, C., 467, 582
Kaufmann, K., 474
Kaunitz, H., 262, 677, 680, 686, 688
Kawaguchi, E., 35
Kawai, T., 512
Kawakami, M., 458, 1189, 1195, 1196, 1205–1207, 1209, 1214, 1350
Kaye, B. M., 734
Kazanskii, B. M., 255
Kearns, J. W., 248, 424, 433, 434
Keast, J. A., 1342
Keaty, C., 267, 517
Kedem, O., 757
Keene, C. M., 1392
Keene, M. F. L., 163
Kehl, R., 253, 284, 688, 1004, 1037–1039, 1041, 1045–1047, 1052, 1054
Kehl, R. M., 1050, 1051, 1054
Keiffer, M. H., 1018
Keith, N. M., 988
Kellar, R. J., 992
Keller, A. D., 281, 283
Keller, A. G., 1457
Keller, E. B., 654
Keller, K., 52, 77

Keller, T. B., 180, 189, 190
Kellerman, G. M., 382
Kelley, K., 457
Kelley, R. M., 647
Kellner, G., 451, 455
Kellog, M., 823
Kelly, T. L., 184, 242
Kelsey, F. O., 165, 200
Kemeny, T., 690
Kemp, F. H., 626, 627
Kemp, T., 337
Kempf, R., 271, 530
Kendall, E. C., 612
Kendall, K. A., 691
Kendeigh, S. C., 1270, 1271, 1284, 1285, 1288, 1298, 1299, 1356
Kennaway, N. M., 427
Kennedy, A., 989
Kennedy, H. S., 482
Kennedy, J., 741, 742
Kennedy, J. S., 1332
Kenneth, J. H., 961
Kenny, J. F., 988, 990
Kensler, C. J., 1108, 1126
Kent, G. C., Jr., 1188, 1206
Kenyon, A., 1174
Kenyon, A. T., 1390
Kerkhof, A. M., 127
Kerly, M., 653
Kerr, W. E., 33
Kerr, W. R., 749
Kerrigan, S., 1317, 1331
Kertesz, P., 690
Kessell, H. R., 346
Kestel, L., 270, 342
Ketterer, B., 201
Keye, J. D., Jr., 322
Keys, A., 261, 262, 668
Khayyal, M. A., 653, 655
Kiddy, C. A., 749, 750, 773,
Kihara, H., 40
Kihlström, J. E., 709, 722, 747, 751
Killian, J. A., 381
Kim, J. N., 1003
Kimball, R. F., 44, 65
Kimeldorf, D. J., 315
Kimming, J., 385
Kinder, E. F., 1306, 1309, 1337, 1346
King, A. B., 322
King, E., 242
King, E. J., 390, 391
King, E. S. J., 746
King, F. A., 1307
King, G. M., 1180, 1184
King, H. D., 851, 959
King, J., 1355
King, J. A., 1254, 1357
King, J. T., 346, 684
King, L. S., 523
King, R. L., 810
King, S. L., 275
King, T. E., 384, 385, 756
King, W. A., 676
Kingery, H. M., 504, 804
Kinney, T. D., 679
Kinney, W. C., Jr., 728
Kinochita, M., 252
Kinoshita, T., 1063
Kinoshita, Y., 1044, 1045, 1052, 1060, 1061

SUBJECT INDEX

1517

Adrenal corticoids (*cont.*)
  levels during pregnancy, 1007
    hypophysectomy and, 1006
  plasma binding, 475–476
Adrenal functioning, hypophyseal stalk transection and, 283
Adrenal progesterone and mammary development, 599–600
Adrenal weight, ratio to body weight in wild compared with domestic turkeys, 1354
Adrenalectomy
  and hypophyseal cytology, 196–197
  and nest-building in rat, 1308
  androgen replacement therapy in ducks, 1104
Adrenaline (see Epinephrine)
Adrenogenital syndrome (see Hyperadrenocorticism)
Aeguidens latifrens, aggressive behavior, reproductive state and, 1254
Agapornis fischeri, egg-laying determinate, 1144
Agapornis roseicollis, egg-laying determinate, 1144
Agapornis taranta, egg-laying determinate, 1144
Age and uterine responsiveness to estrogen, 265–266
Agelaius tricolor
  egg-laying, suppression of by addition of eggs, 1283
  incubation behavior and broodiness, interchangeability, 1303
  nest, 1269
  nest-building, temporal relation
    to copulation, 1271
    to egg-laying, 1273
    to follicular growth, 1274
  parental behavior, new nestlings and, 1301
Age of animal
  and acid phosphatase in prostate, 390
  and androgen content of bull testis, 1204
  and estrogen secretion in chick, 1113
  and hypophyseal gonadotrophin secretion, 256–258, 503, 1129
  and induction of ovulation, 514–515
  and mating behavior, 1202–1204
    tissue responsiveness or hormone reduction?, 1204
  and ovarian follicular growth, 457, 807
  and ovarian functioning, 476–478
  and ovarian responsiveness to gonadotrophins, 263–264, 477–478, 1127–1128, 1130
  and oviducal response to bronchitis in birds, 1125
  and parental behavior, 1334–1335
  and prostate zinc, 381
  and response of testis
    to androgen, 338, 1104
    to cortisone, 1104
  and responsiveness
    of prostate to estrogen, 428
    of testis to gonadotrophins, 337
  and running activity in rats, 1203–1204
  and seminal fructose secretion, 383
  and testis atrophy in fishes, 1036
  and testis structure, 309
  and tissue responsiveness
    to androgen, 419–420, 422, 1202–1203, 1214
    to estrogen, 1214
Aggressive behavior
  androgen and, 1197, 1247–1248, 1254–1255, 1258–1259, 1387
  genetic basis, 1244–1246, 1355
  in birds, relation to color, 1260
  in mice, isolation after birth and, 1358
  methods of study, 1242–1250
    control of the substrate, 1244–1250
  ovarian hormones in hamster and, 1256
  releasers, 1260

Aggressive behavior (*cont.*)
  reproductive state and 1250, 1256
  sex dimorphism in response to androgen, 1254–1255, 1258
Aggressive-submissive behavior, dual mechanisms? 1257
Agkistrodon contortrix, sperm storage in female, 1055
Aipysurus, ovoviviparity, 1057
Alces americana
  development of behavior, parental care and, 1358
  social behavior, reproductive state and, 1250
Alcidae, egg-laying pattern, 1277
18-Aldo-11-desoxycorticosterone and aldosterone biosynthesis, 646
Aldolase in male accessory reproductive glands, 392
Aldosterone
  biosynthesis, 644–647
  during pregnancy, 979–980
  levels in pregnancy toxemia, 979
Alectura lathami
  incubation, 1295
  nest-building
    androgen and, 1275
    role of sexes, 1275
Alkaline glycerophosphatase, estrogen and amount of, 652
Alkaline phosphatase
  histochemical differentiation, 890
  in coagulating gland, androgen and, 413
  in epididymis, androgen and, 715
  in male accessory reproductive glands, 391
    functional significance, 419
  in placenta, 938–942
    functional significance, 938–940
  in prostate, androgen and 402, 406, 411–412
  in seminal vesicles, androgen and, 409–410, 415
Alligator
  adrenal cortex development, 1062
  breeding season, 1050
  gonads, development of, 1062
  hermaphroditism in, 1065, 1067
  hypophyseal gonadal relations, 253
  mesonephros, androgen and, 1047
  Müllerian duct, development, 1062
  ovary of immature animal, 1050
  oviduct
    androgen and, 1047
    of immature animal, 1052
  penis, 1042
    androgen and, 1047
  pseudohermaphroditism in, 1065, 1067
  sex differentiation
    estrone and, 1069
    testosterone and, 1069
  spermatogenesis, seasonal occurrence, 1037
  testis, interstitial cells, 1039
Allopregnane-3-(α)-ol-20-one in pig testis, 332
Allopregnane-3-(β)-ol-20-one in pig testis, 332
Alosa, hermaphroditism, 1063
Alouatta ursina
  behavior maturation, critical periods, 1404
  social organization, 1242
Altricial young, birds, 1298
Alytes mesonephric duct, sperm storage in, 1040
Alytes obstetricans, transport of developing eggs by male, 1048
Ambystoma
  chromosome pattern, 44–45
  gonad transformation
    dominance of testis, 87–89
    gonadal hormones and, 94, 95
    histologic changes, 88

Androgen (*cont.*)
  and amplexus, 1046
  and arousal mechanism of male, 1207–1208
  and bill color, 1091
  and bursa of Fabricius in fowl, 1091
  and citric acid in prostate, 401, 405
  and claws of reptiles, 1047
  and cloacal gland
    in amphibia, 121–122, 1047
    in *Coturnix*, 1091
    in female *Triton*, 1055
  and coagulating gland, 402, 403, 408, 412–414
  and comb growth, 659, 1090, 1125
  and consummatory mechanism in male, 1207
  and courtship behavior in *Bathygobius*, 1254
  and development
    of central nervous tissues, 1348–1349
    of epididymis, 121
    of neural tissues mediating mating behavior, 1348
    of penis in mammals, 122, 126–128
    of seminal vesicle in rat, 121
  and dorsal prostate, 406
  and dorsonuchal crest of *Anolis*, 1047
  and epididymis
    of *Eumeces*, 1047
    of mammals, 711, 715–716
    of *Sceloporus*, 1047
  and ergothioneine content of semen, 659
  and erotic arousal
    in human female, 1208, 1390, 1391
    in human male, 1388–1389, 1390–1391
  and erythrocytes in fowl, 1091
  and female prostate, relative potencies, 421
  and feminine behavior
    by female vertebrates, 1196
    by male vertebrates, 1195
  and femoral glands of *Sceloporus*, 1047
  and fertilizing capacity of fowl sperm, 1095
  and fructose in prostate, 405, 406, 408
  and glycosidase levels in epididymis, 392
  and gonad transformation in female amphibia, 92, 94
  and gonopodium, 1046
  and head furnishings in turkey, 1091
  and hemipenes of *Sceloporus*, 1047
  and hypophyseal gonadotrophins, 268–271, 342–343, 530, 531, 1101
  and incubation behavior, 1288, 1291–1292
  and inhibition of parental behavior in birds, 1300
  and inositol secretion by seminal vesicles, 385
  and inhibition of intrasplenic ovarian graft development, 271
  and lateral prostate, 404–405
  and masculinization of liver in *Oryzias*, 1046
  and lymphomatosis in fowl, 1091
  and male accessory reproductive glands, 399–425
  and male genital ducts in lampreys, 1046
  and masculine behavior by female vertebrates, 1196–1198
  and masculinization of behavior in female guinea pig, 1199–1200
  and mating behavior
    in male rat, maintenance dose, 1202
    in male vertebrates, 1180–1186
    mechanism of action, 1207–1209
  and maxillary teeth in amphibia, 1047
  and mesonephros of reptiles, 1047
  and micturition pattern in dog, 1347–1348
  and middorsal skin from female *Triton*, 1047
  and mitotic activity in male accessory reproductive glands, 401, 410, 411, 414, 415

Androgen (*cont.*)
  and Müllerian duct
    development
      in mammals, 114
      in reptiles, 1047, 1070
    differentiation, 113–120, 1047, 1070
  and muscles in males, 660, 1186, 1387
  and nest-building in birds, 1274, 1275
  and nitrogen metabolism, 1387
  and nuptial pads in amphibians, 1046
  and olfactory perception, 1208, 1398
  and ovarian suppression in rat, 269–270
  and ovary in birds, 1131
  and oviduct
    in amphibians, 1046
    in birds, 1125
    in reptiles, 1047
  and ovulation
    in amphibians, 1046
    in rat, 269, 514
  and pelvic glands in amphibia, 1047
  and penis
    in Anserinae, 1091
    in mammals, 122, 126–128
    of reptiles, 1047, 1070
  and phallus in fowl, 1091
  and plumage in *Phylomachus*, 1091
  and precocious dominance behavior in fowl, 1258
  and precocious sex behavior in male rat, 1202
  and precocious vaginal patency in rats, 473
  and prenatal patterning of sex in guinea pig, 1222
  and prostate respiration, 659
  and prostatic carcinomas in Muridae, 420–423
  and prostatic hyperplasia in dogs, 429
  and respiratory enzymes in male accessory reproductive glands, 394–396
  and secondary sex characters in black-crowned night heron, 1275
  and seminal citric acid, 659
  and seminal fructose, 383, 659
  and seminal vesicles
    in amphibians, 1046
    in birds, 1091
    in Muridae, 409–410, 414–417, 422
  and sense organ acuity, 1260
  and sex behavior
    in female canaries, 1351
    in guinea pig, organizing action, 1199–1200
  and sex differentiation
    in fish, 1065, 1067
    in hamster, 136
    in rat, 136
    in reptiles, 1067–1069
  and sex reversal
    in fish, 46–47, 1065, 1067, 1070
    in reptiles, 1067–1069
  and sexual segment in reptiles, 1047
  and skin color
    in amphibians, 1046
    in fish, 1046
  and sperm viability, 713
  and spermatogenesis
    in fish, 1045
    in mammals, 270, 338–343
  and survival of adrenolectomized ducks, 1104
  and testis
    in *Fundulus*, 1045
    in mammals, 270, 338–343
  and urinary estrogen, 342–343
  and uropygial gland in fowl, 1091
  and vas deferens in *Sturnus*, 1091
  and ventral prostate, 401–403, 407, 411–412

Chimpanzee (*cont.*)
  urinary androgen, levels in female, 508
  urinary estrogen, levels in female, 507–508
Chinchilla laniger
  litter-size, 960
  pregnancy, length, 960
Chiroptera (see Bat)
Chlamydoselachus anguineus, intromittent organ,
      1041
Chloride ions and spermatozoa vitality in fowl,
      1110–1111
Chloris chloris
  ovarian follicular growth, pregnant mare serum
      and, 1128
  ovulation, pregnant mare serum and, 1128
  seminiferous tubules, cholesterol in, 1093
  sperm, 1096
Cholesterol
  adrenocortical, ACTH-depletion of, 531
  and steroid biosynthesis, 644–646
  biosynthesis, 644–645
  conversion to pregnenolone, hydroxylation re-
      action, 648
  depletion, similarity of luteotrophin and ACTH
      actions, 531
  estrogen and synthesis of, 653
  in corpus luteum of rat, 531
  in seminiferous tubules of birds, 1093
  luteal, lactogen-depletion of, 531
Choline derivatives
  biosynthesis, 386–387
  in male accessory reproductive glands, 386–387
  in semen, 386–387
Choline esterase in semen, 392
Chondrodystrophy, chromosome idiogram, 65
Chordeiles minor, incubation, ambient temperature
      and, 1295
Chorionic gonadotrophin
  and ovulation, 451
  excretion, hypophysectomy and, 1006
Chromosomes (see also Sex chromosomes)
  abnormalities
      and Klinefelter syndrome, 64
      and Mongolism, 63–65
      and syndromes not related to sex, 63–65
  "accessory," 6
  alterations
      drugs and, 8
      radiant energy and, 8
  and sex
      absence of Y chromosome and development
          of male genital system, 60
      accessory chromosome in *Xiphidium*, 6
      aneuploids, 8
      contributions from cytogenetics, 7–8
      determination
          in fishes, 45–47
          in *Humulus*, 43
          in *Melandrium*, 35–40
          in *Rumex*, 40–42
          mechanisms, 4–13
      gene mutations in *Drosophila*, 12
      genetic linkage group, 8
      historical, basic literature, 3–4
      in plants, 7
      in *Sciara*, 28–32
      polyploids, 8
      W in *Bombyx*, female sex factor in, 34–35
      XO + 2A type, species comparisons, 59
      Y chromosome, 23–25
  and types in *Drosophila americana*, 16–17
  animals, tabulations, 4
  autosomes in relation to sex, 10–11

Chromosomes (*cont.*)
  balance
      and sex determination, 5
          in fish, 46
          in *Melandrium*, 35–40
      and sex types in man, 59
      in sex deviates, species comparisons, 59
  behavior in parthenogenetic *Drosophila*, 22
  differentiation in *Sciara*
      in germinal tissue, 32
      in somatic tissue, 32
  Drosophila, female elements in X, 10
  identification in man, 54–55
  idiograms for man in disease conditions, 65
  in tortoiseshell cats, 51
  "limited" in *Sciara*, deoxyribonucleic acid in,
      30–31
  lineage and sex in *Sciara*, 29
  Lymantria, female elements in W, 10
  man, 52–55
  mosaics, in man, 53, 61
  nondisjunction and concept of genic balance, 9
  numbers, racial similarity in man, 53
  pairing
      mutant genes and, 7
      variations in, 6
  pattern
      amphibia, 44–45
      and sex differentiation, 6–7
      and sex ratios in *Sciara*, 29
      birds, 47
      Bombyx mori, 34–35
      cat, 51
      digametic females, 6–7
      digametic males, 6–7
      dioecious plants, 7
      Drosophila, 10
      haploid-diploid relations, 7
      hermaphroditic plants, 7
      homogametic females, 6–7
      homogametic males, 6–7
      human sex types, 62
      Humulus, 43
      Lebistes, 45
      Lymantria, 10
      Melandrium album, 36
      mouse, 50
      sex-reversed amphibians, 45
  plants, tabulations, 4
  Sciara, 29
  sex values
      in *Melandrium*, 37–38
      in *Rumex*, 41
  translocations, role in deviation, 40–41
  types
      in amphibia, viability of WW males, 45
      in man
          autosomal trisomics, 63–65
          hermaphrodites, 60
          superfemales, 57–58
          trisomic of chromosome, 18, 64
          trisomic of chromosome 22 (Sturge-Weber
              syndrome), 64
          trisomic of D group chromosomes, 64
          XO + 2A (Turner's syndrome), 59
          XXXY + 2A, 61–63
          XXY + 3A, 63
          XXY + 2A (Klinefelter's syndrome), 58–59
          XXYY + 2A, 59
  variations in *Spinacia*, 42
  zygotic formulae, 7
Chrysemys
  hermaphroditism, 1066
  pseudohermaphroditism, 1066

Dog (*cont.*)
  pseudopregnancy, 532–533
  relaxin in blood, 973
  reproduction, hypophyseal stalk transection
      and, 281, 283
  scrotum
    absence of sweat glands, 320
    temperature gradient, 318–319
  seminiferous tubules, motility, 712
  site of insemination, 727
  social behavior
    development, 1257
    genetic basis, 1244
  sperm
    antigens, 745
    hyaluronidase concentration, 829, 830
    transport in female, 731
  spermatogenic cycle, 328
  spermatogenesis, thyroid and, 347
  testicular tumors, 349–350
  testis
    adrenalectomy and, 347
    artery of, 318, 319
    high temperature and, 319
    hypophysectomy and, 335–336
    stress and, 322, 323
Dolichonyx oryzivorus, aggesssive behavior, breed-
      ing cycle and, 1250–1251
Dominance
  among males, and reproduction, 1246–1247
  behavior
    fowl
      experience and development of, 1258
      precocity, androgen and, 1258
    psychologic state and, 1255
  reproductive state and, 1251–1254
Dormouse, breeding season, 502
Dorsal crest, salamanders, orchiectomy, and, 1045
Dorsal fin rays, *Monocanthus*, testosterone and,
      1069
Dorsonuchal crest, *Anolis*, androgen and, 1047
Dove
  egg-laying
    conditioning to atypical stimuli, 1343
    handling and, 1143
  hybridity and phenotype, 20
  parental behavior, role of the sexes, 1299
DPN (Diphosphopyridine nucleotide)
Drill, mating behavior of male, castration and,
      1183
Drive-interaction, 1249–1250
  and conflict behavior, 1250
Drosophila
  chromosomes
    pattern, 10
    sex loci, 4
  embryology, 4
  hybridity
    and phenotype, 20–21
    and sexuality, 20–21
  intersexuality, genetic basis, 13–20
  meta females, 11
  parthenogenesis, 22–23
    and rudimentary females, 23
  sex comb teeth
    as measures of sexuality, 11–12
    chromosome balance and, 11–12
  sex determination
    genic balance and, 8
  sex differentiation
    cytoplasmic factors, 21
    Hr gene and, 49
    tra gene and, 50
  sex dimorphism, 11–12

Drosophila (*cont.*)
  sex genes, 13–20
  sex mosaics, origin, 60–61
  sex types, 13–20
  supermales, 11–12
  X chromosome, female elements in, 10
  Y chromosome
    and phenotype, 24
    variegation effects, 24
Drosophila affinis
  sex ratios
    female, 26
    male, female-male interactions, 28
Drosophila americana
  intersexes, 17
  sex types, 16–17
  triploids, phenotypes, 17
Drosophila asteca, female sex ratios, 26–27
Drosophila athabasca, female sex ratios, 26–27
Drosophila bifasciata
  female sex broods, 25
  female sex ratios, maternal cytoplasmic agents
      and, 25–26
Drosophila borealis, female sex broods, 26
Drosophila busckii, sex genes, 19
Drosophila mangabeirai
  parthenogenetic development, 34
  thelytokous reproduction, 23
Drosophila melanogaster
  gene mutations, and sexuality, 12
  genetics of sex, 3
  gynandromorphs, 21, 22
  Hr gene, sex effects, 15
  hybridization with *Drosophila simulans*, 14, 20
  intersexuality, sex genes and, 15
  male sex ratio, 27
    Ne gene and, 27
  maternal cytoplasmic agent, and susceptibility
      to CO_2 poisoning, 26
  microchromosome, 19
  parthenogenetic development, 34
  sex differentiation
    autosomes and, 18–20
    IV chromosome genes and, 18–20
    gene action and, 17–18
    X chromosome and, 17–18
    Y chromosome and, 18
  sex genes, 15–20
    autosomal, 18–20
  sterility factor in Y chromosome, 23–24
  tabulation of mutants, 4
  tra gene
    and mating bahavior, 16
    and sexuality, 16
    and sterility, 16
    phenotypic effects, 16
  Y chromosome, function, 23–25
Drosophila neorepleta, hybridization with *Dro-
      sophila repleta*, 20–21
Drosophila obscura, female sex ratios, 26
Drosophila parthenogenetica
  parthenogenesis, incidence, 22
  parthenogenetic development
    embryonic mortality, 22
    manner of, 34
Drosophila paulistorum
  female sex broods, 25
  female sex ratios, maternal cytoplasmic agents
      and, 25
Drosophila polymorpha, parthenogenesis, inci-
      dence, 22
Drosophila prosaltans
  female sex broods, 25

Estrogen (cont.)
  methods of assay, 472–473
  paradoxical effects on *Platypoecilus*, 1053
  plasma binding, 475–476
  prepubertal administration to rat, and reproductive functioning, 1201
  prepubertal treatment of female mouse, and reproductive functioning, 1201
  rate of production
    ovarian, 455
    problems of measurement, 471–473
  role in pregnancy, 964
  secretion
    androgen suppression, 342–343
    birds, 1117
    by Sertoli cell tumors, 350
    fowl, age of animal and, 1113
    inanition and, 262, 683
    luteinizing hormone and, 246
    man, malnutrition and, 262
    measurement, problems of, 507
    rate, 507–508
    ring dove, courtship by male and, 1276, 1281
  synergism with luteotrophic hormone in rat, 531
  synthetic, 450
  threshold, vagina compared with tissues mediating mating behavior, 1349
  turnover time, 475
Estrogen-androgen interrelationships
  antagonism, 426–429, 467
  coagulating gland, 426, 429
  cooperative, 426–429
  oviduct of birds, 1123–1124
  potentiating, 467
  prostate, 379–380, 426–429
  seminal vesicle, 426
  seminal fructose test and analysis of, 384
  synergism, 426–429
Estrogen-DOCA, and secretion of aridin, 1123
Estrogen-progesterone
  effects on uterus, monkey compared with rodents, 567
  in compensation for vitamin E deficiency, 691–692
  interrelationships
    aggressive behavior in female hamsters, 1256
    cervix uteri, 575, 1011–1012
    formation of mucus layer of ovum, 815
    in hypervolemia, 991
    implantation, 851–852
    incubation patch in male birds, 1106
    lactation, 615–616
    luteinizing hormone secretion, 541
    maintenance of deciduomas in rat, 531–532
    mammary development, 599–601
    mating behavior, female, 1174, 1189, 1206
    menstruation, 578–583
    myometrium, 570–571, 661, 1013–1015
    oviducal albumen in fowl, 1278
    oviduct
      of birds, 1123–1124, 1125
      of *Bufo*, 1054
      in mammals, 823
    ovulation in rabbit, 518–519
    pelvic relaxation, 1009–1010
    pregnancy, 1004
    protein synthesis, 660
    secretion of avidin, 1123
    sex skin, 577–578, 580
    tubal transport of ova, 823
    uterus, 559, 567–571, 582
    vagina, 559, 576
  thresholds in guinea pig, vagina *vs.* mating behavior, 1189

Estrogen-progesterone-relaxin, and cervical dilation, 1011–1012
Estrogen-prolactin
  and incubation patch, 1289
  finches compared with cowbirds, 1353
Estrogen-relaxin
  and cervical dilation, 1011
  and pelvic relaxation, 1009
Estrone
  adrenal cortical synthesis of, 647
  and cloacal epithelium of *Anolis*, 1054
  and ductus deferens in *Anolis*, 1054
  and epididymis in *Sceloporus*, 1054
  and foreclaw growth in *Pseudemys*, 1054
  and isocitric dehydrogenase activity, 656
  and Müllerian duct of male toads, 1054
  and ovary of *Anolis*, 1054
  and oviducts
    in amphibia, 1054
    in reptiles, 1054
  and parental behavior in rat, 1331
  and skeletal parts in *Oryzias*, 1069
  and testis of *Anolis*, 1054
  and vas deferens of male *Sceloporus*, 1054
  biosynthesis, 644–647
  placental synthesis, 647
  testicular synthesis, 647
Estrone-estradiol interconversions, 647
Estrous behavior (see Mating behavior, female)
Estrus
  cat, hypophyseal carminophil cell activity, 179
  during pregnancy, 458
  ferret, during anestrum, hypothalamic lesions and, 510
  persistent, 499
  postpartum, 260, 458–459
  progesterone and termination of, 1189
  progesterone-suppression, 517
  rat, time of day and, 514
  sheep, visual stimuli and, 277
  temporal relation
    to follicular growth, 1192–1193
    to ovulation, 514, 1187, 1192–1193
Ethinyl-Δ⁵-androstenediol, comparison with progesterone, 517
Ethinyl testosterone
  and spermatogenesis, 345
  comparison with progesterone, 517
Ethionine
  and liver damage, 674
  and testis structure, 679–680
17α-Ethyl-19-nortestosterone, anti-estrogenic action, 1113
Etiocholanolone
  cholesterol derivative, 644
  testosterone catabolism and, 649
Euarctos americanus (see Bear)
Eumeces
  breeding season, 1050
  epididymis
    androgen and, 1047
    seasonal changes, 1040
  male, lack of response to estradiol, 1054
  orchiectomy, 1045
  sexual segment of metanephros, androgen and, 1047
Euphagus cyanocephalus, nest building, temporal relation to copulation, 1271
Euplectes
  bill color, luteinizing hormone and androgen and, 1120
  feather coloring, luteinizing hormone and, 1120
  in luteinizing hormone assay, 249, 1152
Euplectes orix, bill color, androgen and, 1091

Ovulation (*cont.*)
  fowl (*cont.*)
    progesterone and, 1130–1133, 1150, 1277–1278
    temporal relation to oviposition, 1146–1152
  guinea pig, induction of, 505
  hypophyseal gonadotrophins and, 246, 248, 450, 513
  hypophyseal portal vessels and, 523
  hypothalamo-hypophyseal interactions and, 540–541
  hypothalamus and, 520–523
  interval after gonadotrophin release, 514
  mammals, temporal relation to estrus, 1187
  man, time of, 457
  mechanism of, 449, 456–457
  monkey, time of, 558
  Mustelidae, copulation and, 533
  nervous system and, 520–523
  neurohumoral control, 541
  priming action of estrogen, 516, 518
  progesterone and, 260, 267–268, 271, 506, 517–518, 527–528, 531, 1005, 1132–1133
  rabbit
    electrical stimulation and, 278
    epinephrine and, 524
    estrogen-progesterone synergism, 518–519
    norepinephrine and, 524
    protein deficiency and, 684
    rhinencephalon and, 523
    sequence of events, 521–522
  rat
    androgen and, 269
    progesterone and, 521
    reflex stimulation of, 498–499, 517, 520
  reptiles, seasonal occurrence of, 1049–1050
  reticular activating system and, 520
  sheep
    olfactory stimuli and, 277
    visual stimuli and, 277
    stimulation of genitalia and, 520
  temporal relation
    to estrus, 513–514
    to ovum maturation, 816, 818
  tuber cinereum and, 278
  vaginal stimulation and, 517
  without estrus, 503
  Xenopus, androgen and, 1046
Ovulation-oviposition cycle, fowl
  activity and, 1149, 1150
  feeding and, 1149
  light and, 1149
  regulation, 1146–1152
Ovum
  activation, 827, 837
  age at fertilization
    and developmental defects, 848–850
    and sex ratio, 848
  amphibia, transport in female, 1051
  and follicular growth, 807
  biochemical components, 810–811
  changes following penetration of sperm, 840–841
  collection of, 798–799
  culture of, 799–800
  cumulus-cell dispersal, 828, 829–831
  cumulus oophorus and sperm penetration, 830
  cytoplasmic components, 808–810, 813–814
  development of perivitelline space, 812
  dogfish, estradiol-17β in, 1070
  fate of unfertilized, 836–837
  fertilizable life, 849–850
  fowl, deposition of membranes, 1122–1123, 1147
  Fundulus, delayed hatching and development, 1070

Ovum (*cont.*)
  growth, 807
    deposition of yolk, 1116–1117
    independence of follicle-stimulating hormone, 243, 245
    temporal relation to follicular growth, 807
  maturation divisions, 816–817, 837–838
    gonadotrophins and, 817
    sperm penetration and, 829, 835
    temporal relationship to ovulation, 816, 818
  mucous (albuminous) coat, 815–816
    and penetration of sperm, 815
    chemical properties, 816
    formation, estrogen-progesterone and, 815
  polarity, 811
  postovulatory corona radiata, 818
  size, 811–812
  sperm penetration, 822, 834–835
  transfer, 800–801
  tubal, 828
    progesterone and, 826
    transport, 819–823, 845–846
  vitamin content, 686
  yolk distribution, 811
  zona pellucida
    formation, 449, 811–813
    physicochemical properties, 814–815
    sperm penetration of, 832–833
Oxytocin
  and galactopoiesis, 628–630
  and hypophyseal gonadotrophin secretion, 512
  and lactation, 284, 537
  and luteotrophin secretion, 628
  and luteolysis, 537
  and mammary gland involution, 598
  and milk-ejection, 272, 609–610, 621–625, 630, 1323–1325, 1341
  and parturition, 1015–1016, 1018
  and prolactin secretion, 272, 628–630, 1329–1330
  and pseudopregnancy in rats, 272
  and sperm transport in female, 732
  and uterine contractions, 732
  bioassays using fowl, 1153–1154
  plasma concentration, 623
  release during coitus, 732
  secretion, suckling and, 272, 1329–1330
Oxytocinase

Paedogenesis, in salmon parr, 1036
Pagellus
  hermaphroditism, 1063, 1064
  sex reversal, 1064
Pair formation, *Larinae*, sequence of behavior, 1242
Palade granules in adenohypophysis of rat, 214, 222
Pan satyrus (see Chimpanzee)
Pantothenic acid
  deficiency and developmental mortality, 692
  in cod ovaries, 686
Pan troglodytes (see Chimpanzee)
Pangolin (see also Short-tailed manis)
  hypophysis, anatomy, 165, 167
  intermedin, cellular origin, 200
Papio hamadrys (see Baboon)
Papio porcarius (see Baboon)
Papio ursinus (see Baboon)
Paraguayan anaconda, sexual dimorphism, 1044
Parakeets, egg-laying, sounds from other birds and, 277
Paramecium aurelia, mating types, 44
Paramecium bursaria, mating types, 44
Paraplacental hematomas and placental transport, 947

Placenta (*cont.*)
  source (*cont.*)
    of relaxin, 976
    of somatotrophin, 981
  spongiotrophoblastic zone in rat
    histology, 913
    role in protein synthesis, 913
  site
    of gonadotrophin production, 931–937
    of steroid production, 930–931
  structure
    in man, 891–892, 894
    in monkey, 886, 891–892, 894
  surface area, 944, 946
  syncytium
    and steroid production, 930–931
    comparison with nephron, 899–900
    lipid droplets in, 930, 936
    origin, 936–937
    physiologic role, 936–937
    protein synthesis in, 895
    site of steroid synthesis, 886–887, 892–893, 896
  transhydrogenase in, 651
  trophoblastic labyrinth in rat, 1078–1079
Placental barrier
  changes with age, 947
  definition, 908
  layers, 899
    in cat, 916
    in pig, 896, 900–901, 916, 932–933
  lipids in, 942
Placental enzymes, mechanism of estrogen action, 656–657
Placental gonadotrophins, 982–986
  origin in horse, 937
Placental histochemistry, 922–930
  cytoplasmic basophilia, significance, 937
  cytotrophoblast, ground substances, 905
  decidua, matrix, 900–901, 904, 905
  decidual cells, distinction from peripheral trophoblasts, 905
  Langhans cells, succinic dehydrogenase in, 895, 910–911
  lipid droplets, 892–893, 896, 923–925, 928–929, 938–939, 940–941, 948–949
  maternal decidua, 905, 924–925, 926
  metachromasia, indicator of mucoid degeneration, 900
  peripheral cytotrophoblast, "fibrinoid" (ground substance), 890, 904, 926
  peripheral trophoblasts, 890, 900–901, 903–907, 910–911, 920–921, 926
    distinction from decidual cells, 905
  spongiotrophoblast in rat, 913
  stroma of villi, 886–887, 892–893, 898, 900–901, 906–907, 910–911, 926
  syncytium, 886–887, 890, 892–893, 895–897, 900–901, 906–907, 910–911, 914–915, 926
    acetylcholine, 897
    acid phosphatase, 896–897, 914–915
    alkaline phosphatase, 886–887, 896, 914–915
    cytochrome oxidase-cytochrome *c* system, 897
    esterase, 897, 910–911
    glycogen in, 895
    lipids, 886–887, 892–893, 895, 896, 910–911
    PAS-positive substances, 895–896, 906–907, 926
    phospholipids, 899, 900–901
    ribonucleic acid in, 886–887, 890, 895
    succinic dehydrogenase in, 895, 910–911
    sulfhydryl groups in, 895, 910–911
Placental histology, 884–885, 886–887, 891–892, 909–914
  basal plate, 903, 918–919
  basal zone, 892

Placental histology (*cont.*)
  chorionic villi, epithelial plates, 892–893, 899, 900–901, 924–925
  cytotrophoblasts, 886–887, 891
  decidua basalis, 892
  decidual cells, 892
  Langhans cells, 890, 891, 892, 894, 910–911, 912, 926
  paraplacental border, 912
  peripheral cytotrophoblast, 884–887
    "fibrinoid" (ground substance), 890, 898, 903, 904, 920–921, 926
  peripheral trophoblasts, 891
  placental barrier, 894
  septae placentae, 903, 918–919
  stratum compactum, 892
  stratum spongiosum, 892
  stroma of villi, 886–887, 890, 892–893, 897–898, 900–901, 906–907, 926
    Hofbauer cells, 892–893, 898, 900–901, 926
  syncytium, 890, 892–893, 894–897, 899, 900–901, 906–907, 912, 924–925
    mitochondria, 896, 899
  trophoblastic cell columns, 890, 891
Placental permeability, 943–950
  gestation age and, 917, 943
  placental type and, 943–950
  to ACTH, 1008
  to estrogens, 1006–1007
  to serum gonadotrophin, 478
Placental ribonucleoprotein, significance, 937
Placental transmission, 908
  manner of, 947–948
  pinocytosis and, 948, 950
Placental transport
  antibodies, 943–944
  proteins, 943–944
  sodium, 944
Placental types
  comparative, 915–916
  endotheliochorial, 908, 914
  epitheliochorial, 908
  Grosser's classification, 908–909
  hemochorial, 908
  hemoendothelial, 908–909, 914
  syndesmochorial, 908
Placentophagy, 1312–1313
  hormonal basis, 1313
Plants
  dioecious types, 7
    sex determination, 4
  hermaphroditic types, 7
  mutants, tabulation of, 4
Plasma binding of steroids, 475–476
  and hormone antagonisms, 476
  in pregnancy, 476
Plasma proteins during pregnancy, 993–994
Platydactylus, pseudohermaphroditism, 1066
Platypoecilus
  effects of pregneninolone, 1053
  gonopodium in females, androgens and, 1046
  masculine behavior by female, androgen and, 1197
  paradoxical effects of estrogens, 1053
  sex chromosome variations, 46
  sex reversal in females, androgens and, 1067
  sperm storage in female, 1055
  spermatogenesis, estrogen-suppression of, 1053
Platypoecilus maculatus
  feminine behavior by male, 1179
  sex determination, chromosomes and, 46
Platystacus, transport of developing ova, 1047
Play, monkeys, parental care and, 1359
Plectrophenax nivalis
  incubation, temporal relation to egg-laying, 1284

Rat (cont.)
  exploratory behavior, selective breeding and,
      1355
  female genital tract, physico-chemical deter-
      minations, 741–742
  feminine behavior
    by females, androgen and, 1196
    by males, 1179
      androgen and, 1195
      estrogen and, 1195
  fertilization
    changes in ovum, 840–841
    changes in sperm, 838–844
    cytology of, 827
    polyspermy, 845, 850
    pronuclei, 841
    sperm penetration
      of ooplasm, 834–835
      of zona pellucida, 832
    supernumerary sperm, 844
  fetal gonad differentiation, gonadal hormones
      and, 100
  fetal hypophysis, functioning of, 163
  fetal loss
    adrenal corticoids and, 963
    body temperature and, 962–964
    folic acid deficiency and, 692
    hypoxia and, 963–964
  fetal testis, interstitial cells, 145
  gonad differentiation, pituitary and, 133
  gonaduct differentiation, pituitary and, 133
  Graafian follicle size, 505
  hair growth, progesterone and, 1347
  hoarding, selective breeding and, 1355
  hypogonadism in male, unilateral tubular
      atrophy, 348–349
  hypophyseal acidophils, thyroidectomy and, 176
  hypophyseal basophils, corticotrophin in, 176
  hypophyseal cytology
    adrenalectomy and, 196–197
    basophils, 185–188, 203, 209
    castration cells, 172
    castration compared with thyroidectomy
        cells, 188–190
    during pregnancy, 204, 205
    during pseudopregnancy, 204
    during sexual maturation, 201–202
    estrogen and, 202
    suckling and, 1327
    thyroidectomy cells, 172
    thyroxine deficiency and acidophils, 174
  hypophyseal gonadotrophin
    luteinizing hormone actions, 246
    secretion
      age of animal and, 257, 501, 503
      androgen and, 268–271, 531
      diabetes and, 673
      dietary proteins and, 675–676
      estrogen and, 202, 265–268, 503–504, 531
      follicle-stimulating hormone luteinizing
          hormone ratios, 259
      gonadectomy and, 259
      inanition and, 674–675
      progesterone suppression of follicle-stimu-
          lating hormone secretion, 518
      sex differences, 257, 259
      vitamin deficiency and, 676–677
  hypophyseal prolactin, selective breeding and,
      1355
  hypophyseal structure, inanition and, 674
  hypophysis
    anatomy, 165, 273, 275, 1099
    electron microscopy, 214–223
    masculinization of, 530

Rat (cont.)
  implantation
    delayed, 459
    endometrial response, 862
    estrogen-progesterone and, 851
    lactation delay, 851
    progesterone and, 851
  in pregnancy tests, 986, 987
  intermedin, cellular origin, 94
  lactation
    adrenal corticoids and, 612–613
    biochemical correlates, 607–609
    hormone requirements, 609–612
    neurohumoral blocking agents and, 630–631
    ovarian hormones and, 613–614, 616
    parathyroids and, 619
    pars nervosa ablation and, 1147
    prolactin levels, 205
    suckling induced, 1325, 1326, 1328, 1329–1330
    thyroid and, 617
    tranquilizing drugs and, 631–632
  litter size, thyroid and, 669
  luteotrophic substances, 530
  male accessory sex glands
    estrogen and, 426–427
    glycosidases in, 392
    progesterone and, 425–426
    rate of castrational involution, 420–421
    respiratory metabolism, 394–396
  mammary development, 595–596
    adrenal corticoids and, 604
    hormone requirements, 599, 602–606
    insulin and, 605
    thyroid hormone and, 605
  mammary gland
    after weaning, 598–599
    postparturitional, 596
  mammary tissue RQ, insulin and, 619–620
  masculine behavior
    by female, 1190–1191
      androgen and, 1197–1198
    by male, estrogen and, 1194, 1202
  masculinization, by ovarian androgen, 465–466
  maternal behavior, pars nervosa ablation and,
      1147
  mating behavior
    age of animal and, 1202–1204
    comparison with guinea pig, 1220
    duality of mechanisms, 1177–1179
    experience and, 1340
    hypophysis and, 1210
    in female, 1186–1187
      adrenal corticoids and, 1209–1210
      development of capacity in absence of
          ovaries, 1201, 1203, 1222
      estrogen-progesterone and, 1188, 1205
      individual differences, 1187
      measurement of, 1187
    in male, 1175–1176
      androgen and, 1184, 1185–1186
      androgen and development of, 1186, 1202
      castration and, 1177, 1180, 1181, 1182
      cerebral decortication and, 1178
      cortisone and, 1209
      experience and, 1216, 1219–1220
      hyperexcitability, 1182, 1208
      maintenance dose of androgen, 1202
      methods of scoring, 1177
      protein deficiency and, 679
      stability of patterns, 1179–1180
      thyroid and, 1211, 1212
  strain differences, 1214

Transvestism (see also Berdache), 1425–1428, 1451–1453, 1471
  genotypic sex and, 1427
  gonadal hormones and, 1426
  social learning and, 1427–1428
Trichoptera, digametic females, 7
Trichosurus vulpecula, pregnancy, length, 961
Triglycerides, histochemical differentiation, 889
Triiodothyronine, and sperm production, 669
Tringa totanus
  development of song, example of foster species and, 1357
  nest-building, role of sexes, 1270
Trionyx, pseudohermaphroditism, 1066
Triphosphopyridine nucleotide
  and adrenal corticoid synthesis, 647
  in estrogen biosynthesis, 647
  in steroid biosynthesis, 645, 647
  in steroid hydroxylations, 648
Triploids, phenotypes in *Drosophila americana*, 17
Tryptophan peroxidase-oxidase, cortisone and amount of, 652
Triton (see *Triturus*)
Triturus
  chromosome pattern, 44–45
  corpus luteum, 1058
  gonaducts, castration and, 112
  male accessory sex structures, androgens and, 1047
  mesonephric duct, seminal vesicle-like structure, 1040
  middorsal skin from female, androgen and, 1047
  orchiectomy, and secondary sex characters, 1045
  oviducts, diethylstilbestrol and, 1054
  sex dimorphism, cloacal glands, 1043
  testis, seasonal changes, 1038
  Wolffian duct
    development, castration and, 120–121
    diethylstilbestrol and, 1054
Triturus alpestris, mesonephric epithelium, 1040
Triturus cristatus
  cloacal glands, conversion to spermathecae, 1055
  mesonephric epithelium, 1040
Triturus torosus, gonad transformation, dominance of testis, 87
Triturus viridescens
  dominance, hypophyseal gonadotrophins and, 1254
  hypophyseal cytology, during sexual maturation, 202
  pars intermedia functioning, 199
  responsiveness to gonadotrophins, in cross-species tests, 252
  sex dimorphism, hind limb warts, 1042–1043
  sperm storage in female, 1055
  spermatogenesis, seasonal occurrence, 1036
Trochilidae
  altricial young, 1298
  parental behavior, role of sexes, 1299
Troglodytes aëdon
  egg production, environmental temperature and 1141
  incubation, temporal relation to egg-laying, 1285
  nest-building
    correlation with copulation, 1271
    role of sexes, 1270
    regulation of body temperature, in nestlings, 1356
Troglodytes troglodytes
  incubation, ambient temperature and, 1295
  nest-building, role of sexes, 1270

Troglodytes troglodytes (cont.)
  ovarian follicular growth, inhibition by parental behavior, 1302
Trogonophis, oviduct, 1052
Trophotaeniae, 1057
Tropidoclonion lineatum, sperm storage in female, 1055
Tropidonotus (see also *Natrix*)
  genital tract, development, 1061
  gonad, development, 1061
  pseudohermaphroditism, 1066
  testicular, interstitial tissue, seasonal changes, 1039
Tropidonotus natrix
  sexual segment in, 1041
  testis regeneration, 1045
Tropidonotus viperinus
  breeding season, 1050
  mating and ovulation, temporal separation, 1050
  sexual segment, 1041
Trout
  genital tract, development, 1060
  hermaphroditism, 1063
  sexual differentiation, estrogen and, 1067
Trygon, viviparity, 1057
TSH (Thyrotrophin)
Tube intermédaire, 1041
Tupaiidae (see Shrew)
Turbellarians, sperm, penetration of somatic tissue, 744
Turdus merula
  feeding of young, 1356
  incubation, temporal relation to egg-laying, 1285
Turdus migratorius, nest, 1269
Turdus philomelos, sperm, 1096
Turkey
  adrenal, wild compared with domestic birds, 1354
  aggressive behavior in male, castration and, 1254
  broodiness, testosterone and, 1292
  congenital malformations, vitamin A and, 691
  copulatory organ, 1095
  egg production, enviromental temperature and, 1142
  head furnishings, androgen and, 1091
  hypophyseal gonadal relations, 253
  incubation
    environmental temperature and, 1142
    estrogen and, 1292–1293
    presence of eggs and, 1294
    progesterone and, 1132, 1293
  male feathering, 1119
  masculine behavior by female, 1190
  mating behavior
    castration and, 1181
    isolation and, 1216
  maturation of behavior, parental behavior and, 1357
  ovarian follicular growth, progesterone and, 1131
  parental behavior
    prolactin and, 1299
    strain differences, 1354
  parthenogenetic development, 48, 1115–1116
  seasonal breeding cycle, synchronization of male and female, 1144–1145
  sinistral ovariectomy, 1114
  sperm, 1096
    age and fertilizing capacity, 1109–1110
    metabolism, 760
    storage and embryonic mortality, 1110
  spermatogenesis, environmental temperature and, 1141–1142